THE NEUROANATOMICAL BASIS FOR CLINICAL NEUROLOGY

The Neuroanatomical Basis for Clinical Neurology

TALMAGE L. PEELE, M.D.

Associate Professor of Anatomy in Charge of Neuroanatomy
Assistant Professor of Medicine, Duke University School of Medicine

THE BLAKISTON DIVISION
McGRAW-HILL BOOK COMPANY, INC.

New York Toronto London

1954

Library of Congress Catalog Card Number: 53-9002

III

ACKNOWLEDGMENT

Six illustrations, on pages 85, 343, 345, and 431 of this book, were taken from "Handbuch Der Neurologie," 5th and 6th volumes, edited by O. Bumke and O. Foerster, Berlin, Julius Springer, 1936. The copyright in each volume was vested in the Attorney General of the United States, and the illustrations are reproduced pursuant to License No. JA-1528 of the Attorney General.

FOREWORD

THE PRESENT integrated interest in the whole of neurology is relatively modern and yet remarkably similar to that which directed the creators of this discipline. Between these two extremes in time lie many years—years which witnessed a debilitating partition of neurology into specialized fields of laboratory research separated by impenetrable hedges of scorn and of prejudice. Now, however, the hedges are cut. Investigators may trespass upon a neighboring field without fear of arrest.

Initially, neurology grew and later flowered with its roots firmly embedded in the clinic, for it was essentially man's study of man's nervous system. Since those early days, cross fertilization from laboratory experimentation has occurred, and the fruit produced is a great increase in the comprehension of the human brain, its intimate structure and diverse function. This mutual interaction between studies of the nervous system of man in the clinic and those of the nervous systems of animals in the laboratory is a prerequisite for determining the critical data to understand this discipline. For example, the control of visceral and emotional activity by the central nervous system was discovered and developed by investigators in clinic and in laboratory alike. Such results have served to entrench neurology more firmly within the matrix of the medical curriculum and to lend to medicine its axioms and methods of analysis for assay of disease in general. Indeed, neither neuroanatomy nor neurophysiology can be adequately presented without the use of data which stem from clinical investigations. This recognized and useful unity within the subject of neurology challenges the ability of the teacher. Dr. Peele has met this challenge in a manner all his own.

As preparation for teaching neurology in the Department of Anatomy at Duke University, Dr. Peele has studied neuroanatomy and neurophysiology and received training in clinical neurology under Foster Kennedy. Such triple experience with neurology has given Dr. Peele an unusual orientation in this discipline and has enabled him to use and to evaluate critically clinical symptoms in the manner of a laboratory investigator.

The annotated data, both physiological and anatomical, are meticulously presented in this textbook of neurology. Each part of the nervous system is visualized in its functional integrity within the whole. In spite of its length, the text itself held my interest when I read it in manuscript. Although the discussions may be too detailed as an introduction to this subject in some medical schools, nonetheless, even in the first course of neurology, it would be a reliable and interesting reference book. For more experienced students, however, it contains information unavailable in any other book and is therefore in a class all its own.

Finally, Dr. Peele has tested this type of presentation of neurology to medical students for many years. He offers his experience in teaching this subject to other teachers and students because he has found it good.

MARION HINES

Emory University

PREFACE

In the present text an effort has been made to combine with descriptive neuroanatomy some principles of neural physiology and some applications of these to clinical neurology. Without some demonstrations of function of the neural organization, pure neuroanatomy tends to become uninteresting and complex to many medical students. It is just as necessary to integrate the instruction concerning the nervous system as it is to demonstrate the essential function of nerve tissue, integration. Certainly, the presentation during a neuroanatomy course of a patient suffering with a neurological disorder has served many times to provoke renewed interest and much incentive in learning a little more in the formative preclinical years. Such results, I think, justify a composite treatment of the nervous system that may prove helpful to medical students of all class years.

By frequent reference in the text to the work of the outstanding researchers in the field, it is hoped that more interest in the study of the nervous system will be encouraged. Experimental arguments are not completely banned. Conversely, they are at times presented in sufficient detail to allow the student to make up his own mind. It is a good policy to let him learn early that all is not cut and dried and that dogmatism has no place in medicine. It is possible to achieve this without too much confusion.

Chapters 1 and 6 are concerned with the elements of nervous tissue, nerve cells and fibers. These are described in more detail than is usual in a neuroanatomy text. The mechanism of nerve impulse conduction is discussed, and the changes consequent to axon severance are described. Function, normal and deranged, is thus emphasized from the outset. Chapter 2 dealing with supportive elements is similarly developed. Next, in the third chapter, the development of the nervous system is described, and for this section I am indebted to Dr. C. H. Sawyer. The next section is given to macroscopic anatomy of the brain, its coverings, and its blood supply as a necessary orientation procedure.

The gross anatomy of the spinal cord is covered early in the following chapter, which deals later with a discussion of spinal cord pathways. Recent clinical observations of the lateral spinothalamic tract are given space, and the position of this tract in the brain stem according to these researches is adhered to. Physiological principles of conduction in the central nervous system are described and are followed by a discussion of various clinical disorders involving the spinal cord.

Descriptive sections concerned with the external and intrinsic features of the various divisions of the brain stem follow. These sections are liberally illustrated with photographs from a human brain stem series. Cranial nerves are considered separately, and the various clinical disorders of them are emphasized. The blood supply of the brain stem is given in some detail in order to describe the common vascular syndromes briefly.

The cerebellum receives treatment in a separate section as does the vestibular system. In each instance more space is given to physiology and to disease than is usual. The discussion of the thalamus is based on the recent work of Walker, Sheps, and Toncray and Krieg. The experimental work on the diffuse thalamic reticular system is introduced. The vascular syndromes of the thalamus are described, and the relations of the thalamus to the cerebral cortex, point-to-point and diffuse, are emphasized.

The autonomic nervous system is treated in detail in two sections: in one, the general anatomical features of the system as a unit are presented; in a second, the hypothalamus is described. Again physiological and clinical approaches are utilized.

A general section concerned with the intrinsic anatomy of the cerebral cortex is followed by complete discussions of the various systems of the nervous pathways. Thus, the motor pyramidal and extrapyramidal, the sensory, the auditory, visual, gustatory, and olfactory systems are covered in separate sections. Experimental and clinical researches are relied on to a great extent in these sections in order to make the discussions complete. Clinical syndromes are considered at some length.

Insofar as possible original illustrations have been used, but in those cases where it has been found expedient and helpful, permission has been sought to use outstanding, familiar ones. To their creators and publishers I express my thanks for this permission.

To Dr. D. C. Hetherington, Mr. George Lynch, Mr. Robert Blake, Mr. O. A. Parkes, and Mr. Sam A. Agnello, I am indebted for many of the original illustrations, and Mr. Agnello has typed and retyped considerable portions of the manuscript. I offer all these colleagues my sincere thanks.

Dr. H. W. Magoun and Dr. Marion Hines have read the manuscript and Dr. Hines, particularly, has offered much valuable and constructive criticism. Dr. J. E. Markee has given much encouragement. To each of them, I am deeply grateful.

TALMAGE L. PEELE

CONTENTS

CHAPTER 1

NERVE CELLS AND FIBERS

SHERRINGTON USED the word integration to describe one of the characteristics of the central nervous system. The process of integration characterizes other biological systems also. To integrate is to unite parts to form a whole, as to unite a part with something else, especially something more inclusive. The digestive system displays an integrative ability in its conversion of glucose to glycogen, of amino acids to protein; the blood-forming tissues integrate essential elements to form blood cells; the endocrine system combines individual parts to form hormones.

It is not an exaggeration, however, to say that the nervous system is, of all these, the most capable integrator. The inherent qualities of its components, irritability and conductivity, contribute the technique necessary for integration. The nervous system is composed of millions of functional components, nerve cells, of diverse sizes and shapes, all demonstrating irritability and conductivity. Through their irritability, they collect impressions; through their conductivity, they assemble and coordinate impressions and then transmit them to neighboring cells which initiate a change or an adaptation fitting to the impressions.

Within the skin of man, inside his muscles, and within the substance of his viscera are receptor representatives of the nervous system, the terminals of nerve cells. Their function is to collect and to send in impressions of activity occurring within their locale. Assembled in the organs of special sense, the nose, the eyes, the ears, and the taste buds, are highly developed mechanisms receiving and sending into the brain impressions from their environment.

Within the muscles, striated skeletal, cardiac, and smooth, and about and within glandular tissue are terminals of effector representatives of the nervous system which set into play an efficient and harmonious response to the changes of the environment inside and outside the body. The receptor mechanisms bearing a certain amount of specificity are part of a nerve cell just as the effector endings are parts of other nerve cells.

The nerve cells and their processes are, then, the mediators in integration. Groups of neurons of similar function are formed, and they are related to other groups of similar or different function. Receptor, or sensory, neurons may be in conductive relation with other sensory neurons; with effector, or motor, neurons; or with liaison agents, the associative or intercalated neurons which serve for elaborating and prolonging the harmonious relations between sensory and effector nerve cells. The greater the number of suitable associative neurons there are involved in a process, the more advanced the integration. It will be useful to consider at this point the physical character of the neurons, and to observe how these characters are adapted to irritability and conductivity and their integrative ability.

NEURONS AND NEURONAL INTERRELATIONSHIPS

The structural unit of the nervous system is, therefore, the neuron, a nerve cell with all its processes (Fig. 1). Nerve cells possess a body of cytoplasm and a nucleus. The cytoplasm of the body is called **perikaryon** and contains fibrils and a variety of other **inclusions**. The cytoplasm of many nerve-cell bodies is continued into a number of expansions or processes, the **dendrites** and the **axis cylinder,** or **axon.** Nerve cells are the conductors of nerve impulses, their processes constituting the nerve fibers seen throughout the various parts of the nervous system. The relationship existing between nerve cells was for a time greatly debated, and the

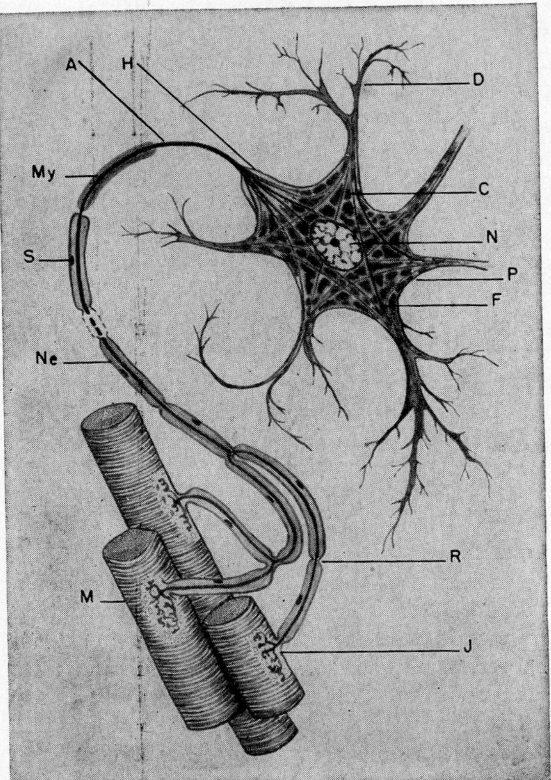

FIG. 1. Diagram of a motor neuron. The nerve cell, its axon, and the terminals in muscle fibers constitute a motor unit. *A*, axon; *C*, Nissl substance; *D*, dendrite; *F*, neurofibrils; *H*, axon hillock; *J*, motor end plate; *M*, striated muscle fiber; *My*, myelin sheath; *N*, nucleus; *Ne*, neurolemma; *P*, perikaryon; *R*, node of Ranvier; *S*, nucleus of Schwann cell. ×1300.

ideas of such relationship have been expressed in two chief doctrines, the so-called **reticular doctrine,** and the **neuron doctrine.** The latter is now almost universally accepted.

THE RETICULAR DOCTRINE

This doctrine considers nerve cells and their processes to be interconnected and holds that by a merging of their substances, they form systems of nerve nets. Nerve fibers are thought to be formed by the fusion of many cells. Certain adherents of this doctrine believed that the neurofibrils described later are the conducting elements in the nerve cells and that they pass from one cell into another at the synapse, the point at which processes of two cells come into contact.

THE NEURON DOCTRINE

The neuron doctrine assumes that each cell and its processes originate from a separate primitive cell, the neuroblast. The axon develops or grows out from the neuroblast and does not result from fusion of cells. This was observed by Harrison (1908–1910) in tissue-culture experiments, confirming earlier opinions of His, Cajal, and Kupffer (see references 338, 339, 340). Further, the neuron doctrine assumes that the nerve cell is an independent cellular unit capable of independent action and existence. Histological methods designed to make a neuron and its processes visible by virtue of metallic impregnation have shown the relationship between two neurons to be one of surface contact only. With such technique isolated cells only are usually impregnated, and such cells may be beautifully and sharply outlined, with cell body and processes visible down to the finest ramification. Remaining completely unimpregnated are cells with which the stained cell is in synaptic contact—a neat denial of the existence of nerve nets, but a vexing problem when one is attempting to stain all neurons in a given area of nervous tissue!

Within the principles of the neuron doctrine the processes of the nerve cells are dependent on the body and the nucleus; when cut they degenerate, regenerating anew in peripheral nerves from the cell body. The neuron theory predicates a degree of **polarity** in the nerve cells and their processes; the *dendrites receive* impulses arriving from other neurons and transmit them *to* the cell body, while the *axon carries* the impulse *away from* the cell body to other neurons or to end organs such as glands and muscles. Actually, the cell body may have a minor role in the process of transmission, but it is essential for the maintenance of the conducting processes. When artificially stimulated, an axon can transmit excitation in either direction. At a synapse, however, an impulse can pass in only one direction. A functional polarity of the synaptic membrane exists, permitting the nerve impulse to pass only from the axon of one neuron to the dendrites or body of a related neuron.

Nerve cells vary in their independence of one another. In a group of cells not connected directly or indirectly, one cell may die without affecting any other. A degenerative process may pass through one cell and throughout the length of its axon to the synapse with another cell without affecting this other cell. On the other hand, in some instances degeneration of one neuron may involve another with which it is synaptically related by a process of **trans-synaptic or transneuronal degeneration.** This is particularly true in the visual and auditory pathways and perhaps in the connections of certain of the spinal-cord neurons with the incoming posterior root fibers, as will be seen later.

According to the neuron doctrine, also, nerve

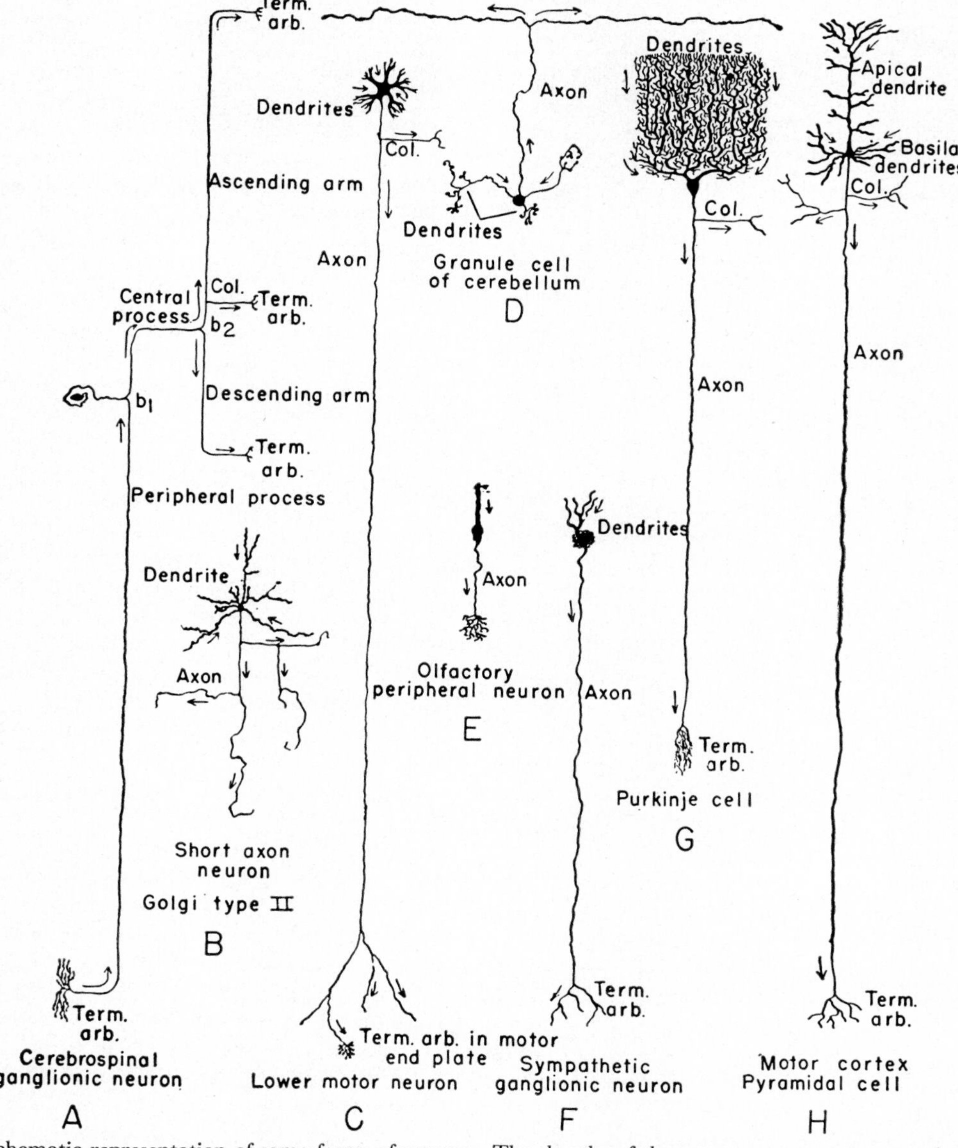

FIG. 2. Schematic representation of some forms of neurons. The sheaths of the neuron processes are not shown. The axons, except in *B*, are shown much shorter in proportion to the size of cell body and dendrites than they actually are. Arrows denote the direction of conduction. b_1, b_2, branches 1, 2; *Col.*, collateral branch; *Term. arb.*, terminal arborization. (*From "Bailey's Textbook of Histology," courtesy of The Williams & Wilkins Company.*)

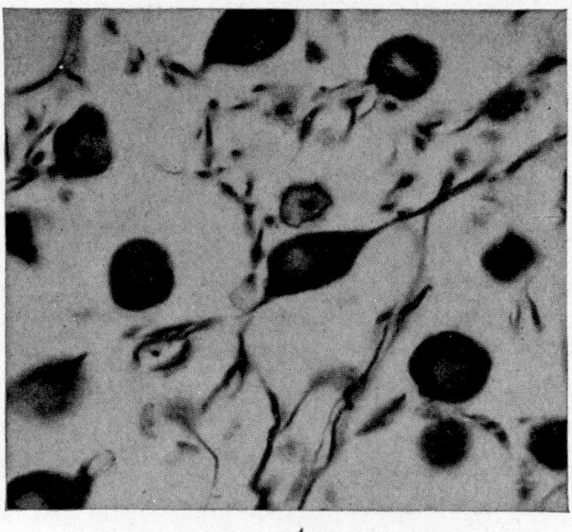

A

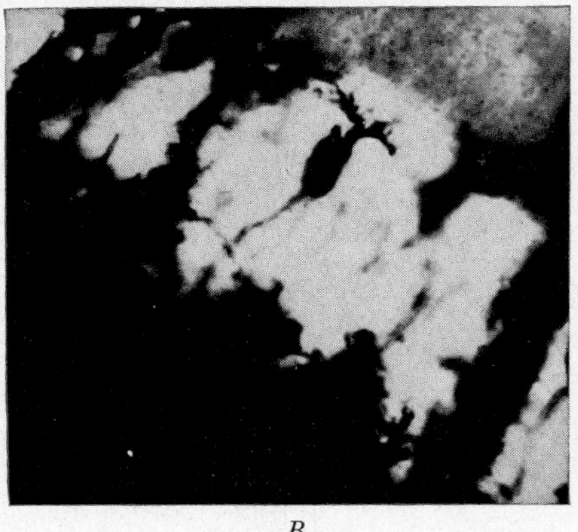

B

FIG. 3. *A*, bipolar neuron, vestibular ganglion. Bodian stain. ×645. *B*, bipolar neuron, retina, ox. Golgi. ×404. Photomicrographs.

cells exhibit physiological or functional specificity. They vary in their chemical and physical make-up, in the type and number of their expansions, and in the types of synaptic relationships they establish; finally, they react differently in normal and in pathological reactions. In summary, the neuron doctrine assumes (*a*) an independent development of the cell body and an outgrowth of its processes from a single neuroblast; (*b*) a certain polarization of the neuron; (*c*) a complete independence of (or only a partial dependence upon) other neurons synaptically related to it; and (*d*) a specificity of function.

NEURON TYPES

Functionally nerve cells are classed as **sensory** or **motor,** although there is a third type, the **associative** or **intercalary** neuron, which connects the first two. Structurally they have been classed, according to the length of their axons, as Golgi type I (long) and Golgi type II (short) (Fig. 2). A motor cell with a diameter of 50 μ in the spinal cord may send an axon 7 μ in diameter by way of a peripheral nerve for a distance of a meter to a muscle of the foot; such a cell would belong to the Golgi type I. The axon of many nerve cells terminates near the parent cell; such a cell would belong to type II. The most useful structural classification of nerve cells, however, is based upon the number of processes and lists **unipolar, bipolar,** and **multipolar** cells.

Unipolar cells possess only an axon and are rare except in embryonic stages of the nervous system. Bipolar neurons have one main dendrite and one axis cylinder projecting from opposite ends of a fusiform cell body; bipolar neurons are found in the retina and in the vestibular and cochlear ganglia (Figs. 3*A*, *B*). Multipolar neurons are most numerous, and their shape depends on the number and pattern of their dendrites. Large star-shaped motor cells are found in the ventral gray columns of the spinal cord; pyramidal-shaped neurons, in the cerebral cortex; and Purkinje cells, in the cerebellar cortex (Fig. 4). The last possess two main treelike stalks of dendrites (Fig. 181). Very small cells with a few short dendrites radiating in all directions and a short axon are called granule cells. These would belong to Golgi's type II class, because of the short processes (Fig. 182). The majority of the neurons of the ganglia of spinal and cranial nerves are pseudo-unipolar. Although they possess a single process, which divides like the letter T into a dendrite and an axon, they are physiologically bipolar (Fig. 5). The single, branching process arose through a fusion of two original processes, which, however, maintain their intrinsic anatomical constituents (neurofibrils) individuate (Fig. 6). Neurons, within the neural axis, of similar morphology and function are grouped in **nuclei;** similarly, related neurons, lying without the neural axis, compose **ganglia.**

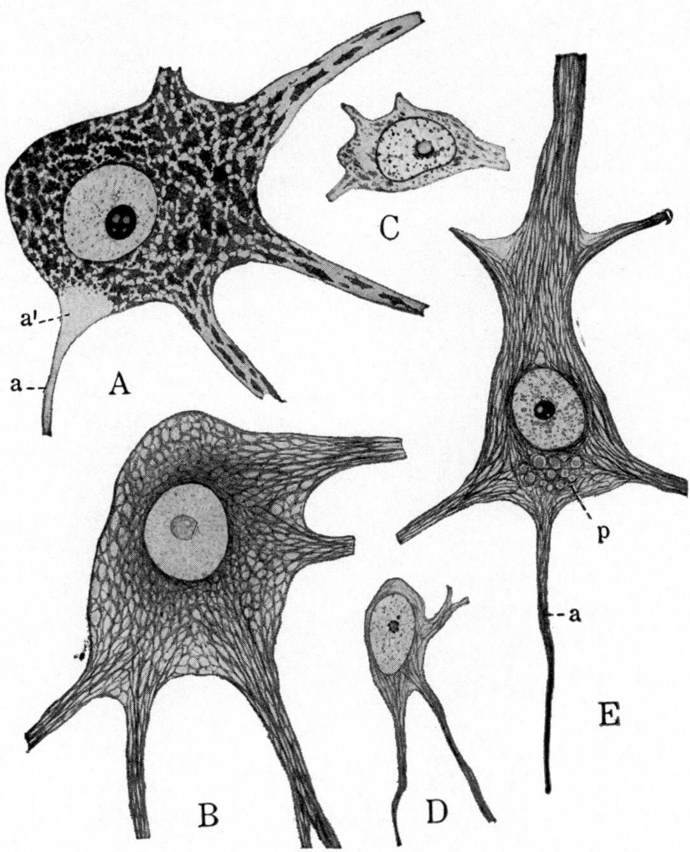

FIG. 4. Multipolar neurons. *A* and *B*, motor cells of a kitten's spinal cord stained by Nissl and silver methods; *C* and *D*, small interneurons of the spinal cord stained by Nissl and silver methods; *E*, neuron of the cerebral cortex stained by silver; *a*, axon; *a'*, axon hillock; *p*, pigment. ×900. (*From Nonidez and Windle, "Textbook of Histology," courtesy of McGraw-Hill Book Company, Inc.*)

CYTOLOGY OF NEURONS

The **cell body (perikaryon)** may vary, within the above structural types, in both shape and size. It may be round, stellate, pyramidal, or spindle-shaped and may measure from 4 to 120 μ in diameter (Figs. 7, 8). The nucleus is round, has a definite membrane, and contains little chromatin material but has a definite linin structure. Although the nucleus is usually centrally placed, in certain neurons it is located near the cell periphery (Fig. 9). A prominent nucleolus is present (Figs. 4, 8). The cytoplasm (neuroplasm) is a semifluid, viscous substance in the living state. There are several types of intracellular structures, including (*a*) **Nissl substance,** (*b*) **Golgi apparatus,** (*c*) **mitochondria,** (*d*) **neurofibrils,** and (*e*) other inclusions

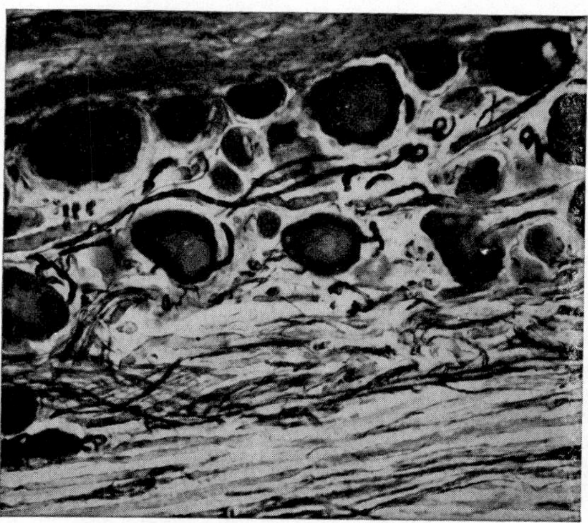

FIG. 5. Pseudo-unipolar neurons. Posterior root ganglion, cat. Pyridine silver. Photomicrograph, ×185.

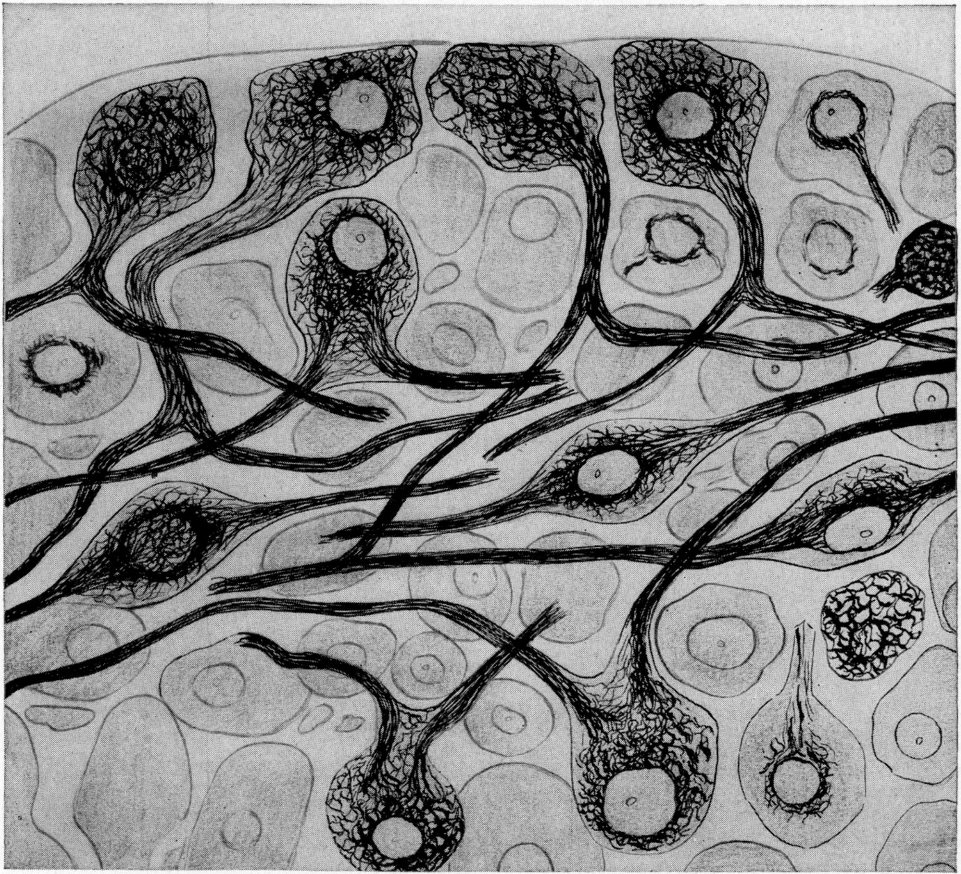

Fig. 6. Development of pseudo-unipolar neurons from bipolar cells. Two bipolar neurons are shown in the center of the illustration. (*From Cajal, "Histology," courtesy of The Williams & Wilkins Company.*)

described later. Two substances are present in a colloidal state in the perikaryon: one is a fluid which represents the dispersed phase and which, after coagulation, forms the Nissl bodies; the second is a viscous semisolid or plastic substance which forms the continuous phase and conditions the typical formation of the pattern of the Nissl bodies (236, 237).

NISSL BODIES

The structures in nerve cells first described by Flemming in 1882, but stained by, and named for, Nissl, have produced much argument (Figs. 7*A*, 8). Tigroid bodies and chromidial substance are synonymous names for them. They have been considered products of fixation, inasmuch as they have not been seen in undamaged living cells. It is believed generally now, however, that they are present in the living cell, for they have been seen in rapidly frozen-dried material. The Nissl bodies are nucleoproteins with combined iron. They disappear when treated with ammonia, and they stain with basic dyes. Nissl bodies are present in larger nerve cells but are not satisfactorily demonstrated in the smaller or granular cells. When present they are usually scattered uniformly through the cell-body cytoplasm except near the point from which the axon arises, the **axon hillock;** they are present in the dendritic cytoplasm. In some cells the Nissl bodies are normally collected about the periphery of the cell (Fig. 9). An attempt has been made to correlate function of cells with the amount of Nissl bodies and with the size of the particles. In an ultracentrifuging study, Nissl bodies were

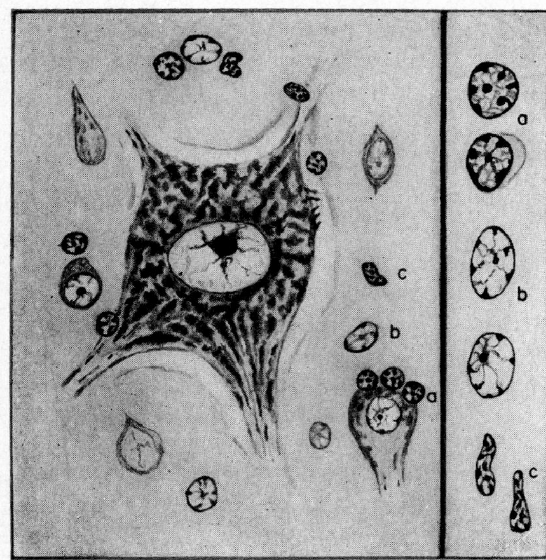

FIG. 7*A*. Drawing of giant multipolar neuron and nuclei of glial cells. *a*, nucleus of oligodendrocyte; *b*, of astrocyte; *c*, of microglia. Cerebral cortex, cat. Toluidine blue. ×715.

FIG. 7*B*. Nuclei of glial cells. *a*, *b*, and *c* same as in Fig. 7*A*. ×1430.

found to be heavier than the neuroplasm (68). Though the Nissl bodies were displaced to the centrifugal pole, they still retained a discrete form.

Some cytologists believe the Nissl substance arises from the nucleoproteins of the nucleus and they speak of nucleoli, presumably Nissl bodies, passing through the nuclear membrane. Nissl substance is described as being first formed embryologically about the nucleus adhering to the nuclear membrane. In normal Purkinje cells, Nissl bodies, while diffusely arranged through the cell, are also condensed at a certain place in the nuclear membrane to form a cap. Similar nuclear caps of Nissl substance are described in motor cells recovering from injury to their axon in the reaction designated as chromatolysis and described later. As recovery proceeds, the substance becomes again diffused throughout the cytoplasm (236, 404).

The importance of the Nissl bodies with respect to the metabolism of the cell is attributed to their iron content, the iron serving as a catalyst. Through its oxidation reactions it is thought to assist in the passage of the nerve impulse. As stated before, the Nissl substance takes part in the reaction of nerve cells to injury, *e.g.*, to severance of the axon. Early signs of injury exhibited by Nissl substance are its disappearance from the dendrites, and near the nucleus, and a shift to the periphery of the cell (Fig. 115). Later it becomes diffuse and disappears. The reaction is called **chromatolysis.** Upon exposure to certain toxins and after fatigue, Nissl bodies diminish and disappear. When the nerve cell does not die, certain of the changes in chromatolysis are reversible, and the Nissl substance assumes its previous appearance.

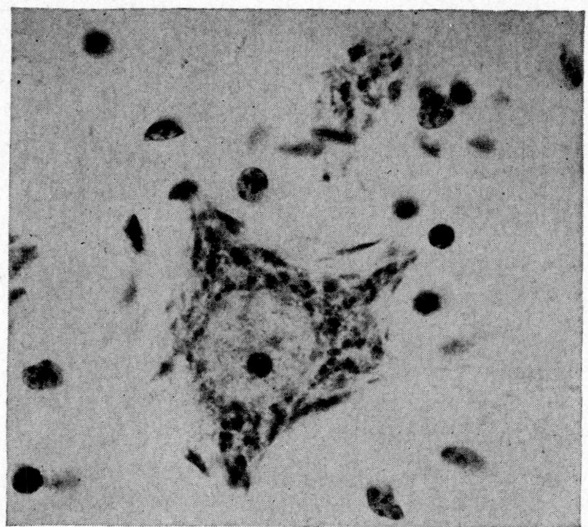

FIG. 8. Neuron of anterior spinal gray. Monkey. Gallocyanin. Photomicrograph, ×645.

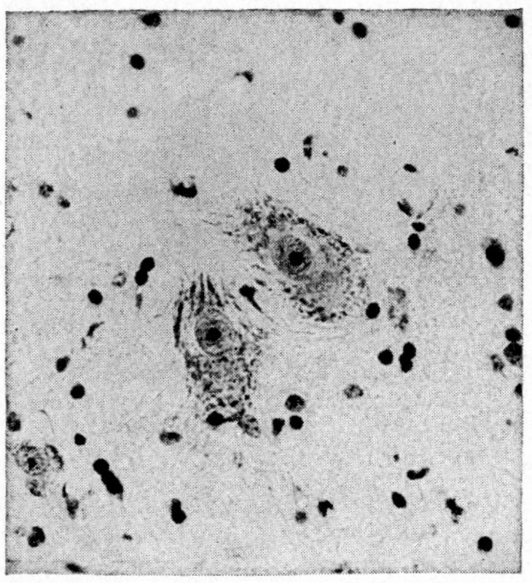

FIG. 9. Neurons of posterior spinal gray, Clarke's nucleus. Note eccentric position of nucleus. Gallocyanin. Photomicrograph, ×305.

GOLGI APPARATUS

Golgi first described in nerve cells the "apparatus" or network named for him, but it has since been shown to be present in all normal living cells. Experimental evidence has been offered to show that the Golgi apparatus in fixed cells results from the action of the techniques on droplets of material stainable with neutral red in freshly teased nerve cells. Covell and Scott watched the droplets become arranged in series, take up osmium or silver as the case may be, and become confluent to form a Golgi network (179). In the nerve cells it lies around the nucleus and on rare occasions may enter the dendrites. In material stained by silver impregnation methods, the Golgi apparatus has the appearance of a reticulum (Figs. 10*A, B*). It responds to injury to the cell or its axon by undergoing certain changes which are grouped under the term "retispersion" (608). These changes involve a displacement of the "apparatus," then its dissolution, and finally its reconstruction in its normal pattern. These events are a part of the general neuronal reaction, chromatolysis, to cutting the axon, and they occur before any change takes place in the Nissl substance.

MITOCHONDRIA

Mitochondria in nerve cells are granular, or more often filamentous, and are more abundant in younger cells and in those containing little fat (Fig. 11). These facts suggest a relationship between the rate of oxidation within the cells and the amount of mitochondria present. Chemically they are phospholipids, possibly in combination with protein. Unlike the Nissl substance, they do not contain iron. The number of mitochondria varies considerably in nerve cells in different parts of the nervous system. Pyramidal motor cells of the cerebral cortex and sensory cells of the brain stem, spinal cord, and posterior root ganglia contain more mitochondria than do motor cells of the brain stem and spinal cord.

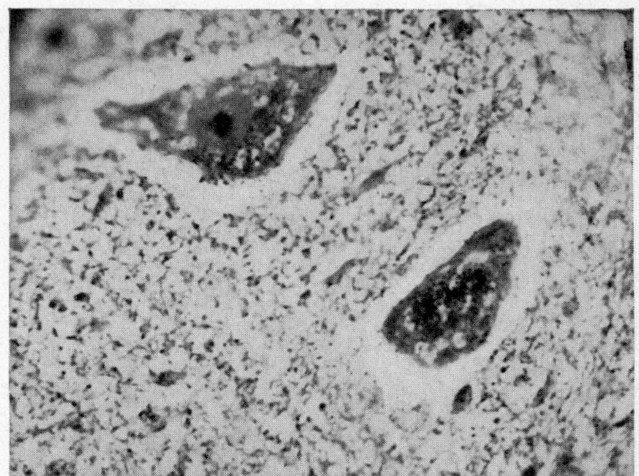

FIG. 11. Neurons of anterior spinal gray, showing mitochondria stained and Golgi apparatus in negative image. Kitten. Fain-Wolf. Photomicrograph, ×645.

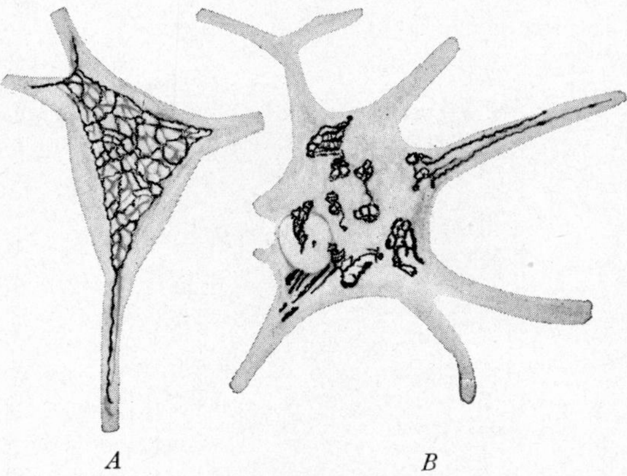

FIG. 10. Golgi apparatus, motor neurons, rabbit. *A*, normal appearance, in cell of sublingual nucleus; *B*, appearance in similar cell, 4 days after cutting the sublingual nerve. (*Redrawn after Marcora, from Maximow and Bloom, "Textbook of Histology," courtesy of W. B. Saunders Company.*)

Mitochondria in normal cells occupy a position immediately adjacent to the Nissl substance, retain this position in chromatolysis, and remain after Nissl substance has disappeared. A progressive increase in the mitochondria of anterior horn cells of the spinal cord occurs after section of a spinal nerve (342). The increase of mitochondria follows approximately the same time course as does chromatolysis, and they increase also in size as well as develop an intensified affinity for certain stains. The changes are possibly related to a higher metabolic level in the affected cells. It is an interesting fact that mitochondria disappear less rapidly than Nissl bodies when the neuron is attacked by the poliomyelitis virus (402).

NEUROFIBRILS

Neurofibrils, like Nissl substance, have been debated structures in so far as their existence in living cells is concerned. They were first discovered by Remak in 1853 and have since been referred to many times as occurring in fixed and stained material (Figs. 4, 12). Neurofibrils appear to run through the nerve cells from the dendrites, around the nucleus, and into the axon. With microscopic dissection techniques they have been observed in normal living cells and fibers in invertebrates and in some of the lower mammals. De Renyi described them in the living nerve fibers of the lobster (662, 663). By methods of silver impregnation the fine fibrils can be seen running through a nerve-cell body and its processes (Fig. 12). Neurofibrils have also been demonstrated in living nerve cells grown in tissue cultures (834).

Electron-microscope studies of fixed and unfixed nerve-fiber axoplasm from vertebrate and invertebrate material have given some information concerning axonic structure (667, 679, 709). The presence of elongate filaments *within* the axon has been verified. These filaments are nodose and frequently contorted. They are of indefinite lengths and of widths ranging between 75 and 200 A. In formalin-fixed material from a variety of vertebrates and invertebrates dense-edged fibrils have been observed (709). These were thought at first to be axonic structures also. Since these fibrils appeared to have a tubular structure, they were tentatively called "neurotubules." In view of subsequent studies of fixed and unfixed axoplasm from invertebrates and vertebrates, it has been suggested that the "neurotubules" are really connective-tissue derivatives.

The origin of the neurofibrillar substance is unknown. It has been considered as a coagulation product. In regeneration experiments neurofibrils have been described as arising from Schwann cells, though Speidel in observations on living nerves disagrees with this (741). If they develop from Schwann cells (see later) in the peripheral nerves, their origin within the central nervous system must be different since no Schwann cells occur there.

Neurofibrils have been considered as wholly or partly concerned in conduction of the nerve impulses. Adherents to this theory present as evidence examples of supposed continuity of neurofibrils from one cell into another. Such evidence is very flimsy, since continuity of substance between neurons does not exist in accordance with the neuron doctrine outlined above. The passage of a nerve impulse along a nerve fiber is now generally recognized as being a surface phenomenon, in which a wave of depolarization sweeps along the surface of the axon. Other authors have considered neurofibrils to be related to the metabolism of the cell and have looked on them as transporters of nutriments from the cell body to the axon limits. It is probable that neurofibrils are only an expression of the longitudinal orientation of micellae in an otherwise homogeneous substance. It is of interest, however, that they become differentiated embryologically in relation to the onset of functional activity (843).

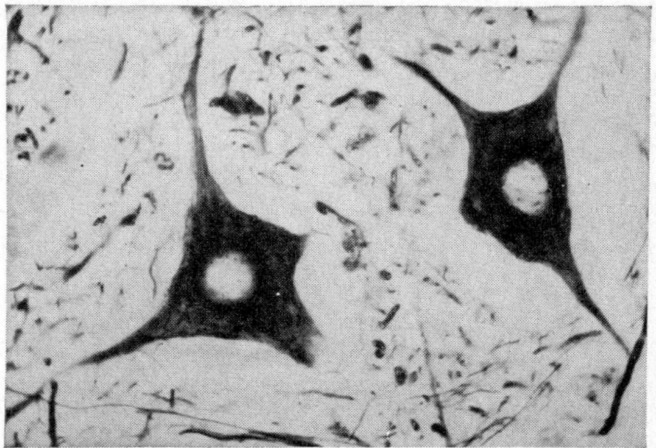

FIG. 12. Neurons of anterior spinal gray, showing neurofibrils. Silver. Photomicrograph, ×498.

OTHER INCLUSIONS

In addition to the above intracellular structures a variety of inclusions are found in neurons. Mineral deposits are seen only in the nucleolus and Nissl granules. Calcium and iron are present in both, and a trace of silica is also found in the nucleolus. Pigment granules are present, and of these the most striking are the dark brown granules, almost certainly melanin, found especially in the cells of the substantia nigra of the midbrain, in the locus caeruleus in the wall of the fourth ventricle, in the dorsal vagus nucleus, and in the spinal and sympathetic ganglia. Lipochrome granules and fatty substances are present in the cytoplasm of many neurons, but their exact significance is not clear.

Cytology of Nerve-cell Processes

Nerve-cell processes are of two kinds, **dendrites** and **axons.** The long bundles of nerve fibers seen in sections of the brain and spinal cord are made up of axons. Peripheral nerves are composed of both axons and dendrites functionally, although the dendritic processes derived from the posterior root ganglion cells resemble structurally the axons (of spinal-cord motor neurons).

DENDRITES

A cell may have many dendrites. These as a rule are short processes; occasionally only one may occur (Fig. 3*A*). Dendrites are direct expansions of the cell body and contain Nissl bodies and mitochondria. They arise from a wide base, rapidly becoming slender at their ends, and branch repeatedly (Fig. 1). The branchlets vary extremely but are typical for each neuron variety. The free tips and surfaces of dendrites may have "spines" or gemmules which are slightly swollen and serve as synaptic organs for receiving nerve impulses.

AXON

A neuron has only one axon (axis cylinder), which is a much longer and thinner process than the dendrite. The axon may occasionally arise from a dendrite, but more often it arises from a part of the cell body known as the **axon hillock,** identifiable through its lack of Nissl substance; the axon itself also does not contain Nissl substance (Figs. 1, 4). Along its course the axon may give off collateral branchlets, but the chief branching is at its termination into many telodendria. The terminal branches may assume, or be grouped into, a variety of shapes. They may entwine about the cell body or the dendrites of another neuron, or there may be only a simple contact. A single axon, by means of its branches, may synapse with several other neurons, always transmitting the nerve impulse to them. In the spinal cord many of the terminal axonal branches are swollen into little button-like structures (end feet, terminal buttons, *boutons terminaux*) which are in contact with the cell bodies and processes of other neurons (Fig. 13).

Nerve fibers (axons and dendrites) are supplied with one or more sheaths which vary according to the type of fiber and its location (Figs. 14, 15). For example, most fibers are closely enveloped by a demonstrable acellular sheath of myelin, of variable thickness. The

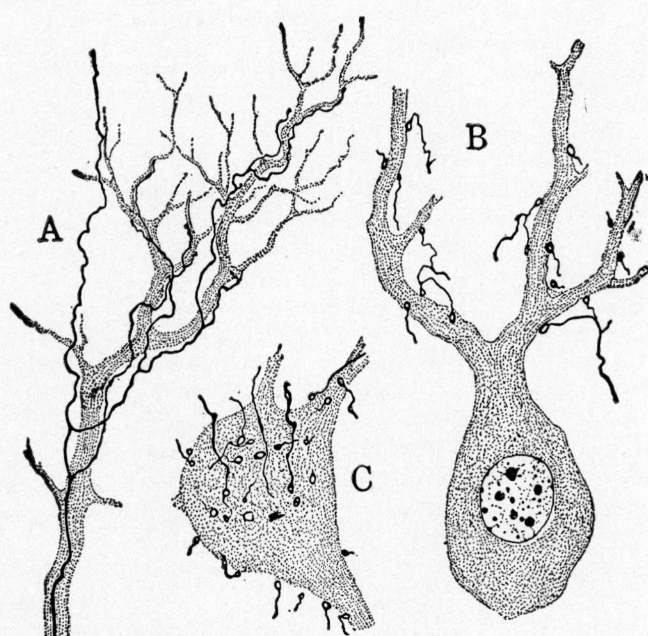

FIG. 13. Synapses. *A* and *B*, climbing fibers and end bulbs on dendrons of Purkinje cells of the cerebellum; *C*, end bulbs on a motor neuron of the spinal cord. Silver stains. (*From Nonidez and Windle, "Textbook of Histology," courtesy of McGraw-Hill Book Company, Inc.*)

myelin is periodically interrupted at the **nodes of Ranvier.** Around the **myelin sheath,** in peripheral nerves only, there is another, the neurolemma sheath (sheath of Schwann). Beneath the neurolemma, between it and the myelin, are **Schwann cells,** protoplasmic structures with a centrally placed nucleus and granular cytoplasmic inclusions. All fibers in peripheral nerves have a neurolemma and Schwann cells, but no fibers in the brain or spinal cord have either, nor do the optic-nerve fibers.

In a consideration of the physical characteristics of peripheral nerve fibers and their sheaths, the experiments of de Renyi, Young, and others are quite helpful (662, 663, 862, 863, 864). From his microdissection studies upon living nerve fibers of the frog, de Renyi describes the axon substance, or **axoplasm,** as of jellylike consistency, soft, easily flattened, and readily deformed. The substance of the nodes of Ranvier is more viscous or solid than is that of the internode, but there are no dissectible differences in physical consistency between the surface and the interior of the axon. The axis cylinder is thinner at the nodes, sometimes only one-half the diameter shown at the internodes. De Renyi could find no fibrillar structures of the axis cylinder as long as it could be considered normal; but as soon as it began to degenerate or dry and to become granular, it assumed a fibrillar appearance. In normal nerve fibers of the lobster, however, neurofibrils were found in a sort of central core of the axon. Young described axoplasm as a complex mixture of semifluid consistency containing some long submicroscopic rodlets (neurofibrils) arranged parallel to the long axis of the fiber. It was stated above that these have been identified by electron-microscope studies. The viscous axoplasm can probably flow down the axon during life. When a nerve fiber is cut, for example, the axoplasm flows out the central end. It appears that a pressure exists in the fiber normally originating in, and maintained by, the cell body, because if a fiber is constricted, it swells central to the constriction. When the obstruction is removed, flow is resumed and the swelling disappears.

The diameter of the axon (or dendrite, in peripheral nerves) has an important influence on function; larger axons conduct more rapidly. The periphery of the axoplasm shows no demonstrable anatomical membrane, but since chemical and physical properties inherent in a membrane are evident, a surface membrane is assumed and is called an **axolemma.** The membrane is differentially permeable to ions. Within the living fiber is a high concentration of potassium and little sodium; outside the fiber these relations are reversed. The membrane also possesses important electrical properties, and these together with its variable permeability are probably essential features of the mechanics by which impulses are propagated.

Axis cylinders and dendrites of peripheral nerves when severed, or injured in other ways, mechanically or chemically, degenerate distal to the point of interruption but have the faculty of regenerating (see Chap. 6).

MYELIN SHEATH

Myelin is composed of proteins and various lipoids, phosphatids, cerebrosides, and sterols, cholesterol being the most important of the sterols. Proteins occur as thin sheets wrapped about the axon, with two layers of lipoids interspersed between adjacent protein layers (710). All nerve fibers may have a myelin sheath, though on many it is not demonstrable with present histological techniques, and these have customarily been called "unmyelinated" fibers. The sheath of the small so-called "unmyelinated" fibers (of about 2 μ size) has a preponderant protein make-up. In the thicker myelin sheaths, the protein and lipoid layers are concentrically arranged, with protein layers and lipoid layers repeated periodically in a radial fashion. The thickness of the myelin sheath varies from fiber to fiber. Those which have no histologically demonstrable myelin sheath are called **Remak's fibers.**

In fixed preparations of peripheral nerves the myelin may appear to have incisions running obliquely into it from its surface, the Schmidt-Lantermann clefts (Fig. 15). They have also been observed with polarized light in fresh, teased nerve fibers. They also occur in the fibers of the central nervous system. It has been suggested that they represent a mechanism for extension in peripheral nerve fibers when they are subjected to stretch (303). Myelin is *organically* connected to the axon but has no connections with the neurolemma. The myelin

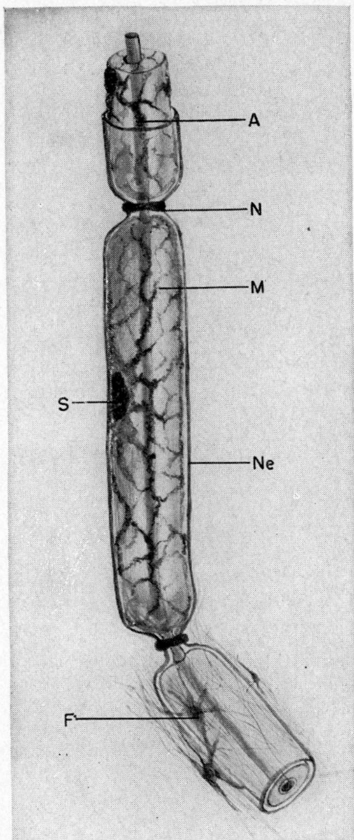

FIG. 14. Diagram of a peripheral nerve fiber to show the sheaths. *A*, axis cylinder; *F*, fibroblast of endoneurim; *M*, myelin sheath; *N*, node of Ranvier; *Ne*, neurolemma; *S*, nucleus of Schwann cell.

sheath is interrupted at intervals by the **nodes of Ranvier,** which give the fibers a segmented appearance caused by the regular constrictions of the axis cylinder and interruptions in the myelin sheath. The segment between nodes is designated the **internode** (Fig. 14). The latter is covered by a single Schwann cell. The nodes of Ranvier are more frequent in the terminal portion of the peripheral nerve fiber. The length of the internodes varies from 50 to 1,000 μ in different fibers and in different animals. Branching of the nerve fiber occurs at the nodes only. Nodes of Ranvier also occur on nerve fibers within the brain and spinal cord.

The origin of myelin is unknown. It appears developmentally after the axis cylinder and the neurolemma. Ranvier thought that it arises from the neurolemma; others believe it to arise from the axis cylinder. In the brain and spinal cord, the oligodendrocyte, one of the supportive neuroglial cells, is thought to be concerned with the formation of myelin. In regeneration experiments Speidel found by direct observation that newly formed nerve sprouts were at first devoid of both neurolemma and myelin sheaths (740). Sheath cells appear before myelin does, and the latter appears near the nucleus of the sheath

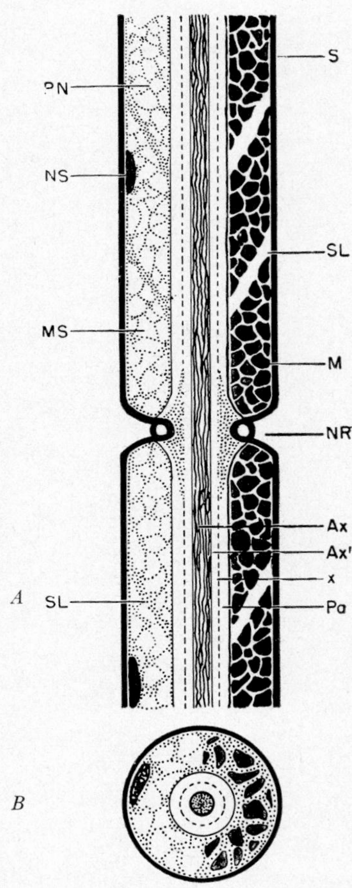

FIG. 15. Schematic representation of peripheral nerve fiber. *A*, in longitudinal section; *B*, in cross section. On the right side of each, the myelin is indicated as if stained with osmic acid; on the left, as if dissolved. *Ax*, axis cylinder; *Ax′*, peripheral zone of axis cylinder devoid of fibrillar substance; *x*, edge of axis cylinder, axolemma; *M*, myelin droplet; *MS*, myelin space; *NR*, node of Ranvier; *NS*, nucleus of Schwann cell; *Pa*, periaxial space about axolemma, indicating shrinkage; *PN*, protoplasmic net; *S*, neurolemmal sheath; *SL*, Schmidt-Lantermann's incisures. (*Redrawn with modification after Nemiloff.*)

cells first and spreads proximally and distally along the nerve fibers. Myelinization as a rule begins close to the body of the neuron.

The function of myelin is also unknown, but it has been considered as an insulator, and it is of importance in determining the velocity of conduction of nerve impulses. The presence of a thick myelin sheath apparently increases the speed of conduction of impulses. Degeneration of the myelin always accompanies degeneration of the axis cylinder, but the converse is not true, as the axis cylinder may remain fairly normal while the myelin degenerates.

SCHWANN CELLS

Heretofore these cells around peripheral nerve fibers have been included as constituents of the neurolemma, or "sheath of Schwann." It seems correct now to interpret them as forming a separate sheath between the neurolemma and the myelin sheath. The cells are thinned out and more or less completely invest the axon or its myelin sheath if this is demonstrably present. One cell is said to occur in an internode length (Fig. 14). Schwann cells have a flat, oval-shaped nucleus, and their cytoplasm contains a Golgi net and mitochondria. The protoplasm is probably homogeneous during life, but occasionally contains granular lipoid inclusions with advancing age.

Schwann cells arise from the neural-crest elements and are thus ectodermal in origin. They are thought to be concerned in the metabolism of the axon and in the maintenance of the myelin sheath. They do not occur along the nerve fibers within the brain and spinal cord. Oligodendrocytes are considered to be their counterpart within the central nervous system (see Chap. 2). Schwann cells are important in regeneration of peripheral nerves (see Chap. 6).

NEUROLEMMAL SHEATH

About the peripheral nerve fibers the neurolemma is a continuous thin, tubular, membranous sheath without interruption at the nodes of Ranvier, where nothing separates it from the axis cylinder (Fig. 14). This fibrillar sheath is most probably derived from the Schwann cells, according to Speidel (740). It holds in place the underlying Schwann cells and with them is of great importance in nerve fiber regeneration. There is no neurolemma in the central nervous system.

The neurolemmal sheath of the spinal nerves, and of those cranial nerves possessing it, terminates (or begins) a short distance from spinal cord or brain stem. At its point of termination the myelin is also interrupted in a node of Ranvier. Proximal to this point, the **Obersteiner-Redlich zone,** the nerve fibers have glial elements entwined about them. The connective-tissue sheaths of peripheral nerve fibers are described in Chap. 6.

NERVE ENDINGS

The terminations of axons and dendrites of peripheral nerves in skin, connective tissues, muscle, and glands are known as nerve endings. Sensory and motor endings or receptor and effector endings exist, therefore. Sensory endings vary considerably in their structural arrangements and are classed as either **free** or **encapsulated** (Fig. 267). They are described in detail in Chap. 19. Motor endings are more simple in arrangement. Those in striated muscle are found ramifying in the motor **sole plate,** a mass of sarcoplasm beneath the sarcolemma (Fig. 113). Many nuclei are present between this mass and the contractile elements beneath it. The naked axis cylinder penetrates the sarcolemma and breaks into many terminal grapelike arborizations. Motor endings in epithelial structures have not been well differentiated. Without regard to a definite histological structure, the functional contact between motor nerve and muscle is called the **myoneural junction.**

SYNAPSE

The point of contact of the terminals of an axon with the dendrites or with the cell body of another neuron is known as the synapse. A synapse is, therefore, the point of contact between axon terminal and the cell membrane (body or dendrite) of another neuron. **Axosomatic** synapses occur between axon terminations of one neuron and the cell body of another; **axodendritic,** between axon terminal and the dendrites of another neuron. **Axoaxonic** synapses have also been described. Various methods of contact exist and include contact by end feet, by gemmules, and by parallel apposition, according to the type of endings of the axon and the receptive spines or gemmules of the dendrite (Fig. 13). About nerve cells in the spinal cord or brain a rich fibrillar plexus of synaptic endings can be demonstrated with metallic impregnation; such collections are known as **neuropile.**

Synaptic association is so intimate that it is not usually possible microscopically to demonstrate two membranes at the point or surface of contact, and yet two must be present (264). Bodian has demonstrated that axon terminals are separated from the cell body and dendrites of a synaptically related neuron by interface plasma membranes (84). The physicochemical organization of the material intervening between the two cells is important, because it is polarized so that the nerve impulse passes across in one direction only, from axon to dendrite or to cell body. Further, of two synapsing neurons, one may die while the other continues to live. The fact that the "giving" cytoplasm is axonic and the "receiving" cytoplasm is not, and the probability that the two are not the same physicochemically, may underly the polarization. The rate of conduction of the nerve impulse is slower at the synapse than elsewhere. The synapse is very susceptible to fatigue and drugs.

The Nerve Impulse. Its Character and Method of Transmission

The unit of activity or response in the nervous system is the nerve impulse, and this in turn is conducted by the unit of structure, the neuron, its cell body and processes. In the living body a neuron normally is thrown into activity in one of two ways: by a stimulus picked up in a sensory end organ and transmitted to the cell body by way of the dendrite; or by a stimulus transmitted from an axon terminal of some other neuron with which it is related synaptically, the stimulus being received by the cell body or its dendrites. Experimental studies have utilized for the most part nerve trunks (or fibers) and nerve-muscle preparations, the stimuli being electric currents. Analysis of the nerve impulse has involved a recording of the **action current,** or **action potential,** the electrical change that accompanies a nerve impulse. Conduction of a nerve impulse without an associated action current has not been found, and action currents do not arise in resting nerves. In making recordings of action currents the cathode-ray oscillograph has been used.

A stimulus of threshold value will set up in a nerve fiber a nerve impulse. This response is followed immediately by a **refractory period,** divisible into two parts. During the first part, or **absolutely refractory period,** there is no response by the nerve regardless of the strength of the stimulus; during the second part, or **relatively refractory period,** it is possible to set up a response, but the stimulus necessary is greater than that required by the resting nerve. The duration of the refractory periods varies for fibers of different size and structure. As the nerve impulse passes along the nerve fiber there follows in its wake for each point of the fiber a refractory period.

The frequency of impulse transmission along a nerve fiber is thus limited by the absolutely refractory period, and similarly, activity in nerves is discontinuous or rhythmic. The duration of the refractory period is of the order of milliseconds. Persistent conduction of excitation along nerves is in the form of a succession of discrete outbursts and has been compared to a stream of bullets from a machine gun (57). Impulses to skeletal muscles are transmitted over motor nerves at frequencies varying from 5 to 50 per sec., and occasionally at a rate of 100 per sec.; impulses in sensory fibers, set up by receptor stimulations, travel at similar frequencies. The most rapidly conducting and most excitable mammalian fibers are permitted by their rate of recovery of excitability to conduct nearly 1,000 impulses a second. It is likely that a part of the recovery of excitability depends on energy derived from chemical changes, since it has been learned that the absolutely refractory period has a temperature coefficient characteristic of a chemical process (57).

The energy for the conduction of a nerve impulse is not dependent on the energy of the stimulus. The size of the impulse in any particular portion of a fiber depends on the condition of that portion. This has been shown by working with fibers injured or narcotized at certain points. During the passage of the impulse through an injured point, a drop in the action potential can be measured, but once the impulse has passed into normal fiber again, the action potential regains its normal size. If a fiber conducts an impulse at all, it will be of the maximum strength possible for the condition of the nerve at that time. Conduction in nerve fibers follows therefore an **all-or-none law.** If a stimulus is adequate, it sets up an impulse in a fiber of maximum magnitude. If the stimulus is below threshold, no impulse is set up.

The fact that the energy of the nerve impulse is derived from the nerve fiber itself is of value in the functioning of nerves. An impulse may thus be conducted along an axon and through all its numerous branchings with undiminished intensity. Through the possible multiple connections (synapses) of the various branchings the impulse may spread from one neuron to many without becoming diminished in strength. Another fact of importance is that an impulse set up by electrical stimulation can travel in either direction along the length of a fiber. In such a manner, a stimulation of an axon branch near its termination in muscle will result in an impulse passing not only into the muscle but also up into the stem fiber and into all its other branches. The conduction of an impulse from the peripheral branch back up into the axon stem fiber and into other branches is said to be **antidromic.** Antidromic conduction is a feature of certain mechanisms of dilating blood vessels in the skin. A sensory fiber near its ending may divide into two branches, *e.g.*, one terminating in skin and one terminating about a blood vessel. Impulses arising in the skin terminal can pass up the fiber to the branching and thus pass downward or antidromically in the blood-vessel branch to bring about a vasodilation of the vessel. Certain physiological mechanisms of sensation apparently involve antidromic conduction (see Chap. 7).

As seen above, nerve fibers are histologically different, there being fibers myelinated in heavy or moderate amounts, and fibers with only the thinnest sheath of myelin. Thickly myelinated axons are usually larger in diameter than thinly myelinated ones and also conduct impulses more rapidly (293). Axon diameter as well as thickness of myelination is important in the speed of transmission of impulses. The speed of conduction varies from a fraction of a meter per second in small fibers to 120 m. per sec. in large fibers. On the basis of their conduction velocities, nerve fibers have arbitrarily been grouped into three classes (see also Chap. 19). *A* fibers have the highest velocity of conduction; *C* fibers, the slowest; and *B* fibers, intermediate velocities. *A* fibers generally are large, heavily myelinated fibers, carrying motor impulses to skeletal muscle and afferent (sensory) impulses from proprioceptive receptors in skeletal muscles and tactile receptors in the skin. *B* fibers are small myelinated fibers occurring in certain nerves of the autonomic nervous system. *C* fibers are the small, most thinly myelinated or so-called "unmyelinated" ones and are found in the autonomic nerves and also as mediators of certain sensations of pain and temperature throughout the body (Fig. 267).

The properties of a nerve may be altered by changes in the chemical composition of the surrounding fluid. Small changes in the concentration of calcium and potassium, for example, cause marked alterations in the properties of nerve fibers. Increasing amounts of potassium may at first cause an increase in excitability, and later a reduction; a decrease in potassium below normal level tends to decrease the excitability. Treatment of a peripheral nerve with a calcium-free solution increases excitability to such an extent that several responses may be elicited by a single electric shock. Prolonged treatment of a nerve with calcium-free solution may cause the nerve to go into spontaneous activity. An increase in calcium reduces the excitability. Increased excitability of nerves is seen clinically in the condition **tetany,** which is characterized by a calcium deficiency.

The mechanism of transmission of the nerve impulse is perhaps best explained by the **core-conductor theory,** or **membrane hypothesis.** According to the membrane theory the nerve-cell membrane and that of its axon, the axolemma, are the seat of an electromotive force which gives rise to the resting potential of the cell. Mechanisms which maintain in the interior of the axon ionic distribution different from the external medium determine the resting potential. Sodium and potassium exchange takes place through the resting membrane, however. No flow of current occurs, since the potential is the same at all places on the resting cell membrane. Application of a threshold stimulus at a point on the nerve fiber causes a breakdown of the membrane at that point and locally abolishes the membrane potential (Fig. 16).

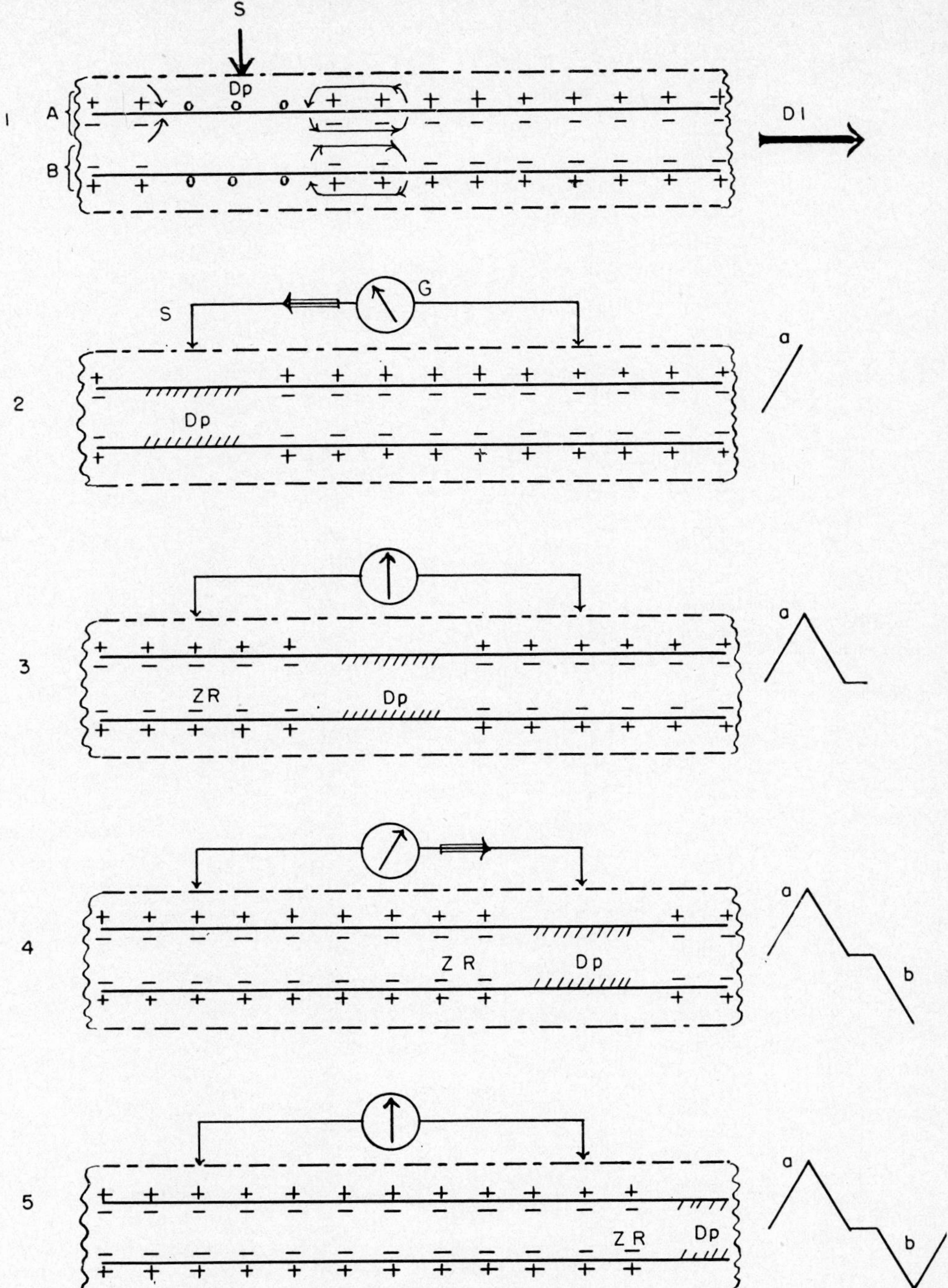

FIG. 16. Diagram of a nerve fiber suggesting the sequence of events during the passage of an impulse and the production of a diphasic action current registered galvanometrically. *A* and *B*, axon membranes with positive charges on the exterior surface and negative charges on the interior surface. The axon membrane is lying within a fluid medium immediately surrounding it and itself enclosing the axoplasm. *DI*, direction of propagated impulse flow; *Dp*, zone of depolarization of the membranes; *G*, galvanometer for registering the action current; *S*, stimulus. Arrows indicate the flow of current and the swing of the needle in the galvanometer as the zone of depolarization passes beneath the leads. *ZR*, zone of reconstitution where the original electrical signs of the membrane are restored; the membranes are repolarized.

A potential difference is thus brought about between normal regions of the nerve and this region of breakdown, and local currents are set up. These currents cause a breakdown of membrane potential of a neighboring segment with setting up of local currents there, and the breakdown process spreads along the fiber like a flame along a fuse. The breakdown is repaired rapidly, and at any one time only a small segment is broken down. As an impulse travels along a nerve the region of breakdown is in absolutely refractory state. Adrian described the mechanism of impulse transmission as a little patch of surface leakage spreading along the fiber and being sealed up again as soon as it has formed (13, 14). During activity in the axon, potassium is lost through the membrane and sodium is gained.

The mechanism of transmission of the nerve impulse from nerve to muscle (across the myoneural junction) and from neuron to neuron (across the synapse in peripheral ganglia and in the central nervous system) has not been uniformly agreed upon. It is known that transmission in both instances is in only one direction, from nerve to muscle and from axon to dendrite or to cell. Two theories have been postulated concerning the mechanism of transmission across the myoneural junction (and also across the synapse), the **electrical** and the **chemical.** The electrical theory holds that the muscle fiber is stimulated in the same way that one segment of a nerve is excited, as a result of a change in membrane potential in an adjacent segment.

According to the chemical theory, transmission is effected through the liberation of certain chemical mediators (125). These mediators were first discovered in the autonomic nervous system, which controls the activities of glands, smooth muscle, and cardiac muscle. They are acetylcholine and sympathin. **Acetylcholine** is produced when impulses arrive in outlying autonomic ganglia, particularly in parasympathetic endings and also at sympathetic preganglionic endings. Acetylcholine is quickly destroyed by **acetylcholinesterase,** a substance found in nerve tissues and blood. **Sympathin** is the substance liberated at the postganglionic sympathetic endings and is apparently similar to, but not identical to, adrenaline. On the basis of the chemical substance liberated, autonomic nerve fibers have been classed by Dale as **cholinergic** (acetylcholine liberated) and as **adrenergic** (sympathin liberated, the term "adrenergic" being derived from the word adrenaline). This pharmacological classification does not parallel the anatomical divisions of the autonomic nerve fibers, as will be seen later. There is evidence that liberation of acetylcholine is an important factor in the transmission of nerve impulse to skeletal muscle fibers, but an evaluation of data makes it unwise to say that this is the only process involved (193). A combination of the chemical and electrical theories is perhaps the best explanation of all the factors involved in the excitation of skeletal muscle, as well as in nerve-impulse conduction and transmission generally.

It seems likely that acetylcholine plays a role in the conduction of the nerve impulse along the nerve fiber as well as in its transmission across the synapse. The manner in which it acts is not clear as yet. It has been suggested, however, that acetylcholine acts to alter the permeability of the nerve-fiber membrane. By the movement of ions, particularly sodium and potassium, local currents are set up. A repetition of this activity along the fiber leads to the propagation of a flow of current and thus the conduction of the nerve impulse. Similar processes have been suggested as underlying impulse transmission across synapses and myoneural junctions. In accordance with this scheme, acetylcholine liberated in the terminal membrane of the presynaptic fiber leads to the generation of electric currents. These flow across the synaptic barrier to the postsynaptic membrane and lead to the liberation of acetylcholine there. This in turn alters the permeability of the postsynaptic membrane wherein currents are set up. Acetylcholinesterase and other enzymes are involved in the processes, since conduction in a fiber appears to depend on the liberation and removal of acetylcholine. Acetylcholinesterase has been found in all types of nerve tissue.

Neurons are thus well equipped structurally for their role of collection of stimuli and conduction of impulses. Intracellular inclusions, which are numerous, are perhaps essential for the rapid metabolic exchanges which the neurons undergo. Protection and isolation are furnished the nerve-cell processes by myelin, neurolemma, and endoneurium (see Chap. 6). Where better functional results will be obtained the structure varies, *e.g.,* in the many branched dendrites of the Purkinje cell. Speed of conduction is increased through fibers of larger diameter and thicker myelin sheaths. Slower-conducting and perhaps longer-acting elements are smaller and less myelinated, *e.g.,* the pain fibers, and it will be seen later that pain endings adapt more slowly to stimuli than other types of endings. Specificity of function is served by having endings of varied composition and type, as will be seen especially when sensory terminals are considered in more detail. Nerve-muscle relationships are structurally well adapted and nerve-fiber physical characteristics are well suited for excellent performance. And finally, the ability to regenerate, inherent in many neurons, offers a certain margin of safety to the organism.

Before describing the development of the nervous system and manner in which neurons are collected into functional groups such as simple spinal reflex arcs and longer circuits in the spinal cord and brain, it is necessary to consider first those elements in the nervous system that do not exhibit a conductive ability. These cells, next to be described, are astrocytes, oligodendrocytes, and microglia.

CHAPTER 2

NEUROGLIA AND MICROGLIA NEUROHISTOLOGICAL METHODS

In addition to neurons, there are in the central nervous system other elements, neuroglia, of ectodermal origin, which are nonconductive but are supportive in character and which also take part in the reaction of the nervous system to injury or infection. The ectodermal nonnervous tissue within the central nervous system differentiates along three lines, leading to the formation of three types of structural elements. These are the ependyma, the chorioid plexuses, and the neuroglia. The first two will be considered in the section dealing with the meninges and cerebrospinal fluid (Chap. 4). Certain mesodermal cellular elements are present in the central nervous system whose functions are supportive and phagocytic. These are the microglia.

Neuroglia and microglia are relatively recently discovered components of the nervous system possibly because more or less specific techniques are required for their staining and identification. Neuroglia are of two types, **astrocytes** and **oligodendrocytes** (611). The astrocytes were identified first, and later the microglia and the oligodendrocytes were recognized. These latter two cell types were first accurately described by Del Rio Hortega in 1919. It is necessary to use metallic stains (gold or silver) for demonstrating astrocyte cell bodies. Oligodendrocytes and microglia require special silver solutions for impregnation and identification. The nuclei only of the three cells are stained with ordinary hematoxylin and Nissl stains.

In the central nervous system, therefore, it is correct to refer to three types of cellular elements exclusive of meninges, blood vessels, and ependyma. These include **neuronal** elements concerned with the propagation of the nerve impulse and thus with integration; **neuroglia** (astrocytes and oligodendrocytes) serving in a supportive and protective function; and **microglia** associated with the task of taking up, transforming, and removing the products of normal and abnormal disintegration of neurons. In disease processes the neurons undergo **degenerative** changes, the neuroglia become **proliferative** in scar-tissue formation, and the microglia are **phagocytes.** The pathological substratum of a disease will vary according to (*a*) the site of the most severe injury, (*b*) the way in which neurons degenerate and neuroglia react, and (*c*) the phagocytic activity of the microglia. Most of the tumors of the central nervous system arise from neuroglial elements. Rarely microglia have been found as the cell type in a tumor of the central nervous system. With a few of these, proliferations of comparable reticulo-endothelial cells have been found in other organs such as the spleen, kidney, bone marrow, and lung (696).

Astrocytes

Two chief types of astrocytes have been described, **fibrous** and **protoplasmic** (611) (Figs. 17, 18, 19, 20). The former can form fibers which serve, as connective tissue elsewhere serves, as a supporting element. The protoplasmic astrocytes are normally more prevalent in the gray matter of the nervous system. They do not normally form fibers but may do so under stimulus of disease. Both types of astrocytes have one or more **vascular feet** which are extensions of the cell to or toward a neighboring blood vessel (Figs. 18, 19). Dispute exists regarding the exact physical relationship between the astrocyte foot and the blood-vessel wall. Whether or not actual continuity exists

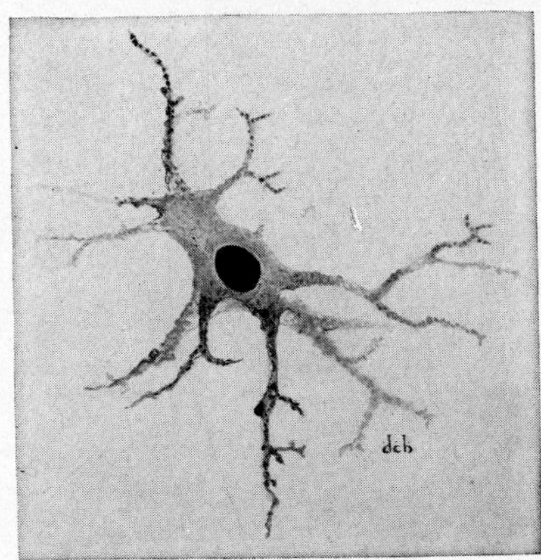

Fig. 17. Drawing of protoplasmic astrocyte. Many gliosomes are evident. Human. Cerebral cortex. ×975.

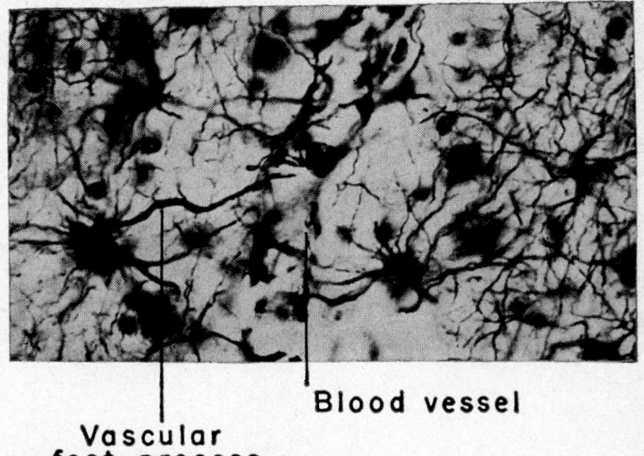

Fig. 19. Fibrous astrocytes with foot process. Cerebral cortex. Dog. Cajal's gold chloride sublimate. Photomicrograph, ×497.

with the vessel endothelium is debated. Though astrocytes are not actively phagocytic, certain materials can penetrate their cell membrane, and it has been suggested that such substances are then disposed of by means of the vascular feet. Another suggestion is that the foot process serves as a channel for emptying the secretion of certain astrocytes into the blood stream. On the basis of assays for cholinesterase in human embryos and in brain tumors, it has been suggested that the formation of this enzyme may be rather intimately related to the astrocyte or its younger form, the astroblast (868).

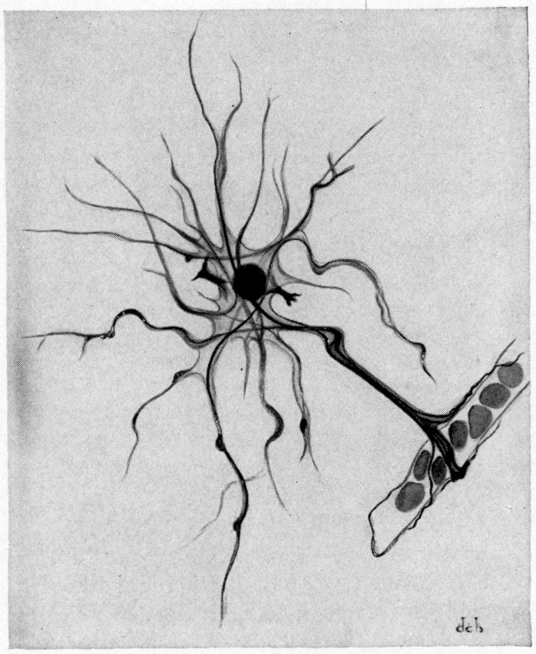

Fig. 18. Drawing of fibrous astrocyte. The cell has a vascular foot process, and several fibrils are seen crossing the cell. Human. Cerebral cortex. ×975.

In addition to the vascular foot processes, astrocytes have numerous expansions from the cell body, and these branch. The expansions of the fibrous astrocytes are less numerous, and are straighter, than those of the protoplasmic. The nucleus of the astrocyte is irregularly oval and contains a small amount of chromatin, and the cells can be identified in Nissl preparations by the character of their nuclei (Fig. 7*B*). These are round or oval, about the size of a nucleus of a small neuron, contain only a few chromatin particles, and do not possess a nucleolus. It is difficult to stain the astrocyte nucleus and cell body well with a single technique. The cytoplasm is granular when stained with gold, and granules can also be seen at intervals along the cell processes. They are called **gliosomes** and are thought to be similar to the secretion granules of certain gland cells. Fibrous astrocytes have fibrils coursing "through" them, and it is difficult to say whether they are intracellularly or extracellularly placed, though there is some evidence that the fibrils are covered by cell protoplasm everywhere. The fibrils do not pass from one cell to another, nor are the astrocytes joined to one another.

In response to abnormal conditions astrocytes are either destroyed or stimulated to hypertrophy and to multiplication by amitotic

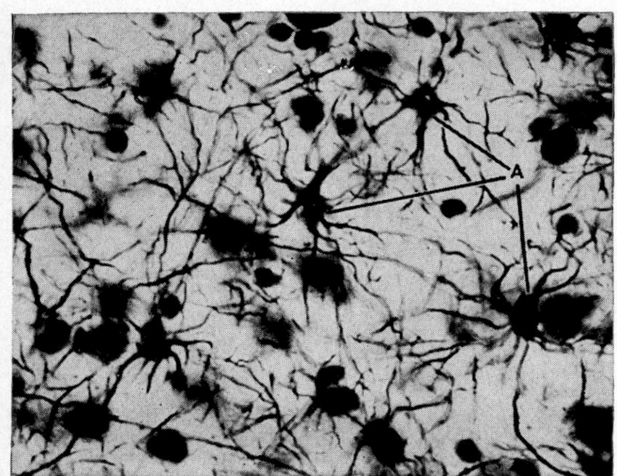

Fig. 20. Protoplasmic astrocytes indicated at *A*. Cerebral cortex. Monkey. Cajal's gold chloride sublimate. Photomicrograph, ×608.

division into several daughter cells. Each daughter cell from a dividing astrocyte receives a part of the vascular foot process. The fibrils disappear from a swollen fibrous astrocyte about to divide. After division, however, all the daughter cells show fibrils regardless of whether the mother cell was a protoplasmic or fibrous type. Astrocytes may be stimulated to **gliosis,** which includes hyperplasia and hypertrophy. The latter is associated with an increase in the size and number of fibers in those astrocytes already containing fibers. On the other hand, astrocytes may disintegrate in response to injury. Degeneration frequently involves a swelling and subsequent fragmentation of the cells (**clasmatodendrosis**).

Oligodendrocytes

These are the most difficult of the supporting cells to stain, and again it is seldom possible to stain simultaneously both cell body and nucleus (609) (Figs. 21, 22). Oligodendrocytes have no vascular feet, do not form fibers, and have more delicate and fewer expansions than do astrocytes. The cytoplasm is granular, and the expansions are frequently studded with gliosomes. Regardless of their position, oligodendrocytes always have about the same shape. They are more numerous in white matter and are not motile. According to their chief locations they are classified as **satellite** (around neurons), **perivascular,** and **interfascicular** (along nerve fibers). The last type are perhaps most

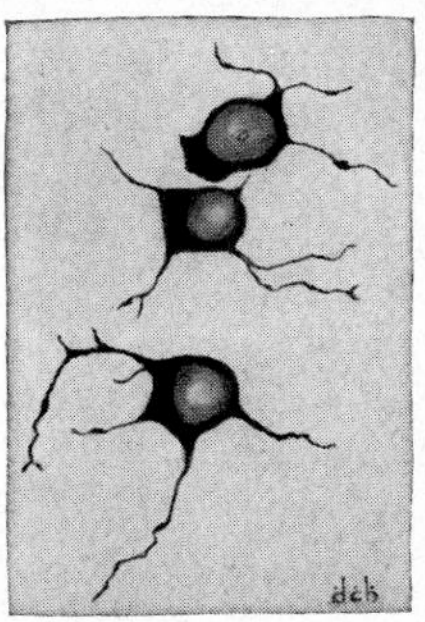

Fig. 21. Drawing of oligodendrocytes from a preparation stained with silver carbonate. Thalamus. Monkey. ×975.

numerous and are frequently seen in rows of 2 to 20 along nerve fibers, the processes entwined about the fiber. In Nissl preparations these cells are identifiable only by their nuclei. These are small, are round, and contain varying amounts of chromatin (Fig. 7*B*).

Round or oval cells, similarly located in the nervous system as those previously described, are found lacking processes (30). Their cytoplasm is difficult to impregnate, variable in amount, causing difference in cell size, and is, for the most part, clear. Their nuclei are rich in chromatin and are round. These cells are thought to be related to the oligodendrocytes and have been named **adendroglia,** since they lack processes.

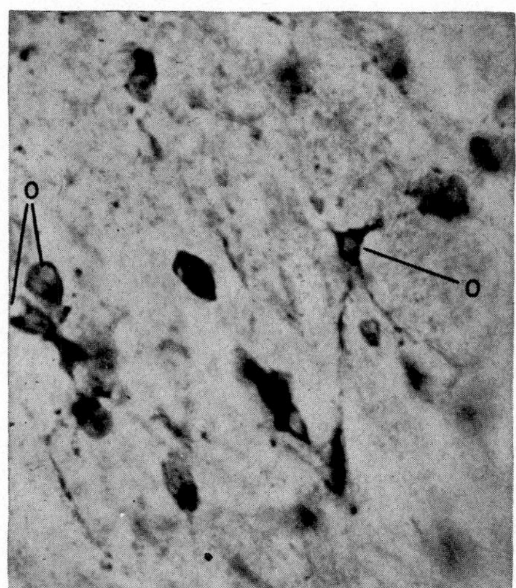

Fig. 22. Oligodendrocytes indicated at *O*. Thalamus. Monkey. Penfield's modification of Hortega's silver carbonate. Photomicrograph, ×736.

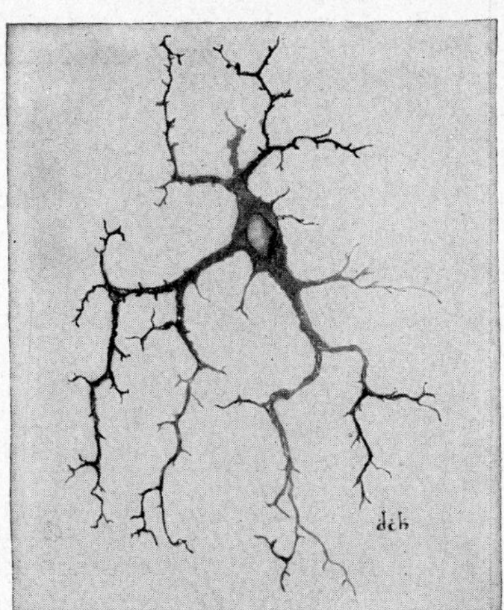

FIG. 23. Drawing of microglia from preparation of cerebral cortex of rabbit. Silver carbonate. ×975.

In response to injury the neuronal satellite cells increase in numbers. There is usually an increase in, or an adsorption to, their bodies of amounts of iron and fats. Oligodendrocytes with processes are said not to be phagocytic; the adendroglia are described as being actively phagocytic, especially in cases in which death of neurons occurs. In disorders in which myelin is destroyed, interfascicular oligodendrocytes decrease in number, while astrocytes increase in number, and it is considered likely that certain of the oligodendrocytes become astrocytes. Degenerative changes in oligodendrocytes take several forms. In one form the cell and its processes become swollen and watery, and the nucleus is shrunken. These large cells may fragment and be phagocytized. In a second form the cells show an enlargement with a material like mucin; this reaction is called **mucoid degeneration.**

Oligodendrocytes are considered to be important functionally, either in the formation of myelin in the central nervous system or in its maintenance. They are thought to bear the same relation to nerve fibers in the central nervous system that Schwann cells bear to nerve fibers in the peripheral nerves.

MICROGLIA

These cells, the origin of which has been the subject of much dispute, are now generally believed to arise from **mesodermal** elements and subsequently to have invaded the developing central nervous system at the time when meningeal and vascular organization of the developing brain reached its height (436, 678). They are seen first on some surfaces of the brain immediately below the pia. They enter in several regions, the chief of which are (*a*) the pia which lines the fornix and a part of the thalamus; (*b*) the portion of pia covering the cerebral peduncles; and (*c*) the medullocerebellar and medullopontine folds of pia. At first they are rounded cells, looking like lymphocytes. As they spread by active migration through the nervous system they are successively globose, round, and branched in appearance.

The microglia are most abundant in gray matter, and their appearance varies according to location and their state of activity (Figs. 23, 24). The nuclei are polymorphic and may be twisted to resemble an S or a C; they have abundant chromatin and possess a nucleolus. With Nissl stains they are easily recognized by their very deep stain and irregular contour (Fig. 7*B*). A very scanty amount of protoplasm is present in the cell body, from which arise several prolongations of diverse lengths. These processes become thinner distally, branch, and are covered with fine spikes. According to location and shape monopolar, bipolar, multipolar,

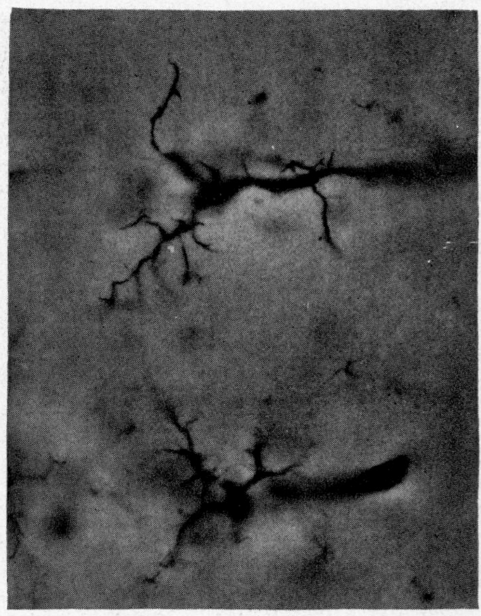

Fig. 24. Microglia. Cerebral cortex. Rabbit. Silver carbonate. Photomicrograph, ×645.

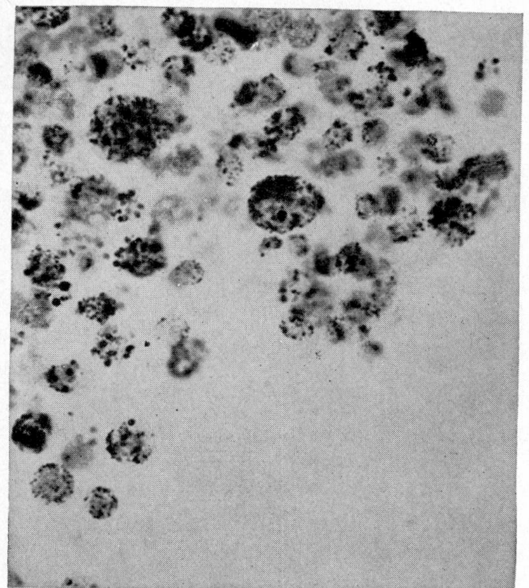

Fig. 25. Microglia in a phagocytic phase, filled with neuronal debris stained black. Preparation from edge of experimental lesion in cerebral cortex of monkey. Marchi technique. These cells are sometimes referred to as "gitter" cells. Photomicrograph, ×425.

and lamellar forms of microglia are described. Vascular feet are not present, but sometimes the cell processes are entwined about blood vessels.

When inactive, microglia have their many processes. In phagocytic activities, however, they undergo a change in shape. They round up, draw in the elongations, and become swollen in appearance (Fig. 25). The cytoplasm becomes vesicular and reticulated, and the cells resemble the ordinary macrophages of other tissues. In this stage they have phagocytic (and hemolytic) functions, are actively motile, and increase in number through mitotic division. Once they have phagocytized cellular debris they transport it to the vicinity of blood vessels, where it is possible that it may be taken up by the endothelial cells of the vessels. The microglia are important in infections of the nervous system and in clearing away the debris of normal cellular disintegration. The microglia in the central nervous system of animals ingest vital dyes, such as trypan blue, injected into the animals, and they react just as macrophages of the reticulo-endothelial system elsewhere react.

Cytogenesis of Neuroglia

These cells have been studied in the developing nervous system of human embryos from 8 weeks age to term (435, 436). The origins of astrocytes and oligodendrocytes are similar. Both arise from neuroepithelial cells in the ependymal layer of the developing nervous system, and as they develop they move out into the mantle and marginal layers (see Chap. 3). A brief sketch of development will suffice. The development of neurons and ependyma is also included.

Table 1. Development of the Neuron, Neuroglia, and Ependyma

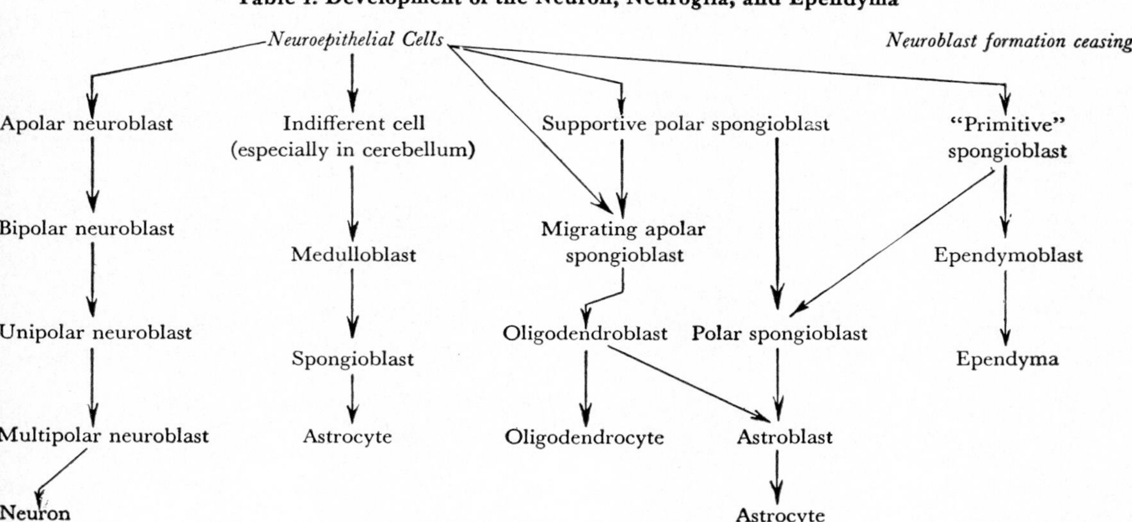

The medulloblasts are called indifferent cells also, because potentially they can develop into neurons or astrocytes. They are more frequently called medulloblasts, and they form the principal cell type of a fatal tumor occurring in children, the **medulloblastoma.** In the human-embryo material in which neuroglial cytogenesis was studied, these cells were found only in the cerebellum, and this is in keeping with the fact that medulloblastomata are practically never known to occur primarily in any region except in the cerebellum (435). Medulloblastomata, being of a primitive cell type, grow rapidly, are sensitive to x-ray treatment, but are prone to recur.

In addition to their part in medulloblastoma formation, neuroglial elements are found as the principal cell type in other brain tumors classified therefore as **gliomas.** These form about 40 per cent of all intracranial tumors (805). Astrocytes are the predominant cell type in **astrocytomata;** astroblasts, in **astroblastomata;** and spongioblasts, in **spongioblastomata.** Oligodendrocytes are the predominant cell type in **oligodendrocytomata,** and oligodendroblasts in **oligodendroblastomata.**

In order of frequency, astrocytomata are perhaps most common; next, usually spongioblastoma (glioblastoma) multiforme; medulloblastoma; astroblastoma; spongioblastoma (polare); oligodendroglioma. Astrocytomata and oligodendroblastomata usually show the longest survival times; glioblastomata and medulloblastomata, the shortest. Astrocytomata occur in the cerebrum of adults and in the cerebellum in children and sometimes in adults. Slow-growing, they tend to be circumscribed and may be associated with cyst formation. Glioblastomata occur in the cerebral hemispheres, are rapid in growth, and may invade large areas of the brain. Oligodendrogliomata occur nearly always in the cerebral hemispheres, are very cellular, are hard, slow-growing, and tend to show calcification.

HISTOLOGICAL METHODS OF STUDY FOR NERVOUS TISSUE

Histological studies of nervous tissue represent a relatively modern field, and several different techniques are necessarily used. In the following brief discussion the dates in parentheses show approximately the first application of the various fundamental methods. Neurons have been impregnated with silver to bring out such elements as the Golgi apparatus (1875) and neurofibrils (1897) as well as to outline the contour of the cell. Silver techniques are also useful in studying nerve endings such as terminal buttons. Nissl (1892) first stained with methylene blue the bodies named for him. Other basic dyes stain Nissl substance and nuclei and give information about the physiological and pathological state of the cell. Normal myelin can be stained by various of the Weigert techniques (1884–1891). Degenerating myelin may be stained with osmic acid, and the Marchi technique (1886) utilizes this fact. Osmic acid also stains normal myelin, but treatment with dichromates or iodates as in the Marchi technique prevents this, while the degenerating myelin is still stained.

In endeavoring to learn something of the anatomical groupings and relations of neurons, as well as something of their function, research on the nervous system has involved removal of certain parts (especially cerebral and cerebellar cortex) with subsequent study of the animal for physiological changes. After sacrificing the animal, anatomical connections of the brain tissue removed may be learned by seeking degenerating fibers of neurons removed, as well as degenerating fiber endings. On the other hand, the origin of fibers can be determined anatomically by searching for the neurons undergoing chromatolysis after nerve fibers (axons) have been divided. The distribution of certain neuron processes can be determined, if myelinated, by sectioning them and applying the Marchi technique to the parts distal to the cut within a week or so. This technique will demonstrate the degenerating myelin sheaths. Degenerating end organs, such as terminal buttons, will also serve to point out the distribution of axis cylinders.

The technique known as physiological neuronography, devised by Dusser de Barenne, has proved useful in defining neural connections (217, 221). The method utilizes the fact that a solution of strychnine sulfate applied to neurons or their dendrites will bring those neurons to discharge through their axons. The activity thus created in the vicinity of the synapses of the axon terminals can be recorded through an implanted electrode. Although strychnine stimulation is most often used in physiological neuronography, electrical stimulation may also be utilized. Much has been learned also by stimulating peripheral end organs physiologically and recording the induced electrical activity in brain stem, thalamus, and cerebral and cerebellar cortices. Functional localizations also can be ascertained with respect to motor activities, by stimulating the exposed cortex of an animal electrically or with a drug such as strychnine which causes neurons to discharge. The representation of muscles or movements in the cortex can be determined by stimulating the cortex and observing muscle contraction obtained thereby or measuring change in tensions in isolated muscles. It is customary to combine anatomical and physiological experiments for best results in an investigation of the nervous system.

Thus far only individual components of the nervous system, the neurons and the nonconductive elements, have been considered. Before investigating how these individuals are combined into the gross structure of the brain and spinal cord, it will be wise to consider the embryology of the nervous tissues.

CHAPTER 3

DEVELOPMENT OF THE NERVOUS SYSTEM

THE EMBRYONIC central nervous system at an early stage is a hollow tube. This **neural tube** develops by the rolling up of a flat sheet of cells, called the **medullary plate,** after the manner illustrated (Fig. 26). Thus the anlage of the central nervous system is first recognizable at about the time of gastrulation, when it appears as a thickening in the primitive ectoderm overlying the notochord. Experiments with amphibian embryos indicate that the notochord induces this development in the ectoderm; a neural tube failed to develop when this relationship was not maintained (391, 742). The medullary plate is composed of columnar epithelium (Fig. 27) and in the human embryo occupies the anterior part of the embryonic disk (Fig. 26). A longitudinal furrow (medullary groove) appears in the mid-line (of the plate), and ridges grow up on each side, eventually to meet above and form a tunnel. This process may be followed in Figs. 28 and

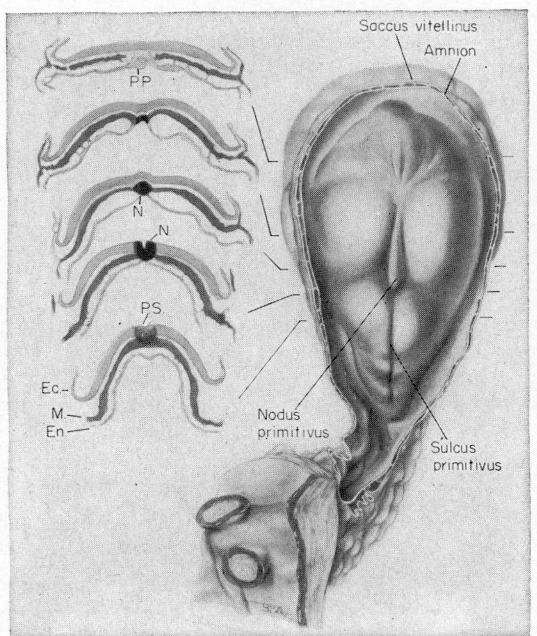

FIG. 26. Dorsal sketch of model of embryo to show medullary plate. Menstrual age, 32 days. The drawings to the left show representative sections at planes indicated. *Ec*, ectoderm; *En*, entoderm; *M*, mesoderm; *N*, notochord; *PP*, prochordal plate; *PS*, primitive streak. ×37. (*Redrawn from C. H. Heuser, Contrib. Embryol., vol.* 23, *Carnegie Inst. Wash. Publ.* 433.)

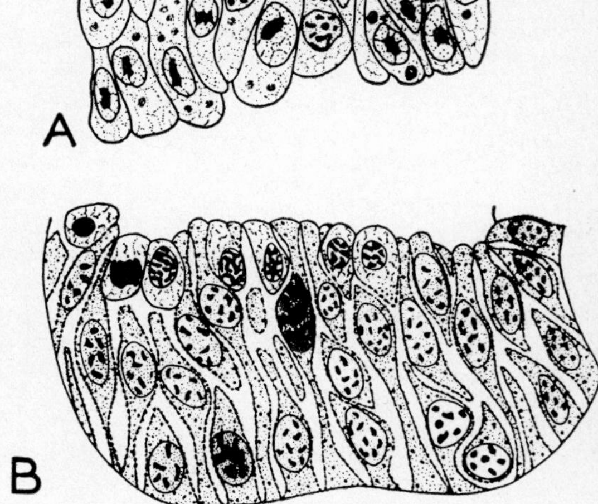

FIG. 27. *A*, camera-lucida drawing of neural plate of a chick embryo, showing the columnar form of the interkinetic cells, the rounded form assumed in mitosis, and the attachment of the cells to each other by terminal bars. *B*, one side of the neural tube of a 24-somite toadfish embryo, illustrating the columnar form of the cells. The figure indicates the appearance at one focus level; the majority of the cells could be traced through their entire length by focusing. Drawn at ×1800; reduced to ×750. (*After F. C. Sauer, J. Comp. Neurol., vol.* 63.)

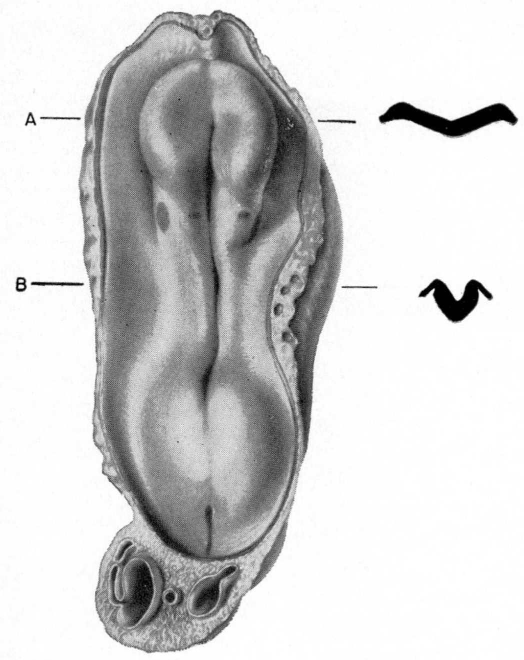

FIG. 28. Dorsal sketch of model of embryo showing medullary groove. Figures at the right represent sections taken at planes indicated. ×50. (*Redrawn from N. W. Ingalls, Contrib. Embryol., vol.* 11, *Carnegie Inst. Wash. Publ.* 274.)

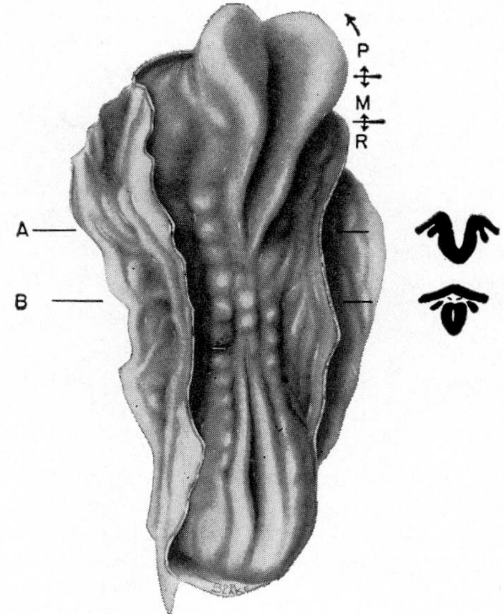

FIG. 29. Dorsal sketch of model of seven-somite embryo showing the neural tube. Drawings at the right show sections at the planes indicated. *P*, *M*, and *R* indicate the regions of the future prosencephalon, mesencephalon, and rhombencephalon, respectively. ×33. (*Redrawn after F. Payne, Contrib. Embryol., vol.* 16, *Carnegie Inst. Wash. Publ.* 407.)

29, and especially in the cross-section diagrams *A* and *B* of each. After the tube is formed it loses its connections with the overlying ectoderm.

DIVISIONS OF THE NEURAL TUBE

Even before the neural tube is completely closed cephalically, three primary brain vesicles may be recognized (*P, M,* and *R* of Fig. 29). They are known as **prosencephalon, mesencephalon,** and **rhombencephalon**—or, more commonly, as **forebrain, midbrain,** and **hindbrain,** respectively. Their subsequent division and modification is summarized in Figs. 30, 31, 32, 33, and 34 and in Table 2. Unequal growth rates and migration of cells result in flexures, constrictions, thickenings, invaginations, and evaginations. By the time the human embryo has reached a length of 5 mm., marked mesencephalic and cervical flexures are present, and the optic vesicle, an evagination of the forebrain, has become converted into an optic cup (Fig. 30). In an 11-mm. human embryo (6 weeks after fertilization) a third, or pontine, flexure, compensatory to the other two, has become marked, and the rhombencephalon can be subdivided into **myelencephalon** and **metencephalon** (Fig. 31). Evaginating cerebral vesicles now constitute the **telencephalon,** while

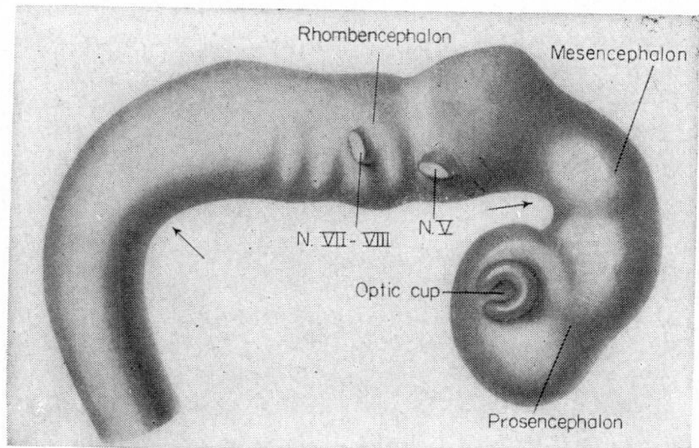

FIG. 30. Reconstruction of the external form of the right half of the cranial part of the central nervous system in a 5-mm. human embryo. The arrows indicate the mesencephalic and cervical flexures. (*After Hochstetter*, 1919. *Redrawn courtesy of Hamilton, Boyd, and Mossman, "Human Embryology," W. Heffer & Sons, Ltd.*)

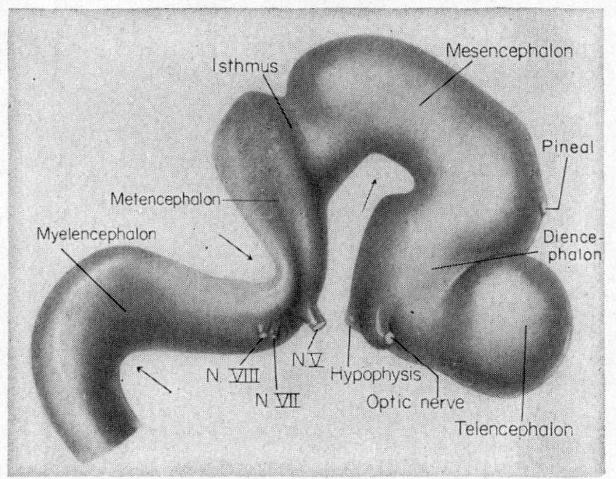

FIG. 31. Reconstruction of the external form of the right half of the cranial part of the central nervous system in an 11-mm. human embryo. The dorsal arrow indicates the pontine flexure; the ventral arrows, the mesencephalic and cervical flexures. The thin rhombencephalic roof is not shown. (*After Hochstetter*, 1919. *Redrawn courtesy of Hamilton, Boyd, and Mossman, "Human Embryology," W. Heffer & Sons, Ltd.*)

the medially situated remainder of the prosencephalon is the **diencephalon.** Dorsal and ventral diencephalic evaginations, apparent at this stage, become the primordia of the pineal gland and posterior hypophysis, respectively. Later features of brain growth, illustrated in Figs. 32, 33, 34, include dorsolateral thickenings of the metencephalon to form the cerebellum and the tremendous expansion of the cerebral vesicles to constitute the cerebral hemispheres.

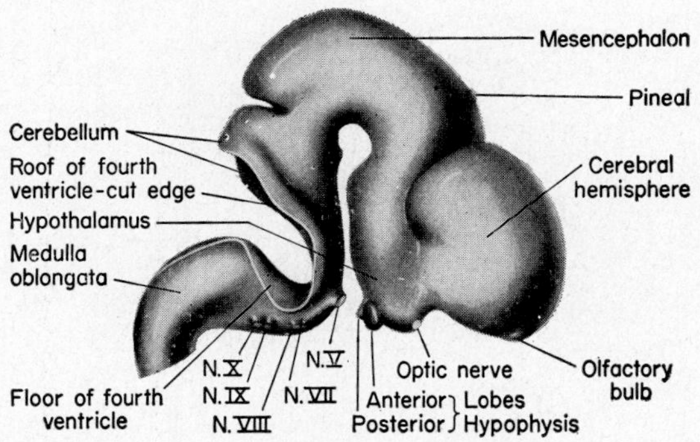

FIG. 32. Reconstruction of the external form of the right half of the cranial part of the central nervous system in a 15-mm. human embryo. The roof of the fourth ventricle has been removed. (*After Hochstetter*, 1919. *Redrawn courtesy of Hamilton, Boyd, and Mossman, "Human Embryology," W. Heffer & Sons, Ltd.*)

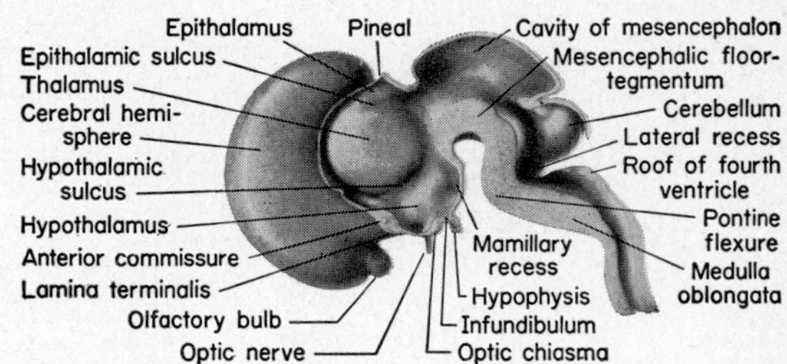

FIG. 33. Medial surface of a reconstruction of the right half of the cranial part of the central nervous system in a 43-mm. human embryo. (*Courtesy of Dr. Marion Hines, J. Comp. Neurol., vol.* 34.)

The functional analysis of different regions of the central nervous system is best understood on the basis of the nerve-fiber connections, which are treated in the later sections. There is recognizable very early, however, a gross division between the regions which mediate motor functions and those which mediate sensory ones. Sensory impulses are discharged into the dorsal half of the neural tube, the **alar** or **sensory** plate (Fig. 35). Motor impulses emerge from the ventral half of the neural tube, the **basal** or **motor** plate. These two regions are sharply demarked on the internal surface of the lateral wall of this tube by a groove, the **sulcus limitans.** The relationship between the sensory and motor plates at the cephalic end of the

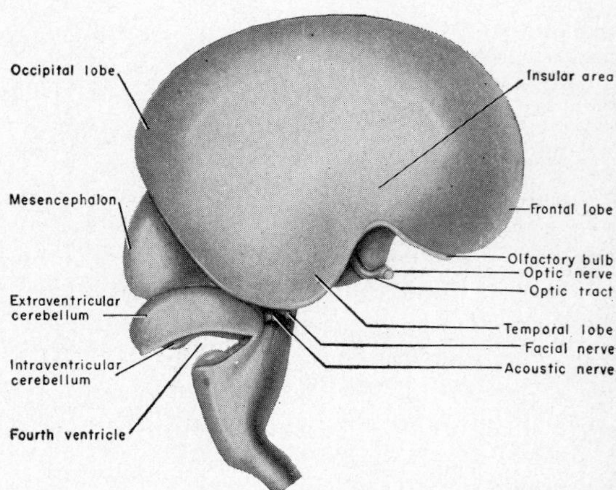

FIG. 34. Reconstruction of the external form of the right half of the cranial part of the central nervous system in a 53-mm. human embryo. The roof of the fourth ventricle has been removed. (*After Hochstetter*, 1919. *Redrawn courtesy of Hamilton, Boyd, and Mossman, "Human Embryology," W. Heffer & Sons, Ltd.*)

Table 2. Derivatives of the Neural Tube

Primary divisions	*Subdivisions*	*Derivatives*	*Cavities*
Prosencephalon	Telencephalon (endbrain)	Cerebral cortex (pallium) Corpora striata Rhinencephalon Pars optica hypothalami	Lateral ventricles Rostral part of third ventricle
	Diencephalon (twixtbrain)	Epithalamus Thalamus Hypothalamus Tuber cinereum Mamillary bodies Posterior lobe of hypophysis	Greater part of third ventricle
Mesencephalon	Mesencephalon (midbrain)	Corpora quadrigemina Crura cerebri Tegmentum	Cerebral aqueduct
Rhombencephalon	Metencephalon (afterbrain)	Cerebellum Pons	Fourth ventricle
	Myelencephalon (spinal brain)	Medulla oblongata	
Myelon or spinal cord	Spinal cord	Spinal cord	Central canal

neural tube has been clarified by the careful studies of Kingsbury, indicating that the sulcus limitans ends in the region of the mamillary recess in the ventral part of the diencephalon (Fig. 33) (438). One should not expect to find, therefore, any motor nerves emerging from the brain anterior to the mamillary recess. Since all neural tissue rostral to this point represents an anterior extension of the alar plate, the function of the higher brain centers must be regarded as sensory or associational.

Histogenesis in the Neural Tube

While the central nervous system is in the medullary-plate stage it is composed only of tall columnar epithelial cells. This is also true later of the neural tube, but the true character of the columnar epithelium is not so obvious when the wall of the tube begins to thicken. In fact, the idea has been long held that there is a stage in the development of the neural tube when the epithelium breaks up and forms a syncytium. Careful studies by Sauer have proved this to be a false impression based on the altered structure resulting from delayed fixation of the tissue after the death of the animal (703, 704). Another significant observation by Sauer is that the nuclei of the neural tube migrate to the lumen of the tube to effect mitosis, and the nuclei of the daughter cells either migrate or are crowded back again into the substance of the wall.

The spinal cord of a 10-mm. human embryo presents well-defined zones about the central canal, which are designated **ependymal, mantle,** and **marginal** layers, proceeding from within out (Fig. 35). The mantle layer differentiates into the gray matter of the spinal cord which contains the nerve cells and their dendrites. The marginal layer develops into the white substance of the adult spinal cord by the growth into it of axons of the nerve cells in the mantle layer. These axons form association fibers which ascend and descend through the marginal layer and serve to connect one level of the neural tube with another. It is only after these longitudinally coursing fibers acquire their myelin sheath that the white substance

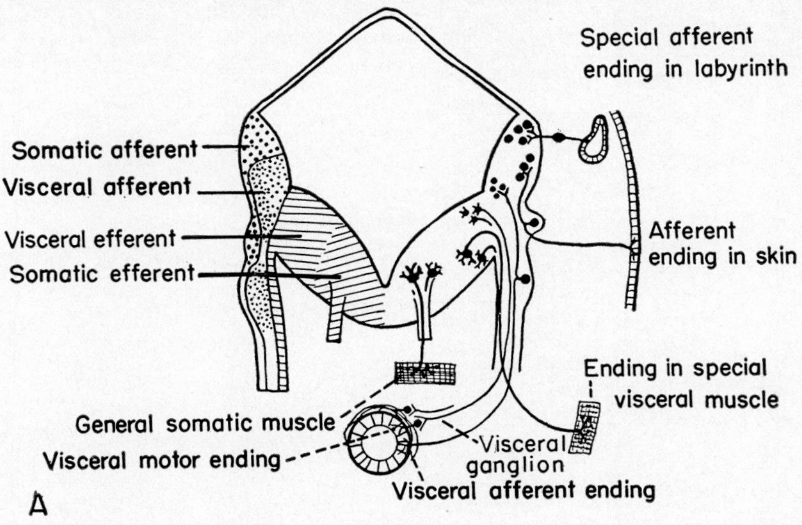

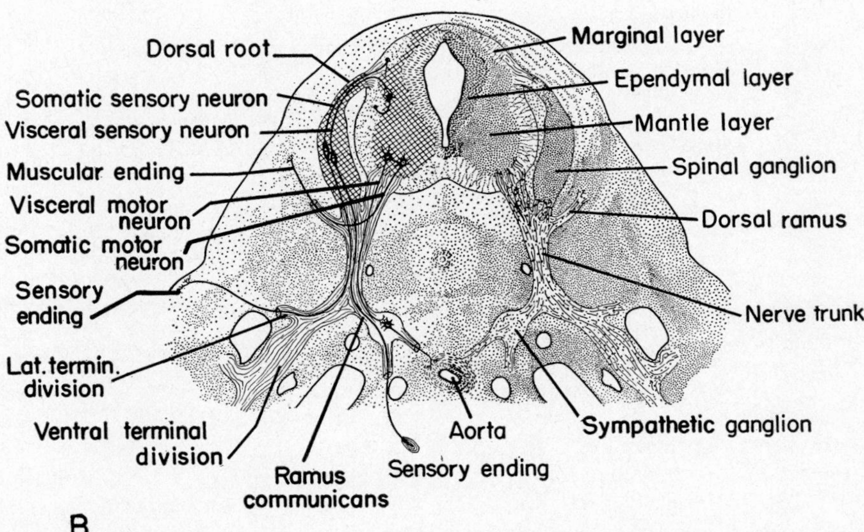

FIG. 35. *A*, Diagrammatic cross section through medulla oblongata. On the left side, the four principal functional cell columns are shown; on the right side, the distribution of afferent and efferent fibers from these columns, including special somatic afferent fibers from the ear and special visceral efferent (branchiomeric) fibers to the branchial musculature. (*After Larsell, "Anatomy of the Nervous System," courtesy of the author and Appleton-Century-Crofts, Inc.*) *B*, a transverse section of a 10-mm. human embryo showing a spinal nerve and its functional components. Approximately ×25. (*After Arey, "Developmental Anatomy," courtesy of the author and W. B. Saunders Company.*)

acquires its characteristic color. There is, however, nothing in the way of behavior capacity to correlate with the development of the myelin sheath (31). The fiber systems have been shown to be functional long before the myelin appears (459, 460, 684).

Cytogenesis of the neural tube has been restudied with an emphasis on neuroglial development by Kershman (435, 436). His illustration and its legend summarize the story of early histogenesis in the spinal cord (Fig. 36).

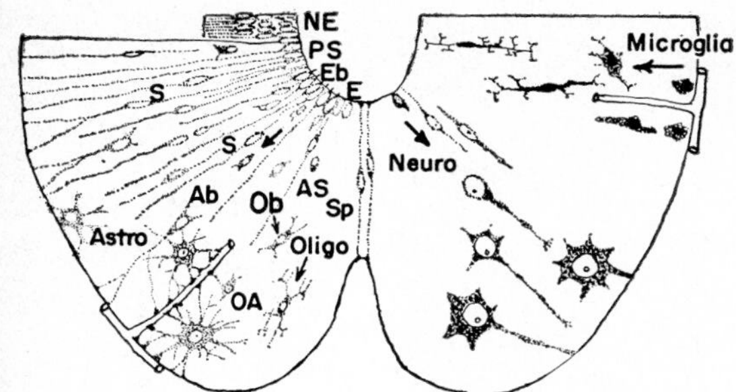

Fig. 36. Diagram illustrating cytogenesis in the spinal cord. *Ab* indicates an astroblast; *AS*, apolar spongioblast; *Astro*, astrocytes; *E*, ependyma; *Eb*, ependymoblast; *NE*, neuroepithelium; *Neuro*, neuroblastic cells; *OA*, oligodendroblast acquiring a vascular foot to become an astroblast; *Ob*, oligodendroblast; *Oligo*, oligodendrocyte; *PS*, primitive spongioblast; *S*, spongioblasts (polar forms), and *Sp*, supportive spongioblasts. "Neuroepithelial cells give rise to neuroblasts and spongioblasts. After neuroblast formation has ceased, the cells remaining in the ependymal zone may be called primitive spongioblasts; gradually the remaining cells become ependymoblasts and finally ependyma. In the meantime from the ependymal region there is constant discharge of polar and apolar spongioblasts which develop into astrocytes and oligodendroglia cells. In the median raphe of the spinal cord supporting spongioblasts persist as the adult mature cell of this region. Microglia migrate into the spinal cord from the mesenchyme." (*Courtesy of Dr. John Kershman, Arch. Neurol. & Psychiat., vol.* 40.)

Cytogenesis in the brain is much the same as in the spinal cord with the exception of the development of the cortices, cerebral and cerebellar. The primarily distinctive feature of cortex formation is a migration of neuroblasts from the ependyma outward and the establishment of a myelinated mass between the externally and internally located aggregations of neurons.

The manner in which the cerebral cortex develops is illustrated in Fig. 38. During the early weeks ependymal, mantle, and marginal layers are established (*A*). During the second month neuroblasts begin to wander out to the edge of the mantle layer. By the middle of the third fetal month they have established a definite zone of young, pyramidal cells (primordial cortical gray, *B*) beneath the primitive marginal zone. Between this pyramidal layer and the ependyma is a cell-poor intermediate layer, the outer part of which is destined to become the sixth layer of definitive cortex. The inner part of the intermediate layer later becomes myelinated and makes up the central white mass of the cerebral hemispheres. Eventually from the primitive marginal zone, the outer part of the intermediate layer, and especially from a subdividing of the primitive pyramidal layer, six distinct layers are established in the cortex. These layers, pictured in Fig. 38*E* and discussed in detail in Chap. 15, are recognizable over the whole hemisphere between the sixth and eighth fetal month, according to Brodmann (104, 170).

The distinctive features of cytogenesis of the cerebellum have been described by Kershman and are presented in another illustration and legend (Fig. 37).

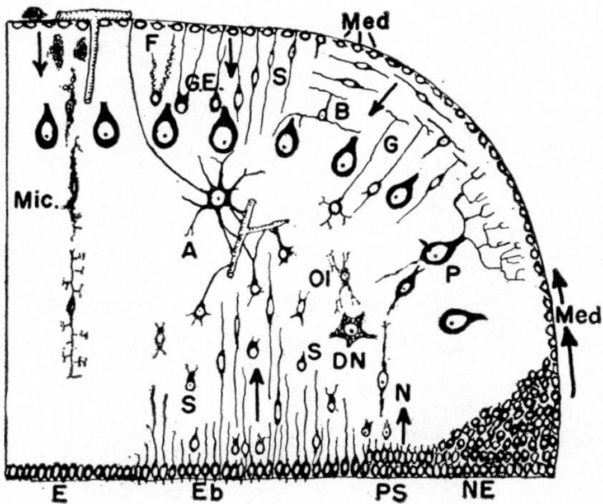

Fig. 37. Diagram illustrating cytogenesis in the cerebellum. Cells in the region of *A* show astrocytic development; *B*, basket cells; *DN*, deep nuclei of the cerebellum; *E*, the ependyma; *Eb*, ependymoblast; *F*, Fañana's cells; *G*, granule cell; *GE*, a Golgi epithelial cell; *Med*, medulloblasts; *Mic*, microglial development; *N*, neuroblast forms; *NE*, neuroepithelium; *Ol*, oligodendroglial development; *P*, a Purkinje cell; *PS*, primitive spongioblasts; *S*, spongioblast forms, apolar and polar. "Medulloblasts originating from the neuroepithelium of the roof of the fourth ventricle form the external granular zone. From these medulloblasts are derived granule cells, basket cells and spongioblasts. The last form the Golgi epithelial cells (*GE*) and Fañana's cells (*F*). The rest of the cerebellum is formed in the same way as the spinal cord and cerebrum. As in the spinal cord and brain, microglia cells are derived from mesenchymal elements and begin as ameboid cells which invade the nerve parenchyma when intracerebral blood vessels make their appearance." (*Courtesy of Dr. John Kershman, Arch. Neurol. & Psychiat., vol.* 40.)

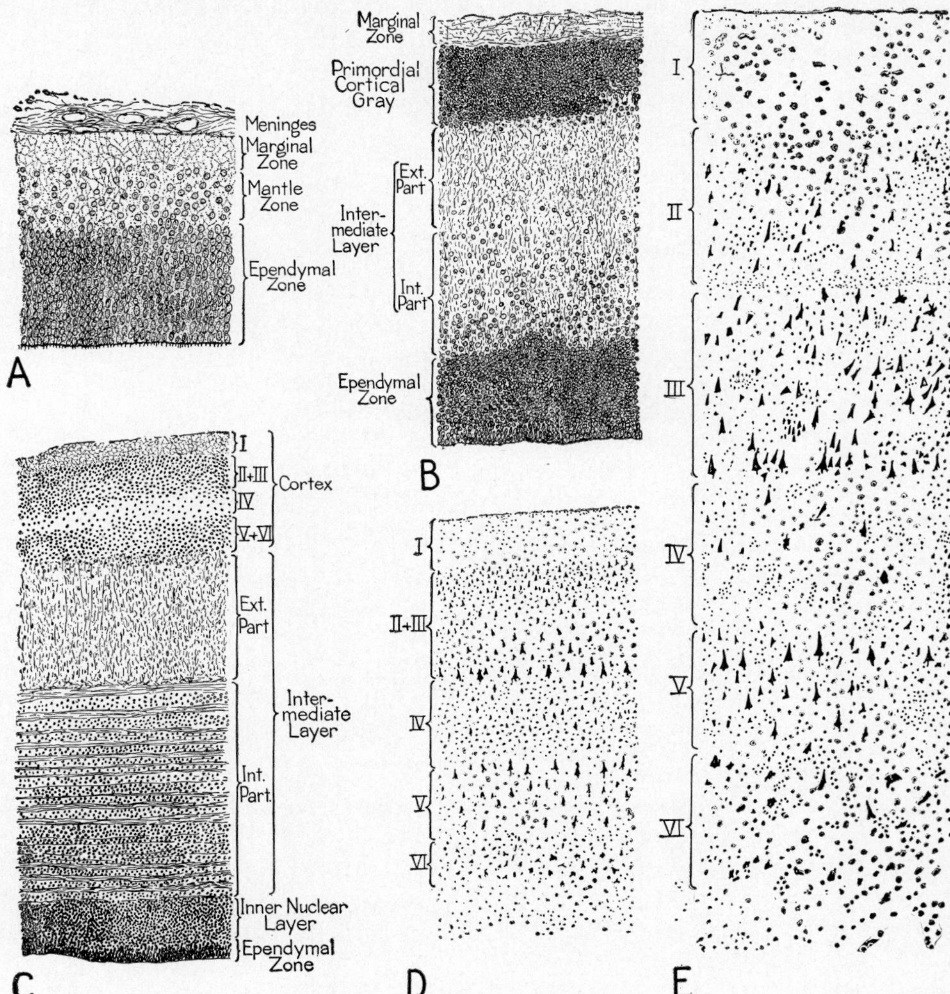

FIG. 38. Histogenesis of cerebral cortex. *A*, entire thickness of telencephalic wall from a human embryo at beginning of the eighth week, ×200. *B*, entire thickness of telencephalic wall in an embryo of the tenth week, ×125. *C*, entire thickness of telencephalic wall in an embryo of the fourteenth week, ×22.5. *D*, cortex only, from fetus of about 6 months, ×33. (*Redrawn from Brodmann*). *E*, Adult parietal cortex, ×40. (*Redrawn from Kappers, Huber, and Crosby.*) Roman numerals used in labeling of *C–E* stand for the cortical layers: I, molecular layer; II, external granular layer; III, external pyramidal layer; IV, internal granular layer; V, internal pyramidal layer; VI, fusiform layer. (*After Patten, "Human Embryology, The Blakiston Company.*)

It is to be noted that a secondary migration from the exterior inward is involved in the derivation of granule cells, basket cells, and spongioblasts, and that Purkinje cells merely migrate out to their definitive position from the inner mantle zone. The medulloblasts are indifferent cells capable of developing into neurons or astrocytes. These cells are the cell type of a common brain tumor of childhood (Chap. 2).

The types of neurons and neuroglial cells derived from the primitive neuroepithelial cells are illustrated in Fig. 39. Microglia are mesenchymal derivatives which, as ameboid wandering cells, migrate into the central nervous system chiefly along blood vessels (Figs. 36, 37). They have been described in Chap. 2.

Development of the Peripheral Nervous System

Peripheral nerve fibers are formed as outgrowths of nerve cells of the spinal cord, spinal ganglia, or autonomic ganglia rather than by a coalescence of multicellular peripheral elements (Fig. 35*B*) (338, 341). Motor fibers start their outgrowth in the human as early as the 4-mm. stage. The primitive fiber soon attaches to an embryonic muscle and is thereafter rather passively towed to its definitive site of termination (833). Attempts to demonstrate that growing fibers are oriented by chemical or electrical forces have yielded largely negative results; mechanical or contact forces are considered to have more effect in determining the nerve pathway. Marsh and Beams, however, have recently claimed that direct electric currents of physiological intensities induced nerve fibers in their tissue cultures to grow toward the cathode (532).

The primary differentiation of **motor neurons** in the mantle of the spinal cord is independent of peripheral influences (33). The number of neurons which differentiate in a given region, however, does depend on the muscle mass innervated, for in the congenital absence of a limb the appropriate motor-cell columns are missing (189, 682, 683). The exact nature of the influence is unknown, but Barron has advanced the hypothesis that dendrites grow out from primary neuroblasts only after they have established peripheral connections; these dendrites in some way stimulate the further differentiation of neuroblasts from indifferent mantle cells (63, 65, 66). If a fetal limb is amputated, the primary neuroblasts serving this field fail to sprout dendrites (67).

Sensory ganglion cells develop from an embryonal organ known as the **neural crest,** which may be recognized before the neural tube has closed. This organ is of ectodermal origin and to a considerable extent is derived from the neural tube itself, although the portion forming the dorsal spinal ganglia is usually diagrammed as coming from the lips of the medullary plate

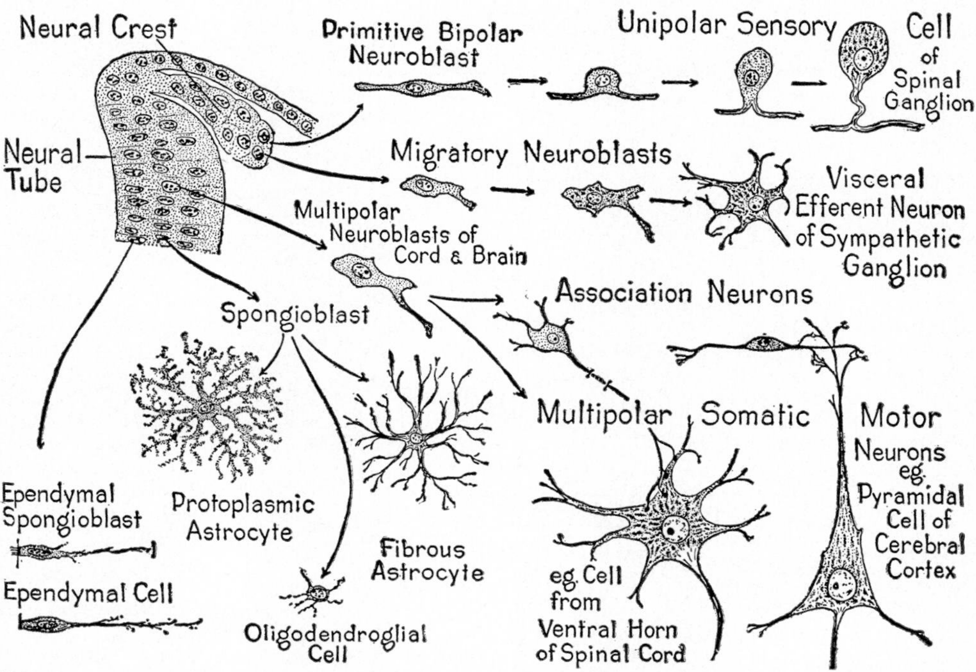

Fig. 39. Diagrammatic representation of the types of nerve cells and neuroglial cells derived from the primitive cells of the neural crest and the walls of the neural tube. (*After Patten, "Human Embryology," The Blakiston Company.*)

during closure of the neural tube (see Figs. 28 and 29). The subsequent development of primary sensory nerve cells and their transformation from bipolar to unipolar cells are illustrated in Figs. 6, 39. Recently, primary sensory neurons have been observed within the marginal and mantle layers of the spinal cords of young human fetuses and even within the central canal (396, 397, 867). These are all considered to be neural-crest derivatives.

In addition to sensory ganglion cells, **sheath cells** of Schwann develop from neural-crest tissue. In their young form the sheath cells are quite ameboid and migrate from one growing nerve fiber to another until they settle down on one and secrete outside themselves a **neurolemma sheath.** This process has been extensively studied in the transparent tail fin of the tadpole by Speidel (740). The fatty myelin sheath which lies between the axon and the Schwann sheath cells in all larger peripheral fibers may be derived from the axon, the sheath cells, or both.

Several investigators have studied the development of **nerve endings** in human embryos (187, 188, 378, 643, 772). The muscle spindle appears in the eleventh week and by 14 weeks has acquired all its different components (187). Cuajunco could not demonstrate motor-nerve endings in the biceps brachii of a human fetus 38 mm. crown-rump length, though Hooker reports that the biceps brachii responds reflexly to stretching by contraction in a fetus of 33 mm. crown-rump length (188, 393). Since all methods for demonstrating nerve endings are capricious, little reliance can be placed on negative results in one embryo. Dickson, however, observed in sheep fetuses that distinct motor end plates were not found until 3 months after the initiation of fetal movements (211).

The **autonomic** or **visceral nervous system** is composed of preganglionic fibers, whose cell bodies are in the central nervous system, and postganglionic fibers, whose cell bodies are in the ganglia of the sympathetic chain and in some cases in the walls of the viscera (Fig. 35). The peripheral autonomic ganglia are derived from neural-crest tissue, as is also the medulla of the adrenal gland (325). When the visceral nerve fibers become functional is not known, but anatomical evidence suggests that it is relatively early in the fetal period. Adrenaline is said to be formed by the adrenal gland at 12 weeks menstrual age (time since the onset of the mother's last menstrual cycle) (427).

Further Development of the Central Nervous System and the Cerebrospinal Pathways

During development of the central nervous system, nerve cells sometimes change their relationship with each other. The factors responsible for this change are somewhat obscure but seem to involve the source from which a nerve cell receives its principal stimulation as well as the location of the object of its discharge. The actual movement of the neurons has been called **neurobiotaxis.** This process is illustrated in Fig. 40 *A–E*. In Fig. 40 *C–E*, the nucleus of the facial nerve which innervates the muscles of facial expression is seen to be lying cephalad to that of the abducens nerve. Only later does it acquire the adult position by migration of the nerve cells caudolaterally toward the direction from which they receive most of their stimuli, namely, the spinal trigeminal nucleus, which receives pain, thermal, and some tactile impulses from the skin of the face.

The medial longitudinal fasciculus is the first descending cerebrospinal pathway to develop. It is considered an important factor in the integration of the first movements of the embryo. The fibers of the medial longitudinal fasciculus cross in the ventral commissure of the spinal cord to end on motor neurons before these same motor neurons are brought under the influence of any sensory fibers. Thus, in the rat, the anatomical basis for a total pattern reaction (see later) matures before local reflex connections are established (32). Rhines and Windle disagree with the claim that all the early longitudinal fibers are descending, but their results do not rule out the medial longitudinal fasciculus as an early integrator of motor activity (666).

The study of the development of the cerebrospinal pathways is the most difficult, time-consuming, and incompletely explored field of human embryology. That the embryological approach may be helpful is illustrated by Fig. 41, which depicts certain structures more clearly than they could be seen at other stages of

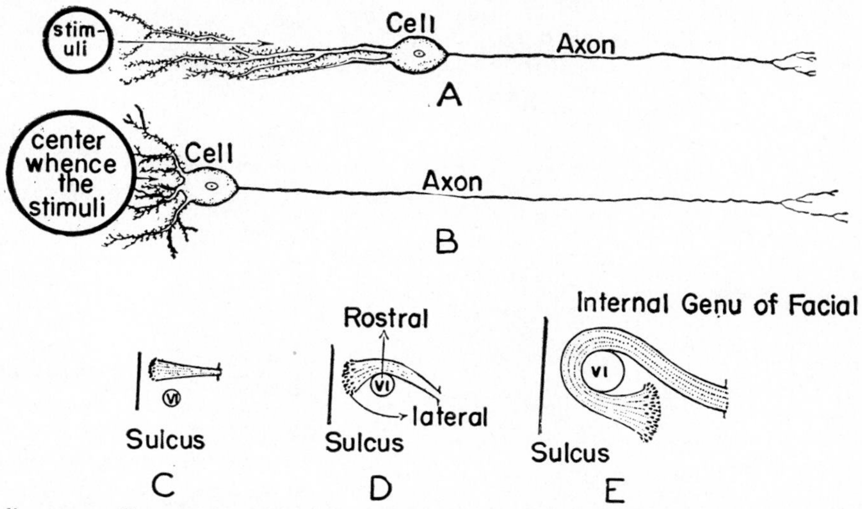

FIG. 40. *A, B*, diagrams to illustrate the principle of neurobiotaxis. The dendrites grow out toward the center of stimulation, and the cell body shifts in the same direction. The axis cylinder grows away from the center of stimulation. (*From Kappers, Huber, and Crosby, "The Comparative Anatomy of the Nervous System of Vertebrates," courtesy of Dr. J. F. Huber.*) *C, D, E*, diagrams illustrating three stages in the shift of position during development of the sixth and seventh cranial nerve nuclei, examples of neurobiotaxis leading to the formation of the genu of the facial nerve. *C* corresponds to the condition in the 10-mm. embryo; the oldest, *E*, to that in the newborn child. *Sulcus* refers to the median sulcus of the rhomboid fossa. The abducens nucleus moves toward the stimuli coming to it over the medial longitudinal fasciculus, and the facial nucleus moves caudally toward the stimuli coming to it, principally, from secondary sensory fibers of the spinal fifth. (*After Streeter in Keibel and Mall, "Manual of Human Embryology," J. B. Lippincott Company.*)

development. Thus by selection of different developmental stages one may virtually dissect the nervous system. This approach has already given some interesting data to correlate with the knowledge of the functional development of the human fetus, and it should give much more.

Development of Behavior

Morphological development of neurons and nerve pathways, as outlined above, is a prerequisite to the genesis of neural function and patterns of behavior in the embryo. Before reflex activity is possible, sensory and motor neurons must have established their central and peripheral connections.

The sequence in which patterns of reflex activity are laid down in the embryo has been the subject of numerous correlated anatomicophysiological studies, classic among which are those of Coghill (167, 168, 169, 637). For many years he studied the development of behavior patterns in salamander embryos and was able to demonstrate by anatomical methods the progressive structural changes in the nervous system related to the appearance of new reflexes. Coghill concluded from these studies that the embryos' earliest activity is in the nature of a total pattern from which localized reflexes are subsequently individuated. For instance, early limb movements are merely a part of the total swimming reaction of the animal and only later does the limb acquire an individuality, the capacity to move independently of the trunk. The anatomical basis for individuation of the limb movements was discovered by Youngstrom, who found a secondary motor system of fine fibers growing out to the arm coincident with the onset of capacity for local reflexes (865).

Whereas there is general agreement with Coghill's sequence for developing behavior in salamanders, not all neurologists agree that the total-pattern-and-individuation plan applies to mammals. Windle, for example, holds that the earliest fetal movements of mammals including man are simple localized reflexes and that these are subsequently integrated into a secondary total pattern (250, 842). Proponents for the Coghill thesis counter with the claim that such local "reflexes" are the result of direct excita-

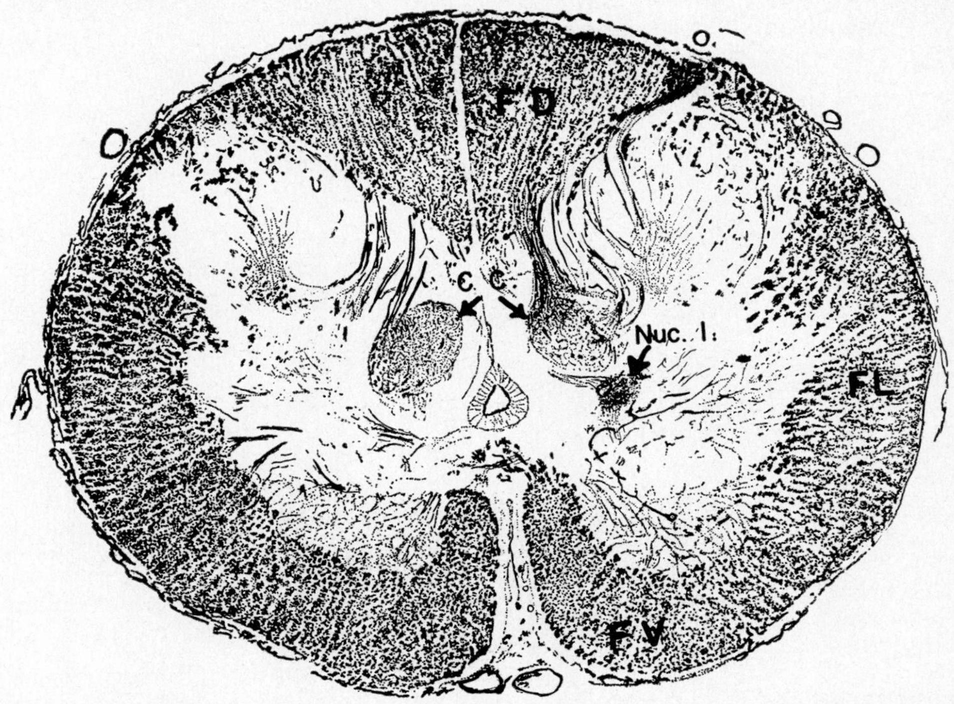

Fig. 41. Cross section of the spinal cord in the thoracic region of 145-mm. human embryo. The dorsolateral nucleus or Clarke's column, *C*, on each side and the nucleus intermedius of Cajal, *Nuc. I*, on the right are made conspicuous by their neuropile or close network of fine nerve fibers, though the cells are relatively inconspicuous. *FD*, *FL*, and *FV*, dorsal, lateral and ventral funiculus, respectively.

tion of muscle fibers rather than of indirect stimulation of sensory nerve endings as required in true reflexes.

The outstanding student of fetal behavior in man, Davenport Hooker, supports the Coghill sequence (392, 393). He has studied and photographed the neuromotor responses in nearly a hundred human fetuses from 7½ weeks menstrual age through full term. The earliest response, at about 2 months menstrual age, consisted of lateral flexion of the neck in response to light stimulation about the mouth with a hair. The anatomical basis for this total response may include the simple intramedullary sensory neurons described by Humphrey and Youngstrom (397, 865). During the third month the extent of the response includes the entire length of the trunk, and the area which may be stimulated increases to contain almost the whole body surface. A few localized reflexes such as forearm pronation and contraction of the muscle of the eyelids in response to local stimulation appear during this period. The fourth month introduces a variety of new reflexes and a new grace and fluidity to the former marionettelike movements. During the last 5 months of intrauterine life, although spinal reflex activity is largely suppressed, the fetus develops the ability for successively more complicated reflexes including grasp, the suctorial response, respiration, and "tendon" jerks. At 27 weeks of menstrual age one fetus was sufficiently well fitted with neural mechanisms to prove viable.

Reflex grasping, which is present at birth, gradually disappears by the third postnatal month; voluntary grasping begins at 4 months, and reaching for objects at 6 months. The Babinski phenomenon, characterized by dorsiflexion of the great toe on stroking the sole of the foot, is normal for the human fetus up to 3 months after birth and in 10 per cent up to 26 months, after which time plantar flexion of the toes occurs in response to the plantar stimulus (202). Some of the most important studies of the early postnatal development have been made by Gesell and associates (92, 295, 296, 297, 298).

Anatomical differentiation of neurons must precede but does not necessarily denote physiological differentiation. There is no morphological criterion of the attainment of functional maturity by a nerve cell. As suggested by Barron, "the immediate transition from an unresponsive to a responsive stage in ontogeny is probably due to some physiological change in the structural elements already present" (64). One such physiological change might be the maturing of the neurochemical acetylcholine-cholinesterase system (578, 579). Indeed the onset of rapid reflexes in salamander embryos coincides precisely with a sharp rise in the cholinesterase content of the neuromuscular apparatus (705). In the human fetus the morphological differentiation and functional development, as evidenced by behavior patterns, take the following order of regional development: spinal cord, medulla and midbrain, diencephalon and cerebral hemispheres. The period of most rapid increase in the concentration of cholinesterase follows the same temporal sequence (866).

CHAPTER 4

GROSS ANATOMY OF THE BRAIN ITS BLOOD SUPPLY AND MENINGES

As a means of orientation for the descriptions of the intrinsic neural pathways in the following sections, a description of the macroscopic anatomy of the brain, its blood supply and meninges, should prove useful. As a general rule when the brain is removed from the cranium during a post-mortem examination a transection is made as far caudad through the medulla as is possible through the exposure. An ideal section would be placed just anterior or rostral to the rootlets of the first cervical nerve. The mass of tissue removed then would include that which developed about the three primary brain vesicles of the neural tube. Let us assume that such a specimen is available for study.

GENERAL TOPOGRAPHY

Beginning at the caudal point of transection and proceeding rostrally, the following visible divisions can be made: **medulla, pons,** and the **cerebellum** overlying them, the **cerebral peduncles,** and **cerebral hemispheres.** The medulla (or bulb), pons, and cerebellum are **rhombencephalon** or **hindbrain.** The cerebral peduncles are **midbrain.** The midbrain and hindbrain excluding cerebellum are two of the components included in the term **brain stem** in common usage. The remaining large bulk of the brain is **forebrain** or **prosencephalon.** Within this last portion, however, are two divisions, **telencephalon** and **diencephalon,** though only slight indications of this can be noted externally on the whole brain.

Ventral Aspect of the Brain Stem

The medulla on its ventral surface presents a prominent longitudinal, median sulcus. On either side of the sulcus are rounded masses, the **pyramids,** containing motor fibers passing from cerebral cortex to spinal cord (Fig. 42). Lateral to these in the rostral half of the medulla are two oval swellings, the **inferior olives,** also concerned with movement, and emerging between olive and pyramid on each side are **hypoglossal nerves** for innervating the muscles of the tongue. As a rule, in the whole brain the remaining part of the medulla is concealed from view by the cerebellum. The rounded mass of cerebellum immediately adjacent the medulla laterally composes the **tonsils.** The medulla is separated from the pons on its ventral surface by a transverse groove. The pyramids, prominent on the ventral medullar surface, appear to dive into the substance of the pons.

The ventral surface of the pons frequently shows transverse striations indicating transversely coursing fibers between pontine nuclei and cerebellum. If these fibers are followed laterally, it will be seen that the pons has two arms (**brachia**) or lateral extensions which pass dorsally and slightly in a caudal direction into the cerebellum (Fig. 51). If the ventral part of the cerebellum be pushed laterally away from the medulla and pons, and the **cerebellopontine** or **cerebellomedullar angle** be thus widened several cranial nerves come into better view (Fig. 42). Within the angle near the rostral end of the medulla is a group of threadlike nerve filaments composing the **ninth** (taste, especially for posterior one-third of the tongue), **tenth** (pharynx, palate, abdominal and thoracic viscera), and a part of the **eleventh** (larynx) **cranial nerves.** Frequently a small cord of nerve tissue will be seen running free along the lateral wall of the medulla from the spinal region, and this will join the threadlike filaments above (Fig. 42). This free portion represents the spinal fibers of the **eleventh nerve** which in-

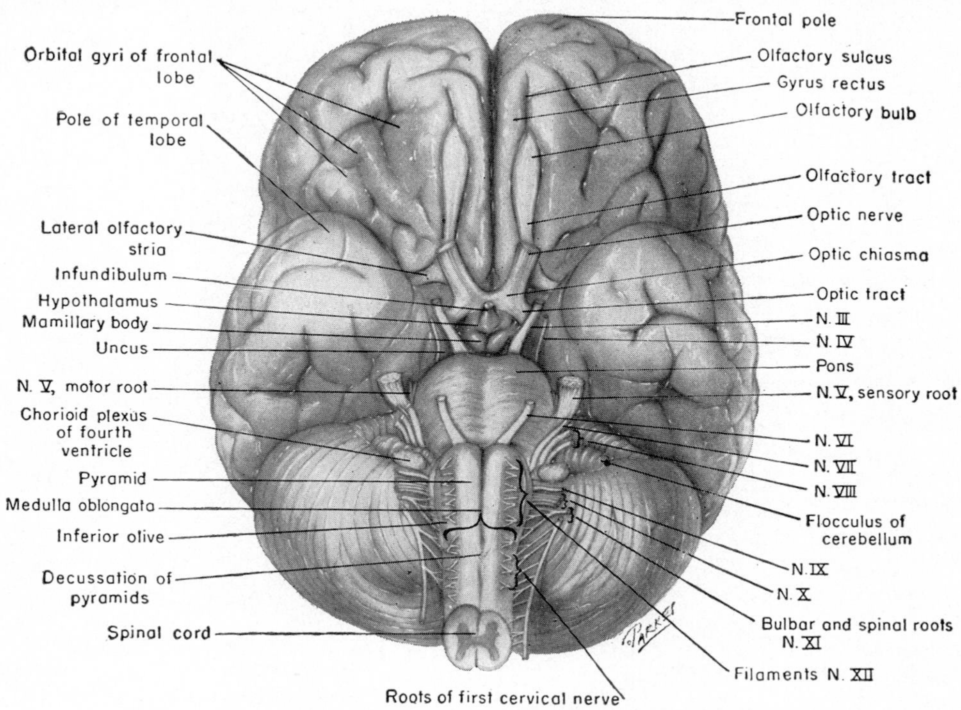

FIG. 42. Base of the human brain. Approximately 1:2.

nervate the sternocleidomastoid and trapezius muscles. They are only briefly associated within the cerebellomedullar angle with their medulla or "bulbar" relative nerve fibers.

Within the cerebellopontine angle at the level of the transition from medulla to pons two other cranial nerves are seen, the **seventh** (to muscles of facial expression) and **eighth** (hearing and equilibrium). They rest posteriorly on a rounded finger of cerebellum, the **flocculus,** and just posterior to that a small spongelike mass can usually be seen. This last is **chorioid plexus,** which can be traced into the lateral recess of the fourth ventricle and is concerned with spinal-fluid formation (Fig. 42).

Near the caudal end of the pons or from within the transverse groove between pons and medulla, the **sixth cranial nerve** (external rectus muscle of the eye) emerges (Fig. 42). Its point of exit is about 4 to 5 mm. from the mid-line. At a level near the rostral tip of the cerebellum ventrally, a large cranial nerve, the **trigeminal** (sensory to head, motor to masticator muscles), can be seen emerging from the lateral pons. Just rostral to the trigeminal a very small nerve, the **trochlear** (superior oblique muscle of eye), can usually be seen, and it can be followed dorsally along the lateral pontine surface until it disappears from view. It is the only cranial nerve that emerges from a dorsal brain stem site.

The rostral end of the pons is flanked on either side by the medial pole of the temporal lobes of the cerebrum. It is only after removal of these that the structures rostral to the pons may be seen (Fig. 43). The **cerebral peduncles** continue forward from the pons as two large, diverging, fingerlike processes. They contain fibers interconnecting cerebrum and brain stem and spinal cord and also contain certain large cell masses. Between the peduncles is a space, the **interpeduncular fossa,** and emerging into this space are the **oculomotor** or third cranial nerves. These innervate all ocular muscles except superior obliques and external recti. The **posterior perforated substance,** the perforations made by entering blood vessels, is just rostral, to the point of attachment of the third nerves.

Running transversely across the rostral end of the cerebral peduncles are the **optic tracts**

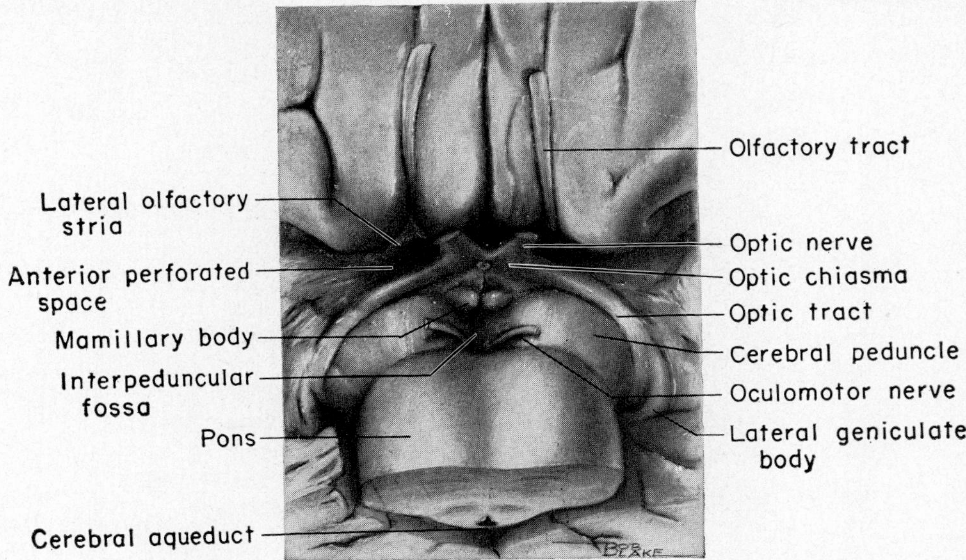

FIG. 43. Part of base of human brain, ventral view, with temporal lobes removed.

(vision) (Fig. 43). These have diverged anteriorly from the **optic chiasma** in which many fibers cross. Entering the rostrolateral poles of the chiasma the **optic nerves** can be seen. Within the mid-line, just posterior to the main bulk of chiasma, the **infundibulum,** or pituitary stalk, can be seen; about its point of attachment the brain floor is rounded into the **tuber cinereum.** Just back of this are two discrete, rounded masses which merge rostrolaterally into the tuber cinereum. These are the **mamillary bodies** and with the tuber cinereum are part of the **hypothalamus.** This is a part of the diencephalon, in turn derived from the prosencephalon. Dorsal to the hypothalamus and hidden from view in the intact brain is the rest of the diencephalon. The diencephalon, or interbrain, is a component also of the brain stem.

THE TELENCEPHALON

The remaining portion of the brain to be seen while it is whole composes the telencephalic portion of the prosencephalon. This is by far the largest bulk of the brain, and it is divided longitudinally by the **longitudinal fissure** into the two **cerebral hemispheres.** The surface of the hemispheres is thrown into folds, the **gyri,** or **convolutions;** between these folds are **fissures,** or **sulci.** Immediately beneath the surface of the gyri are the layers of neurons composing the **gray matter,** or **cerebral cortex.** Beneath these cell layers is the **cerebral white matter.** This is composed of fibers interconnecting various gyri, fibers coming to end in cortical gray from brain stem centers, and fibers arising in cortical gray and passing down into the brain stem and spinal cord.

The telencephalic divisions have been listed in Chap. 3 as **cerebral cortex, corpora striata,** and **rhinencephalon.** These arise through evaginations on the lateral walls of the primitive telencephalon. Within these evaginations the lumina are the **lateral ventricles** (Fig. 69). The corpora striata and the rhinencephalon are ventrally placed parts of the cerebral hemispheres. Portions of them are the oldest regions of the telencephalon phylogenetically. The corpora striata are obscured from view in the intact whole brain. On the basis of phylogenetic age the rhinencephalon, or olfactory brain, is subdivided. The divisions are called **archipallium** and **paleopallium** as distinct from the **neopallium** or somatic brain, described below. The rhinencephalon can be seen in part in the most medial and ventral parts of the hemisphere adjacent to the rostral pons and also in the ventral surface of the hemisphere lateral and rostral to the optic chiasma (Figs. 43, 304). The **olfactory tracts** can be traced along the ventral floor of the rostral part of the hemisphere and will be seen to pass into the rhinencephalic area.

The corpora striata and rhinencephalon become overgrown by the widely growing third derivative of the telencephalon, the cerebral cortex, or **neopallium.** This begins, as noted, in the dorsolateral wall of the telencephalon but grows rostrally, dorsally, and caudally enclosing always the lateral ventricle which enlarges progressively. In the shifting of the latter, it becomes elongated and thinned out as it follows the enlarging lateral ventricle. As it develops, the neopallium displaces parts of the archipallium, especially. This growth of neopallial cerebral cortex is not everywhere equally rapid, however. That portion immediately lateral to the corpora striata lags and in time comes to be covered from external view by the more rapidly developing rostral, dorsal, and caudal portions. This covered portion of cortex is known as the **insula** or **island of Reil** (Fig. 44).

The rostral growth of the neopallial telencephalon includes the **frontal lobe;** the dorsal portion, the **parietal lobe;** and the caudal portion, the **occipital** and **temporal lobes.** It is the convergence of the ventral portions of frontal and parietal lobes with the superior part of the temporal that covers over the insula. These divisions of the adult cerebral cortex are in part made by sulci and fissures. Fissures of the brain surface are usually considered more primitive in development and of greater depth than sulci, though the two words are frequently used interchangeably. A large fissure is left between the ventral parietal region and the fold of pallium developing into the temporal lobe. This fissure is known as the **lateral,** or **sylvian, fissure** (Fig. 45). In its floor is the insula, and those parts of the frontal, parietal, and temporal lobes overhanging the insula are known as **opercular portions** of those lobes (Fig. 45). The lateral fissure is divisible into three parts (Fig. 46*A*). Near its anterior end are two limbs. One passes rostrally and somewhat horizontally in the opercular part of the frontal lobe; this is the **anterior horizontal ramus.** Caudal to this, another limb opens vertically and superiorly into the frontal opercular portion also; this is the **anterior ascending ramus.** The largest part

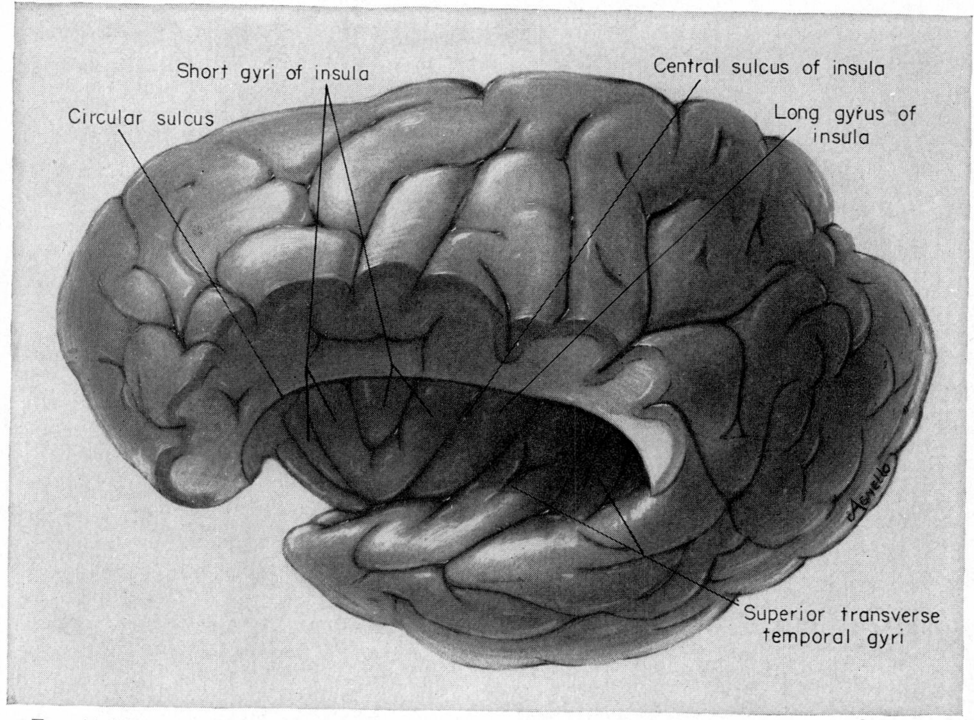

FIG. 44. Dissection of human brain to show insula and superior surface of the temporal lobe.

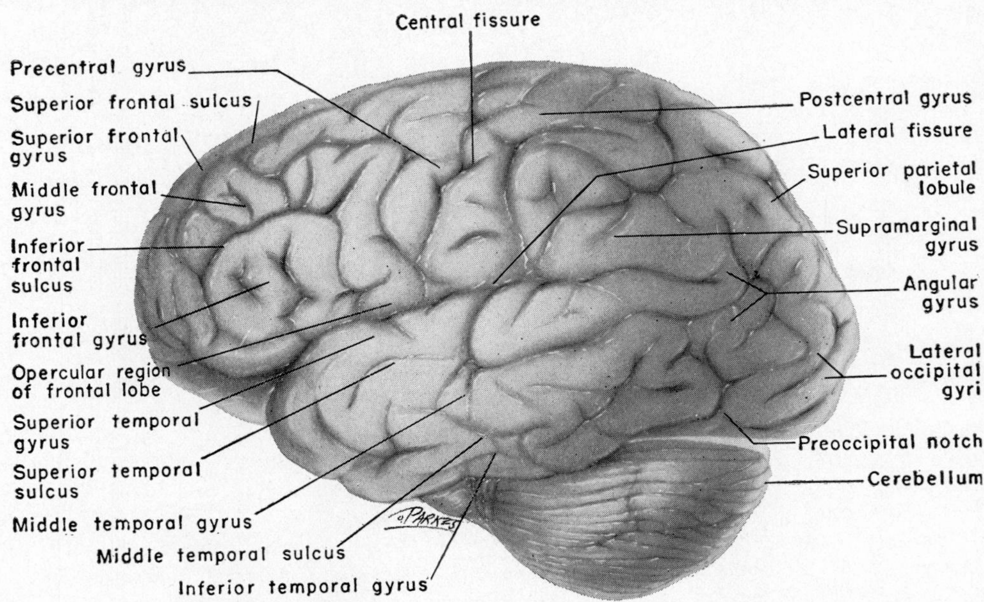

FIG. 45. Lateral view of human cerebral hemisphere and cerebellum.

of the lateral fissure, extending posteriorly between parietal and temporal lobe, is the **posterior ramus.**

Another fissure, of importance in delimiting lobes of the pallium, is the **central fissure,** or **fissure of Rolando** (Fig. 45). This separates frontal from parietal lobe. It extends from the dorsal aspect of the lateral hemispheric surface to the opercular region shared by frontal and parietal lobes. The superior limb of this fissure is more caudad than the inferior, or opercular, end, and in the adult brain the fissure may show several bends in its course. A superior bend usually has a frontally directed concavity. An inferior bend usually has a concavity directed toward the parietal lobe. No continuous fissures on the lateral hemispheric surface serve to indicate separations between parietal and occipital lobes and posterior temporal and occipital lobes. The divisions are somewhat arbitrary.

The various lobes of the cerebral hemispheres can be studied if a cut be made through the depths of the longitudinal fissure and the whole brain be divided in its mid-line. In the bottom of the longitudinal fissure the brain knife will encounter first the **corpus callosum,** a very large **commissure** of fibers interconnecting homologous portions of the cerebral hemispheres. Beneath the corpus callosum the knife will pass through the **transverse cerebral fissure** before encountering the roof of the third ventricle. Continuing through the ventricle it will sever portions of the diencephalon, midbrain, pons, and medulla and thus complete the division for study.

THE FRONTAL LOBE

Within the frontal lobe on its lateral surface are several sulci. The **superior** and **inferior precentral sulci** follow a course nearly parallel to that of the superior and inferior parts of the central sulcus (Fig. 46*A*). The **gyrus** between the precentral and central sulci is the **precentral,** and it is concerned with voluntary movement (Fig. 45). Two long sulci have a somewhat horizontal course in the rostral portion of the frontal lobe. These are the **superior** and **inferior frontal sulci** and they separate **superior, middle,** and **inferior frontal gyri** (Figs. 45, 46*A*). The inferior frontal gyrus has several divisions caused by the two anterior limbs of the lateral fissure and the inferior precentral sulcus.

The superior frontal gyrus continues over onto the medial surface of the frontal lobe and forms the major portion of the lobe on the medial surface. Ventrally, the superior frontal gyrus is continuous with the **gyrus rectus** along

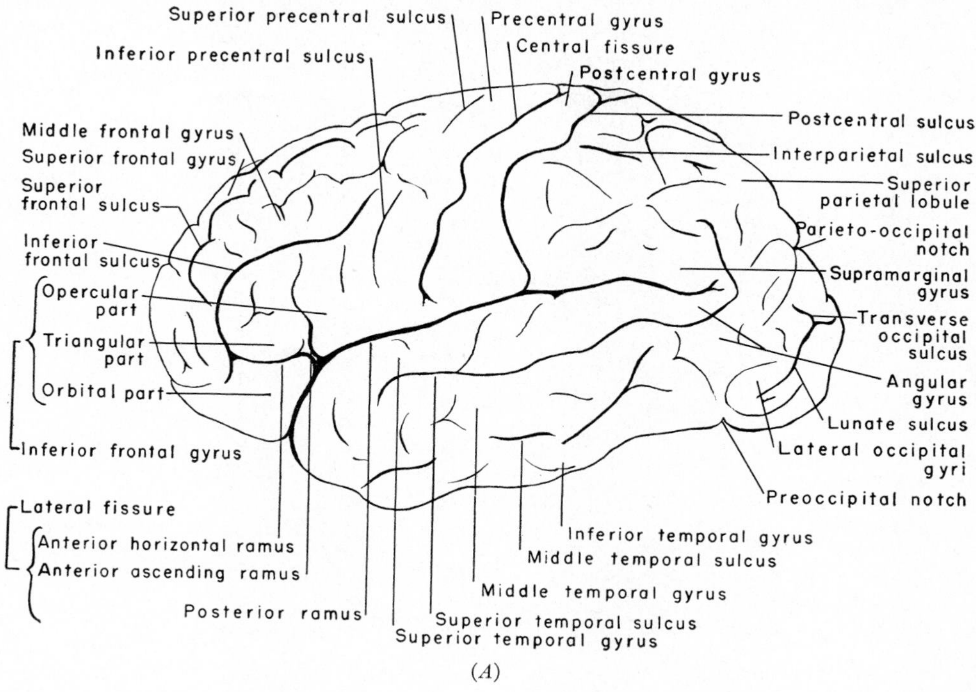

(A)

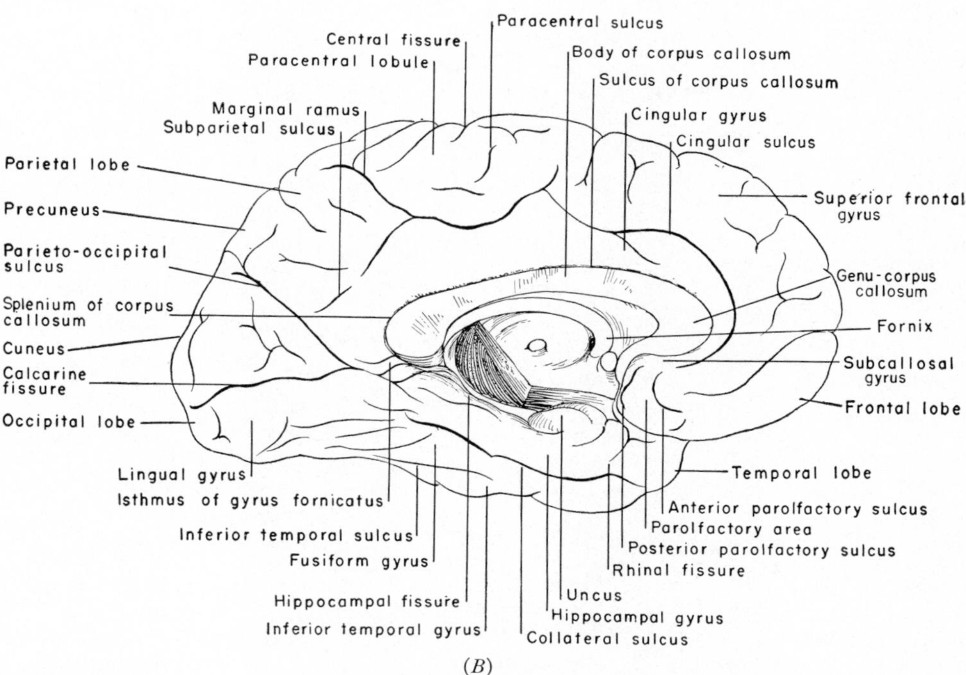

(B)

FIG. 46. Semidiagrammatic representation of sulci and gyri on the lateral surface (*A*) and on the medial surface (*B*) of the human cerebral hemisphere.

the inferior medial margin of the hemispheric surface. The remaining gyri of the ventral frontal surface are the **orbital gyri** (Fig. 42). The precentral gyrus continues medially around the superior limit of the central fissure and forms with the medial extension of the postcentral gyrus the **paracentral lobule.**

A deep sulcus, the **sulcus of the corpus callosum,** is seen just above the extent of that commissure. Superior to the sulcus is a large gyrus, the **gyrus cinguli,** and above this the **sulcus cinguli** (Fig. 47). This sulcus does not extend the length of the gyrus cinguli, however, but turns superiorly as a **marginal portion** which almost extends to the summit of the medial surface several centimeters caudal to the superior limit of the central fissure. Just below the most anteroventral part of the corpus callosum is the **subcallosal gyrus.** A continuation just in front of the lamina terminalis is sometimes called the paraterminal area. The **parolfactory area** is just ventral and anterior to the subcallosal gyrus and is separated from it by the **parolfactory sulcus** (Figs 46*B*, 47).

THE PARIETAL LOBE

Within the parietal lobe on its lateral hemispheric surface are several sulci. The **postcentral sulcus** follows somewhat the course of the central, and between it and the central sulcus is the **postcentral gyrus** which has a sensory function (Figs. 45, 46*A*). Passing caudally from the postcentral sulcus in a horizontal and inferior course is the **interparietal sulcus.** Dorsal to it is the **superior parietal lobule,** below it, the **inferior parietal lobule.** The latter has two divisions. That portion around the posterior end of the lateral fissure is called the **supramarginal gyrus;** that part about the posterior end of the superior temporal sulcus is the **angular gyrus.**

The parietal lobe is separated from the occipital on the medial hemispheric surface by the prominent **parieto-occipital sulcus.** This sulcus passes inferiorly toward the splenium of the corpus callosum near which it intersects, and becomes continuous with, the **calcarine fissure** of the occipital lobe. The marginal portion of the sulcus cinguli and the parieto-occipital sulcus bound the **precuneus,** medial portion of the superior parietal lobule. The **subparietal sulcus** separates the precuneus from the gyrus cinguli (Figs. 46*B*, 47).

THE TEMPORAL LOBE

The lateral hemispheric surface of the temporal lobe shows two sulci roughly paralleling the course of the lateral fissure. These are **superior and middle temporal sulci,** and they separate **superior, middle, and inferior temporal gyri** (Figs. 45, 46*A*, *B*). Near the posterior end of the superior temporal gyrus, on its superior surface and within the banks of the lateral fissure, are two smaller gyri, running transversely. These are the **superior transverse temporal gyri,** anterior and posterior (Fig. 44). The anterior is the cortical center for hearing.

In order to see the full extent of the inferior temporal gyrus it is necessary to turn to the ventral surface of the temporal lobe. The **inferior temporal sulcus,** pursuing a longitudinal course, separates the inferior temporal gyrus from the **fusiform gyrus** on the ventral surface of the temporal lobe (Figs. 46*B*, 48). Medial to this latter gyrus is another long fingerlike gyrus, the **hippocampal,** running the extent of the ventral temporal surface, and the **collateral sulcus** separates fusiform and hippocampal gyri. Near the anterior end of the hippocampal gyrus is the **uncus.** This lies adjacent to the rostral end of the pons, as noted above. The collateral sulcus at its rostral end may continue into the **rhinal fissure** which separates the rostral portion of the hippocampal gyrus (paleopallium) from the rest of the temporal lobe (neopallium).

THE OCCIPITAL LOBE

The occipital lobe occupies only a small portion of the lateral hemispheric surface. This part is triangular in shape, with an apex at the posterior end of the hemisphere, the **occipital pole.** The base of the triangle is an imaginary line extending from the **parieto-occipital notch** above to the **preoccipital notch** below (Fig. 46*A*). Several small twisting gyri compose the lateral occipital surface. Their course is chiefly horizontal. A transverse sulcus, the **transverse occipital,** may divide the **lateral occipital gyri** into superior and inferior groups. The **lunate sulcus** curves inferiorly and slightly rostrally from near the caudal end of the transverse occipital sulcus (Fig. 46*A*).

The medial surface of the occipital lobe is divided into superior and inferior portions by the **calcarine fissure** which extends to the occipital pole (Figs. 46*B*, 47). The region about the calcarine fissure serves as a primary visual receptive area. That part of the occipital cortex above the calcarine fissure is the **cuneus.** The inferior occipital cortex composes the **lingual gyrus,** which becomes continuous rostrally with the hippocampal gyrus on the ventral surface of the temporal lobe.

THE INSULA

If the opercular parts of the parietal, frontal, and temporal lobes are removed, the insular cortex is exposed (Fig. 44). This cortex, forming a thin covering over the lateral surface of the corpora striata, has a cone shape with apex forward and slightly inferior. The **central sulcus** of the insula passes obliquely downward across the cortex to separate the **short gyri** rostrally from the **long gyrus** behind. The insula is perhaps concerned with sensory and motor activity of the abdominal viscera.

THE CORPUS CALLOSUM

The cut surface of the corpus callosum reveals it to stretch horizontally with a gentle arch (Fig. 47). Its posterior end is rounded off roll-like, forming the **splenium.** Its anterior end takes a rather sharp curve ventrally, forming the **genu,** and continues into a thin **rostrum.** This in turn becomes continuous with the **lamina terminalis** within which the callosum develops originally. Another **commissure,** the **anterior,** connecting olfactory areas and temporal-lobe cortex of the two hemispheres, is also seen cut across in the lamina terminalis (Fig. 47).

Mid-line Aspects of the Brain Stem

The lamina terminalis can be followed ventrally to become continuous with the lateral wall of the **optic recess** above the optic chiasma. The stalk of the **pituitary** with its **recess** can be seen posterior to the optic chiasma (Fig. 47). These two recesses are extensions from the floor of the **third ventricle** which was opened when the brain was bisected.

The posterior floor of the third ventricle extends superiorly toward the **mamillary bodies.** The lumen of the ventricle continues posteriorly, narrowing greatly, into the **iter,** or **cerebral aqueduct.** Superior to the aqueduct is

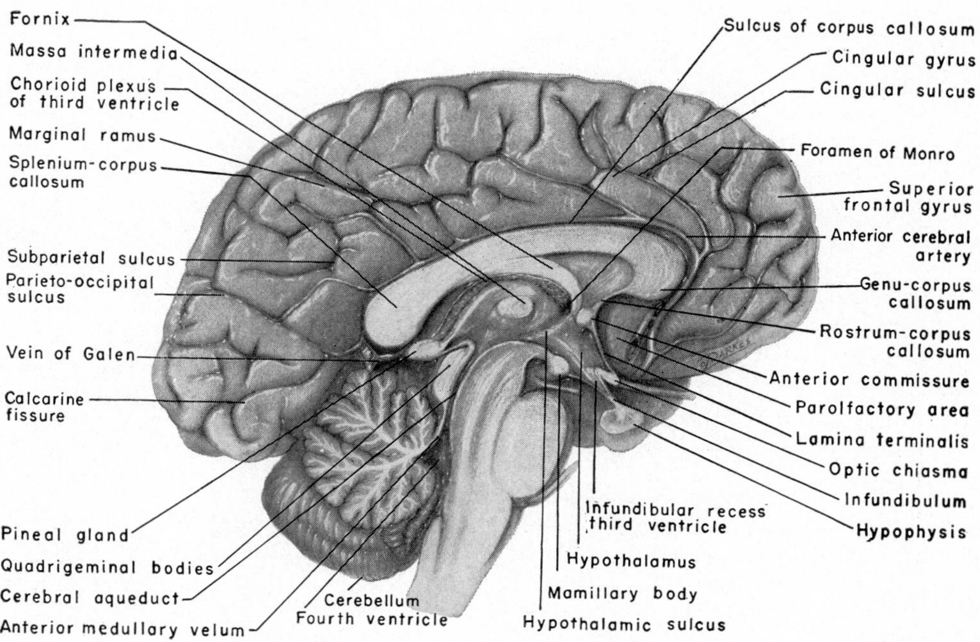

Fig. 47. Medial aspect of human cerebral hemisphere and brain stem. The brain has been sectioned through the longitudinal fissure.

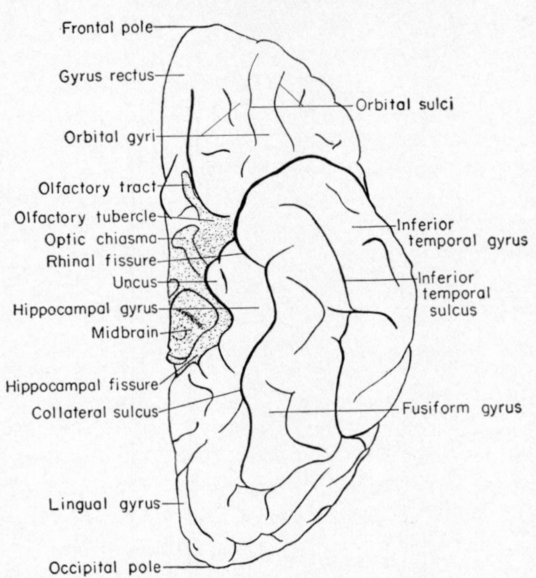

FIG. 48. Ventral surface of a human cerebral hemisphere showing sulci and gyri.

the **quadrigeminal plate,** including the **superior and inferior colliculi** (Fig. 47). These are the **tectum** of the midbrain. Anterior to them is the **posterior commissure** connecting brain stem centers of the two sides. Above the posterior commissure another extension of the third ventricle is seen, the small **pineal recess.** This extends into the stalk of the **pineal gland.** The **habenular commissure,** interconnecting the habenular ganglia, crosses just rostral to the pineal. These ganglia, their commissure, and the pineal gland compose the bulk of the **epithalamus.**

The lateral walls of the third ventricle are formed by the **hypothalamus** inferiorly and the **thalamus** superiorly. The **hypothalamic sulcus** indicates the divisions (Fig. 47). These, with the epithalamus, are derivatives of the diencephalon of the prosencephalon. The remaining derivative, **subthalamus,** lies lateral to the hypothalamus and is hidden from view. Occasionally the lumen of the third ventricle is bridged by thalamic gray, the **massa intermedia.** Above and just rostral to the anterior limit of the ventricle, a band of fibers can be traced from beneath the corpus callosum extending inferiorly to merge into the substance of the hypothalamus. This is the **fornix,** composed of many fibers arising in the hippocampus (Figs. 46*B*, 47). Some of the fibers cross beneath the splenium of the corpus callosum as a hippocampal commissure. The majority end in the hypothalamus. Just posterior to the point at which the fornix merges into hypothalamus is the **foramen of Monro** leading from third into the lateral ventricle (Fig. 47). The terms foramen of Monro and interventricular foramen are nearly always used synonymously. Strictly speaking, they are not the same (372). The interventricular foramen is the space above the foramina of Monro, forming the rostral, or telencephalic, part of the third ventricle, or that region lying beneath the primitive telencephalon medium. The **chorioid plexus** of the roof of the third ventricle is continuous through the foramina of Monro with that of the lateral ventricles and also with a small extension into the rostral or telencephalic part of the third ventricle. Extending between the fornix and the rostrum and genu of the corpus callosum is the **septum pellucidum** which forms the medial hemispheric surface and medial wall of the lateral ventricle in this region. If the septum pellucidum be removed and the ventricle thus opened, the **caudate nucleus** of the corpora striata can be seen forming the lateral walls of the lateral ventricles (Figs. 144, 208). These nuclei are usually included in the term brain stem.

Those parts of the pons and medulla that are visible on the medial surface of a half brain will not be described here in detail, since they are considered in later chapters. Only a few structures will be mentioned at this time. The lumen of the **fourth ventricle** is easily visible, showing its continuity rostrally with the cerebral aqueduct (Fig. 47). Its caudal end, overhung by the **obex,** is usually not continuous by a patent lumen with the central canal of the spinal cord. The roof of the fourth ventricle is of two parts, pitched transversely in its middle region beneath the cerebellum. The anterior roof is the **anterior medullary velum** (Fig. 47). It is lined within by ependyma, as are all walls of the ventricles. The posterior roof is thin and is composed of a layer of ependymal epithelium within reinforced by the inner meningeal layer, the pia. This latter is rich in blood vessels, tufts of which, covered by ependyma, are invaginated into the ventricle to form the chorioid plexus of the fourth ventricle. Before vascularization this posterior roof of the fourth ventricle was the **posterior medullary velum.**

Above the fourth ventricle is the mass of the **cerebellum.** It is constructed of many transversely arranged folia, and on cut surface these appear treelike (Fig. 47). The cut medial surface further shows also the characteristic composition of the cerebellum, an inner core of white matter covered by many small folds of gray, or cellular, cortex. The medial part of the cerebellum when viewed from above and posteriorly looks like an arched worm and has therefore been called the **vermis.** Except for its posterior portion, this is continuous with the two lateral lobes or **hemispheres.**

THE BLOOD SUPPLY OF THE BRAIN

Histologically, the cerebral and dural arteries described below have relatively thin walls in comparison to the size of their lumina. The internal elastic membrane is very well developed. The media contains practically no elastic fibers, however, and the adventitia contains chiefly collagenous tissue. The majority of the cerebral veins possess no smooth-muscle tissue.

Pattern and Control of Cerebral Circulation

Much variation exists in the relative vascularity of different parts of the nervous system. In general, gray matter contains many more capillaries than does white. The higher metabolic rate and greater oxygen consumption by neuronal elements than by fiber paths bear a relation to the difference in relative vascularity. The number of synapses and the amount of neuropile more closely parallel the increase in capillaries than does the number of neurons. Further, the amount of neural activity of a center bears a relation to the vascularity of the gray matter; sensory nuclei and associative centers have a greater vascularity than do motor nuclei, for example.

Normally, well-organized physiological mechanisms regulate the cerebral circulation (265, 266, 267). The systemic arterial pressure, and especially the difference between it and the venous pressure, is the chief agent in the regulation of the volume of blood flow through the brain, but it is not the sole regulator. Venous pressure in the dural sinuses and the jugular and vertebral veins plays a part in the regulation of cerebral flow. Other factors include changes in caliber of vessels through chemical stimuli (hormones, drugs); through nervous stimuli (sympathetic vasoconstrictor and parasympathetic vasodilator nerves); through local neuronal activity (increase in metabolism, increase in carbon dioxide tension, and subsequent regional vasodilation); and finally, through changes in resistance to flow within cerebral capillaries or venules caused by extreme hydration or dehydration of the brain.

Quite a large percentage of diseases of the nervous system have as their basis a disorder of some part of the vascular supply to the brain and spinal cord. Over the surface of the brain and spinal cord the various arteries have many communications with one another. Within the substance of the neural parenchyma, too, some anastomoses take place between neighboring vessels through capillary beds. Such anastomoses are usually not adequate to care for the supply of the neural tissue if an occlusion occurs in one of the contributing vessels. When any vessel entering into the nervous tissue is occluded, that tissue supplied by it undergoes necrosis. By a correlation of clinical signs and anatomical findings our knowledge of the cerebral and spinal circulation has been increased, and frequently on the basis of signs alone it is possible to say with certainty which cerebral or spinal vessel is at fault.

The Arterial Supply of the Brain

The brain derives its blood supply from the **internal carotid** and **vertebral arteries** (Fig. 49). The meninges derive their blood supply via the ophthalmic artery, a branch of the internal carotid, the middle meningeal, and the occipital. The internal carotid divides into the **middle** and **anterior cerebral arteries,** the **anterior chorioidal,** and **ophthalmic arteries.** The vertebral arteries of each side join to form the **basilar,** which runs forward along the basal surface of the pons and divides into the two **posterior cerebral arteries.** A **posterior communicating artery** joins each posterior cerebral artery with the ipsilateral internal carotid artery, and an **anterior communicating artery** joins the two anterior cerebral arteries. By means of these communicating arteries, an unbroken vascular chain is established around the base of the brain, the so-called **circle of Willis** (Fig. 49).

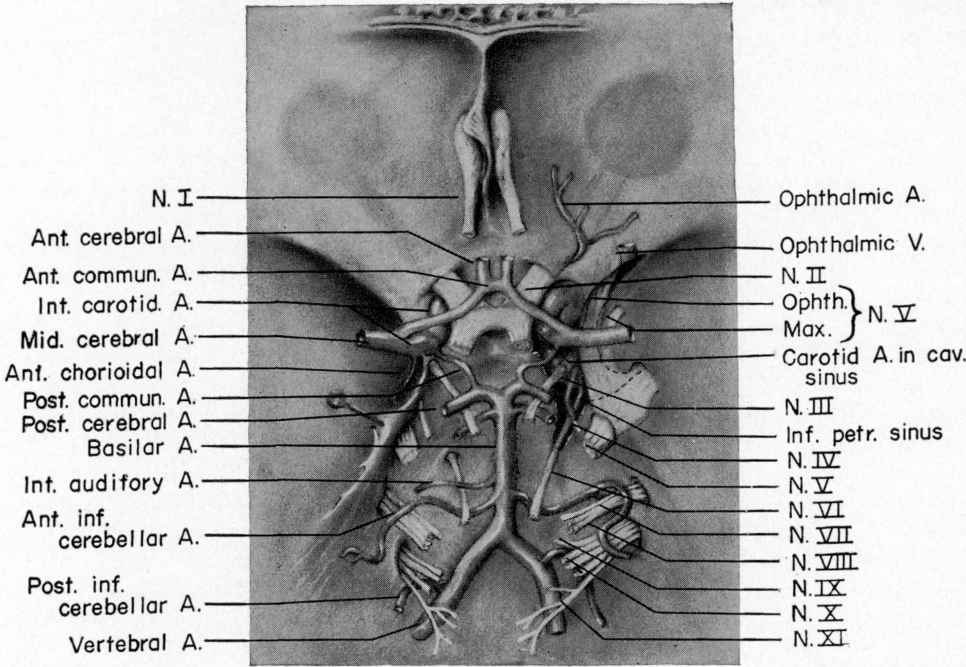

FIG. 49. The usual relationships of the cranial nerves to the intracranial arteries at the base of the brain. On the right the arteries and nerves traversing the cavernous sinus are shown in this relationship. (*Courtesy of Dr. Frank Walsh, from Arch. Ophth., N.S., vol.* 27.)

THE CIRCLE OF WILLIS

The circle of Willis is in effect an anastomosis between the vertebral and carotid arterial systems. The system is nearly always a closed

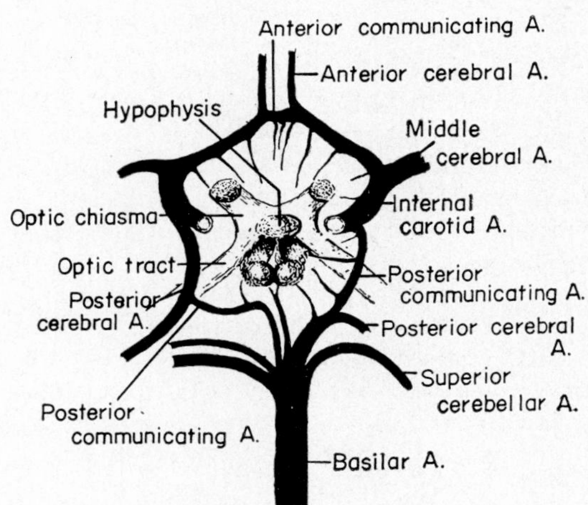

FIG. 50. Drawing of the circle of Willis from a human brain showing derivation of the posterior cerebral artery from the internal carotid, on the left. The typical pattern is shown on the right. Only a few of the basal penetrating arteries arising from the arterial circle are shown.

"ring," but it is fairly common that a component vessel is quite small without giving rise to noticeable clinical disturbance under normal conditions. One of the communicating vessels may be small, and the anterior or posterior cerebral arteries of the two sides may be of unequal size. The value of the circle as an anastomosis under normal conditions is more potential than actual. If one of its source arteries becomes occluded before it enters into the formation of the circle, however, the anastomosis may open up and all the branches from the circle will be supplied with blood from the normally patent source arteries. Under normal conditions little mingling of the blood carried by the several source arteries occurs, that in the internal carotid of one side passing almost exclusively into the anterior and middle cerebral arteries of the same side, and that of the basilar passing into its main branches (442, 681, 719). Furthermore, blood entering via the right internal carotid artery is distributed almost entirely to the right hemisphere. These facts are demonstrated in cerebral arteriography. In this procedure it is possible to outline aneurysms or anomalies of the chief cerebral arteries by injecting a radiopaque substance such as Thorotrast or Diodrast. If such a substance is injected into the right internal carotid only, the carotid system of that side is outlined. Normally, an insignificant amount, or none, passes into the carotid system of the opposite side or into the posterior cerebral arteries.

Though the posterior cerebral arteries are functionally branches of the basilar in the adult human brain, they are really branches of the internal carotid morphologically, as are the posterior communicating arteries (Fig. 50). In the adult human brain the posterior cerebral arteries have wandered far from their parent stream, approaching nearer another source of blood via the basilar. Strictly speaking, the short terminal branches of the basilar artery, uniting with the posterior cerebral arteries, represent the "communicating" arteries between internal carotid and vertebral sources of blood (2, 838).

INTERNAL CAROTID SUPPLY

Each of the three large cerebral arteries, anterior, middle, and posterior, gives off **basal penetrating branches** to supply the centrally placed nuclei and central white matter of the cerebral hemispheres (Fig. 51). Then each artery spreads out over the cortex to give off a second set of **cortical branches** which supply the cortex and subcortical white matter. The cortical branches in general are named for the area supplied. The arterioles and capillaries form some anastomoses with the branches of other arteries and with the branches of the penetrating arteries of the base. Only the general area of supply by these vessels will be given here. Some of the details of supply will be found in later sections.

The anterior cerebral artery passes dorsally to, and in close association with, the optic chiasma and optic nerve (Figs. 51, 52). While passing in a medial direction along the ventral brain surface it gives off several basal penetrating branches, the largest being called the **recurrent artery of Heubner.** These basal vessels are frequently called **striate arterioles** since they supply part of the corpora striata and the internal capsule, a large mass of fibers passing between cortex and brain stem. The recurrent artery usually pierces the lateral edge of the

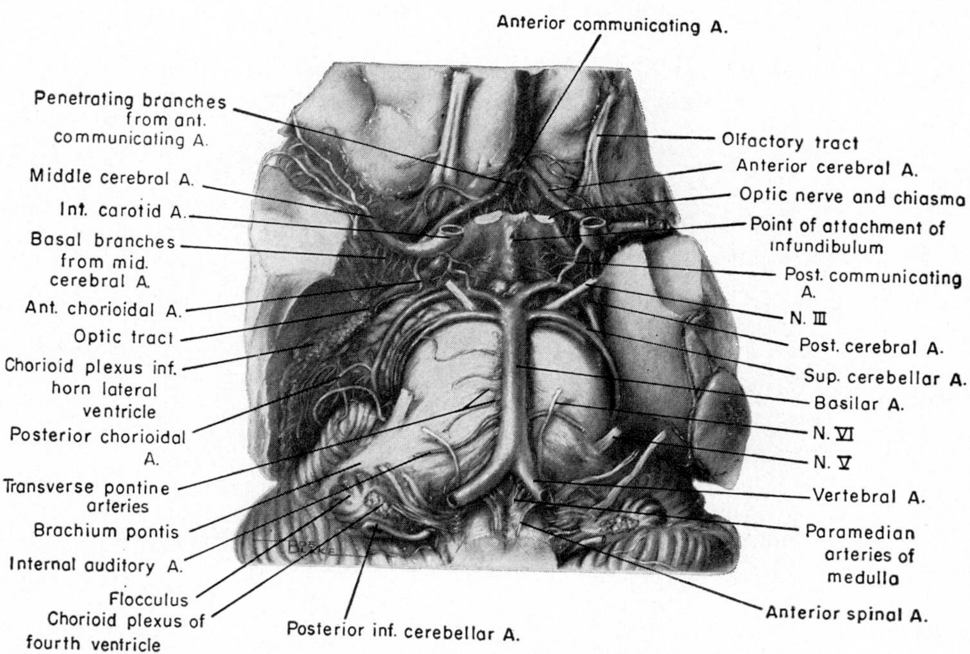

FIG. 51. The principal arteries at the base of the brain and especially those forming the circle of Willis. The temporal lobes have been partially dissected away, and on the left the inferior horn of the lateral ventricle has been opened.

anterior perforated space after giving small branches to the space (olfactory tubercle) and to the olfactory tract. The main trunk of the anterior cerebral artery passes dorsally into the longitudinal cerebral fissure. As it enters the fissure the vessel is connected by the short anterior communicating artery to the opposite anterior cerebral artery. Once within the fissure the anterior cerebral artery turns upward and forward to reach the genu of the corpus callosum (181). It gains the superior surface of that structure along which it runs and to which it gives numerous branches. It also supplies cortical tissue on the medial hemispheric surface of frontal and parietal lobes. Its terminal branch is usually in the parieto-occipital sulcus. The branches of the anterior cerebral given off in its cortical course are noted in Fig. 52. Several of these vessels may arise from a single trunk.

In the majority of cases the two anterior cerebral arteries do not have any intercommunication distal to the anterior communicating trunk. Rarely, however, one of the anterior cerebral vessels may distribute to each hemisphere. The various branches of the anterior cerebral pass over the crest of the hemisphere to terminate on the lateral surface (Fig. 53). A posterior callosal vessel may unite with a branch of the posterior cerebral (Fig. 55).

The middle cerebral artery gives off a number of small, basal penetrating branches, **striate arterioles,** soon after its origin from the internal carotid (Figs. 51, 53). These supply the corpora striata and internal capsule, especially the posterior limb of the latter. The main trunk of the vessel then passes across the insula and into the sylvian fissure wherein its course continues. **Cortical branches** supply the tip, superior, and lateral surface of the temporal lobe, and several vessels, frequently corresponding with the chief sulci, pass onto the lateral surface of the frontal and parietal lobes. The cortical territory supplied extends posteriorly to the rostral border of the occipital lobe, and superiorly almost to the crest of the hemisphere.

A schematic, common arrangement of the cortical branches of the middle cerebral is given by Foix and Levy (262). A large anterior temporal artery is first given off. This usually supplies branches to the temporal pole and the superior and lateral surfaces of the temporal lobe, anteriorly. Next, a large trunk arises

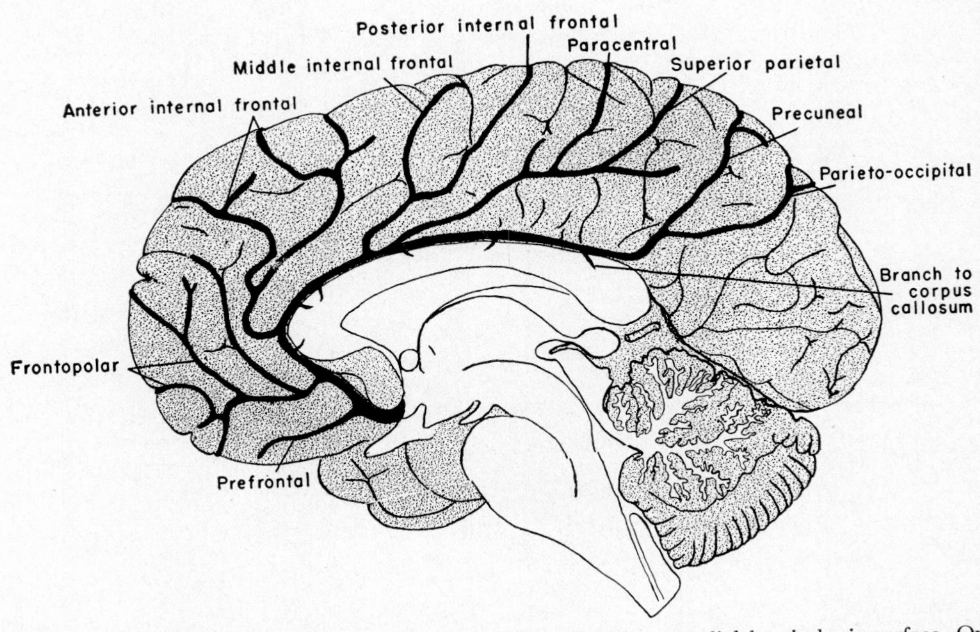

Fig. 52. The chief branches of the human anterior cerebral artery on the medial hemispheric surface. Only a few branches to the corpus callosum are shown.

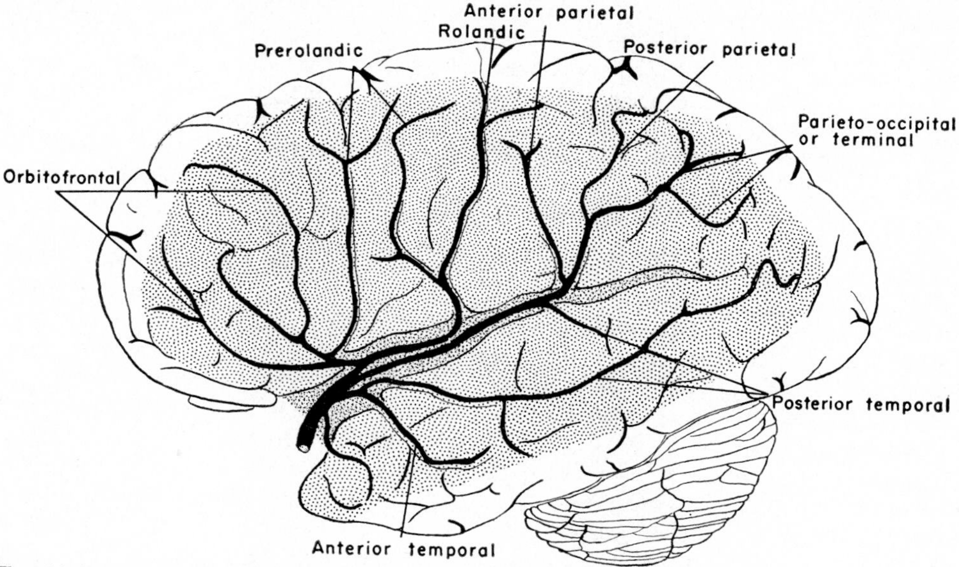

FIG. 53. The chief cortical branches of the human middle cerebral artery in a pattern of origin frequently seen. The approximate area of supply is shaded. Terminal branches of anterior and posterior cerebral arteries are also indicated.

which may run parallel with the middle cerebral for a short distance. From this trunk several smaller ascending vessels spring. These include the orbitofrontal, prerolandic, rolandic, and anterior parietal arteries. After a fairly long course without giving any branches, the middle cerebral then has posterior temporal, posterior parietal, and terminal parieto-occipital branches. The middle cerebral artery illustrated in Fig. 53 shows a slight variation in the pattern of origin of the temporal and terminal branches. Aneurysms are common at the sites of the first and second branches of the middle cerebral artery.

The posterior cerebral artery, soon after its origin from the basilar, arches caudally around the cerebral peduncle to gain the cleft between temporal lobe and brain stem. It comes into close association with the oculomotor and trochlear nerves (Figs. 49, 51, 54). **Basal penetrating branches** are of two varieties, short and long, according to the extent of their course around the brain stem before entering it. They supply the thalamus, cerebral peduncles, tectum, and chorioid plexus of the third ventricle. Details concerning the distribution of some of these vessels will be found in Chap. 8. After these branches have arisen, the

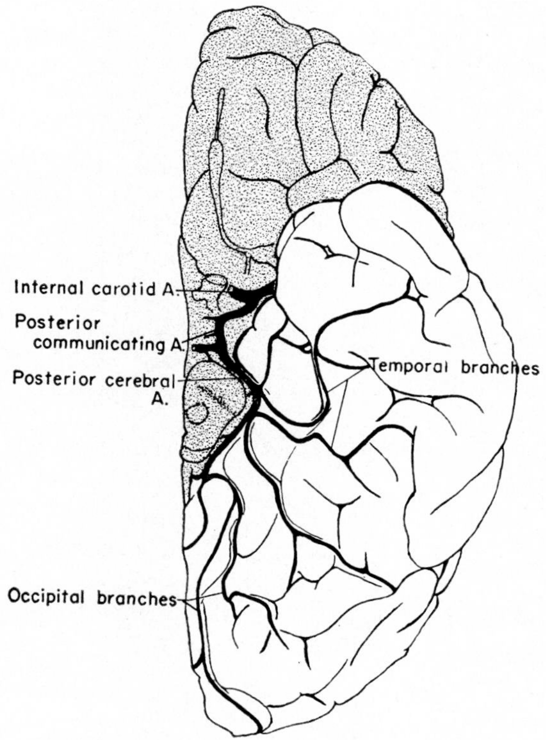

FIG. 54. The cortical branches of the posterior cerebral artery on the ventral surface of the temporal and occipital lobes.

posterior cerebral artery crosses the free edge of the tentorium cerebelli to gain the ventral surface of the temporal lobe and pass finally onto the medial surface of the occipital lobe. It usually has three large **cortical branches** which supply the entire medial surface of the occipital lobe, the major portion of its lateral surface, the ventral surface, and ventrolateral crest of the major portion of the temporal lobe (Fig. 55).

The anterior chorioidal artery is frequently a branch of the middle cerebral rather than of the internal carotid (Fig. 51). It passes posteriorly from its origin and runs between the uncus of the temporal lobe and the brain stem. It runs somewhat parallel but ventral to the optic tract and several of its branches overlie the lateral geniculate (Fig. 56). Terminal branches of this artery anastomose with branches of the middle and posterior cerebral and posterior chorioidal arteries.

Branches supplying the head of the caudate nucleus (of the corpora striata) and the anterior commissure arise near the origin of the anterior chorioidal. Next arise branches to the amygdaloid nuclei and those other rhinencephalic structures in the temporal lobe (1). More posteriorly branches arise which penetrate the optic tract and enter the base of the brain to nourish the posterior limb of the internal capsule, some of the nuclei of the corpora striata, and the first parts of the radiations between geniculates and cortex. Other vessels are given off to the optic tract itself. Branches are also given to the cerebral peduncle, lateral geniculate body, and chorioid plexus of the inferior horn of the lateral ventricle. Occasionally, a branch can be followed along the chorioid plexus superior to the thalamus to the level of the foramen of Monro.

Branches from the **posterior communicating artery** (Fig. 51) supply the optic chiasma, tuber cinereum of the hypothalamus, subthalamus, rostral part of the cerebral peduncle, internal capsule, globus pallidus of the corpora striata, and medial and lateral thalamic nuclei. Some of the branches with this distribution may at times come from the posterior cerebral. The **anterior communicating artery** may have a small number of branches or none. It usually sends a small vessel into the rostral hypothalamic region (Figs. 50, 51). The points of union between this artery and the anterior cerebrals are frequent sites of aneurysms.

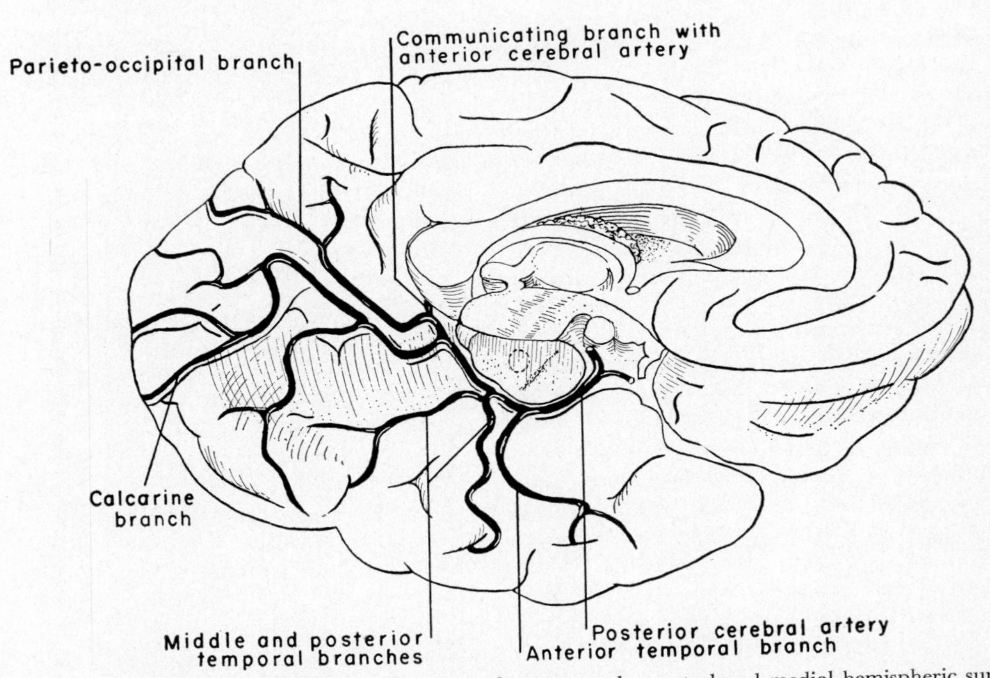

FIG. 55. The cortical branches of the posterior cerebral artery on the ventral and medial hemispheric surfaces.

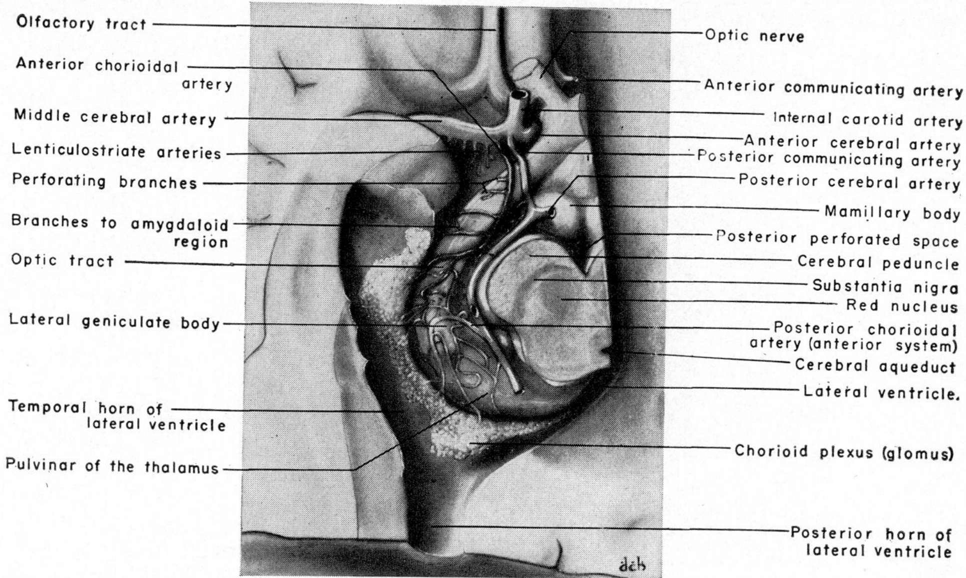

FIG. 56. The anterior chorioidal artery on the ventral surface of the human brain. Some of the posterior chorioidal supply is also shown. (*From an original dissection and in part after Abbie.*)

VERTEBRAL ARTERY SUPPLY

The medulla, pons, and cerebellum are supplied by branches of the vertebral and basilar arteries (Figs. 49, 141). All the brain stem, exclusive of the basal ganglia and diencephalon, is supplied by branches of these vessels. As the two **vertebral arteries** course first along the lateral and later along the ventral surface of the medulla, they show an inequality of size in about 90 per cent of human brains (759). The left is larger in the majority of cases in which significant difference in size is present. They give rise to bulbar (medullar) branches which pass into the median and ventrolateral region of the medulla, the **anterior spinal arteries, arteries of the lateral fossa,** and the **posterior inferior cerebellar arteries.** In some cases they give rise to **posterior spinal arteries.** These last more frequently arise, however, from the posterior inferior cerebellar arteries (Fig. 57). The vertebral arteries in their course are closely related to the last three cranial nerves; in most brains they unite at the caudal end of the pons to form the basilar.

The **basilar** is a fairly constant artery in its size, course, and relations. It usually divides at the rostral end of the pons into the two posterior cerebral arteries, or into shorter "communicating" branches which join the posterior cerebrals. In many brains the posterior cerebral arteries maintain their early developmental relationship and stem directly from the internal carotid. In such cases they may or may not be joined to the basilar by a communicating vessel. At any rate the "communication" between basilar and carotid trunks is susceptible to much variation in size and point of union. Branches of the basilar artery are the **median** and **transverse pontine,** the **anterior inferior cerebellar, internal auditory,** and **superior cerebellar arteries.** The close relationship of the basilar artery to the abducens nerve, of the anterior inferior cerebellar and internal auditory arteries to the facial and auditory nerves, and of the superior cerebellar artery to the oculomotor and trochlear nerves should be noted (Fig. 49).

The general plan of blood supply is the same to the medulla, pons, and midbrain and involves a classification of the vessels listed above into three types according to their course (261). There are paramedian, short circumferential, and long circumferential vessels according to their point of entry into the substance of the brain stem. The intramedullary distribution of these vessels is described in Chap. 8. Interesting syndromes have been described as a result of disturbed blood supply

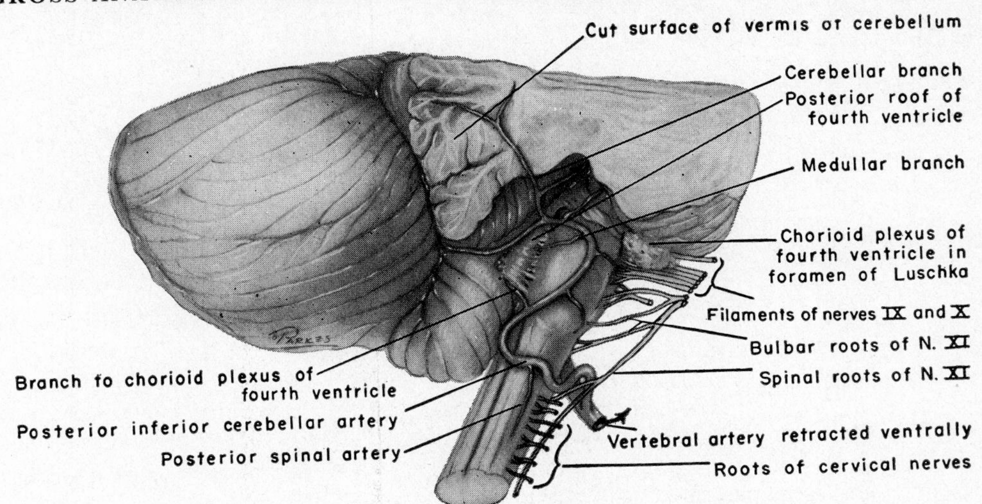

FIG. 57. A dissection to show the posterior inferior cerebellar artery and some of its branches.

in the area of distribution of some of these vessels. Some of these will be alluded to in later sections.

Venous Drainage of the Brain

The venous drainage of the cerebral hemispheres can be divided arbitrarily into two systems, a **superficial** and a **deep,** or central, system. This does not imply, however, that a territory of drainage is peculiar to veins of one system. Anastomoses are numerous between the two sets of veins, and much of the cerebral tissue can be drained by either of the systems as the necessity arises (708).

superficial veins

The superficial cortical veins are superior and inferior ones with reference to their position on the brain (Fig. 58). The **superior cerebral veins** can be grouped into four large divisions, the **frontal, precentral, postcentral,** and **occipital,** draining upper medial hemispheric surface and the superior region of the lateral surface (Figs. 58, 59). All these superior veins drain into the longitudinal venous sinus and open into this obliquely. These veins receive a small cuff of arachnoid as they move to enter the sinus. It is of interest also that many of these open into the walls of the sinus in such a fashion that they pour their blood in a direction opposite to that of the sinus blood flow. The venous sinuses are described later.

The inferior cerebral veins drain the ventral hemispheric surface and the inferior part of the lateral (Fig. 60). Veins draining the ventral surface of the frontal lobe may drain into the inferior sagittal sinus, into the cavernous sinus, or into the basal vein, described below. The inferior temporal veins may drain into either the superior petrosal or transverse sinuses. The **inferior lateral occipital veins** usually drain into the transverse sinus. The **inferior medial occipital** veins, sometimes forming a **posterior cerebral vein,** may drain into one of several vessels: into the superior petrosal sinus, directly into the great vein of Galen described below, or into the basal vein and thence into the great vein of Galen.

The superficial middle cerebral vein occupies the rostral portion of the sylvian fissure. It drains chiefly the inferior convexity of the lateral hemispheric surface by a series of tributaries. It empties ventrally into the cavernous sinus or runs caudally along the ventral brain surface to drain into the superior petrosal sinus. The superficial middle cerebral vein nearly always has one or more anastomotic connections with the superior longitudinal sinus via the **veins of Trolard** (Fig. 58). The **anastomotic vein of Labbé,** running obliquely across the posterior temporal surface, may connect either the superficial middle cerebral vein or a posterior superior vein with the transverse sinus. These two anastomotic channels between the superior longitudinal sinus and the cavern-

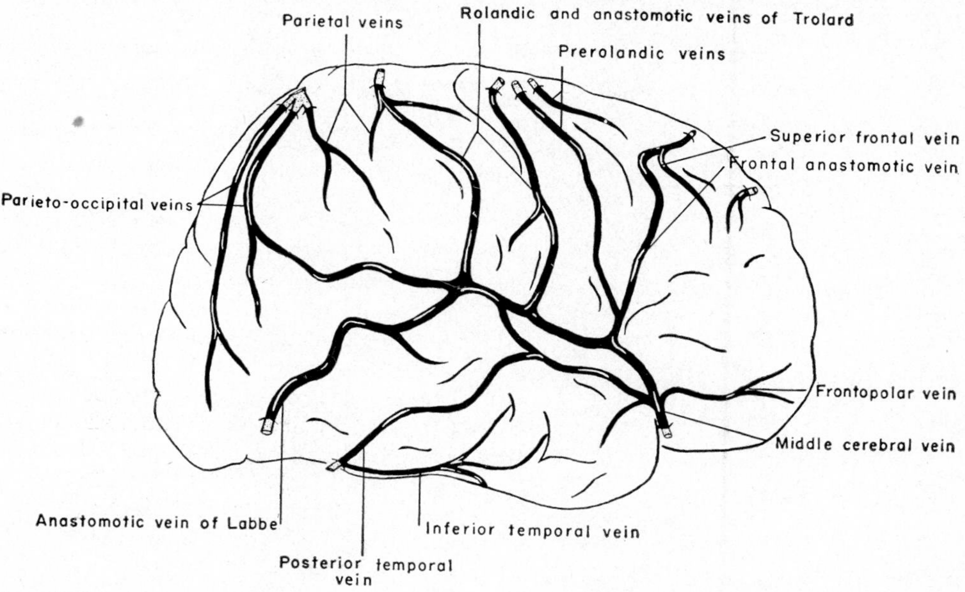

FIG. 58. A semischematic representation of the veins of the lateral hemispheric surface of the human. Small cuffs are shown to illustrate the point of entry of the veins into the dural sinuses.

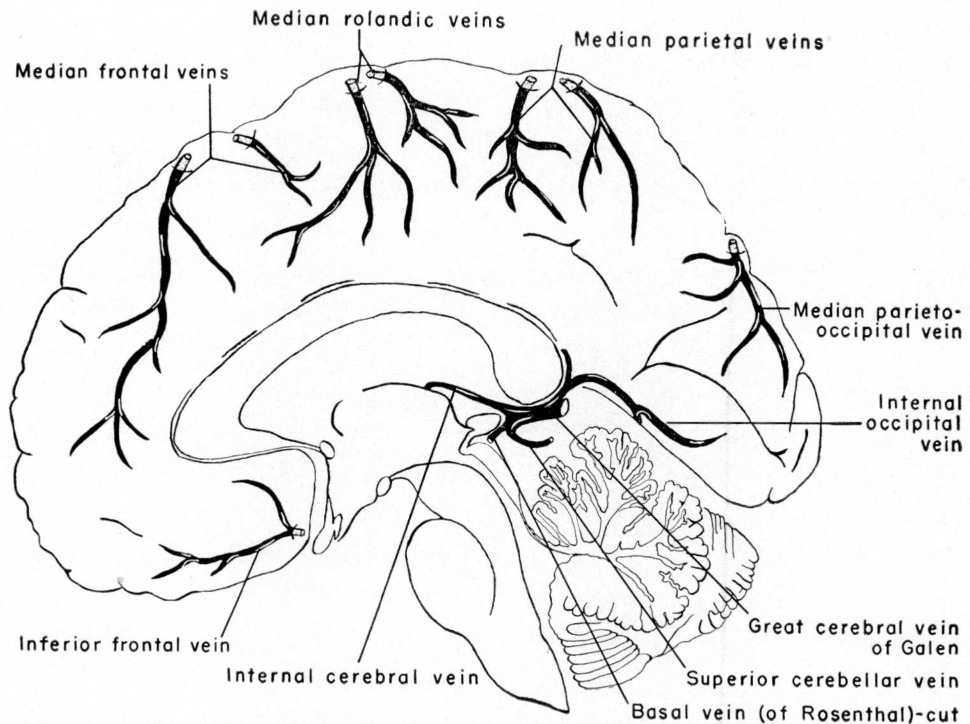

FIG. 59. A semischematic representation of the veins of the medial hemispheric surface of the human.

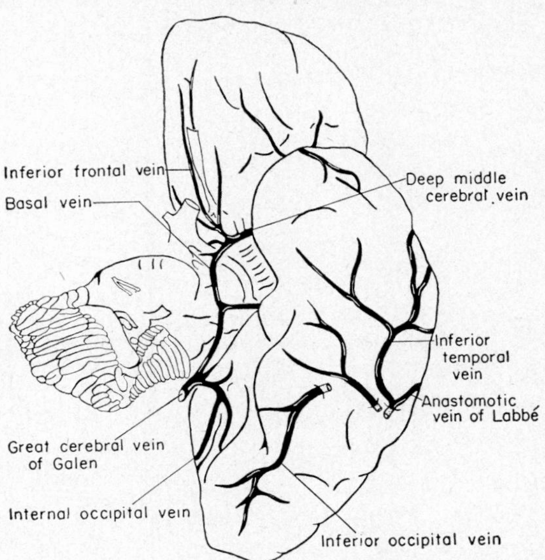

Fig. 60. A semischematic representation of the veins on the basal surface of the cerebral hemisphere of the human. The pons and cerebellum are rotated and retracted medially.

ous and transverse sinuses may be of great value in certain alterations of the intracranial pressure.

The anterior cerebral vein runs with the artery of the same name and drains the inferior medial hemispheric surface of the frontal lobes. It is joined near the optic chiasma by the **deep middle cerebral vein** which arises in, and drains, the insular region and opercular cortex and passes ventrally, deep within the sylvian fissure. Other veins, chiefly **striate veins,** draining the corpora striata, join this common trunk, commonly known as the **basal vein (of Rosenthal).** This vessel passes posteriorly and dorsally around the cerebral peduncle and colliculi to join the great vein of Galen (Figs. 60, 208). In its course it receives tributaries draining the peduncular region, midbrain, inferior horn of the lateral ventricle, and occasionally certain of the occipital veins. The basal vein is an important anastomotic channel between the superficial venous system and the deep system described just below. In some instances, however, the basal vein drains into the superior petrosal sinus rather than into the vein of Galen.

DEEP VEINS

The **great vein of Galen** collects a number of tributaries from the central parts of the hemisphere. This vein, a very thin-walled structure, can be seen projecting posteriorly just beneath the splenium of the corpus callosum. It empties into the straight sinus. Its two largest tributaries aside from the basal vein, described above, are the two small veins of Galen, or the

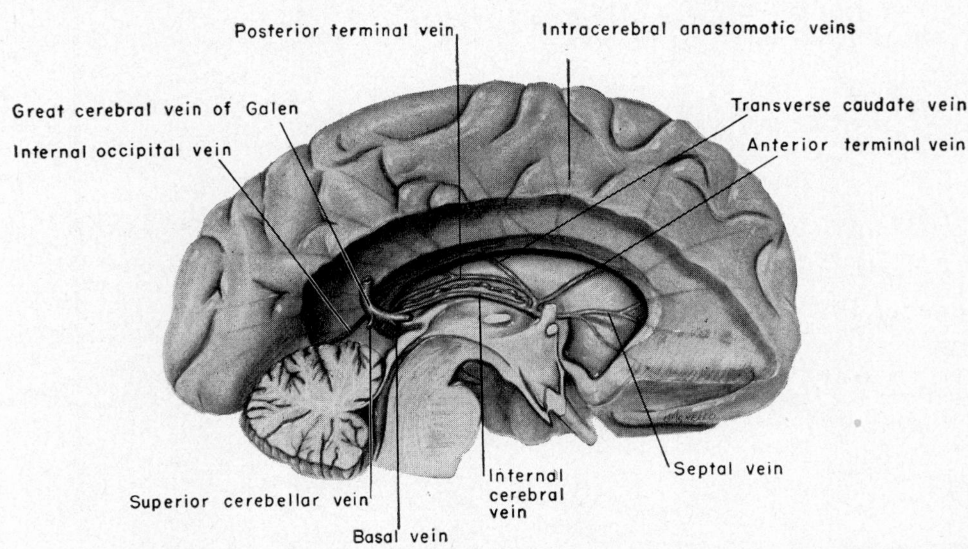

Fig. 61. Schematic representation of the galenic, or internal, system of cerebral veins. Only two of the intracerebral anastomotic veins are labeled. (*Modified after Schlesinger, from Brain, vol. 62.*)

internal cerebral veins (Figs. 61, 208). These latter first appear on each side as they pass caudally near the interventricular foramen, and each receives the following tributaries: **septal, anterior terminal, transverse caudate, posterior terminal, superior chorioidal,** and **epithalamic veins.** The internal cerebral veins drain the white matter of the cerebral hemispheres about the lateral ventricles and in the inferior frontal lobe, the basal ganglia (corpora striata), the chorioid plexus of the lateral ventricles, and a small portion of the dorsal thalamus. Each of these territories can be drained by veins of the superficial venous system. Many intracerebral anastomoses exist between the terminal tributaries of the central and superficial veins and thus provide a margin of safety in conditions in which increased intracranial pressure may alter the drainage by one system or the other (Figs. 62*A*, *B*).

The remaining parts of the thalamus, the midbrain, pons, and medulla are drained by many small local veins which drain into the sinuses at the base of the brain. The veins of the medulla have communications with those of

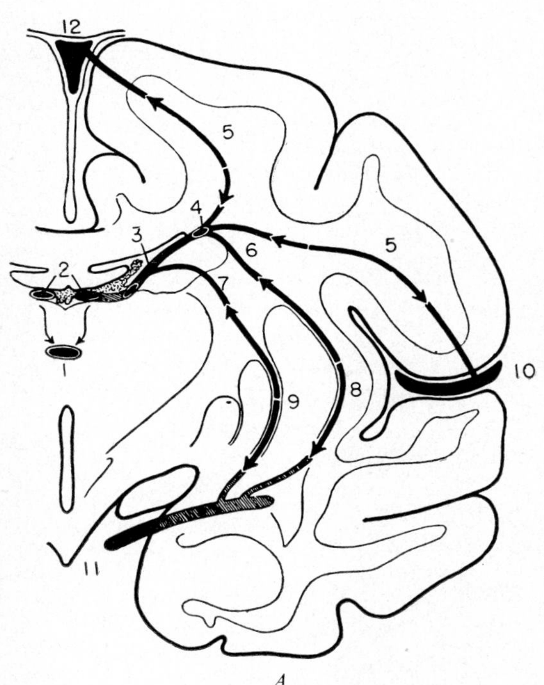

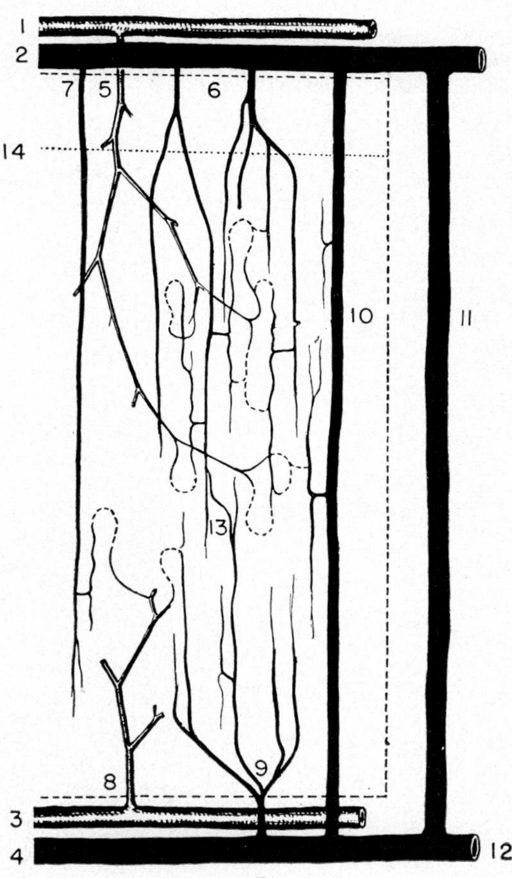

Fig. 62. *A.* Diagrammatic cross section through the brain of a rhesus monkey, showing the connections between the galenic system and the veins on the surface of the brain: 1, great vein of Galen; 2, small veins of Galen; 3, transverse caudate vein; 4, longitudinal caudate vein; 5, venous channels, connecting the great vein of Galen with the superior longitudinal sinus and the superficial sylvian vein; 6 and 7, superior external and internal lenticular veins; 8 and 9, inferior external and internal lenticular veins; 10, superficial sylvian vein; 11, deep sylvian vein; 12, superior sagittal sinus. (*After Schlesinger, from Brain, vol.* 62.)

B. Diagram showing the venous circulation in the white matter and the connections between the superficial cortical and the ventricular veins through the intracerebral and extracerebral anastomotic veins: 1, pial artery; 2, pial vein; 3, basal artery; 4, basal vein; 5, cortical artery; 6, cortical veins; 7, cortical and long subcortical vein; 8, subventricular artery; 9, subventricular vein; 10, intracerebral anastomotic vein; 11, extracerebral anastomotic vein; 12, great vein of Galen; 13, intervenous anastomosis; 14, junction of cortex and white matter. (*After Schlesinger, from Brain, vol.* 62.)

the spinal cord. The cerebellum is drained by two chief groups, **superior** and **inferior cerebellar veins.** The superior veins drain the upper surface and empty into either the straight, the transverse, or superior petrosal sinuses. The inferior veins drain into inferior petrosal, transverse, and occipital sinuses.

VENOUS SINUSES

All these veins, central and superficial, drain into the large **venous sinuses** located within the layers of the dura. These are merely endothelial lined channels lying within the dura (Figs. 63, 64). There are six chief dural sinuses.

The superior longitudinal, or sagittal, sinus begins at the foramen caecum anteriorly, receives the frontal, precentral, postcentral, and occipital veins, and extends posteriorly to the "confluence of the sinuses" (confluens sinuum) or the torcular Herophili. As described above, some of the cortical veins, after running obliquely in the wall of the sinus, empty their blood into the sinus in a direction opposite to that of the sinus flow. The longitudinal sinus has lateral enlargements or lacunae into which protrude the arachnoid villi.

The inferior longitudinal, or sagittal, sinus occupies the inferior margin of the falx cerebri and empties into the straight sinus. It drains the corpus callosum and the inferior part of the medial surface of the hemispheres.

The straight sinus lies within the dura at the junction of the falx cerebri and tentorium cerebelli. It receives the inferior sagittal sinus, the superior cerebellar veins, and the vein of Galen. The straight sinus ends posteriorly in the confluence of the sinuses with the longitudinal sinus, if a confluence of the sinuses is present (see later).

The cavernous sinuses are at the base of the skull on either side of the sella turcica. They receive veins from the frontal face region, from the orbit including the central retinal vein, and may also drain the superficial middle cerebral

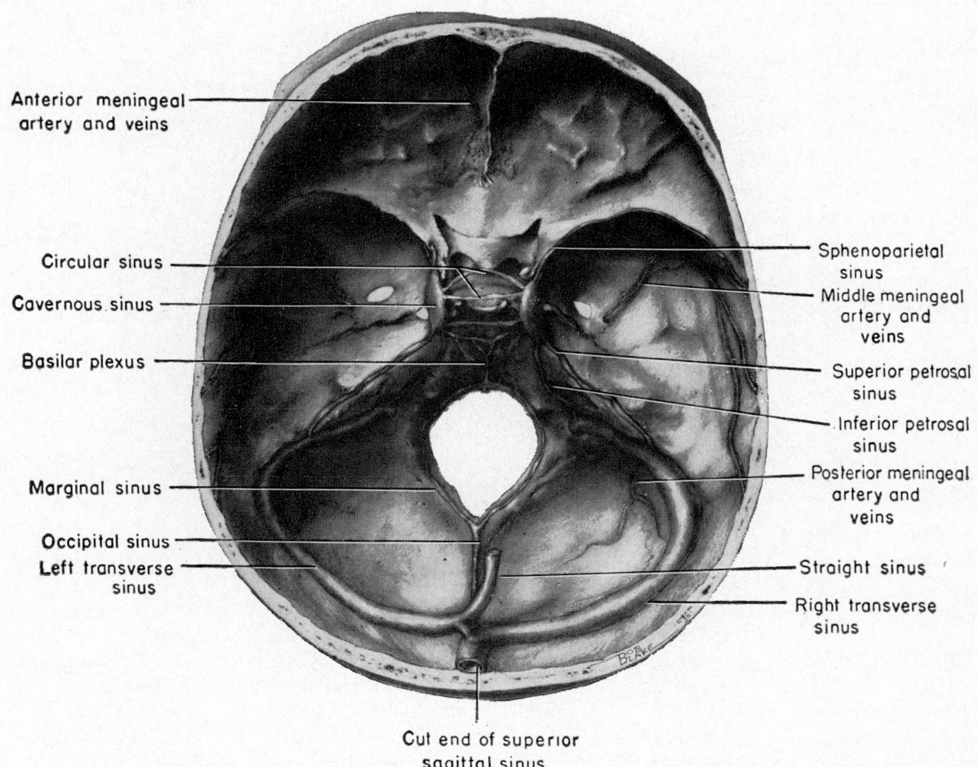

FIG. 63. Schematic representation of the dural venous sinuses about the base of the brain. The meningeal arteries and veins are also shown. Drawn as if dura were closely cut away from each sinus.

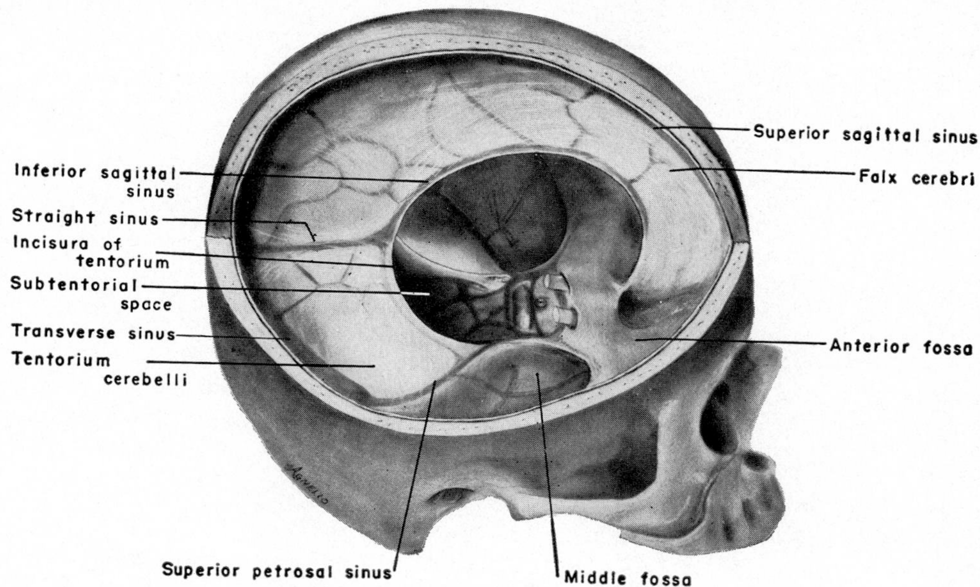

FIG. 64. The dural septa, intracranial fossae, and dural venous sinuses.

vein and some veins from the inferior frontal cortex. The **circular sinus** connects the two cavernous sinuses.

The superior and inferior petrosal sinuses, beginning in the posterior portions of the cavernous sinus, pass caudalward into the transverse sinus and the first portion of the internal jugular vein, respectively. The superior petrosal sinus runs along the attached margins of the tentorium cerebelli; the inferior petrosal sinus passes along the lines of the petro-occipital sutures. The superior petrosal sinus may receive the superficial middle cerebral vein and usually receives veins from the temporal cortex, and veins from the superior surface of the cerebellum; in some instances it receives the basal vein. The inferior petrosal sinus receives veins from the inferior surface of the cerebellum, from the medulla and pons, and from the internal ear.

The lateral, transverse, or sigmoid sinuses arise from the confluence of the sinuses when it is present, and pass laterally and anteriorly in the margin of the tentorium to the base of the petrous portion of the temporal bone. They then leave the tentorium and pass inferiorly into the jugular bulb and thence into the internal jugular vein. The mastoid emissary veins (see later), the superior petrosal sinuses, and the veins of the diploë empty into the lateral sinuses. Veins from the posterior inferior region of the cerebral cortex occasionally drain into the lateral sinus also.

Lesser sinuses are the **occipital, sphenoparietal,** and the **basilar plexus.** The occipital sinus is formed by two smaller **marginal sinuses** encircling the foramen magnum. It passes upward to end in the confluence of the sinuses if such be present. The marginal sinuses receive certain cerebellar veins and communicate with the vertebral vein and with the external vertebral plexus through a plexus of veins traversing the hypoglossal canal. The sphenoparietal sinuses run along the inferior surface of the lesser wings of the sphenoid and empty into the cavernous sinus. They usually originate from a meningeal vein. The basilar plexus is located in the dura over the basilar part of the occipital bone and the body of the sphenoid. It communicates with the inferior petrosal and marginal sinuses, as well as with the internal vertebral venous plexus. It receives veins draining the pons and medulla. It should be noted that the medullar veins are connected with those draining the upper spinal cord.

THE CONFLUENS SINUUM

For many years it was considered typical that the superior longitudinal, straight, and occipital sinuses empty into a common pool, from which

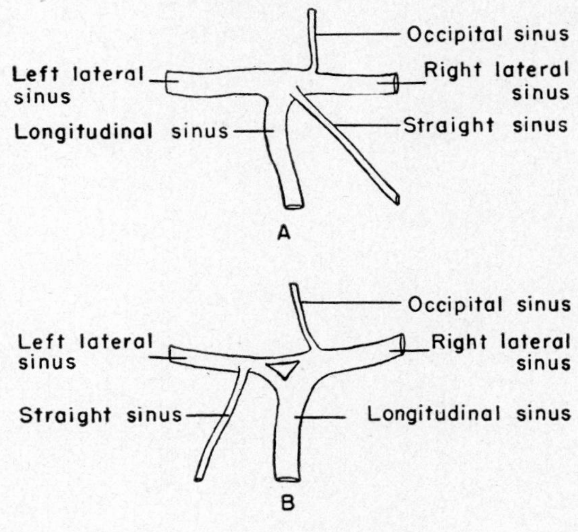

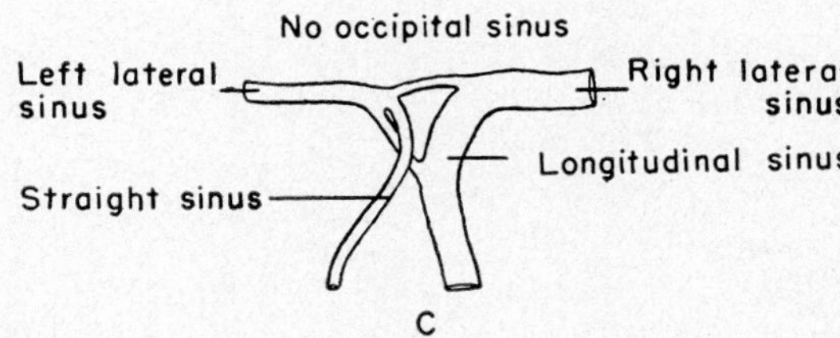

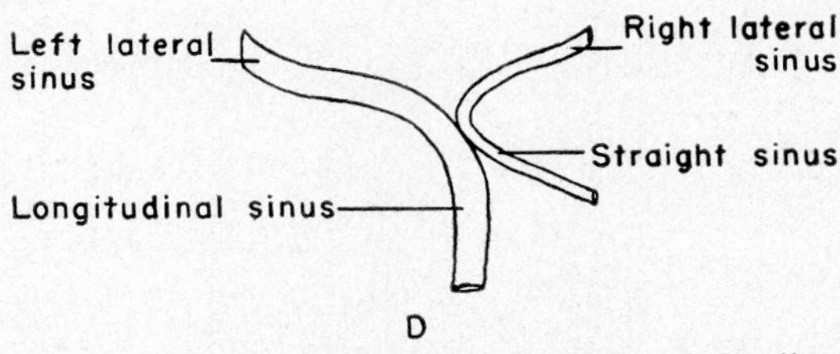

Fig. 65. Various types of arrangements of the "confluence of the sinuses." *A*, "common pool"; *B*, plexiform; *C*, ipsilateral; *D*, a second variant of the ipsilateral. (*Courtesy of Dr. Barnes Woodhall, Laryngoscope, vol.* 49.)

a transverse or lateral sinus arose on either side. This common pool has come to be known as the "confluence of the sinuses" (confluens sinuum) or the torcular Herophili. Actually such a **common reservoir** type is not the most common one encountered (235, 851). More common types are the **unequal deviation** and the **plexiform** (Fig. 65). In the former, the superior longitudinal sinus deviates to one side or the other, becoming continuous with the transverse sinus of that side and sending only slender communications, if any at all, to the transverse sinus of the other side. This type was found in 18 of 50 cases, and in 11 of these the superior longitudinal sinus was continuous with the right transverse. In the plexiform type both the superior longitudinal and straight sinuses bifurcate into divisions of equal or unequal size. A division of the superior longitudinal unites with one from the straight sinus to form a transverse sinus of one side. A rather unusual type of arrangement of these sinuses is the **unilateral deviation** type. Both the superior longitudinal and straight sinuses deviate to one side to form a transverse sinus. Only slender branches are sent to the other side to form a transverse sinus. In these last three variations, the occipital sinus may join either transverse sinus. It is very common, in view of these various types of sinus arrangement, that the two transverse sinuses are of unequal size. The left is more often the longer one also.

It was mentioned above that the blood entering the skull via the right internal carotid artery supplied almost exclusively the right cerebral hemisphere. It is of interest that this right stream is drained predominantly by the right internal jugular vein (719). Furthermore, the blood in each internal jugular vein is fairly representative of the drainage from both cortical and central structures. This is understandable when the ample connections between the superficial and deep cerebral veins are recalled. The blood in the internal jugular veins is relatively free of blood from extracerebral sources. On the other hand the blood in the external jugular veins contains a significant fraction of cerebral venous blood.

The sinuses may become occluded by a thrombosis during intracranial infections, or they may sometimes be ruptured during trauma or in the course of operative procedure (389). Lateral-sinus thrombosis occurs at times with an infection of the mastoid air cells; cavernous-sinus thrombosis, with an infection of the nose, upper face, or teeth. Thrombosis of the cerebral veins is apt to lead to softening of the cortex they drain. This is especially prone to occur in marantic individuals with or without some chronic infection.

EMISSARY VEINS

Many communications exist between the sinuses within the dura and the veins outside the skull. These are the emissary veins. The **diploic veins** contained within the laminae of the skull also drain into the sinuses or into the external veins. Various other emissary veins usually present other important pathways for the spread of infection inside and outside the cranium. The chief connections between the sinuses and the extracranial veins are as follows. A vein connects the anterior end of the superior longitudinal sinus and veins of the nose through the foramen caecum. A mastoid emissary vein passes between the transverse sinus and the posterior auricular and external occipital veins. A parietal emissary vein connects the superior longitudinal sinus and the scalp veins. A vein in the condyloid foramen connects the transverse sinus and the deep neck veins. A vein passing via the hypoglossal canal joins the occipital (or marginal) sinus and the deep neck veins. Ophthalmic veins connect the cavernous sinus with the angular vein of the face. Connections pass between the cavernous sinus and pterygoid plexus via the foramen ovale. Connections via middle meningeal veins are formed between the longitudinal sinus and the pterygoid plexus.

THE MENINGES AND CEREBROSPINAL FLUID

Immediately surrounding the relatively soft brain and spinal-cord tissue within their rigid bony encasement are three covering membranes, the meninges (Fig. 66) (830). The very fibrous and strong **dura mater** is outermost, the rather delicate cellular-fibrillar **pia mater** is innermost, while between them is the filmy **arachnoid,** also cellular and fibrillar. Through popular usage the word "mater" is customarily dropped, and the membranes are called simply the dura and the pia. Because of their relative thickness, the dura is often termed the **pachymeninx,** the pia and arachnoid together, the **leptomeninges.** Sometimes indeed the two inner layers are considered to be one, the pia-arachnoid, with the pial portion forming an intimate investment for the brain and spinal cord as a visceral layer while the arachnoidal portion, as a parietal layer, forms the outer wall of the subarachnoid space. Whether this concept is helpful or not, there is no doubt about the pia mater and arachnoid being continuous, the one with the other, along the trabeculae, denticulate ligaments, and nerve roots which appear to "traverse" the subarachnoid space.

Dura Mater

The dura mater is of two layers closely united in the cranial region. It is composed principally of white fibrous connective tissue arranged in crossing and interlacing fashion, but it also contains a few elastic fibers. The outer layer of the dura serves as the periosteum of the bones of the skull, and between it and the inner layer are the large intradural venous sinuses, described in the previous section. The innermost surface of the dura is lined with a layer of flattened mesothelial cells. The **subdural space,** which contains tissue fluid, everywhere separates the dura from the arachnoid. In the spinal region the vertebrae possess their own periosteal lining. This last membrane is separated from the single layer of true spinal dura by a moderate amount of fatty connective tissue and a plexus of vertebral veins. The space between spinal dura and periosteum is the **epidural space.** The spinal dura mater is firmly fused with the periosteum of the skull at the foramen magnum and is continuous at that point with the outer layer of cranial dura.

SEPTA OF INTRACRANIAL DURA MATER

In the cranium the dura mater forms four septa which tend to divide the intracranial cavity into compartments. The largest septum, the **falx cerebri,** is sickle-shaped and represents a fusion of the two inner layers of dura as they dip down between the cerebral hemispheres. The falx extends anteriorly to the crista galli of the ethmoid bone; posteriorly, to the upper surface of the tentorium cerebelli in its midline; inferiorly, to the corpus callosum.

The tentorium cerebelli, as a double-layered reflection of the inner dural sheet, forms a roof for the cerebellum and supports the occipital lobes of the cerebral hemispheres. It is roughly semicircular in shape and lies almost horizontally. Its posterior circumference borders the transverse sulcus of the inner surface of the occipital bone. Its anterior edge, known as the **incisura** of the tentorial dura, is free and fits snugly around and just behind the midbrain (Fig. 64). The relation of the tentorium to the midbrain and several cranial nerves, the oculomotor and trochlear especially, is an important one. Under certain conditions, as described below, the free anterior edge of the tentorium may compress these cranial nerves and the cerebral peduncles of the midbrain. Dipping down in the mid-line from the under surface of the tentorium, to simulate a division of the cerebellum, is the **falx cerebelli.** The sella turcica containing the pituitary is bridged over by the **diaphragma sellae,** with only a small opening left in it to accommodate the stalk of that gland as it passes to its attachment at the base of the hypothalamus.

VESSELS AND NERVES OF THE DURA

The dura mater receives its blood supply principally through the **middle meningeal artery,** a branch of the internal maxillary artery, which enters the skull through the foramen spinosum. It runs in a groove on the inner surface of the parietal bone, its branches spreading extensively within the dura overlying the major portion of the frontal and parietal lobes. It anastomoses with the middle meningeal artery of the opposite side. **Anterior meningeal branches** of the ophthalmic artery supply the most rostral dura and **posterior meningeal branches** of the occipital and vertebral arteries, the tentorial and infratentorial dura. The middle meningeal artery is important clinically in that it may be lacerated in fractures of the parietal bone, thus constituting the source of a rapidly accumulating, and frequently fatal, extradural hemorrhage (extradural hematoma). **Meningeal veins** draining into the dural sinuses accompany the meningeal arteries. In its supratentorial portion the dura receives a sensory innervation from the trigeminal nerve (620). The infratentorial dura in the vicinity of the lateral sinus is innervated by a meningeal branch of the vagus nerve. Fine fibers from the hypoglossal nerve, derived originally from vagus or cervical nerves, supply the dura around the foramen magnum.

THE ARACHNOID

The framework of the arachnoid is composed of a mixture of white fibrous and elastic connective tissue, which forms a continuous membrane. Trabeculae of the same elements are extended inward to the pia. The outer and inner surfaces of this fibrous membrane, as well as the trabeculae projecting from it, are covered with the same structural type of mesothelial cell as that lining the inner surface of the dura (Fig. 66). The cells form continuous sheets.

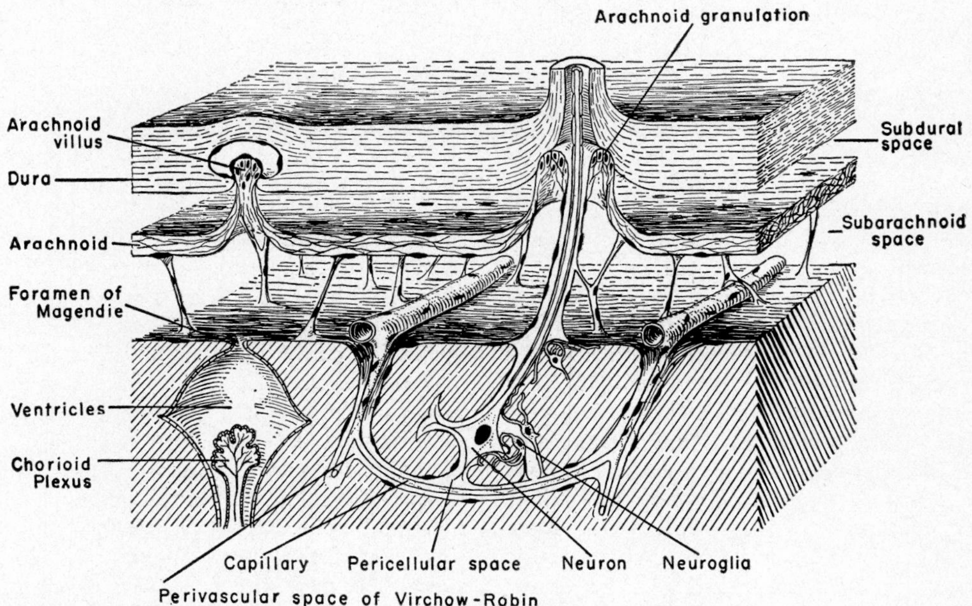

FIG. 66. Schematic representation of the central nervous system with reference to the circulation of the cerebrospinal fluid. (*Courtesy of Dr. W. L. Aycock, Research Publ., A. Nerv. & Ment. Dis., vol.* 4.)

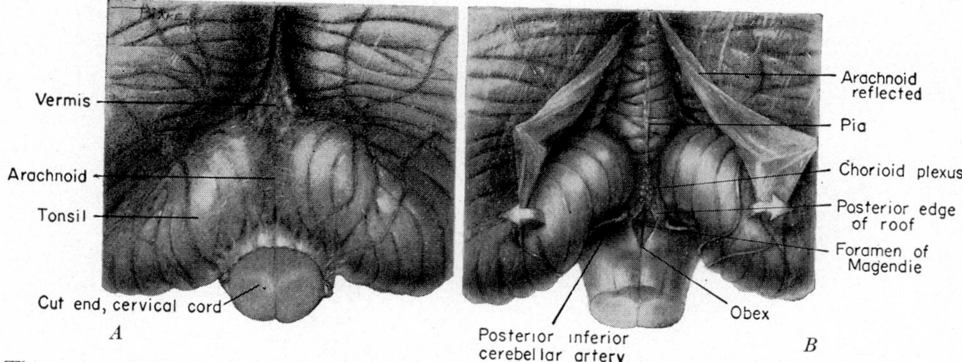

FIG. 67. The region of the cisterna magna. *A*, the arachnoid extending from cerebellum to medulla is intact, and the cistern is visible beneath it. *B*. The arachnoid has been incised and reflected, thus opening the cistern. The tonsils of the cerebellum have been slightly retracted laterally in order to visualize the foramen of Magendie in the posterior roof of the fourth ventricle. Chorioid plexus is seen extending through the foramen. In reality, the foramen is a deficiency in the ventricular roof. The floor of the ventricle can be seen through the foramen. The entire specimen has been pushed a bit forward.

The arachnoid is avascular; it receives sensory nerve fibers from the trigeminal nerve.

Though the subdural space lies between dura and arachnoid, the two membranes come into close contact in certain areas. The most conspicuous type of contiguity is that afforded in the **arachnoidal villi,** which are invaginations of the arachnoid into the lateral walls of the great dural sinuses, the arachnoidal mesothelium being separated from the sinus blood only by the endothelium of the sinus. An arachnoid villus is composed of a core of loose connective tissue, covered by the mesothelial cells, which at the tip of the villus may be heaped up into several layers (Fig. 66). These cranial arachnoidal villi are sometimes the site of calcification, giving rise to the pacchionian (arachnoidal) granulations. Another type of contact of dura and arachnoid occurs where so-called arachnoidal cell columns, representing extensions of arachnoid mesothelium, project into the dura.

The Pia Mater

The trabeculae of the arachnoid and their covering of mesothelial cells become continuous with the similar layers of the third membrane, the pia mater, which is closely applied to the nervous tissue and contains fibroblasts, fixed macrophages, lymphocytes, and pigmented cells, melanophores. Rarely, the melanophores, more numerous in the pia over the ventral medullar and pontine surfaces, give rise to tumors. The pia follows all the contours of the surfaces of the brain and spinal cord; it dips into the fissures and sulci, whereas arachnoid does not. The pia sends many trabeculalike prolongations into the parenchyma of brain and spinal cord, and these as well as the inner pial surface are closely associated with the neuroglia within the cord and brain substance. It is therefore difficult to strip away the pia. The pia, unlike the arachnoid, is perforated in the roof of the fourth ventricle, at the two lateral **foramina of Luschka** and the median **foramen of Magendie.** The foramen of Magendie is often a true deficiency in the posterior roof (Fig. 67). In a recent study it was found that the foramen of Magendie is most often of such form, although in a small proportion of cases the ventricular roof is more complete and the deficiency, or foramen, is narrowed (62). Occasionally the foramen is a tiny aperture with a diameter of 1 mm., and rarely, it is missing entirely. Usually, however, the margins of the foramen are formed by the posterior margins of the pia-ependymal roof, and the lateral margins of the floor of the fourth ventricle. The width of the foramen depends on the points of attachment of the pia-ependymal roof to the lateral walls of the fourth ventricle.

VESSELS AND NERVES OF PIA MATER

The pia is quite vascular, containing the blood vessels whose branches enter and leave the nervous tissue. The layers of pia accompany

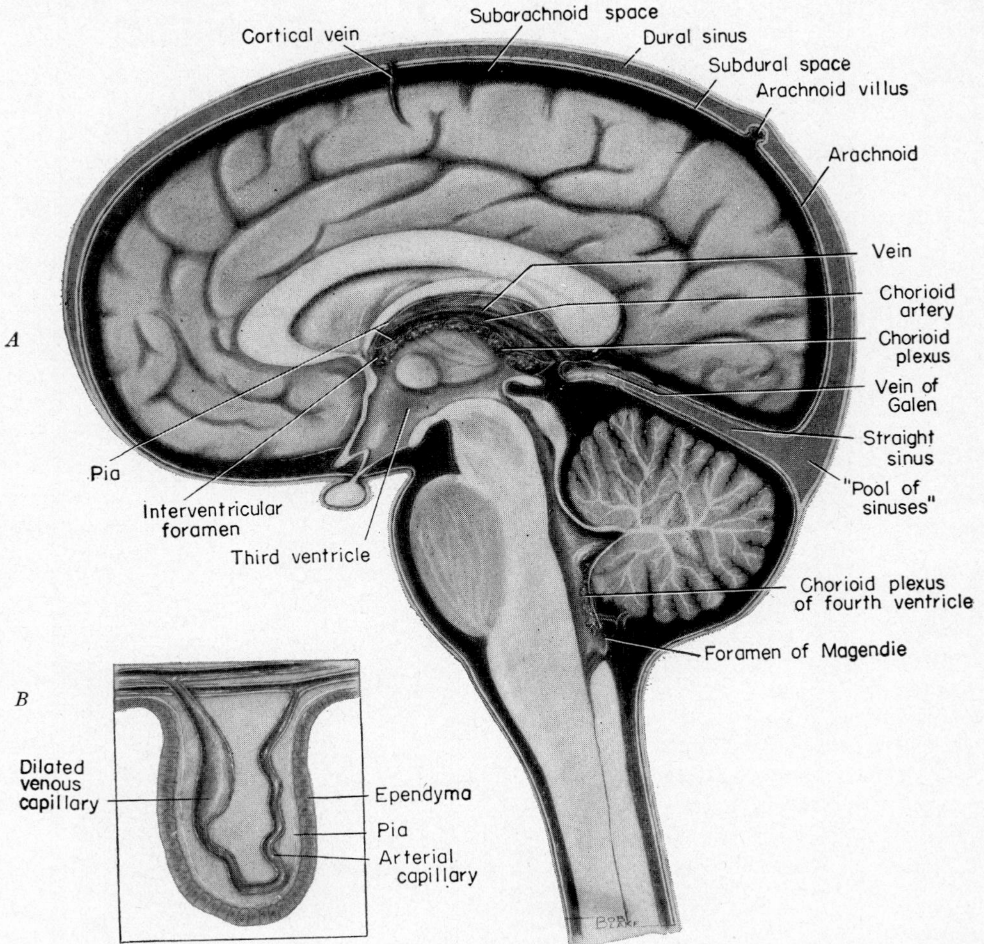

FIG. 68. *A*, semischematic representation of the human brain, meninges, and intermeningeal spaces as seen from the medial surface of a specimen sectioned through the longitudinal cerebral fissure. Adapted particularly for showing the plan of the roof of the thirdventricle and its chorioid plexus. *B*, diagram of a villus of the chorioid plexus.

these blood vessels, surrounding them like a cuff as they dip into the tissues. The subarachnoid space is also continued into the neural substance for a short distance, but more deeply only a potential space, the **space of Virchow-Robin,** exists (Fig. 66). The intracranial pia receives sensory innervation from the trigeminal nerve especially. Sympathetic nerves from the cervical sympathetic chain reach the vessels in the intracranial pia via the plexus about the internal carotid artery. These serve chiefly as vasoconstrictors. Parasympathetic nerves reach the pial vessels via the seventh cranial or facial nerve. These are vasodilator fibers. Increase in the caliber of the intracranial arteries, and the extracranial ones also, serves to stimulate the sensory fibers ending about the vessels. Such stimulation frequently produces pain, or headache.

INTERMENINGEAL SPACES

The three meninges about the brain and spinal cord are separated from each other by spaces containing fluid (Fig. 68). The **subdural space,** perhaps more potential than actual, between dura and arachnoid, contains a small amount of fluid which is probably similar to cerebrospinal fluid. The **subarachnoid**

space, incompletely split up by the arachnoid trabeculae, lies between the arachnoid and the pia. Within this space the cerebrospinal fluid circulates. Several large pocketlike areas, or **cisterns,** are present in the intracranial subarachnoid space. Of these the **cisterna magna,** between the posterior aspect of the cerebellum and the medulla, is perhaps of most clinical importance. Other large cisterns, ventrally, are the **pontine, interpeduncular,** and **chiasmatic** which together form the large **basilar cistern.**

The cisterna magna continues inferiorly to become continuous with the posterior portion of the spinal subarachnoid space (Fig. 68). Lateral extensions of the cisterna magna ventrally and around the medulla serve to connect it with the pontine part of the basilar cistern. A superior extension medially leads into a channel that passes over the superior surface of the cerebellum in the mid-line as the **cerebellosagittal channel.**

Large pockets extend laterally and dorsally from the chiasmatic part of the basilar cistern (497). These follow the sylvian fissure on either side to make the large **lateral cerebrocortical channels** overlying a portion of the frontal, parietal, and temporal lobes. Other lateral extensions of the basilar cistern pass posteriorly and superiorly around the brain stem on each side to unite and form a median **internal cerebral channel** overlying the midbrain. A rostral extension of the chiasmatic portion of the basilar cistern continues superiorly around the corpus callosum whose contour it follows as a **cerebrosagittal cistern.** This joins the internal cerebral channel, which also is continuous with the cerebellosagittal channel. The large subarachnoid pocket formed by the union of the internal, cerebrosagittal, and cerebellosagittal channels is sometimes called the **ambient cistern.** Posterior extensions from this pocket continue as subarachnoid channels over each occipital lobe. These large subarachnoid cisterns and channels are of importance in the spinal fluid circulation; the flow in them is usually more rapid than elsewhere.

Cerebrospinal Fluid and Cerebrospinal Spaces

The subarachnoid space is filled with the watery cerebrospinal fluid. Its presence in the subarachnoid space was known before information was obtained regarding its formation or its entry into, and escape from, this space.

Ventricular System

The method of origin and site of formation of the cerebrospinal fluid are still debated. Within the spinal cord is a **central canal** lined with ependyma, which is composed of simple epithelial cells derived from the neuroepithelial cells of the neural tube. Because of the small size of the lumen and its incomplete patency in the adult there is, practically speaking, very little fluid in the central canal. Rostrally, the lumen widens into a rhomboid-shaped chamber, the **fourth ventricle,** in the medulla. The anterior end of this chamber continues into a narrow somewhat diamond-shaped channel, the **iter** or **aqueduct of Sylvius,** which traverses the midbrain. The aqueduct in turn enlarges into the **third ventricle,** the cavity of the diencephalon. From each side of this ventricle, a foramen of Monro passes slightly rostrally and lateralward into the **lateral ventricles** (Fig. 69). These paired ventricles are very large and occupy a part of each lobe of the cerebrum. The part of the lateral ventricle extending rostrally into the frontal lobe is the **anterior horn;** that in the

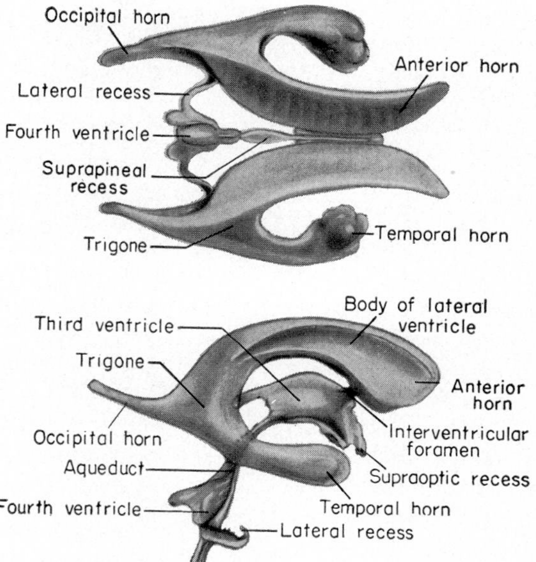

Fig. 69. Casts of the ventricular system. (*Redrawn from Kappers, Huber, and Crosby, after Retzius.*)

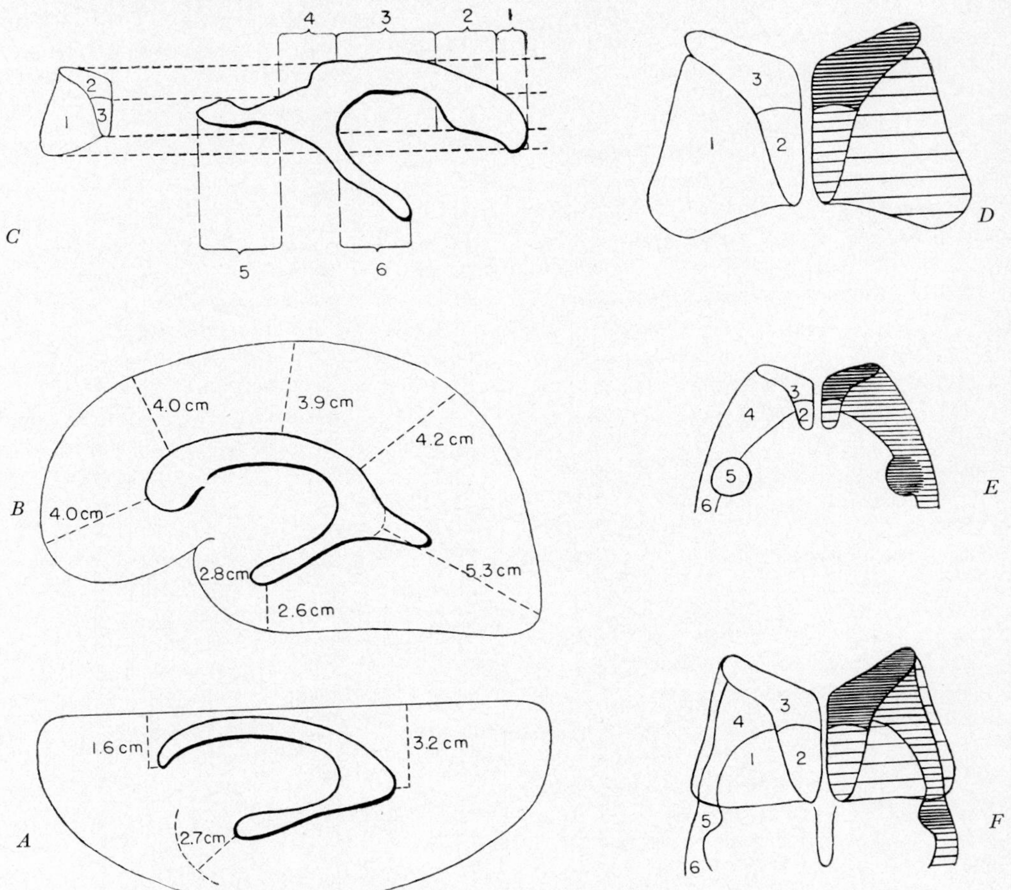

FIG. 70. Diagrams to illustrate the anatomy of the lateral ventricle and ventriculographic interpretations. *A* and *B*, the distances of various parts of the lateral ventricle from the surface of the brain, as determined by study of x-ray films. (*After Torkildsen, J. Anat., vol.* 68.) *C*, the lateral view of the lateral ventricle divided into six portions which are visible as units in anteroposterior views. The dotted lines serve to project portions 1, 2, and 3 on an imaginary plate. The lines would be approximately parallel to the base of the skull. *D*, outlines of portions 1, 2, and 3 in an anteroposterior view. *E*, superposition of ventricular shadows in posteroanterior view of an encephalogram. *F*, superposition of ventricular shadows in an anteroposterior view of an encephalogram. (*After Torkildsen and Penfield, Arch. Neurol. & Psychiat., vol.* 30.)

parietal lobe, **the body;** that in the occipital lobe, the **posterior horn;** and the part which extends into the temporal lobe, the **inferior horn.** The radiologists divide the lateral ventricles into parts designated numerically (Fig. 70) (778).

CHORIOID PLEXUSES

Extensions of the pia mater together with many small vessels project into certain parts of the roof or walls of the ventricles. These capillary tufts, covered with pia mater, push before them the ependymal cells which become specialized and which, together with the vessel tufts beneath them, are known as **chorioid plexuses.** The vessels of the plexus are dilated capillaries and are covered by the epithelial layer of ependyma which in this area is composed of cuboidal cells, said to contain intracellular structures such as secretion granules, lipoid inclusions, and Golgi apparatus (Fig. 68). Chorioid plexuses are found in the roof of the fourth and third ventricles and in the medial walls of the inferior and anterior horns of the lateral ventricles. The plexus in the fourth ventricle projects through the foramina of

Luschka into the space between medulla and cerebellum (Fig. 42).

The ventricular system contains cerebrospinal fluid, and the evidence indicates that nearly all the fluid is formed in the intraventricular structures, the chorioid plexuses. Some small amount may arise from the perivascular spaces of the central nervous system or from the ependymal cells elsewhere in the ventricles. The chorioid plexus cells are, however, generally considered to be the site of the greatest fluid production. The exact mechanism of formation is debatable, some investigators claiming a secretory process, others a filtration of the fluid by the chorioid plexus from the blood in the plexus capillaries. At any rate, the fluid is passed by the cells of the chorioid plexuses, which expend energy or do work in the process (830). The chorioid plexus is called the blood-brain barrier, since normally it maintains a selective filtration process, preventing certain chemical substances and bacteria from passing through into the neural tissue. The rate of formation of spinal fluid by the plexuses is determined by the pressure in the capillaries of the plexus and the osmotic pressure of the nonpermeable constituents of the blood plasma. Increases in the latter such as result from intravenous injection of hypertonic solution will diminish the formation of fluid. This fact is the basis of the relief of intracranial pressure increase following the injection of hypertonic glucose.

CEREBROSPINAL-FLUID CIRCULATION

Cerebrospinal fluid formed in the lateral ventricles enters the third ventricle through the foramina of Monro. From the third ventricle the fluid traverses the aqueduct to gain the fourth ventricle. From the latter, the cerebrospinal fluid enters the subarachnoid space by way of the foramina in the pia overlying the roof of the fourth ventricle, posteriorly. The foramen of Magendie is a mid-line deficiency of the roof (62). The foramina of Luschka are perforations in the lateral walls of the roof of the fourth ventricle. They are identifiable by the chorioid plexus projecting through them (Fig. 57). Once the cerebrospinal fluid has emerged into the cisterna magna of the subarachnoid space, it spreads rapidly via the cisterns and their channels over the surface of the brain and seeps less rapidly down around the spinal cord.

The major portion of the cerebrospinal fluid escapes from the subarachnoid space through the arachnoidal villi into the intradural venous sinuses. The villi penetrate the walls of the venous sinuses to lie just beneath the endothelial lining. Some fluid is absorbed directly into veins from the subarachnoid space. A certain amount escapes in the spinal region through the villi dipping into the segmental veins at that level, and some escapes around the emerging cranial and spinal nerves into the tissue spaces and lymphatics of the nerves. Lymphatics within the central nervous system have not been demonstrated. Under certain pathological conditions some fluid may be absorbed through the chorioid plexuses.

CHEMICAL AND PHYSICAL QUALITIES OF CEREBROSPINAL FLUID

It is estimated that in man there is an average volume of 135 cc. of cerebrospinal fluid, and that the daily production of fluid is about 525 cc. The fluid contains protein, sugar, chlorides, nonprotein nitrogen, and urea, and normally 3 to 5 mononuclear cells per cubic millimeter. The brain and spinal cord are, for practical purposes, suspended in this fluid which forms for them a cushion. Other functions of the cerebrospinal fluid are not understood. Normally the cerebrospinal fluid is under a pressure of about 120 mm. H_2O when measured at the lumbar level in an adult lying on his side. Fluctuations of pressure occur with changes of position, and, perhaps more important, with reciprocal fluctuations in volume in different parts of the cerebrospinal system. This character is perhaps its most useful function.

Cerebrospinal fluid can be readily obtained from the subarachnoid space by inserting a needle between the second and third, or between the third and fourth, lumbar vertebrae, into the lumbar level of the dural sac. It can also be obtained from a needle inserted into the cisterna magna. With a patient in the sitting position, the pressure, in millimeters of water, measured at the lumbar level is approximately equal to the distance in millimeters from the needle level to the vertex level (300 to 400 mm. H_2O). Study of the spinal fluid serologically, cytologically, chemically, and physically as to pressure is important in the diagnosis of disease of the nervous system.

With a patient lying on his side the cerebrospinal fluid pressure is everywhere the same. If the pressure is increased anywhere in the fluid system, the increase is reflected throughout. This fact can be utilized in the **Queckenstedt test,** useful for determining obstruction to the fluid circulation in the spinal region. Compression of the jugular veins, blocking thereby the venous drainage from the brain, increases the intracranial venous pressure and therefore also the intracranial pressure. This increase is measured in the lumbar region with a manometer attached to an inserted needle. If an obstruction to the flow exists along the spinal subarachnoid space, above the level of the needle, the increase in intracranial pressure will not be transmitted to the lumbar level.

RELATIONSHIPS BETWEEN CEREBROSPINAL FLUID AND INTRACRANIAL PRESSURE

The soft brain and spinal cord are protected from the atmospheric pressure by the rigid bony coverings and the semirigid dura. The circulating blood and spinal fluid likewise protect the neural tissue up to a certain point and tend to maintain conditions constant when a foreign body, tumor, bone fragment, blood, or missile encroaches on or within the brain. Such protection is afforded by a variation of rate of blood flow, of the caliber of the intracranial vascular tree, and of the rate of formation of cerebrospinal fluid, as well as by a reciprocal alteration of the spinal-fluid volume at points in the subarachnoid system. When neural tissue decreases in amount, as in a degenerative process, the fluid content is increased and the ventricular system dilates in order to maintain the intracranial contents constant.

Increase in intracranial pressure can be brought about by obstruction to the venous outflow, by obstruction to the flow of fluid within the ventricular system or at its points of escape, by an impairment of the absorption of fluid, and, to a less extent, by increased formation of fluid. Any of the foreign bodies previously listed may cause increased intracranial pressure directly or secondarily through its effect on the blood and fluid content and circulation.

The increase in intracranial pressure results in certain local and systemic alterations in the vascular system. Fundamentally, several factors are of importance in determining the volume and rate of intracranial blood flow. These have been listed previously. The caliber of the intracranial vessels and the systemic arterial pressures and, especially, the difference between intracranial arterial and venous pressure are the most important (849). Several factors influence the difference between arterial and venous pressure. Some of these are variations of systemic arterial pressure, variations in cerebrospinal-fluid pressure, and obstruction to venous outflow from the cranium.

Increase in cerebrospinal-fluid pressure, reflected on the intracranial veins, brings about an increase in pressure on the veins and a stasis of blood. Vasodilation may then occur if the spinal-fluid pressure increase has not been too rapid, and the arterial pressure will be transmitted more readily through arterioles and capillaries into the veins. In such a way the venous pressure will be increased, and the venous stasis overcome. The vasodilation, in spite of the lowered velocity of blood flow, will maintain the blood volume. Rapid increases in intracranial pressure, however, will necessitate an increase in systemic arterial pressure, and a consequent greater difference, therefore, between arterial and venous intracranial pressure, in order to overcome the venous stasis. With the increased difference between arterial and venous pressure, the velocity and intracranial blood flow will return to, or approach, normal. These changes in systemic arterial pressure, as well as the changes in caliber of the intracranial arterioles, are brought about through activity of the medullar vasomotor center, stimulated to activity through its lowered blood supply as a result of the stasis. The systemic arterial pressure is increased through the constriction of the splanchnic vascular bed.

CLINICAL INDICATIONS OF INCREASED INTRACRANIAL PRESSURE

These relationships can be observed in patients suffering with slowly increasing intracranial pressure due to brain tumors and hemorrhages. The increase in systemic arterial

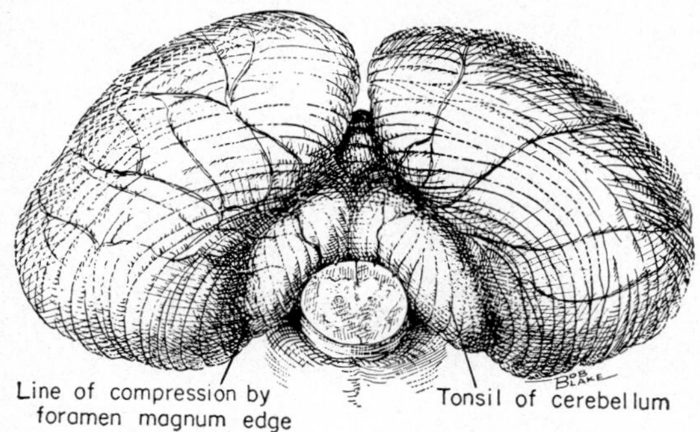

Fig. 71. Herniation of the cerebellar tonsils through the foramen magnum resulting from an increase in intracranial pressure. (*Courtesy of Dr. George Margolis.*)

pressure with increased intracranial pressure is accompanied by slowing of the pulse rate, and these two physical signs should be closely followed in patients with increasing intracranial pressure from any cause. The respiration may also become irregular because of embarrassment of the medullar and pontine centers by pressure or through hemorrhage into them as a result of venous stasis (192). Another important indication of increasing intracranial pressure is the change in the retina. The earliest sign here is an engorgement of the retinal veins. This venous obstruction is contributed to by a compression of the central vein of the retina by the distended dural covering of the optic nerve. The increased pressure in the general cranial subarachnoid space is transmitted into the subarachnoid space about the optic nerve. The compression of the retinal vein as it courses in the optic nerve produces stasis in its branches and leads to small hemorrhages in the retina, a generalized retinal edema, and especially, edema of the optic-nerve head. This last results in an obliteration of the normal cupping of the nerve head and a blurring of the nerve-head outline. Such a condition is known as "choked disk" or **papilledema** (597).

Further signs of increased intracranial pressure are headache, nausea and vomiting, and drowsiness. Headache results from stimulation by distortion of the sensory-nerve fibers in the walls of the vessels of the meninges and brain, as mentioned previously. These signs, together with those already listed, are general results of increased intracranial pressure. Localizing signs of deranged brain function will also occur. Many of these come about directly as a result of compression, lacerations, destruction, or invasion of a definite brain region by the foreign body, blood, or tumor. It is these signs, observed in a neurological examination, that help one decide on the locus of injury. Other indications of disordered function may also be present and will occasionally confuse the picture. These result indirectly from the increased pressure and displacements of the brain.

Certain gross physical alterations occur to the brain in cases of rapidly increasing intracranial pressure. The nervous tissue is relatively incompressible, and it therefore makes an effort to escape from within the confines of its restraining dural envelope. The tonsils of the cerebellum are pushed into the foramen magnum, the uncus and inferomedial portion of the temporal lobe are pushed through the free edge of the tentorium cerebelli, a cingular gyrus is herniated beneath the falx cerebri, and the inferior surfaces of the frontal lobes are pressed hard against the sphenoid ridges (Figs. 71, 72, 73). The cerebral peduncles and certain

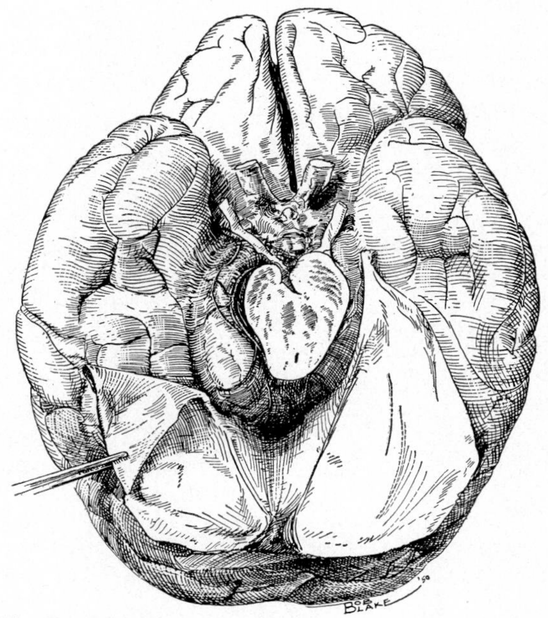

Fig. 72. Herniation of the hippocampal gyri through the incisura of the tentorium cerebelli. Note the compression of the oculomotor nerves, and the distortion of the midbrain. The tentorium has been reflected on the left to indicate the line of compression. Supratentorial tumor. (*Courtesy of Dr. George Margolis.*)

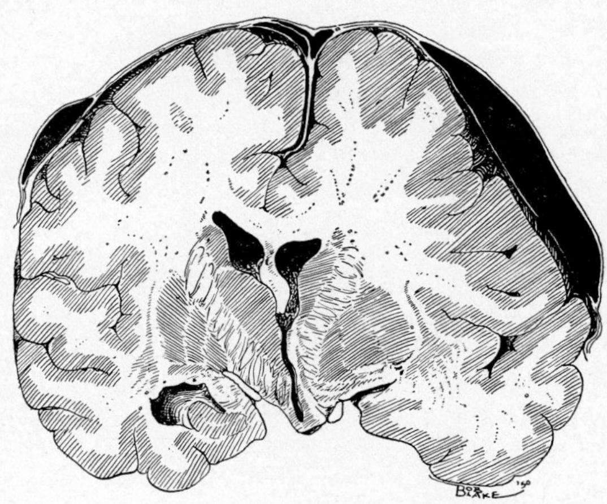

FIG. 73. Compression and displacement of the right cerebral hemisphere by a large subdural hematoma. Note the herniation of the cingular gyrus beneath the falx cerebri. A small hematoma is present also on the left. (*Courtesy of Dr. George Margolis.*)

cranial nerves, especially the oculomotor, trochlear, and abducens, are apt to be compressed by the free tentorial edge (852). Signs of motor disorder of the skeletal and ocular muscles will thus be brought about as an indirect result of the neural lesion. The posterior cerebral and superior cerebellar arteries are also compressed by the tentorial edge. Softenings of the occipital lobe occur in the area of distribution of the posterior cerebral artery, because of defective blood supply resulting from compression of the vessel. Such a softening may lead to a homonymous visual defect (See Chap. 21) which will lead the examiner astray in his localization of the original cerebral lesion. Because of compression of brain stem arteries and veins either directly by the pressure increase or as a result of constriction by the tentorium cerebelli, areas of hemorrhage and softening are frequently found in the brain stem in cases of intracranial pressure increase. Such areas of destruction may lead to respiratory embarrassment and noticeable alterations of muscle tone as a result of damage to reticular systems.

The changes in systemic arterial pressure and the pulse rate in response to increased intracranial pressure are compensatory efforts of the organism to promote normal intracranial blood flow. Such compensation can be carried only to a certain point. The vasomotor center may ultimately fail, the intracranial vasomotor tone may be paralyzed, more extravasation of fluid will then occur into the neural tissue from the capillaries to increase the cerebral edema, and consequently the intracranial pressure will increase more and more, ultimately to paralyze the respiratory centers completely and bring about death.

OBSTRUCTIONS TO CEREBROSPINAL-FLUID CIRCULATION

When obstructions to the circulation and absorption of cerebrospinal fluid occur, the consequences are serious. An obstruction at a foramen of Monro by tumor will obstruct the lateral ventricle of that side. The chorioid plexus within the ventricle continues to produce cerebrospinal fluid, and the ventricle enlarges gradually at the expense of the hemispheric neural tissue. An obstruction in the aqueduct resulting from inflammation or tumor growth will lead to a symmetrical dilatation of the two lateral and the third ventricles. A blocking of the foramina of Luschka and Magendie by inflammatory reaction or by tumor will lead to progressive dilatation of the entire ventricular system. Such a progressive accumulation of the fluid within the ventricles is known as an **internal hydrocephalus.** Occasionally, the fluid escapes into the cerebellomedullar and basal cisterns only to find the subarachnoid spaces otherwise blocked. This constitutes a **communicating internal hydrocephalus.** It is possible for this type to become an **external hydrocephalus.** The dilated cisterns, especially the basal, gradually enlarge dorsally and laterally. The fluid may rupture the arachnoidal cistern wall, escape into the subdural space, and here collect gradually. The progressive enlargement of the subdural space occurs at the expense of the brain again, this becoming gradually shrunken and left attached to dura and the longitudinal sinus by enlarged cortical veins only. Internal hydrocephalus may be congenital or acquired. In the former the child's head progressively enlarges to great size if untreated. The cause of the congenital form is not definitely known, though this type is frequently associated with other anomalies of the cerebrospinal-fluid system and the surrounding bony parts. Operations are devised for relieving the congenital form of hydrocephalus if it is caused by obstruction along the aqueduct or in the fourth ventricle. These involve the introduction of a catheter into the system above the block and into the cisternal or spinal subarachnoid space below the block to establish a shunt around the point of obstruction (779). Tumors in the fourth ventricle or in the midcerebellum may lead to acquired internal hydrocephalus. Scar tissue remaining from a meningitic process may seal off the foramina of Luschka and Magendie, or the posterior and basal cisterns, and lead to hydrocephalus. If the patient is a child below the age of ten, the cranial sutures will spread before the progressive enlargement of the ventricular system and brain, only the scalp protecting the brain in certain areas.

Developmental anomalies may occur in the formation of the cerebrospinal fluid channels, and these frequently involve the cranial and spinal bony structures. A failure of closure of the vertebrae, **spina bifida,** may be associated with a herniation of meninges and, at times, of spinal-cord tissue. A herniating meningeal sac with fluid is called a **meningocele;** if the spinal cord is also herniated, a **meningomyelocele. Encephaloceles** are protrusions of the brain through anomalous clefts in the skull. Derangements in the formation of the occiput, due to maldevelopment or disease, may lead to compression of the medulla and cisternal cerebrospinal pathways. In the condition **basilar impression,** or **platybasia,** the angle between the basisphenoid and the basilar part of the occipital bone is widened beyond its normal 110 to 140 deg. A thinning of the occiput occurs, with or without an associated assimilation of the atlas and a dislocation, anteriorly, of the atlas on the axis. The foramen magnum is asymmetric and narrowed, and the odontoid process protrudes into the skull. Medulla, cervical spinal cord, cranial nerves, cerebellum, and cerebrospinal pathways may be compressed, and the cerebellar tonsils may be herniated into the vertebral canal. Developmental anomalies of the cervical spine may be associated with a pulling down into the vertebral canal of the medulla and cerebellum, with a posterior kinking of the spinal cord (**Arnold-Chiari malformations**). Various neural pathways would be blocked, and abnormal motor and sensory activities would be observed in a neurological examination of a patient suffering such malformations as these.

RADIOLOGICAL EXAMINATION OF CEREBROSPINAL-FLUID PATHWAYS

Intracranial tumors sometimes produce also a distortion and displacement of the ventricles (and brain) or a filling up of some part of the cranial subarachnoid space. As an aid to the location of such tumors the ventricles and subarachnoid space can be visualized by x-ray if air or oxygen is injected into them. There are two ways of doing this. In one procedure, the air or oxygen is put into the lumbar subarachnoid space through a needle, after a certain amount of spinal fluid has been withdrawn. In another procedure, the air or oxygen is introduced by tapping the posterior horn of a lateral ventricle after a small area of bone has been removed and fluid withdrawn. After either type of injection, x-rays of the head in various positions are made. The ventricular injection outlines the ventricles quite well, and sometimes also the subarachnoid space if the air escapes into it by paths usually taken by the cerebrospinal fluid. The spinal injection of air outlines the subarachnoid space well and usually the ventricles also. The ventricular procedure is known as **ventriculography;** the spinal, as **encephalography.**

CHAPTER 5

THE SPINAL CORD AND SPINAL PATHWAYS

THE NERVOUS SYSTEM, as noted previously, is constituted on a series of levels each of which is capable of certain activity or integration, independently. Each level cooperates with the others usually, however, in the performance of maintaining and activating the organism. It is customary to refer to the anterior horn cells and the reflex arcs they complete with incoming dorsal spinal root fibers as the lowest, or **segmental,** level of spinal neural activity. Similar segmental arcs exist between cranial-nerve sensory and motor neurons. Above these lowest neuronal arcs are series of more complex arcs of second, third, fourth, and fifth or more orders. Those arcs in cerebellar and cerebral cortices have been called **suprasegmental.** The simple spinal-cord arcs are capable of activity of a certain stereotyped character when acting alone. Other neurons, located in the spinal cord, at times join in the neural activity of the simple arcs, giving to the performance variation and more complexity. These neighboring neurons are associative, internuncial, or intercalary neurons, and they are capable of coordinating many spinal segments into a unified neural mechanism. Finally, supraspinal neurons through their projections into the spinal cord can organize spinal neurons of several segments into small but efficiently acting groups, or they can blend many spinal segments into harmonious skillful activity. The success of the activity these higher levels bring about will depend in part on the messages relayed to them from spinal neurons. The anatomical structure for these various neural performances will be described in this section.

MACROSCOPIC FEATURES

In adult man the spinal cord does not extend through the entire length of the vertebral canal. The explanation for this fact is to be found mainly in the continued growth of the vertebral column after the spinal cord has reached its full length. Below the upper cervical level, any particular spinal cord segment lies somewhat higher than its correspondingly numbered vertebra. This discrepancy increases in the lower vertebral levels, because the caudal end of the vertebral column and the pelvis continue growing as the individual develops (Fig. 74). The lower end of the spinal cord proper, the **conus terminalis** or **conus medullaris,** is usually found at the level of the intervertebral disk between the first and second lumbar vertebrae. The discrepancy between cord and vertebral column lengths is offset by the increase in length of the anterior and posterior roots in the lumbar and sacral levels. The collection of long roots is known as the **cauda equina.** That part of the vertebral canal formed by the last four lumbar vertebrae and the entire sacrum contains only the cauda equina and the **filum terminale** (Fig. 74). The relation between point of emergence of spinal nerves from the spinal canal and the body of the vertebra also varies. In the cervical region, it is to be recalled, the mixed spinal nerves emerge via foramina above the respective vertebral bodies. In the thoracic, lumbar, and sacral levels the spinal nerves emerge from foramina below the respective vertebral bodies.

A knowledge of the relations between spinal-cord segments and vertebrae is extremely important in the diagnosis and surgical treatment of certain spinal-cord disorders, *e.g.,* spinal-cord compression by tumor. It is necessary to recall the relation of spinal segment to overlying vertebra and spinous process when laminectomy is contemplated for the relief of the spinal-cord compression. A good working rule is as follows: Between the levels of the second cervical and tenth thoracic, add 2 to the number of the spinous process and this will give the number of the underlying spinal segment. The sixth cervical spinous process accordingly overlies the eighth cervical spinal segment; the sixth thoracic, the eighth thoracic. The eleventh and twelfth thoracic spinous processes overlie the five lumbar segments, whereas the first lumbar spinous process overlies the five sacral segments.

Longitudinal fissures separate the cord into symmetrical halves and each half into thirds (Fig. 80). The **anterior and posterior median longitudinal fissures** mark the division of the cord into halves. The **posterolateral** and **anterolateral** fissures are less evident and are placed at the points of entrance and emergence of the fasciculi composing **posterior** and **anterior roots,** respectively. The halves of the spinal cord are joined in the mid-line by commissures of gray and white substance, anterior and posterior to the central canal. The central canal, lined by ependyma, usually does not contain fluid in the adult, nor can its fetal, rostral continuation with the fourth ventricle be grossly demonstrated.

The full-grown spinal cord shows outwardly cervical and lumbar enlargements, the former being the larger. Between these is the smaller, but longer, thoracic or dorsal portion, and caudal to the lumbar enlargement, the sacral portion rapidly tapers into the conus medullaris and an insignificant coccygeal region. The cervical and lumbar enlargements are the natural result of the great increase in neurons and their processes at these levels for the innervation of the limb musculature and skin.

The Meninges of the Spinal Cord

The three membranes, dura, arachnoid, and pia, are continuous with the corresponding membranes inside the skull. They have the same histological structure as do the intracranial meninges. The spinal dura, it should be recalled, is disposed somewhat differently from the intracranial. The two layers of intracranial dura are in close apposition except where the venous sinuses intervene. The outer layer serves as periosteum for the inner surface of the skull. In the spinal region the vertebrae have their own inner periosteal lining. This is continuous at the foramen magnum with the outer layer of cranial dura, and is, in fact, often looked upon as the outer layer of spinal dura. The inner

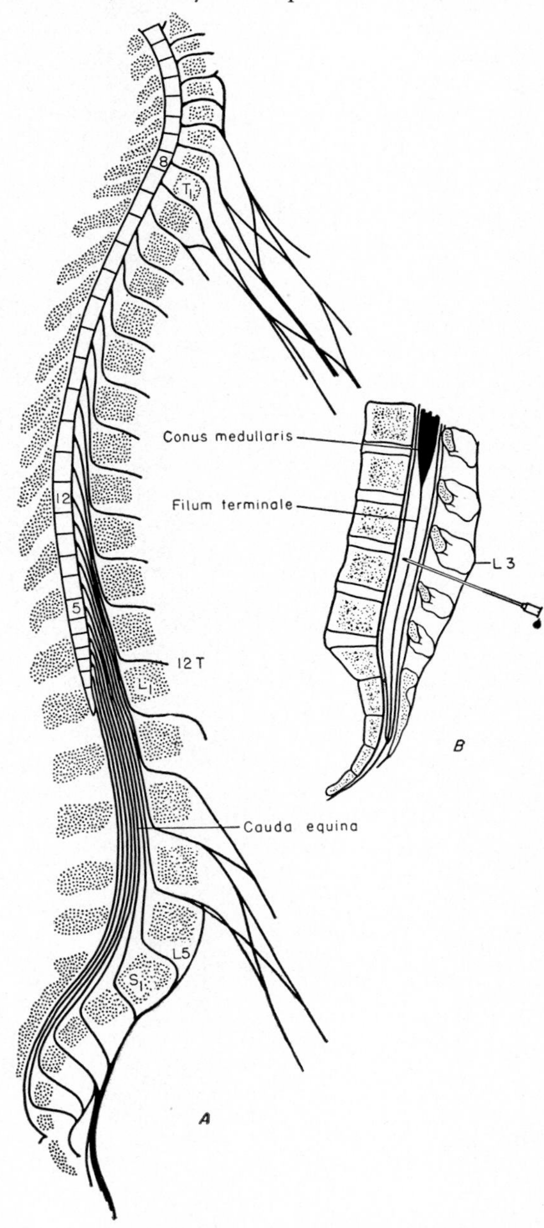

Fig. 74. *A*, relation between spinal-cord segments and vertebrae. The cervical nerves take exit through intervertebral foramina above their respective vertebral bodies; the other nerves, through foramina below their respective bodies. *B*, diagram of relations between neural structures in lumbar puncture.

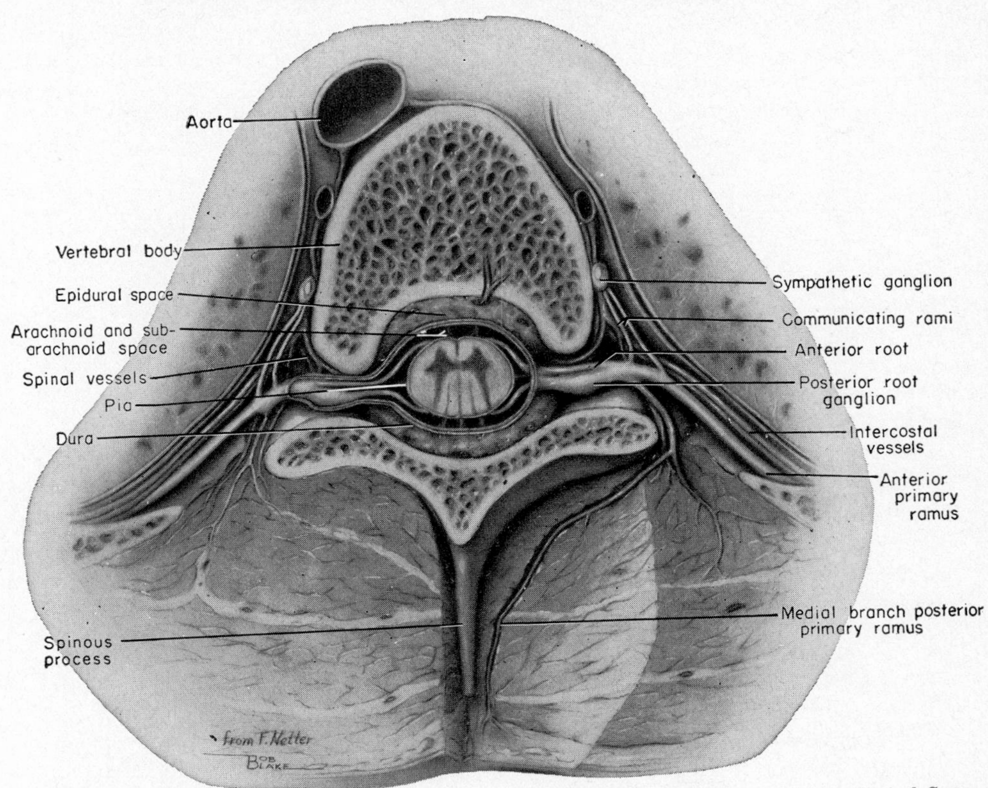

FIG. 75. Transverse section through thoracic spine and spinal cord. (*Redrawn after F. Netter, Clinical Symposia, vol. I,* 1949, *courtesy of Ciba, Inc.*)

layer of spinal dura, or the true spinal dura, is continuous at the foramen magnum with the inner layer of cranial dura. Between the true spinal dura and periosteum of the vertebra the **epidural space** intervenes (Fig. 75). Within this space are the internal intervertebral venous plexuses and usually some fat.

The true spinal dura mater forms a tubular sac which extends to a level opposite the second sacral vertebra (Fig. 76). In addition to its firm attachment at the foramen magnum, the spinal dura is usually attached to the periosteum of the posterior surfaces of the second and third cervical vertebrae. It is also attached loosely to the posterior longitudinal ligament of the vertebrae throughout its length, but especially in the cervical and lumbar regions. At the level of the second sacral vertebra the dural sac is pierced by the **filum terminale** which at this level is primarily a tube or fold of pia mater, although more cephalad it contains the tapering inferior end of the spinal cord. The dura mater provides an external covering for the filum terminale and the two membranes proceed caudalward to become continuous with the periosteum of the dorsal surface of the coccyx as the **coccygeal ligament.** The spinal dura receives sensory innervation from the spinal nerves. Its blood supply is furnished by small branches of the regional spinal arteries.

The spinal arachnoid has an arrangement comparable to that of the intracranial arachnoid. Small arachnoid villi are present and project into the lumina of the segmental veins. Beneath the arachnoid, the subarachnoid space, bridged by arachnoid trabeculae, contains spinal fluid.

The spinal pia is closely adherent to the spinal cord, dipping into the anterior and posterior fissures. The **septum posticum** attaches the pia to the arachnoid along the posterior longitudinal fissure. The pia along each side of the cord extends laterally as a double-layered fold, the **denticulate ligament** (Fig. 76). The edges of the latter are arranged as a series of about twenty-one dentate processes, known individually as **dentate ligaments,** which are attached to the inner surface of the dura, either by traversing the arachnoid or by crowding it against the dura. The highest dentate ligament is a bit cephalad to the first cervical roots, the lowest usually between the last two thoracic roots or the last thoracic and first lumbar roots. Hyndman has shown that the ligaments arise from the cord in a plane that separates approximately a posterior one-third of the cord from an anterior two-thirds (407). The dentate ligaments thus anchor the spinal cord to the dura, and in compressions of the cord, especially from the anterior and lateral directions, they may serve to produce unusual lines of stress, which lead to unexpected symptoms (422).

The spinal pia mater receives innervation from meningeal branches of the spinal nerves. The blood vessels in the pia receive sympathetic innervation also by way of the meningeal nerves from the paravertebral sympathetic ganglia. The blood vessels themselves are branches of the regional spinal vessels. The spinal dura and leptomeninges form surrounding cuffs for the spinal nerves. About the latter they extend to encompass the posterior root ganglia and the dura terminates in the intervertebral foramina. A potential subarachnoid space is present about the posterior root ganglia.

Spinal Roots

The anterior and posterior roots appear with monotonous regularity from each so-called segment of the spinal cord. Many fine fascicles of neuron processes entering or emerging from the cord in a longitudinal pattern compose the **posterior** and **anterior spinal roots,** respectively. The roots in turn are bundled together into **spinal nerves.** The spinal nerves are described in the following chapter. The anterior roots contain small, medium, and large fibers which arise from neurons in the anterior and lateral gray columns to be described presently. These fibers are motor, carrying effector impulses to striated, cardiac, and smooth muscle. The posterior roots contain fibers which arise from neurons in the posterior root ganglia and they transmit sensory impulses from the periphery of the organism to the spinal-cord neurons. The neurons of the posterior root ganglia are of a variety of sizes. They are described in more detail in the following chapter. The majority of the posterior root ganglion cells in the adult human show a single process. This divides like a T into a branch which runs into the cord via the posterior root and a branch which enters the spinal nerve to transmit impulses from the receptor endings in the skin, subcutaneous tissue, muscles, and viscera. The fibers in the posterior roots are large and small; some are heavily myelinated, some are practically devoid of myelin. As they enter the spinal cord the fibers are grouped somewhat according to size. The larger fibers form a medial division; the small, poorly myelinated fibers, a lateral one. Their subsequent course will be followed after a description of the intrinsic spinal-cord neurons is given.

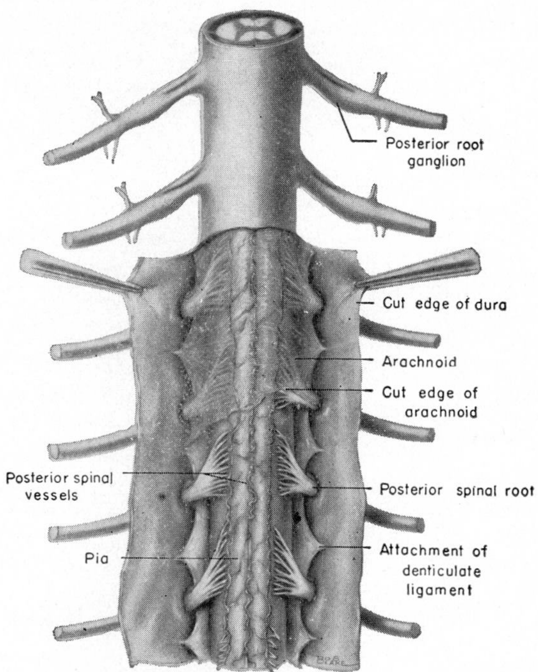

Fig. 76. A portion of the spinal cord viewed from behind, with dura incised and some arachnoid cut away to show relations of meninges to cord and roots. The spinal subarachnoid space can be visualized through the filmy arachnoid.

MICROSCOPIC ANATOMY OF THE SPINAL CORD

Intrinsic Neurons

The spinal-cord gray matter contains a grouping of cell columns about the small central canal, and in a cross section these gray columns have roughly the appearance of an H. The upper halves of the sides of the H would be **posterior columns;** the lower, the **anterior;** and the small, connecting middle zone, the **intermediate columns.** These columns are frequently referred to as "horns." Cell columns of the two sides are joined across the mid-line by **gray commissures,** anterior and posterior to the central canal. Through and adjacent to these gray commissures, fibers cross from one side to the other, thus forming also **anterior** and **posterior white commissures.** Outside the gray columns the fibers, or white substance, are grouped. The number of fibers and of cells as well as the general contour of the gray columns, or "horns," varies from level to level, and a knowledge of these variations is useful in ascertaining the level of any particular section being studied (Fig. 77). In the cervical and lumbar enlargements of the cord, for example, more cell columns and cells are found than at other levels.

Within the gray matter of the spinal cord the cells are of all sizes and are probably all multipolar. The largest cells appear in the anterior gray, some there measuring more than 100 μ. Many of the cells are arranged in

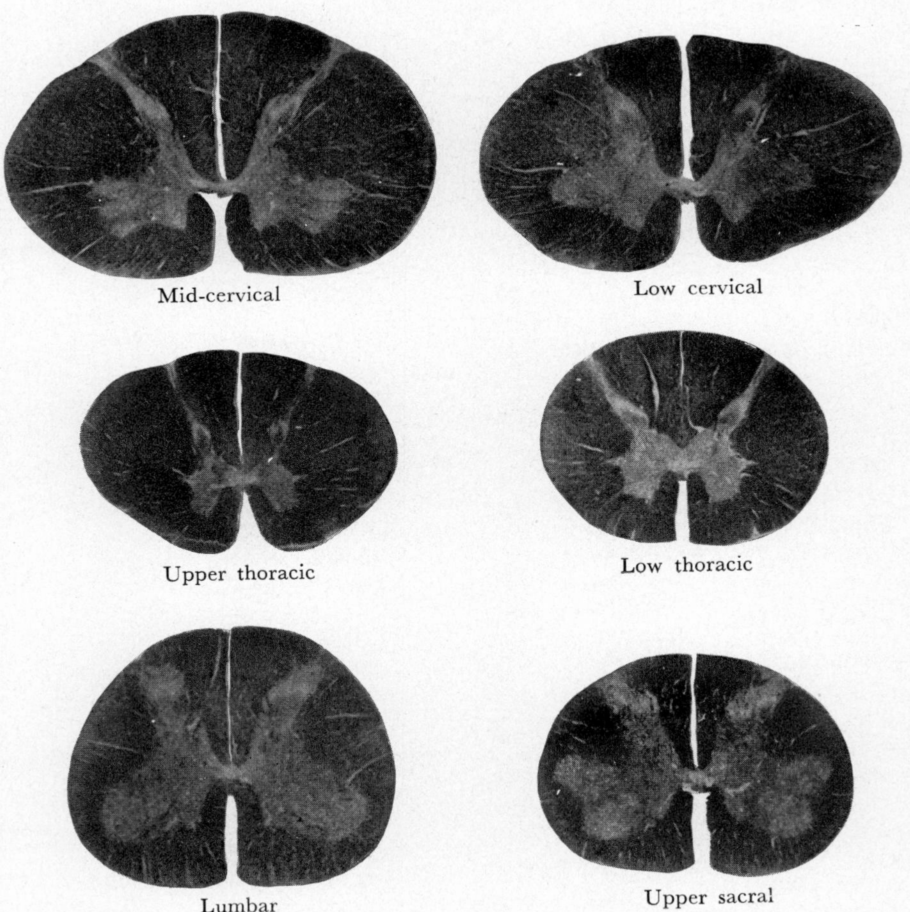

Fig. 77. Representative sections from various levels of the human spinal cord. The alteration in contour of the gray at various levels will be noted. Weigert technique. Photographs, approximately $\times 5.4$.

columns as mentioned above, and some of the columns extend without interruption throughout the length of the cord. Other columns are discontinuous, appearing well populated only in certain levels of the cord. A column or group of neurons, all of which have similar function, is referred to as a **nucleus.** The majority of the anterior columns of large cells are **motor** in function; the majority of the posterior columns of medium-sized and large cells are **sensory;** and the intermediate lateral ones of moderate-sized neurons are **autonomic motor.** The axons of many of these column neurons are long ones. The anterior and intermediate lateral neurons send their axons out by way of anterior roots to innervate striated muscles and smooth muscles and glands, respectively. The axons of the larger, posterior column neurons pass into the white matter to form the longitudinal, ascending fibers, some of which may run a great distance before terminating.

Scattered among the large column-neurons are other cells of small and medium size. Many of these cells have short axons and fall into the Golgi type II classification of nerve cells. Others have axons of medium length; *i.e.,* the axon may run across to the gray of the other side of the cord, or may ascend or descend on the same side through several cord segments. These neurons with axons of short and medium length occur in groups scattered among the long columns of large neurons. These are **associative** or **intercalary** neurons. If their axon passes across to end in the opposite cord gray, they are called **commissural associative** neurons. If the axon ascends or descends for several segments, the neurons may be called **intersegmental associative** ones. The Golgi type II cells, with axons terminating usually within the gray of the same segment, are **intrasegmental associative** cells. These associative neurons are very important in the intrinsic spinal neural mechanisms, and they also serve as intermediaries in the relations between supraspinal and spinal neurons on the one hand and peripheral sensory endings and spinal neurons on the other.

ANTERIOR AND INTERMEDIATE CELL COLUMNS

Within the anterior gray throughout the length of the cord, and with the exception of

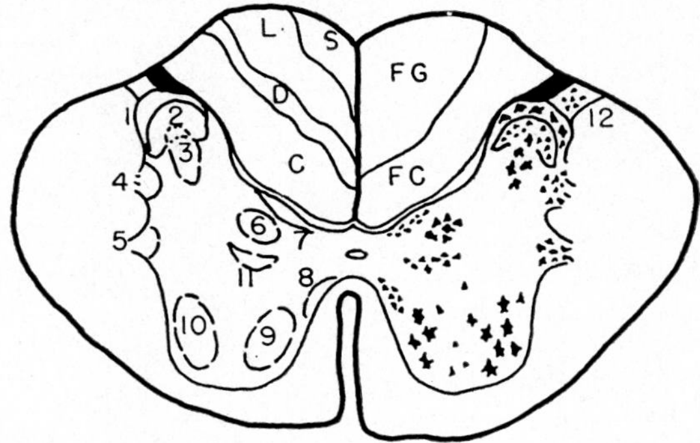

FIG. 78. Diagram of a spinal-cord segment showing lamination of the dorsal funiculi and principal nuclear divisions of the anterior and posterior gray columns. *S, L, D,* and *C,* representations, respectively, of sacral, lumbar, dorsal (thoracic), and cervical spinal-cord segments in the fiber tracts; *FC,* fasciculus cuneatus; *FG,* fasciculus gracilis. 1, posteromarginal nucleus; 2, substantia gelatinosa; 3, central nucleus of dorsal horn; 4, reticular nucleus; 5, intermediolateral nucleus; 6, dorsal nucleus (Clarke's nucleus); 7, posterior commissural nucleus; 8, anterior commissural nucleus; 9, medial motor nucleus; 10, lateral motor nucleus; 11, intermediomedial nucleus; 12, fasciculus dorsolateralis (Lissauer).

the last lumbar and first sacral segments, subsidiary medial columns of large cells are present (Fig. 78). These are usually regarded as neurons for innervation of trunk musculature, principally, since they have been found to remain intact after amputation of the extremities. Subsidiary lateral columns of large cells, more numerous and more populated in cervical and lumbar enlargements, are for the innervation of limb musculature (Fig. 79). The flexors and adductors of the extremities are supplied by the more posterior groups of cells in the subsidiary lateral columns; the extensors and abductors, by the more anterior groups. Some overlapping of innervations exist: *i.e.,* some medial neurons probably innervate limb muscles, some lateral neurons, axial musculature (238, 682, 754). The anterior gray neurons whose axons pass out in anterior roots are the so-called **lower motor neurons,** or the **final common motor path of Sherrington.** The axons of many associative neurons, the axon terminals or collaterals of descending fiber systems, and those of the incoming dorsal root fibers end about these anterior gray motor neurons (259, 771). The product of the various neural mechanisms is

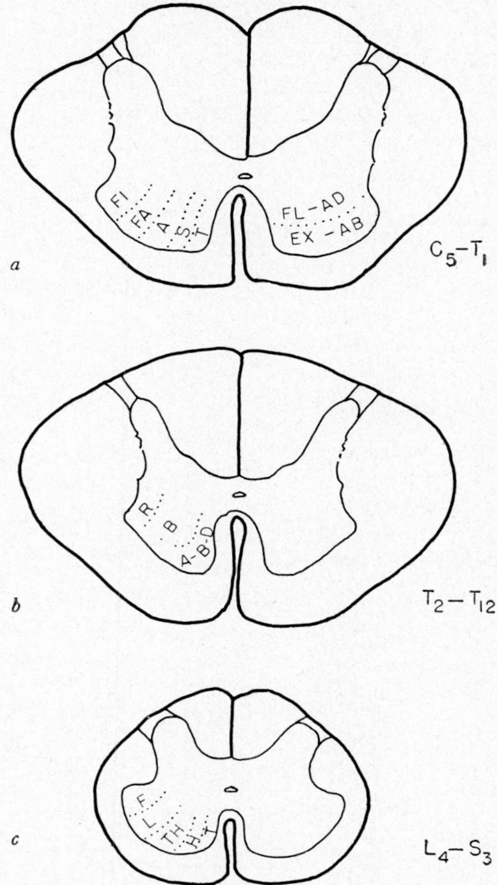

FIG. 79. Diagrams of cord segments indicating approximate topographical representation of muscle groups in the ventral-horn cell columns. *a*, fifth cervical segment to first thoracic: *FI*, fingers; *FA*, forearm; *A*, arm; *S*, shoulder; *T*, trunk. *b*, second to twelfth thoracic segments: *R*, ribs; *B*, back; *A-B-D*, abdomen. *c*, fourth lumbar segment to third sacral: *F*, foot; *L*, leg; *TH*, thigh; *H*, hip; *T*, trunk. Flexor and adductor groups are represented in the dorsal portion of the anterior horn; extensors and abductors, in the ventral portion.

expressed by these "final common paths" to the muscles. Since the muscles are derived from somites of dorsal mesoderm, these neurons for their motor innervation are classed as *general somatic motor*.

In addition to these neurons, sending their axons out to innervate striated muscle and serving a somatic motor function, associative neurons are also found in the anterior columns as noted above. A group is present in the most medial part of anterior gray on either side of the gray commissures. For this reason, and also because they send their axons across the commissure to end about anterior column cells of the opposite side, they are known as the **anterior commissural nuclei.** Small neurons of Golgi type II are scattered throughout the central portions of the anterior gray. Medium-large cells in the lateral periphery of the anterior columns have been found to undergo chromatolysis after a contralateral hemisection of the spinal cord several segments above (173). These cells were present in the lowest thoracic segment and in the next six succeeding ones caudally. Their axons, in the monkey at least, appeared to contribute to the ventral spinocerebellar tract (see later).

In that region of the spinal cord between the first thoracic segment and the second lumbar segment, medium-sized multipolar cells form columns in the lateral part of the intermediate gray. Their presence gives a lateral projection of the gray, and they constitute the **intermediolateral cell columns** (Fig. 78). These cells are motor to smooth muscle, cardiac muscle, and glands. In a corresponding position, but without a marked lateral projection, in the second to fourth sacral segments of the spinal cord, are cells of a similar type which send their axons to the smooth muscle of the pelvic viscera and blood vessels. These cells are, respectively, **preganglionic motor neurons** of the spinal sympathetic and spinal parasympathetic divisions of the autonomic nervous system. Their axons are classed as **general visceral motor.** Medial columns of neurons, less well circumscribed than the lateral ones described above, are referred to as the **intermediomedial nuclei.**

POSTERIOR CELL COLUMNS

Sensory endings have been classified topographically as exteroceptive, from skin; proprioceptive, from muscles, tendons, and joints; and visceral or interoceptive, from the interior of the body. Whatever their source, all sensory impulses enter the spinal cord by way of the axons of the pseudo-unipolar cells of the posterior root ganglia—the **primary sensory neurons.** Once within the spinal cord, the course of impulses through it and to the brain stem, to the thalamus, and cortex, as well as to the cerebellum, differs. Certain neurons of the posterior cell columns take part in their transmission, and these are denoted as **secondary neurons** in the conduction pathways. Other neurons involved at higher levels are **tertiary** and **quaternary.**

Essentially, three chief divisions of posterior gray may be made. These include a **marginal zone,** the **substantia gelatinosa,** and the **body** proper of the posterior gray (Figs. 78, 80). The last is sometimes referred to as the (ventral) **spongiosa substance.** The "body," or spongiosa, is subdivided into a ventrally placed **basal** part adjoining the intermediate gray columns, a dorsally placed **"cervix"** or neck, and a **"caput"** or head. The last is surrounded by the substantia gelatinosa. These divisions differ in contour and hence in cell content at various levels of the spinal cord. The cell population is greater in the low cervical and lumbar levels.

The marginal zone constitutes the most dorsolateral portion of posterior gray often referred to in part or totally as **Lissauer's fasciculus** (423). Some authors include this with the white matter of the spinal cord. In it and running through it are many very fine, unmyelinated or very thinly myelinated fibers, and scattered among these are some small cells whose function is probably that of segmental and intersegmental associative neurons. The lateral division incoming posterior root fibers pass through this marginal zone and some of their branches and collaterals ascend in it for short distances.

The substantia gelatinosa forms a hood over the "caput," or head, of the posterior columns. It varies in contour and amount at different levels, as noted above. It has a gelatinous appearance in the fresh condition because of the presence in it of many unmyelinated and finely myelinated fibers. The cells in this zone are of small size. The dendrites of many spongiosa cells ramify in the gelatinous zone.

Just dorsal to the substantia gelatinosa is a rim of large neurons. These constitute the **posteromarginal nucleus.** The site of this nucleus is sometimes referred to as the apical zone of the posterior gray or as the **dorsal spongiosa** region.

The three parts of the body of the posterior gray column, or the ventral spongiosa substance, contain many cells larger than those of the gelatinosa. These large and medium-sized cells are grouped especially into two quite prominent columns. One of these, constituting the **central nucleus,** or **proper sensory nucleus,**

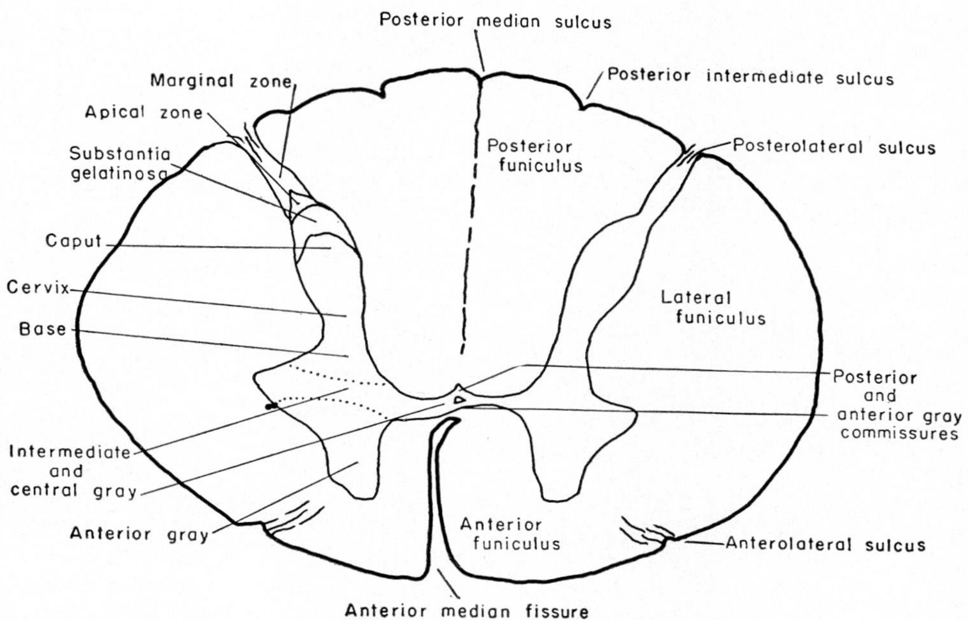

FIG. 80. Diagram of divisions of gray and white matter within the spinal cord.

is located in the central portion of the "caput" and "cervix" of the spongiosa. The proper sensory nucleus is present at all spinal levels. A second column is found in the medial part of the basal zone. Between the second lumbar and middle cervical levels this mediobasal column is composed of prominent large neurons. The nuclei of these cells are placed eccentrically. Below the second lumbar level the neurons are smaller and the column is less distinct. The entire column is known as the **dorsal nucleus.** In the low lumbar and sacral levels it is the dorsal nucleus of Stilling, in the other levels, the dorsal nucleus of Clarke (166).

Also present in the mediobasal region of posterior gray adjacent to intermediate gray is the **posterior commissural nucleus.** The cells of this nucleus are not as large as those of the dorsal nucleus. The posterior commissural nucleus is not well developed in thoracic levels. In the lateral part of the basal zone of the posterior gray, at all levels, a fairly prominent column of neurons constitutes the **reticular nucleus.** Its cells are about the same size as those of the posterior commissural nucleus. Scattered between these several distinct columns of neurons in the spongiosa are many small cells.

The exact function of these various posterior gray nuclei is not settled. Some have synapses with posterior root fibers, some with axons of intrinsic spinal neurons, and some with descending spinal tracts. Certain of the cells send axons to the thalamus; others project to spinal levels, regional and distant. According to Foerster and his colleagues, incoming posterior root fibers of the macaque have synapses with neurons in Clarke's nucleus, in the proper sensory nucleus, and in intermediate gray, though not with autonomic neurons (259). By studying transneuronal degeneration resulting from cutting posterior root fibers in the monkey, they found no synapses between posterior root fibers and neurons in the substantia gelatinosa. Szentagothai and Kiss, studying degenerating end organs after incisions into posterior roots, reported such synapses (771). Many fine fibers entering the gelatinosa from the posterior funiculus and from Lissauer's zone have been observed to end there in the human fetus (A. A. Pearson, 1952). Whether or not the neurons of substantia gelatinosa receive incoming posterior root fibers, they do not appear to contribute axons to the long ascending spinal tracts. Like the small neurons in the zone of Lissauer, they may serve as links in short-chained ascending systems, or they may have purely an associative function.

The cells of the proper sensory nucleus send their axons into spinothalamic and spinotectal tracts. The neurons in Clarke's dorsal nucleus contribute their axons to the dorsal spinocerebellar tracts. Those of Stilling's and of the posterior commissural nuclei are thought to contribute to the ventral spinocerebellar tract. It has been suggested that interoceptive, visceral sensory fibers terminate about cells near the base of the posterior columns in the medial intermediate zone and about the central canal, but substantial proof is lacking. The posteromarginal cells and the scattered neurons of the posterior gray serve an associative function, their axons contributing to intersegmental and intrasegmental connections. The neurons of the reticular nucleus receive some of the corticospinal fibers and send their axons into the anterior gray.

Foerster thought that there is precise localization of cells in the posterior columns according to function and body topography, and with Brouwer also, he thought that medially placed cells in the posterior columns receive impulses from the most lateral (limbs) parts of the body and laterally placed cells, from the proximal (axial) parts of the body (254). This would represent a reversal of the arrangement in the anterior columns. Recent evidence has been presented that the lateral half of the substantia gelatinosa receives impulses from dorsal parts of the dermatome, the medial half from the ventral parts of the dermatome (771).

White Matter—Fiber Tracts

The white matter of the spinal cord is composed of **fiber tracts** made up of myelinated and nonmyelinated fibers which are grouped in large bundles called **funiculi.** For each half of the cord there are a posterior, a lateral, and an anterior funiculus, the longitudinal fissures being the boundaries of these. These funiculi contain tracts, or **fasciculi,** of ascending (**sensory**), descending (**motor**), and **associative** fibers, the last being short and both ascending and descending (Figs. 81, 82). The long ascend-

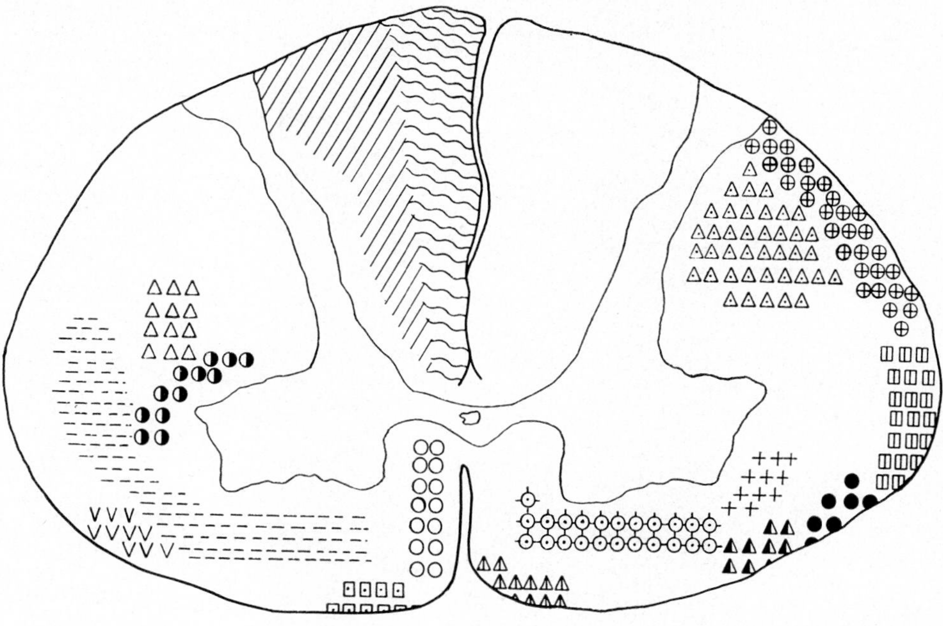

ASCENDING

/ FASCICULUS CUNEATUS
⟍ FASCICULUS GRACILIS
--- SPINOTHALAMIC TRACTS
● SPINO-OLIVARY (& OLIVOSPINAL)
V SPINOTECTAL
⊕ DORSAL SPINOCEREBELLAR
◫ VENTRAL SPINOCEREBELLAR

DESCENDING

△ LATERAL CORTICOSPINAL
O VENTRAL CORTICOSPINAL
△ RUBROSPINAL
▲ MEDIAL TECTOSPINAL
+ LATERAL TECTOSPINAL
⊙ MEDIAL RETICULOSPINAL
◑ LATERAL RETICULOSPINAL
⊡ MEDIAL VESTIBULOSPINAL
▲ LATERAL VESTIBULOSPINAL

Fig. 81. Diagram of spinal-cord pathways. For purposes of clarity no pathway is duplicated on the two sides. Those in the anterior funiculus in particular are shown more discretely than they actually are. Associative tracts are not shown.

ing and descending pathways are given names implying their origin and termination. The long descending pathways arise in the cerebral cortex and brain stem centers, and the majority terminate directly, or through intercalary neurons, about cells in the anterior and intermediate gray columns of the spinal cord; some (the corticospinals) end in part about intercalary neurons in the posterior columns. The long ascending tracts arise from neurons in the spinal cord and terminate either in the medulla, pons, midbrain, cerebellum, or thalamus.

ASCENDING TRACTS (FIG. 81)

It is now necessary to return to the posterior root fibers as they enter the spinal cord. Sensory fibers in the spinal nerves, aside from functional types, are known as **general somatic** and **visceral afferents**, according to their peripheral distribution. The somatic fibers transmit sensory impulses from striated muscles, skin, and subcutaneous tissues; visceral fibers transmit sensory impulses from smooth muscle, cardiac muscle, and glands. The fibers in each root sort themselves, as noted above, into two distinct groups, the lateral and medial bundles. The lateral bundle is composed of finely myelinated fibers of small and medium size, and the larger medial division is composed of large, heavily myelinated fibers.

Lateral spinothalamic tract. The lateral bundle enters Lissauer's fasciculus at the tip

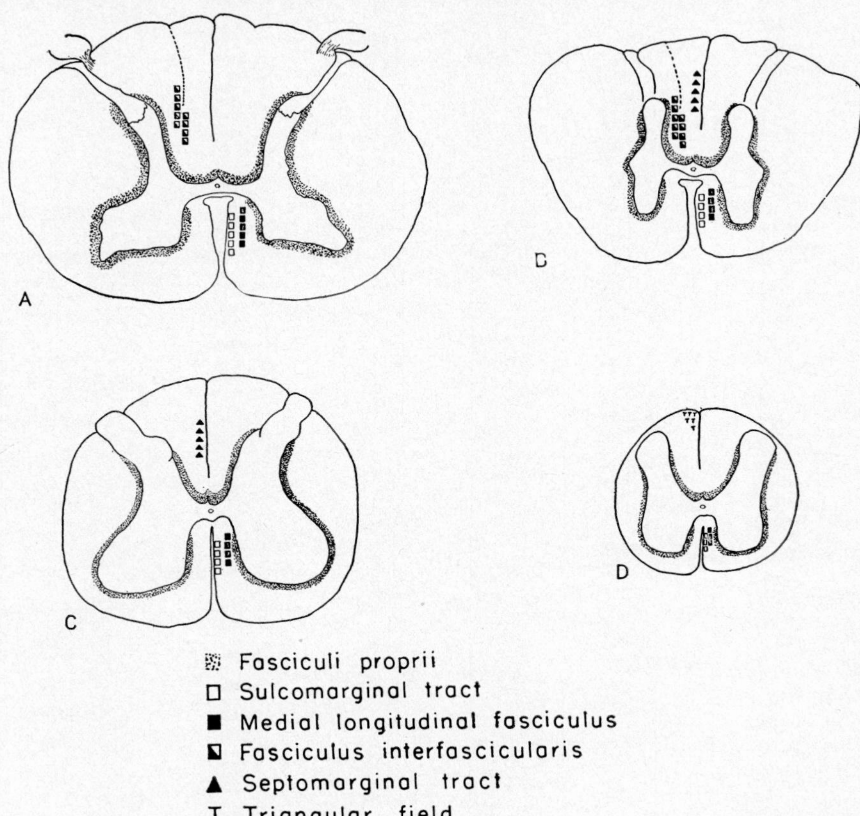

Fig. 82. Diagram of associative tracts in the spinal cord. *A*, cervical; *B*, thoracic; *C*, lumbar; *D*, sacral level.

of the posterior gray horn (Figs. 83, 84). These fibers carry temperature and pain impulses from the body surface and viscera (646, 650). Some few tactile impulses may also be brought in by them. In Lissauer's fasciculus the incoming fibers divide into short ascending and descending branches. From these short branches, collaterals arise also. Many of the ascending and descending branches synapse within the segment of entry directly about neurons in the proper sensory nucleus of the spongiosa. These neurons are then the **secondary neurons** in the conduction of painful and temperature impulses. From them, thinly myelinated axons arise, *cross* in the anterior white commissure, and turn rostrally to ascend as the **lateral spinothalamic tract.** Separate fibers exist for pain, warmth, and cold impulses. Collaterals from the ascending and descending limbs of the incoming lateral root fibers may synapse about small neurons in Lissauer's fasciculus. Many neurons in Lissauer's fasciculus in turn send their axons up a few segments, where they synapse about other neurons in Lissauer's tract; these in turn project cranialward for several segments. In such fashion is formed an *uncrossed,* short-chain tract for transmitting pain and temperature impulses to brain stem centers. Some perhaps reach the thalamus in this fashion. The posteromarginal neurons and the small cells of the gelatinosa may receive axons from neurons in Lissauer's fasciculus and send their axons in turn as intrasegmental and intersegmental fibers to synapse about motor neurons for the completion of spinal reflex arcs in response to pain and temperature stimuli. Some of their axons may relay in the proper sensory nucleus, and in such fashion impulses may gain lateral spinothalamic tract fibers after the several relays. The spinothalamic tracts probably contain fibers of several orders, therefore.

The branching of the incoming posterior root fibers serves a useful purpose of diffusing impulses to those segments wherein they may play upon effector neurons with which they are more closely related. The sixth cervical posterior root, for example, supplies a strip of skin which stretches from upper arm to fingers. Muscles under this skin area are supplied by neurons located in the fifth to eighth cervical cord segments inclusive. The ascending and descending limbs of the posterior root fibers entering the sixth segment can therefore transmit impulses to these cephalad and caudad segments, respectively, wherein they may come into direct contact with the motor neurons innervating the muscles which lie beneath the skin area supplied by the sixth posterior root fibers.

The lateral spinothalamic-tract fibers are scattered in the anterior half of the lateral funiculus medial to the ventral spinocerebellar tracts, and in the posterior half of the anterior funiculus, in which they are mingled with the fibers of the ventral spinothalamic tract carrying touch and pressure impulses (see later). Pain and temperature fibers in this overlapping of the two spinothalamic systems are more concentrated posteriorly; touch and pressure fibers, anteriorly. In a diagram of Foerster's, pressure is most ventral, then touch, pain, and temperature (Fig. 85*C*).

As these lateral spinothalamic pain and temperature fibers, arising in a given segment, cross in the anterior white commissure, they take an anterior position in the lateral funiculus (or in posterior part of anterior funiculus), and as they ascend they are pushed posteriorly and laterally by fibers arising from higher segments. In this manner, fibers arising in the sacral segments of the spinal cord are situated posteriorly and laterally in the tract, and fibers representing successive segments upward disperse themselves more and more anteriorly and medially (Figs. 85*B, C*). Incoming impulses for pain and temperature, entering over a particular root and traversing secondary neurons, are sent directly across the anterior commissures into the lateral spinothalamic tract, within one segment of their entrance. The lateral spinothalamic tracts have long and short fibers. The long fibers terminate in the thalamus; the short

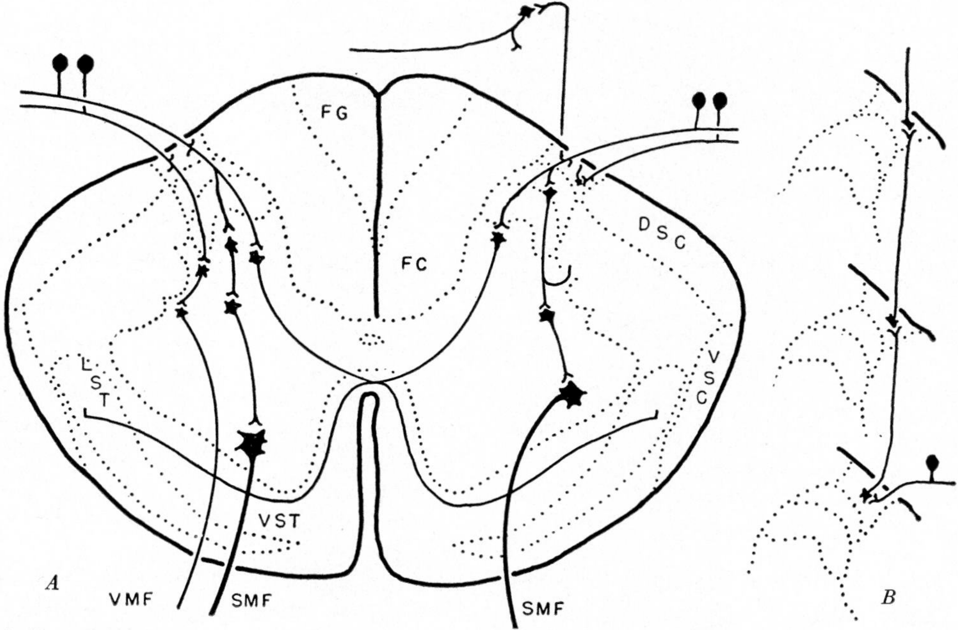

FIG. 83. *A*, diagram of dorsal-root fibers for pain and temperature conduction and reflex connections. *B*, diagram of ipsilateral pain conduction. *DSC*, dorsal spinocerebellar tract; *FC*, fasciculus cuneatus; *FG*, fasciculus gracilis; *LST*, lateral spinothalamic tract; *SMF*, somatic motor fiber; *VMF*, visceral motor fiber; *VSC*, ventral spinocerebellar tract; *VST*, ventral spinothalamic tract.

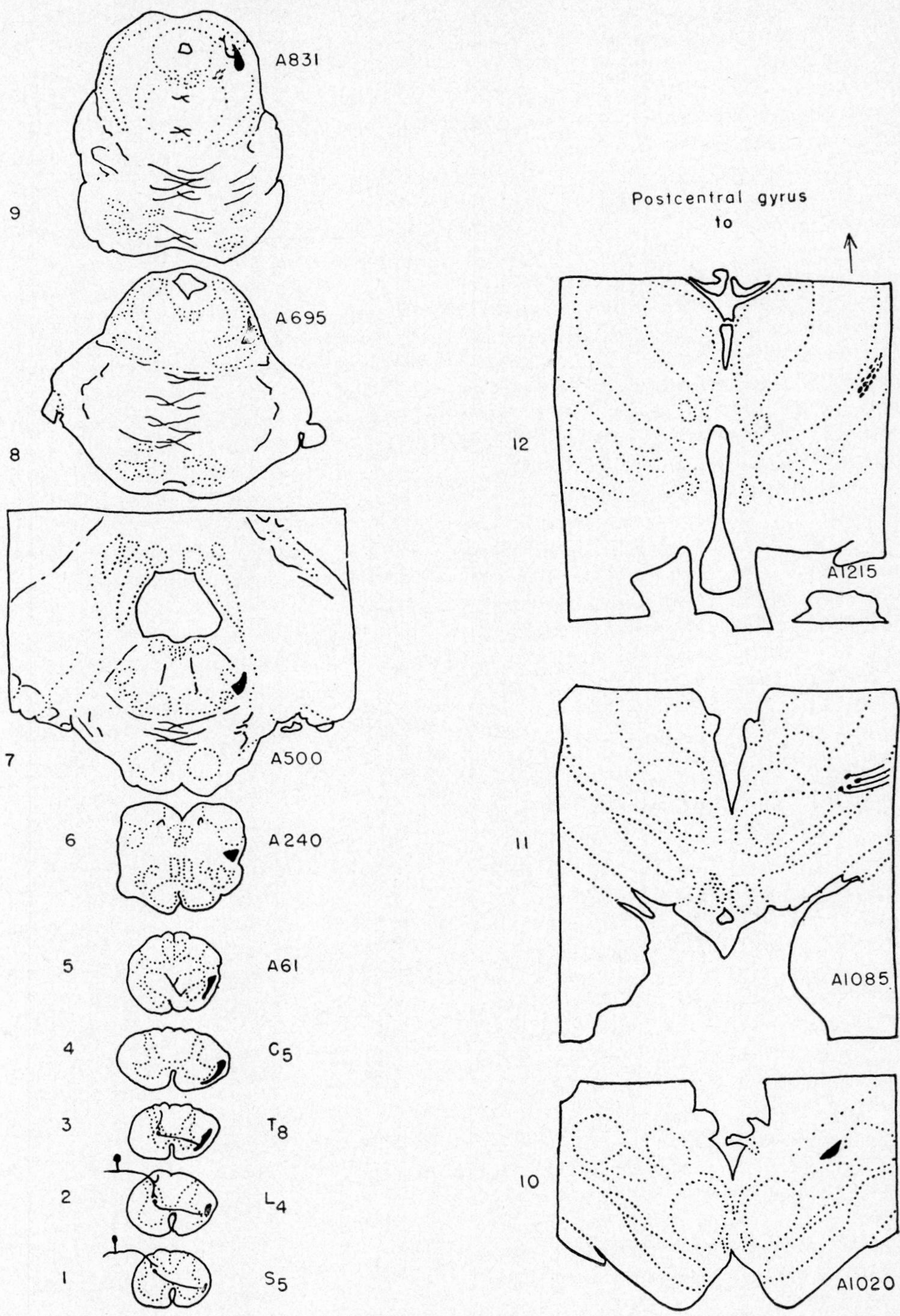

FIG. 84. Diagram of the spinothalamic and spinotectal tracts. Tactile impulses traversing these paths traverse one to three spinal segments on the side of entry before crossing. This is illustrated in the small figures 2 and 3. The serial numbers, such as A 1020, refer to the sections of a human brain stem series.

ones, about neurons in the posterior gray at spinal cord levels and about neurons of reticular formation throughout the brain stem.

In the medulla, the lateral spinothalamic tract is just dorsal to the inferior olive. The fibers are scattered lateromedially from near the medulla edge to a point about one-third the distance to the mid-line. They ascend through the pons and midbrain in the ventrolateral tegmentum in company with, but dorsal and lateral to, the medial lemniscus (see later). As they reach the rostral part of the pons, the fibers move more dorsally and pass either just medial to, through, or lateral to, the nucleus of the inferior colliculus, pass medial to the brachium of the inferior colliculus and medial geniculate body, and terminate in the posterolateral ventral nucleus of the thalamus (Fig. 84) (654, 796). Lateral spinothalamic fibers have been described in the spider monkey as crossing again in the posterior commissure to end in the posterolateral ventral nucleus (133). Impulses carried over these fibers would therefore end in the thalamus of the same side as that into which they entered the spinal cord originally. A long uncrossed pain and temperature tract then apparently exists in this animal; a similar condition appears to be present in man. The lateral spinothalamic tract also sends collaterals to the tectum and mid-line nuclei of the thalamus, to the substantia nigra, and probably also to certain of the hypothalamic nuclei (796).

In their midbrain course, the lateral spinothalamic fibers carrying impulses from the lower limbs are most dorsal; those from the arms, next most dorsal. The secondary pain and temperature tracts carrying impulses arising from the head (quintothalamics) are associated in the midbrain with the spinothalamics, and these fibers are most ventral of the group in the midbrain passage (Fig. 86). The lateral spinothalamic tract has been interrupted surgically in man at the medullar and mesencephalic levels, since it is near the surface at these levels. If interrupted at the latter level the fibers transmitting impulses from the head may also be sectioned, and a complete contralateral anesthesia for pain and temperature sense will result. Throughout the course of the tract, the topographical arrangement of fibers persists, and a definite order of termination of them in the posterolateral ventral nucleus of the thalamus is established. Having reached this level, the pain and temperature impulses may gain conscious recognition. A certain amount of appreciation of painful and thermal stimuli may be dependent also on the mid-line thalamic nuclei, especially in disease of the lateral nuclei (793). From the thalamic relay neurons, certain pain and temperature impulses pass over axons running through the internal capsule to terminate in the postcentral gyrus of the parietal lobe. At this level the impulses are integrated with others arriving there, and in addition to perception of pain or temperature as such, discriminative, comparative, and topographical qualities of the stimuli are

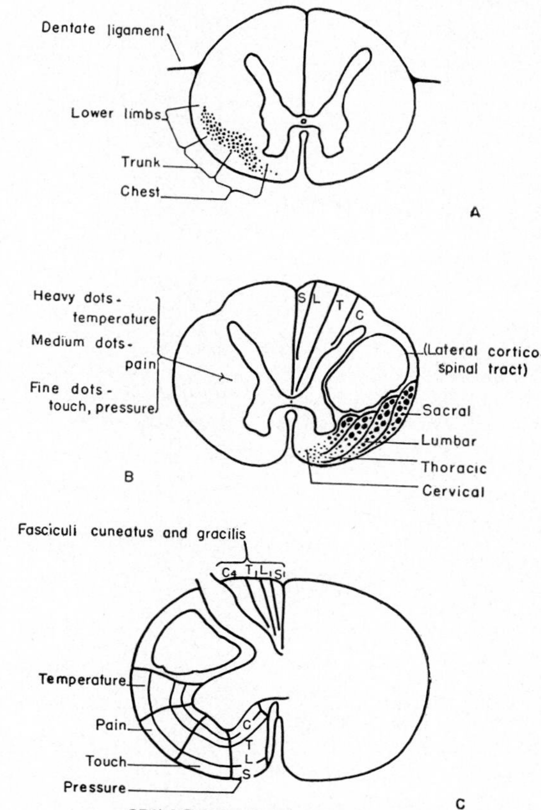

FIG. 85. Diagrams to illustrate various concepts of the spinothalamic tracts. (*A, after Hyndman and Van Epps, Arch. Surg., vol.* 38; *B, after Walker, Arch. Neurol. & Psychiat., vol.* 43; *C, after Foerster, in Bumke and Foerster, "Handbuch der Neurologie," copyright* 1936 *by Julius Springer in Berlin. Printed in Germany. Vested in the U.S. Attorney Gerneral.)*

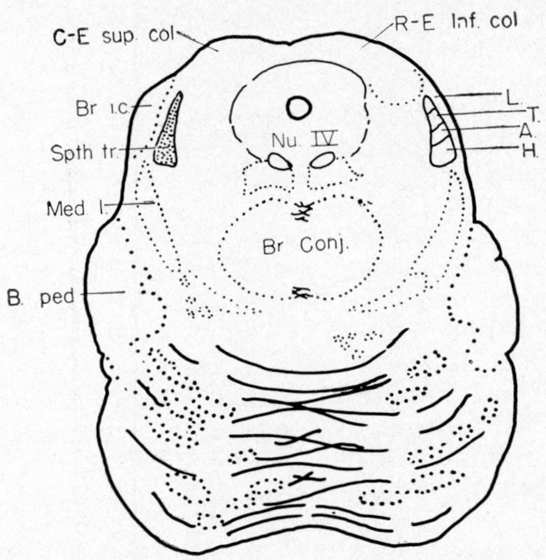

Fig. 86. Diagram of spinothalamic tracts at the mesencephalic level. *C-E Sup. col.*, caudal edge of superior colliculus; *R-E Inf. col.*, rostral edge of inferior colliculus; *Br. i.c.*, brachium of inferior colliculus; *Spth. tr.*, spinothalamic tracts (*L*, leg; *T*, trunk; *A*, arm; *H*, head); *Nu. IV*, trochlear nuclei; *Med. l.*, medial lemniscus; *Br. conj.*, brachium conjunctivum; *B. ped.*, basis pedunculi. (*Based on studies of Walker, Arch. Neurol. & Psychiat., vol.* 43, *and of Rasmussen and Peyton, Surgery, vol.* 10.)

recognized. One is therefore able to compare painful stimuli and to localize them accurately, through the integrations of painful impulses at a cerebral cortical level.

As a result of studies in humans who have had the lateral spinothalamic tracts sectioned at a spinal level for relief of intractable pain, much information about the course and position of the fibers in the cord mediating pain and temperature impulses has been obtained (251, 286, 407, 408, 796) (Fig. 85). Hyndman describes the lateral spinothalamic tract as occupying a space bounded by "a point about midway from the dentate ligament to the anterior roots to a point about midway from the anterior roots to the anterior median fissure." In the anterolateral funiculi it is believed that temperature fibers are most posterior, then pain, then touch, then pressure as the medial edge of the anterior funiculus is approached. This arrangement accords also with schemes worked out by Walker and Foerster, who in their diagrams did not separate the fibers into lateral and ventral spinothalamic tracts (Fig. 85). They refer to the entire group as the spinothalamic tracts. General touch and pressure fibers are usually allocated, however, to a separate bundle, the ventral spinothalamic tract, described below. It is possible for disease processes to injure fibers transmitting impulses of one modality and to spare others of the lateral spinothalamic tract. Dissociation of pain and temperature sensibility has thus been described by a number of investigators (723).

Chordotomy, or section of the spinothalamic tracts, is most advantageously performed in humans at a high thoracic segment in relieving intractable pain. The sections may be done unilaterally or bilaterally depending on the nature of the disorder to be treated. Following a successful chordotomy, there is observed contralateral loss of appreciation of pain and temperature stimuli beginning one dermatome below that one corresponding to the level of section. According to Foerster's experiences, the affective sensations of itching and tickle are lost when the ventral spinothalamic tracts are sectioned bilaterally in a chordotomy. Hyndman found sensation of tickle undisturbed and itching sensations abolished, in his patients with chordotomy. Bilateral chordotomy is necessary to render the viscera analgesic, and is also the procedure most certain to render a permanent loss of response to pain and temperature stimuli over any given area of skin. After unilateral chordotomies some appreciation of these stimuli may sometimes return, indicating uncrossed as well as crossed fibers transmitting painful and thermal impulses. Chordotomy necessarily also inflicts damage on the ventral spinocerebellar tract and certain descending motor tracts located in the anterior funiculi, but symptoms resulting from such injury are usually temporary.

In contrast to the results of Hyndman, Walker also described, in his chordotomy patients, bilateral disturbances of tactile sense, though these began at a lower level than the pain and temperature loss did. These tactile disturbances manifested themselves as a reduction in the number of touch points (groups of tactile end organs) per given area of skin surface and in an increase in the threshold of an individual point. It is, however, safe to assume that quite a margin of safety exists in severing so-called ventral spinothalamic fibers, since tactile impulses are carried also by other tracts, notably the fasciculi cuneatus and gracilis (see later).

Fasciculus gracilis and fasciculus cuneatus (fasciculus of Goll and fasciculus of Burdach, respectively) (Figs. 81, 87, 88). The large incoming fibers of the medial bundle of the posterior root enter the spinal cord just dorsomedial to the tip of the posterior gray columns and divide into long ascending and shorter descending branches as they reach the medial border of the posterior gray. Collateral fibers arise from the stem fibers as well as from both branches throughout their length, but they are more numerous near the point of entry and bifurcation. These medial division root fibers transmit impulses arising in neuromuscular and neurotendinous spindles, from pacinian corpuscles, and from encapsulated and naked tactile endings. These fibers represent, therefore, the primary neuron for all the ascending tracts described in the following sections.

The descending branches run in the posterior funiculi, as association bundles, and ultimately synapse around cells in the gray columns. They are described below. The collateral fibers have any one of several destinations; some ascend several segments and terminate about cells in the body of the posterior columns; others terminate about posterior column cells within the segment of entrance; others may pass into the intermediate and anterior gray columns to synapse around cells located there. The stretch, or myotatic, reflex arc is completed in this way and involves only two neurons, therefore, in dorsal root ganglia and anterior gray (494). Some collaterals may cross to the other side by way of the posterior white commissure just posterior to the central canal and synapse in the opposite gray, especially about cells of Clarke's nucleus.

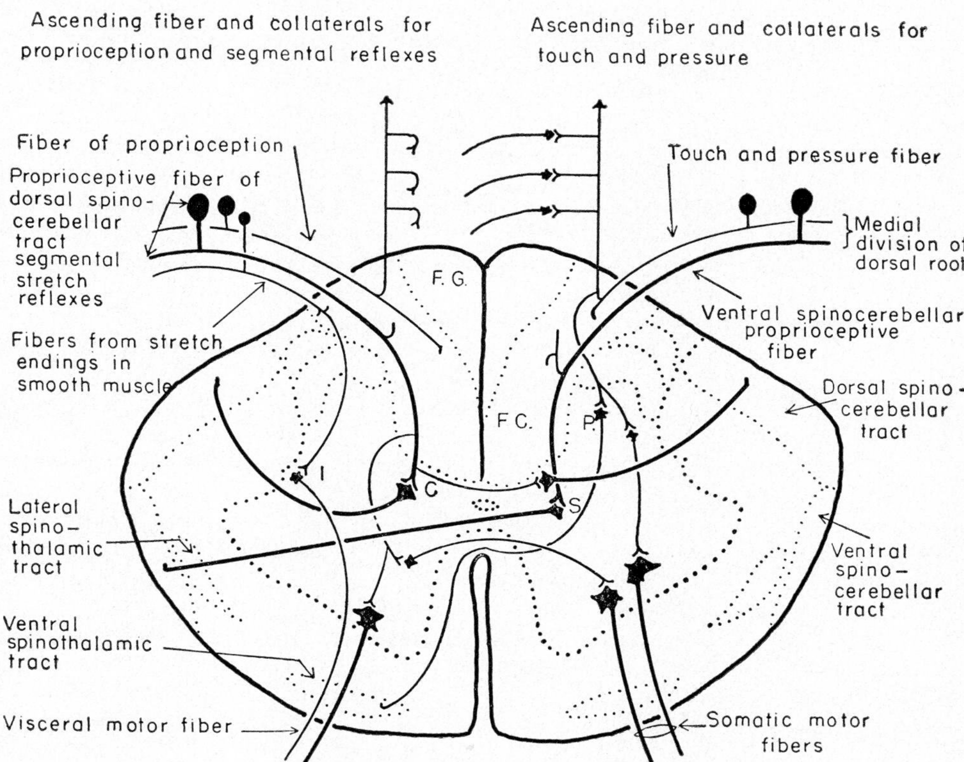

Fig. 87. Diagram of dorsal-root fibers contributing to dorsal and ventral spinocerebellar tracts, the dorsal columns, and the ventral spinothalamic tract. *C*, nucleus dorsalis of Clarke; *I*, intermediolateral cell column; *F.C.*, fasciculus cuneatus; *F.G.*, fasciculus gracilis; *P.*, nucleus proprius of dorsal horn; *S*, Stilling's cell column.

The ascending limbs of the medial division fibers constitute the large fasciculi in the posterior funiculus. In this funiculus from the middle thoracic level upward two distinct bundles are present, a medial and a lateral. These are the **fasciculus gracilis** carrying impulses from those segments of the body innervated by the lower six thoracic, lumbar, and sacral posterior roots; and the **fasciculus cuneatus** carrying impulses from that part of the body innervated by the upper six thoracic and cervical posterior roots.

The impulses arising in the end organs located in muscles and tendons are set up by changes in the tension of the muscle fibers and tendons. The neuromuscular spindles are activated by the relaxing, and thus elongating, muscle fibers. The sense of position of a part of the body in space, and the amount of contraction in and about joints are ascertained through the conduction of these impulses to, and their integration in, the parietal lobe. Through the cortical integration of the impulses arising in tactile organs, sensations of light touch, discrimination of two simultaneously applied stimuli (tactile discrimination), and localization of tactile stimuli are determined. Recognition of rapidly successive stimuli, as vibrations, depends on impulses conducted by these tracts also. The ability to recognize shape, size, and quality ("stereognosis") depends on the cerebral integration of the impulses transmitted to the cortex by these tracts of the posterior funiculi. Stereognosis, strictly speaking, refers to ability to appreciate the *form* of an object, but is frequently loosely used to denote ability to appreciate shape, size, and quality. It is a function of the cerebral cortex, especially the parietal lobe.

The fibers in the fasciculi cuneatus and gracilis are so arranged that those transmitting impulses from the lower segments of that part of the body represented in each are medial; those from the upper segments, lateral (Figs. 78, 85*B*, *C*). Thus fibers for impulses from the legs and feet are found along the medial border of gracilis, those for impulses from the upper arm and neck are most lateral in the fasciculus cuneatus. These long ascending fibers give collaterals to the gray column at many levels, but most of them (the long ascending fibers) reach a **secondary neuron** in the **nuclei gracilis and cuneatus** in the lower medulla. The **clava** and the **cuneate tubercle** are external landmarks for the identification of these nuclei, respectively.

From these nuclei, **internal arcuate fibers** swing medially and ventrally around the central canal and beneath the fourth ventricle, cross in the mid-line, turn rostrally and ascend as the **medial lemniscus.** This large bundle, at first placed in the medial and ventral part of the tegmental portion of the brain stem, gradually moves laterally but remains in the ventral tegmental region through medulla and pons (656). In the midbrain, however, it is lateral and slightly dorsal to the red nucleus, and it terminates in the posterolateral ventral nucleus of the thalamus. In this nucleus are located the **tertiary neurons** of this conduction path. The medial lemniscus gives collaterals to the reticular formation of the brain stem, to the midline thalamic nuclei, to the substantia nigra, possibly to the globus pallidus, and to some of the hypothalamic nuclei. From the posterolateral ventral nucleus of the thalamus, axons of the tertiary neurons pass into the internal capsule to run to the postcentral gyrus and adjacent areas of the parietal lobe.

Destruction of the fibers in fasciculi cuneatus and gracilis results in impairment of appreciation of lightest touch, of tactile discrimination, of sense of position and movement, and of vibration. The ability to discriminate differences in size, weight, and texture is lost, since the impulses necessary for this do not reach the parietal lobe. The reflex arc underlying the maintenance of muscle tone is broken, and the resistance of skeletal muscles to passive stretch is accordingly lessened, a condition known as hypotonia. The muscles feel relaxed and flabby. The hypotonia combined with faulty or lost sense of movement results in disordered voluntary movement, manifested as awkwardness or **sensory ataxia.** In unilateral destruction all these disturbances are on the same side as the spinal lesion and are more severe in the distal parts of the extremities. If the injury occurs in one of the medial lemnisci, the disorders are contralateral to the site of the injury.

As seen previously, the majority of the stem fibers of the posterior roots pass into the posterior funiculi directly, divide, and give off

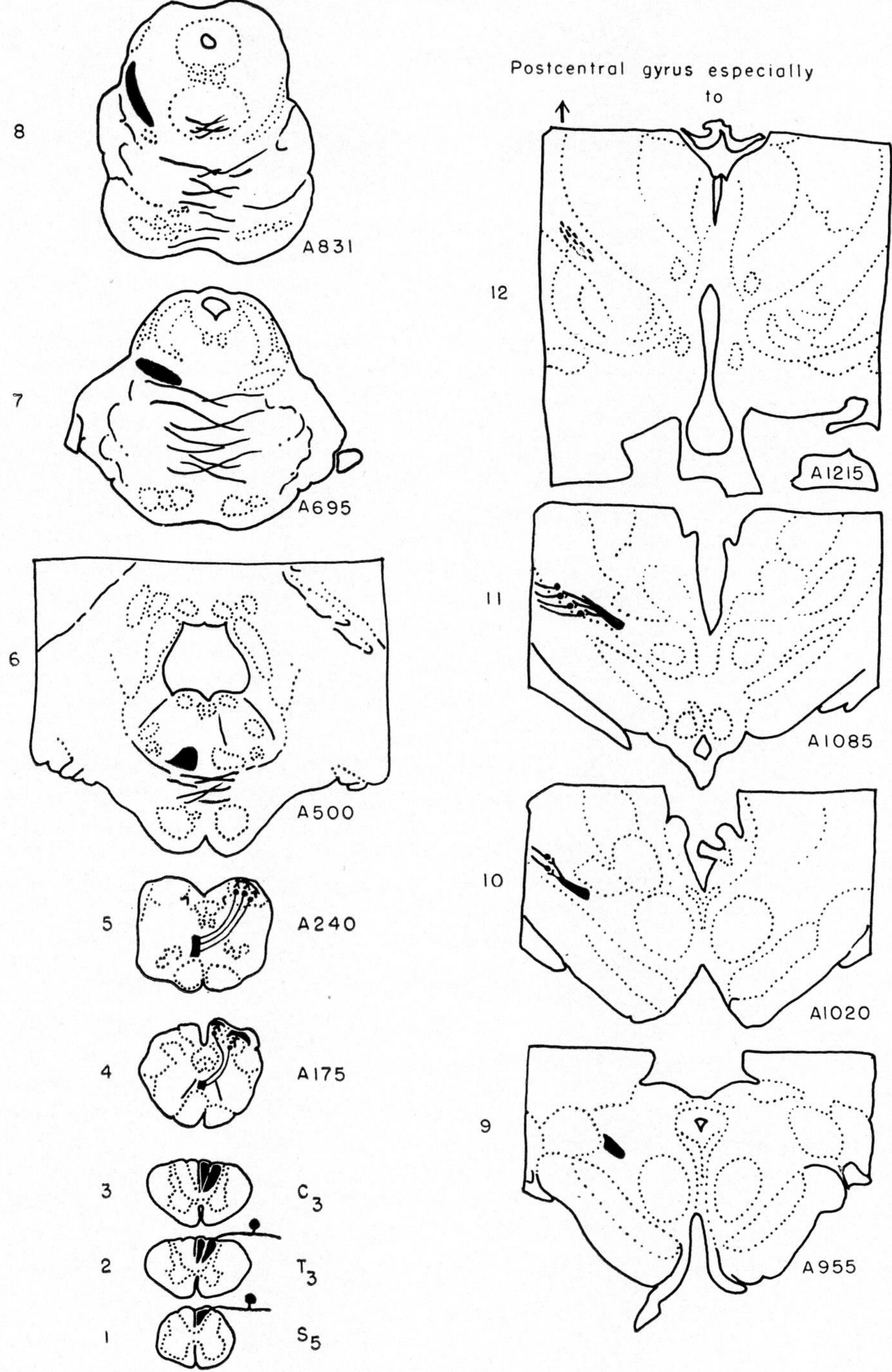

FIG. 88. Diagram of the medial lemniscus. The serial numbers, such as A 1215, refer to the sections of a human brain stem series.

collaterals. These collaterals, as described above, together with a few direct stem fibers entering each segment, synapse about cells in the posterior gray, which in turn give rise to other ascending tracts. These are described next.

Ventral spinothalamic tract (Figs. 81, 85, 87). The medial bundles of the posterior roots carry impulses of touch and muscle sense, as mentioned. Not all impulses arising in tactile end organs and in pressure endings, however, are transmitted by the fasciculi cuneatus and gracilis. Only those necessary for appreciation of very light contact, tactile discrimination, and stereognosis are carried by the fibers in those fasciculi. Fibers transmitting impulses for general contact sense and deep pressure take another course, to be described now.

The ascending limbs of certain stem fibers of the medial division of the dorsal roots climb for a distance of several segments in the posterior funiculi, then enter the posterior gray column of the same side, synapsing about cells of the neck and basal part of the posterior gray. Collaterals of certain medial division fibers, given off in the segment of entry, and in the next above, also synapse about these cells of the neck and basal zone. The axons of these **secondary neurons** pass ventrally and cross to the other side in the anterior white commissure to collect in the **ventral spinothalamic tract,** placed superficially on the lateral and anterior edge of the anterior funiculus (Figs. 81, 85). Since the collaterals and stem fibers of any one posterior root synapse in several segments, a variable number of segments are traversed before all the tactile impulses from that root, destined for the opposite ventral spinothalamic tract, are crossed. Many secondary fibers traverse the ventral spinothalamic tract of the same side. It should be remembered, then, that unilateral spinal cord lesions do not give complete loss of tactile sense on any one side because of this and especially because two touch pathways, cuneatus-gracilis and ventral spinothalamic, are present.

The exact position of the ventral spinothalamic tract through most of the lower brain stem is unknown. At rostral brain stem levels it comes to be associated with the medial lemniscus and lateral spinothalamic tracts and passes into the posterolateral ventral nucleus of the thalamus. Here the **tertiary** neurons are found. From these, axons pass to the postcentral gyrus of the parietal lobe.

Spinotectal tract (Figs. 81, 84). A small path, the **spinotectal,** of origin similar to that of the lateral and ventral spinothalamic tracts, ascends superficially in the lateral funiculus, then becomes associated in the medulla with the lateral tectospinal and spinothalamic tracts, and ends in the **nuclei** of the **superior** and **inferior colliculi,** the **tectum** of the midbrain. It carries somatic sensory impulses (pain, thermal, and tactile) to this midbrain region which is primarily concerned with optic and auditory impulses. Many authors consider this tract merely as a collateral of the spinothalamic tracts because of its association with them in its origin and course.

Spinocerebellar tracts (Figs. 81, 87, 89). Many impulses, arising in receptors in muscles and tendons, reach the cerebellum by way of the two spinocerebellar tracts, dorsal and ventral. The finer details of the origin of these tracts, especially of the ventral, are not clear, however. Ascending limbs of fibers of the medial division of the posterior root and, especially, collaterals of the fibers pass into the posterior gray columns within the segment of entrance or several segments above. The majority of these stem fibers and collaterals terminate about **secondary neurons** on the same side; a few may cross first in the posterior white commissure to synapse about neurons on the opposite side.

In the thoracic and upper lumbar segments these fibers synapse about cells in **Clarke's column.** Axons of these **secondary neurons** in Clarke's column run through the gray to the periphery of the cord on the same side, where they turn rostrally and ascend in the lateral funiculus just ventral to Lissauer's tract; these compose a **dorsal spinocerebellar tract** (763). A few of these secondary axons may cross in the ventral white commissure to gain the dorsal spinocerebellar tract of the other side. Since Clarke's column is best developed above the second lumbar segment, the dorsal spinocerebellar tract is found only above that level. Some authors have reported that impulses destined for this tract, and entering the spinal cord with lower lumbar and sacral roots, reach Clarke's column by way of the ascending limbs and

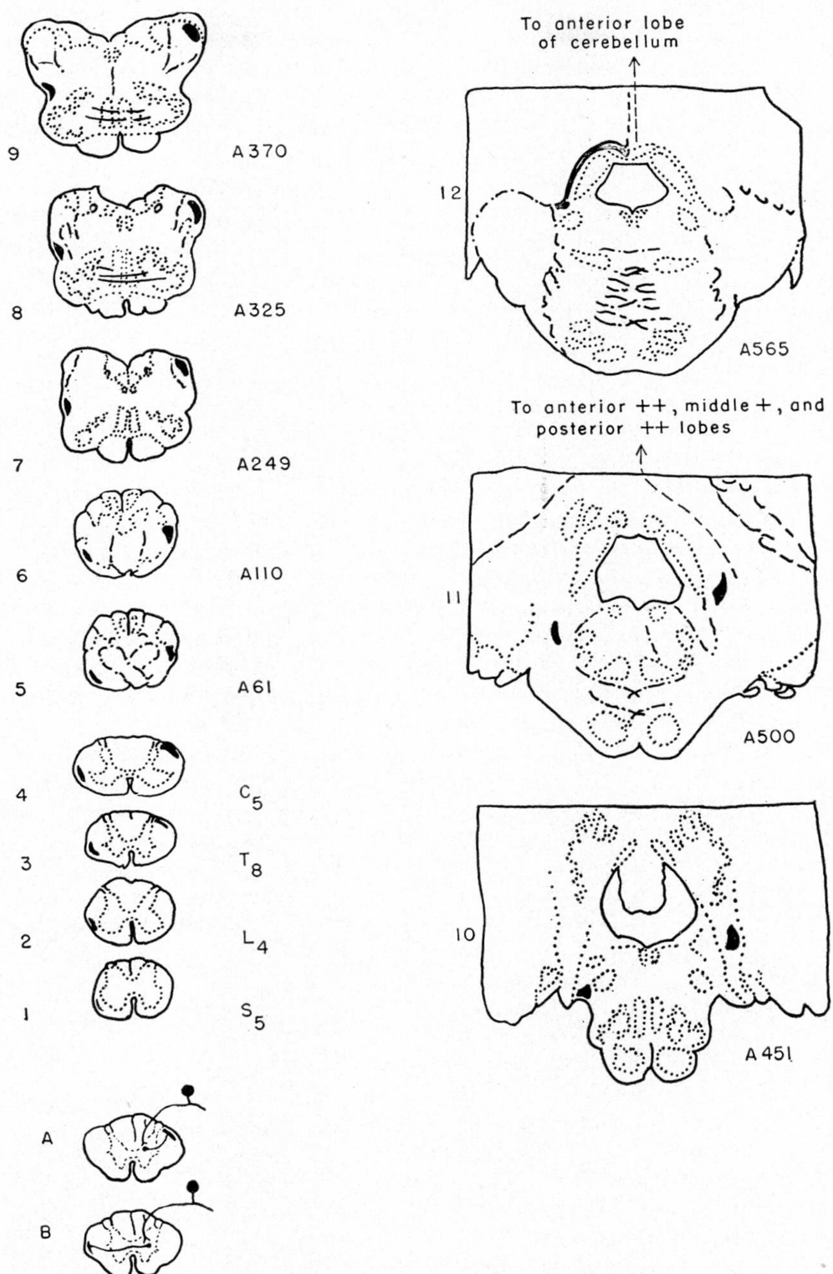

FIG. 89. Diagram of the spinocerebellar tracts. *A*, dorsal tract from nucleus dorsalis; *B*, ventral tract from Stilling's nucleus. Only the origin of the ventral tract from Stilling's nucleus is shown. The serial numbers, such as A 565, refer to the sections of a human brain stem series.

collaterals from these fibers. That the dorsal spinocerebellar tract may arise also from neurons at cervical levels, in the monkey at least, was shown by Cooper and Sherrington (173). After spinocerebellar-tract section at a high cervical level, they found chromatolytic neurons in the dorsal nucleus at the sixth and seventh cervical levels.

The origin of the ventral spinocerebellar tract is even more disputed. Cooper and Sherrington reported that it arises from the lowest thoracic and the next six successive caudal spinal segments in the monkey. The cells of origin were large neurons placed ventrolaterally about the anterior gray columns. According to their studies the ventral spinocerebellar tract is predominantly a crossed one. It is of interest, however, that recent investigation in the cat has failed to reveal contralateral electrical activity in any part of the lateral funiculus in response to peripheral "proprioceptive" stimulation (J. M. Sprague, 1951). Sprague concluded that the border neurons, described by Cooper and Sherrington as giving rise to ventral spinocerebellar fibers, were not under the influence of activity coming directly from the periphery in the cat. Before the investigations of Cooper and Sherrington, it was believed that the ventral spinocerebellar tract has a more extensive origin. It has been reported as arising in all levels of the spinal cord, and especially in those levels which innervate the extremities (423). Neurons in the posterior gray, especially in Stilling's nucleus and in the posterior commissural nucleus, have been described as the origin of the ventral spinocerebellar tract. The majority of axons from these various **secondary neurons** are said to cross by way of the anterior white commissure to gain the periphery of the spinal cord in the opposite lateral funiculus, turn rostrally and ascend just ventral to the dorsal spinocerebellar tract as the **ventral spinocerebellar tract;** some axons pass through the gray to join the ventral spinocerebellar tract of the same side.

In summary, then, the dorsal spinocerebellar tract arises from Clarke's column, is chiefly an uncrossed tract, and carries impulses to the cerebellum from endings in muscles and tendons of the trunk, upper thigh, and to some extent, of the arm. These impulses are evoked through changes in tension in the muscle fibers and in the tendons and arise in neuromuscular spindles and neurotendinous endings. The ventral spinocerebellar tract arises in all levels of the cord and is chiefly a crossed tract. It carries impulses to the cerebellum from the muscles of both upper and lower limbs, chiefly from the lower.

These two bundles end in the granular layer of the cortex of the anterior and posterior lobes of the cerebellum. The dorsal bundle holds its lateral position as it passes into the medulla and thence with the fibers of the restiform body (inferior cerebellar peduncle) into the cerebellum. The ventral bundle also remains laterally placed until the level of the inferior colliculus is reached, then turns about on itself and passes into the cerebellum around the brachium conjunctivum. Injury to these tracts results in hypotonia in skeletal muscle and poor regulation of movement expressed as awkwardness or ataxia. Muscular contraction and relaxation in voluntary movements of gait and other skilled acts are ill-timed. Familial degenerations of unknown causes are prone to involve the spinocerebellar tracts, leading to severe **cerebellar ataxia.** Friedreich's ataxia is an example (see later).

Spino-olivary and spinoreticular tracts (Fig. 81). In all levels of the spinal cord certain other medial division, stem fiber-collaterals synapse about cells of the posterior gray column, which in turn give rise to fibers terminating in the medulla (Brodal and others, 1949, 1950). Spino-olivary fibers are predominantly crossed and ascend in the dorsolateral corner of the ventral funiculus and in the adjacent region of the lateral funiculus. They end in the more caudal parts of the inferior olive, particularly—in the cat, at least—in the dorsal and medial accessory olivary nuclei. Spinoreticular fibers arising in all levels ascend in the lateral funiculus and terminate in the lateral reticular nucleus of the medulla. In the cat they appear chiefly uncrossed, and they terminate in a localized fashion in the caudal parts of the reticular nucleus. The inferior olive and lateral reticular nucleus in turn relay these spinal impulses to the cerebellum.

ASSOCIATIVE TRACTS (FIG. 82)

Within the spinal cord are many short fiber systems that begin and end within the cord itself. Included in these are ascending and descending fibers. The greater portion of these fibers run just outside the gray column as the **fasciculi proprii,** or **propriospinal system.** The entire gray columns are thus ringed by these paths, the fibers of which travel up or down for a distance of only several spinal-cord segments as a rule. These fibers are axons of neurons located within the gray, neurons belonging to the internuncial, or associative nuclei; the axons of these neurons terminate in the gray about motor neurons and other associative neurons. As has been seen, these associative nuclei are present in both anterior and posterior gray.

Included among the anterior proprius fibers are some representing the spinal continuation of several associative paths of the brain stem. The **medial longitudinal fasciculus** is thus a component of the spinal associative tracts. The **sulcomarginal tract,** bordering the anterior median longitudinal sulcus, is the spinal continuation of the **interstitiospinal and commissurospinal** *tracts* (see later).

Other associative paths in the spinal cord are composed of descending branches of incoming, medial division, posterior root fibers. These branches course within the posterior funiculi running for several segments before entering the gray to terminate. Some of them end about neurons in the anterior gray columns for the completion of reflex arcs. These descending branches form the **septomarginal fasciculus** and the **fasciculus interfascicularis,** or **comma bundle.** The former varies in its position and goes by different names at various levels. It is known as the **triangular fasciculus** in sacral levels and is located at the medial tip of the posterior funiculus. In the lumbar levels, it is known as the **oval bundle** and is found along the mid-portion of the posterior median longitudinal septum. In the thoracic levels, the septomarginal fasciculus is along the posterior periphery of the posterior funiculus. The comma bundle, or fasciculus interfascicularis, placed along a line joining the fasciculi cuneatus and gracilis, is best developed at thoracic levels. Other short associative connections are made by collaterals of incoming medial and lateral division posterior root fibers, by collaterals of the long ascending and descending tracts. The intrinsic spinal-cord neural mechanisms are thus under influences coming from the peripheral sensory end organs, from the supraspinal levels, and from other intraspinal nuclei.

Through the activity of these associative pathways the intrinsic spinal neural mechanisms are coordinated. Cervical spinal-cord activity may be correlated with, and may influence, lumbar activities, for example. Many of the descending associative tracts directly influence motor neurons of the same side. Within the anterior gray, the commissural nuclei, however, exert their effect on motor neurons located in the anterior gray of the opposite side. The propriospinal systems are the first tracts in the spinal cord to be myelinated. They are pathways through which the earliest movements of the fetus are integrated. Another example of activity mediated by these intrinsic spinal cord paths is the "scratch reflex" demonstrable in many normal dogs and in laboratory preparations of "spinal" animals, described below.

VISCERAL SENSORY TRACTS

Before starting the discussion of the descending pathways, it may be said that the position of pathways for the transmission of visceral sensory impulses, if there are separate tracts, is unknown. Visceral pain impulses enter the spinal cord via the thinly myelinated fibers of the lateral division of the posterior root. Without adequate evidence, neurons in the medial portion of the intermediate gray columns have been thought to serve as **secondary neurons** for an ascending visceral sensory tract. It is customary usually to include any ascending visceral sensory tracts with the spinothalamic tracts, and at present it is not possible to differentiate within this tract fibers transmitting impulses of visceral origin from those carrying impulses of somatic origin.

DESCENDING TRACTS

The intrinsic spinal-cord motor neurons and the internuncials related to them are almost constantly bombarded by impulses descending from supraspinal neurons in the medulla, pons, midbrain, and cerebral cortex as well as by those entering over posterior root fibers. The cerebellum and basal ganglia also influence spinal neurons, but perhaps they exert their effect not directly but through neurons located in one of the levels previously listed. Certain impulses descending into the spinal cord via the tracts now to be described are concerned with the initiation and coordination of skeletal movement and of its relaxation, and with the promotion and proper distribution of muscle tone. Impulses which initiate, regulate, and coordinate the motor activity of smooth and cardiac muscle and of glands utilize other descending tracts, which also will be briefly described.

The descending somatic motor tracts may be separated into two major groups according to their method of passage into the spinal cord. One group, composed of a large compact group of fibers, traverses the medullar pyramids; these are therefore called the **pyramidal,** or corticospinal, tracts. The second group of descending fibers does not traverse the medullar pyramid, but rather descends through the tegmentum of the medulla to enter the anterior and lateral funiculi of the spinal cord. These are the **extrapyramidal** tracts, and of these there are several.

Recent physiological experiments have served to differentiate many of the descending tracts according to their influences on the spinal-cord motor neurons and the reflex arcs of which they are a part. Impulses carried over certain descending paths enhance or facilitate the activity of the spinal neurons when properly coordinated with other impulses of spinal or peripheral origin; those carried over other descending paths are inhibitory or suppressive to the activity of spinal neurons. Thus, the descending motor tracts have been classified as facilitative or inhibitory, and this division, it will be seen, does not parallel the pyramidal-extrapyramidal classification (528).

Corticospinal or pyramidal tracts (Figs. 81, 90). Corticospinal fibers are present in the lateral and ventral funiculi of the spinal cord. Those fibers whose origin is known arise chiefly from cells in area 4 of the precentral gyrus and, to a lesser extent, in area 6 of the precentral gyrus, in areas 3, 1, and 2 of the postcentral gyrus, and in areas 5 and 7 of the superior parietal lobule (388, 472, 478, 479, 606, 782). The origin of nearly 50 per cent of the corticospinal fibers, however, is unknown at present. Those whose origin is known descend from the cortex through the internal capsule, into the cerebral peduncle and through the basilar part of the pons. As they enter the medulla they are grouped along the ventral border in the "pyramids"; hence the name **pyramidal tract,** as noted above. A more detailed description of the course of these corticospinal fibers through the brain is to be found in Chap. 16.

In the caudal end of the medulla, a decussation takes place and the pyramidal paths enter the spinal cord as ventral and lateral corticospinal fibers. About 85 per cent or more of the fibers usually cross over and pass dorsolaterally to form the **lateral corticospinal tract** which descends into the spinal cord, taking a position in the posterior part of the lateral funiculus just lateral and anterior to the posterior gray columns. This tract contains also some uncrossed fibers. In some individuals other uncrossed fibers descend into the cord in a superficial ventrolateral position in close association with the olivospinal tract (see below). This **ventrolateral tract** is known as **Barnes' tract** (60). The remaining uncrossed fibers form the **ventral corticospinal tract,** which lies medially in the anterior funiculus. It may distribute throughout the length of the cord, though in man the majority of fibers terminate in cervical and thoracic levels. Some of the fibers are thought to cross finally in the anterior white commissure before synapsing, but many end ipsilaterally. Cases have been described in which no pyramidal decussation occurred. In some individuals the ventral tract is the larger; in others it has been almost nonexistent.

The termination of corticospinal fibers is chiefly contralateral, as seen from the decussations; fibers in the ventrolateral and ventral bundles, especially, end ipsilaterally. The fibers terminate in several ways, if evidence from animal experimentation can be transferred to man: directly about the large multipolar motor cells in the anterior gray; about an intercalary neuron in the lateral basal portion of the posterior gray (reticular nucleus), which then projects to a motor neuron directly or indirectly; about an intercalary neuron in the intermediate gray, which in turn projects to a motor neuron; about neurons of Clarke's column. When the motor area is removed from macaque or chimpanzee and the termination of cortico-

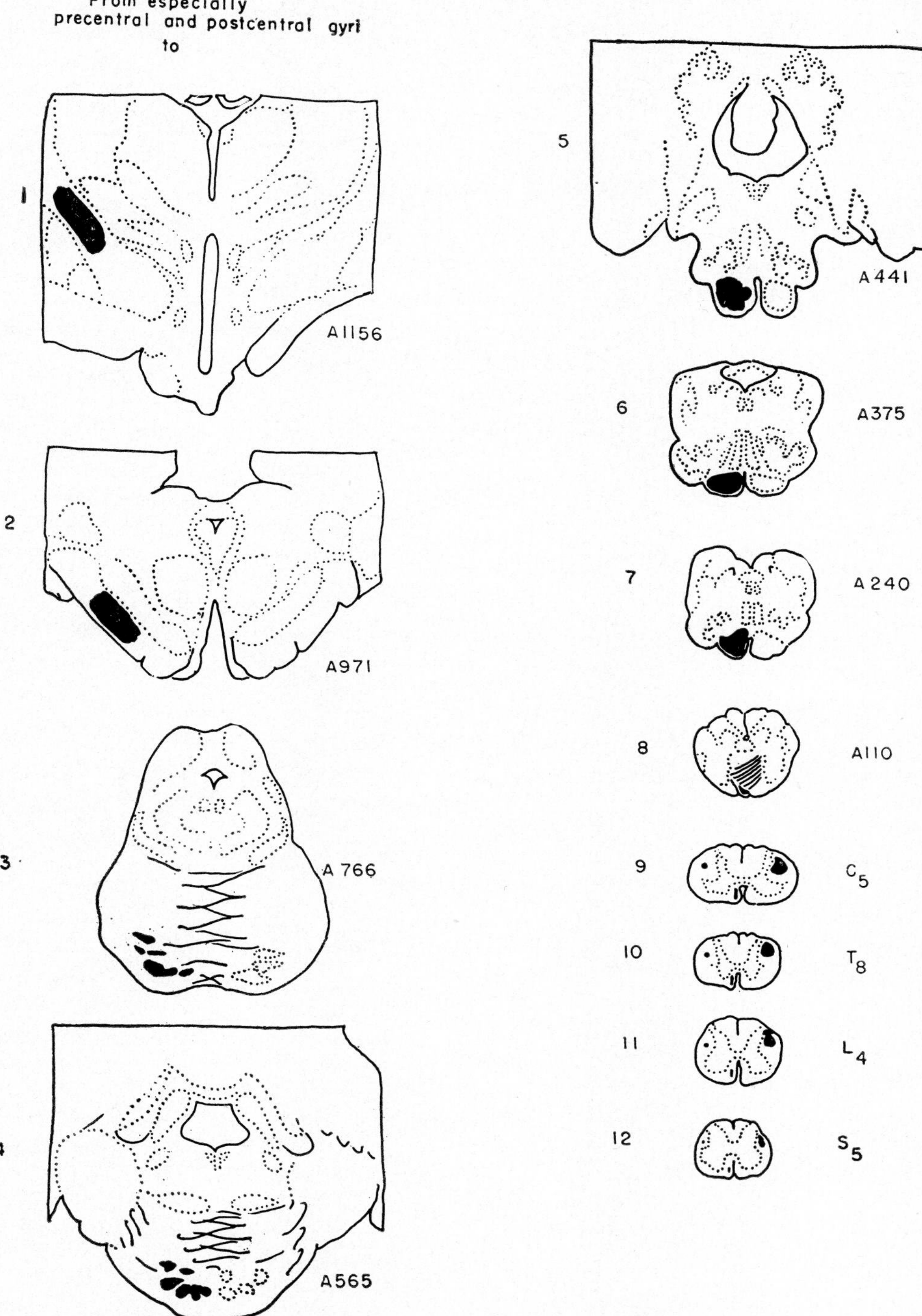

FIG. 90. Diagram of the corticospinal tracts. The ventrolateral tract (of Barnes) is not shown. The serial numbers, such as A 1156, refer to the sections of a human brain stem series.

spinal fibers determined by the study of terminal-button degeneration, the loci are found in intermediate and ventral gray. Those terminating in intermediate gray appear more prominent (377).

The corticospinal tracts are composed of large and small, myelinated fibers, the latter being more numerous. The largest fibers arise from the largest cells in the fifth cortical layer, so-called Betz cells, and transmit impulses for initiation of volitional movement in individual or small groups of skeletal muscles, particularly those moving the hands, fingers, feet, and toes. The corticospinal impulses are facilitative for the spinal motor neurons. Inability to contract selectively the muscles of the distal parts of the extremities and hypotonia are the most striking disturbances resulting from injury to these tracts such as commonly occurs in a so-called "stroke." This deficit and other results of corticospinal-tract injury are described in detail in Chap. 16.

In the transmission of an impulse for volitional movement of trunk or limb muscles at least two, and usually three or more, neurons are involved, as outlined above. The first neuron is located in the cerebral cortex and, with its axon, is commonly referred to as the **upper motor neuron.** The second and third, or more, neurons are located in a spinal-cord segment, depending on the destination of the impulse for movement to arm, hand, trunk, leg, or foot. The second, third, or fourth neuron is a large multipolar neuron in the anterior gray columns, and together with its axon constitutes the **lower motor neuron** or the **final common path of Sherrington.** It comes by the latter name through the fact that the axon of the anterior gray motor neuron is the only pathway by which impulses for movement may reach a given muscle fiber from a given neuron. The final, anterior gray motor neuron, however, receives impulses from many sources: from incoming posterior root fibers or intercalary neurons about which they synapse; from neurons in the posterior and intermediate gray which serve as intercalaries for the descending corticospinal tracts, or from the corticospinal fibers directly; and from fibers in other descending motor tracts now to be described, or from intercalary neurons about which these tracts terminate (Fig. 101).

The rubrospinal tract (Fig. 91). This tract arises from the large cells of the **red nucleus** of the midbrain and decussates at once after leaving the nucleus. It descends in a lateral position through the tegmentum of the brain stem and takes up a spinal-cord position just ventral to the lateral corticospinal tract (Fig. 81). It is said to terminate about neurons in intermediate gray. The rubrospinal tract is smaller in man than in lower animals and is perhaps in man not a very important direct extrapyramidal projection path. It appears to end in thoracic levels (758). The red nuclei may influence spinal neurons in large measure indirectly, acting through certain reticular nuclei of the brain stem. In animals its impulses acting via spinal neurons serve in the proper distribution of muscle tone and in the coordination and alternation of contractions in groups of muscles. Whether the rubrospinal fibers belong to the facilitative or inhibitory groups of motor fibers has not been determined.

Reticulospinal tracts (Figs. 81, 92). These are at least two in number (592). Throughout the brain stem tegmentum are continuous groups of cells many of which possess short processes. These usually occupy the medial portion of the dorsal half of the brain stem, or tegmentum, and they are collectively grouped as the **reticular formation** or **reticular nuclei.** At certain levels these neurons are so arranged that they form discrete nuclei (see Chap. 11). In the medulla at the level of entrance of the eighth nerve and at the level of the motor nuclei of the vagus, discrete medial reticular nuclei are located, and these contribute fibers to the **medial reticulospinal tracts** of the two sides. Reticular nuclei in the pons also contribute to these paths. Certain of the fibers of the medial reticulospinal tracts end on the side of origin, others cross; they travel near the median raphe of the brain stem in company with, but lateral to, the medial longitudinal fasciculus, enter the spinal cord in the anterior funiculus especially, and become scattered among the associative tracts there. They synapse directly about anterior gray column motor cells or about internuncial neurons located in the anterior gray.

At the level of the motor nucleus of the trigeminal nerve, especially, other discrete reticular nuclei give rise to the **lateral reti-**

culospinal tract. These fibers chiefly are crossed and hold a ventromedial position throughout most of the brain stem tegmentum. In the lower medulla, they lie just ventral to the rubrospinal tract and enter the cord in a position ventromedial to the lateral corticospinal and rubrospinal tracts. These fibers end chiefly about motor and internuncial cells in the anterior gray columns. Some fibers following the course of this lateral reticulospinal tract, however, have been described as ending about autonomic motor neurons in the intermediate gray

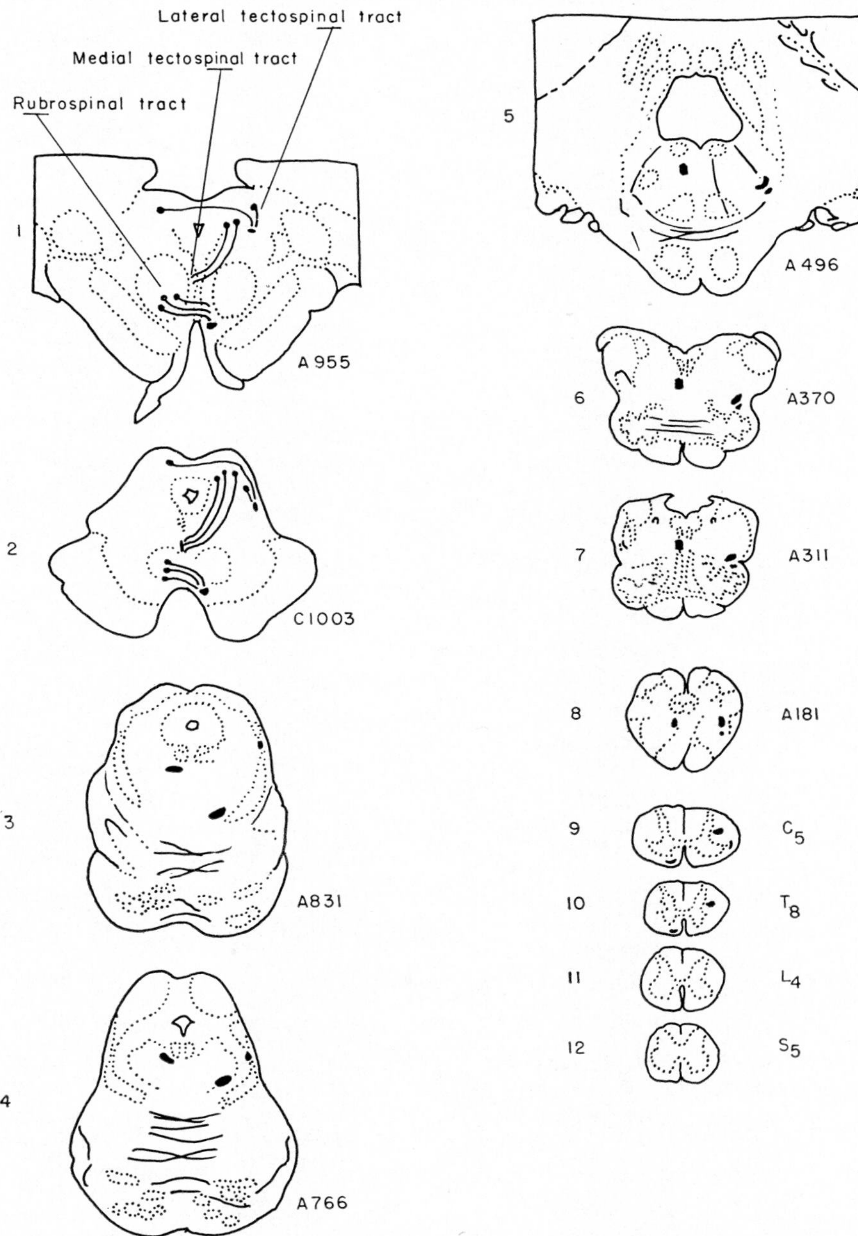

FIG. 91. Diagram of the rubrospinal and tectospinal tracts. The rubrospinal tract, as a continuous path, does not pass below thoracic levels. The serial numbers, such as A 955, refer to the sections of a human brain stem series.

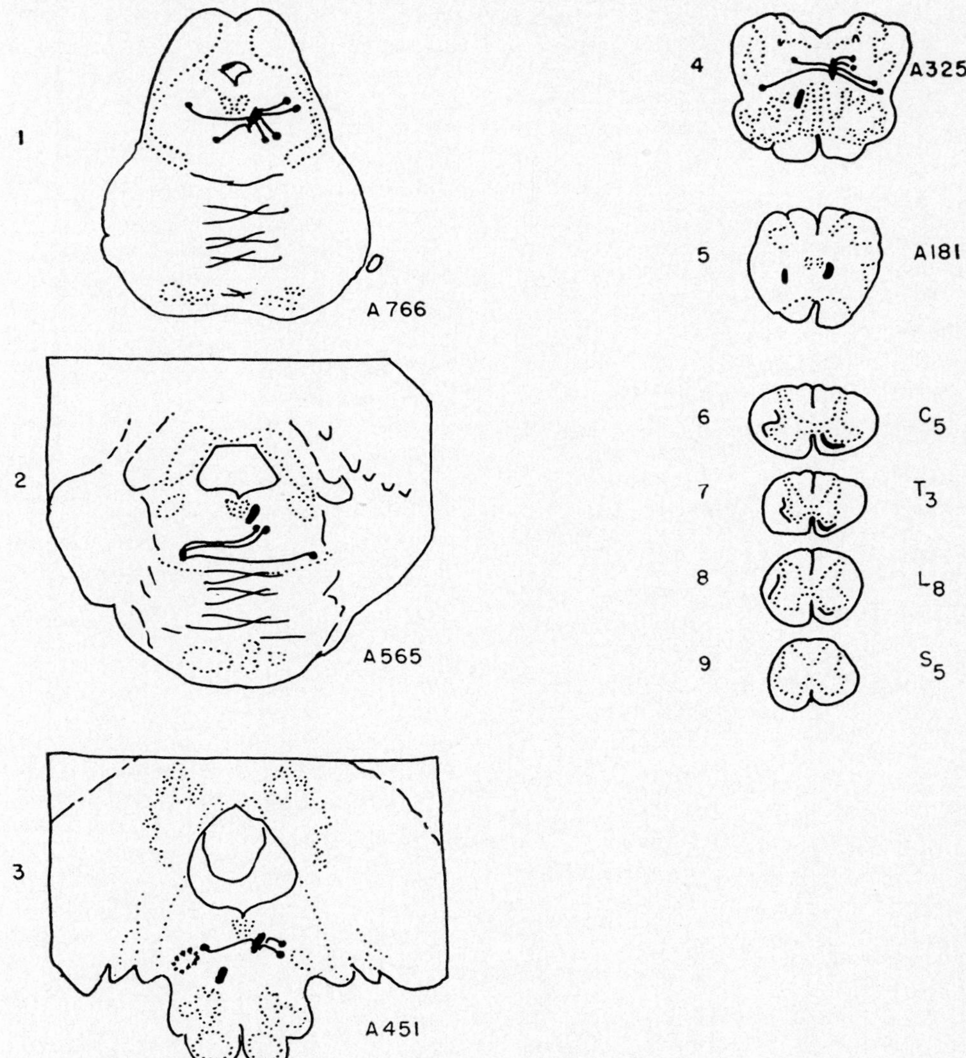

FIG. 92. Diagram of the medial and lateral reticulospinal pathways. Medial reticulospinal tract (right side of spinal cord) arises from medial and lateral reticular nuclei at midbrain, pontine, and medullar levels to descend, mostly uncrossed, into the ventral funiculus of the spinal cord. Lateral reticulospinal tract (left side of spinal cord) arises from medial and lateral reticular nuclei at midpontine level, crosses, and descends as far as lumbar levels, in the lateral funiculus of the spinal cord. The serial numbers, such as A 766, refer to the sections of a human brain stem series.

columns. Impulses traversing those fibers terminating about motor neurons in the anterior cell columns and about internuncial neurons are important in the coordination of skeletal movement involving large groups of muscles and are of great importance in the maintenance of, and distribution of, proper amounts of muscle tone (see Chap. 17).

In the analysis of reticulospinal tracts with reference to their influence on spinal motor neural mechanisms, it was found that certain of them transmit facilitative impulses and others inhibitory impulses. The medial reticulospinal tracts perhaps transmit the majority of the inhibitory impulses. The fibers transmitting inhibitory influences arise from a medullar reticular center and pass into both anterior and lateral funiculi of the spinal cord, especially the former. In the cat, at least, the medullar inhibitory center of one side may exert influence on both sides of the spinal cord via reticulospinal fibers. A spinal decussation for certain of these inhibitory impulses has been described. The facilitatory reticulospinal fibers have a more diffuse brain stem origin, arising from each level. In the spinal cord they travel especially in the ventral half of the lateral funiculus. Both brain stem and spinal crossings are made by these fibers in the cat. The reticulospinal fibers are widely scattered in the ventral and lateral funiculi in the cat. Overlapping of facilitative and inhibitory fibers exists, but in general, facilitative ones have a posterior concentration, while inhibitory fibers are more dense anteriorly (582).

Certain reticulospinal fibers form the central efferent limb of paths for certain reflex acts such as respiration and vomiting. Many of these reflex fibers may be grouped as a **solitariospinal tract** which runs with the reticulospinal fibers. They arise from the **nucleus** of the **tractus solitarius** and adjacent neurons in the medulla and are crossed and uncrossed. How far they descend into the spinal cord in man is not known, but apparently they terminate in the cord in a manner similar to the corticospinal fibers. In the future, when the large mass of fibers, now grouped under the name reticulospinal, is further analyzed, many discrete component tracts may be listed.

Tectospinal tracts (Figs. 81, 91). These arise from the neurons in and adjacent to the colliculi, cross over, and descend into the cord as **medial** and **lateral tectospinal** tracts, so-called because the collicular region is known also as the tectum. The colliculi are optic and auditory reflex centers. The lateral tectospinal tract is thought to be a spinal continuation of a tectopontine tract of the upper brain stem. This latter tract arises from neurons laterally placed in the superior colliculus and contains crossed and uncrossed fibers (Fig. 91). The tract is placed laterally to the brachium conjunctivum and for a part of its course it is quite peripherally located in the brain stem. It moves into the ventrolateral tegmental region in the rostral medulla and holds such a position as it runs spinalward. The majority of the medial tectospinal fibers cross in the dorsal tegmental decussation of the midbrain soon after their origin and hold a median tegmental position through the brain stem. The medial tract is ventromedial to the anterior gray columns in the anterior funiculus of the spinal cord, near the anterior median fissure; it terminates in cervical and thoracic levels. The lateral is in the ventral part of the lateral funiculus just lateral to the anterior gray columns; it terminates chiefly in cervical levels. Both tracts terminate about anterior column cells or internuncials and transmit impulses for skeletal postural movements in response to auditory and visual stimuli (423). Their facilitative or inhibitory quality has not been analyzed; they are perhaps facilitative. Some fibers having a course and position similar to that of the medial tract have been described as ending about sympathetic neurons in the lateral intermediate gray columns, especially in upper thoracic levels. They would thus probably compose a link in the reflex paths serving pupillodilation in response to darkness (see Chap. 21).

Vestibulospinal tracts (Figs. 81, 93). These are two in number, one of which, the lateral, is distinct in position; the other, the medial, is closely associated—in its spinal course, at least—with the medial longitudinal fasciculus, and some authors do not separate the two. These tracts are not so prominent or so important, apparently, in man as they are in animals, and little accurate information exists with regard to them in man. The fibers of the **lateral vestibulospinal tract** arise from the lateral vestibular nucleus of Deiters, and in the medulla they are placed dorsolateral to the inferior olive (Fig. 93). They enter the spinal cord, remaining on the side of origin, and descend in the anterior white columns. The fibers end about anterior column cells or internuncials at all levels of the spinal cord.

The fibers of the **medial vestibulospinal tract** arise from lateral, spinal, and medial vestibular nuclei; many of them cross the mid-line soon after their origin, and enter the spinal cord in the ventromedial portion of the anterior funiculus in company with the fibers of the medial longitudinal fasciculus. They synapse about anterior column cells or internuncials in the cervical cord predominantly. The lateral of these two tracts, at least, transmits impulses for regulation of, and promotion of, muscle

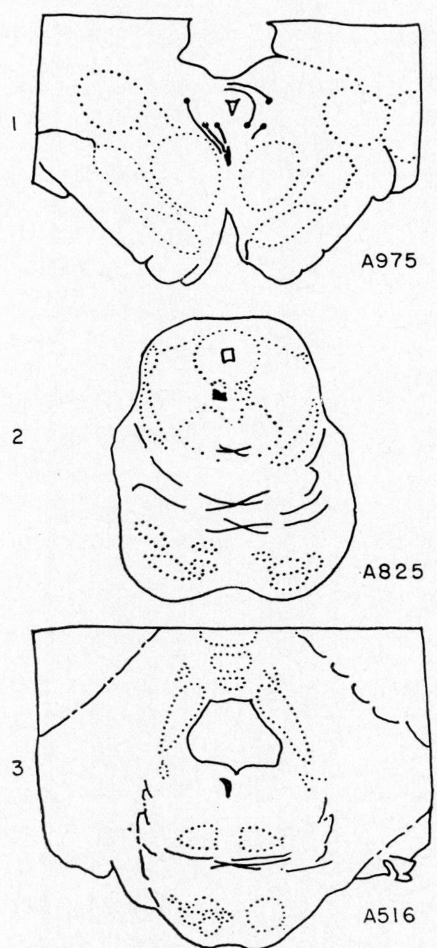

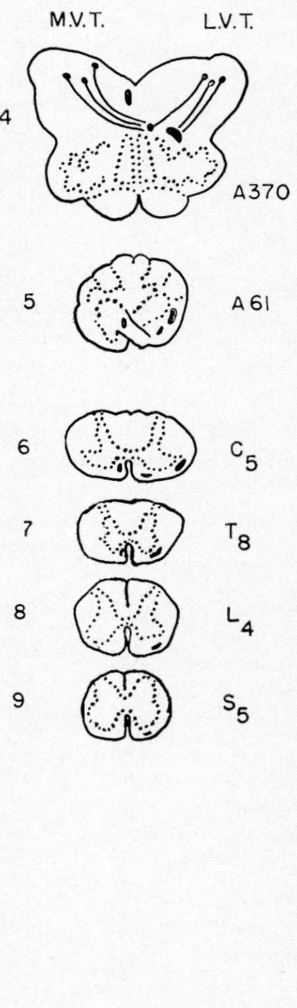

FIG. 93. Diagram of the medial longitudinal fasciculus, medial and lateral vestibulospinal pathways. *M.V.T.*, medial vestibulospinal tract crossed from origin in medial, lateral, and spinal nuclei with some uncrossed fibers from lateral nucleus. *L.V.T.*, lateral vestibulospinal tract descends uncrossed from origin in the lateral vestibular nucleus. The serial numbers, such as A 975, refer to the sections of a human brain stem series.

tone. With the medial tract, it also transmits impulses for carrying out reflex postural movements in response to proprioceptive stimuli arising within the labyrinth (see Chap. 10). It has been thought that the cutting of these tracts in cats causes "spinal shock" (discussion later). The impulses traveling over the lateral vestibulospinal tract are facilitative for the spinal motor mechanisms (41). The medial, though not analyzed as such, may be a component of the inhibitory mechanisms.

Medial longitudinal fasciculus. This is a great coordinating and associating system of fibers running through brain stem and spinal cord. It has been alluded to above as a component of the spinal associative tracts. In the brain stem it contains both ascending and descending fibers (see Chap. 10). In the spinal cord descending fibers predominate. The fibers are placed in a ventromedial portion of the anterior funiculus, between the anterior gray columns and the anterior median fissure, and serve as short-chained paths as a part of the ventral proprius bundles. Associated with the medial longitudinal fasciculus in its brain stem course, but somewhat separated in the spinal cord, are the interstitiospinal and commissurospinal fibers (Figs. 81, 93). The **interstitiospinal tract** is uncrossed and arises from the interstitial nucleus of Cajal in the dorsal tegmentum of the midbrain. The **commissurospinal fibers arise** from the nucleus of the posterior commissure and from the nucleus of Darkschewitsch, just ventral. Both tracts enter the spinal cord in the most medial part of the anterior funiculus and are frequently called collectively the **sulcomarginal tract.** Some investigators group the medial tectospinal and medial vestibulospinal tracts with the medial longitudinal fasciculus also.

Olivospinal tract. The olivospinal tract arises from the inferior olivary nucleus and descends in the ventral part of the lateral funiculus near the surface of the spinal cord (Fig. 81). It is distributed to the motor neurons supplying the neck musculature. Its facilitative or inhibitory qualities have not been analyzed. It is probably facilitatory. It may represent an important relay in the projection of the basal ganglia to the spinal motor neurons, since these ganglia send many impulses through reticular relays to the inferior olivary nucleus.

DESCENDING AUTONOMIC PATHWAYS

That the autonomic motor cells in the lateral half of the intermediate gray columns and in the thoracic, upper lumbar, and mid-sacral cord levels are under control of higher autonomic centers is well understood. The higher centers are located in the cerebral cortex, hypothalamus, and certain reticular nuclei of the medulla and pons. Crossing of fibers in the descending tracts occurs at upper brain stem and spinal levels. The pathways over which they exert their control on spinal neurons have not been identified as yet as distinct tracts in the spinal cord. They are located especially in the anterolateral funiculi at a cervical level (143, 520, 812, 814). It is quite likely that such fibers may take part in a long series of short-chain systems and that they may also be small and poorly myelinated, thus making their identification difficult. It is through observation of patients with spinal-cord damage, naturally or surgically induced, that an approximate position of descending autonomic tracts has been learned and will be further clarified (254).

From the "respiratory" center in the medulla, impulses pass by way of the solitariospinal tract and possibly also by short-chained reticulospinal fibers (see Chap. 7). These fibers descend in the anterior funiculus and anterior portion of the lateral funiculus, on the basis of evidence obtained in animals, and they terminate about neurons innervating intercostal muscles, the diaphragm, and bronchiolar smooth muscle.

The autonomic tracts to spinal-cord neurons for innervation of the smooth muscle of **bladder** and **rectum** contain crossed and uncrossed fibers; they run in the anterior funiculi and the anterior portion of the lateral funiculi. Crossing occurs in upper brain stem and lumbar levels (520). The pathways to neurons involved in genital reflexes are thought to be similar to those of bladder and rectum. The descending fibers from the cerebral cortex for innervation of the external sphincters of bladder and rectum are closely associated with the corticospinal tracts (513). The fibers promoting **vasoconstrictor** processes and **sweat secretion** are in the anterior part of the lateral funiculus and are anterior to the general area of the lateral corticospinal tracts. The fibers for the legs are anterior and lateral; those for the arms, anterior and medial, between corticospinal fibers and the gray cell columns (254). **Pupillary dilator** fibers and **thermoregulatory** fibers are in the lateral and anterolateral columns of the spinal cord and are almost exclusively uncrossed at spinal levels. In fact, any crossings occurring in these systems appear to take place at upper brain stem levels. The fibers for **innervation** of **bronchial musculature** are diffusely scattered in the spinal cord and are apparently not limited to the anterior and lateral funiculi.

It is quite possible that "reticulospinal" fibers, described as terminating about cells in the lateral intermediate gray columns, form in

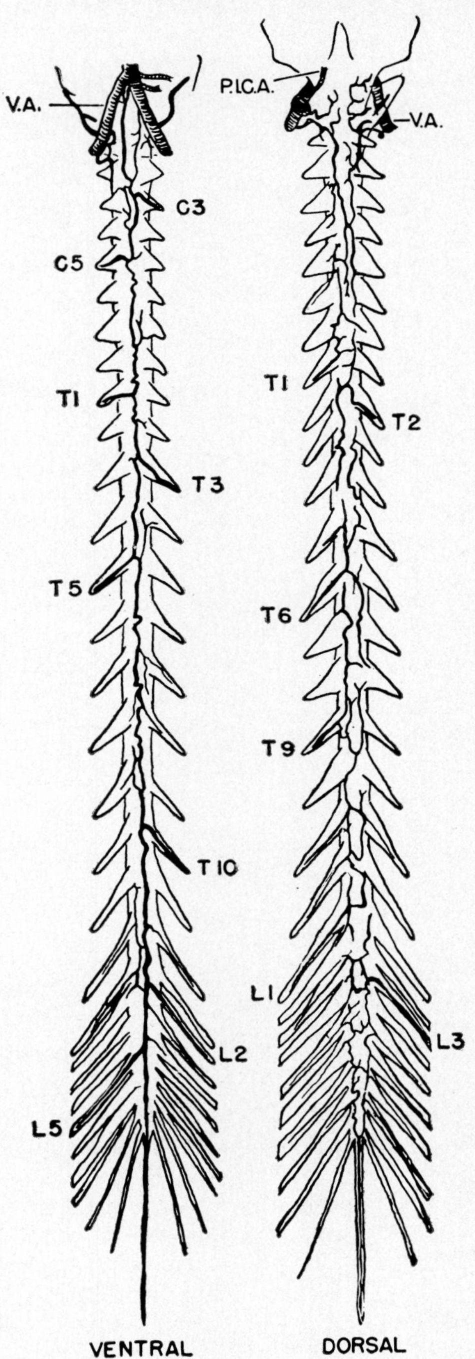

FIG. 94. Diagram of the arterial supply of the human spinal cord. A single anterior spinal artery is shown on the ventral surface, this arising from the vertebrals and being reinforced by branches of significant radicular vessels entering at the levels indicated. On the dorsal surface two discontinuous posterior spinal arteries are shown, arising from vertebral or posterior inferior cerebellar arteries and being reinforced by branches of significant radicular vessels entering at the levels indicated. (*After Suh and Alexander, Arch. Neurol. & Psychiat. vol.* 41.)

fact a large component of the descending autonomic tracts. The reticulospinal system is a diffuse one arising from neurons at many levels, and it may well encompass many autonomic tracts, including "respiratory tracts." Certainly, evidence has been presented that various autonomic activities are disturbed when injury occurs to tracts diffusely scattered in the brain stem tegmentum; in time, the individual tracts will no doubt be identified.

BLOOD VESSELS OF THE SPINAL CORD

THE ARTERIAL SUPPLY

The spinal cord is nourished through branches from the vertebral artery, from the posterior inferior cerebellar artery, and from regional vessels arising from thoracic and abdominal aorta. Branches of the deep cervical, intercostal, lumbar, and lateral sacral arteries take part in the supply. From all these vessels, **lateral spinal arteries** arise and enter the intervertebral foramina. These lateral spinal arteries supply the vertebrae, the periosteum, and the neighboring dura mater in addition to dividing into **anterior** and **posterior radicular arteries.**

Within the cranium a small artery arises from each vertebral artery and runs caudally along the ventral surface of the medulla (Figs. 94, 141). These two descending arteries usually unite to form a single vessel near the rostral end of the spinal cord. This single trunk is continued as the **anterior spinal artery,** and it runs caudally within the anterior longitudinal sulcus. As it descends it is joined by the **anterior radicular arteries** entering from each side; these divide into cephalad and caudad branches which make the anterior spinal artery a continuous trunk. Although anterior radicular arteries may enter with nearly every anterior root, it is usually true that only six to eight of them on both sides together are of a size sufficient to carry a significant amount of blood to the spinal-cord substance (357, 768). The distribution of the significant radicular arteries varies, but the largest one most frequently enters with the left second lumbar root. Two significant anterior radicular arteries are usually present in the cervical levels, three in the thoracic levels, and two in the lumbar levels.

From the anterior spinal artery smaller vessels, the **sulcal arteries,** arise to run into the spinal-cord substance. Altogether about two hundred of these entering vessels are present throughout the length of the spinal cord. A single vessel supplies either the right or left side of the spinal cord, and successive sulcal arteries do not necessarily alternate in the territory of supply, right and left (Fig. 95). Rarely, left and right branches arise from a single sulcal artery. The caliber of the anterior spinal artery varies at different levels. It is also probably true that the direction of predominant blood flow, cephalad or caudad, varies at the several levels in which the anterior radicular arteries join the anterior longitudinal arterial trunk with their ascending and descending branches.

Once within the spinal cord, the entering sulcal arteries, right and left, branch into successively smaller radicles, the **intramedullary vessels.** The plane of distribution of the longer intramedullary arteries is predominantly transverse in the sacral and lumbar regions, predominantly longitudinal in the thoracic region, and about midway between these two planes in the cervical region. The thoracic region is, therefore, relatively poorly supplied. The intramedullary branches of the anterior spinal artery supply the gray commissures, Clarke's dorsal nuclear column, the anterior and lateral gray columns, and the anterior and lateral funiculi. In addition to these intramedullary branches, other branches of the anterior spinal artery, **coronal arteries,** are found at many spinal-cord levels. They run circularly outside the spinal cord on its anterolateral aspect to supply peripheral white matter in the anterolateral funiculi (Fig. 95).

Also within the cranium small branches arise either from the vertebral or posterior inferior cerebellar arteries and pass caudally along the posterior medulla surface into the spinal cord. These vessels are usually continued caudad as separate trunks, the **posterior spinal arteries,** and they run along just medial to the line of entrance of the posterior spinal roots. Connecting branches may join the two posterior spinal trunks, and either vessel may have interruptions in its continuity. Long, continuous posterior spinal arteries are infrequent.

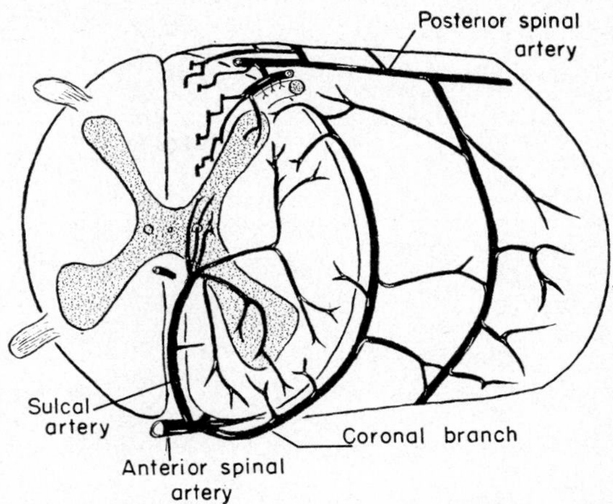

Fig. 95. Diagram of intrinsic arterial supply of the human spinal cord. (*Redrawn after Herren and Alexander, Arch. Neurol. & Psychiat., vol.* 41.)

The **posterior radicular arteries** of significant size number from five to eight, including those of both sides, throughout the spinal-cord length. Again, the largest vessel is usually present at an upper lumbar level, and the plan of distribution of the posterior radicular arteries follows that of the anterior radicular arteries. Branches of the radicular arteries follow the root fibers into the spinal cord substance, and terminal ascending and descending branches contribute to the posterior spinal arterial trunk. Branches from these trunks pass into the spinal substance in steplike fashion. From the posterior radicular arteries and their contribution to the posterior longitudinal trunk, the posterior white columns and the posterior gray, exclusive of Clarke's column, are supplied (Figs. 94, 95).

Spinal Veins

The pattern of the **veins** draining the spinal cord is similar to that of the arteries (Figs. 96, 97). Six to eleven **anterior radicular veins** of significant size are distributed in nonsymmetric fashion. They usually do not leave the spinal cord by the same roots on which the larger radicular arteries enter. Usually one larger vein is present in the lumbar region, and the others are scattered along the length of the spinal cord in a fashion similar to the

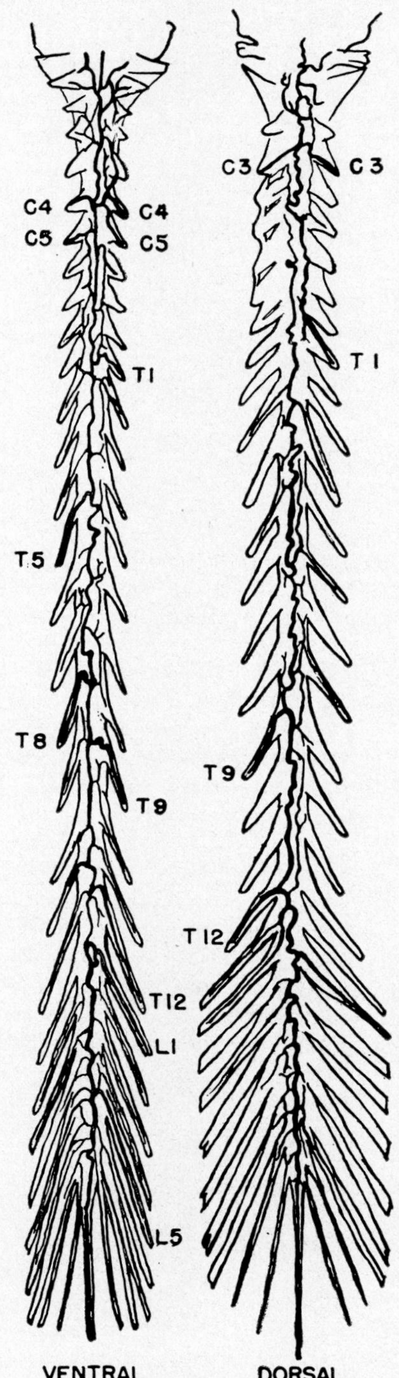

Fig. 96. Diagram of the venous drainage of the human spinal cord. At spinal levels the blood is drained by significant radicular veins at the levels indicated. (*After Suh and Alexander, Arch. Neurol. & Psychiat., vol.*, 41.)

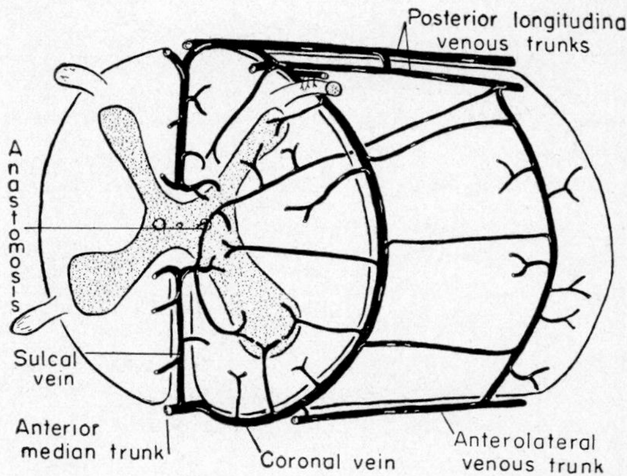

Fig. 97. Diagram of the intrinsic venous drainage of the human spinal cord. (*Redrawn after Herren and Alexander, Arch. Neurol. & Psychiat., vol.* 41.)

arteries. An **anterior longitudinal venous trunk** connects the radicular veins, and it is usually to one side of, and just dorsal to, the anterior arterial trunk. Anterolateral longitudinal venous trunks are also present. There are fewer **sulcal veins** than there are arteries, and they do not run in pairs with each sulcal artery as do the venae comitantes elsewhere in the body. Each sulcal vein, however, usually drains both sides of the spinal cord. The sulcal veins drain the anterior and medial intermediate gray columns and the medial anterior white columns. Frequently a sulcal vein sends an anastomotic branch from the region about the central canal to the posterolateral surface of the spinal cord to join a posterior venous trunk at the same level. This anastomotic branch is thought to serve for equalization of venous pressure, when alterations exist in one or the other of the venous streams.

Posteriorly a mid-line venous trunk is usually present and occasionally a posterolateral one also. Sulcal veins draining both sides of the spinal cord in the region of the posterior commissure, posterior white columns, posterior gray columns, and Clarke's column enter the mid-line posterior venous trunk. The anterior and posterior longitudinal venous trunks are connected by large veins which circle the spinal cord on either side, and these in turn drain the white matter in the anterior and lateral funiculi as well as the lateral and anterior gray columns.

The syndrome of **anterior spinal artery**

thrombosis usually can be diagnosed if the blood supply of the spinal cord is recalled. This syndrome includes a loss of motor power bilaterally in those muscles innervated by segments below the level of thrombosis, together with bilateral impairment of appreciation of pain and temperature stimuli, but with preservation of tactile sense and deep sensibility. Cutaneous pain and temperature sensibilities are, however, usually not completely lost because penetrating branches of the coronal vessels supply the peripherally placed fibers of spinothalamic tracts. The more caudal dermatomes usually show some sparing, therefore. Urinary and rectal sphincter disorders also usually occur.

MECHANISMS OF SPINAL-CORD NEURAL ACTIVITY. SOME PHYSIOLOGICAL PRINCIPLES OF IMPULSE CONDUCTION IN THE SPINAL CORD AND CENTRAL NERVOUS SYSTEM

In an earlier chapter certain characteristics of conduction of the nerve impulse in nerve fibers have been considered; the information was based on studies of peripheral nerves. It is not amiss to include here, therefore, a brief discussion of conduction in reflex arcs and in the spinal cord. Though the neuronal patterns and chains in the central nervous system are complex as compared to a peripheral nerve, the fundamental features of conduction in the two are probably similar. Studies of reflex arcs and spinal-cord pathways, electrically and physiologically, in spinal animals have served to furnish much information (726).

Physiological Interrelationships of Spinal Neurons

Spinal-cord neurons are under the influence of peripheral end organs as well as supraspinal neurons. These latter exert their influence through the descending pathways previously described. The integration and effector activity produced by spinal-cord neurons at any time depends to a great extent on the influence of peripheral and supraspinal mechanisms. The electrical studies of Lloyd and Eccles, especially, have served to elucidate the functional organization of the spinal cord (106, 228, 490, 491, 492, 493).

So-called **simple spinal reflex arcs** involve two or three neurons at least (Fig. 98). In a two-neuron arc the individual parts would be a sensory receptor; a dendrite; its parent neuron in the posterior root ganglion; an axon, or its collateral, of the ganglion neuron; the axon terminals about the body or dendrites of the anterior motor cell; the anterior gray motor neuron; the axon of the motor neuron; the endings of the axon about a skeletal muscle fiber; and the muscle fiber. In a three-neuron or multineuron arc, one or many **internuncial neurons** would be interposed between the central process of the posterior root ganglion cell and the anterior motor cell. Many reflex arcs formed by medial division posterior root fibers involve only two neurons; those formed by lateral division root fibers are most often multineuron arcs.

Though conduction may occur in either direction along a nerve fiber, axon or dendrite, conduction in life over a reflex arc is in only one direction: from sensory neuron to motor neuron and thence to motor neuron ending. Conduction within the spinal cord, or central conduction, is also slower than conduction along either the afferent or efferent nerve fiber, and this slowness is in great part apparently due to delay at the synapse between incoming posterior root fiber and anterior motor neuron. Since only a few incoming posterior root fibers (or their collaterals) end directly about anterior motor cells, and most of them have collaterals ending around internuncial neurons, it is likely that most spinal reflexes, except the myotatic ones described below, involve at least three neurons and probably more.

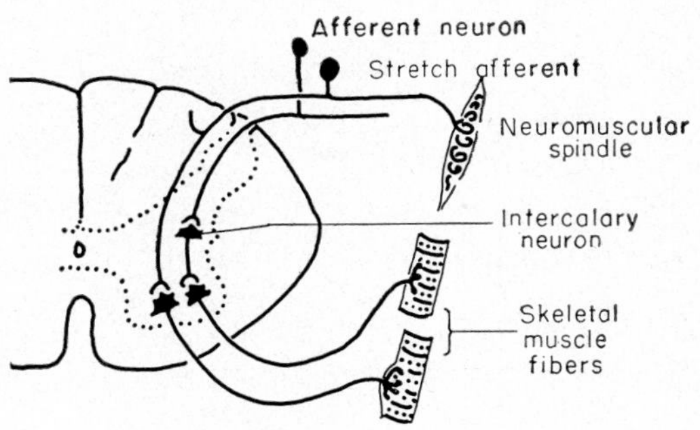

Fig. 98. Diagram of simple reflex arcs.

Similarly, collaterals of any one posterior root fiber may terminate about many internuncial neurons, and the body and dendrites of an anterior motor cell may have synaptic relations with processes of many root fibers and internuncial neurons. So-called "pools of neurons" are involved in much of the activity initiated as a result of impulses entering over posterior root fibers. In "neuron pools," probably much overlap exists in the terminations of incoming afferent fibers and descending motor fibers, as well as of the intrinsic spinal fibers.

CENTRAL EXCITATION

As yet no agreement has been reached on the mechanisms involved in transmission of impulses through central nervous system synapses. Lloyd describes two components involved in the **excitation** at the synapse with a motor neuron when an excitatory volley is sent in over an afferent fiber (493). The first is a brief, powerful one, capable of stimulation of the motor neurons, and is known as the detonator action. The second component is of longer duration and is less powerful but is capable of complementing or facilitating the action of the first component; this Lloyd calls "residual facilitation." Eccles considers synaptic transmission in excitation to involve a more gradual train of events (227). The posterior root fiber, or presynaptic, impulses set up local responses of the postsynaptic membrane (motor-neuron membrane) immediately under the synaptic knobs (terminal buttons), and thence activity spreads to the remaining surface membrane of the motor neuron. When the local responses create sufficient involvement in an area of the cell membrane, an impulse develops and spreads throughout the cell plasma and down the axon. If the local responses do not create sufficient activity they gradually die out.

CENTRAL INHIBITION

Mechanisms involved in **inhibition** in the central nervous system are also not completely understood. Lloyd has studied inhibition in two-neuron-arc systems. He believes that inhibition can be initiated by impulses traversing afferent fibers similar to the fibers that create excitation of motor neurons. He sees inhibition as an active process in itself leading to a depression of excitability of a neuron. Inhibition is commonly involved in the neural mechanisms utilized in walking, for example, or in practically any skilled movement. Certain muscles actively contract while others relax in a pattern of reciprocal innervation; other muscles, the synergists, cooperate in the activity with the contractors. The quadriceps femoris and biceps femoris, for example, are antagonistic in their activity about the knee joint. Lloyd describes the following sequence of events when an afferent volley arises in the nerve of a part of the quadriceps (494). If the volley is above threshold for the motor neurons of this quadriceps part, these are caused to discharge. The motor neurons supplying the other parts of the quadriceps are facilitated, as are those of other cooperating or synergistic muscles. The activity of motor neurons supplying the biceps is, however, inhibited. The inhibitory activity is transmitted over a monosynaptic path, according to Lloyd, the impulses traversing posterior root fibers or collaterals to reach the motor nuclei supplying the biceps. This inhibitory volley is in opposition to an excitatory volley reaching the biceps over its own afferent fiber.

Eccles called Golgi neurons into play in his first theory of inhibition (106, 227). The Golgi type II interneurons can serve as inhibitors under certain conditions, as excitators under others. Inhibitory impulses passing into a Golgi cell create activity in the synaptic knobs which it has with motor neurons. Unless the impulses are of a certain strength, a discharge is not set off but areas of anelectrotonus are set up in the motor neuron's cell membrane under the synaptic knobs. Excitatory impulses traversing an afferent fiber ending directly about the motor neuron set up local excitatory responses in the motor-neuron membrane. These, however, would be vitiated through spread into, or fusion with, the anelectrotonic areas set up by the Golgi knobs. Inhibition would thus occur. If the inhibitory volley to the Golgi cells created enough activity in them to cause their discharge into the motor neuron, the initial inhibition effect would give way to excitation, and this would be added to the excitation set up by the excitatory monosynaptic arc. Eccles now finds fault in this Golgi-cell theory. By measuring intracellular potentials he has studied direct inhibition of motor neurons. He believes that a specific transmitter substance is liberated from the inhibitory synaptic knobs. This causes an increase in polarization of the membrane of the motor neuron. Similarly, he thinks that synaptic excitatory action depends on a specific transmitter substance. The transmitter substances have not been identified although acetylcholine has been considered.

SUMMATION—SPATIAL

The activity of these "neuron pools" of Golgi cells serves best to explain certain other physiological concepts of neural activity, *e.g.*, **spatial summation.** Afferent impulses arriving in a neuron pool may stimulate certain neurons in the pool liminally (at threshold) causing them to discharge. Other neurons in the pool will be subliminally stimulated. Summation occurs when the subliminal stimulation thus caused by one group of afferent impulses is sufficient to bring that produced by a second group of afferent impulses to the threshold level. The number of motor neurons thus brought to discharge at any one time and the consequent magnitude of the reflex contraction produced thereby are determined by summation.

FACILITATION

This characteristic is frequently observed in central conduction, and this too involves "neuron pools." A stimulus of a certain strength may be sent into a motor neuron directly from a posterior root fiber. Through other collaterals of the posterior root fiber the stimulus also passes into internuncial neurons which are in synaptic contact with the motor neuron. The motor neuron may discharge by virtue of the stimulus reaching it directly and give a response of a certain magnitude. A second stimulus of similar strength to the first, however, may elicit a discharge of greater magnitude from the same motor neuron. The second impulse from the root fiber apparently reaches the motor neuron simultaneously with the impulse set up in the internuncial pools by the first stimulus (these were delayed by the additional synapse involved) and the combined result of the converging impulses is a discharge of greater magnitude. Internuncial neurons or circuits may sustain activity within their pool for some time after an impulse enters the pools from any source. By bombarding effector units with small impulses repeatedly, they may create and promote the readiness of certain effector neurons to respond to sudden incoming impulses from another source. Posterior root impulses from the periphery may traverse internuncial connections and facilitate spinal neurons to respond to impulses descending to them over pathways from the brain stem, and the resultant motor discharge is more effective.

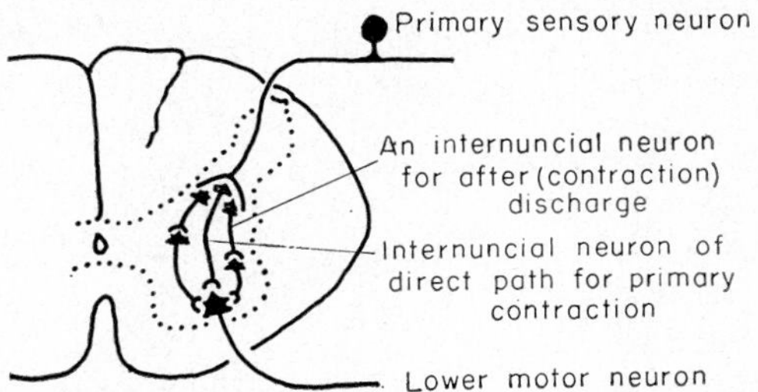

FIG. 99. Diagram to explain after-discharge.

AFTER-DISCHARGE

This phenomenon is noted in certain reflex activities. That is, a single stimulus sent into a motor neuron through internuncials may produce prolonged repetitive discharge. Such discharge results from the continuous reverberating activity in the internuncials and a repeated activation of the motor neuron thereby. Such reverberating circuits of neuronal activity are numerous in cortical neural mechanisms (Fig. 99).

RECRUITMENT

Internuncial neurons are involved in the **recruitment** exhibited in reflex discharges. A single volley sent into a neuron pool, and thence into a motor neuron, will result in a discharge of certain magnitude, and as a result of the impulses passing into the pool, a certain number of internuncials will be activated. Repeated volleys entering by posterior roots will promote activation of more and more internuncials, and their bombardment of motor neurons will be enhanced. The tension of the motor neuron responses will be slowly increased, and recruitment will occur thereby.

CONVERGENCE AND OCCLUSION

A motor neuron, as previously noted, may be in synaptic relation with several afferent nerves,

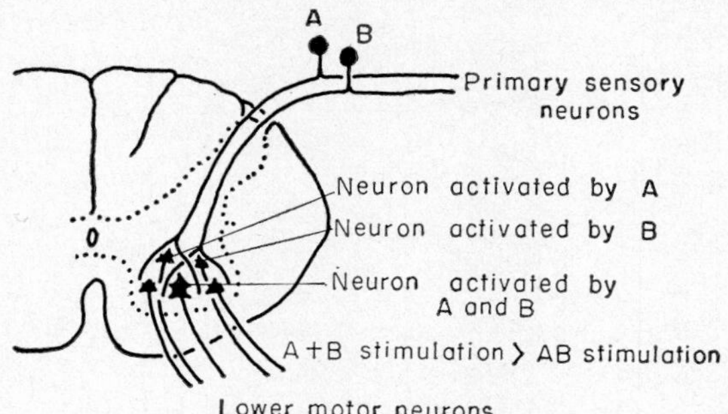

FIG. 100. Diagram to explain occlusion.

and this is the basis of the physiological **principle of convergence,** an important factor in coordinated activity in the nervous system. This central overlap is also the basis for **occlusion;** it has been shown that simultaneous impulses over two afferent fibers having connections with the same neuron pool and thus having access to a given muscle will not produce as much reflex tension as the sum of the tension produced by separate volleys of impulses over the two fibers (Fig. 100).

ORGANIZATION OF SPINAL-CORD ACTIVITY

SEGMENTAL ORGANIZATION

The reflex response of a skeletal muscle to stretch is to shorten. Such a reflex is called the **myotatic** or **stretch reflex.** This is especially well developed in those muscles which normally maintain postures against the forces of gravity, *e.g.,* the quadriceps femoris, the biceps of the upper arm in man, and the muscles which close the jaw. Flexor muscles also contract in response to stretch but do not maintain the activity. The stretch reflex is the fundamental mechanism promoting muscle tone, a condition inherent in muscle at rest, expressed simply as a posture-maintaining activity and readiness for active phasic contraction. Electrical studies have revealed that the myotatic reflex involves a two-neuron arc. The afferent limb is a large fiber of the medial division of the posterior roots having a neuromuscular spindle as end organ. It transmits impulses rapidly. The efferent limb is the anterior gray motor neuron and its axon. The stretch reflex is limited to the muscle or the part of the muscle stimulated. Other two-neuron-arc reflexes involve flexor muscle pathways.

PLURISEGMENTAL ORGANIZATION

When the medium and small myelinated posterior root fibers of either cutaneous or muscular origin are stimulated electrically the reflex response involves principally flexor muscles. The reflex discharge involves a multineuron arc, the shortest arc involving one internuncial neuron between posterior root fiber and motor neuron. A common example of the flexor reflex is the withdrawal or flexor response to painful stimulation. Through the apposition of an internuncial neuron it is possible to promote diffusion of activity and thus involve other synergically acting flexor muscles in the response. Contractions of many flexor groups together are frequently the result of painful stimulation.

Lloyd has learned that intrinsic spinal-cord mechanisms may involve long and short intersegmental, or associative, tracts (491). Long intrinsic fibers of the ventrolateral columns may relay to short ones after synapse. Lumbar motor neurons can be activated as a result of reflex stimulation of one side of the upper body. Transmission involves crossed as well as uncrossed fibers, and the neurons of the nucleus of the anterior commissure are important in the crossed conduction of long spinal reflex activity. Intersegmental fibers traversing the ventral columns are active in bilateral transmission through internuncial neurons of the commissural nucleus. Intersegmental fibers in the lateral columns transmit unilaterally. Internuncial activity arising in the lumbar cord as a result of afferent volleys to the cervical enlargement is confined to the ventral horn. The same locus is activated by descending extrapyramidal systems, as will be seen below.

The relation of spinal neurons to certain supraspinal ones has also been investigated electrically. Since these studies are best adapted in fibers of large size, the posterior columns and spinocerebellar tracts have been used thus far. Conduction in the posterior white columns is slower than that in the dorsal spinocerebellar tracts (320). The conduction rate in the cat's dorsal spinocerebellar tract was found to be almost twice that in fasciculus gracilis, and in spite of the synaptic delay involved in the spinocerebellar tract, impulses traveling those fibers reached medulla levels before those traversing the gracilis. Larger fiber size of spinocerebellar fibers was correlated with increased conduction rate. The dorsal spinocerebellar tract can be activated as a result of stimulation of the neuromuscular spindles and their large posterior root fibers, presumably the same fibers which are responsible for transmission of impulses underlying the stretch reflex. Lloyd thinks that the dorsal spinocerebellar tracts are activated simultaneously with the stretch reflexes. Clarke's column neurons, as judged by electrical studies, receive collaterals from more than one primary sensory neuron, and they are probably activated by internuncial chains of varying complexity. It should be recalled that some pyramidal-tract terminals have been traced to the vicinity of Clarke's neurons. Through such connections ascending activity, initiated in Clarke's column neurons simultaneously with the stretch reflexes, may be influenced by impulses traversing the descending pyramidal tract.

ORGANIZATION OF DESCENDING-TRACT ACTIVITY IN THE SPINAL CORD

Lloyd found differences in the sites of action in the pyramidal and extrapyramidal tracts in his electrical researches (489, 490). According to his investigations in the cat, extrapyramidal tracts including vestibulospinal and reticulospinal fibers end principally about internuncial neurons in the anterior gray and, to a less extent, directly about motor neurons. Though they exert little activity on the motor neurons directly, they have a powerful influence indirectly through the activation of many internuncial neurons. When motor neurons are discharged through the convergence of extrapyramidal influences exerted over direct fibers and the internuncial neurons, the discharge is controlled by the internuncial activity. If internuncial activity set up by primary afferent (posterior root) stimulation converges with the descending extrapyramidal tract activity, the motor-neuron discharge control then passes to the direct-tract fibers, and the direct pathway to motor neurons supersedes the indirect one. It is possible thus to have continuous but alternating activation of spinal neurons under the control of extrapyramidal fibers alone. This central activity thus depends to a certain extent on the activity in sensory receptors.

Pyramidal-tract fibers acting alone seem to have little direct effect on motor-neuron discharges. In the cat, at least, they act chiefly through internuncial neurons in the posterior and intermediate gray. Single-shock stimulation of the pyramidal tract serves only to activate interneurons in the basal part of the posterior gray adjacent the lateral corticospinal tract. With repetitive stimulation, activity spreads further to intermediate gray interneurons. When they in turn are brought to discharge, motor neurons in turn are facilitated, and principally these are neurons involved in flexor-reflex arcs.

Conduction of impulses over pyramidal fibers in the cat is slower than over extrapyramidal ones, and it is to be recalled that the majority of pyramidal fibers are of small caliber, whereas the extrapyramidal fibers studied experimentally are of large size. The faster-traveling extrapyramidal impulses arrive among ventral column neurons after a number of synaptic relays (Fig. 101). The slower-traveling, but more direct, pyramidal impulses reach internuncial neurons in the posterior gray neurons. Activity simultaneously induced over the two systems conceivably would result in that traveling over extrapyramidal fibers reaching the spinal mechanisms first. As a result this latter mechanism could be "set" for the working of the more slowly arriving pyramidal activity. In such manner the correct postural adjustments could be made for the oncoming phasic voluntary movements initiated by pyramidal impulses. It was noted above that the nature of extrapyramidal activity depends also on activity in peripheral receptors. Central integration and subsequent discharges to peripheral effectors depends necessarily for best results on adequate information from the peripheral field of action.

THE STRETCH REFLEX AND MUSCLE TONE

As mentioned earlier, the activity of spinal reflex arcs is in turn under the influence of descending impulses from supraspinal levels. This has been well illustrated in studies of the myotatic or stretch reflexes subserving **muscle tone.** In order to effect smooth, purposeful

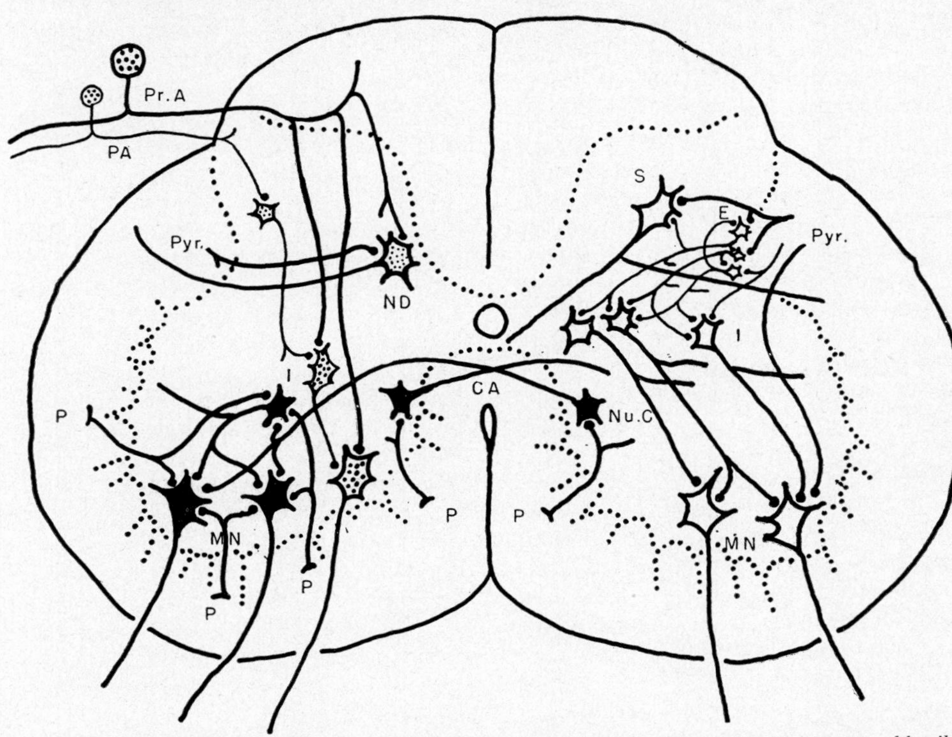

FIG. 101. A diagram of intrinsic spinal mechanisms. *CA*, anterior commissure; *E*, small cells of external basilar region of dorsal horn; *I*, internuncial neurons; *MN*, motor neurons; *ND*, nucleus dorsalis; *Nu. C*, nucleus of anterior commissure; *P*, propriospinal fibers of long spinal reflex systems; *PA*, pain afferent; *Pr. A*, proprioceptive afferent; *Pyr.*, pyramidal-tract fibers; *S*, solitary cells of the dorsal horn. (*After Lloyd in part.*)

motor performance, skeletal muscle must remain in a certain state of preparedness, or awaiting, for the phasic contraction. A certain amount of activity or tension persists in the muscle at all times normally serving to maintain its posture. This arises in large measure through activity in the stretch reflexes. The normal response of a muscle fiber to stretch is for it to shorten, and this activity is carried out over a two-neuron-arc, as seen above. This constant state of tension in muscle fasciculi is defined as **muscle tone.**

This quality in a resting muscle may be determined clinically by palpation of the muscle or, better, by evaluating the resistance encountered in the muscle when attempts are made to stretch it passively. If the resistance to passive stretch is increased, the condition of **hypertonia** is said to exist. If the resistance to passive stretch is diminished or absent, **hypotonia** is present. The resistance, or muscle tone, met with in passive stretch, however, is not completely produced by motor-unit activity in response to myotatic reflexes. Other factors enter into the mechanisms at play. The emotional attitude of the subject examined, the intramuscular conditions relating to intramuscular blood volume, and the reaction of the muscle to temperature are factors which themselves can effect the resistance met with in passive movement. They may enhance the normal motor-unit activity in response to stretch, or by their nature they may not contribute to, but rather lessen, the total response. Wide variations are therefore met with in the muscle tone of normal muscles, when this muscle tone is evaluated by passive stretch. The factors listed above will also enter into the picture when the muscle tone or resistance is evaluated in patients suffering with various disorders of their central neural pathways which transmit impulses that influence the distribution of muscle tone. Normally the myotatic reflex arcs are under the control of impulses descending into the cord over the various motor pathways described above. These will be alluded to again, below.

The **tendon reflexes** such as the knee jerk which are studied in a neurological examination are also subserved through the mechanism of stretch reflexes. In reality, they should more properly be called muscle reflexes, or deep reflexes. In eliciting a deep reflex the muscle concerned is placed in a position in which minimal pull is exerted on it, and the tendon is briskly tapped with a percussion hammer. This tapping force tends to displace and stretch the tendon and its muscle, and the muscle reflexly contracts. With practice one comes to recognize the range and extent of the normal response. The quadriceps muscle, for example, may contract more briskly and with greater excursion in response to the stretching tap in certain conditions, usually associated with hypertonia, and in such states, this increase in reflex activity is designated **hyperreflexia.** Frequently when the reflex contraction of a muscle is thus increased, its contraction serves to stretch quickly its antagonist muscle, and this muscle in turn reflexly shortens. A persisting alternation of stretching and contraction will ensue in the two muscles. Such a performance is known as **clonus.** Hypertonia, hyperreflexia, and clonus are all manifestations of increase in stretch-reflex activity, or lowered threshold of stretch reflexes, and the triad is denoted clinically as **spasticity.** Hypotonia and hyporeflexia characterize **flaccidity,** and in this condition the stretch reflexes are diminished, their arcs depressed or interrupted. Those deep reflexes usually evaluated in a neurological examination are listed below. The segmental spinal level concerned with the reflex arc is also shown.

Reflex	*Segmental level*
Biceps	Fifth and sixth cervical
Triceps	Sixth to eighth cervical
Brachioradial	Fifth and sixth cervical
Quadriceps (knee)	Second to fourth lumbar
Gastrocnemius (ankle)	First and second sacral

The character of the stretch reflexes can be altered by neural factors in addition to those extraneural ones mentioned in the discussion of muscle tone. Interruptions can be made in the afferent or efferent limb, and as a consequence no motor response will be obtained and hypotonia will exist. Increased activity in the receptor organs may serve to enhance the stretch reflexes to a certain extent. As stated previously, important influences on the stretch reflexes are exerted via pathways descending into the spinal cord, pyramidal and extrapyramidal. The stretch reflex activity can be inhibited especially by impulses traversing certain of the reticulospinal tracts located in the anterior funiculus. The impulses utilizing this tract may have originated in cerebral cortex, basal ganglia, anterior lobe of cerebellum, or brain stem neurons; but whatever their source, they converge upon, and are relayed in, a reticular center in the rostral medulla (521, 527, 528). From this center they are discharged via reticulospinal fibers. Stretch reflexes may be enhanced or facilitated by impulses traversing pyramidal, vestibulospinal, and certain reticulospinal fibers, these last two being concentrated especially in the anterior funiculus, and in the anterior half of the lateral funiculus, respectively. The middle cerebellar lobes also facilitate the stretch reflexes, perhaps indirectly via reticulospinal tracts. Normally a certain balancing or integration of these supraspinal facilitative and inhibitory influences exists. In certain disease conditions inhibitory pathways may be interrupted and facilitatory paths may be dominant, so that spasticity would result. In certain disorders facilitatory tracts may be damaged either alone or with inhibitory tracts, and hypotonia would result. Such alterations of stretch reflexes can be produced in experimental animals, and they are also frequently produced in man in disease of the neural pathways.

EXPERIMENTAL AND CLINICAL DISORDERS OF THE SPINAL CORD

The "Spinal" Animal

If in a cat the spinal cord is separated from the brain by a transection (below the fourth cervical segment, if to be kept for a time) a condition of depression sets in which affects all the spinal-cord reflex arcs. This condition is known as **spinal shock.** In addition to the depression of all skeletal muscle activity, the disturbances also include an inability to maintain a normal body temperature, an inability to empty the bladder normally, and a fall in the arterial blood pressure. A few days after the transection the animal begins to show signs of spinal reflex activity, though voluntary movement is permanently lost. All the reflex activity is performed by spinal neurons acting spontaneously or in response to impulses from peripheral receptors and other intrinsic spinal neurons. In the "spinal" cat it is thought that the initial depression of reflexes is due to the interruption of impulses descending from higher centers. In this animal it has been shown that "spinal shock" develops when the facilitative vestibulospinal and reticulospinal paths are cut (284, 755).

"Spinal" Man

On the basis of studies of Second World War veterans with a traumatic transection of the spinal cord, it has been necessary to revise certain concepts concerning the capabilities of "spinal" man (450, 451). The classical descriptions of spinal-cord transections for many years have been those of Head and Riddoch (349, 672). In their cases the neurological status could be described in three phases. Following immediately upon the trauma the patient demonstrated the condition of spinal shock. This was characterized by complete absence of all movement of muscles innervated by the isolated spinal-cord segment, profound depression of muscle tone, and usually the presence of urinary and fecal retention for a number of hours. In spinal shock the blood pressure also may be lowered, no sweating may occur in those skin areas innervated by sympathetic fibers from the isolated spinal cord, and the skin may become dry and thick and discolored.

In favorable cases a second phase would be entered within a period of one to several weeks; this was characterized by a development of reflex activity in the isolated spinal cord. The distribution and nature of this activity depended on the level of the transection. With cervical and thoracic transections, the reflex activity involved not only striated muscles but smooth muscles of abdominal and pelvic viscera, blood vessels, and sweat glands. In this phase the patients usually developed involuntary flexor movements of the lower limbs and of the abdominal muscles after upper or midthoracic transections. The involuntary flexor movements of a leg could be induced by pinching or pricking the sole of the foot or other part of the leg; those of the abdominal muscles could be obtained by pinching the skin over the lower abdominal wall. The induced flexor movement occasionally involved the other leg, and frequently the two legs flexed simultaneously, apparently without stimulation other than that of the overlying bedclothes. The contractions of the flexor muscles were associated with an inhibition of their antagonists, and the movements usually persisted for several seconds or minutes. Feeble deep reflexes usually returned in the lower limbs, and in response to plantar stimulation the toes were usually extended. The extension of the great toe in response to plantar stimulation, except in infancy, is usually denoted as a **Babinski reaction** and is considered to be an indication of injury to the corticospinal tracts. In "spinal" man it is considered to be a fragment of the primitive withdrawal or flexor reflex in response to nociceptive or potentially harmful stimulation of the sole of the foot. In the well-developed flexor reflex, there might also be dorsiflexion at ankle, and flexion at hip and knee as well. The flexor activity in the legs of "spinal" man were considered, therefore, to be protective reflexes. The development of flexor movements was usually accompanied by a return of muscle tone, this being especially noticeable in the flexor muscles, and in some patients a persistent flexor position of the legs was assumed.

The heightened reflex activity of smooth muscle during the second phase was manifest by episodes of profuse sweating of the skin innervated by the isolated spinal cord, by erection of the penis, by contraction of the dartos, by ejaculation of seminal fluid, and by evacuation of the urinary bladder and rectum. These occurred separately or collectively. In late stages of the second phase of spinal transection, the flexor movements of the legs and abdomen were occasionally associated with the widespread autonomic discharge just described in a so-called **mass reflex.** This could be elicited by impulses entering from skin, striated muscle, or from a viscus, and the most effective stimulus was usually visceral in origin, arising from rectum or bladder. It was interpreted as an irradiation of impulses throughout the isolated spinal cord, setting off activity in many motor neurons whose threshold to discharge was lowered. Usually, the second stage of spinal transection gave way to a third, in which reflex activity was lost. This was usually brought about by a deterioration of the patient's general systemic condition as a result of intercurrent urinary-tract infection, the development of pneumonia, or infected bedsores. The situation most often terminated in death.

With the development of knowledge concerning the nursing care of the paraplegic or quadriplegic patient, the state of "spinal" man is now more favorable. This care involves attention to the urinary bladder, to the skin, and to the paralyzed muscles, and in successful cases the paraplegic patients may be rehabilitated sufficiently that they can earn a living (573, 574, 575). The successive phases of spinal man in favorable cases can now be characterized as follows: the phase of "spinal shock"; the phase in which development of minimal reflex activity occurs; the phase in which flexor spasms develop; the phase in which flexor and extensor spasms alternate; the phase in which extensor spasms predominate (450). These stages of "spinal" man have been described on the basis of observations of 27 cases of verified spinal-cord transection. The length of time that different patients remained in a given stage varied, but in general the stage of spinal shock persisted for 1 to 6 weeks. Stages 2 and 3 persisted for 6 weeks to a year; stage 4 rarely began earlier than 4 months, and usually terminated within a year. Stage 5 might appear as early as 6 months after injury and persist indefinitely. Early signs of reflex activity were reflex emptying of the bladder, penile erection elicited by manipulation, and involuntary twitching movements of the toes. Flexor withdrawal movements, involving merely the foot or the entire lower limb in a triple flexion pattern, would soon develop. Later the flexor movements were alternated with extensor patterns. The extensor phenomena were manifest as spontaneous extension of one or both limbs in steppinglike movements. These could be elicited by pressure beneath the knee of either relaxed extremity, but were noticeable especially when the position of the patient was being altered from a sitting to a supine position. Pressure on the sole occasionally induced an extensor thrust in the ipsilateral leg such as occurs in the assumption of weight bearing by the limb. In some patients transient reflex standing was present, and a number were able to stand in water. The deep reflexes became quite active, and ankle clonus frequently was demonstrable as alternating contractions in the flexor and extensor muscles about that joint. Triple flexion- or extensor-type withdrawal movements were demonstrable when a limb was placed in cold or hot water, although no withdrawal occurred from water at 37.5°C. It was believed that the withdrawal in response to cold involved activation of cold sensory endings; that in response to hot water, pain endings (517). It is of interest that the "mass reflex" was not demonstrable in these patients. This might be accounted for partially by the fact that the distention of the urinary bladder was kept at a minimum, and bladder training was encouraged. This frequently has resulted in good reflex emptying of the bladder at definite times. Five of the patients remained in the stage of spinal shock even in spite of excellent systemic condition.

Certain other examples of heightened reflex autonomic activity in "spinal" man have been described in more detail in recent years. This activity is more pronounced in cases of cervical or high thoracic transection. The inciting stimulus has been most often distention of the bladder or rectum, and in response to this, there have occurred excessive sweating, flushing of the face, pilomotor erection, shivering, headache manifest as general fullness, slowing of the pulse, elevation of the blood pressure, and, if the stimulus is maintained, convulsions (774). The mechanisms underlying this widespread autonomic discharge are not understood. This so-called "full-bladder syndrome" may not occur over a very long period of time, but it can be very bothersome.

In the light of the recent studies the isolated human spinal cord, in successful cases, is capable of promoting much reflex activity. Not only protective flexor skeletal movements are performed, but also postural extensor ones. Excretory activities can be adequately carried out, and generative functions maintained, in those cases of spinal-cord transection in which no damage occurs to the thoracolumbar and sacral segments which initiate those reflex acts (see Chap. 7). It is not possible to state accurately in a given case of spinal-cord trauma whether the spinal cord is anatomically transected or not, unless the site of damage is explored through laminectomy. It has been customary to assume in the past that the spinal cord was not completely transected in those cases in which extensor movements occur and muscle tone is normal or increased in extensor muscles. Two categories of neural status have been described in severe spinal-cord damage with paraplegia, whether this be induced traumatically or result from long-standing, unrelieved compression which leads to progressive functional block of impulse transmission. If the paraplegic patient demonstrates marked or complete sensory loss below the level of injury and shows involuntary extensor spasms with heightened extensor muscle tone and reflexes, he has been said to have **paraplegia-in-extension.** This has been thought to indicate that the spinal cord was not completely transected anatomically or functionally. When transection is considered complete, the patient has been said to have **paraplegia-in-flexion,** since the involuntary movements were always flexor in pattern, extensor muscle tone was diminished, the extensor tendon reflexes were not greatly increased, and the legs frequently assumed a flexion posture.

On the basis of experimental sections in animals, a paraplegia-in-extension was said to be converted into a paraplegia-in-flexion when the vestibulospinal tracts were severed (284). As long as these tracts were intact the extensor mechanisms were sufficiently facilitated to be dominant. It is known now, however, that facilitatory reticulospinal tracts closely associated in their course with vestibulospinal fibers also contribute to the extensor mechanisms, and their section along with vestibulospinal fibers leads to the development of paraplegia-in-flexion. It appears likely, however, that the isolated spinal cord in complete spinal transection is capable of the production of extensor mechanisms as well as flexor ones through the activity of intrinsic facilitative neuronal activity. The term paraplegia-in-flexion is not always to be applied, therefore, to complete spinal transection; extensor as well as flexor movements may be present.

The forceful involuntary flexor, or extensor, spasms may become quite bothersome, interfering with the patient's general care and disturbing his rest. They have been relieved by section of the anterior roots of the lumbar levels. The mechanisms underlying the production of the involuntary movements in "spinal" man are not completely understood. It has usually been considered that impulses from a viscus, from the periphery, or from a muscle may set off the activity by bringing to discharge anterior horn cells which have previously been facilitated by intrinsic spinal neuronal activity. It has also been observed that certain of these intrinsic impulses may arise from the area of scarred neural tissue in traumatic transection (707). A more bothersome symptom in the paraplegic patient is the occurrence of spontaneous pain in the distal parts especially of the paralyzed limbs. This is often described as deep-seated and burning or boring in character. The mechanisms underlying the production of the pain are not completely understood. It has been suggested, however, that the painful impulses arise in the scar tissue about the transected end of the proximal segment of the spinal cord.

Other Clinical Disorders of the Spinal Cord

In a study of the spinal cord with reference to clinical findings occurring in its disorders, it is well to keep the following factors in mind: The arrangement of the various types of sensory fibers into similar groups; the lamination of the fibers in the bundles, depending on the origin of the impulses peripherally; the possibility of bilateral derivation of the fibers in any one tract or funiculus; the restriction of preganglionic autonomic cell bodies to certain levels of the spinal cord; and the arrangement of the blood supply. It is important to know whether a given patient with spinal-cord disorder has disturbance of the gray or white matter or both, whether the signs follow segmental or tract distribution, and whether the disorder, if it be a tumor, is inside the spinal cord (intramedullary), outside the spinal cord (extramedullary), inside or outside the dura. A study of the neurological signs should aid in differentiating the problem.

Diseases affecting the spinal cord frequently give characteristic syndromes. Some of those seen can be described briefly. In an examination of a patient with spinal-cord disease, it is well to differentiate the signs due to involvement of tracts and those due to involvement of segmental gray matter, or of nerve roots. The distribution of the motor and sensory changes will vary accordingly.

The **Brown-Séquard syndrome** is due to unilateral compression or transection of the spinal cord. Partial syndromes are frequently seen in patients with unilaterally placed tumors growing outside the spinal-cord substance. Knife or bullet wounds most commonly produce hemisections, however. On the side of the injury, after the acute phase has subsided, one finds paralysis of voluntary motion and a Babinski phenomenon due to involvement of the corticospinal tracts. The deep reflexes of the same side and the muscle tone are increased because of damage to the inhibitory extrapyramidal tracts which normally hold the segmental neural mechanisms in abeyance. The effect of this supersedes the loss of the supraspinal facilitating influences which also are severed. The loss of inhibitory restraint plus the facilitating influence of intrinsic proprius neurons leads to the heightened tone and reflexes. Also on the side of injury, the patient has loss of position sense, impaired vibratory sense, impaired tactile discrimination, and stereoanesthesia, because of injury to the posterior columns. Because of damage to the lateral spinothalamic tracts, the patient has loss of sensation to painful and thermal stimuli on the side of the body opposite the lesion. This level of sensory loss is usually not equivalent to that of the lesion but reaches a dermatome or so below, because the spinothalamic fibers arising in any one cord segment require at least one segment to cross completely. Because of associated damage to gray matter and anterior and posterior roots, the patient may have cutaneous sensory loss in a segmental pattern on the side of the injury as well as atrophy of the muscles innervated by the spinal-cord segment or root destroyed.

A not too uncommon disease of the spinal cord is **syringomyelia.** This word literally means cord cavitation. Cavitation or softening of the spinal cord can result from several factors, congenital or acquired. Anomalies of neural-tube closure, together with abnormal overgrowth of glia with secondary necrosis, may lead to cavitation of the spinal cord, especially about the central canal. Inadequate blood supply because of diseased vessels, hemorrhage into its substance, and tumors can lead to spinal-cord softening in the acquired types. The characteristic lesion of the disease, however, is around the central canal—more often, anterior to it. A softening so placed will interrupt spinothalamic fibers crossing in the anterior gray and white commissures. The patient therefore presents segmental or dermatomal losses of pain and thermal sensibility bilaterally, as well as some lesser impairment of touch sensation. Deep sensibility, dependent on the posterior white column transmission, is usually normal, and the patient therefore presents a **dissociated sensory loss.** The spinal-cord cavitation can begin or extend posteriorly or laterally and thus damage other tracts or gray matter. Because of anterior gray damage the patient frequently has paralysis and atrophy of muscles innervated from the diseased spinal segment and trophic changes in skin and bone. Involvement of the posterior white columns would result in loss of deep sensibility; that of lateral white columns, in loss of voluntary motion with increased reflexes and spasticity, below the level of the lesion. Involvement of intermediate gray and autonomic tracts results in a Horner's syndrome (miosis of the pupil, ptosis of the upper eyelid, and loss of sweating on the same side of the face). Syringomyelia is seen most often in the cervical cord.

As a result of trauma, severe straining and exertion, or disease of blood vessels, hemorrhage may occur into the spinal-cord substance, a condition called **hematomyelia.** Usually rapidly developing, the signs will depend on the particular portion of spinal cord involved. The characteristic **syndrome** of the **anterior spinal artery,** usually due to obstruction to blood flow in that vessel, has been described earlier. In these conditions, and with neoplasms growing within the spinal-cord substance, one customarily sees early neurological disorders distributed over segmental patterns. The syringomyelic cavity or intramedullary neoplasm located centrally in the last cervical and first thoracic segments, for example, leads early to a segmental loss of cutaneous sensation over the hands. As the cavitation extends laterally and destroys anterior gray of those segments, the intrinsic muscles of the hand become paralyzed and gradually waste. If the cavitation or neoplasm continues to enlarge laterally and encroaches on, or compresses, the white columns, the distribution of the abnormal neurological signs increases and a "tract pattern" of sensory loss is added to the segmental. With such disturbances of the lateral spinothalamic tracts, for example, the most medially placed fibers which have most recently joined the tract and which transmit impulses from dermatomes just caudad to the first thoracic will be damaged first. If the compression or destruction extends more and more laterally, ultimately the outermost fibers of the spinothalamic tracts will be damaged. Since these transmit impulses from most caudad dermatomes, the distribution of sensory loss will gradually enlarge to encompass all the dermatomes below the level of the lesion. Similarly, as lateral corticospinal fibers are encroached upon, motor disorder will progress in those parts of the body and limbs below the lesion.

Spinal-cord compression by tumors outside the spinal cord frequently develops, with characteristic story. The neurological signs depend to a certain extent on the site of the compression, whether it be lateral, anterior, or posterior. A history is frequently obtained of pain over the distribution of a nerve root due to compression of the posterior root. This may be followed by gradual impairment of motility and sensation as spinal tracts are compressed. The patient may have bilateral paralysis of volitional movement, hypertonia, hyperreflexia, and some impairment of both cutaneous and deep sensibility. In addition to the sensory loss over the distribution of the compressed posterior root, the patient may soon show evidences of a tract pattern. This differs in its distribution from the tract pattern described in the preceding paragraph. Tumors growing laterally outside the cord frequently give sensory loss first over the sacral areas, because the most peripherally placed spinothalamic fibers first compressed transmit impulses from sacral dermatomes. As the compression increases more fibers are damaged and the level of sensory loss rises, ultimately to reach the level of the lesion. Blockage of spinal-fluid circulation by the tumor may also frequently be demonstrated.

Syphilis of the spinal cord, most often in the form of **tabes dorsalis,** characteristically first involves posterior roots and posterior columns. Tabes dorsalis is a descriptive name, since in the late stages of the disorder, the degeneration of the posterior funiculi leads to a flattening of the posterior portion of the spinal cord. The disorder most often begins by involving the posterior roots at lumbar levels, and especially it is prone to damage the large fibers of the medial division of the posterior root. This therefore leads to a loss of appreciation of muscle and joint sensibility with impaired sense of position, sense of contraction, and loss of vibratory sensibility. The deep, or postural, sensibilities are thus deranged, and tactile sensation may be mildly impaired. The patient has **sensory ataxia** because of the deficit of postural sensibility, and unless he can watch every movement of his lower limbs and voluntarily correct his errors, he is quite awkward, stumbling about. Because of frequent involvement of posterior roots in the sacral levels, the afferent limb of the stretch reflexes underlying normal function of the urinary bladder and rectum is interrupted, and the patients develop large atonic bladders with overflow incontinence as well as constipation and fecal incontinence. If the cervical dorsal roots are involved also, the patient develops sensory ataxia of the upper limbs, with stereoanesthesia. Pupillary disorders, including the characteristic Argyll Robertson pupils, are also frequently seen in tabes (see Chap. 7).

A frequent involvement of the spinal cord occurs in **multiple sclerosis,** a disease characterized by widespread small patches of demyelination, axis-cylinder destruction, and glial overgrowth. The most frequent syndrome is a spastic paresis of both legs, usually with some impairment of deep sensibility or vibratory sense. Associated with **pernicious anemia,** one sees some involvement of the spinal cord. The posterior and lateral columns are most often the site of the lesions, leading to disorders of deep sensibility, especially, and motor power. Superimposed involvement of the spinal nerves may complicate the picture by adding more or less complete sensory loss over certain nerve distributions.

Poliomyelitis, or infantile paralysis, characteristically involves gray matter of the spinal cord, especially the anterior and lateral intermediate columns. The patients usually show total paralysis of certain muscle groups, depending on the spinal-cord segments involved. In addition to the paralysis, the muscle reflexes are ultimately lost, muscle tone gradually is lost, and muscle atrophy usually develops. This combination of disorders composes a **lower-motor-neuron syndrome.**

Primary muscular atrophy is a degenerative disease which involves anterior horn cells. It is apt to involve cervical segments especially, beginning in the seventh or eighth segment, and it is usually bilateral, leading to symmetrical wasting of intrinsic muscles of the hands. Commonly associated with the atrophic or "lower-motor-neuron" signs are indications of disease of the upper motor neurons or their axons supplying other muscles, especially those of the legs. In such cases, a combination of upper-motor-neuron and lower-motor-neuron signs is found, and this combined syndrome is called **amyotrophic lateral sclerosis.**

In the so-called **upper-motor-neuron syndromes,** loss of movement and disorders of muscle tone are present. These come about through injury to pyramidal and extrapyramidal fibers. The loss of movement results from damage to the corticospinal fibers. This loss of volitional movement involves all muscles innervated by segments caudad to the level of damage, and especially the muscles of the distal parts of the limbs. The disorder of muscle tone most commonly is one of hypertonia, occasionally hypotonia. This depends on the relative numbers of inhibitory and facilitatory extrapyramidal fibers that are interrupted.

Before describing the intrinsic anatomy of the brain stem wherein these same spinal-cord tracts will be encountered, it will be worth while to investigate in more detail the spinal roots and the spinal nerves. Within these are somatic motor fibers passing to innervate striated muscle, visceral motor fibers to innervate smooth and cardiac muscle and glands, and sensory fibers bringing in impulses arising in receptors located in skin, subcutaneous tissue, striated muscle, mucous membranes, and viscera. The somatic motor and sensory elements will be discussed first.

CHAPTER 6

THE PERIPHERAL NERVES

THE NEURONS of the neural axis in the brain stem and spinal cord are in contact with peripheral receptors and effectors via cranial and spinal nerves, respectively. The cranial nerves are described in Chap. 9. The spinal nerves are composed of axons of neurons located in the anterior and intermediate gray columns, and of dendrites of the pseudo-unipolar cells of the posterior root ganglia. Much variation exists both in component-fiber size and also in amount of myelination. Connective-tissue coverings bind the fibers into nerves, which are well supplied with blood. Specificity of sensory end organs for various qualities of stimuli exists, and the morphology of the receptors is adapted to the type of stimulation. Since certain individual nerve roots split and regrouping of fibers takes place in the various plexuses, a peripheral nerve may include fibers of several roots. The motor and sensory disorders following injury will vary, therefore, according to site of injury, root, plexus, or nerve. Unlike axons and dendrites wholly within the spinal cord, those in peripheral nerves have the capacity of regeneration after interruption.

Spinal nerves are arbitrarily divided into groups as follows, eight cervical, twelve thoracic, five lumbar, five sacral, and one coccygeal (Fig. 74). Some spinal nerves, or rather portions of them, take part in the formation of plexuses, such as the cervical, brachial, and lumbosacral plexuses; other spinal nerves remain as individual elements. In the following discussion the gross features of the roots and nerves will be presented first. A description of the histological and functional characters of the root and nerve fibers will then be given, and finally nerve and muscle relationships and reaction to injury will form the concluding section.

MIXED SPINAL NERVES

A **spinal nerve** is formed by the union of anterior and posterior **spinal roots.** Since anterior roots contain motor elements and posterior roots contain sensory ones, the spinal nerve formed by their union is known as a "**mixed spinal nerve**" (Fig. 102). The union of the anterior and posterior roots occurs just prior to entry into the intervertebral foramen or within it, the point of union of the posterior root being just distal to the posterior root ganglion. The meninges and intermeningeal spaces accompany the roots to the site of union (Figs. 75, 76). The arachnoid and pia blend and terminate as meninges here; the dura fuses firmly with periosteum of the intervertebral foramen. The connective tissue sheath of the spinal nerves begins where the meninges end, blending in with them.

The lumbar and sacral anterior and posterior roots are longer than those of the cervical and thoracic cord, since they must pursue a long intradural course before reaching the proper intervertebral foramen where they join, and from which they emerge as "mixed spinal nerves." It should be recalled that each cervical nerve leaves a foramen immediately above the body of the vertebra corresponding to it segmentally, while the thoracic, lumbar, and sacral nerves leave foramina below their corresponding vertebrae (Fig. 74). The fifth cervical nerve, for example, emerges above the body of the fifth vertebra; the fifth thoracic, beneath the fifth thoracic vertebra.

"TYPICAL" SPINAL NERVE

The majority of the thoracic spinal nerves take no part in the formation of plexuses, and one of them can be used as an illustrative

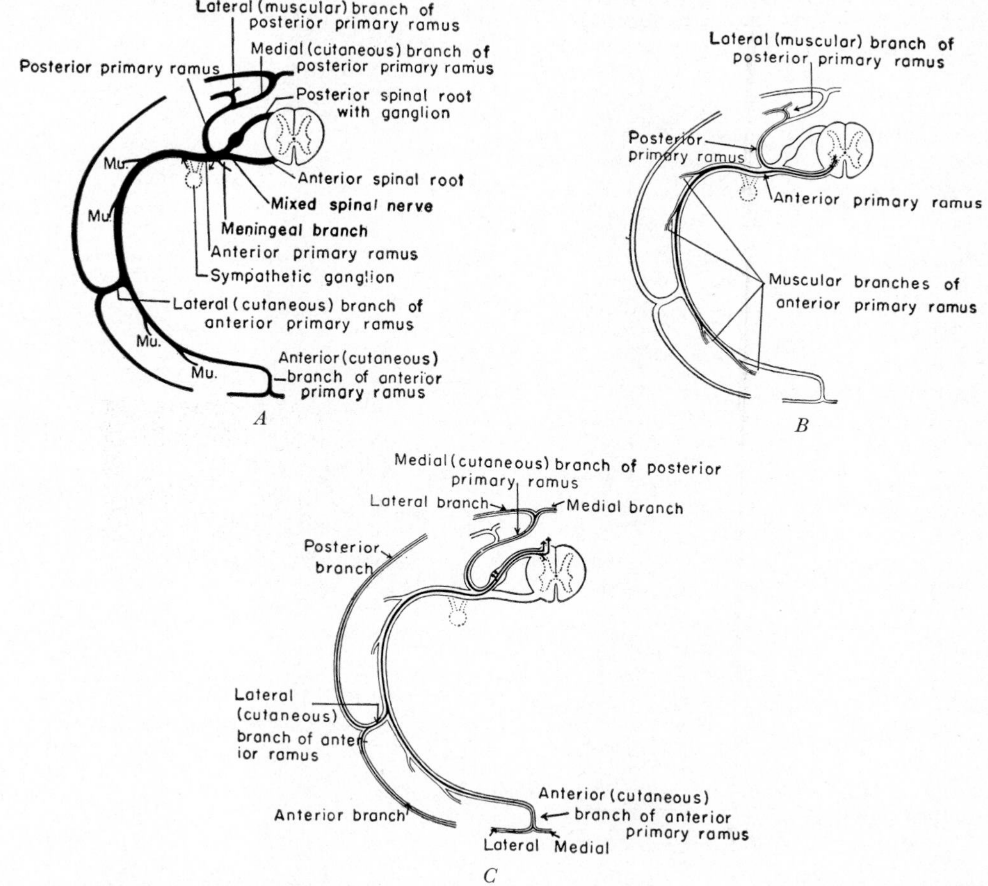

FIG. 102. Diagrams of segmental peripheral nerves. *A*, components of a segmental nerve (*Mu.*, muscular branches given off by anterior primary ramus); *B*, segmental nerve, routes traveled by efferent fibers to muscles; *C*, segmental nerve, course of sensory neurons from periphery to spinal cord. (*After Haymaker and Woodhall, "Peripheral Nerve Injuries," W. B. Saunders Company.*)

example of a "typical" spinal nerve. The "typical" mixed spinal nerve gives off a very small branch, the **recurrent meningeal,** and then divides, as it emerges from the intervertebral foramen, into larger **posterior** and **anterior primary rami** (Figs. 75, 102*A*). The meningeal nerve contains sensory fibers for the meninges, and motor fibers (autonomic) for the blood vessels of the meninges. The anterior and posterior "primary rami" also are mixed, containing motor and sensory fibers. The posterior primary rami of all the mixed spinal nerves except the first three cervicals are smaller than the anterior. The "typical" posterior primary ramus penetrates the deep back muscles and divides into medial and lateral branches, for innervation of the back muscles and the overlying skin. In the upper half of the body the medial branches, in general, supply the skin as well as the muscles; in the lower half, the lateral branches, chiefly, supply the skin. The posterior primary rami of the first cervical, fourth and fifth sacral, and coccygeal nerves do not divide.

The anterior primary ramus of the "typical" thoracic spinal nerve runs laterally and anteriorly around the body wall. Near the midaxillary line a lateral branch is given off. This penetrates the muscles and within the subcutaneous tissue divides into anterior and posterior branches which supply in turn the lateral part of the ventral trunk wall, the side, and lateral part of the posterior trunk wall. The remaining part of the anterior primary ramus, now referred to as an anterior branch, continues around the body wall innervating the muscles and bones along its course. Near the mid-line of the anterior body wall this anterior branch penetrates the muscle remaining over it and divides into medial and lateral branches which supply the skin over the anterior trunk wall.

The anterior primary rami of the twelve thoracic and first two lumbar nerves are usually connected to the paravertebral chain of sympathetic ganglia by **communicating rami.** These latter are of two types, **white** and **gray,** so-called because of their gross appearance due to the presence or absence of myelin about their component fibers. The white ramus contains motor (sympathetic) fibers, which come from the spinal cord via anterior roots, and sensory fibers which carry impulses from viscera to the posterior root ganglia and spinal cord. The gray ramus contains fibers which arise in the paravertebral sympathetic ganglia and travel via the spinal nerve division to blood vessels and glands of the skin in the limbs and trunk walls. The anterior primary rami of the second, third, and fourth sacral nerves give off branches corresponding to white rami in that they carry motor (parasympathetic) fibers to pelvic viscera. These fibers do not pass to the paravertebral sympathetic ganglia, but run to ganglionated plexuses near the viscus to be supplied.

MESODERMAL COVERINGS OF PERIPHERAL NERVES

Around the tubular neurolemmal sheath about each peripheral nerve fiber is a sheath of connective tissue, the **endoneurium** or **sheath of Key and Retzius** (Fig. 14). It is composed of a sticky homogeneous substance which is rich in delicate fibrils, the majority of which run parallel to the long axis of the nerve fibers; others run obliquely. Fibroblasts and macrophages are also present. At the nodes of Ranvier the connective-tissue sheath is more developed and is resistant to injected fluids; it, rather than the neurolemma, is the strong substance at the nodes. The endoneurium continues about the nerve fiber to its finest terminals. Variable numbers of nerve fibers, each of which is enclosed in an endoneurial tube, are collected into bundles or fasciculi surrounded by **perineurium.** This connective-tissue sheath is composed of collagenous fibers with scattered fibroblasts. The fibers are arranged both in longitudinal and in oblique or spiral fashion about the bundle of nerve fibers. Many bundles of nerve fibers surrounded by perineurium are united into a nerve and are bound together by the **epineurium** (Fig. 103). This also is composed of fibrillar connective tissue, chiefly collagenous, but blended with elastic fibers. The fibers, the majority of which are oriented longitudinally, are interspersed with many connective-tissue cells, including some fat. From the inner layer of epineurium more loosely arranged connective-tissue fibers pass into association with the perineurium about groups of nerve fibers. Perineurial spaces within a nerve are thus formed.

BLOOD SUPPLY OF NERVES

Blood vessels are present in all three layers of connective tissue. Nerves receive an abundant supply of blood from regional arteries. The amount of regional supply varies with the size and length of the nerve. Each regional nutrient artery enters the nerve and divides into ascending and descending branches, which pass in a longitudinal direction along the nerve (5). Each of these longitudinal branches gives off several side branches which in turn give off smaller longitudinal branches. Through anastomosis of the ascending and descending branches of a regional nutrient artery with those of the next successive one, a continuous, centrally placed, longitudinal arterial channel is established in nerves (Fig. 104). Blocking of a single incoming nutrient vessel is therefore not apt to lead to much impairment of nerve function. The venous drainage, in general, is similar in its pattern to that of the arterial supply. The veins usually drain into deeper muscular veins whether the nerve be superficial or deep. Lymphatics are present in the perineurial spaces, these being continuous with the subarachnoid space about the spinal roots.

Peripheral Nerve Plexuses

The anterior primary rami of the upper four cervical nerves take part in the formation of the cervical plexus; those of the lower four

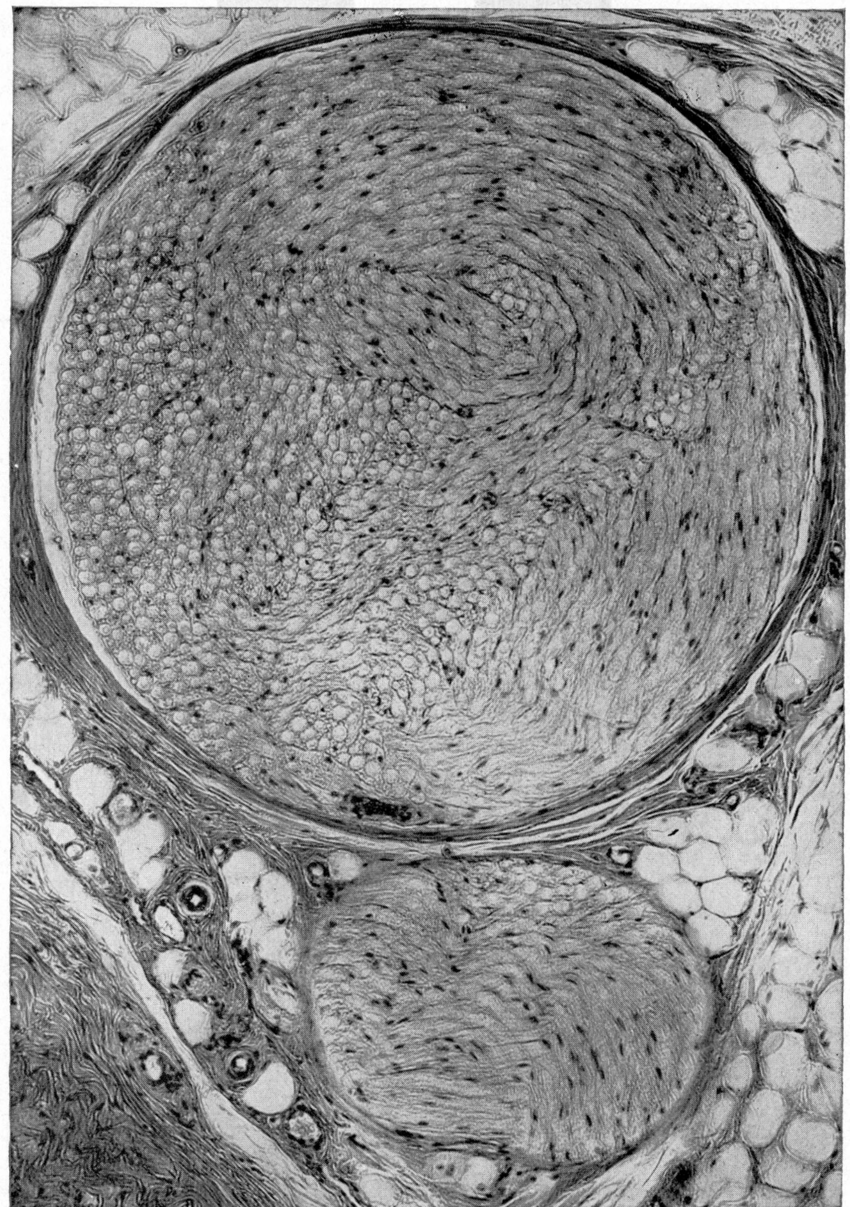

FIG. 103. Nerve fascicles of the human femoral nerve, stained with hematoxylin. Note the dense fibrous connective-tissue sheaths of perineurium and fat cells around them. Photomicrograph, ×150. (*From Nonidez and Windle, "Textbook of Histology," courtesy of McGraw-Hill Book Company, Inc.*)

cervical and first thoracic nerves, in that of the brachial plexus; those of the first three or four lumbar nerves, in that of the lumbar plexus; those of the lower one or two lumbar and all the sacral nerves, in that of the lumbosacral plexus. From those various plexuses arise the peripheral nerves. Because of the sorting and regrouping in the plexuses a peripheral nerve may contain fibers from several anterior and posterior roots; conversely, the fibers of a single anterior or posterior root may be distributed through several peripheral nerves. Such disper-

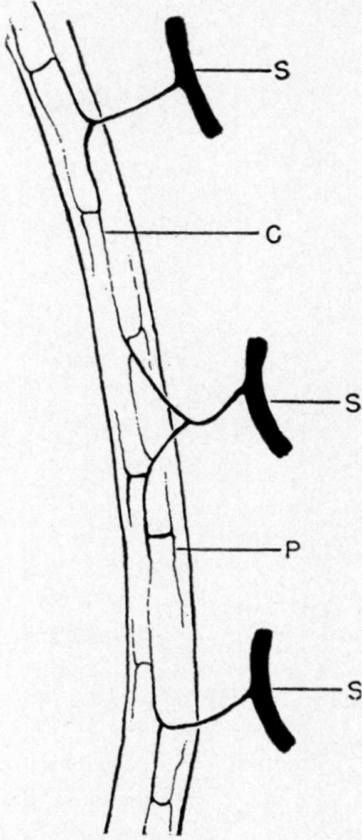

FIG. 104. Diagram to show the pattern of the blood supply to nerves. *S*, regional arteries; *C*, central longitudinal arterial supply; *P*, peripheral, or secondary, longitudinal arterial trunk. (*Modified from Adams.*)

sion comes about as a result of the splitting, migration, and regrouping of myotomes, the primitive muscle segments of the embryo. Each myotome originally is connected to the spinal cord by a definite pair of spinal roots. The relation between root and myotome is a persistent one, and when a myotome splits and its parts regroup with parts of other myotomes, each myotome-part retains a portion of the original nerve root. In the thoracic region the segmental myotomic arrangement is retained to a great extent, and the majority of the thoracic nerves contain fibers from only one pair of spinal roots, anterior and posterior. They are referred to as **unisegmental nerves.** In the limbs wherein individual muscles are derived from parts of several myotomes, a nerve supplying such a muscle will contain fibers from several roots and is thus a **plurisegmental nerve.**

Within the proximal portions of the peripheral nerves the fibers destined for any one muscle or skin area are diffusely arranged. Distally a rearrangement takes place, and fibers of similar destination are grouped in definite fasciculi prior to their branching away from the main trunk. A discrete injury to the proximal part of the nerve will be likely to result in little noticeable disorder of innervation to a muscle or skin area; distally, a small injury might sever completely the fascicle destined for a large muscle and thus result in a paralysis of the muscle. In certain nerves (*e.g.,* radial) the fascicles destined for some muscles are grouped together for several centimeters above their point of breaking away.

DERMATOMES

The reshifting of posterior root fibers through several peripheral nerves follows that of the anterior root fibers. That area of skin supplied by the fibers of any one posterior root

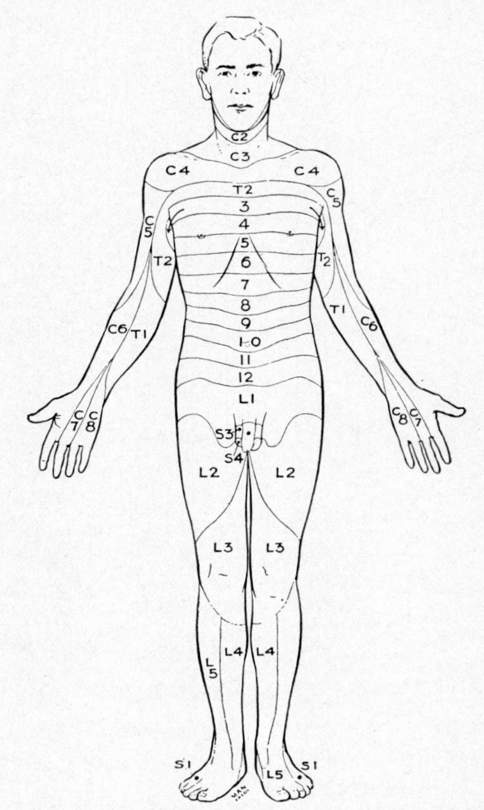

FIG. 105. The segmental innervation of the skin on the anterior aspect of the body. The uppermost dermatome, the second cervical, is adjacent to the cutaneous field of the mandibular division of the trigeminal nerve. The arrows indicate the lateral extensions of the third thoracic dermatome. (*After Foerster, from Haymaker and Woodhall, "Peripheral Nerve Injuries," W. B. Saunders Company.*)

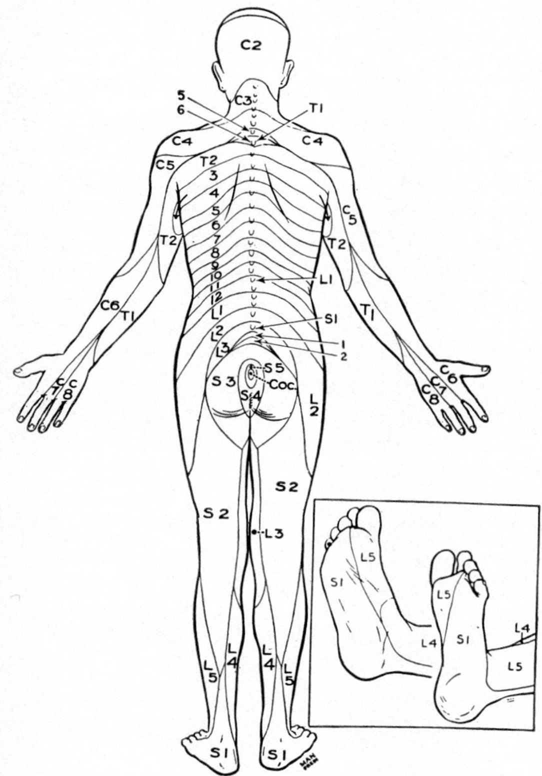

FIG. 106. The dermatomes on the posterior aspect of the body. The first cervical spinal segment usually has no cutaneous supply. The arrows in the axillary regions indicate the lateral extent of the third thoracic dermatome. The first thoracic, first lumbar, and first sacral spinous processes are indicated. (*After Foerster, from Haymaker and Woodhall, "Peripheral Nerve Injuries," W. B. Saunders Company.*)

is referred to as a **dermatome;** the sensory fibers may reach this skin area via several peripheral nerves. Maps of the cutaneous innervation by specific posterior roots (dermatome maps) have been constructed on the basis of clinical observation and experimentation. In the virus inflammation of cells in a posterior root ganglion, shingles or herpes zoster, small vesicles and discoloration of the skin occur over the skin area supplied by sensory fibers from this ganglion, and it was by studying many cases of this disorder that Head compiled dermatome maps. By utilizing several surgical procedures, Foerster also constructed maps (Figs. 105, 106, 107). In one procedure he would section individual posterior roots and outline the area of cutaneous sensory loss. In another he would section one root immediately above, and another root just below, a third root, and outline the cutaneous "island" in which sensation remained. He also observed the cutaneous area of vasodilatation (flushing) resulting from his stimulating the distal stump of sectioned posterior roots (253). By carefully studying the area of sensory impairment resulting from compression of a single posterior root by a herniated nucleus pulposus, Keegan has published maps slightly different from those of Foerster (425, 426).

SPINAL ROOTS

In the anterior and posterior roots the nerve fibers are of a variety of sizes. More fibers are present by count in the posterior roots, but the fact that the anterior root fibers in general are coarser makes the discrepancy in numbers less

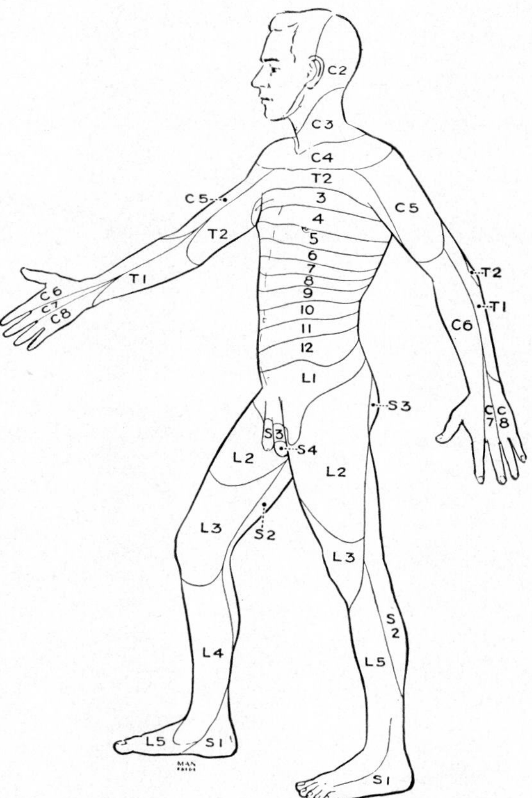

FIG. 107. The dermatomes from a lateral view. (*After Foerster, from Haymaker and Woodhall, "Peripheral Nerve Injuries," W. B. Saunders Company.*)

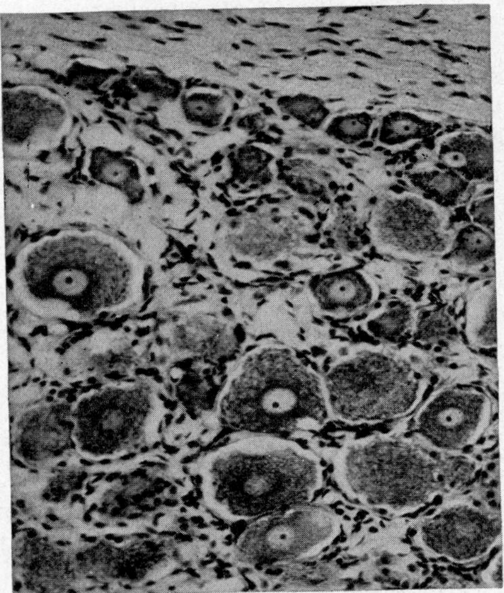

Fig. 108. Neurons of the posterior root ganglion. Large and small cells are present and the capsules about many are visible. The axon hillock, indicated by absence of Nissl substance, may be seen on several of the neurons. Nissl stain. Photomicrograph, ×202.

apparent. The root fibers are scantily myelinated, moderately myelinated or heavily myelinated, and great variation exists in their individual cross-sectional area. It will be recalled that the myelin sheaths of the nerve fibers of spinal roots and nerves are interrupted by constrictions at the nodes of Ranvier. Further, the incisures of Schmidt-Lantermann are found in the myelin sheaths of the peripheral nerves. It has been suggested that these incisures represent a mechanism for permitting extension (303).

According to the Bell-Magendie law, all anterior roots convey motor (efferent) impulses; all posterior roots, sensory (afferent) impulses. From time to time certain authors, however, have presented evidence that some motor fibers are present in posterior roots and some sensory ones in anterior roots (254, 776). A ganglion is present on each posterior root, with the frequent exception of the first cervical. Occasionally there is more than one ganglion on a root.

POSTERIOR ROOT GANGLIA

A posterior root ganglion contains large, medium, and small pseudo-unipolar cells, each of which is surrounded by two cellular capsules (Fig. 108). Small cells are more numerous but are less conspicuous. The inner capsule about the neurons is composed of Schwann cells which are continuous with those surrounding the cell's single process and its branches; the outer capsule is formed by a modification of the surrounding interstitial connective tissue and is comparable to endoneurium. A lipoid surface film, similar to myelin, lies about the cell body within the cellular capsule. The single process of the ganglion cells is surrounded also by a variable amount of myelin and divides like the letter T into two branches. One passes out by way of the peripheral nerve as a functional dendrite; the other passes centrally into the posterior root as an axon. Many complex types of neurons have been found in the ganglia in addition to the typical ones described above, though their functions are not clear. Some of these have den-

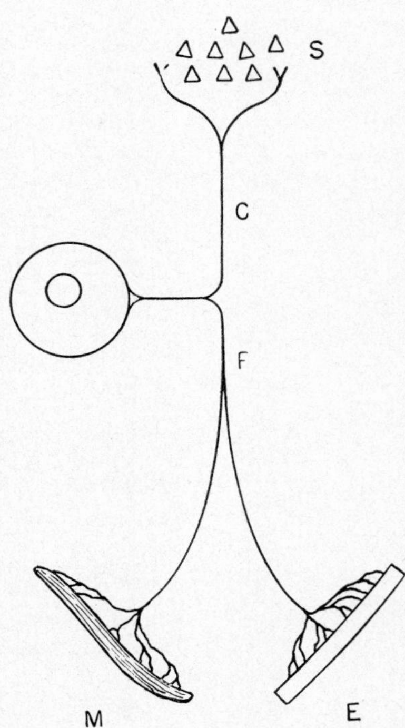

Fig. 109. Schematic representation of posterior root ganglion cell with branching dendrite. *C*, central or axonic process entering spinal cord; *E*, terminations in skin; *M*, terminations in muscle; *P*, peripheral or dendritic process; *S*, spinal neuron pool. (*Modified from Weddell, Sinclair, and Feindel.*)

dritic processes which ramify near the cell body and terminate within the ganglion about what are thought to be sensory endings; the axon of such cells passes into the spinal cord.

It has been observed in certain animals that the peripheral process of a single ganglion cell may divide and send one branch into the posterior primary ramus, and another into the anterior primary ramus. One branch may have terminals in skin, one in muscles (Fig. 109). Another ganglion cell may have terminals in skin as well as in a visceral structure. It has been presumed that some posterior root ganglion cells in man may have similar dividing dendrites, and the mechanisms involved in referred pain have been explained by bringing this assumption into play. This hypothesis as well as others concerning referred pain will be described in Chap. 7.

The ratio of numbers of ganglion cells to posterior root fibers is approximately 1:1 in the thoracic levels. The fibers of the posterior root are small, medium, and large. Some have very thin sheaths of myelin, some have sheaths of moderate thickness, and others are heavily myelinated. In general, the smallest and most poorly myelinated fibers transmit impulses arising from pain and temperature receptors, although some pain impulses also traverse medium-sized fibers.

In the mixed peripheral nerve the diameter of the myelinated fibers ranges from 1μ to 20μ (Figs. 110, 111). Many other small fibers are also present whose myelination is so scanty that it is not detectable with ordinary histological techniques. That the speed of impulse conduction is related to the diameter of the nerve fiber has been noted in Chap. 1. In a peripheral nerve, therefore, the conduction rate of impulses will show a wide range. In fact, it has been learned that in mammals the conduction rate ranges from 120 m. per sec. for the largest fibers to 10 m. per sec. or less for the finely myelinated and "unmyelinated" (histologically) fibers.

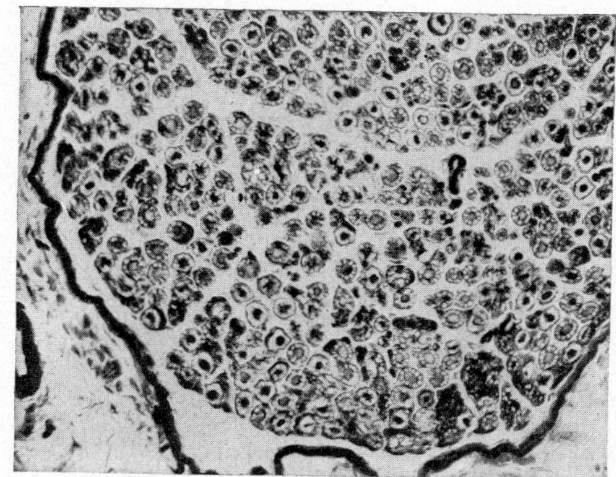

FIG. 110. Cross section of fascicle of normal sciatic nerve of cat. The myelin sheaths are easily visible. The variation in fiber diameter should be noted. Several groups of very small, thinly myelinated fibers are also present. Weil stain. Photomicrograph, ×240.

The sensory fibers in a peripheral nerve vary

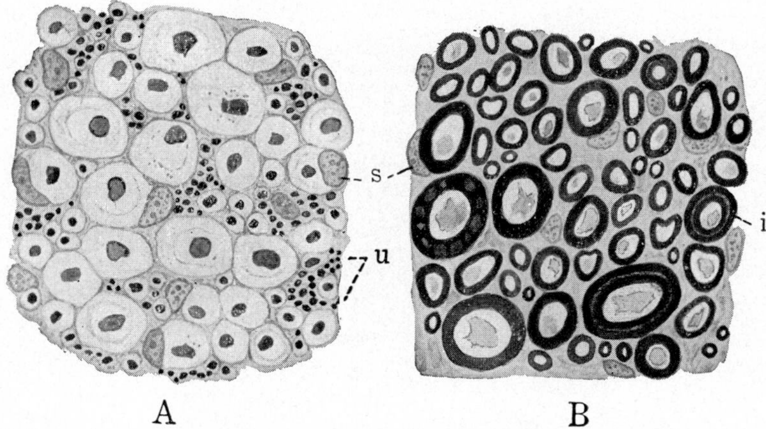

FIG. 111. Drawings of cross sections of nerve fibers of peripheral nerve. *A*, stained with silver for axis cylinders; *B*, with osmic acid for myelin sheaths; *i*, myelin; *s*, Schwann cell nucleus; *u*, unmyelinated fibers, not visible in *B*. (*From Nonidez and Windle, "Textbook of Histology," courtesy of McGraw-Hill Book Company, Inc.*)

not only in size and amounts of myelination, but also in their type of terminals. In general, sensory nerve endings, or receptors, can be divided into encapsulated and nonencapsulated forms. It is now known that a sensory fiber transmitting a certain quality of sensibility has a characteristic ending, or in other words, specificity of sensory endings exists with reference to the type of stimuli that activate them. The various sensory endings and cerain principles of their mechanisms are described in Chap. 19.

FUNCTIONAL COMPONENTS IN SPINAL ROOTS

The fibers of a posterior root fall into two functional categories, **general somatic afferent** and **general visceral afferent.** The former transmit impulses from receptors in cutaneous areas, muscles, and tendons; the latter transmit impulses from receptors within the walls of viscera. These reach the posterior root via the communicating rami, after having traveled the peripheral paths of the autonomic nerves. Impulses arising in the cutaneous areas are classed as **exteroceptive;** those arising in muscles and tendons, as **proprioceptive;** those arising in viscera as **interoceptive.**

As the posterior roots approach the spinal cord, the fibers are grouped into a medial and a lateral bundle. The medial bundle contains medium and large fibers transmitting impulses of all qualities except pain and temperature. The pain- and temperature-conducting fibers are grouped into the lateral bundle. The subsequent course of these fibers within the spinal cord has been described in the preceding chapter.

The anterior roots, as stated above, are composed of axons of cells located in the anterior gray columns throughout the spinal cord. These innervate skeletal or striated muscle and are called **general somatic efferent** or **motor.** In the thoracic and upper two or three lumbar segments and in the second, third, and fourth sacral segments, autonomic motor cells in the intermediate gray cell columns contribute axons to the anterior roots also. These axons innervate smooth and cardiac muscles and are called **general visceral efferent** or **motor.** They leave the anterior primary ramus of the spinal nerve via the white communicating ramus. The somatic efferent axons are considerably larger than the visceral efferent ones and in general have a heavier myelin sheath.

It will be seen from the preceding discussion that the mixed spinal nerves formed by union of anterior and posterior roots contain components of four categories: general somatic efferent; general visceral efferent; general somatic afferent; general visceral afferent. The general somatic afferent fibers have receptors in cutaneous areas and in muscles and tendons. They are responsible for cutaneous and striated muscle, or deep, sensibility. The sensory fibers with terminals in muscles and tendons and deeply placed blood vessels travel with the somatic efferent or motor fibers, within the deep branches of peripheral nerves. Superficial branches of the peripheral nerves contain sensory fibers, somatic and visceral, with endings in cutaneous and subcutaneous areas, and visceral efferent fibers to the smooth muscle and glands in the skin layers.

Nerve-muscle Relationships

A single motor neuron through branching of its axon may have endings in contact with 150 muscle fibers in the large, powerfully contracting muscles of limbs and trunk. In small muscles capable of finer degrees of contraction and movements of precision, a single axon does not innervate so many muscle fibers. The motor neuron, its axon, and all its terminals constitute a **motor unit.** Motor-nerve fibers in muscles terminate in many grapelike arborizations. The branching terminals of the axon lose their myelin, penetrate the sarcolemma of the muscle fiber, and arborize with little brushlike or grapelike endings in contact with the sarcoplasm of the muscle. The neurolemma of the nerve fiber becomes continuous with the sarcolemma. In the granular sarcoplasm beneath the nerve endings are many nuclei which with the sarcoplasm constitute a **sole plate** (Figs. 112, 113). The point of union between nerve fiber and muscle constitutes the **myoneural junction.** It is of interest that the muscle fibers of each motor unit are grouped in close relationship in a muscle, at times constituting a muscle fascicle.

The sensory endings on muscle fibers are of two types, simple unencapsulated and encapsulated; both are epilemmal in their position with

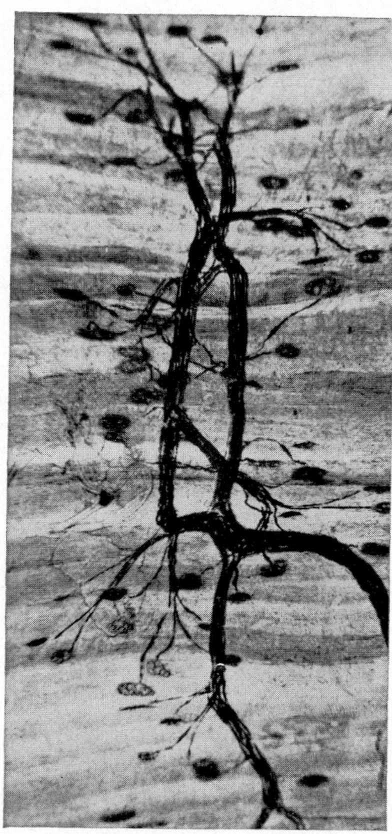

FIG. 112. Motor-nerve endings in striated muscle. Ranvier gold chloride. Photomicrograph, ×142.

reference to the sarcolemma. It will have been noted that motor endings in muscle are beneath the sarcolemma and are, therefore, hypolemmal.

Not all the motor fibers to striated muscle are the same size, and in fact, a small-fiber motor system as well as a large-fiber motor system has been described in many of the limb muscles of frogs, certain mammals, and man (322, 446, 447, 448, 475, 664). In man the cervical anterior roots contain as many as 15 to 25 per cent small fibers having a diameter of about 4 to 5 μ. Haggquist described a different type of ending for the small fibers, one whose terminals swell into grapelike enlargements in the sole plate. Some investigators report that a single muscle fiber may receive both large and small fibers; others state that the small fibers pass only to the intrafusal fibers about which the proprioceptive neuromuscular spindles are entwined. The function of the small-fiber system is also disputed. Haggquist conceived it as furnishing the efferent limbs of the reflex mechanisms underlying muscle tone (322). When large fibers to the limb muscles of a rabbit had been rendered inactive by anoxia, a condition of spastic paralysis resulted, the spasticity maintained, presumably, by small fibers. A sensory function has also been ascribed to them, Leksell considering them as sensory fibers only indirectly which facilitate the neuromuscular spindle endings, enabling them to have more selective and efficient action (475). It has been demonstrated in the frog, at least, that the small-fiber system can evoke slowly developing, nonpropagated contraction of muscle fibers (448). It is possible that the small fibers innervate the small motor units, although it does not seem illogical to suspect that the variation in fiber size in the motor fibers indicates variable functional types, large fibers transmitting motor impulses rapidly to fast-contracting muscles, small fibers conducting more slowly and innervating more slowly and persistently contracting muscles.

A simple sensory ending in striated muscle is

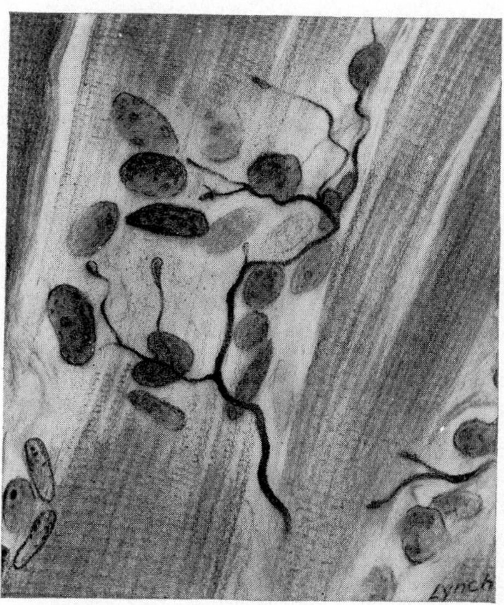

FIG. 113. Drawing of "myoneural junction" from preparation of striated muscle of guinea pig, prepared by Dr. C. H. Sawyer. Many nuclei of the sole plate are visible, and the nerve-fiber terminations ramify among them. Stain, Mallory's technique with fast green and Holmes' silver. ×900.

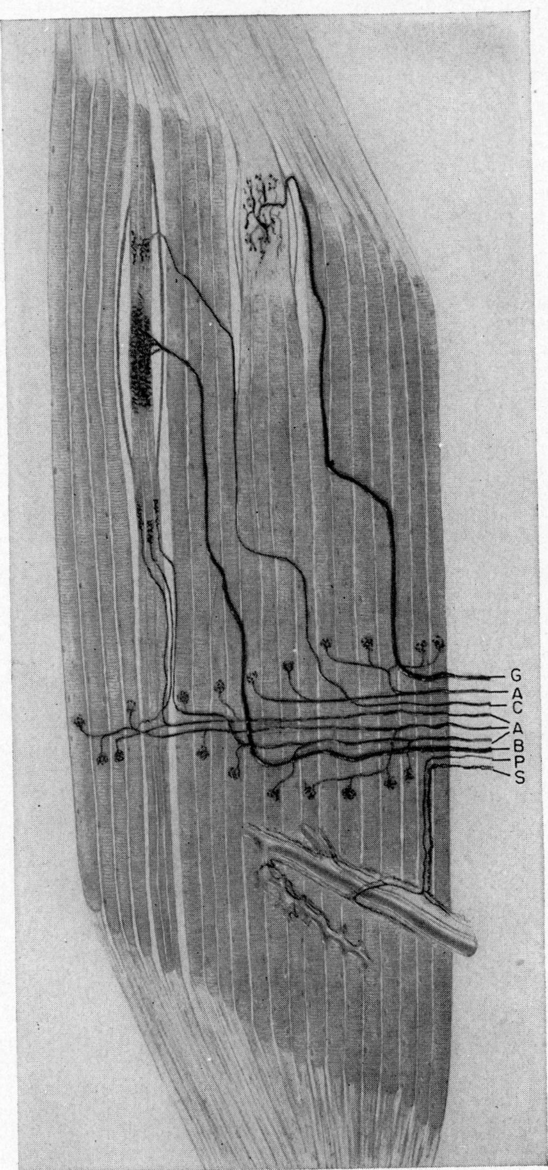

FIG. 114. Drawing to illustrate nerve-muscle relationships. *A*, motor fibers; *B*, sensory fiber to neuromuscular spindle, the intrafusal fibers of which are innervated also by *A*; *C*, fiber innervating flower-spray ending in the neuromuscular spindle; *G*, fiber to a single tendon organ of Golgi; *P*, pain fiber from small blood vessel; *S*, sympathetic fibers to blood vessel. (*Redrawn courtesy of Dr. D. Denny-Brown from Creed, Denny-Brown, Eccles, Liddell, and Sherrington, "Reflex Activity of the Spinal Cord," The Clarendon Press.*)

formed as follows: A myelinated nerve fiber passing along a muscle fiber, in close relation with the sarcolemma, loses its myelin and entwines about the muscle fiber. Small side branches arise from the fiber as it spirals about the muscle fiber, and these end in tiny nodular swellings. These endings are sometimes called flower-spray endings.

The encapsulated endings are more numerous in those muscles subserving posture and intrinsic muscles of the hands, and in these they are more often found near the musculotendinous junction. Several muscle fibers, thinner than the others but abundant in sarcoplasm, are encircled by the branching terminals of a myelinated nerve fiber in a dense spiral arrangement to form a neuromuscular spindle (Fig. 114). The muscle fibers, known as intrafusal fibers, and the spindle are surrounded by a connective-tissue sheath. The nerve fiber loses its myelin as it branches within the connective-tissue capsule, and the terminal spirals have only a thin neurolemma about the axis cylinder. Neuromuscular spindles are arranged longitudinally in muscles with their long axis parallel to the long axis of the muscle fibers. They respond to stretch, being stimulated by the lengthening of the encompassed muscle fibers during passive stretch and relaxation. These endings form the receptors on the afferent limb of the reflex arc which maintains **muscle tone.** In response to impulses sent into the spinal cord by them, the anterior column motor cells send effector impulses to motor endings for bringing about graded amounts of contraction in muscle fibers. In such a way suitable degrees of tension or tone are maintained in skeletal muscles, constituting in them an "awaiting for call to action" in phasic contraction. The tendon organs of Golgi are stimulated by tension arising either through passive stretch of the muscle or through active contraction (536).

It is of interest that more proximal limb muscles (femoral group) of the cat receive afferent fibers of larger diameter than do the more distal muscles (crural group), and that extensor muscles which are classed as "pale" histologically receive larger nerve fibers than do their flexor antagonists. Many afferent fibers to "pale" muscle fibers are larger than those to the "red" muscle, when both "pale" and "red" muscle fibers are present in the same muscle (495).

Muscle-fiber activity follows principles similar to those of nerve action. A stimulus of threshold strength brought to a muscle fiber (or a muscle) will set it into contraction, and the contraction follows again the "all-or-none law." Properly spaced stimuli can set into action a greater response in a muscle, a summative effect taking place. At any one time not all the groups of motor units of a muscle are in the same stage of contraction; *i.e.*, all the motor neurons to a muscle do not discharge at the same time and to the same extent. The discharge, and hence the motor-unit activity, is asynchronous, but the total smooth performance is again the product of a canceling out and summative effect. The integration of efficient muscle activity is primarily brought about by the timing of the discharges of the motor units, and these in turn are controlled or integrated by neurons of other nervous-system levels. In normal and efficient muscle activity, an **agonist** (or active) muscle contracts to the maximum of its ability, its cooperating or **synergist** muscle contracts equally maximally for the condition at hand, and the **antagonist** offers the proper, graded amount of opposition (or relaxation).

As stated in Chap. 1, acetylcholine is liberated at the myoneural junction in association with the passage of the discharge from nerve to muscle. Normally, the cholinesterase-acetylcholine ratio is such that efficient muscle contraction can take place. Disordered or enfeebled contraction can occur, presumably, through inadequate acetylcholine formation, too rapid destruction of it, or interference with its reaching the muscle. In the disease **myasthenia gravis,** weakness of contraction develops in the muscles of the face and head and, at times, also of the extremities. The basic disorder appears to involve a disturbance occurring at the myoneural junction, bringing about an interference with the acetylcholine gaining access to the muscle. A similar condition can be developed experimentally by the application to a muscle-nerve preparation of curare, a poison formerly used on arrows by South American Indians. In spite of a normal amount of acteylcholine for initiating contraction, no contraction will occur through nerve stimulation of the muscle. Stimulation of the muscle directly will result in contraction, however, indicating that the curare prevents the acetylcholine from acting. Some agent apparently behaves in curarelike fashion in myasthenia gravis. Clinical treatment is reasonably successful with a drug, prostigmine or neostigmin, which protects acetylcholine from destruction. After an injection of this drug the patients lose their facial weakness, are again able to swallow, and can perform other muscular activities impossible before. The drug treatment must be a continuous one, however.

Reaction of Neurons to Severance of Axon

Nerve cells are very susceptible to changes in blood and oxygen supply, to bacterial toxins, viruses, chemicals, and direct trauma. With reference to the last, severing the axon of a nerve cell brings forth interesting alterations in the cell body and also in the axon. After injury peripheral nerve axons may successfully regenerate, but those within the spinal cord and brain do not. In peripheral axons, also, regeneration may not be attempted or be successful if the axon is severed very near the cell body. The neuron may die. With a more distant severing, however, a process involving degenerative as well as regenerative activity takes place.

CELLULAR REACTION

The reaction occurring within the cell body when the axon is cut is called **chromatolysis,** since it involves most strikingly the chromidial bodies when the changes are studied with the Nissl staining technique. Early changes are a disappearance of Nissl chromidial substance from the dendrites together with a dissolution of it near the nucleus. Subsequently the nucleus begins to move toward the periphery, the nucleolus becomes more prominent for a short time, and the Nissl substance throughout the cell may undergo dissolution to dustlike particles (Fig. 115). Some small amount of it may remain around the periphery of the cells. The cell usually swells. If the cell does not die, the Nissl bodies may gradually be reformed, the cell shrinks, and the nucleus returns to its central position. As mentioned in Chap. 1, it is thought that the Nissl bodies are re-formed through the activity of nuclear substance. It

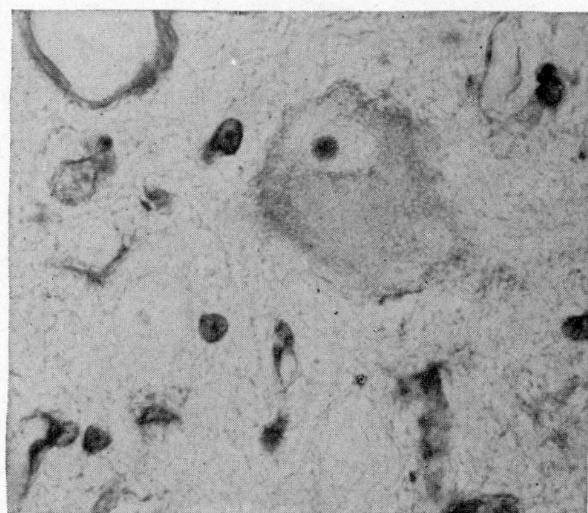

FIG. 115. Motor neuron of anterior spinal gray, undergoing chromatolysis, 72 hr. after section of its axon. Cat, thionin. Photomicrograph, ×645.

has been suggested that chromatolysis involves a breaking up of the nucleoprotein of the Nissl bodies through the activity of an intracellular enzyme. The cell swells and the nucleus is displaced through the taking up of water by virtue of a lowered osmotic pressure. In recovery the nucleoproteins are resynthesized (294).

AXONAL REACTION

Equally striking events are occurring in the axon at the site of section and distal to it (862, 863, 864). Within a few hours the axis cylinders distal to the cut begin to swell and to fragment. Soon thereafter the myelin sheaths suffer a similar fate, and these fragmentations proceed progressively down the isolated nerve stump (Figs. 116, 117). The neurolemma tubes and endoneurium remain unchanged, and the Schwann cells begin to proliferate. Macrophages wander in from the surrounding endoneurium and begin to remove the debris of the axis cylinders and the myelin. With the removal of this and with the continued proliferation of the Schwann cells, the neurolemma tubes may for a time be distended only by Schwann cells.

Soon after the section, the Schwann cells sprout out the cut end of the isolated stump and grow toward the central cut end, and with the proliferation of endoneurial fibroblasts, a bridge of the gap may be laid down. Meanwhile, in the cut central end of the nerve, the axis cylinders and myelin sheaths may degenerate for a very short distance and be removed. Soon, however, the axis cylinders begin to divide longitudinally and to sprout (or flow) out the central end. Many sprouts encounter the Schwann-cell-and-fibroblast "bridge" and are thereby conducted to a neurolemmal tube. Some sprouts go astray, growing laterally and even recurrently toward the cell body. A large excess of sprouts occurs, however, through the axon splitting, and as many as 100 smaller branches may appear from one parent fiber.

Once across the gap, the axon sprouts enter the neurolemmal tubes and begin to grow down into them, edging along between the Schwann cells. A growth of 1 to 2 mm. per day occurs in the nerves of man (715). Many sprouts may enter a single tube. Eventually end organs are reached. Later one of the new fibers will gradually increase in size and regain a thicker myelin sheath, at the expense of the other fibrils within the tube. The fiber successful in reaching an end organ similar to that which belonged to its predecessor is apparently the fiber that survives and increases in size, while the unsuccessful ones disappear.

As the new fibrils grow down, myelination proceeds also, most likely under the influence of the Schwann cell or through a cooperative activity of it and the axis cylinder. With the attainment of a proper end organ, the full development of the new fiber proceeds. Some reorganization of the end organ may be necessary, but ultimately a restoration of function

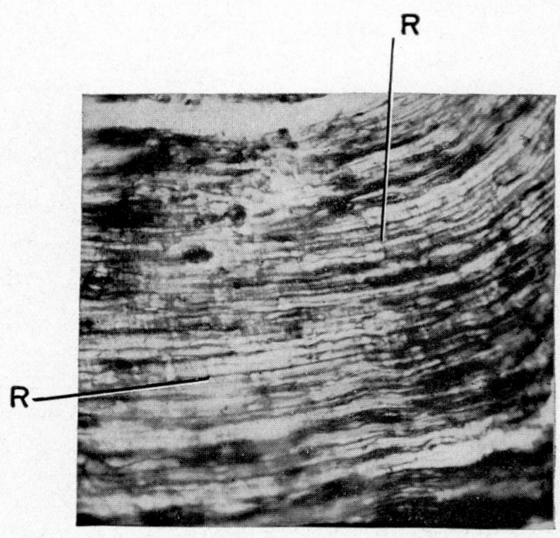

FIG. 116. Normal sciatic nerve, cat. Nodes of Ranvier are present at R. Weil stain. Photomicrograph, ×260.

approaching that normal for the nerve before injury will take place.

Of course the full picture of peripheral nerve regeneration is not as simple as this. Many elements of chance are present, in addition to mechanical obstacles. The nature of the injury has some influence on the success of regeneration and restoration of function. Crushing injuries in which the neurolemma is perhaps not severed are followed by best results. Gaps of 1 to 3 mm. in a nerve of a man may be successfully bridged by the Schwann-cell-and-endoneurial-fibroblast growth, and the new axis-cylinder sprouts will march across. A gap larger than this will probably require suture, with or without a graft. Nerve grafts may be used successfully to bridge the gap of a cut nerve, and these work better if they are portions of some other nerve of the patient, *e.g.,* a small segment of an anterior cutaneous femoral nerve.

The successful restoration of a completely severed nerve trunk depends very much on when the suture is done. Open exploration of the wound very soon after the injury with suture of the nerve is known as **primary suture** and was formerly practiced widely. In many instances, however, it has been necessary later to re-explore the fields, resect portions of the nerve about the suture, and resuture. It appears now that delayed or **secondary suture** of the nerve gives better results. If the initial wound of skin and muscles be allowed 3 or 4 weeks to heal, and exploration then be done, it will be easier at that time to denote the actual extent of the intraneural damage in the nerve stumps and more adequate resection of the severed ends can be made. Secondary suture can then be performed. At this time of secondary suture the neurolemmal, and especially the endoneurial, sheaths will have thickened by proliferation, thus furnishing a more firm and stable tissue for suturing (714). Later or secondary suture may not be followed by successful results if too long waiting results in a degeneration of end organs and if the muscle or skin to be innervated also undergoes atrophic change.

Elements of chance in nerve regeneration are somewhat overcome through the excess of the nerve sprouts, and through the proliferation of fibroblasts and Schwann cells and their out-

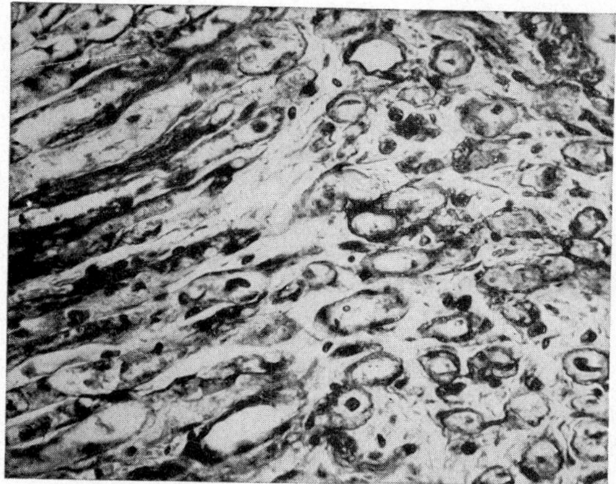

FIG. 117. Longitudinal section of fascicle of sciatic nerve in region just distal to point of transection 120 hr. previously. Only neurolemmal tubes filled with myelin debris and a few Schwann cells are visible. Weil stain, cat. Photomicrograph, ×260.

growths. Many fibers may enter a single neurolemmal tube, and one or more will be likely to reach a suitable end organ. On the other hand, some motor fibers will reach sensory terminals, and some sensory fibers will reach motor terminals; or a tactile fiber may reach a temperature ending, for heat or for cold. It is common that sensory "mix-ups" occur following regeneration. In achieving a successful result the following anatomical factors are more important: Schwann cells must proliferate, axis cylinders must divide and sprout, and especially, proper end organ must be reached. The ultimate completeness of regeneration and successful restoration of function apparently depends on this last factor. These inherent activities of nerve fibers should be given every opportunity through proper surgical care.

The disorders of sensation arising as a result of interruptions in the sensory pathways at various levels, nerve, root, cord, thalamus, and cerebral cortex are described in Chap. 19. It should be emphasized here that within the peripheral sensory pathways it is of great importance to distinguish among root, plexus, and nerve interruptions. Root lesions result in cutaneous sensory losses in a dermatomal pattern, which frequently contrasts greatly with the distribution of sensory loss in the peripheral nerve pattern. Similarly, a single anterior root lesion may cause paralysis of only a certain part of several muscles and may go unnoticed clinically, whereas a nerve lesion may completely paralyze one or several muscles. It is essential, therefore, to know the segmental (root) and nerve innervation of the skin and muscles.

The peripheral nerves suffer a change in anatomical structure under a variety of conditions. Mechanical pressure, chemical (alcohol, arsenic), infective (diphtheria), metabolic (diabetes), and vascular conditions (arteritis, sclerosis, thrombosis) serve as etiological agents for producing disordered structure and hence disordered function. To all these agents, the changes in the axis cylinder, myelin, and Schwann-cell sheaths are basically the same as those described above in a mechanical or traumatic disorder of nerve fibers. The reaction in the connective tissue sheaths may be nil or inflammatory in nature, with dilation of blood vessels, collection of fluids in the perivascular and lymphatic spaces and in the perineurial connective tissue, and mobilization of white blood cells into the tissues. Unless inflammatory changes are demonstrable, it is best to group all these disorders of peripheral nerves under the general classification of **neuropathy;** when inflammation is observed, **neuritis** can be said to exist.

CHAPTER 7

THE AUTONOMIC NERVOUS SYSTEM

THIS IS BY no means a separate "nervous system" but an integral part of the general nervous system (452, 717). Activity in this component of the nervous system also involves the gathering of impulses from peripheral receptors, the transmission and integration of them with association links, and the sorting of them for the initiating of effector responses. The receptors and the fibers transmitting the impulses from them to neurons within the spinal cord or brain stem are customarily thought of as elements of the single large sensory system that are distributed with the autonomic fibers peripherally. By definition the autonomic system is only a motor one innervating those structures whose functions are primarily outside voluntary control; it is frequently thus designated a **visceral motor** system. Among these structures are smooth muscle, cardiac muscle, and glands. Certain viscera, *e.g.*, the urinary bladder, innervated by the autonomic system are influenced in their activity to a considerable extent by voluntary control. Fibers of the autonomic nervous system are distributed to the smooth muscles of all parts of the body, and the system was originally separated by Langley into **sympathetic** and **parasympathetic** divisions on the basis of certain anatomical, physiological, and pharmacological differences of component fibers and their endings. Other names have been suggested for these divisions, as will be seen below, but for better understanding it is best perhaps to adhere to Langley's original nomenclature (455, 456, 457).

Fibers of the sympathetic division leave neurons located in the spinal cord gray via anterior roots and their communicating rami at segmental levels between the first thoracic and second lumbar, inclusively. This division is therefore sometimes referred to as the **thoracicolumbar** outflow of the autonomic system. Certain fibers of the parasympathetic division leave their neurons in the brain stem via several of the cranial nerves, while others leave their spinal-cord neurons via the second, third, and fourth sacral nerves. This is, therefore, the **craniosacral outflow.** These fibers of each division leaving the neural axis, and the cells from which they spring, are designated **preganglionic;** they synapse in peripheral ganglia about neurons whose axons are in turn designated as **postganglionic,** and these latter fibers pass to the structure to be innervated. For the sympathetic division these postganglionic fibers arise in the ganglia of the paravertebral sympathetic trunk and the prevertebral or collateral ganglia, such as the celiac, superior and inferior mesenteric, hypogastric, and pelvic. For the parasympathetic division the postganglionic fibers arise from neurons located within ganglia near, or within the walls of, the viscus innervated. Peripheral autonomic innervation thus involves a two-neuron chain as opposed to the direct innervation of voluntary muscle by an axon from a cell in the cerebrospinal axis. Many of the structures innervated by the autonomic system receive fibers from both divisions. Some apparently receive only a single set, sympathetic or parasympathetic. These peripheral autonomic elements are regulated by supraspinal autonomic centers in brain stem and cerebral cortex.

SYMPATHETIC DIVISION

Within the lateral intermediate gray columns of the spinal cord, between the first thoracic and second lumbar levels, inclusively, medium-sized multipolar neurons are located. These

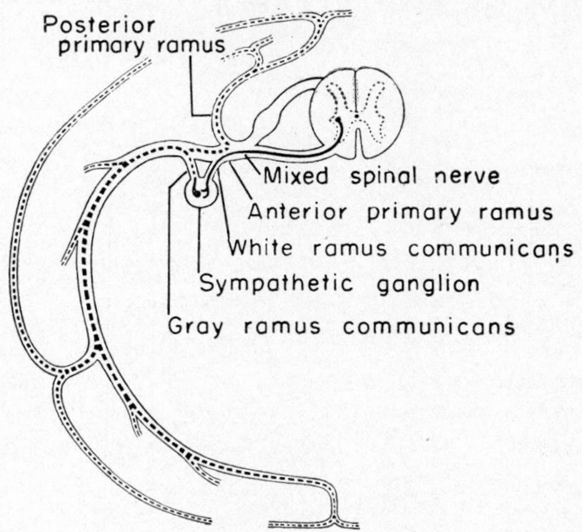

FIG. 118. Diagram to show course of sympathetic fibers in a segmental nerve. (*From Haymaker and Woodhall, "Peripheral Nerve Injuries," W. B. Saunders Company.*)

have been referred to above and in Chap. 5 as **preganglionic sympathetic motor** neurons. They send their axons, also designated as **preganglionic,** out of the spinal cord with the anterior roots.

COMMUNICATING RAMI

Just distal to the point of union of anterior and posterior spinal roots to form a spinal nerve, one or several communicating rami interconnect the spinal nerves and the **paravertebral ganglionated sympathetic chain** (Fig. 118). Of these communicating rami some are designated **white,** some **gray,** according to the histological characteristics of their contained fibers. The white rami, in general, contain larger and more heavily myelinated fibers. The preganglionic sympathetic fibers pass from the spinal nerves to the ganglionated sympathetic chain via the white rami. According to the levels of origin of the sympathetic fibers, white rami are present only on the 12 thoracic and first 2 lumbar nerves. Gray rami, however, are found interconnecting every spinal nerve with neighboring ganglia of the sympathetic chain. They contain fibers which have arisen from cells in the chain ganglia. These pass into the spinal nerves for distribution to blood vessels of the limbs and trunk and to the glands and hair follicles of the skin. The point of connection of the white ramus with the spinal nerve usually is lateral to that for the gray. One or two white and gray rami may be found on any spinal nerve.

PARAVERTEBRAL GANGLIONATED CHAINS

The paravertebral ganglionated chains show much variation from one individual to another (718). The number of ganglia varies, and in certain levels, especially the lumbar, it is impossible to identify, *e.g.*, an independent "third" or "fourth" lumbar ganglion, as such. The chain of connected ganglia extends on each side from the base of the skull to the level of the second coccygeal vertebra (Fig. 119). From two to four ganglia are usually present in the cervical region; superior, middle, intermediate, and inferior ones are usually identified when the larger number are present. Passing superiorly from the superior cervical ganglion, large bundles of nerve fibers, the **carotid nerves,** follow the internal and external carotid arteries into the various regions of the head inside and outside the skull. Eleven or twelve ganglia are usually present in thoracic levels, and four in each of the lumbar and sacral levels. The first thoracic ganglion frequently fuses with the inferior cervical to form a **stellate ganglion.** The two chains end at the lower coccygeal level by fusing into one ganglion, the **ganglion impar.** Occasionally the interconnecting portion of the sympathetic trunk between two consecutive ganglia is double. The right and left ganglionated chains are seldom connected by fibers crossing anterior to the vertebrae.

THE GANGLIONIC CELLS AND SYNAPSES

The neurons of the paravertebral and prevertebral sympathetic ganglia are multipolar, and their Nissl bodies are finely granular. The majority of the cells measure between 25 and 32 μ in greatest diameter (129, 453). Nearly every cell is enclosed within a capsule composed of ectodermal cells that resemble endothelium. The cells are classified according to the length of dendrites. Some have very short dendrites, a number of which end within the cellular capsule; some have long dendrites; and others have short and long dendritic processes (Fig. 120). Many more cells are found in a

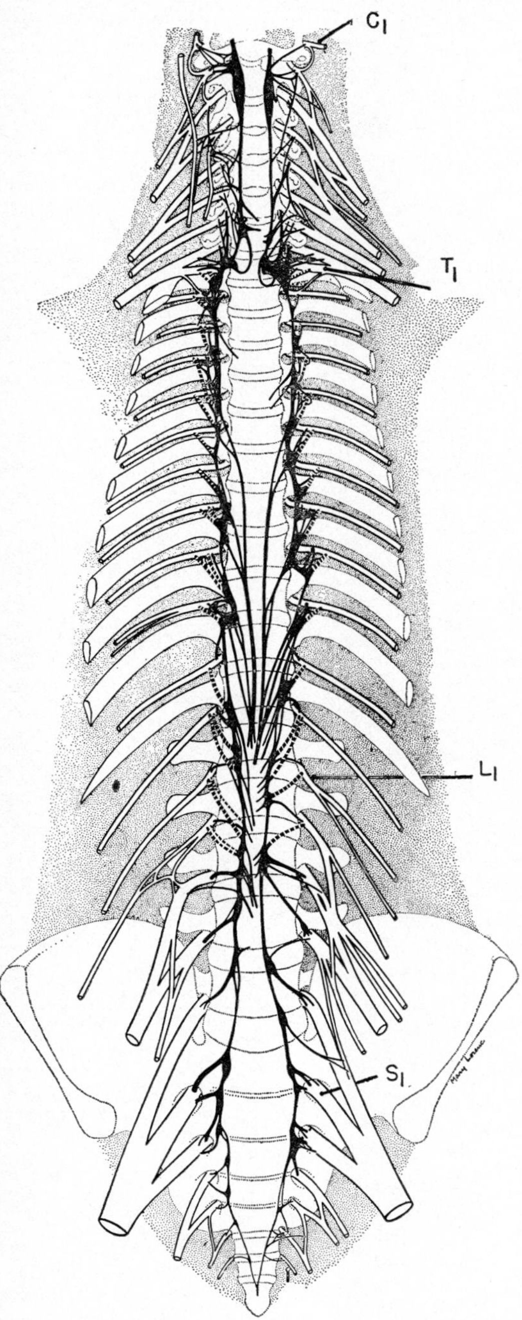

FIG. 119. The sympathetic ganglionated chain, communicating rami and splanchnic nerves of an adult human. The first cervical, first thoracic, first lumbar, and first sacral spinal nerves are indicated. The preganglionic (white) rami are indicated by dash lines. Those at the second and third thoracic levels, right, are indistinct. The postganglionic rami, the sympathetic chain, and the splanchnic nerves are shown in black (*From Pick and Sheehan, J. Anat., vol.* 80.)

given ganglion than there are entering preganglionic fibers, and sympathetic activity along one preganglionic fiber can be discharged into many postganglionic neurons.

DISTRIBUTION OF PREGANGLIONIC FIBERS

The course of the preganglionic fibers of the white rami varies (Fig. 121). Some synapse in the first ganglion of the chain they enter. Others, especially those of the upper thoracic levels, may enter the chain, turn rostrally, and run cephalad to find a synapse in a cervical ganglion. Preganglionic fibers entering the trunk at lowest thoracic and the two upper lumbar levels turn caudally and pass into the lower lumbar and sacral ganglia to find synapse. Other preganglionic fibers enter the sympathetic chain only to pass through it and into outlying prevertebral ganglia such as the celiac, superior mesenteric, inferior mesenteric, and hypogastric, to find synapse. The three thoracic splanchnic nerves, for example, are constituted for the most part by such preganglionic fibers (Fig. 121). Other "splanchnic" nerves may be present at lumbar and sacral levels, and their fibers find synapse in the lower prevertebral ganglia such as the inferior mesenteric and hypogastric. As their names imply, these prevertebral ganglia are found in association with the major branches of the thoracic and abdominal aorta.

POSTGANGLIONIC FIBERS

Wherever the preganglionic sympathetic fibers find synapse, in the chain of ganglia, or in the prevertebral ganglia, the neurons about which they terminate are designated **postganglionic.** A single preganglionic fiber may synapse about many postganglionic neurons, as described above. These neurons send their axons as **postganglionic fibers** to supply the smooth and cardiac muscles and the various glandular structures of the organism. Many postganglionic fibers leave the sympathetic trunk via the gray rami and pass to the lowest cranial and all the spinal nerves to follow these to their ultimate distribution. Other post-

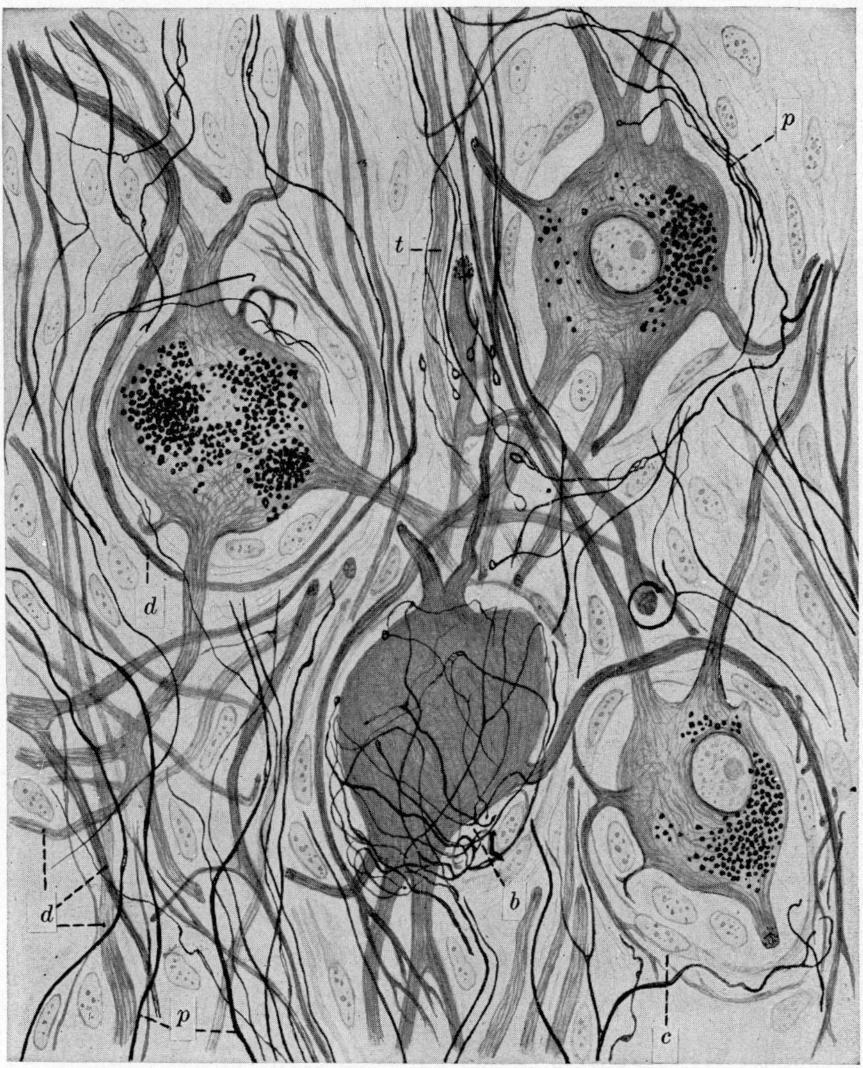

Fig. 120. Autonomic ganglion cells. *b*, terminal plexus of preganglionic fiber; *c*, capsule; *d*, dendrites of ganglion cells; *p*, preganglionic fibers in the intercellular plexus; *t*, long dendrite of ganglionic cell. Note the pigment in the ganglion cells. Silver stain. ×900. (*From Nonidez and Windle, "Textbook of Histology," courtesy of McGraw-Hill Book Company, Inc.*)

ganglionic fibers leaving the trunk pass into the plexuses formed about the prevertebral ganglia, to traverse these and follow intrathoracic and intra-abdominal vessels to the viscera. A sympathetic impulse leaving the spinal cord apparently never traverses more than one synapse in its course to muscle or gland. Because of the multiplicity of synapses made by one preganglionic fiber, however, the sympathetic activity may be discharged over a wide distribution. Arrangements are provided for localized discharge as well as for a diffuse one, however.

Apparently several alternate peripheral paths are available for preganglionic sympathetic impulses. Neurons which, in so far as can be determined, are postganglionic in character have been described in the anterior roots of certain levels, especially the first and second thoracic and the first and second lumbar, and in the white rami of these roots (453). Postganglionic fibers from those neurons in the ventral roots do not necessarily traverse the sympathetic ganglionated trunk, whereas those of neurons in the white rami may take such a course. Furthermore, postganglionic neurons have been described in gray rami at these thoracic and lumbar levels. Those sympathetic fibers which reach their end organs without a circuit through the ganglionated chain naturally would escape in the usual surgical procedures for removing sympathetic innervations.

Parasympathetic Division

This division of the autonomic system is known as the craniosacral outflow, arising as it does from the neural axis at certain cranial and sacral levels (Fig. 122).

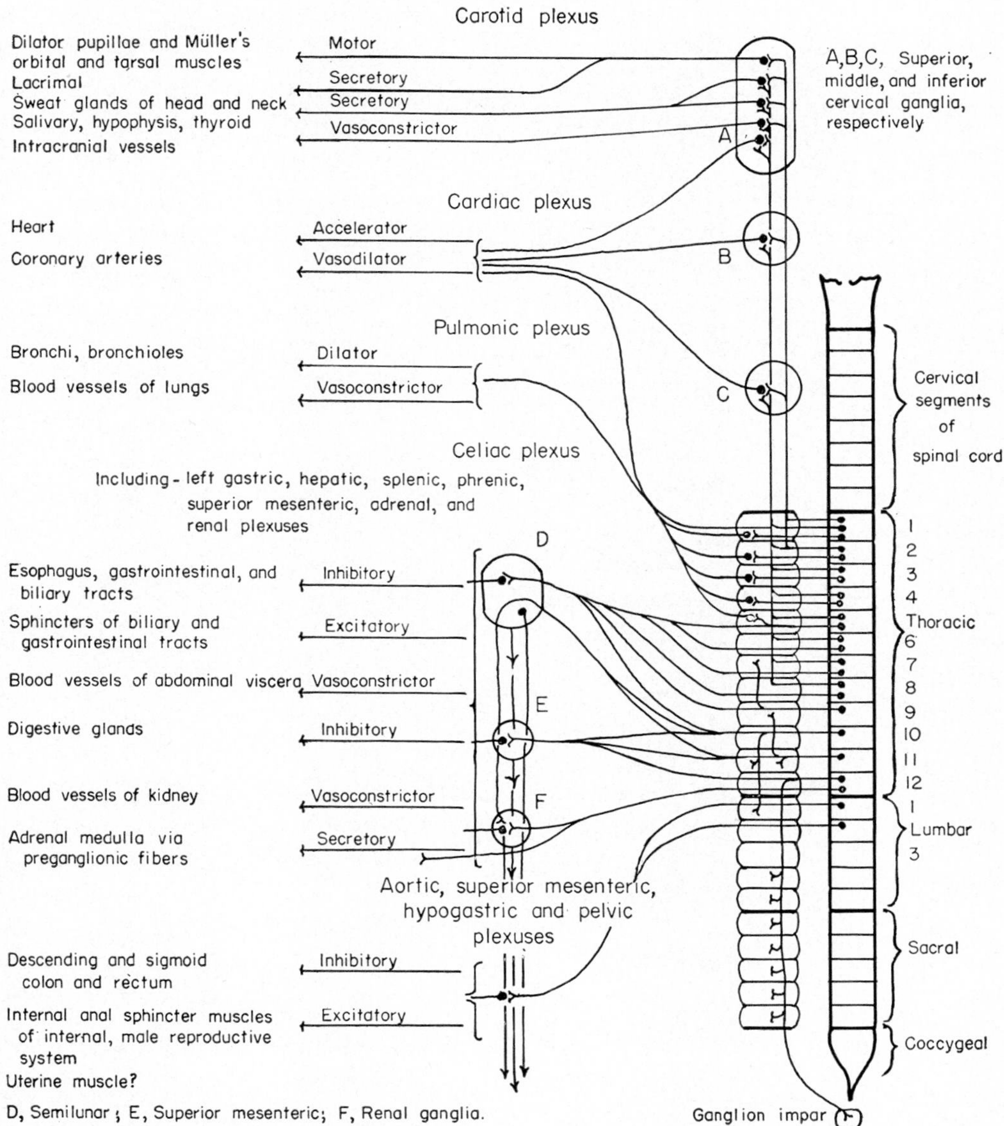

Fig. 121. Diagram of the thoracicolumbar division (sympathetic) of the autonomic nervous system. The diagram does not indicate the connections of the vasomotor, pilomotor, or sudomotor fibers to the skin, or of the vasomotor fibers to vessels of the trunk and extremities.

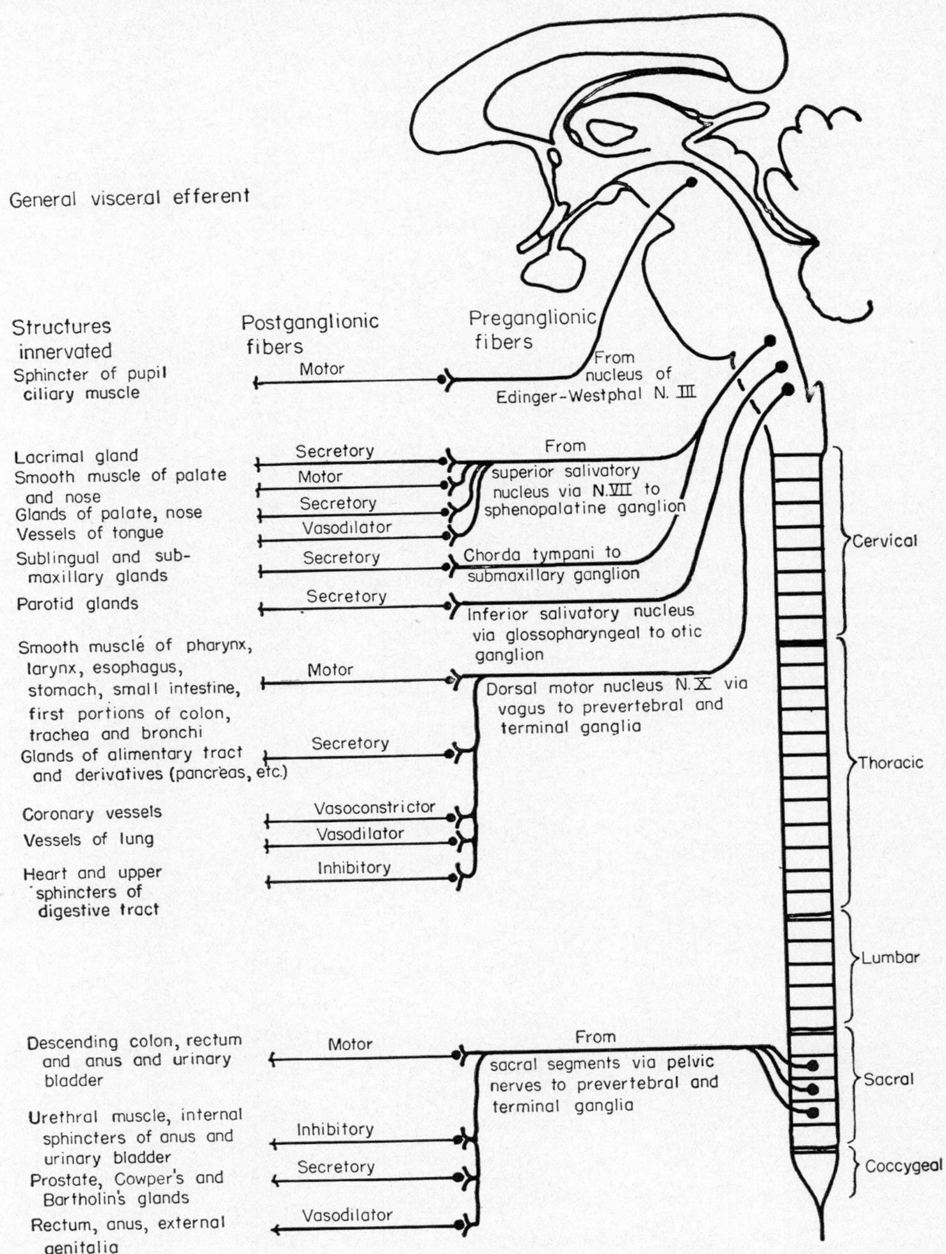

FIG. 122. Diagram of the craniosacral (parasympathetic) division of autonomic nervous system.

CRANIAL OUTFLOW

Certain nuclei within the brain stem, to be described in more detail in later chapters, contain **preganglionic parasympathetic neurons** whose axons pass out with one of several cranial nerves. **Postganglionic neurons** are located within cephalic ganglia and within the walls of thoracic and abdominal viscera. From the Edinger-Westphal nucleus in the midbrain, preganglionic axons pass via oculomotor nerves to find synapse about postganglionic neurons in the ciliary and episcleral ganglia within the orbit. Postganglionic fibers travel to constrictor muscles of the iris and to the ciliary muscles. From the superior and inferior salivatory nuclei in the rostral medulla, preganglionic fibers pass out with the seventh and ninth cranial nerves, respectively, to find postganglionic neurons in the submaxillary, sublingual, and otic ganglia. From these, postganglionic fibers pass into the salivary glands. A lacrimal nucleus, also in the rostral medulla, sends preganglionic fibers via the facial nerve to find postganglionic neurons in the sphenopalatine ganglion. It will be noted that all these outlying cranial parasympathetic ganglia are closely attached to some branch of the trigeminal nerve. In the caudal medulla, the dorsal motor nucleus of the vagus sends out many preganglionic fibers via the vagus nerve, principally, and by the bulbar part of the spinal accessory nerve. These find postganglionic neurons in ganglia located just outside, or within, the walls of the thoracic and most of the abdominal viscera. The plexuses of Auerbach and Meissner contain postganglionic neurons for these vagus fibers.

SACRAL OUTFLOW

From the lateral intermediate gray columns in the second, third, and fourth sacral levels **preganglionic parasympathetic fibers** pass out with the anterior roots of these levels. These fibers leave the sacral nerves to pass separately into the hypogastric and pelvic plexuses, or they unite into a pelvic nerve which passes into the plexuses. Some of the preganglionic fibers may synapse about postganglionic neurons within these plexuses; many of them, however, pass into the walls of the pelvic viscera, or into the connective tissue immediately about the viscera, to find **postganglionic neurons.** The postganglionic fibers of the parasympathetic division usually have a short course in contrast to many postganglionic sympathetic fibers. Peripheral parasympathetic connections are so arranged that the activity initiated through this system may be localized, but diffuse activity is also possible when demanded.

SENSORY FIBERS IN THE PERIPHERAL AUTONOMIC DISTRIBUTION

Sensory receptor endings, naked and encapsulated, subserving almost exclusively pain and stretch impulses respectively, are found in blood vessels, within glands, and within the walls of the viscera. Many corpuscles of Vater-Pacini are found within the mesenteries. The sensory fibers to which the receptor endings belong travel in company with the autonomic nerves, and traverse the autonomic plexuses and ganglia, probably without synapsing. Sensory fibers from the viscera travel with both sympathetic and parasympathetic fibers and are frequently referred to as **visceral sensory fibers.** The neurons giving rise to these sensory fibers are located within the ganglia of the cranial nerves and within the posterior root ganglia of the spinal nerves. Sensory fibers traveling with sympathetic fibers traverse the ganglionated sympathetic trunk and reach the spinal nerves and posterior root ganglia via the white communicating rami.

These neurons in cranial nerve and posterior root ganglia send axonic processes into the brain stem into certain nuclei and into the gray of the spinal cord. Reflex connections are made with autonomic motor neurons and somatic motor neurons, and secondary relays are sent via spinal-cord and brain stem sensory neurons and ascending sensory tracts to higher spinal-cord, brain stem, and cortical centers. It is probably true that these paths transmitting sensory impulses which arise in viscera are in no way different in their general behavior from those transmitting sensory impulses from somatic structures. In fact, it is customary to consider the visceral afferent fibers, distributed to viscera with autonomic nerves, and the secondary ascending visceral sensory spinal pathways, as components, with somatic sensory fibers and tracts, of a single sensory system. Some sensory impulses affecting visceral activity may, however, traverse spinal tracts that are separate from somatic sensory spinal tracts. In the cat, for example, stimulation of the sciatic, splanchnic, or trigeminal nerves sets up impulses that bring about reflex pupillodilatation; these impulses do not travel over the lateral spinothalamic tract (335).

Specific Autonomic Innervations

Many visceral structures receive innervations from both sympathetic and parasympathetic neurons. The salivary glands, the heart, the bronchial muscles, and the gastrointestinal tract receive such dual innervation. The blood vessels of the skin and of the voluntary striated muscles, the sweat glands, and smooth muscles of the skin receive sympathetic fibers only, it seems. The urinary bladder and the iris are apparently innervated predominantly by the parasympathetic system, the uterus, predominantly by the sympathetic. When a structure receives dual innervation, stimulation of the two sets of fibers may produce opposite effects. Stimulation of the parasympathetic, for example, slows the heart; stimulation of the sympathetic accelerates heart action. In certain other structures the sympathetic supply exerts a control chiefly on the vessels of the structure, while the parasympathetic innervates the parenchyma. In the pancreas, for example, such a condition is thought to exist.

It will perhaps be useful to list some of the structures receiving autonomic fibers, including where possible the location of the preganglionic and postganglionic neurons (717). It should be emphasized that the plan of innervation, especially by the sympathetic component, is variable, and this fact perhaps accounts for some of the unsuccessful results of surgery on the sympathetic nerves. This variation of sympathetic distribution has been well demonstrated by the researches of Richter. He has devised an instrument, a neurodermometer, which measures the electrical resistance of the skin. Sympathetic stimulation decreases the resistance; removal of sympathetic innervation increases it (668, 669, 671).

BLOOD VESSELS

On the basis of anterior root stimulation in humans, Foerster has shown that stimulation of the first and second thoracic level results in vasoconstriction in the face and neck, respectively; of the third thoracic to the sixth or seventh, in the arm; and of the tenth thoracic to the second lumbar, in the leg. These levels then probably also represent the spinal segmental localization of **preganglionic sympathetic neurons** in the spinal cord for the innervation of these regional blood vessels. **Postganglionic** fibers for the blood vessels of the cephalic area arise in the superior cervical ganglion, chiefly. Others arise in the inferior cervical or stellate ganglia, and some of these pass via vertebral artery and external carotid to their destination. It is of interest that upper thoracic sympathectomies do not always denervate the face completely, nor does removal of the stellate ganglion always do so (669). **Postganglionic neurons** for the arteries of the arm, according to Foerster, are in the middle and inferior cervical ganglia and in the first, second, and perhaps third thoracic ganglia; for the leg, in the third lumbar to third sacral ganglia. The second thoracic ganglion contains the majority of postganglionic neurons for the hands. By stimulating anterior roots and measuring skin resistance in human surgical cases, Ray and co-workers found the levels of **preganglionic innervation** to the hand to vary in upper and lower levels within the limits of the first and tenth thoracic (660).

The sympathetic fibers to the arteries of the extremities are predominantly vasoconstrictors, but vasodilator fibers are thought to be present also, especially for the vessels in the forearm and leg, while the vasoconstrictor fibers are concentrated in the hand and foot. Proximally, the large arteries of the trunk and limbs may receive this innervation directly from the sympathetic trunk. Sympathetic fibers from the ganglionated trunk join spinal nerves via gray rami to be distributed to the distal vessels. They leave the spinal nerves at intervals to pass onto the blood vessels.

The **intracranial arteries** receive sympathetic fibers also. **Preganglionic fibers** traverse the anterior roots and white rami of the uppermost two thoracic levels. They synapse in the stellate and superior cervical sympathetic chain ganglia. Postganglionic fibers from the stellate ganglion travel into the skull about the vertebral artery to supply it and the basilar artery. From the superior cervical ganglion one group of **postganglionic fibers** follows the external carotid and thence passes to the middle meningeal artery; another group follows the internal carotid to the circle of Willis and its larger branches. These sympathetic fibers are chiefly vasoconstrictor.

Parasympathetic innervation of the vessels of the limbs has not been proved. Parasympathetic dilator fibers to the vessels of the tongue and pia are thought to run in the seventh cranial nerve. Experimental stimulation of the nerve within the medulla produced flushing and turgidity in the tongue, and stimulation of the nerve just outside the medulla resulted in vasodilation of the pia vessels (177). The middle meningeal arteries and certain of the larger divisions of the circle of Willis receive vasodilator fibers via the facial nerve and its branch, the great superficial petrosal nerve.

Afferent fibers also terminate within the walls of the arteries proximally and distally. Vater-Pacini corpuscles are found in the adventitial coat of the arteries. Pressor receptors in the aorta and in the carotid arteries are important mechanisms in the regulation of blood pressure. Sensory fibers and endings are fairly numerous about the larger branches of the external and internal carotid arteries and about the venous sinuses. The trigeminal nerve supplies those to the middle meningeal artery, the external carotid branches, the larger arteries about the base of the brain anteriorly, and to the longitudinal venous sinuses. The infratentorial meningeal arteries and venous sinuses of the posterior fossae are supplied with sensory fibers by the vagus and upper cervical nerves.

The *veins* likewise receive sympathetic motor and sensory fibers. The sensory endings are located within the adventitia of the veins and are of free and encapsulated varieties.

ORGANS OF THE SKIN

Sympathetic fibers alone innervate the sweat glands and arrectores pilorum, the smooth muscles that erect the hairs. **Preganglionic** fibers for the skin of the head and neck arise from upper thoracic spinal cord segments, especially the first and second. **Postganglionic** neurons are located in the middle and superior cervical ganglia, and postganglionic fibers follow the branches of the external and internal carotid arteries to be distributed with branches of various cranial nerves.

For the skin organs of the upper extremity, **preganglionic** fibers arise from the third to the seventh thoracic segments. **Postganglionic** neurons are located in the inferior cervical and first three thoracic ganglia. The postganglionic fibers leave these ganglia via gray rami and join the spinal nerves to the upper limb with which they travel. For the lower extremity, **preganglionic** fibers arise in the spinal-cord segments from the tenth thoracic to the second lumbar inclusively. **Postganglionic** neurons are located in the chain ganglia from the third lumbar to the third sacral inclusively, and the postganglionic fibers travel via the gray rami to reach the spinal nerves which innervate the lower limb. The terminals of the postganglionic fibers end around the muscular elements and the secretory cells of the sweat glands, and about the smooth muscles that erect the hairs. Stimulation of these fibers to sweat glands and to arrectores pilorum induces sweat secretion and piloarrection. The sympathetic fibers to the sweat glands are classified as cholinergic. They react to drugs like parasympathetic fibers.

EYE

Sympathetic preganglionic fibers to the eye arise from the first to the third thoracic segments inclusively. By observing pupillary dilatation in man in response to anterior root stimulation, it has been found that sympathetic innervation to the pupil travels through one or more roots and between the eighth cervical level and the fourth thoracic (660). This rostral level shows again the variation in sympathetic innervation, since it implies preganglionic fibers (and a white ramus) in the lowest cervical root in some individuals. This has been indicated by other researches also. **Postganglionic fibers** arise for the most part in the superior cervical ganglion and innervate the dilator pupillae muscle. Stimulation of these fibers causes dilatation of the pupil, through contraction of radially arranged muscle fibers in the iris.

In addition to their innervation of the muscles of the iris and its vessels, the sympathetic fibers innervate also the smooth muscles of the eyelids, the superior and inferior tarsal muscles. Those fibers of the upper lid, especially, serve with the superior levator palpebrae muscle in maintaining the lid open.

Parasympathetic preganglionic fibers to the eye are thought to arise in the nucleus of Edinger-Westphal in the midbrain. In fact, some investigators divide the outflow from the nucleus of Edinger-Westphal into two parts. The preganglionic fibers from the rostral portion of the nucleus pass via the oculomotor nerve, and its inferior branch, especially, to the ciliary ganglion wherein the **postganglionic** neurons are located. These neurons discharge postganglionic fibers via the short ciliary nerves to the constrictor fibers in the iris. This outflow is responsible for constriction of the pupil in response to light. From the caudal portion of the Edinger-Westphal nucleus, other preganglionic fibers are thought to travel with certain branches of the oculomotor nerve to find postganglionic neurons in episcleral ganglia (302, 581). These in turn discharge postganglionic fibers to the muscles of the ciliary process and to the constrictor muscles. This outflow apparently mediates constriction of the pupil and the associated mechanisms involved in accommodation for near objects. It seems well established that removal of the ciliary ganglion does not result in a loss of this activity. A constriction mechanism, therefore, appears to exist outside the ciliary-ganglion relay.

Langworthy has recalled some interesting data to the effect that the presence and function of radial smooth-muscle fibers in the iris for dilating the pupil have been exaggerated (461). He feels that the sympathetic fibers influence the pupil through the medium of the blood vessels of the iris. The pupillary amplitude varies with the amount of constriction and the circulation in the vessels of the iris, a dilated pupil occurring when vasoconstriction is prominent. The reflex control of pupillary diameter is mediated almost entirely through parasympathetic fibers. Relaxation of the parasympathetic constrictor mechanism leads to pupillary dilatation, and reflex pupillary dilatation probably arises through inhibition of oculomotor constrictor activity (374, 375). After sympathetic section, the amplitude of pupillary movements is diminished, but reflex responses are still present (461).

A section of the sympathetic fibers to the orbit will result in **ptosis** of the upper lid and a **miosis** of the pupil. These two signs are part of the **Horner's syndrome,** which also is usually said to include an enophthalmos. This latter is more apparent than real in man. The palpebral fissure is narrowed not only because the upper lid drops but because the lower lid rises in the absence of the sympathetic innervation to the smooth muscle of the lower lid. Horner's syndrome will occur with interruption of central sympathetic fibers descending through the brain stem tegmentum to the spinal-cord preganglionic neurons, as well as with interruption of the peripheral sympathetic outflow to the orbit; in the first thoracic ventral root especially, or the first thoracic white ramus; in any part of the cervical sympathetic trunk or in the sympathetic fibers as they course along the branches of the internal carotid artery finally to reach the orbit. If the fibers are interrupted within the cervical parts of the sympathetic chain, other signs are added to the Horner's syndrome, namely, vasodilatation of the vessels of the skin of the face and an anhidrosis, or lack of sweating, on the affected side of the face. Injury to the total parasympathetic innervation to the eye results in midriasis or dilatation of the pupil and a disorder of accommodation. Usually paralysis of certain extraocular muscles is also found, since the somatic efferent fibers of the oculomotor nerve are nearly always damaged along with the visceral efferent or parasympathetic fibers.

A peculiar type of apparent autonomic disorder of the iris is the "Argyll Robertson pupil." This is, briefly, a pupil which does not react to light or darkness, but does react by constriction on accommodation. It involves, therefore, a disorder of sympathetic and some parasympathetic innervation and a sparing of certain other parasympathetic mechanisms. Several other characteristics are usually described in this pupillomotor disorder. The disorder is nearly always a bilateral one, the retinae are sensitive to light, the pupils are small, and they dilate imperfectly with midriatics. When all these features are present, the diagnosis of "Argyll Robertson pupils" is justified, and such pupils are almost pathognomonic of central-nervous-system syphilis, especially tabes dorsalis. The most vexing problem concerning these pupils is the lack of knowledge as to the site of the damage to sympathetic and parasympathetic fibers. It is most often assumed to be in the midbrain adjacent the periaqueductal gray, although some investigators think the lesion is a peripheral one in the iris or in the ciliary ganglion.

The so-called **tonic pupil,** or Adie's pupil, is usually a dilated pupil which reacts very slowly to light and darkness and on accommodation. It is characteristically a unilateral disorder and the pupil will react normally to drugs. Such a pupil has no known pathologic significance. Its importance lies in the fact that it may be confused with the Argyll Robertson pupil unless the features of the latter are kept in mind and all the above criteria for its diagnosis are satisfied.

LACRIMAL GLANDS

Sympathetic preganglionic fibers arise in the first two or three thoracic segments and pass into the sympathetic trunk to synapse in the superior cervical ganglion. **Postganglionic** lacrimal **fibers** ascend along the internal carotid artery from the superior cervical ganglion. They branch off to join the deep petrosal and the vidian nerves and follow the parasympathetic fibers described below. Sympathetic stimulation produces vasoconstriction of vessels in the glands, chiefly, and to a less extent, secretion.

Parasympathetic preganglionic fibers for the lacrimal glands leave the brain stem with the facial nerve in its intermedius branch. They leave the facial at the geniculate ganglion, traverse the great superficial petrosal and vidian nerves to reach the postganglionic neurons in the sphenopalatine ganglion. From this ganglion the **postganglionic fibers** reach the lacrimal gland by way of the zygomatic nerve (of the maxillary division of the trigeminal) and the lacrimal branch of the ophthalmic division of the trigeminal. Parasympathetic stimulation increases secretion of the gland. **Sensory** fibers are supplied to the lacrimal gland by branches of the trigeminal nerve.

SALIVARY GLANDS

Sympathetic preganglionic fibers emerge from the spinal cord with the upper two or three thoracic white rami and synapse in the superior cervical ganglion. **Postganglionic fibers** to the salivary glands travel along the external carotid and external maxillary arteries to the glands. Stimulation of these sympathetic fibers produces vasoconstriction of the vessels in the glands; in fact, the sympathetic fibers appear to supply only the blood vessels of the glands (454).

Parasympathetic preganglionic fibers to the **parotid** gland arise in the inferior salivary nucleus and leave the brain stem with the glossopharyngeal nerve. They pass by way of its tympanic branch (nerve of Jacobson) through the tympanic plexus and thence through the small superficial petrosal nerve to the otic ganglion where synapses about postganglionic neurons are made. **Postganglionic** fibers reach the parotid gland by way of the auriculotemporal branch of the trigeminal nerve. Stimulation of the parasympathetic fibers causes increased parotid secretion. Only parasympathetic fibers, apparently, innervate the glandular elements of salivary glands.

Parasympathetic preganglionic fibers to the **submaxillary and sublingual** glands arise in the superior salivary nucleus and leave the brain stem with the facial nerve. They leave the facial nerve through the chorda tympani nerve to reach the lingual branch of the trigeminal. Synapse about postganglionic neurons occurs in the **submaxillary ganglion,** and **postganglionic fibers** enter the submaxillary and sublingual glands by many small branches of this ganglion. Parasympathetic stimulation increases salivation. Some observers report that parasympathetic stimulation leads to the production of thin, watery saliva; sympathetic stimulation, to that of thick saliva filled with cells. It has been shown that some overlapping of parasympathetic innervation of the salivary glands exists (Fig. 163). Fibers traveling with the glossopharyngeal nerve reach the submaxillary and sublingual glands, and fibers traveling with the facial nerve supply the parotid (661). If the parasympathetic nerves to the salivary glands are destroyed, no reflex salivation is possible in response to olfactory, gustatory, or psychic stimuli.

HEART

Sympathetic preganglionic fibers emerge from the spinal cord with the upper five or six thoracic white rami. They enter the ganglionated chain and synapse in the three cervical ganglia and in the upper five or six thoracic ganglia. **Postganglionic fibers** arise in the cervical ganglia and travel to the heart by way of the superior, middle, and inferior cardiac nerves and the cardiac plexuses. Many other postganglionic fibers arise from the upper five or six thoracic ganglia and pass into the cardiac plexuses directly. These latter postganglionic fibers are apparently more numerous than those arising in cervical ganglia. Stimulation of sympathetic nerves causes cardioacceleration.

Parasympathetic preganglionic fibers arise in the dorsal motor nucleus of the vagus, and pass with that nerve and its branches into and through the cardiac plexuses to the terminal cardiac ganglia, located within the auricular muscles. From these ganglia **postganglionic fibers** carry impulses to the sinoauricular and atrioventricular nodes, to the auricular muscle, and to the atrioventricular bundle. Innervation of the sinoauricular node is predominantly right vagal; that of the atrioventricular node, left vagal. It is not definitely known whether vagus fibers reach the ventricular muscle in man. Vagal activity slows cardiac rhythm through the sinoauricular node and causes weakening of contraction of the auricles; it slows the rate of conduction through the auricle and the atrioventricular bundle of His.

Sensory fibers from the heart travel principally by way of sympathetic nerves. Some of them pass directly to the thoracic sympathetic ganglia and through them via white rami to the spinal nerves and posterior root ganglia neurons at the second to fifth thoracic levels, inclusively. The major portion of sensory fibers from the richly supplied coronary vessels travel this route. Many sensory fibers travel via the inferior cardiac nerves through the inferior cervical ganglia to cell bodies in the first thoracic posterior root ganglion, especially, and in the eighth cervical to a less extent. A moderate number of sensory fibers travel with the middle cardiac nerve through the middle cervical ganglion to find posterior root ganglion cells at the first thoracic level, especially, and to a less extent in the fifth, sixth, and seventh. No sensory fibers travel with the superior cardiac nerve. A few sensory fibers travel with the vagus to cervical levels, where they join the second, third, and fourth cervical nerves to find neurons in posterior root ganglia at these levels. The pain fibers travel almost exclusively with the sympathetic nerves, and the majority of pain impulses enter the left side of the spinal cord.

The exact plan of autonomic innervation, however, to the coronary arteries in man has long been debated. It is apparently true that sympathetic stimulation evokes dilatation of these vessels, while parasympathetic stimulation results in vasoconstriction. Results of certain experimental and clinical studies, however, indicate that the sympathetic nerves normally either contain vasodilator fibers also or that sympathetic activity varies with the condition of the vessels, diseased coronary arteries being constricted by sympathetic impulses (34, 424). It is a matter of some practical importance that the details of coronary innervation be understood, in view of the fact that it is believed that coronary constriction plays a role in the mechanisms underlying the pain of angina pectoris (see later). It is more likely that sympathetic nerves to the coronary arteries contain both vasoconstrictor and vasodilator fibers. Surgical section of vasoconstrictor and sensory fibers for the relief of such pain may be carried out, and the most successful procedures have involved either removal of the upper four to six thoracic sympathetic ganglia, or section of the gray and white rami interconnecting these ganglia with the spinal nerves (645). In some individuals it appears necessary to include the inferior cervical or stellate ganglion in the resection.

RESPIRATORY SYSTEM

Sympathetic preganglionic fibers to the respiratory system have segmental origin similar to that of the sympathetic preganglionic fibers to the heart. They arise in the upper four to five thoracic spinal segments, traverse the corresponding thoracic white rami, synapse in the upper four to five thoracic and, to a less extent, in the cervical chain ganglia. **Postganglionic fibers** travel by way of nerves from these ganglia to the pulmonary plexuses about the hilus of the lung whence they are distributed to the bronchial musculature.

Parasympathetic preganglionic fibers leave the brain stem with the vagus nerve and pass by way of its mediastinal branches to synapse in the anterior and posterior pulmonary plexuses about the bronchi in the hilus of the lung. In these plexuses sympathetic and parasympathetic fibers are intermingled. From these plexus neurons **postganglionic fibers** run into the lung tissue along the bronchial tree.

The sympathetic fibers are thought to be bronchodilator in function, but this has not been proved in man (673). Sympathetic and parasympathetic fibers become mingled through cervical and thoracic connections between the sympathetic trunk and vagus, and clear-cut activity of one system has been difficult to prove. It is generally accepted that the vagal fibers are bronchoconstrictor; the sympathetic ones, if active, bronchodilator.

Sensory fibers from the lungs pass by way of the vagus and the sympathetic nerves and have cell bodies in the nodose ganglion and in the upper two or three thoracic posterior root ganglia, respectively. Sensory endings are numerous in the epithelium of the various orders of bronchi and bronchioles, in the atrial walls, and within the smooth muscles of the bronchial tree. The vagus transmits the afferent impulses concerned in the regulation of alveolar size. Inspiration with its associated distention stimulates stretch receptors within the alveolar walls. The impulses thus set up act through the vagus and medullar respiratory center to stop inspiration. Expiration then begins, the alveolar ducts deflate, and receptor endings are stimulated. These discharge impulses via the vagus, and the respiratory center is subsequently enabled to discharge inspiratory impulses again. This reflex pattern is termed the **Hering-Breuer reflex,** and it is most likely true that the inhibitoinspiratory receptors are the ones which normally function, these responding to stretching of the alveolar ducts. The excitoinspiratory receptors can be demonstrated experimentally and perhaps come into play only in certain disease processes. Sensory fibers transmitting pain impulses from the parietal pleura pass through the intercostal nerves, from diaphragmatic pleura, through the phrenic nerves.

ESOPHAGUS

Sympathetic preganglionic fibers leave the spinal cord principally by way of the fifth and sixth thoracic white rami, but also by way of some upper thoracic rami. These synapse in the chain ganglia and in the celiac ganglia. **Postganglionic fibers** pass from upper chain ganglia to upper esophagus directly; other postganglionic fibers pass to the lower portion of the esophagus by way of filaments from the celiac ganglia and from the periaortic plexus. No fibers pass directly from the chain to the lower thoracic portion of the esophagus.

Stimulation of the sympathetic fibers increases tone in the cardiac sphincter, diminishes tone and motility in the lower third of the esophagus, and augments contraction of the upper third, resulting from vagal stimulation (440). It is to be recalled that the upper third of the esophagus in man is composed of striated muscle. The chief action of the sympathetic fibers on the lower third of the esophagus is, however, on the blood vessels in the normally acting organ. After section of the extrinsic parasympathetic fibers, the sympathetic effect on the esophageal musculature is noted.

Parasympathetic preganglionic fibers arise in the dorsal motor nucleus of the vagus and travel by way of the pharyngeal and thoracic branches of the vagus to the esophageal plexuses and postganglionic neurons in the walls of the viscus. From these neurons **postganglionic fibers** pass to the smooth muscles throughout the esophagus and its cardiac sphincter. Stimulation of the vagus causes increased contraction and motility in the upper third of the esophagus (nucleus ambiguus axons), increased tone and motility in the lower third (dorsal motor nucleus axons), especially in the longitudinal muscle layer, and relaxation with an aftereffect of strong contraction in the cardiac sphincter.

Sensory impulses (pain) from the esophagus travel by way of the sympathetic nerves, the cells transmitting them being located in upper thoracic posterior root ganglia, especially the fifth and sixth. Other sensory impulses from the pharynx and upper esophagus travel by way of the vagus and glossopharyngeal nerves.

STOMACH AND INTESTINES

Sympathetic preganglionic fibers for the stomach, small intestine, ascending and transverse colon, arise from the fifth or sixth thoracic segments to the tenth or eleventh. These for the most part pass *through* the paravertebral chain of ganglia as splanchnic nerves to the celiac and superior mesenteric plexuses. **Postganglionic fibers** arise from cells scattered in these plexuses and pass along the arteries to the viscera. **Preganglionic sympathetic** fibers for the descending colon, sigmoid, and rectum arise from the first and second lumbar spinal cord segments. They probably pass through the ganglionated chain to find synapses in the inferior mesenteric, hypogastric, and pelvic plexuses. From **postganglionic neurons** in these plexuses fibers run to the descending colon, sigmoid, and rectum, respectively. Stimulation of these fibers inhibits peristaltic movements and increases tone of the sphincters. Secretion of digestive juices is inhibited.

Parasympathetic preganglionic fibers travel with the vagus through the celiac and mesenteric plexuses to synapse about the intrinsic neurons in Meissner's and Auerbach's plexuses within the walls of the stomach, small intestine, ascending and transverse colon. From these latter neurons in the enteric plexuses, **postganglionic fibers** arise. Stimulation of the vagi increases peristaltic movements, promotes secretion of intestinal juices, and brings about relaxation of the sphincters.

The descending colon, sigmoid, and rectum receive **preganglionic parasympathetic fibers** from the second, third, and fourth sacral cord segments. These pass from the anterior roots perhaps to mingle in the pelvic nerve and travel thus to the postganglionic neurons in the pelvic plexuses and walls of the viscera; from these latter neurons, **postganglionic fibers** arise.

The parasympathetic innervation is very important in the neural mechanisms of defecation, since it promotes increased tone and motility in the rectum and relaxation of tone in the internal anal sphincter. The sympathetic innervation has a minor or negligible function. A reciprocal relationship exists between the action of the rectum and the anal sphincters, and when the rectum is distended, the sphincter has a tendency to become relaxed. A certain amount of voluntary control over the external sphincter for inhibiting the relaxation is mediated through the internal pudendal nerves. This voluntary inhibition of defecation is not as powerful as that maintained over micturition (see later).

Sensory fibers pass from the stomach and intestines via both vagus and sympathetic nerves, but pain impulses traverse the sympathetics predominantly, and those from the stomach enter the spinal cord through the seventh and eighth thoracic posterior roots, especially. The sensation of nausea depends in part on vagus transmission.

Vagotomy performed in many cases of peptic ulcer has afforded opportunity to study the effects of the autonomic system on the stomach. Such a procedure results in a lessening of gastric motility, a decrease in the acid secretion by the fasting stomach, and because of this, a decrease in the pre-existing pain. Combined acid content remains relatively high. Pain sensation itself in the stomach is not lost, and hunger sensations remain normal. The procedure is apparently not as beneficial as at first thought, because of the postoperative complications such as the development of other ulcers. Even after combined section of parasympathetic and sympathetic fibers to the stomach, a great deal of secretory and peristaltic activity returns in time. This apparently comes about through the activity of the intrinsic plexuses within the walls of the stomach.

BILIARY SYSTEM

Sympathetic preganglionic fibers from lower thoracic white rami pass through the paravertebral chain of ganglia and into the splanchnic nerves. **Postganglionic neurons** are located in the celiac ganglia, from which fibers pass along the blood vessels to the gall bladder, hepatic, cystic, and common ducts (23).

Sympathetic impulses are thought to be inhibitory to the musculature of the biliary tract.

Parasympathetic preganglionic fibers pass in the vagus through the celiac plexus and along the blood vessels into the intrinsic plexuses in the walls of the ducts and gall bladder. **Postganglionic neurons** are located in these plexuses and send fibers to the muscles of the gall bladder and bile ducts. Parasympathetic impulses are thought to promote increase in tone and motility of the gall bladder and to inhibit contractions of the sphincter.

Sensory fibers pass by way of the phrenic nerve and by way of the sympathetic nerves. Cells of origin would be in third and fourth cervical posterior root ganglia and in midthoracic and lower thoracic posterior root ganglia, respectively.

LIVER AND PANCREAS

The liver apparently receives only sympathetic innervation; the pancreas, both sympathetic and parasympathetic. The **preganglionic** fibers arise from the fifth to the ninth thoracic levels and pass by way of the greater splanchnic nerve to the celiac plexus, wherein **postganglionic** neurons are located. The sympathetic innervation to the pancreas, derived similarly to that of the liver, is chiefly directed to the blood vessels of the gland. The parasympathetic innervation to the pancreas promotes secretion of pancreatic juices and insulin. The **preganglionic fibers** arise in the dorsal motor nucleus of the vagus; the **postganglionic fibers** arise from ganglion cells about the vessels in the gland.

URINARY BLADDER

The activities of the urinary bladder are regulated by both autonomic and somatic motor innervations in response to sensory impulses arising in the bladder. Somatic motor fibers leave the spinal cord from the second to fourth sacral levels and travel via the internal pudendal nerve to the external sphincter of the bladder and to the perineal muscles.

Sympathetic preganglionic neurons are located in the lower thoracic segments of the spinal cord; preganglionic fibers pass out as white rami *through* the chain ganglia, for the most part, and synapse in the hypogastric and vesical ganglia. From these latter **postganglionic fibers** pass to the bladder.

Parasympathetic preganglionic fibers leave the spinal cord with the second, third, and fourth sacral anterior roots and pass by way of the pelvic nerve through the hypogastric and vesical plexuses to terminate about postganglionic neurons in the bladder walls. From these latter cells **postganglionic fibers** are distributed to all the bladder musculature.

Langworthy and his associates have some interesting findings with regard to autonomic innervation of the bladder (463, 464). Sympathetic nerves pass into the smooth muscle of the blood vessels, to the trigone, to Bell's muscles (bands of muscle fibers running from the ureteral orifices to the medial longitudinal elevation of the trigone, the so-called uvula), and to the crista urethrae (verumontanum). There is no evidence of sympathetic innervation to the bladder detrusor muscles or to the urethra proper.

Stimulation of sacral roots containing parasympathetic fibers causes emptying of the bladder. Section of them leads to inability to empty the bladder, and micturition occurs only after the bladder walls are stretched and the intravesical pressure is raised sufficiently to open the urethra. Late after section the bladder often develops rhythmical contraction waves and opens automatically, but some residuum of urine remains because of the feeble contraction of the organ.

Stimulation of sympathetic fibers to the bladder causes the ureteral orifices to close and to be pulled to the mid-line. The bladder base moves down, carrying a portion of the mucosa toward the vesical orifice. In males there is also a contraction of the prostatic musculature and of the smooth muscles of the seminal vesicles and ejaculatory ducts. Section of the sympathetics produces no modification of vesical activity. Langworthy believes that the sympathetic action is only on the prostatic urethra and has only a sexual and vasomotor function in relation to the bladder and urethra.

Sensory fibers transmitting stretch impulses from the bladder walls and pain impulses from the neck of the bladder travel with the parasympathetic nerves and enter the spinal cord at the second to fourth sacral levels. The sympathetic nerves may be accompanied by sensory fibers transmitting pain from the bladder wall and vague sensations resulting from bladder filling, but these latter are considered unimportant. These impulses apparently enter the lowest two thoracic levels of the spinal cord. Profound disturbance of bladder function results from lesions of the second, third, and fourth sacral posterior roots, since such a lesion interrupts the flow of proprioceptive (stretch) impulses into the cord. These proprioceptive impulses arise as a result of stretch of the muscle fibers.

The ascending sensory tracts from the human bladder have been found to lie in the lateral and posterior funiculi (580). The impulses of fullness, pain, and temperature traverse lateral spinothalamic tract fibers. Tactile and stretch impulses from the urethra traverse posterior funiculus fibers.

The stretch impulses arising in the bladder play a very important role in the process of micturition. The bladder musculature reacts to distention with urine by contracting. The proprioceptive fibers form the afferent limb of this reflex arc, the efferent limb of which is the parasympathetic nerves to the bladder muscles.

Small peristaltic waves occur almost continually in the bladder, but adaptations are made by gradual relaxation and distention to the increasing amounts of urine (458). When the bladder distention reaches a certain point the peristaltic waves are perceived in consciousness and a desire to void may arise. This can for a time be put aside by a diversion of attention, and by willed effort the peristaltic waves can be suppressed somewhat. On the other hand, willed effort to micturate can bring about increased contraction waves in the bladder. The mechanisms of voluntary micturition may be summarized as follows. The abdominal muscles and diaphragm are contracted and intra-abdominal pressure is thereby increased, even though an associated relaxation of perineal muscles and a descent of the bladder occur. This increased intra-abdominal pressure and the heightened intravesical pressure brought about by the peristaltic waves of the bladder detrusor muscle serve to force open the internal sphincter of the bladder. Urine flows into the posterior urethra. The presence of urine here reflexly brings about an opening of the external sphincter, and urine flows along the urethra. Reflexes set up by this flow enhance the peristaltic bladder activity. The external sphincter cannot be opened voluntarily but can be closed by the will. Normally it closes spontaneously at the end of micturition and probably before the internal sphincter is closed, although there is doubt about this. At the end of micturition or with voluntary inhibition of micturition, the perineal muscles contract and the bladder neck rises.

Micturition is therefore primarily a parasympathetic and somatic motor activity, operating for the most part reflexly (209). Willed or cortical control is chiefly exerted as an inhibitory process; when the time and place for micturition are appropriate, this inhibition is relaxed. Such cortical control is usually gained at an early age, and it is mediated over fibers which follow closely the corticospinal or pyramidal fibers.

UTERUS

Sympathetic preganglionic fibers arise from lower thoracic and upper lumbar spinal segments, to pass into the paravertebral chain of ganglia. Certain of these preganglionic fibers traverse the chain ganglia and, behaving like the splanchnic nerves, enter the preaortic plexuses to pass through the inferior mesenteric, hypogastric, and pelvic plexuses, in one of which a postganglionic neuron is found. From this plexus of synapse, **postganglionic fibers** pass to the uterus. A few preganglionic fibers may enter the ganglionated sympathetic chain and turn caudally to find a postganglionic neuron in one of the lower ganglia of the chain. From the ganglion of synapse, **postganglionic fibers** pass into the hypogastric and pelvic plexuses and thence to the uterus. Several pathways exist, therefore, through which sympathetic impulses reach the uterus. Other sympathetic impulses reach the tubal portion of the uterus from the ovarian plexus.

The terminology for the plexuses in the pelvis and around the uterus is confusing. The plexuses can be looked upon as arranged in a chain, continuous with the prevertebral abdominal plexuses. The inferior mesenteric plexus, about the artery of that name, sends descending branches into the pelvis as do the more cephalad preaortic plexuses. These descending branches vary in their arrangement and may be diffuse and plexiform or organized into several large nerve trunks as they pass down anterior to the sacrum. If the latter pattern prevails the trunks are frequently referred to collectively as the presacral nerve. These fibers, together with branches received from the lumbar sympathetic ganglia, form the superior hypogastric plexus. The superior hypogastric plexus continues into the pelvis where it divides into two parts at about the level of the first sacral vertebra. These two parts are often referred to as the inferior hypogastric nerves or plexuses. They follow the hypogastric arteries and give off branches, along the smaller arteries, which furnish sympathetic fibers to the various pelvic viscera. In the female the inferior hypogastric plexuses take part in the formation of Frankenhaeuser's plexuses (pelvic plexus, uterovaginal plexus, cervical ganglion) to which branches of the parasympathetic pelvic nerves and branches from the sacral sympathetic ganglia also contribute. This plexus is situated in the broad ligament on each side at the level of the cervix. It rests upon the posterior surface of the connective tissue (Mackenrodt's ligament), extending laterally between the uterine cervix, vagina, and pelvic vessels (190, 263). Nerve fibers run into the uterus from this ganglionated plexus. The neurons in the plexus are small and the majority are thought to be postganglionic parasympathetic cells.

Parasympathetic preganglionic fibers leave the spinal cord with the second, third, and fourth sacral anterior roots. The bundles from each root may run singly into the inferior hypogastric plexuses or as a combined trunk, the pelvic nerve. They become intermingled in the Frankenhaeuser plexus with sympathetic fibers as mentioned above. **Postganglionic neurons** are located in this plexus and in the periuterine connective tissue, especially about the cervix. Some observers deny a parasympathetic innervation to the uterus, feeling that the nerve fibers just described pass to other pelvic viscera and vessels.

Sensory fibers transmitting painful impulses from the fundus of the uterus travel with the sympathetic fibers through the presacral nerve, thence into the lumbar portion of the sympathetic ganglionated chain and into the eleventh and twelfth thoracic posterior root ganglia, especially. Sensory fibers transmitting pain impulses from the cervical portion of the uterus and upper vagina travel via the parasympathetic nerves and have their neurons in the second, third, and fourth sacral posterior root ganglia. Sensory fibers from the lower vagina and perineum travel with the internal pudendal nerve and have cell bodies also in the second, third, and fourth sacral posterior root ganglia.

It appears a paradox perhaps that the human uterus, with all its trappings of autonomic nerves, can carry on its normal activities when these nerves are severed, or when the spinal cord is completely transected. In fact, it is not known what role the autonomic innervation plays, and as mentioned above, many authorities think that only a sympathetic innervation exists. This latter, on stimulation, will promote muscular contraction and vasoconstriction. Sensory endings in the uterus are plentiful and are of various types. Here again, however, dispute exists as to the course the fibers take from these endings to reach the spinal cord. Some authors feel that all sensory fibers travel with the sympathetic fibers and traverse the hypogastric plexus, ultimately to reach lower thoracic posterior root ganglia and spinal cord levels. A seemingly more plausible plan, however, is that in which only sensory fibers from the fundus are said to travel with sympathetic fibers, and sensory fibers from the cervix region travel with the parasympathetic fibers to the sacral cord. Various operations have been devised for the relief of the pain of dysmenorrhea as well as for pain arising in association with pelvic cancer. Section of the presacral nerve and removal of the hypogastric plexus are two surgical procedures used with variable success. A chordotomy seems a more logical procedure, especially for relief of pain associated with pelvic cancer. It is rather difficult, obviously, to section all pain-carrying fibers in the pelvis.

MALE INTERNAL REPRODUCTIVE SYSTEM

Sympathetic preganglionic fibers leave the spinal cord by way of lower thoracic and lumbar white rami to enter the ganglionated chain. Some fibers traverse the chain ganglia and pass into the preaortic and inferior mesenteric plexus and into the hypogastric plexus. Traversing the pelvic extensions of this many fibers find **postganglionic neurons.** Other preganglionic fibers continue within the sacral portion of the sympathetic trunk to synapse there and from ganglia in this portion **postganglionic fibers** pass into the pelvic plexuses, the vesical, middle hemorrhoidal, and prostatic plexuses. From these plexuses the sympathetic fibers are distributed to the vas deferens (pelvic portion), ejaculatory ducts, seminal vesicles, and prostate. Postganglionic sympathetic fibers to the testes follow the internal spermatic artery and arise from the preaortic plexuses at the level of the renal arteries.

Parasympathetic preganglionic fibers leave the spinal cord by way of the second, third, and fourth sacral anterior roots, pass by way of individual nerves or by the combined pelvic nerve to the pelvic plexuses. The preganglionic fibers synapse about neurons in these plexuses, especially the prostatic, and **postganglionic fibers** arise here, to pass to the prostate gland and, especially, to the vessels supplying the cavernous bodies.

In the activities of the male reproductive organs the sympathetic nerves promote vasoconstriction and contraction of smooth muscles of the prostate, seminal vesicles, prostatic urethra, and vas deferens. The parasympathetic promotes vasodilation through relaxation of tone in smooth muscles in the cavernous-tissue arteries, and it is essential in establishment of erection of the penis. The sympathetic is important in the mechanisms of ejaculation and the establishment of flaccidity after erection, by increasing muscle tone in the smooth muscles of the arteries of the erectile tissue.

THYROID, ADRENAL, AND HYPOPHYSIS

Sympathetic preganglionic fibers for thyroid innervation arise in the upper thoracic spinal-cord segments. **Postganglionic neurons** are located in the middle and superior cervical ganglia, and fibers from these ganglia follow the superior and inferior thyroid arteries into the gland. **Parasympathetic preganglionic fibers** arise in the dorsal motor nucleus of the vagus and pass with the superior and inferior laryngeal nerves to the thyroid arteries. **Postganglionic neurons** are distributed along the course of the superior laryngeal nerve and within the gland tissue. Periarterial and interfollicular plexuses of fibers are described within the gland (584). The sympathetic fibers bring about constriction of the thyroid vessels especially, though they also contain some vasodilator fibers. Parasympathetic fibers also carry vasodilator impulses.

Sympathetic preganglionic fibers for the adrenal gland arise in the lowermost thoracic spinal-cord segments. They travel with the lesser splanchnic nerves to traverse celiac and adrenal plexuses to reach the adrenals. Some of the preganglionic fibers terminate about scattered **postganglionic neurons** in the capsule of the gland and in the medulla. Postganglionic fibers terminate about the blood vessels of the gland. Many preganglionic fibers end directly about the chromaffin cells of the medulla which serve as **postganglionic neurons.** Sympathetic stimulation promotes vasodilation especially, and to a less extent, vasoconstriction. Of greater significance is the fact that it also increases the ouptut of adrenaline.

Sympathetic preganglionic fibers for the hypophysis arise from upper thoracic spinal-cord segments and find **postganglionic neurons** in the superior cervical ganglion. Postganglionic fibers follow the internal carotid artery and its branches to reach the gland. The majority terminate in the anterior lobe; others, in the posterior. **Parasympathetic fibers** numbering not fewer than 50,000, according to Rasmussen, arise in the supraoptic and paraventricular hypothalamic nuclei, pass ventrally through the infundibulum to end especially in the posterior hypophysis (653). A few fibers end in the pars intermedia, and a negligible number, in the anterior lobe. Though the secretory mechanisms of the hypophysis depend to a great extent on hormonal activity, data are accumulating to demonstrate that certain hypophyseal secretions are initiated through nervous impulses, parasympathetic and sympathetic.

Central Levels of Autonomic Nervous System

In the past few years evidence has been accumulated to show that higher autonomic "centers" are present in the central nervous system (452). Stimulation in the anterior hypothalamic region and in the immediately rostral preoptic area leads to certain activities that can also be obtained by stimulation of peripheral parasympathetic fibers (651). Stimulation in the posterior hypothalamus gives rise to sympathetic responses. These are described in more detail in Chap. 14. Stimulations of various regions of the cerebral cortex have also produced effects in visceral structures. Alterations of blood pressure have been produced by stimulation of frontal-lobe areas, especially the orbital surface (see Chap. 18). Pupillary changes and sweating have also been produced by stimulation of the frontal lobe (374, 375, 821). Increases and decreases in peristaltic activity of the gastrointestinal tract have resulted from stimulation of frontal lobes, and a rise in intravesical urinary pressure in the cat has been produced by stimulation of these lobes (463). Respiration can be increased or inhibited from a variety of cortical foci, especially from the orbital surface of the frontal lobe. Peripheral autonomic activity has been produced by stimulation of the cerebellum. Pupillary dilatation and increase in intravesical pressure in the urinary bladder with resulting micturition have been reported to result from stimulation of the interior of the cerebellum of cats (132).

In addition to those autonomic "centers" defined somewhat anatomically, several other "centers" in the pons and in the medulla have been defined. A vasomotor "center" is located in the central reticular formation in the lower end of the medulla. The medullar respiratory "center" of the cat and monkey is located in the reticular formation of the medulla just dorsal to the rostral four-fifths of the inferior olive, and another has been defined in the rostral pons. A correlation of clinical signs with post-mortem findings in cases of bulbar poliomyelitis has indicated that vasomotor and respiratory "centers" are present in the human medulla. Destruction of medial reticular neurons in the lower medulla bilaterally was correlated with vasomotor collapse; that of lateral reticular neurons in upper medulla bilaterally, with respiratory difficulty (53).

In recent years much information has been learned about the neural mechanics of respiration (627, 628). Respiration, though not mediated entirely through autonomic paths, is in large measure involuntary. A brief description of its mechanisms is, therefore, not amiss here. The medullar respiratory center, dorsal to the rostral four-fifths of the inferior olive, has two components, an inspiratory and a surrounding expiratory one. The inspiratory center is in connection with the phrenic-nerve motor neurons and is sensitive to changes in carbon dioxide tension. Normally its activity is phasic, and this character is dependent on inhibitory influences operating on it from without. The vagal inhibitory system, described above, is one of the outside influences. Inspiration, causing expansion of lung tissue, stimulates stretch receptors, sets up in them impulses which are conducted centralward over the vagus. It is thought that these impulses are relayed through the nucleus solitarius, that they excite the expiratory center, and that through its interconnections with the inspiratory center, they cause an inhibition of the latter and of the phrenic-nerve discharge.

A subsidiary inhibitory system is the "pontile pneumotaxic" center in the ventrolateral tegmentum of the rostral pons. Activity of the medullar inspiratory center is relayed cephalad to higher levels and to this center which in turn exhibits, through its descending connections, an inhibitory effect on the inspiratory center. Other excitatory and inhibitory systems act on either the inspiratory division of the respiratory center or the expiratory division or both. Afferent impulses entering by way of other cranial or spinal nerves fall into this class. Specific chemoreceptor impulses entering over the vagus and glossopharyngeal nerves are important in the regulation of respiration. Cortical and hypothalamic impulses also modify respiration.

Fibers from the diencephalic and medullar "centers" to lower autonomic neurons are scattered in the tegmentum of the brain stem and in the anterior and lateral funiculi of the spinal cord. Many fibers scattered mediolaterally in the reticular formation of the brain stem tegmentum are apparently descending autonomic ones which pass into the spinal cord. The dorsal longitudinal fasciculus of Schütz, immediately ventral to the aqueduct and fourth ventricle, is considered an autonomic tract with synapses in its course in the tegmental and periventricular gray. Some evidence has been presented that autonomic tracts are grouped in the tegmentum as discrete bundles according to function (69, 70, 757). These tracts end in the spinal cord about the cells in the lateral part of the intermediate gray columns, the sympathetic and parasympathetic preganglionic neurons.

Character of Autonomic Activity

To a great extent the somatic component of the nervous system effects the adjustment of the organism to the outside world. Activity in the sensory organs, in response to stimuli arising from the external environment, sets into play central neural mechanisms which in turn effect a suitable motor response or alteration of the organism to the environmental changes. The range of somatic activity extends from the simple withdrawal movements in response to pain to the complex and skilled motor performance executed by the hands and guided by the eyes. The autonomic nervous system promotes and maintains the well-being of the organism by adjusting it to the constant alterations in its internal environment, especially, and to some extent, to changes in the external environment as well. This activity of the autonomic system to coordinate the organism as a whole to most changing conditions was called **homeostasis** by Cannon. Through its homeostatic activity, the autonomic nervous system controls the tone of blood vessels, regulates the heart action, initiates and oversees the activities of the gastrointestinal system and its allied glands in their digestive processes, and promotes proper respiratory exchange throughout the organism. It regulates the amount of light reaching the retina. The conserving and the discharge of body heat are controlled in large measure through the autonomic component. It promotes and, to a large extent, executes the activities involved in excretion of waste products. It regulates the mechanisms by which the organism can promote the continuity of its kind. It plays a part, with somatic components, in the expression of emotion. Further, the autonomic component works constantly with the somatic component in the discharge of the latter's duties. The blood supply of muscles is maintained by the autonomic component in times of muscular performance, and the nutritive materials are mobilized at times of prolonged muscular activity. Through autonomic activity, heart action is increased and adjusted to maintain adequate blood and oxygen supply during the somatic activity. The somatic component, on the other hand, can regulate certain of the autonomic activities to bring them under voluntary control. The activity of the parasympathetic system in micturition and defecation is brought under voluntary control within the first two years after birth. This control is maintained except under circumstances of great fear and occasionally when consciousness is lost.

It is commonly said that when a structure receives a dual innervation from the autonomic system, the activity of the sympathetic and parasympathetic divisions is antagonistic. Such an antagonism does not hold true, however, in many structures. Though stimulation of the two sets of fibers may produce opposite effects, contraction and relaxation, these activities in the normally acting structure are correlated to produce the most effective response, and a proper balancing of their performance is maintained. The long-maintained antagonism of the two systems in the control of the iris, the pancreas, the urinary bladder, the uterus, and the rectum is no longer valid, according to modern researchers.

Autonomic nervous activity is essential for physical well-being. The **sympathetic division** provides tonic impulses to the smooth muscle of blood vessels, maintains the blood pressure, and keeps the cardiac rate relatively increased by means of continuously flowing impulses, in order that the organism may be more efficient. It also mobilizes the blood sugar and conserves the body temperature. Through its innervation of the pilomotor apparatus and the sweat glands, temperature mechanisms are aided. By its anatomical arrangement, it is possible for the sympathetic to act widely simultaneously; *e.g.*, a preganglionic fiber may pass through several chain ganglia, giving collaterals to each and synapsing about many ganglionic neurons. In addition to this anatomical method of diffusion of impulses, the hormone of the adrenal medulla (adrenaline), itself produced by sympathetic stimulation, in turn causes stimulation of sympathetic nerves. Local sympathetic activity is also possible under certain conditions. This acting as a unit is important in that the sympathetic through such activity may in times of stress, fear, or muscular effort serve as an emergency system and mobilize all suitable energies and activities to carry out the muscular effort efficiently or to overcome the stress of fear.

The smooth muscle of the gastrointestinal tract and of the urinary bladder is stimulated to contract and its tone is regulated through the **parasympathetic system.** The secretion of insulin is promoted by this component and excessive increase in blood sugar prevented thereby. The parasympathetic division, furthermore, is not so widely distributed, and its preganglionic fibers terminate for the most part in peripheral or intrinsic ganglia associated solely with the organ innervated. Its activity is thus much more restricted. There is not often need for united parasympathetic activity. Further, there is no hormone, at present known, that acts completely on parasympathetic tissues as adrenaline acts on sympathetic tissue.

It has been found that the transmission of impulses by the autonomic neurons and nerve fibers is associated with the liberation of specific chemical substances at the ganglionic synapses and at the effector end organs. Preganglionic stimulation, in general, leads to the liberation in the ganglia of a substance that resembles **acetylcholine.** Stimulation of the majority of sympathetic ganglion cells or postganglionic fibers brings about liberation of a substance, **sympathin,** which resembles adrenaline; stimulation of some sympathetic ganglion cells or their postganglionic fibers, however, leads to the liberation of acetylcholinelike substance. Stimulation of the majority of parasympathetic ganglion cells or postganglionic fibers results in the liberation of an acetylcholinelike substance, but stimulation of certain parasympathetic ganglion cells leads to the liberation of a sympathinlike substance. On the basis of the substance liberated, the autonomic fibers have been termed **cholinergic** (acetylcholine formed) or **adrenergic** (sympathin formed). It may be added that certain sympathetic fibers act as parasympathetics in their response to drugs. The sweat glands, for example, are innervated by sympathetic fibers anatomically, but adrenaline (the sympathetic stimulator) does not cause sweating. Pilocarpine stimulates sweating and atropine stops it, both these being parasympathetic drugs, and the nerve fibers to the sweat glands are therefore classified as cholinergic.

The denervation of structures supplied by the autonomic nervous system is followed by an increased sensitivity of them to the humoral substances, such as adrenaline and acetylcholine. Sympathetic denervation of certain organs makes them more sensitive to circulating adrenaline, and they react to smaller amounts of the substance than do normally innervated structures. This sensitivity follows a postganglionic section more often than a preganglionic one, but occurs after each. It is thought to account in part for the occasional lack of success in treating certain diseases by surgical excision of the sympathetics. Incomplete denervation and regeneration of cut preganglionic fibers are also factors in failure of surgical therapy.

The reaction of the peripheral structure in response to section of its nerve supply points up a difference in autonomic and somatic components of the nervous system. Skeletal muscle deprived of its motor supply will cease to function, will undergo degeneration, and in time will atrophy. Smooth muscle and cardiac muscle, however, do not degenerate when denervated, and their activities are in large measure maintained without disorder. The urinary bladder, for example, maintains its tone and contractility and can expel its contents to some degree, though without voluntary control. A certain amount of autonomy of action exists in the gastrointestinal tract after section of the extrinsic nerves. This activity depends apparently on the intrinsic neurons and their fibers.

The Autonomic Nervous System in Certain Clinical Disorders

It has been possible to observe in humans the effects of denervation of various viscera, since a number of operative procedures have been devised for the relief of certain disorders to which overactivity of one or the other components of the autonomic nervous system has, presumably, contributed. Such disorders may be associated with increased vasomotor activity and excessive or depressed contractility of smooth muscle. These activities may come about through direct overaction or underaction of the autonomic component, or they may be initiated reflexly through some disorder of somatic structures.

Raynaud's disease is a disorder of the terminal arteries of the extremities characterized at first by intermittent episodes of prolonged tonic contraction of the vessels. Exposure to cold and emotional stimuli will provoke an attack. The disorder is usually bilaterally symmetrical, and during the acute episodes discoloration of the extremity, either by cyanosis or pallid asphyxia, and excessive perspiration occur. Pain is frequently present in the stage of asphyxia. Chronic Raynaud's disease may result in a dry gangrene of the extremities. A section of the preganglionic sympathetic fibers for the extremities affected is the operation of choice if surgery is necessary.

Incomplete lesions of peripheral nerves, especially the median and peroneal, are occasionally associated with severe burning pain, glossy skin, and increased rise in temperature in the distribution of the nerve. The pain is poorly localizable and it can be aggravated by very slight cutaneous stimuli or by emotional upsets. These disorders are looked upon as manifestations of sensory-nerve irritation, and perhaps reflex overactivity of sympathetic fibers underlies certain of them. **Causalgia,** a term brought forth by Weir Mitchell, refers to the burning pain only, and this, together with the signs listed above, plus increased sweating and vesicular eruptions, and finally atrophy of skin, subcutaneous tissues, and bone may be found in irritative lesions of peripheral nerves including sensory and sympathetic fibers. Blocking of sympathetic impulses by procaine, by drugs such as Priscoline, or by surgery, is sometimes helpful.

In **angina pectoris,** excessive vasoconstriction of coronary arteries, leading to ischemia of cardiac muscle and subsequent stimulation of sensory endings, has been proposed as the underlying mechanism. Surgical procedures have been devised to relieve this, and these involve sectioning of sympathetic fibers, of sensory fibers, or of both. Sympathetic fibers are considered to be chiefly vasodilator for coronary arteries normally, though a few vasoconstrictor ones are thought to be present also. In disease of the coronary arteries, vasoconstriction is considered the dominant result of sympathetic activity. Combined gray and white ramisectomy, usually left sided, at the second to fifth thoracic levels inclusively, with a section of the ganglionated trunk between the fifth and sixth chain ganglia, has been called a rational procedure, since it interrupts the majority of sympathetic preganglionic fibers for the heart as well as many sensory fibers from the heart.

In **peptic ulcer,** excessive formation of hydrochloric acid and perhaps increased peristalsis have been considered to underly the severe epigastric pain. Since these activities are normally the result of parasympathetic stimulation, vagotomy has been carried out with some success in selected cases. In the congenital disorder **megacolon, or Hirschsprung's disease,** the entire colon may be greatly dilated and atonic, and the child will be constipated and suffer both abdominal distention and vomiting. The atonia of the upper colon may be due to excessive overactivity of the sympathetic system, which normally inhibits peristalsis, but increased tone and narrowing of the rectosigmoid have been found at times to act as a block. Sympathectomy often has not been successful. Sigmoidectomy may be better. These conditions are but a few of the many disorders for which a blocking of autonomic activity either by medical or surgical regimen has been devised. Perhaps more operations have been performed on the sympathetic nervous system for the relief of essential hypertension than for any other single disorder.

Treatment for these disorders involves surgical and/or medical regimens. Surgical procedures have consisted in tedious removal of sympathetic fibers from about blood vessels (periarterial sympathectomy), section of preganglionic or postganglionic fibers or both (ramisectomy), or removal of various ganglia (ganglionectomy) of the paravertebral chain. The entire abdominothoracic portion of the chain has been removed in certain cases of hypertension. Section of preganglionic fibers is more successful than section of postganglionic ones.

Medical therapy of disorders of autonomic innervation involves the discovery and use of drugs that will emulate or enhance the action of the autonomic components, **sympathomimetic or parasympathomimetic,** or of drugs that will block the activity of both components, or only one, **sympatholytic** and **parasympatholytic** drugs. Drugs fitting these descriptions are numerous, and many new ones are being derived every day. A comparative few, however, are at present applicable clinically.

Autonomic and Somatic Interrelations

Autonomic activity is closely related to somatic activity through the peripheral components of the sensory system. Autonomic motor neurons can be brought into action by sensory impulses arising in either somatic or visceral organs. Somatic motor neurons can be set into activity by impulses reaching them from a visceral origin. **Viscerovisceral** reflex arcs involve impulses arising in a visceral structure bringing about activity in visceral structures. An example is the change of blood pressure and heart rate as a result of pressure changes in the carotid sinus and arch of the aorta. **Viscerosomatic** reflexes involve impulses arising in a visceral structure creating activity in somatic structures. The reflex contraction of the abdominal wall in response to certain disease processes in the abdominal viscera furnishes an example. **Viscerosensory** reflexes involve sensory impulses from visceral structures and the alteration or activity they create in the somatic sensory system. The referred pain experienced in certain skin areas when viscera are diseased is an example, and this will be described below. Finally, **somatovisceral** reflexes involve impulses arising in somatic sensory areas and the motor responses they elicit in the visceral motor system. The vascular responses resulting from stimulation of the temperature endings are an example. These relations between somatic and autonomic neural mechanisms serve to point up the functional dependence of them.

The mechanics of **referred pain** have intrigued investigators for many years, and various theories have been evolved to explain it. In heart disease, for example, pain is frequently felt down into the left arm and hand, especially over the distribution of the ulnar nerve. In diaphragmatic irritation, pain is referred frequently to the top of the shoulder over the skin areas supplied by the third, fourth, and fifth cervical nerves. Disease of various abdominal viscera is frequently related to hypersensitive areas over the abdomen at various places, and a knowledge of the points to which visceral pain is referred helps in the localization of the diseased viscus. It is usually true that visceral pain is referred to that area of the body supplied by neurons whose processes terminate in the spinal cord at the same segmental level as those neuron processes serving the affected viscus. The sensory impulses from the central area of the diaphragm, for example, enter the third, fourth, and fifth cervical segments of the spinal cord. The receptors in the skin over the shoulder and outer surface of the upper arm also discharge into these segments. Sensory impulses from the heart enter the first thoracic segment (among others), and certain skin receptors supplied by the ulnar nerve likewise play into this segment.

It has been indicated above that the sensory fibers from viscera have primary neurons in the posterior spinal root ganglia. It is supposed also that a pool of secondary neurons at these intrinsic spinal levels is common to impulses arriving from the skin and from the viscera. One theory of the mechanics of referred pain depends on the activity in such a common pool of neurons. A sudden influx of impulses from a diseased viscus, for example, creates activity in many neurons of the pool. These neurons normally are constantly being bombarded by impulses arriving from a skin area. These last impulses, however, under ordinary circumstances, do not create activity in a sufficient number of the neurons of the pool to cause a discharge along the ascending spinal tracts to thalamic centers and conscious recognition. When the visceral impulses discharge into the pool they activate certain neurons to discharge and activate others to a subthreshold point (facilitation). The customary impulses from the skin area are then sufficient to bring these last neurons to discharge. Impulses are thus sent to the thalamus and cerebral cortex, and pain is felt over the skin area.

A second theory of referred pain involves a visceroviscerosomatic sensory pattern. An influx of visceral impulses creates activity in autonomic motor neurons in the spinal cord. The discharge of these results in constriction of blood vessels and the formation of "toxic" substances or metabolites in the skin. These metabolites in turn activate the receptors of the somatic sensory neurons whose axons pass to the higher neural levels, where pain is recognized as occurring in the skin area.

Another theory of referred pain is based on the anatomical fact that certain neurons in the posterior root ganglia may occasionally have a branching peripheral process (Fig. 109). One branch has a receptor in a somatic structure, such as the skin; the other terminates about a receptor in a muscle or viscus. Disease of the viscus would result in pain referred to the skin area. Two mechanisms are involved to explain the full sequence of events in referred pain (727, 829). The first embodies a misinterpretation centrally of the true origin of the influx of pain impulses, since pain impulses from skin and viscus would be using a common path to the spinal-cord center. Furthermore, the activity created in the viscus is transmitted not only along the dendrite into the ganglion cell, but also into and along (antidromic conduction) the dendritic branch that passes to the skin area. The second mechanism thus comes into play, and the center is thus bombarded by impulses from the two sources.

This antidromic conduction in the somatic branch results in the liberation of metabolites at the terminals in the skin region where pain is experienced. These metabolites lead to the production of secondary pain impulses which actually have origin in the skin. These impulses may travel up the dendritic branch as well as along nonbranching dendrites from the skin area. The misinterpretation seems more important in the initial phase of reference. The liberation of metabolites which leads first to stimulation of more receptors in the somatic area later produces damage to the nerve endings. A more definite sensation of pain as well as tenderness characterizes the later stages of referred pain. Anatomical evidence of such branching of the dendrites of posterior root ganglion cells in man is scarce, and it is likely that such branching is rare. The paucity of such terminals in the skin is thought to account for the poorly localized referred pain, even though the presence of some branching fibers is necessary for this mechanism of pain referral. The density of pain terminals in the skin is thought to determine the sharpness of localization of pain, as will be seen in Chap. 19.

CHAPTER 8

THE BRAIN STEM

THE SPINAL CORD through its emissaries, the spinal nerves, as has been seen, maintains contact with the environment; in response to alterations of the environment as they affect the organism, the spinal cord is capable of making certain adjustments. It represents the lowest level of neural integration. It will now be useful to consider the next highest levels of integration. That they influence the spinal-cord activity has been alluded to previously, and the manner in which they perform this function is now being analyzed experimentally. The first supraspinal levels to be described are those of the brain stem. It should be realized, however, that within the brain stem are also many lowest-level neurons, the motor neurons of cranial nerve nuclei and their sensory counterparts in sensory root ganglia of certain cranial nerves.

The term **brain stem** is used to denote that part of the brain remaining after removal of the cerebral and cerebellar cortices. It is continuous with the spinal cord by ascending and descending fibers. For purposes of study it can be divided into four parts: the medulla, the pons (these two together being parts of the rhombencephalon), the midbrain (mesencephalon), and the thalamic nuclei and fibers (diencephalon). The most rostral part of the brain stem, the basal ganglia (of the telencephalon), will be considered later. The central canal of the spinal cord, partially patent in adult man, extends forward to widen out as the rhombic-shaped fourth ventricle whose floor, the rhomboid fossa, overlies the medulla and pons; the fourth ventricle becomes constricted into the aqueduct in the cephalad part of the pons and in the midbrain, and the aqueduct widens into the third ventricle in the diencephalon.

In the present and following chapters photographs of brain stem sections will be presented. The majority of these sections have been made in a transverse plane at approximately right angles to the long axis of the brain stem. As will be noted in the key in Fig. 124*A*, the superior portion of each section is a bit more cephalad than is the inferior. Furthermore, the left side of each section is a bit more rostrad than the right. Other illustrations utilize brain stem sections made in a coronal plane with reference to the whole brain. A few sections of a parasagittal series are also used. The planes of these sections are illustrated in Figs. 124*B* and 124*C*.

THE MEDULLA

The medulla, the most caudal part of the brain stem, is limited rostrally by a plane at the level of the striae medullares (see later) dorsally and the caudal part of the pontine fibers ventrally, and caudally it is limited by a plane just rostral to the point of emergence of the first spinal nerve (Fig. 42). The striae medullares (cerebellar striae in illustrations of brain stem sections) can be seen in many gross brain stems as they traverse the floor of the fourth ventricle (Fig. 123). The medulla is composed of nuclei of origin and termination of cranial nerves together with their secondary connections; nuclear groups of the region (other than those of cranial nerves) and their secondary connections; and the fibers of passage.

EXTERNAL LANDMARKS

The location of certain of the cranial-nerve nuclei and other nuclei within the medulla is marked externally by grooves and ridges. (Fig. 123). The caudal end of the floor of the fourth ventricle with its markings of grooves and

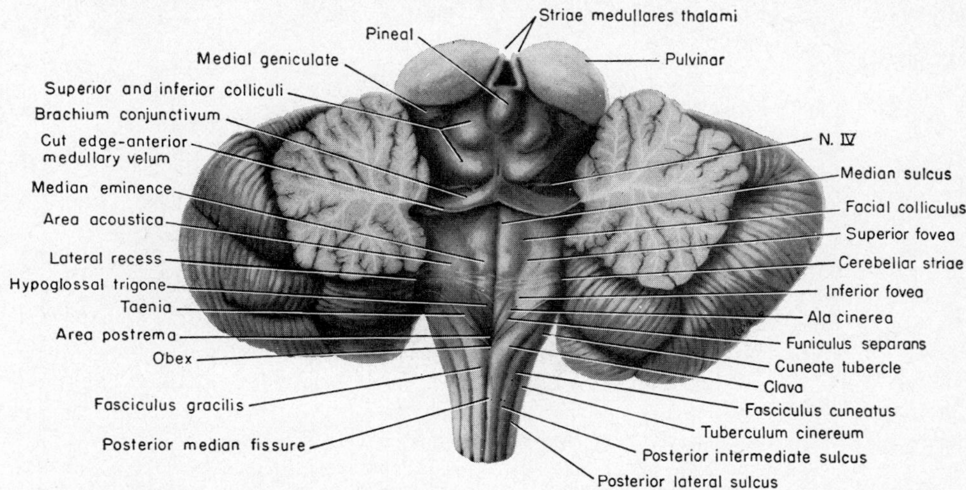

FIG. 123. Dorsal view of human brain stem. A narrow strip of the cerebellar vermis has been removed, and the cerebellar hemispheres are retracted laterally in order to expose the floor of the fourth ventricle.

elevations resembles a writing pen and has been named **calamus scriptorius.** The lateral walls of the ventricle, or the taeniae formed by the line of attachment of ependyma, converge at the caudal end of the ventricle, and this point of convergence is the **obex,** a useful landmark in neurosurgery. Just within the obex on either side is a glial and vascular ridge, the **area postrema.** In the floor of the fourth ventricle the **ala cinerea** marks the location of the **dorsal motor nucleus** of the **vagus nerve.** Cell bodies in this nucleus innervate cardiac muscle and smooth muscle of thoracic and abdominal viscera. The **hypoglossal trigone,** just medial to the ala cinerea, marks the nuclei of the **hypoglossal nerve** which innervate the striated muscle of the tongue; the **acoustic area,** certain of the vestibular nuclei receiving incoming fibers from the labyrinth. In the lateral angle of the ventricular floor, a prominence in the acoustic area, the **acoustic tubercle,** overlies the **dorsal cochlear nucleus,** containing secondary neurons of the auditory, or cochlear, division of the eighth nerve. The following are elevations on the dorsal surface of the medulla just caudal to the fourth ventricle: medially, there is the **clava,** beneath which is to be found the rostral end of the **fasciculus gracilis** and its **nucleus;** lateral to this is the **cuneate tubercle,** beneath which is the **cuneate fasciculus** and its **nucleus;** and next laterally is the **tuberculum cinereum** showing the location of the **spinal nucleus** and **tract** of the **trigeminal nerve.** The tract and nucleus extend from the pontine level of entrance of the nerve to the second cervical spinal cord segment. The tract is composed of central processes of cells located in the **semilunar** or **gasserian ganglion.** These processes end in the nucleus of the tract, the gray matter of which is medial to the fibers.

On the lateral walls of the medulla are to be seen other elevations, the **inferior olivary nuclei,** the **restiform body,** and at times the **ventral cochlear nuclei** (Figs. 130, 177). The cochlear nuclei are discussed in Chap. 22. In some brain stems another ridge can be seen just caudal to the elevation for the cochlear nuclei. This ridge can be traced between the cochlear and facial nerves and along a rostral and ventral direction to the pons. It is the **pontobulbar body.** Its course indicates the direction pontine nuclei took in their original migration from their site of origin close behind the fourth ventricle. A few neurons may remain at the site on the upper edge of the restiform body. The **restiform body,** or **inferior cerebellar peduncle,** consists of fibers entering the cerebellum from the medulla and spinal cord, and fibers leaving the cerebellum to return to the medulla. It is discussed more fully in Chap. 12. The **inferior olivary nucleus** is a large mass of nerve cells belonging **to the reticular system** (Chap. 11). The cells

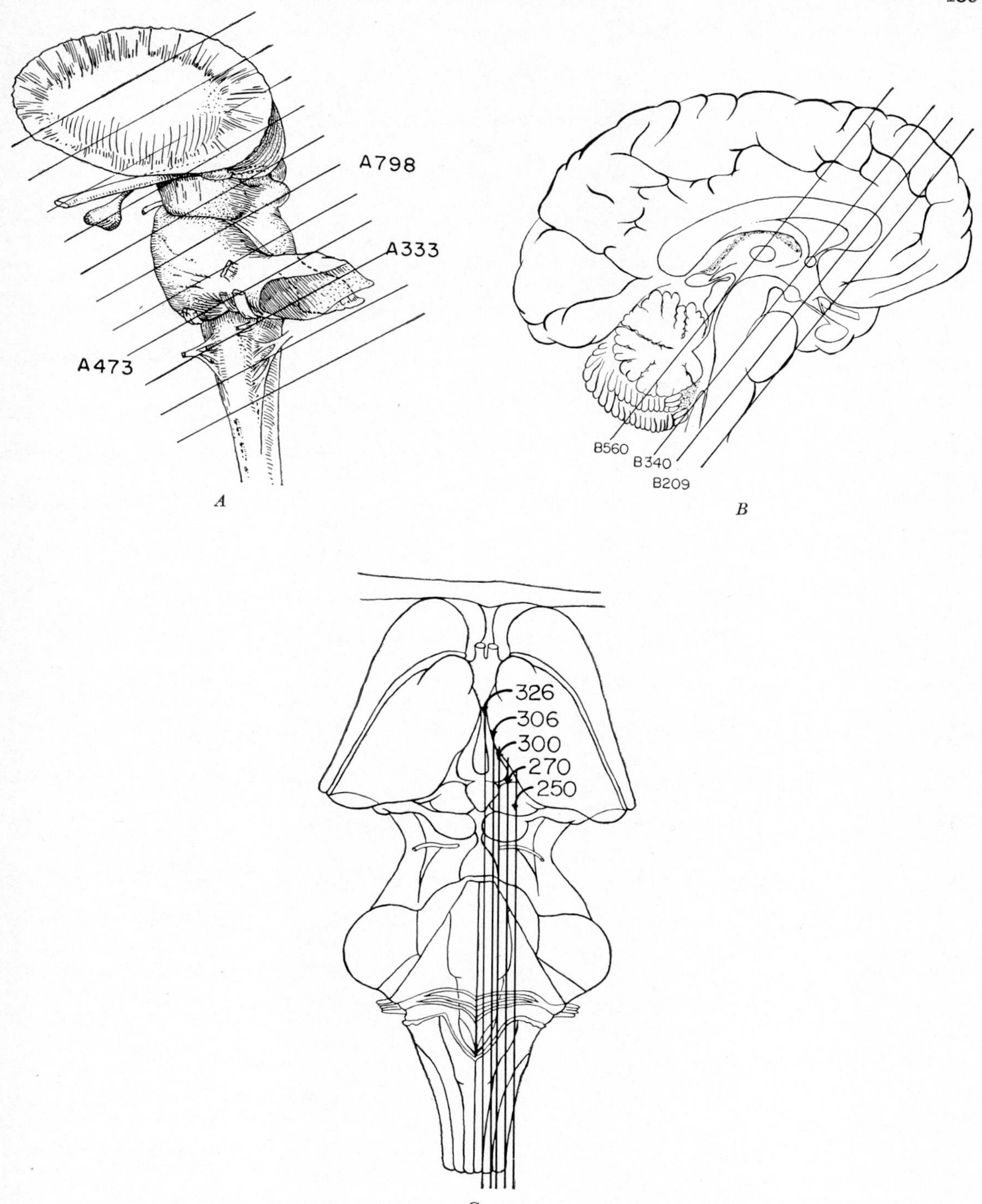

FIG. 124. *A*, key for orientation of plane of transverse sections of brain stem appearing hereafter; the numbers refer to specific sections. *B*, key for orientation of plane of frontal sections; only a few specific sections are indicated. *C*, key for orientation of plane of parasagittal sections.

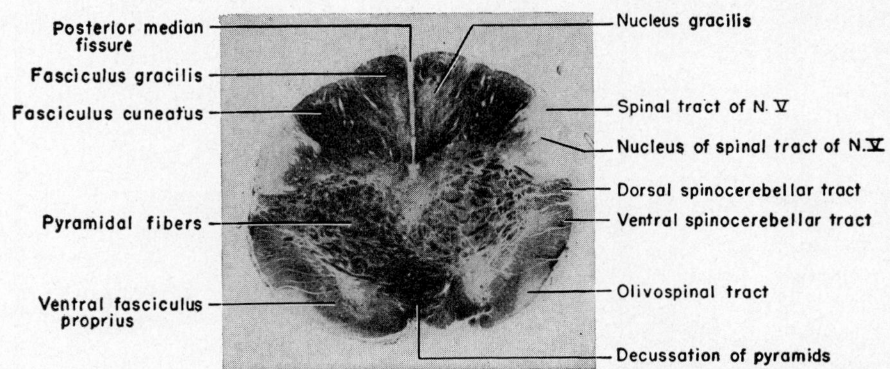

Fig. 125. Transverse section, A 60, caudal medulla, human, through lower third of nucleus gracilis. Weigert stain. Photograph, ×4.3.

are connected to the cerebellum in a definite manner by **olivocerebellar fibers,** to the spinal cord by **olivospinal** or **bulbospinal fibers,** and they receive fibers from the cerebellum, from the red nucleus in the midbrain, and from various other reticular nuclei in the upper brain stem via the **central tegmental tract.** This tract, as the name implies, is a prominent one traversing the central brain stem tegmentum throughout its extent. In midmedullar levels it is just dorsal to the inferior olivary nucleus (Fig. 129). The **tegmentum** forms the dorsal portion of the brain stem except in the midbrain in which the **colliculi** (**tectum**) are superimposed on it. The inferior olivary nucleus also receives fibers from the spinal cord (spino-olivary tract). The efferent fibers of the inferior olive stream out of the hilus medially, intermingle with **medial lemniscus** fibers (see later) as they cross the midline, traverse or pass around the contralateral inferior olive, and join the restiform body with which they enter the cerebellum. The afferent fibers form a capsule, the **amiculum,** around the lateral periphery of the olives. The chief contribution to the amiculum is the central tegmental tract. **Dorsal and medial accessory olivary nuclei** are associated with the inferior olivary nuclei; their efferent connections are with the cerebellum. The eighth, ninth, tenth, and eleventh **cranial nerves** emerge from the medulla laterally; the twelfth nerve emerges ventromedially.

The ventral surface of the medulla is marked by two parallel ridges, the **pyramids,** and their **decussation** (Fig. 42). The pyramids contain fibers coming from the cerebral cortex and descending into the spinal cord, the corticospinal tracts. These have been described in Chap. 5.

Along the ventral surface of the medulla, immediately ventral and lateral to the pyramids, are the small **arcuate nuclei** (Fig. 130). These receive fibers from the contralateral **lateral reticular nucleus** (see later) and perhaps from the contralateral nuclei cuneatus and gracilis, although there is no general agreement concerning these (655, 656). A number of investigators recently have been unable to demonstrate fibers arising in nuclei cuneatus and gracilis and ending in ventral arcuate nuclei. The suggestion has been made that the ventral arcuate nuclei represent aberrant pontine nuclei (see later). If so, they should presumably receive fibers from the cerebral cortex and send fibers to the cerebellum. Ample evidence is at hand for the existence of arcuatocerebellar connections. From an arcuate nucleus, fibers run along the ventral surface of the medulla, and ascend along the lateral walls into the restiform body and thence to the cerebellum. In their course they are joined by fibers from the lateral reticular nuclei. These two groups are **ventral external arcuate fibers** (Figs. 127, 177). Some of the axons arising in the ventral arcuate nuclei appear to pass dorsally into and across the raphe of the medulla (striae medullares), ultimately to gain the floor of the fourth ventricle and pass into the cerebellum via the restiform body. **Dorsal external arcuate fibers** arise in the lateral portion of the cuneate nucleus, the **lateral cuneate nucleus,** and pass into the cerebellum directly via the restiform body.

Internal Structure

In addition to these structures marked externally, other nuclei and fibers of passage are found in the medulla. The pyramids, arcuate nuclei, inferior olivary nuclei, and medial lemniscus form almost the ventral half of the medulla in most of its extent. The **medial lemniscus** is composed of fibers arising in nuclei cuneatus and gracilis, and it transmits the impulses carried in the spinal cord by the posterior columns, fasciculi cuneatus and gracilis (Figs. 125, 128). The fibers, as they arise in nuclei cuneatus and gracilis, sweep ventrally and medially as **internal arcuate fibers** to cross the mid-line and turn rostrally as the medial lemniscus in which they travel to the posterolateral ventral nucleus of the thalamus (Fig. 126). The crossing internal arcuate fibers form the second large medullar decussation; the pyramidal decussation is the other (Figs. 125, 126).

Dorsal to the pyramids, inferior olive, and medial lemniscus, the medulla is not very striking in appearance, when studied in section. Around the periphery of this dorsal medulla, the tegmentum of the medulla, are nuclei, some of which have been mentioned previously. Several others, not marked externally, should be noted. Between the hypoglossal nucleus and the dorsal motor nucleus of the vagus is a collection of small and large neurons forming the **nucleus intercalatus** (Fig. 165). It is thought to receive secondary gustatory connections from the vagus and glossopharyngeal nerve fibers, and also fibers from the **dorsal longitudinal fasciculus of Schütz,** and it is probably important in visceral reflexes. The fasciculus of Schütz is composed, among others, of fibers from hypothalamic nuclei passing into autonomic nuclei of the brain stem and spinal cord, and it runs throughout its course just ventral to the floor of the cerebral aqueduct and fourth ventricle. Its poorly myelinated fibers can be seen just dorsal to the hypoglossal nuclei. The dorsal longitudinal fasciculus of Schütz in the macaque arises in the diencephalic region and contains a variety of fibers. These include interconnections between thalamus and hypothalamus; fibers ending in all the brain stem preganglionic parasympathetic centers; fibers to all cranial-nerve motor nuclei except those innervating the ocular muscles; fibers arising and terminating in the periaqueductal and tegmental gray of the midbrain and pons; and fibers from the dorsal visceral nucleus of the tractus solitarius (E. C. Crosby and R. T. Woodburne, 1951).

Just ventral to the hypoglossal nucleus, a collection of small cells composes the **nucleus of Roller.** It has connections similar to those of the nucleus intercalatus and is considered to be an autonomic nucleus.

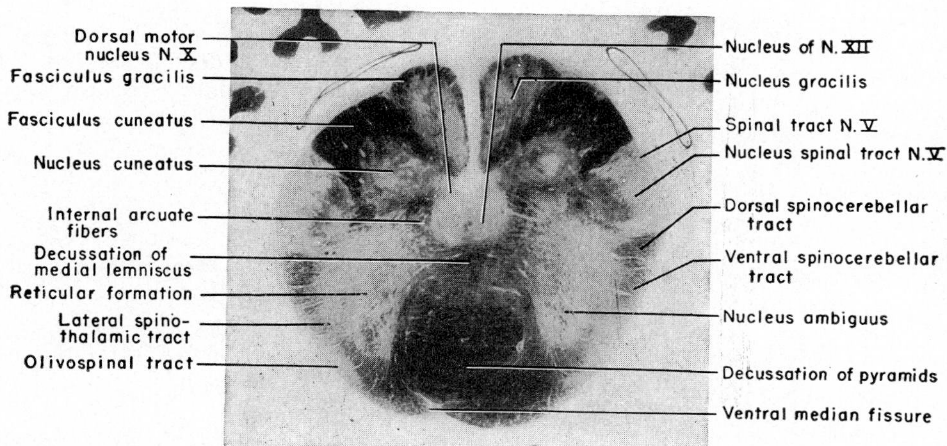

Fig. 126. Transverse section, A 130, caudal medulla, human, through decussation of the pyramids. Weigert stain. Photograph, ×4.3.

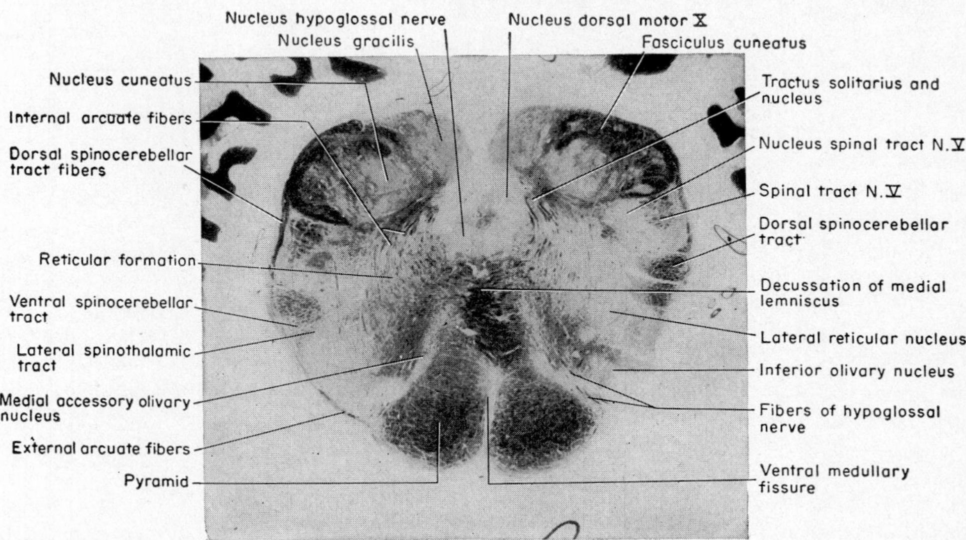

FIG. 127. Transverse section, A 195, medulla, human, through lower end of pyramids. Weigert stain. Photograph, ×4.3.

Lateral and slightly ventral to the dorsal motor nucleus of the vagus is a prominent group of fibers, the **tractus solitarius,** around and in which there are masses of gray, the **nucleus solitarius** (Figs. 127, 128). The tractus solitarius and its gray extend from the level of entrance of the facial nerve to the upper end of the spinal cord. In the spinal cord the gray of the two nuclei becomes continuous across the mid-line, dorsal to the central canal, and many fibers in the tracts cross over also at this level. The tract is composed of incoming fibers of the facial, glossopharyngeal, and vagus nerves and carries impulses of taste and general visceral sensibility. The gray matter surrounding and intermingled with the tract contains secondary neurons for the incoming fibers of these three nerves, the nucleus of the tractus solitarius. In its rostral portion the nucleus is medial and ventral to the tract; at the level of the vagus nerve the nucleus almost surrounds the tract; in its caudal portion the nucleus is lateral and medial to the tract. General visceral sensory fibers turn caudally at their level of entrance and terminate principally in the post-vagal medial portion of the nucleus. This medial part of the solitarius nucleus is adjacent to and continuous with a group of neurons immediately lateral to the dorsal motor vagal nucleus and sometimes designated the **dorsal sensory nucleus of the vagus.** Taste fibers end near their levels of entrance, and the neurons about which they terminate are located principally medioventrally to the tract. The nucleus of the tractus solitarius receives visceral stimuli from many sources and is important in many reflex acts such as coughing and vomiting. Axons arising in the nucleus pass into motor nuclei of cranial nerves and into the spinal cord, at least as far as cervical levels, with the medial reticulospinal fibers (see below). The tract is a short-chained one, with synapses in reticular nuclei, and is known as the **solitario-spinal tract.**

Dorsolateral to the inferior olivary nucleus and separated from the medullar surface by the **ventral spinocerebellar tract** is the **lateral reticular nucleus** (Fig. 127). Cells of this nucleus are large and small, and groups of them extend from caudal olivary levels to the level of entry of the ninth cranial nerve. Fibers of spinal origin end in this nucleus which in turn contributes fibers to the opposite arcuate nuclei. The latter send ventral external arcuate fibers to the cerebellum. The lateral reticular nucleus is also a direct relay center to the cerebellum and is probably interconnected with reticular neurons of upper brain stem levels. Scattered throughout the central tegmental portion of the medulla are numerous other large and small neurons related to each other by short processes. These neurons and fibers constitute the **reticular formation.** They are not often collected into distinct reticular nuclei but are components of the inferior medullar reticular nuclei (see Chap. 11). The lateral reticular and the inferior olivary nuclei are exceptions in that they are easily identified as nuclear groups.

Within the medullar reticular formation are neurons contributing to the **reticulospinal tracts.** Some cells of the medial part of the lateral reticular nucleus may contribute crossed fibers to the medial reticulospinal tract (see later). Other reticular neurons, of a central tegmental position, also contribute fibers to this tract. Also within the central reticular formation dorsal to the rostral three-fifths of the inferior olive are the **inspiratory and expiratory respiratory centers.** They send descending fibers, as components of reticulospinal tracts or solitariospinal tracts or both, into the spinal cord to end around neurons innervating the diaphragm and intercostal muscles; ascending fibers are sent to the **pontine pneumotaxic center.** Another collection of large neurons is found dorsal to the inferior olive in the central reticular formation; these compose the **nucleus ambiguus,** and innervate striated muscles of the pharynx and larynx by way of glossopharyngeal, vagus, and bulbar portions of the spinal accessory nerves. Medial reticular neurons in caudal medulla compose vasomotor "centers."

Certain of the tracts passing through the medulla are well outlined in sections; others are indistinct. The central tegmental tract is the most prominent distinct tract of the ventrolateral tegmentum (Figs. 128, 129, 131). It contains fibers arising from reticular neurons

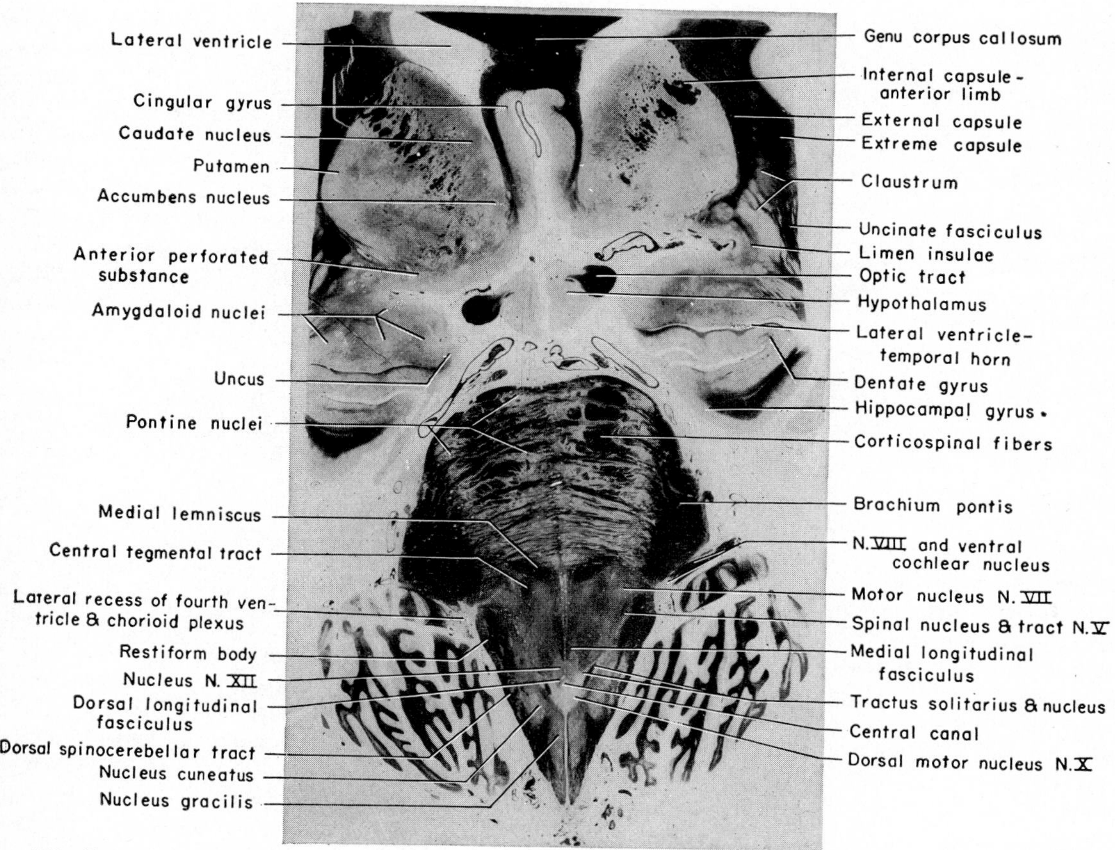

FIG. 128. Frontal section, B 209, through genu of corpus callosum and tuber cinereum. Human, Weigert. Photograph, ×1.25.

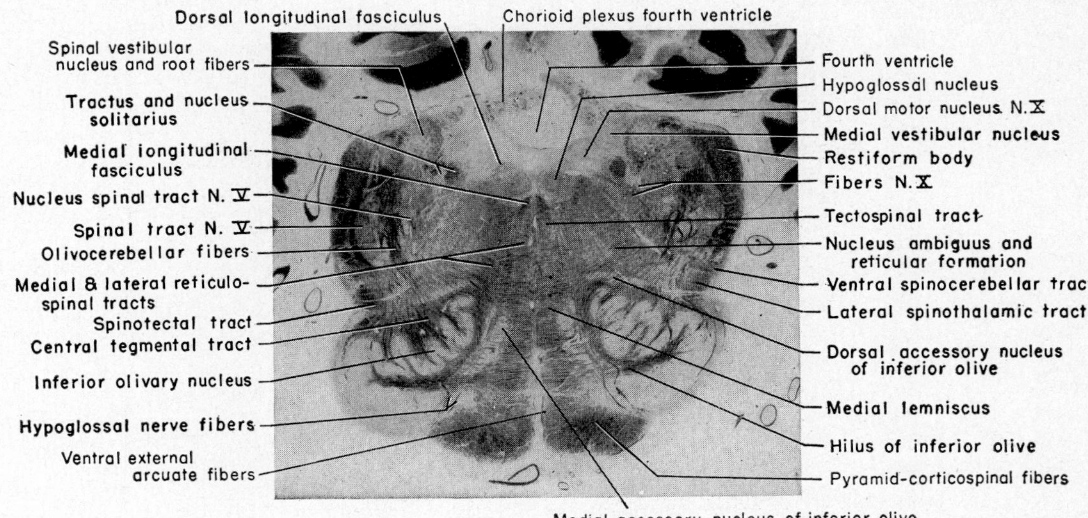

FIG. 129. Transverse section, A 316, human medulla, through caudal end of restiform body. Weigert. Photograph, ×3.25.

throughout the brain stem. Many of the central tegmental tract fibers end in the olive as described, others pass into the spinal cord as reticulospinal tracts. Just ventral to the hypoglossal nuclei in the mid-line is the **medial longitudinal fasciculus.** This is a bundle of ascending and descending fibers extending from the region of the posterior commissure in the midbrain to the spinal-cord levels. It is a connecting bundle, so to speak, and the impulses transmitted over it coordinate movements of the head, eyes, and trunk in response to incoming sensory, auditory, visual, and vestibular (postural) stimuli. It is discussed more completely in Chap. 10. Ventral and slightly lateral to this tract is the **medial reticulospinal tract,** arising from reticular nuclei throughout the pontine and medullar tegmentum, particularly, and containing crossed and uncrossed fibers. Dorsal to this tract and nearer the mid-line is the **medial tectospinal tract,** arising from the superior and inferior colliculi of the midbrain and descending into the spinal cord in the anterior funiculus. Ventral to this tract and slightly lateral is the **medial vestibulospinal tract** composed of fibers from the ipsilateral, lateral, medial, and spinal vestibular nuclei and descending into the spinal cord in the anterior funiculus. Dorsolateral to this tract is the indistinctly outlined **lateral reticulospinal tract,** which is thought to arise principally from reticular nuclei in the pontine tegmentum, to be chiefly crossed, and to descend into the spinal cord in the medial and ventral region of the lateral funiculus.

Proceeding laterally from the region of the lateral reticulospinal tract, and beginning about midway to the lateral medulla wall in a position just dorsal to the inferior and dorsal accessory olivary nuclei, one encounters the following tracts in order: the **lateral vestibulospinal tract;** the **rubrospinal tract** just ventromedial to the lateral reticular nucleus; the **spinothalamic** (the lateral at least) **and spinotectal tracts;** and the **ventral spinocerebellar tract** (Figs. 129, 173, 174). The lateral vestibulospinal tract arises principally in the lateral vestibular nucleus, is chiefly uncrossed, and descends into the spinal cord in the lateral part of the anterior funiculus. The rubrospinal tract arises from the red nuclei of the midbrain and in man is chiefly a crossed short-chained tract, the fibers synapsing and arising in turn from reticular nuclei. The spinothalamic and spinotectal tracts arise from all levels of the spinal cord, are chiefly crossed, and end in the posterolateral ventral nucleus of the thalamus and in the colliculi, respectively. The ventral spinocerebellar tract, principally of crossed origin, arises from neurons in the basal portion of the spinal posterior gray columns, and maintains a lateral and steadily progressing dorsal course to enter the anterior lobe of the cerebellum by looping over its superior peduncle, the brachium conjunctivum.

Along the lateral surface of the medulla, running dorsally into the restiform body, is the **dorsal spinocerebellar tract,** chiefly of uncrossed origin from Clarke's nucleus in the thoracic and upper lumbar cord. It enters the cerebellum by way of the restiform body. Also streaming in a dorsolateral direction to the restiform body are ventral external arcuate fibers along the surface, and the olivocerebellar fibers just inside.

Scattered through the central reticular formation, and indistinguishable as individual bundles, are **descending autonomic tracts** from various autonomic centers in hypothalamus, pons, and medulla. In a dorsolateral position are the indistinct pupillodilator fibers which influence the homolateral pupil; their position has been inferred through a correlation of neurological signs and pathological findings in human cases. Thermoregulatory tracts for heat and cold are similarly placed in the medullar tegmentum.

In the rostral half of the medulla beneath the acoustic area, the secondary **nuclei** associated with the **vestibular** division of the **eighth cranial** nerve can be identified. In those sections wherein the dorsal spinocerebellar tract and the olivocerebellar fibers unite to form the restiform body, two vestibular nuclei are present (Figs. 129, 164). The **medial vestibular nucleus** forms the most lateral part of the floor of the fourth ventricle; lateral to it and separated from it by entering (and descending) vestibular nerve fibers is the **spinal vestibular nucleus.** Near the level of entry of the most inferior vestibular nerve fibers, the **lateral vestibular nucleus** appears. It is first noticeable ventrolateral to the medial nucleus and just medial to the descending vestibular root fibers; it becomes more prominent in levels showing the main bulk of vestibular nerve fibers. The other vestibular nucleus, the **superior,** appears in sections rostral to the level of entry of the eighth cranial nerve, and occupies the ventral portion of the lateral wall of the fourth ventricle. The vestibular nuclear complex extends from midpontine to midmedullar levels.

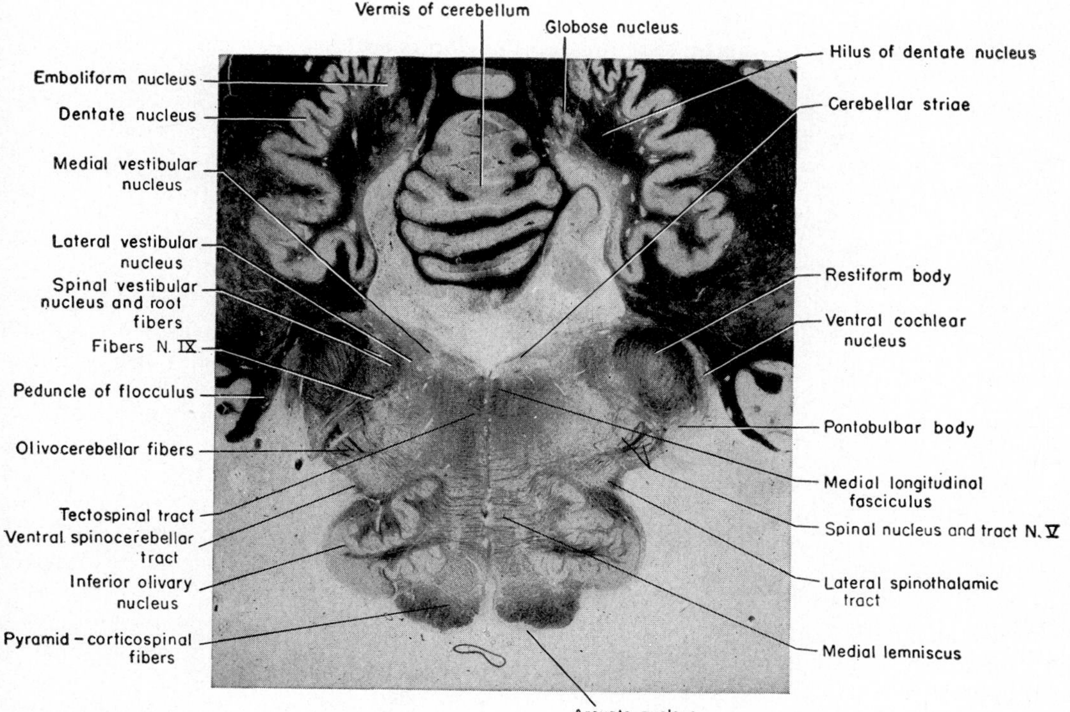

Fig. 130. Transverse section, A 400, upper medulla, human, through area acoustica. Weigert. Photograph, ×2.5.

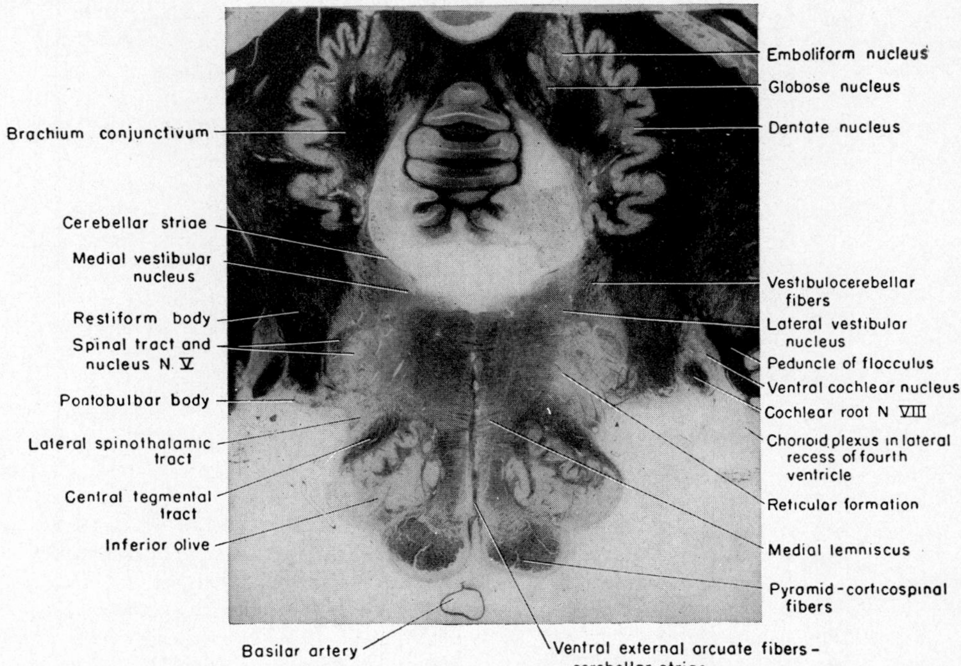

FIG. 131. Transverse section, A 435, rostral medulla, human, through point of entry of eighth cranial nerve. Weigert. Photograph, ×2.5.

In those sections which show the restiform body as it becomes rounded up into a circumscribed bundle of fibers, a continuous column of gray covers over its superior and lateral borders, and within this gray can be seen entering fibers of the **cochlear division of the eighth cranial nerve.** The gray composes the **dorsal and ventral cochlear nuclei,** secondary stations for the entering cochlear nerve fibers (Figs. 130, 174, 294). The secondary cochlear fibers arising in these nuclei will be described briefly below.

At the level of entry of the eighth cranial nerve, other important discrete reticular nuclei are situated. In the ventral half of the tegmentum, within the raphe and especially on each side of it, are prominent centrally placed reticular nuclei, occasionally referred to as central tegmental nuclei (Fig. 132). They constitute in large part the **superior medullar reticular nuclei,** or the medial reticular nuclei (see Chap. 11). Other reticular neurons, which however are not outlined into discrete nuclei, occupy the major portion of the tegmentum dorsal and dorsolateral to the central reticular nuclei (Figs. 131, 132).

The fibers marking the rostral extent of the medulla and crossing in the floor of the fourth ventricle are named **striae medullares** (or cerebellar striae) (Figs. 123, 130, 131). Their exact origin and function are not known, but it has been suggested by several investigators that they arise in the ventral arcuate nuclei, cross the mid-line, and pass dorsally to emerge from the raphe in the floor of the ventricle, across which they run into the restiform body and into the cerebellum (655). Secondary cochlear fibers cross in the tegmentum in three groups at the level of the cochlear nuclei at the rostral medullar level. A dorsal group crosses just ventral to the medial longitudinal fasciculus; a ventral group forming the so-called **trapezoid body** crosses just dorsal to the rostral tip of the inferior olive and is mingled with the fibers of the ascending medial lemniscus. A third group of secondary cochlear fibers crosses in an intermediate position. Other crossing medullar fibers, completely indistinct as definite tracts, are secondary vestibular fibers entering the medial longitudinal fasciculi of each side; and crossing secondary fibers from the spinal nucleus of the trigeminal, to form the **trigem-**

inal lemnisci, ascending to the posteromedial ventral nucleus of the thalamus.

This brief outline of the medulla in no way contains all the nuclei and fibers composing this part of the brain stem. A knowledge of the nuclei and fibers listed, however, is essential. The course and the changes in the course of the fibers through the medulla and other parts of the brain stem are important features to be noted. As can be seen from this brief description, the medulla contains neurons of great importance to the organism. Cardiac activity to a great extent is under the control of a medullar nucleus, the dorsal motor nucleus of the vagus, and vasomotor activity is controlled in part by medullar neurons. A respiratory center is to be found also in the medulla. Protective mechanisms such as coughing and vomiting are under the regulation of reflex arcs traversing medullar neurons. The peripheral organization of speech is a medullar function. The performance of skeletal movement is enhanced and regulated through the maintenance and proper distribution of muscle tone. The medulla, with other supraspinal levels, has a part to play also in this organization of muscle tone, as will be seen later (528). The reticulospinal tracts, especially, and the vestibulospinals seem to be the medullar intermediaries in this activity, bringing spinal-cord neurons under the influence of medullar ones. Finally, a large group of medullar neurons, those of the inferior olive, are active in maintaining communications between extrapyramidal motor nuclei and the cerebellum. A coordination of extrapyramidal and pyramidal influences on motor activity is thus effected at a cerebellar level.

THE PONS

The caudal limit of the pons is the rostral extent of the medulla; namely, a plane passing through the striae medullares, dorsally, and through the caudal end of the pontine fibers, ventrally. The rostral limit of the pons is a plane just posterior to the inferior colliculus, dorsally, and to the cerebral peduncles, ventrally. The pons also can be divided into two parts in a horizontal plane, the dorsal half being the tegmental portion; the ventral half, the pyramidal and pontocerebellar portion. The ventral half develops in association

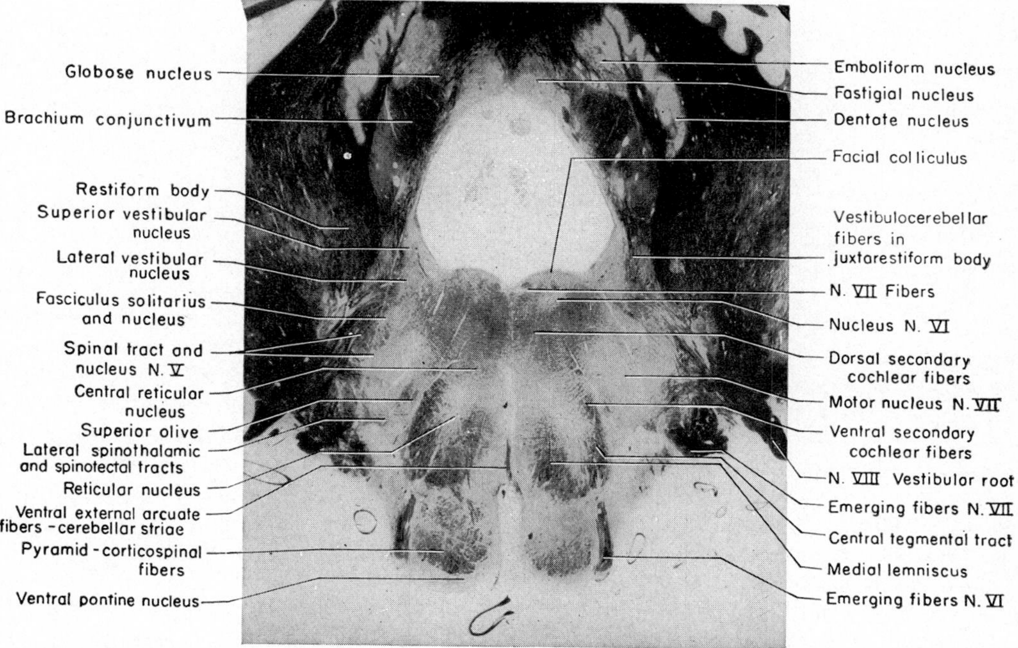

FIG. 132. Transverse section, A 473, medullopontine junction, through facial colliculus. Human, Weigert. Photograph, ×2.5.

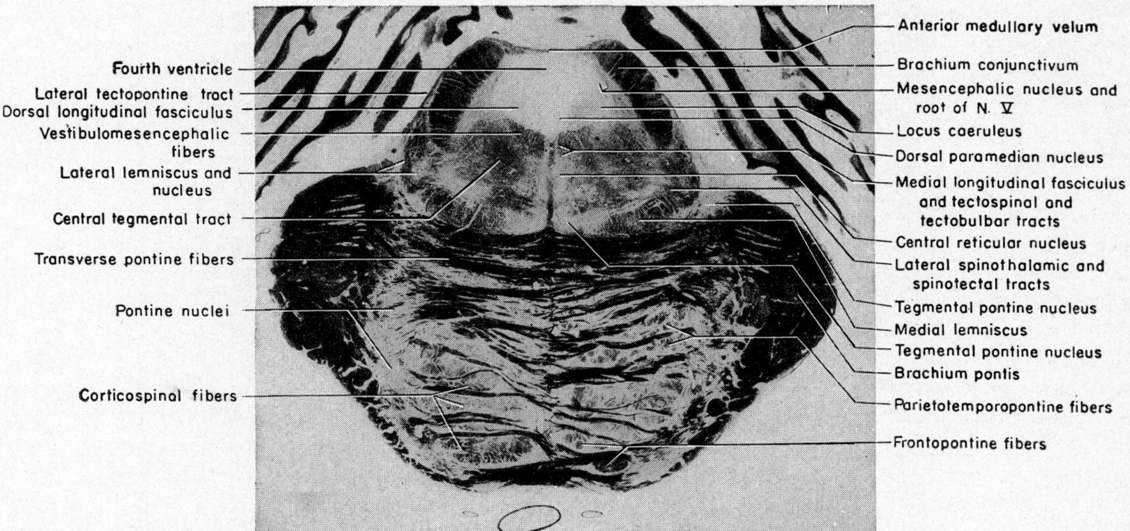

FIG. 133. Transverse section, A 645, midpons, through anterior medullary velum. Human, Weigert. Photograph, ×2.5.

with cerebral and cerebellar cortices. In the tegmentum are found again nuclei of origin and termination of cranial nerves and their secondary fibers, long and short-chained fibers of passage, and reticular nuclei (Fig. 134). Through the pons the fourth ventricle continues, becoming more narrow and shrinking finally to become at the rostral end of the pons the **aqueduct of Sylvius** or **iter,** a small diamond-shaped canal about 2 mm. in lateral, and 3 mm. in vertical, diameter (Fig. 134). The roof of the fourth ventricle in the pons is formed by a thin white membrane, the **anterior medullary velum,** and by the anterior cerebellum overlying that; the lateral walls are bounded by periventricular gray (neurons).

The structures lateral to periventricular gray vary from the caudad to the rostrad end of the pons. Caudally, the **superior cerebellar peduncle (brachium conjunctivum)**, the **inferior cerebellar peduncle (restiform body)**, the upsweeping fibers of the **middle cerebellar peduncle (brachium pontis)**, and the cerebellar hemispheres, in that order proceeding mediolaterally, are placed outside the lateral ventricular walls (Fig. 132). The inferior cerebellar peduncle is composed chiefly of afferent fibers to the cerebellum, including dorsal spinocerebellar fibers, vestibulocerebellar fibers from vestibular nuclei and nerve, olivocerebellar fibers, and dorsal and ventral external arcuate fibers. The superior cerebellar peduncle is principally composed of efferent cerebellar fibers, the **dentatorubrothalamic tract,** passing from dentate and the smaller cerebellar nuclei to the red nucleus and thalamus (Figs. 131, 132, 135). The middle cerebellar peduncle is composed almost exclusively of afferent fibers to the cerebellar hemispheres. The fibers arise from the **pontine nuclei** (Fig. 133). These are large masses of gray surrounding and intermingling with the descending fibers passing through the ventral portion of the pons, the corticopontine, corticobulbar, and corticospinal, to be described below.

In the midpons, the superior cerebellar peduncle and the **ventral spinocerebellar fibers** are lateral to the progressively shrinking fourth ventricle. These latter pass up around the laterodorsal margin of the brachium conjunctivum to enter the medial cerebellar cortex (Figs. 160, 177). In the rostral pons, the ventricle is continuous with the aqueduct, and this latter is surrounded almost exclusively by gray matter. Above it is the superior medullary velum, in the most rostral part of which the **trochlear nerve** decussates; in the floor and small lateral walls are **periaqueductal** gray, containing neurons that are most probably concerned with autonomic tract relays.

In the rostral pons, the brachium conjunctivum fibers move progressively ventromedially in preparation for their caudal midbrain decussation (Fig. 134). As they move medially, a band of gray, composed mostly of glia, separates them from the **lateral lemniscus.** This tract is composed of secondary and tertiary auditory fibers passing from cochlear nuclei, superior olive, and trapezoid nuclei to the inferior colliculus and to the medial geniculate body of the thalamus. Along its medial side is a column of gray, the **nucleus of the lateral lemniscus** (Figs. 133, 135).

In the floor of the fourth ventricle several eminences serve to locate cranial nerve nuclei. Caudally, in the medial position, are the **medial eminences** marking the hypoglossal and associated nuclei. Lateral to these and extending rostrally almost half the length of the pons are other rounded eminences, the **acoustic areas** mentioned in the section describing the medulla. At almost midpons level the medial eminences are enlarged into the **facial colliculi** (Figs. 132, 161). Beneath each of these is the **genu** of a **facial nerve** and immediately beneath the genu, the **motor nucleus** of the **sixth,** or **abducens, nerve.** The fibers of the sixth nerve pass slightly laterally and caudally as they are directed ventrally; they emerge near the mid-line in the caudal pons and supply the lateral rectus muscle of the eye.

Medial to the abducens nuclei and extending to the raphe are the **medial longitudinal fasciculi.** At this level this fasciculus contains vestibular fibers passing to the oculomotor, trochlear, and abducens nuclei and to reticular nuclei of the midbrain; fibers interconnecting the superior olive (see later) and the motor nuclei for the ocular muscles, and other fibers interconnecting these last nuclei with spinal neurons innervating neck musculature; interconnecting fibers between other cranial motor nuclei; and interstitiospinal and commissurospinal fibers arising from neurons in the neighborhood of the posterior commissure at the rostral midbrain level. Ventral to each medial longitudinal fasciculus are the medial tectospinal tract and medial reticulospinal tract.

In the ventral pontine tegmentum, caudally, the fibers of the medial lemniscus are spread in a mediolateral plane, and as they proceed rostrally they become more and more compact and assume a lateral position. Caudally, at the level of the eighth cranial nerve, these fibers are in part intermingled with ventrally

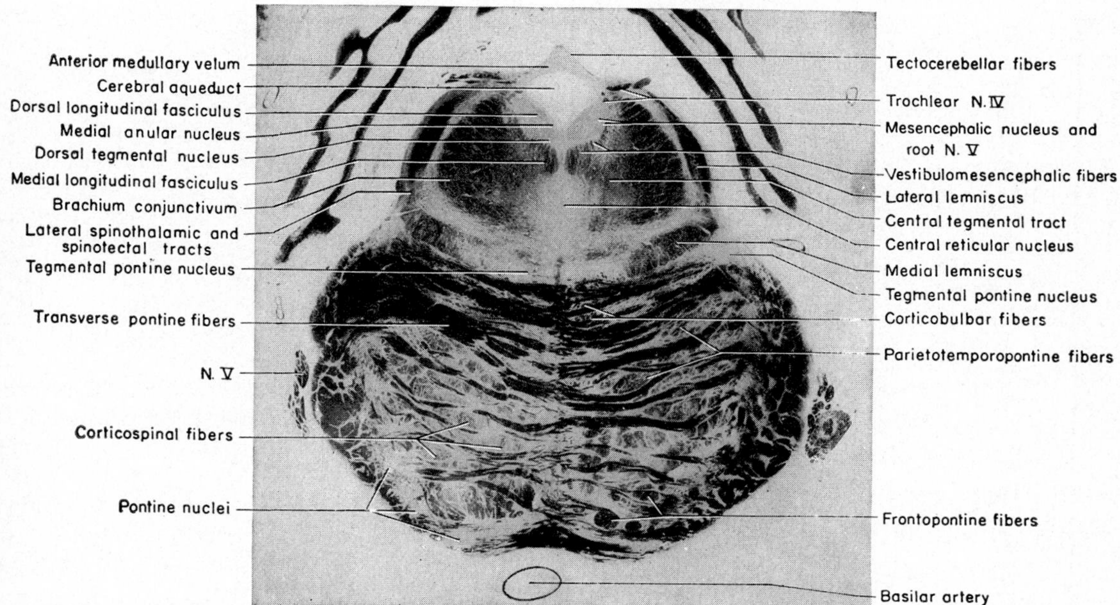

FIG. 134. Transverse section, A 723, upper pons, human, through point of emergence of fourth cranial nerve. Weigert. Photograph, ×2.5.

crossing fibers of the auditory system (**trapezoid body**). These latter are secondary fibers from the ventral cochlear nucleus and pass to form a part of the contralateral lateral lemniscus; some of them in transit across the tegmental floor synapse in the superior olivary nucleus and **nuclei of the trapezoid body.** The trapezoid body gets its name from its shape.

The superior olivary nucleus is very small in cross section when compared with the inferior olivary nucleus, though it extends from caudal pons to a plane at approximately midpons (Figs. 132, 160). It is situated in the ventrolateral tegmental region and is ventromedial to the motor nucleus of the facial nerve. It is dorsolateral to the main mass of the medial lemniscus and is dorsal to other scattered gray, the nuclei of the trapezoid body. It receives secondary auditory fibers and sends many fibers into the lateral lemniscus, medial longitudinal fasciculus, adjacent reticular nuclei, and motor nuclei of the trigeminal and facial nerves.

Dorsolateral to the superior olive, the **motor nucleus** of the **facial nerve** is also located in the caudal ventrolateral tegmentum of the pons (Figs. 128, 132, 159, 161). Fibers innervating the facial muscles of expression pass dorsomedially from the nucleus to loop about the nucleus of the abducens, forming the genu of the facial nerve. Thence the fibers are directed ventrolaterally and emerge from the brain stem. In their course they are joined by fibers from the **superior salivatory nucleus** passing as preganglionic parasympathetic fibers to the submaxillary and sublingual glands. The location of the superior salivatory nucleus is not definitely known, but stimulation in cats and monkeys, medial and dorsal to the facial nucleus, has produced submaxillary secretion. Similarly, stimulation caudally in about the same planes has resulted in parotid secretion, and the **inferior salivatory nucleus** is thus thought to be located here near the level of the dorsal motor vagus nucleus. Somewhere near the superior salivatory nucleus lie cells (**lacrimal nucleus**) supplying preganglionic parasympathetic fibers via the facial nerve to the lacrimal glands.

In the ventrolateral tegmental zone of the caudal pons are also the **spinothalamic tracts,** the ventral spinocerebellar, the lateral lemniscus, and presumably the **rubrospinal** and **lateral tectospinal.** The spinothalamic, ventral spinocerebellar tract, and lateral lemniscus move dorsolaterally as the rostral pons is reached and are superficially placed. Their subsequent course is described elsewhere. The ventrolateral pontine tegmentum is of clinical interest because of the syndromes that arise as a result of damage there. Ipsilateral facial paralysis and anesthesia, bilateral hearing loss, and contralateral anesthesia of the body may be seen with disease of this region.

Sensory nuclei associated with the trigeminal nerve are found throughout the extent of the pons. The **spinal tract** and its **nucleus,** subserving pain and temperature impulses, especially, from skin and mucous membranes of the head, extend from the level of entrance of the nerve in midpons to the second cervical cord segment and maintain a lateral and about middorsal position throughout (Figs. 128, 132, 159). At the level of entrance of the nerve is a circumscribed mass of gray, the **main sensory trigeminal nucleus,** continuous with the spinal, and subserving certain impulses of touch and pressure sense. Rostral to the level of entrance of the nerve, some few fibers can be seen passing mediodorsally toward the gray in the wall of the aqueduct. The gray is the **mesencephalic nucleus of the trigeminal,** and the fibers are the dendrites of cells in this nucleus (primary sensory neurons) bearing proprioceptive impulses from the muscles of mastication (Fig. 134). Intermingled with the mesencephalic nucleus is a column of medium-sized and large pigmented neurons. These neurons constitute the **nucleus of the locus caeruleus,** so named because of the pigmentation, and they extend from the level of entry of the trigeminal nerve to the midbrain (Figs. 133, 160). They are apparently related to the trigeminal nuclei and possibly also to the nucleus intercalatus and dorsal motor vagus nucleus, though their exact function has not been determined. Medial to the main sensory trigeminal nucleus, and separated from it by fibers of the nerve, is the **main motor nucleus of the trigeminal,** sending fibers to the muscles of mastication and several others of similar embryologic derivation. The **oval fasciculus** and its **nucleus** are located between the main motor and sensory nuclei of the trigeminal (Figs. 158, 161). This tract and nucleus extend caudally to the level of the nucleus of the facial nerve. Because of their location and the similarity of their appearance to that of the tractus solitarius and nucleus, it has been suggested that the oval fasciculus and nucleus also have a gustatory function (675).

Within the tegmentum throughout the pontine levels are reticular nuclei and fibers of the **reticular formation.** Most of the fibers are scattered ones, though one well-circumscribed tract is the **central tegmental tract** mentioned in the previous section (Figs. 129, 133, 162). This tract occupies approximately a central tegmentum position. Its composition varies from level to level, but many of its fibers arise in the midbrain tectum, tegmentum, periaqueductal gray and red nucleus, and reticular nuclei of the upper brain stem. The fibers end in the inferior olivary nucleus, especially medullar reticular nuclei, and in the spinal cord as reticulospinal fibers. The reticular nuclei in caudal pontine levels include neurons which inhibit spinal-cord motor neurons and neurons which facilitate them. They are more fully described elsewhere in Chap. 11. Suffice it to say here that a discrete **central tegmental reticular nucleus** of the **pons** is present adjacent to the raphe throughout the pontine tegmentum, medial to the medial lemniscus. Another prominent one is present in the ventrolateral corner of the pontine tegmentum, especially at levels of the main motor and sensory trigeminal nuclei (Figs. 133, 134). Another is in the dorsal part of the central tegmentum, medial to the main motor nuclei. Rostral to the pontine levels of the main motor trigeminal nucleus, other prominent reticular nuclei are found in the central tegmentum. The **superior central tegmental nuclei of the pons** are located just caudad to the decussating brachium conjunctivum fibers. The **dorsal paramedian nucleus** is dorsal to the medial longitudinal fasciculus, through the pontine levels (Fig. 133).

In the lateral part of the cephalic pontine tegmentum is a group of neurons, not discretely located, which have been found to be related to respiration in animals. They form the **pontile pneumotaxic center,** probably composed of one of the reticular nuclei (628). They receive impulses from the medullar "inspiratory center" at the time impulses to initiate inspiration pass spinalward from the latter center. As a result of the reception of the inspiratory impulses the "pontile pneumotaxic center" sends inhibitory impulses to the medullar respiratory center which discharges inspiratory-inhibitor or expiratory impulses from its "expiratory component." The inhibitory impulses from the pontile pneumotaxic center and those received by way of the vagus from the lungs cause rhythmic activity in the medullar "respiratory center."

In the ventral half of the pons, fibers of passage and scattered gray are practically the only constituents. These fibers are **corticospinals, corticobulbars,** and **corticopontocerebellars.** These last begin in various regions of the cerebral cortex, frontal, parietal, temporal, and occipital, descend with the motor fibers through the internal capsule and cerebral peduncles, and synapse about nuclei scattered among the fibers in this inferior half of the pons. From these **pontine nuclei** secondary fibers arise, cross to the opposite side, and form large bundles which pass into the cerebellum on the lateral side of the pons. They constitute the **brachium pontis** or the **middle cerebellar peduncle.** The corticopontocerebellar system is discussed more fully in the section dealing with the extrapyramidal pathways (Chap. 17).

The corticospinal fibers are collected in bundles scattered centrally in the basal pontine gray. The corticobulbar fibers arise in the frontal lobe of the brain and pass to the cranial-nerve motor nuclei of the brain stem. They are closely associated with corticospinal fibers, but at midbrain, pontine, and medullar levels bundles of them continuously pass dorsally, run in company with the medial lemniscus, and enter motor nuclei. A pontine component can occasionally be seen as it passes dorsally in sections through the rostral pons (Figs. 134, 136). The corticobulbars are described in detail in Chap. 16.

In review, the pons has added to our neural-organization mechanisms for feeding and emotional expression (trigeminal, salivatory, and facial nuclei). Secondary hearing centers are introduced. A higher degree of control of respiration, chiefly a phasic quality, has been added. Neurons inhibiting and neurons facilitating spinal motor neurons are also con-

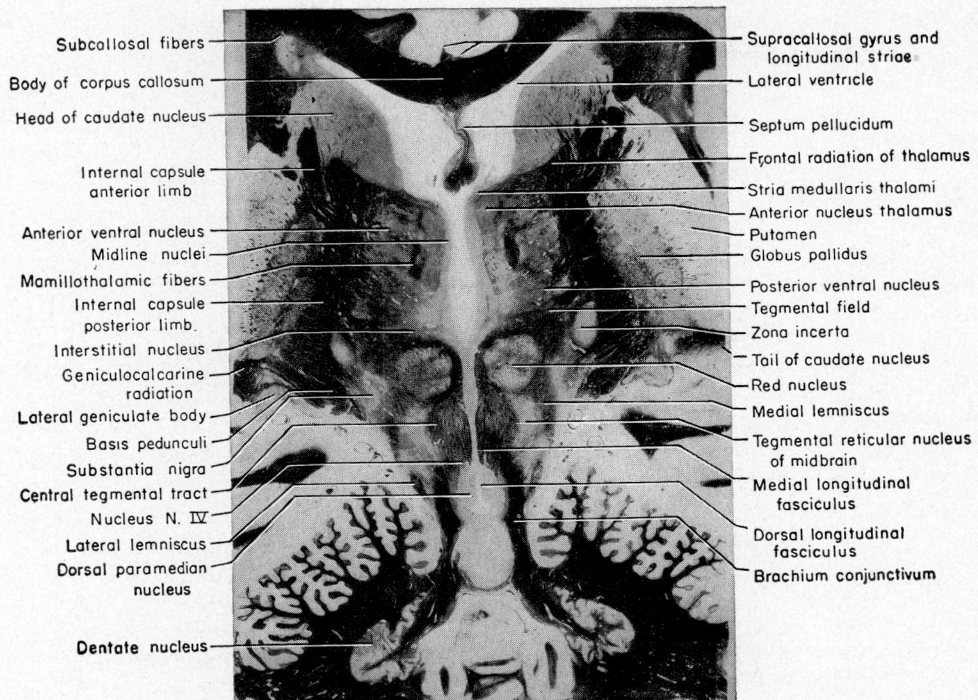

FIG. 135. Frontal section, B 500, through red nucleus and dentate nucleus. Human, Weigert. Photograph, ×1.25.

tained in the pons, as well as again intermediaries in the coordination of cerebral and cerebellar activity.

THE MIDBRAIN

The rostral limit of the midbrain in man is difficult to define because it merges gradually with the diencephalon. For purposes of description a plane passing through the rostral edges of the superior colliculi, dorsally, and through the posterior edge of the mamillary bodies, ventrally, forms the rostral extent of the midbrain; the caudal boundary is a plane passing just caudal to the inferior colliculi, dorsally, and just anterior to the pontine fibers, ventrally.

In this part of the brain stem are again nuclei of cranial nerves and their associated fibers, fibers of passage, long and short, and reticular nuclei of the region and their associated fibers (Figs. 136, 137). The midbrain can be divided by horizontal planes into two general regions. The most dorsal region containing the **colliculi** is the **tectum.** Its ventral limit, roughly, is a plane passing longitudinally through the mid-portion of the aqueduct. The remaining portion of the midbrain is composed of the **cerebral peduncles.** The most ventral part of the cerebral peduncles is the **basis pedunculi** containing corticospinal, corticobulbar, and corticopontine fibers. Immediately dorsal to the basis is a dark brown, pigmented strip, the **substantia nigra,** and above this, the **tegmentum** of the midbrain.

The tectum, or **quadrigeminal plate,** contains the four colliculi, a superior and inferior on each side. These are nuclear masses surrounded by incoming, emerging, and associated fibers. They are connected to the diencephalon by **brachia,** or arms. The nucleus of the inferior colliculus forms a central core for the incoming and emerging fibers. The **inferior colliculus** receives the lateral lemniscus (auditory fibers), fibers from the superior colliculus (optic fibers), and possibly a few fibers from the cortical auditory areas. In addition, it is said to receive collaterals from the ascending sensory pathways, particularly the quintothalamics and spinothalamics and spinotectals. It sends fibers to the superior colliculus, to the opposite inferior colliculus, and, by way of its brachium, to the medial geniculate body of the thalamus.

Fibers to the pontine nuclei composing a tectopontine tract arise here also (Fig. 133). The fibers of the brachium move laterally and rostrally in a superficial position (Figs. 136, 139). In caudal midbrain levels the lateral lemniscus is lateral and ventral to the inferior colliculus, as it approaches.

The **superior colliculus** receives spinotectal fibers and collaterals from ascending sensory tracts, including secondary trigeminal fibers, fibers from the retinae, fibers from probably all three areas of the occipital cortex and from the auditory cortex, fibers from the inferior colliculus (the so-called **acoustico-optic tract**), and fibers from the hypothalamus via the dorsal longitudinal fasciculus of Schütz (Figs. 136, 137). The chief discharge paths from the superior colliculus are to the oculomotor nuclei (tectobulbar tract), to both red nuclei, medial tectospinal fibers, and tectoreticular and tectopontine fibers which may relay into a pontospinal system, completing a lateral tectospinal tract. All these fibers leaving the superior colliculus swing ventrally around the aqueduct except the tectopontine system, which passes from the lateral portion of the nucleus. The superior colliculus shows a complex histological structure which can be conveniently divided into a series of nine alternating layers of fibers and gray matter (Figs. 137, 138). The even-numbered layers are gray; the odd-numbered ones are white, but some contain a few cells. The outermost layer 1, or the stratum zonale, contains fine fibers entering the colliculus via its brachium and some scattered cells. Layer 2, or the stratum cinereum, contains cells whose dendrites extend into layer 1, and about which the fibers from the occipital lobe and optic nerve end. Layer 3, or the stratum opticum, contains fibers from the optic nerve, many of which end in layer 2, while others end in deeper layers. The next four layers are sometimes referred to collectively as the stratum lemnisci. Layer 4, the stratum griseum mediale, gives rise to tectospinal fibers and also receives fibers from the occipital lobe; layer 5, the stratum album mediale, contains some fibers from layer 4 and also the spinotectal tract fibers; layer 6, the stratum griseum profundum, gives rise to some tectobulbar and tectospinal tract fibers; layer 7, the stratum album profundum, contains fibers arising in layer 6; layer 8 is periventricular gray, and layer 9 includes fibers of

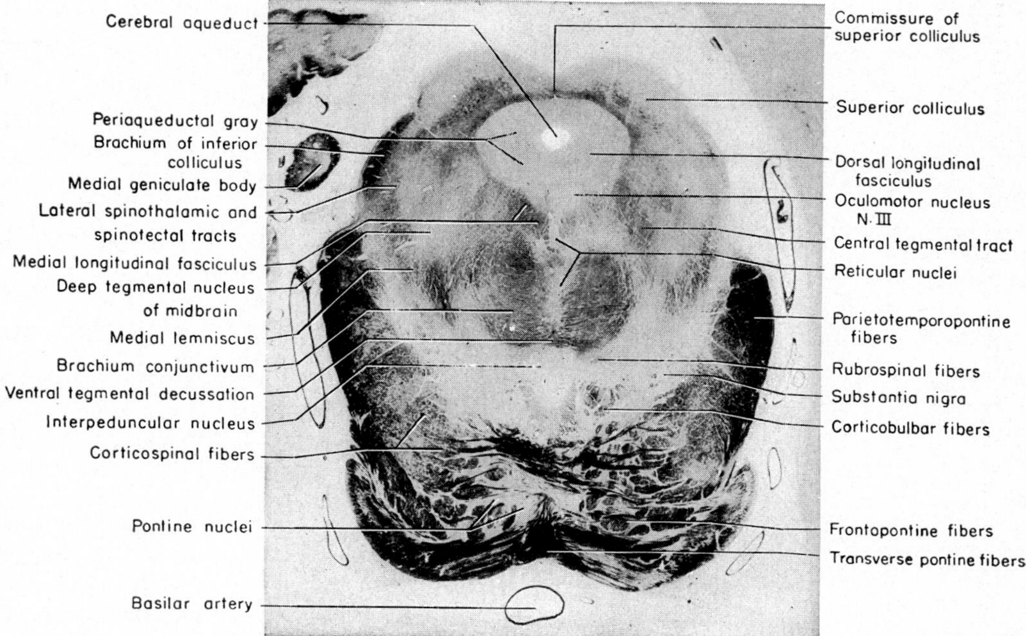

FIG. 136. Transverse section, A 863, through rostral tip of basal pons and caudal end of medial geniculate. Human, Weigert. Photograph, ×2.5.

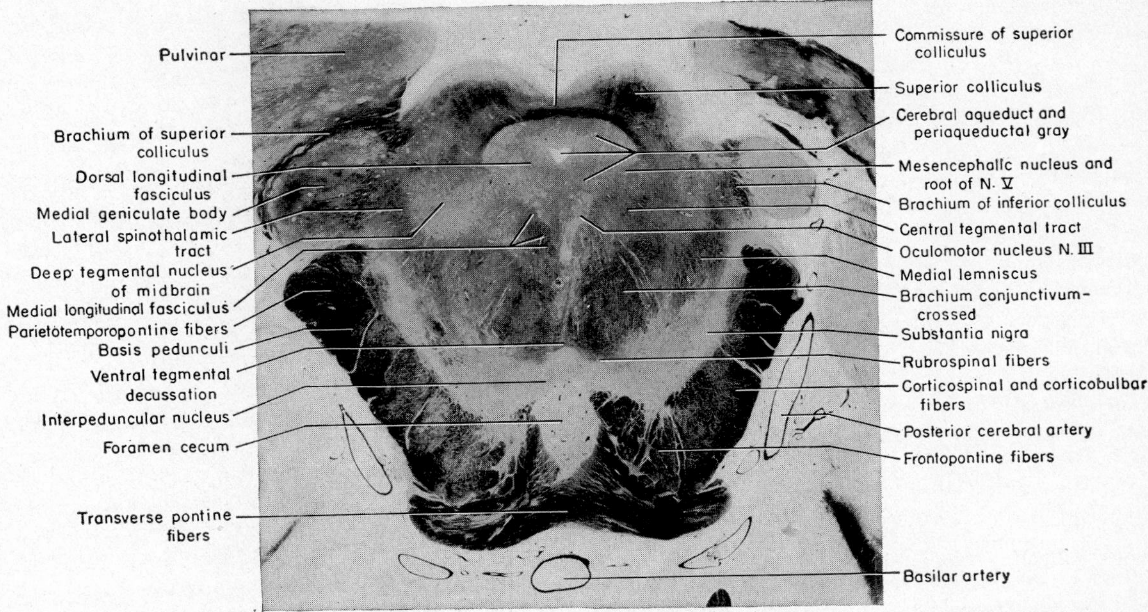

FIG. 137. Transverse section, A 901, through caudal tip of pulvinar and rostral tip of basal pons. Human, Weigert. Photograph, ×2.5.

several origins, tectobulbars, tectospinals, and many arising in the nuclei associated with the posterior commissure. The more specific relations of the superior colliculus with the terminations of the optic nerve and corticotectal fibers will be described in Chap. 21.

The **brachium of the superior colliculus** can be seen in rostral midbrain levels, passing dorsal to the medial geniculate body, and connecting colliculus and lateral geniculate body (Fig. 137). It contains fibers entering the colliculus. Certain of the incoming optic fibers, especially those for the light reflex, terminate in the gray of the superior colliculus; in fact, it is very difficult to separate the caudal border of pretectal area from collicular gray in man. Immediately lateral to the pretectal area in the caudal diencephalic levels is the pretectal nucleus which also merges into the collicular gray. The pretectal region begins in the caudal diencephalon and is medial to the pulvinar, ventral, and medial thalamic nuclei. Certain incoming fibers of the optic tract, especially those mediating light-reflex impulses, end in the pretectal region (Fig. 148).

The cells in the two collicular nuclei give rise to processes that form **tectobulbar** and **tectospinal** tracts. Many of these fibers cross ventral to the aqueduct in the **dorsal tegmental decussation** and form medial tectobulbar and tectospinal tracts. The lateral tectospinal tract of the medulla and spinal cord is a caudal continuation of a **tectopontine tract,** as mentioned above. This arises laterally from the efferent collicular cells, appears dorsal to the brachium conjunctivum, and descends into the lateral pontine tegmental region. The inferior colliculus also contributes fibers to the tectopontine tract. In the caudal pons and medulla the lateral tectospinal tract is thought to be medial to the lateral spinothalamic tracts. Tectocerebellar fibers pass via the anterior medullary velum into the cerebellum. They arise from each colliculus.

As the tectobulbar tract and the medial tectospinal cross the mid-line in the dorsal tegmental decussation, they are known collectively as the **predorsal fasciculus.** They descend through the mediodorsal fibers of the crossing brachium conjunctivum and can be followed through the brain stem thereafter adjacent to the mid-line, ventral to the medial longitudinal fasciculus. The tectobulbar fibers break away and enter motor nuclei of the cranial nerves. By way of the colliculi and these tracts, incoming sensory, auditory, and optic impulses can bring about certain reflex movements of the head, eyes, and neck.

The **oculomotor** and the **trochlear nuclei** are situated near the mid-line in the tegmentum of the midbrain at the level of the superior and inferior colliculi, respectively (Figs. 137, 147, 152). These supply impulses to all the eye muscles except the lateral recti. Nerve fibers can be seen emerging from each of the nuclei. The oculomotor fibers, some of which are crossed, pass caudally and slightly laterally, medial to and through the red nucleus, to emerge between the cerebral peduncles. The trochlear fibers swing dorsolaterally through the periaqueductal gray to decussate in the superior medullary velum, just caudal to the inferior colliculus. Associated with these oculomotor and trochlear nuclei and running near them, principally medially, is the **medial longitudinal fasciculus.** Its components have been identified elsewhere.

Dorsal and dorsolateral to the oculomotor and trochlear nuclei and extending to surround the aqueduct is a mass of gray known as the **anulus of the aqueduct,** or periaqueductal gray (Fig. 137). Dorsal, lateral, and ventral portions are defined. The dorsal portion constitutes the deepest layer of the superior colliculus. The lateral portion shows little differentiation into nuclear groups aside from a component of the nucleus of the posterior commissure (see later). It is best developed at the level of the inferior colliculus and is continuous with the central nucleus of the inferior colliculus. The ventral periaqueductal gray is more extensive than the other divisions and is continuous rostrally with diencephalic periventricular gray, and caudally with pontine periventricular gray. A number of nuclear groups are differentiated in it, but between these groups are scattered neurons (184, 394). Within the gray are some small, poorly myelinated fibers, the **dorsal longitudinal fasciculus of Schütz.** These run throughout the brain stem just ventral to the aqueduct and fourth ventricle. They are thought to contain descending projections from the hypothalamus and reticular nuclei of the midbrain. These synapse

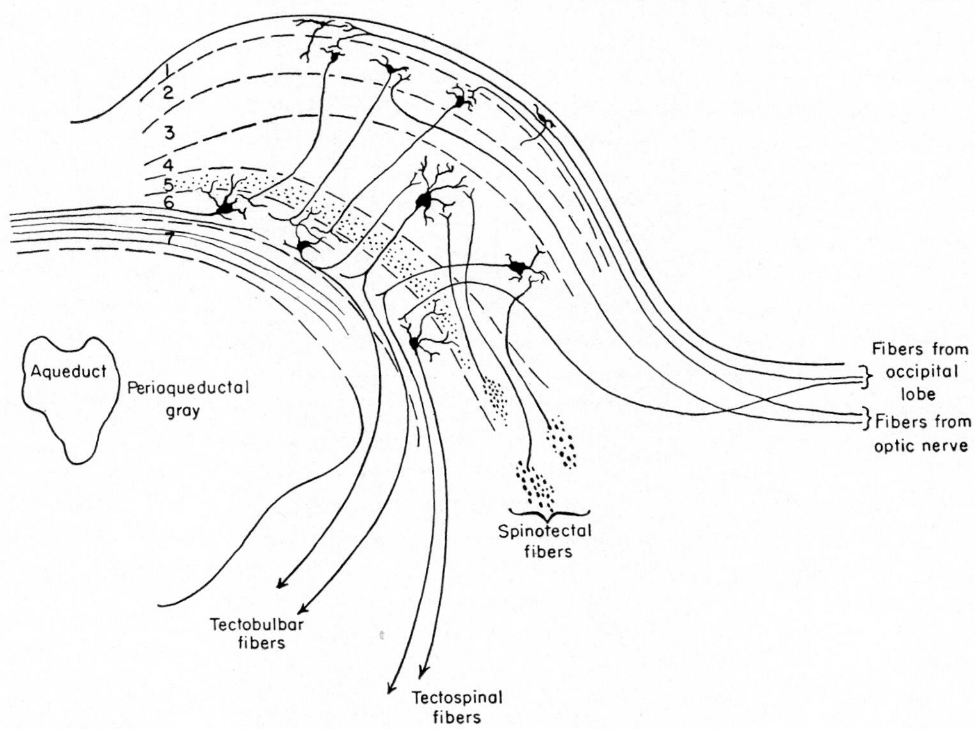

FIG. 138. Diagram of the chief laminae of superior colliculus of human. Only a few of fiber connections are indicated.

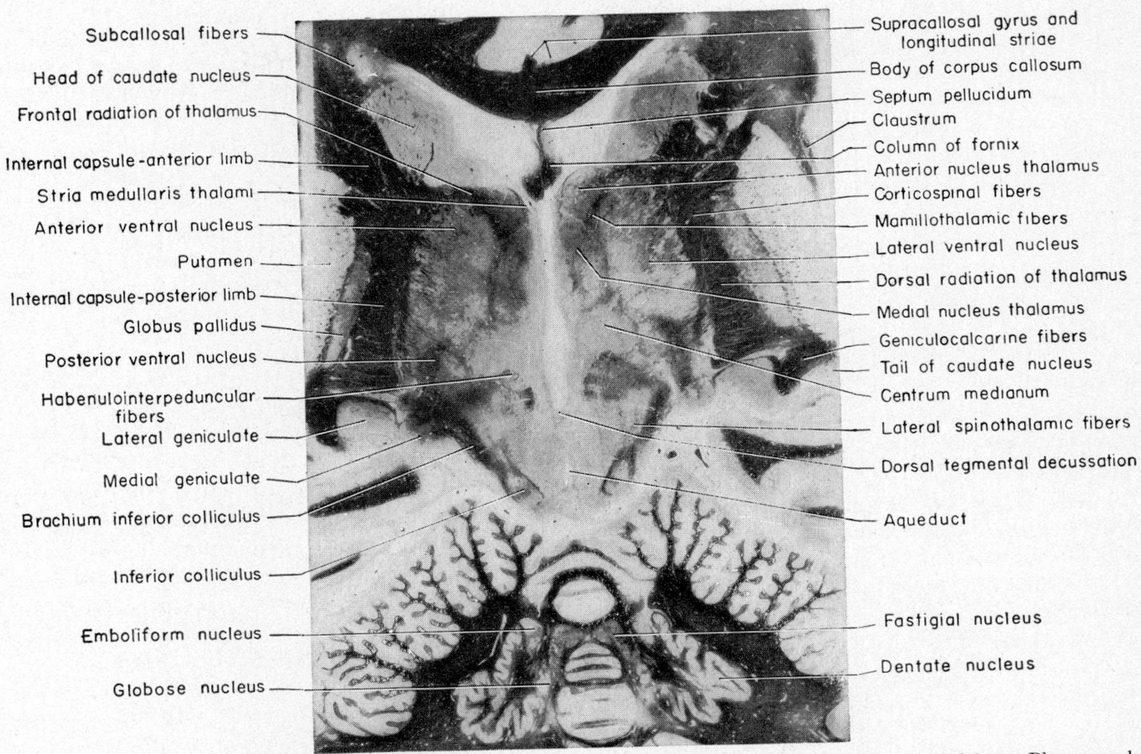

FIG. 139. Frontal section, B 560, of human brain through septum pellucidum and inferior colliculi. Weigert. Photograph, ×1.25.

about periaqueductal neurons and in other brain stem nuclei such as the nucleus intercalatus and dorsal motor vagus nucleus. Partly within the anulus of the aqueduct and partly within tegmentum is the **nucleus of the posterior commissure.** This nucleus surrounds all surfaces of the commissure and is smaller in man than in many lower forms (Fig. 147). It contributes fibers to the commissure and probably to the medial longitudinal fasciculus. The **nucleus of Darkschewitsch** begins near the diencephalic-mesencephalic boundary and is located in the ventral part of the periaqueductal gray. It extends caudally to levels through the Edinger-Westphal complex (Fig. 147). Ventrolateral to the nucleus of Darkschewitsch, and belonging to the midbrain tegmental area, is the **interstitial nucleus of Cajal.** This nucleus also begins in the diencephalic-mesencephalic boundary region and extends further caudally than the nucleus of Darkschewitsch. It overrides the fibers of the medial longitudinal fasciculus, and its cells are medium-sized multipolar and efferent in character. The connections of these three nuclei, and especially the last two, are thought to be similar. They receive fibers from vestibular nuclei, from the basal ganglia, and perhaps from the occipital areas of the cerebral cortex. The nucleus of Darkschewitsch contributes crossed fibers to the medial longitudinal fasciculus, the commissurospinal tract. The interstitial nucleus contributes fibers to both the ipsilateral and contralateral fasciculi, the interstitiospinal tracts. These nuclei would therefore probably correlate head and eye movements.

In the mid-portion of the midbrain tegmentum the **red nucleus** stands out surrounded by its dense capsules of incoming and outgoing fibers (Figs. 135, 147, 148). The red nucleus is a reticular nucleus and, with its connections, is part of a correlating mechanism having to do with motor function. It belongs to the extrapyramidal motor system, and it is described in detail in Chap. 17. The red nucleus receives impulses from the cerebellum via the brachium conjunctivum, from the cerebral cortex, basal ganglia, and diencephalic centers. It discharges rubrospinal, rubroreticular, rubro-oculomotor, and rubrothalamic fibers.

Throughout the tegmentum of the midbrain are many reticular neurons, large and small, some in scattered arrangement and some arranged into discrete nuclear groups. Some are dorsomedial to the red nucleus, some dorsolateral, and some are ventral. They constitute dorsal, lateral, and ventral portions of the large reticular nucleus, the **deep tegmental nucleus of the midbrain** (Fig. 137). The neurons are important relays for the basal ganglia, subthalamus, and associated nuclei.

Within the mid-line near the base of the midbrain, the **interpeduncular nucleus** overlies the interpeduncular fossa (Fig. 136). Its neurons are small and stain poorly. They receive fibers from the habenular complex. They project caudally into the brain stem tegmentum. In the basal part of the midbrain is a broad mass of gray, with entering and emerging fibers, slightly noticeable in the usual stained preparations. In gross sections of the fresh midbrain this mass appears darkly pigmented. This area is known as the **substantia nigra,** and in function it is related to the basal ganglia of the extrapyramidal system. It receives fibers from the cerebral cortex, the globus pallidus, and the spinal cord by way of collaterals of the ascending sensory tracts. It is discussed more fully in Chap. 17.

In the tegmentum also are fibers of passage, long and short. These are, chiefly, in addition to tracts associated with the colliculi, the **spinothalamics,** the **medial lemniscus,** and those fibers of the **brachium conjunctivum** which pass beyond the red nucleus to the thalamus (Figs. 135, 137, 148). The medial longitudinal fasciculus has been mentioned and described earlier. The spinothalamic fibers have a laterodorsal position, and some pass through the nuclear portion of the inferior colliculus. They are medial to the brachium of the inferior colliculus. The medial lemniscus, of a semilunar shape, extends dorsoventrally and is lateral to the decussation of the brachium conjunctivum and dorsal to the lateral portion of the substantia nigra. As it moves rostrally it is laterodorsal to the red nucleus and can be traced into the posterolateral ventral nucleus of the thalamus, as can the spinothalamic tracts.

Coursing rostrally, the fibers constituting the brachium conjunctivum pass from their dorsolateral position to a ventromedial one. In the rostral pontine levels they cross, many fibers then entering the red nucleus and adjacent tegmental gray, others passing laterally and rostrally to end in the lateral ventral nucleus of the thalamus. Some collaterals descend to end in scattered reticular nuclei.

The **posterior commissure** may be described with the midbrain, though it is in the boundary zone between the diencephalon and midbrain (Figs. 147, 148). It is just dorsal to the point at which the aqueduct is continuous with the third ventricle. It contains fibers arising in the globus pallidus and ending in the midbrain tegmental gray and red nucleus; fibers from the occipital cortex to the superior colliculus; commissural fibers between the superior colliculi; fibers from the pretectal area passing to the opposite Edinger-Westphal nucleus; fibers from the globus pallidus to the nucleus associated with the posterior commissure, the nucleus of Darkschewitsch, and the interstitial nucleus of Cajal; and finally, fibers arising in these latter nuclei of one side and passing into the contralateral medial longitudinal fasciculus.

The midbrain has added to our neural-organization mechanisms for moving the eyes and for regulating the light reaching the retinas. A second special sense, hearing, also finds a more complex arc here than in the pons and medulla. Coordination of movement patterns occurs here also. The primitive righting reflexes have a midbrain arc, and alternation of flexor and extensor movement patterns may be controlled here in part by the red nucleus and allied neurons. The substantia nigra is important in the regulation and distribution of muscle tone, as well as in the organization of movement patterns.

It should be noted that lesions in part of the brain stem thus far described frequently cause what is clinically called **crossed paralysis.** In such a syndrome it is customary to find ipsilateral motor and sensory disturbances in whatever cranial nerve is involved, and contralateral sensory and motor disturbances below the level of the lesion. Syndromes involving the oculomotor and abducens nerves and nuclei, the facial nerve, and the trigeminal nuclei are described elsewhere.

THE BLOOD SUPPLY OF THE MEDULLA, PONS, AND MIDBRAIN

The blood supply of these regions may be discussed briefly at this point, since the general plan of arterial supply is the same for all three (261, 759). In fact, the plan of supply for the diencephalon is also similar, but it will be more suitable to describe the vessels of that region later (Fig. 140).

Arterial Supply

From large regional arteries for medulla, pons, and midbrain three types of branches, described according to their course, arise. Vessels penetrating the ventral surface of these levels near the mid-line are called **paramedian** arteries. Vessels running transversely around the brain stem to penetrate the ventrolateral and lateral surfaces form a **short circumferential** group of arteries. Vessels which run completely around the brain stem to enter its dorsal surface constitute **long circumferential** arteries. The large regional vessels at the medulla level are the vertebrals; that at the pontine level, the basilar. At the midbrain level the anterior chorioidal, posterior cerebral, and its branch, the posterior chorioidal, serve as regional arteries. The supply to the tegmental portion of the brain stem and to the floor of the fourth ventricle and aqueduct varies from level to level, but is derived from branches of paramedian and from long and short circumferential arteries—sometimes from all three types, sometimes from only two.

A slight variation exists in the plan of blood supply at the rostral and caudal levels of the **medulla.** In the rostral portion an arterial representative of each of the three types is present. In the caudal part are arteries representing only two of the types. In the rostral part paramedian arteries are represented by small vessels springing either from the basilar or terminal portion of the vertebrals. These supply the rostral part of the pyramids, the medial portion of the inferior olive, the internal arcuate fibers forming the medial lemniscus, the medial longitudinal fasciculus, the medial tectospinal tract, and the hypoglossal nuclei. The short circumferential type of artery is represented by one or two vessels arising from

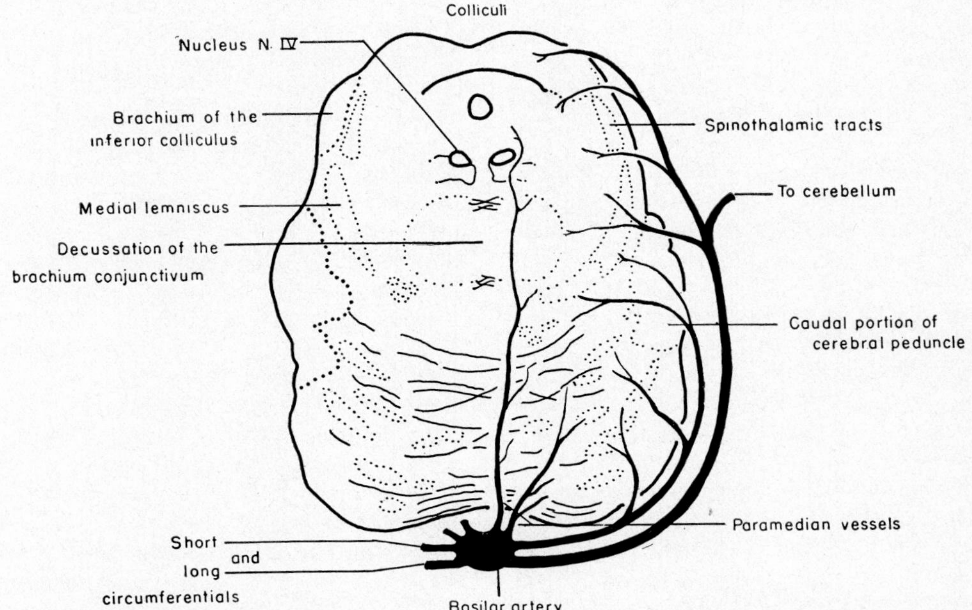

Fig. 140. Diagram of plan of arterial blood supply to human brain stem. (*Based on study of Foix and Hillemand.*)

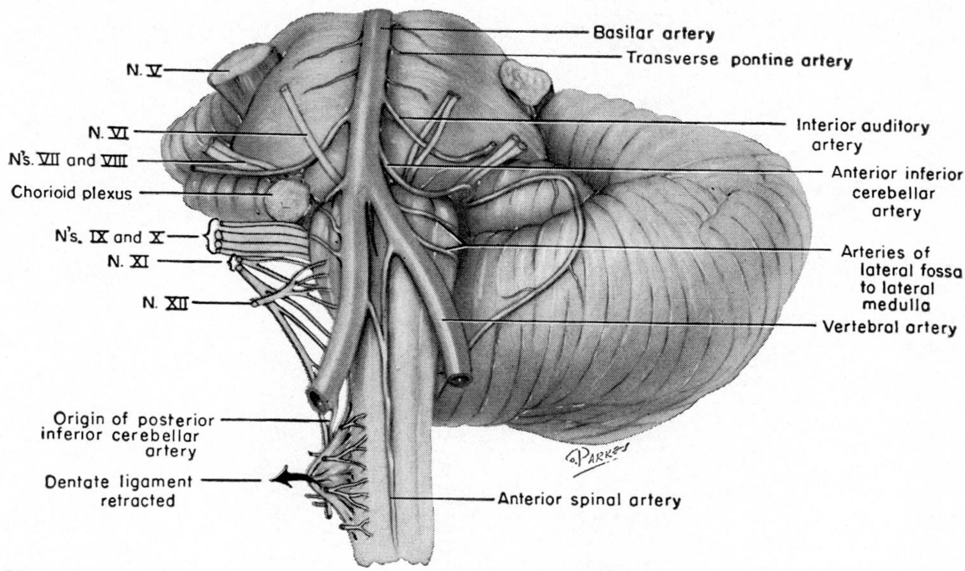

FIG. 141. Ventral surface of human medulla, to show cranial nerves and much of the arterial supply. The major part of the cerebellum has been removed on the left.

the basilar or vertebrals, as the **anterior artery of the lateral fossa** and an accessory artery of the lateral fossa, as well as by a variable number of small arterioles arising from the posterior inferior cerebellar artery (Fig. 141). These vessels supply the lateral territory of the medulla and thus irrigate much of the inferior olive, the lateral spinothalamics, the rostral portion of the nucleus ambiguus, the rostral three-fourths of the spinal root and nucleus of the trigeminal, the internal arcuate fibers, the emerging fibers of the ninth, tenth, and bulbar portion of the eleventh nerves, the medullar respiratory center, and the tracts and other nuclei of the reticular formation. The long circumferential type of artery is represented in the rostral part of the medulla by the **posterior inferior cerebellar artery** (Figs. 57, 141). This usually arises from the vertebrals. It ascends around the medulla and is rather tortuous. In the rostral medulla its region of supply (aside from variable branches supplying some of the inferior part of the lateral territory) is chiefly the restiform body and vestibular nuclei.

In the inferior part of the medulla the vascular plan usually consists of paramedian and long circumferential arteries. The representatives of the former type are branches of the **anterior spinal arteries** which arise from the vertebrals (Fig. 141). These branches supply the pyramids, the medial reticular substance, and the medial portion of the floor of the fourth ventricle including the caudal part of the hypoglossal nucleus. The long circumferential artery of the inferior medulla is the posterior inferior cerebellar artery, which in this region supplies all that portion of the medulla not supplied by the paramedian vessels. It usually sends a branch, the **posterior artery of the lateral fossa,** into territory customarily nourished by short circumferential vessels (22). The **posterior spinal artery,** usually a branch of the posterior inferior cerebellar, nourishes the nuclei cuneatus and gracilis and the caudal end of the restiform body (Fig. 57).

In the **pons** four to six paramedian vessels arise from the basilar and penetrate perpendicularly into the nervous tissue near the raphe. Short circumferential arteries, 5 to 10 in number, arise laterally from the basilar and enter the mass of the middle cerebellar peduncle particularly, though some small radicular vessels supply the trigeminal root and ganglion. Penetrating branches supply the lateral reticular formation and passing fibers. Usually, one or two long circumferential arteries are found. The **superior cerebellar**

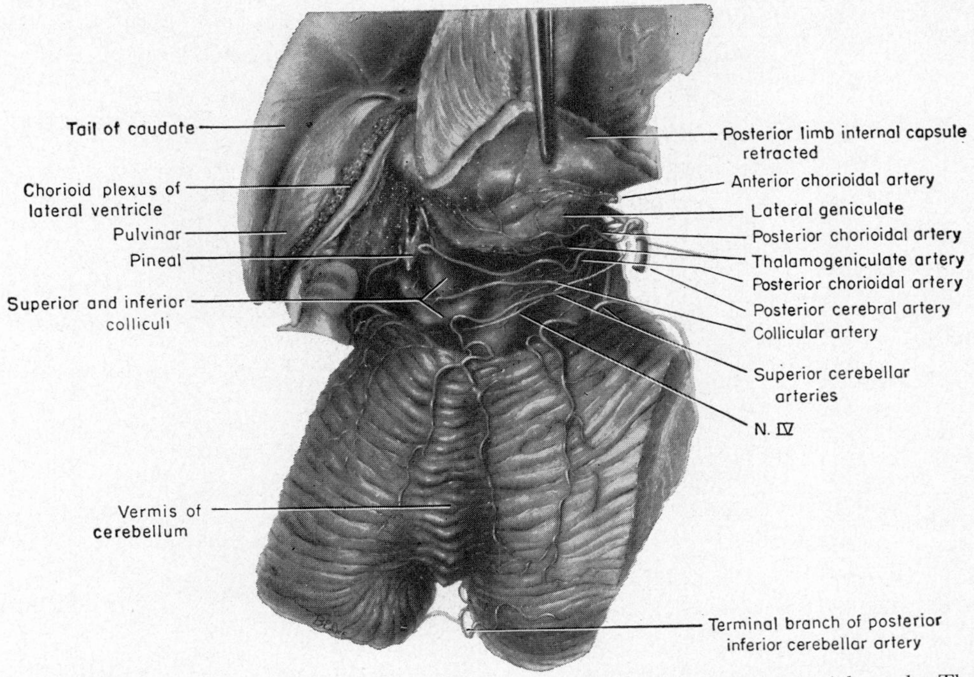

FIG. 142. A dorsolateral view of the human brain stem to show some of the important arterial supply. The superior cerebellar arteries, two in number in this case, arise from the basilar which is not shown. Two posterior chorioidal arteries are also present. Several small arteries entering the dorsolateral pons and midbrain are not labeled.

artery and frequently an accessory vessel run around the middle cerebellar peduncle to the dorsolateral pontine surface (Fig. 142). They supply the middle cerebellar peduncle and the posterior end of the quadrigeminal bodies, but do not appear to supply any of the floor of the aqueduct. Branches from them, especially from the superior cerebellar, may supply the ventrolateral pontine tegmentum wherein are found trigeminal and facial nuclei, spinothalamic tract, and lateral lemniscus. The supply of the dorsal reticular formation and periaqueductal region depends on penetrating paramedian and short circumferential vessels, the latter being almost the only supply at lower pontine levels. The **anterior inferior cerebellar artery** arises from the basilar artery at the junction of the lowest and middle thirds of that vessel (Fig. 141). It is a long circumferential vessel in relation to its supply to the ventrolateral cerebellum and the lateral tegmentum of the lower two-thirds of the pons. The pontine area of supply appears to be a crucial region. Atkinson has made some very provocative observations in a series of cases of acoustic nerve tumors (39). In all the cases he found an infarction of the pontine tegmental region and an occlusion of the anterior inferior cerebellar artery, due either to a clip placed on the vessel at operation or to postoperative thrombosis of the artery. The **internal auditory artery,** accompanying facial and auditory nerves, arises from the anterior inferior cerebellar artery. It may arise as a separate branch of the basilar.

The supply of the **midbrain** and cerebral peduncles follows the usual vascular pattern as noted above. Again paramedian, short and long circumferential vessels are present, but variation in their arrangement is to be noted. Many of the paramedian arteries, for example, necessarily have a short lateral course and direction and are thus similar to short circumferential vessels elsewhere. Several long circumferential vessels sweep around the peduncle to gain the posterior surface of the midbrain. As they wind around, short penetrating vessels arise from them to supply the territory usually supplied by short circumferential arteries.

The long circumferential or peripeduncular arteries are usually five in number, but only one supplies midbrain tissue alone, this being the **quadrigeminal artery,** which arises from the posterior cerebral artery near its origin (Fig. 142). This artery has two terminal branches, one for each colliculus. The superior cerebellar artery, as noted, furnishes a few penetrating branches to the cerebral peduncle, sends a branch also to the superior cerebellar peduncle, and supplies the superior aspect of the cerebellum. The chief **posterior chorioidal** gives several short circumferential arteries to the cerebral peduncle, to the thalamogeniculate supply, some to the lateral part of the superior colliculus, some to the splenium of the corpus callosum, and terminal branches to the medial thalamic nuclei and the chorioid plexus of the third ventricle. The **accessory posterior chorioidal** has a similar but more limited area of supply. The **posterior cerebral** artery gives some short circumferentials, the thalamoperforating vessels, and furnishes some branches to the splenium of the corpus callosum before becoming a cortical vessel. The **anterior chorioidal,** a branch of either the internal carotid or middle cerebral artery, runs across the upper part of the cerebral peduncle and gives in its course some penetrating branches (Figs. 51, 56). It also supplies the chorioid plexus of the lateral ventricle, olfactory centers in the temporal lobe, basal ganglia, optic tracts, and internal capsule.

The paramedian vessels, properly speaking, arise from the posterior cerebrals just after their formation by the bifurcation of the basilar (Fig. 51). They are referred to as the retromamillary trunk, because they enter the nervous tissue just posterior to these bodies. They are composed of two groups of vessels, the thalamoperforating described with the supply to the thalamus, and the peduncular. The peduncular arterioles are numerous, penetrating the nervous tissue to supply the internal portion of the cerebral peduncle, and passing superiorly on either side of the red nucleus to supply to the midbrain tegmentum, including the substantia nigra, red nucleus, and the oculomotor nuclei, especially.

In summary, then, in the midbrain, the interpeduncular region is supplied by the paramedian vessels from the retromamillary stalk. The peduncle is supplied by some of the paramedian peduncular vessels from the same stalk and by arterioles from the long circumferential vessels, the superior cerebellar, the quadrigeminal, and the anterior and posterior chorioidals. The midbrain tegmentum is supplied in its median part by penetrating peduncular vessels of the retromamillary stalk and in its lateral portion by penetrating short circumferential arteries which are in turn branches of the long circumferentials. The tectum is supplied by the quadrigeminal artery, a long circumferential vessel, which branches to supply each colliculus.

Considerable variation exists in the arterial tree supplying these brain stem levels. Often a long or short circumferential artery is missing entirely on one side, or considerable inequality may exist in the size of two corresponding vessels. Variation in the pattern of origin of these arteries also is found. Whereas in one specimen a certain group of medullar circumferential vessels may spring from the vertebral artery, in another they may arise from the basilar. Several may arise from a single trunk. Similar variations are to be seen in the pattern of origin of circumferential vessels from the basilar and posterior cerebral arteries.

Venous Drainage

This has been touched on briefly in Chap. 4. The pattern of venous drainage from the **medulla** is similar to the arterial, although not as many veins are present. They drain into a subpial rete. Anterior and posterior median medullar veins are present and are connected to branches of the subpial plexus. The anterior vein is continuous rostrally with a pontine vein. The posterior vein arises rostrally from the chorioid plexus of the fourth ventricle. These median veins may be continuous caudally with anterior and posterior spinal venous trunks. The posterior median vein may also connect directly with cerebellar veins and with the transverse sinus by way of veins running along the ninth and tenth cranial nerves. The anterior median vein may connect with veins about the hypoglossal nerve which drain into the emissary vein of the hypoglossal canal.

The venous drainage of the **pons** is also similar to the arterial pattern. An anterior median longitudinal pontine vein drains the central and ventrolateral pontine regions by small venous radicles. This vein is continuous caudally with the anterior median medullar vein. Rostrally the longitudinal pontine vein divides and may join either cerebellar veins or the basal vein of Rosenthal. Veins draining the dorsolateral pontine regions empty into an anterior inferior cerebellar vein.

The **midbrain** venous drainage is cared for by paramedian or central and lateral radicles draining ventrolateral and lateral midbrain regions. The former drain into the interpeduncular venous plexus which empties in turn usually into the basal vein. Lateral veins draining the ventrolateral midbrain area also usually empty into the basal vein. The vessels draining the lateral and dorsolateral midbrain, including the tectum, usually empty into the internal cerebral vein or vein of Galen.

THE DIENCEPHALON

The rostral portion of the brain stem, the **diencephalon,** becomes covered from external view, except in its ventral portion, by the developing **telencephalon.** The **transverse cerebral fissure** separates the dorsal portion of the diencephalon from the overhanging part of the cerebral hemispheres (Fig. 145). The **internal capsule,** the large collection of fibers interconnecting telencephalon and brain stem, bounds it laterally, and separates it laterally as well as rostrolaterally from the various divisions of the basal ganglia (Fig. 144). Caudually, the diencephalon merges gradually into the midbrain. From the floor of the diencephalon is suspended the hypophysis by means of the infundibulum. The diencephalic nuclei of the two sides bound the third ventricle.

The diencephalon may be divided into four parts: the most dorsal medial part, the epithalamus, includes the pineal gland (epiphysis), the habenulae and their commissure, and the striae medullares thalami, which are fibers entering the habenulae; the remaining dorsal part of the diencephalon, or "the" thalamus, includes the dorsal thalamus, subdivided into anterior, medial, and lateral nuclear masses, and the pulvinar, and the lateral and medial geniculate bodies; the most ventral part is formed by the hypothalamus; the subthalamus lies between the lateral part of the hypothalamus and parts of the dorsal thalamus (Figs. 143, 145).

The **epithalamus** is continuous caudally with the rostral portion, or the pretectal region, of the superior colliculus (Fig. 144). The **pineal,** somewhat cone-shaped in the human, lies in the intercollicular sulcus with its apex directed posteriorly. Anteriorly, two peduncles or laminae, a superior and an inferior one, attach the body of the structure to the brain stem, and between the peduncles the pineal recess represents a small extension of the cavity of the third ventricle. The superior peduncle blends into the habenular commissure; the inferior one attaches to the posterior commissure.

The human pineal is composed of large and small masses of cells. Groups of cells are surrounded by a framework of reticular connective tissue in which many blood vessels are present. The structure of the pineal varies considerably from one individual to another, and it has been said that no two pineals show a similar grouping of the cell masses (677). Two types of cellular elements compose the cell masses, neuroglia and parenchymal elements. The neuroglial cells have dark nuclei, the parenchymal cells, pale-staining nuclei. The parenchymal cells have a cell body of stellate shape from which a variable number of cytoplasmic prolongations may extend in all directions or all the prolongations may extend in only one or two directions. Many processes end freely with either filiform terminations or club-shaped expansions. The protoplasm of the parenchyma cells shows a reticulum. The cells contain mitochondria, a number of short rod-like processes, pigment granules, and specific secretion granules. The cells are therefore considered to have an intensive secretory activity. They are considered to have a nonnervous function. Neurons have been identified within the pineal in the macaque, but not in other animals.

The neuroglial elements are less numerous than the parenchymal. Astrocytes, especially cells resembling the fibrous type found in the cerebral cortex, are present. A lesser number of astrocytes resemble protoplasmic astrocytes, and these contain gliosomes. Neuroglial cells containing granules are also present; and they resemble the parenchyma cells. They too are thought to have a secretory activity. Regressive changes occur in the neuroglial and mesodermal connective tissues of the pineal, usually

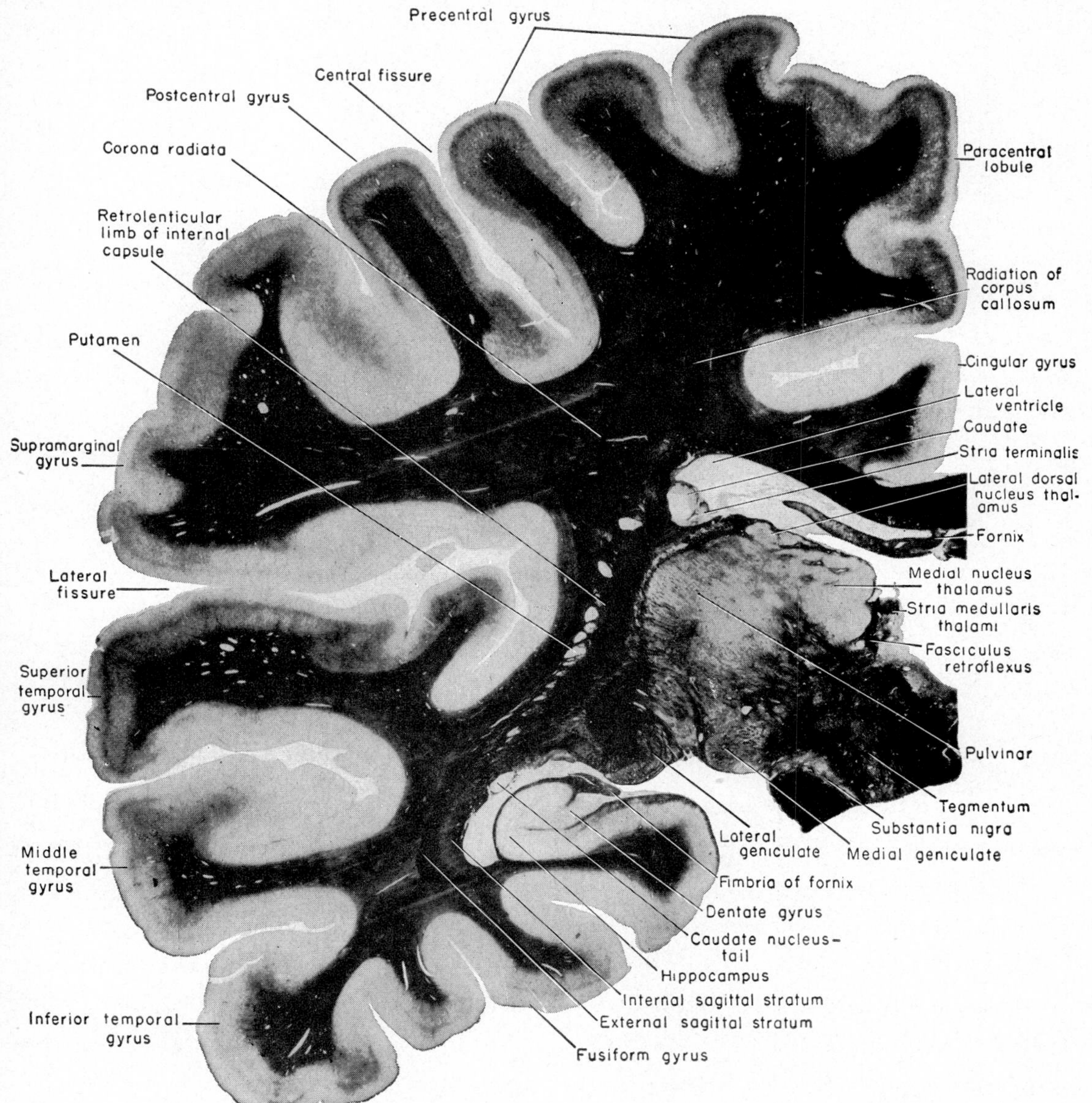

Fig. 143. A frontal section of the human brain through the lateral geniculate body. (*From Jelgersma, "Atlas Anatomicum Cerebri Humani," Amsterdam, Scheltema & Holkema.*)

in the third decade or later, and these involve the formation of calcareous concretions or acervuli. A calcified pineal is a useful landmark to the radiologist.

Nerve fibers, the origin of which is obscure, are said to enter the pineal by way of the habenular and posterior commissures. It happens that these "nerve fibers" are actually aberrant fibers of these commissures and that they do not terminate within the pineal (677). Nerves follow the blood vessels entering the structure from the tela chorioidea of the third ventricle.

Emerging from (or penetrating) the apex of the pineal is a prominent fasciculus of nerve fibers, the nervus conarii. This has been identi-

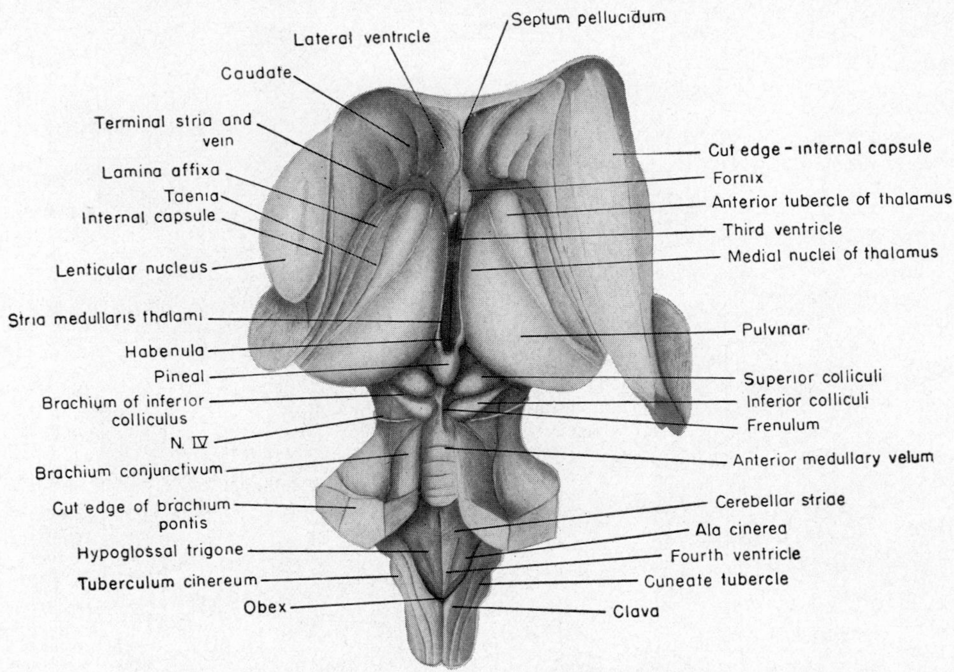

FIG. 144. Dorsal view of human brain stem.

fied in the human (153). The origin and ultimate destination of these fibers are unknown, but the nerve has been traced into the floor of the straight sinus. A peculiar formation of arachnoid, resembling an arachnoidal granulation, has been found in relation to the floor of the straight sinus where the vein of Galen opens into it. This structure contains pial tissue, a sinusoidal plexus of blood vessels, and several blood sinuses. Clark suggests it may exert a ball-valve effect in the wall of the sinus, capable of regulating the venous return from the great vein of Galen. He names this arachnoidal structure the suprapineal body. The nervus conarii apparently traverses the suprapineal body without contributing fibers to it.

A great deal of speculation has been offered from time to time as to the function of the pineal. Galen originally regarded the structure as a gland, and the modern investigations of its histologic structure tend to verify this idea. What the nature of its secretion is, or into what the secretion is poured, are unsettled. The pineal has also been considered as the seat of the soul by Descartes, and as a sensory structure related to the parietal or third eye of certain lizards. Others have regarded it as an organ which functions for the reflex regulation of the cerebrospinal-fluid circulation and pressure. The suprapineal body may indeed have some such function. Many investigations in recent years have been directed toward a possible endocrine nature of the pineal, and it perhaps may in some way be related to sexual maturation in the male.

The **habenular commissure** connects the **habenular nuclei** of the two sides (Figs. 144, 148). These latter are lateral to the pretectal region and are marked dorsally as slightly elevated, rounded arms embracing the posterior superior part of the third ventricle. As the arms continue rostrally, they become thin and merge on either side into a longitudinal ridge formed by the **striae medullares thalami** which marks the division between the dorsal and medial surfaces of the dorsal thalamus. The striae are fibers coming into the habenulae primarily from the amygdaloid nuclei of the temporal lobes and from the medial olfactory areas beneath the rostrum of the corpus callosum. Some fibers from the rostral hypothalamus and the fornix may also be a part of them. The habenular nuclei are olfacto-somatic reflex centers, receiving impulses by way of the striae and discharging to the **interpeduncular ganglion** (between the cerebral peduncles) by way of the **habenulointerpeduncular tract,** or **fasciculus retroflexus of Meynert.** The habenular commissure contains some crossing fibers from the striae medullares thalami.

The **dorsal thalamus** proper is lateral and ventral to the epithalamus. When viewed from above after removal of all cerebral substance above the transverse cerebral fissures, it is seen to be formed of two large, winglike masses, converging rostrally, whose medial surfaces form the walls of the third ventricle (Fig. 144). The dorsal surface of each "wing" presents a groove laterally which separates the dorsal thalamus from the body and tail of the caudate nucleus (of the basal ganglia). Within each groove is a bundle of fibers, the **stria terminalis thalami,** which is composed of commissural fibers between, and projection fibers from, the amygdaloid nuclei to the preoptic region and to the hypothalamus proper (which is just caudad). A small vein, the **vena terminalis,** travels with the stria terminalis (Fig. 144). The most lateral, caudal portion of each of the wings is the **pulvinar.** Rostral and also medial to it are dorsal divisions of the lateral nuclear mass, the **lateral dorsal and lateral posterior thalamic nuclei.** Medial to the rostral part of the latter is the **anterior thalamic nucleus,** protruding somewhat above the general level of the thalamus. Forming the medial surface of the wings and extending in a ventral direction is the **medial nucleus,** part of which is occasionally continuous across the mid-line, through the **massa intermedia** (Fig. 145).

The anterior nuclei receive fibers from the mamillary bodies of the hypothalamus, and send fibers to the cingular gyrus. The connecting fibers from the mamillary bodies compose the **mamillothalamic tract** or the **bundle of Vicq d'Azyr,** which stands out prominently in frontal sections through this region (Figs. 145, 199, 257). The medial nuclei, which are connected with other dorsal thalamic nuclei and with the hypothalamus, project to the rostral part of the frontal lobe and may serve as visceral and somatic sensory associative nuclei. The lateral dorsal and lateral posterior nuclei receive fibers from the ventral nuclei of the dorsal thalamus, project to the parietal lobe, and function as somatic sensory association nuclei. The pulvinar, which is thought by Walker to receive fibers from the geniculate bodies and ventral nuclei of the lateral nuclear mass, projects to the parietal, temporal, and occipital lobes and is probably an association nucleus for auditory and visual impulses, as well as general somatic (793).

Ventral to the caudal portion of each of the wings and nearly obscured by it are the medial and lateral geniculate bodies (Fig. 143). The former may be seen from the dorsal surface, associated medially with a rounded arm of fibers, the **brachium of the inferior colliculus.** The **medial geniculate body** is a thalamic auditory center, and it projects fibers by way of the internal capsule to the auditory cortex (areas 41 and 42) of the temporal lobe. Hidden from dorsal view by the overhanging pulvinar is the **lateral geniculate body,** easily outlined in frontal sections of the brain stem, where it lies just dorsal and lateral to the most lateral part of the cerebral peduncle. This geniculate is connected to the superior colliculus by a brachium, serves as a thalamic visual center, and projects to the cortex of the occipital lobe (area 17).

The medial surfaces of the dorsal thalami form the walls of the third ventricle, as previously mentioned. The lateral surface of each "wing" is not completely visible in a dorsal view but is bounded by the internal capsule, which will be described more completely later in Chap. 15. Forming the capsular surface above and below are the dorsal and ventral parts of the **lateral nuclear mass,** respectively. The dorsal part has been described previously. The ventral portion is composed of three chief nuclei listed in rostrocaudal order: **anterior ventral** (nucleus), **lateral ventral,** and **posterior ventral.** The last nucleus is further divided into medial and lateral portions—the **posteromedial ventral** and the **posterolateral ventral** nuclei. These are all discernible in frontal sections of the brain stem (Figs. 204, 259). The posterolateral ventral nucleus receives the spinothalamic tracts and the medial lemniscus and sends fibers to the parietal lobe (areas 3, 1, and 2, especially) through the internal capsule. The posteromedial ventral nucleus, also known as the **arcuate** or the **semilunar,** re-

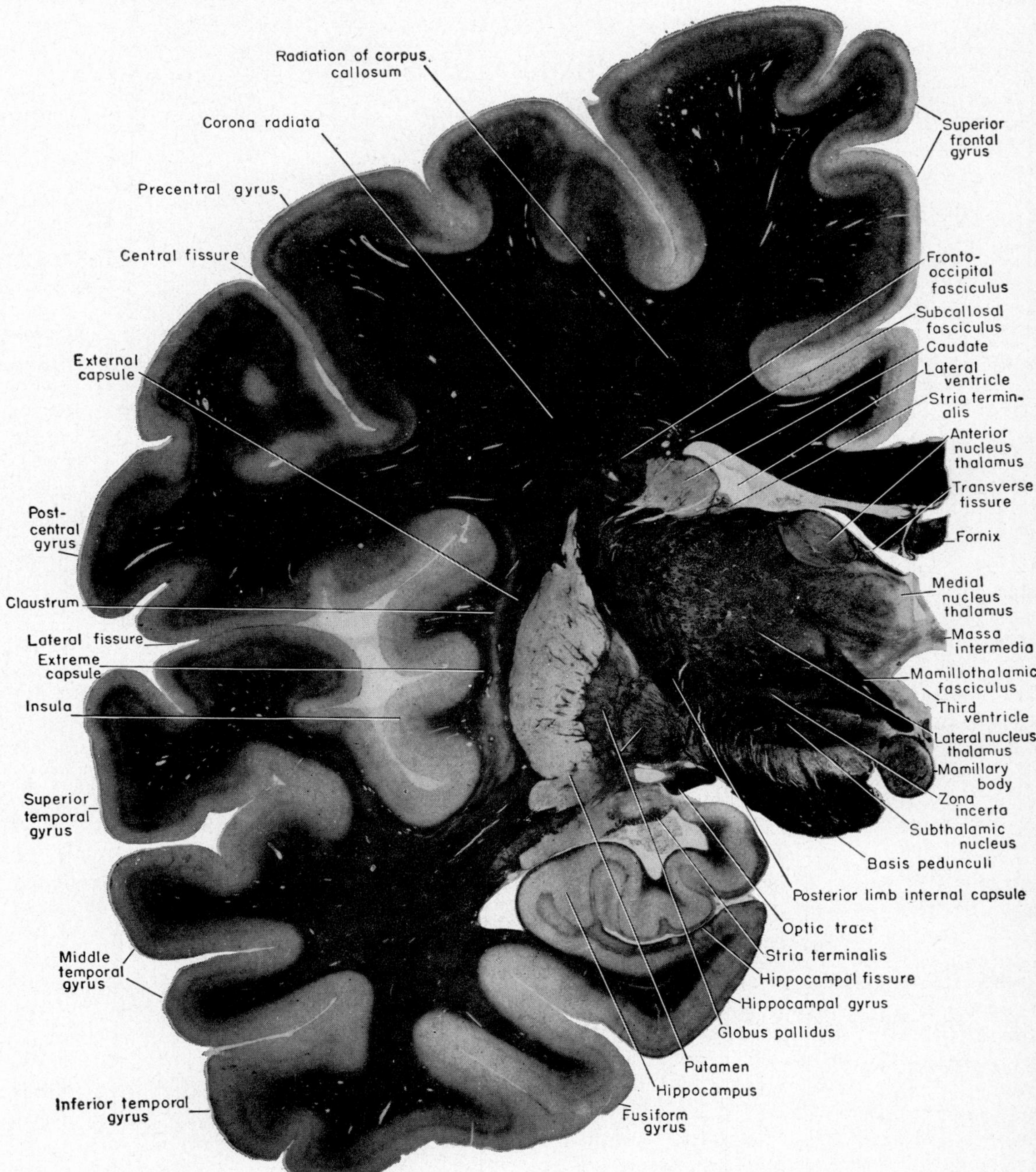

FIG. 145. Frontal section of human brain through mamillary body. (*From Jelgersma, "Atlas Anatomicum Cerebri Humani," Amsterdam, Scheltma & Holkema.*)

ceives the secondary trigeminal fibers and likewise projects to the parietal lobe. The lateral ventral nucleus receives fibers by way of the brachium conjunctivum from the dentate nucleus of the cerebellum and projects to the precentral gyrus (areas 4 and 6) of the frontal lobe. The anterior ventral nucleus receives fibers from the basal ganglia; it projects to area 6.

The large divisions of the dorsal thalamus—anterior, medial, and lateral—are separated by collections of connecting fibers, the **internal medullary laminae** (Figs. 196, 199, 203). A large, prominent nuclear mass within these in the posterior thalamus is the **centrum medianum.** The fasciculus retroflexus of Meynert runs through it, and the posteromedial ventral nucleus is lateroventral to it. Its function is unknown, and its connections aside from those with basal ganglia remain obscure.

In order to see the **subthalamus** it is necessary to use frontal sections of the brain stem (Figs. 145, 204, 259). Dorsally it merges into the dorsal thalamus; laterally it is bounded by the internal capsule; medially and rostrally it is bounded by the hypothalamus; and caudally it merges with nuclei of the tegmentum of the midbrain, the red nucleus, and the substantia nigra in particular. In frontal sections the most dorsolateral part is the **zona incerta,** a nucleus of small cells; the middle part is marked by many fibers of Forel's tegmental fields H, H_1, and H_2 (composed of efferent fibers of the striatum and globus pallidus, with some large cells intermingled among the fibers of H, the most caudad field); the ventromedial part, or **subthalamic nucleus** proper (corpus luysi), is a collection of medium-sized cells well surrounded by a dense capsule of fibers. The connections of the subthalamic region are discussed in Chap. 17.

The **hypothalamus** can be seen in frontal brain sections and from the ventral surface of the brain (Figs. 128, 145, 146). Its rostral portion (**supraoptic**) is hidden from view in the gross brain by the **optic chiasma.** This portion merges into the telencephalic **preoptic area,** interposed between it and medial basal olfactory nuclei. Just caudad to the optic chiasma and projecting ventrally from the hypothalamus is a stalk, the **infundibulum,** to which the hypophysis is attached. A narrow ventral extension of the third ventricle is contained within the infundibulum. The rounded portion of the hypothalamic floor merging into the infundibulum is the **tuber cinereum** which unites laterally with the **lateral hypothalamus.** Posterior to the tuber cinereum and also merging with the lateral hypothalamus are two rounded masses, the **mamillary bodies,** which are connected across the mid-line. The hypothalamic nuclei are divided into the supraoptic, infundibular, retroinfundibular, and mamillary portions. They are described in detail in Chap. 14.

The **third ventricle** is enclosed by the diencephalon and is lined by ependyma (Figs. 68, 144). At the level of the posterior commissure it becomes narrower and merges into the aqueduct of Sylvius. The roof of the third ventricle is formed of a layer of ependyma stretching from points of attachment marked by the striae medullares thalami. Pushing into this ependymal roof from the transverse cerebral fissure are highly vascular folds of pia; these, together with the ependymal cells, which become specialized here into secretory elements, form the **chorioid** plexus of the third ventricle (Fig. 68). The chorioid plexus is quite extensive, stretching all along the roof on either side. Caudally the ventricle shows an extension into the suprapineal recess.

The walls of the third ventricle are formed by the medial thalamic nuclei, which in part are frequently joined across the mid-line to form the **massa intermedia.** The rostral, ventral extent of the ventricle is limited by a thin membrane, the **lamina terminalis,** extending dorsally from the optic chiasma to the anterior commissure. The lamina terminalis connects the two cerebral hemispheres at this point (Figs. 68, 150). The **anterior commissure** is a large rounded bundle of fibers connecting the olfactory centers and other parts of the two hemispheres. Just caudal to it and forming a rounded elevation in the rostral, dorsal boundary of the third ventricle on either side are the **columns of the fornix,** connecting the hippocampus with the mamillary bodies of the hypothalamus. Just caudal and lateral to the columns of the fornix and emerging from the third ventricle are passages into the lateral ventricles ("first" and "second"), the **foramina of Monro.** There are thus three openings into

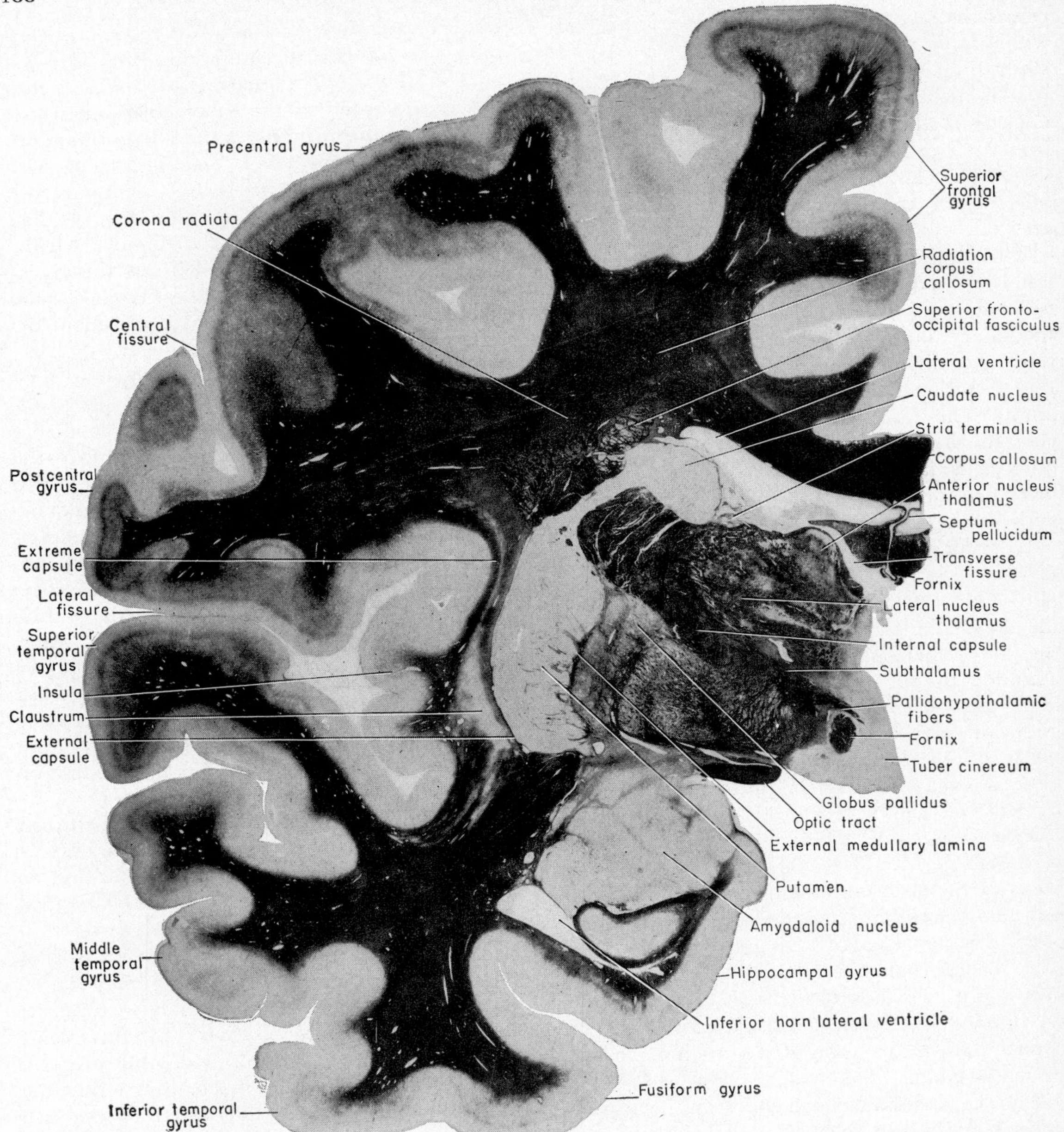

FIG. 146. Frontal section of human brain through tuber cinereum. (*From Jelgersma, "Atlas Anatomicum Cerebri Humani," Amsterdam, Scheltema & Holkema.*)

the third ventricle: these two foramina, rostrolaterally, and the aqueduct of Sylvius, caudally. The floor of the ventricle is formed by the hypothalamus and shows medially two ventral extensions: the **optic recess,** dorsal and rostral to the optic chiasma, and the **infundibular recess** within the infundibulum.

These diencephalic additions to the brain stem contribute somatic and special sensory relay centers, nuclei which are further able to elaborate motor mechanisms, and nuclei which appear to be instrumental in the expression of emotion and autonomic activities. In fact, within the dorsal thalamus the qualitative element of painful and thermal impulses may gain conscious recognition. Neurons within, or adjacent to, the subthalamus and its fibers of passage take part in the correlation of progression movements. The mamillary nuclei and their anterior thalamic projections have to do with the expression of emotion, and much of the remaining parts of the hypothalamus can bring about peripheral autonomic discharges.

In these descriptive sections concerned with the brain stem, reference has been made to a number of nuclei, motor and sensory, related to the cranial nerves. Certain of the fibers of these latter, like the spinal nerves described in earlier sections, are concerned with the transmission of impulses from receptor endings in the skin, mucous membranes, and organs of special sense within the head, as well as from those in the mucous membranes lining thoracic and abdominal hollow viscera. Other cranial nerve fibers discharge effector impulses to the striated and smooth muscles about the head and to the cardiac and smooth muscles of the thoracic and abdominal viscera. These cranial nerves and their nuclei will be described in the chapter that follows.

PAGE NUMBERS FOR BRAIN STEM SECTIONS

TRANSVERSE SERIES—CAUDO-ROSTRAL ORDER

Section No.	*Page No.*	*Section No.*	*Page No.*	*Section No.*	*Page No.*
A 60	160	A 463	478	A 901	174
A 130	161	A 473	167	A 973	192
A 195	162	A 495	209	A 1003	192
A 245	225	A 520	479	A 1058	283
A 288	219	A 530	205	A 1105	386
A 316	164	A 560	203	A 1155	282
A 333	216	A 595	264	A 1198	382
A 381	477	A 645	168	A 1245	279
A 400	165	A 678	481	A 1275	381
A 418	234	A 723	169	A 1356	276
A 435	166	A 798	482	A 1383	379
A 450	259	A 836	195	A 1430	378
A 455	235	A 863	173	A 1560	378

FRONTAL SERIES—VENTRO-DORSAL ORDER

Section No.	Page No.	Section No.	Page No.
B 209	163	B 539	277
B 230	380	B 560	176
B 280	299	B 610	280
B 340	381	B 650	281
B 360	384	B 690	281
B 440	262	B 750	284
B 500	172	B 800	285

PARASAGITTAL SERIES—MEDIO-LATERAL ORDER

Section No.	Page No.
A 326	194
A 300	298
A 270	210
A 250	204

CHAPTER 9

THE CRANIAL NERVES

LIKE THE SPINAL nerves which connect spinal-cord neurons and periphery, the cranial nerves supply information from outlying sensory receptors to the brain stem neurons and bring about the necessary alterations in the peripheral effector apparatus. During the examination of the brain stem in the immediately preceding chapter, nuclei of the cranial nerves have been encountered at various levels. Thus far these nuclei have been identified only according to name. Cranial nerves are not as simply composed as the spinal; as a group they contain functional components in addition to the **general somatic efferent and afferent,** and **general visceral efferent and afferent** fibers of the spinal nerves. The additional cranial nerve components are **special somatic afferent, special visceral afferent,** and **special visceral efferent.** The first of the additional groups includes sensory fibers from the eye and internal ear, structures of ectodermal origin serving special senses. The special visceral afferent fibers are those of the first cranial nerve subserving olfaction, and those fibers of several other cranial nerves subserving taste. The special visceral efferent fibers innervate striated muscle derived from the branchiomeric apparatus. The muscle fibers themselves, however, are histologically similar to those of somite origin.

Cranial-nerve components have been classified in general according to function and also according to embryological origin of the structure innervated. A few fibers have been oddly classified, however, and for this there is only slight explanation. These will be mentioned later under the individual nerves containing these fibers. No one cranial nerve contains fibers of all categories, and conversely, very few cranial nerves contain fibers of only a single category.

The spinal-cord neurons related to spinal nerves are arranged in columns of nuclei according to function and also partly according to locus of structure innervated. The nuclei of the cranial nerves are also arranged in columns, though some of the columns have long gaps in them. Generally speaking, the afferent nuclear columns are lateral to the efferent ones. Such an arrangment might be said to come about because of the opening of the angle of the sulcus limitans in the medullar and pontine levels and a consequent lateralward movement of the alar-plate tissue containing the afferent columns. Beginning near the mid-line of the brain stem, beneath the floor of the aqueduct and fourth ventricle, and moving laterally, successive neuron columns are encountered (Fig. 35). Moving from near the mid-line to the lateral edge of the brain stem, one encounters somatic motor, visceral motor, visceral sensory, and somatic sensory columns. With one exception, however, no column extends without interruption through midbrain, pontine, and medullar tegmentum.

The **general somatic efferent** column, innervating striated muscle of somite origin, is found near the mid-line of the brain stem and contributes fibers to the oculomotor, trochlear, abducens, and hypoglossal nerves. It is therefore an interrupted column. The ocular muscles and the intrinsic muscles of the tongue are the only cranial muscles customarily considered to be of myotomic origin.

The **general visceral efferent** column is next most medially placed. These nuclei innervate ciliary and iridial muscle, smooth muscle, cardiac muscle, salivary, lacrimal, and mucous glands, and send their fibers out via oculomotor, facial, glossopharyngeal, and vagus nerves. They have been described in Chap. 7 and constitute the cranial parasympathetic nervous system; they are the **Edinger-Westphal nucleus,** the **superior** and **inferior salivatory,** the **lacrimal nucleus,** and the **dorsal motor vagal nucleus.** Their column is also an interrupted one.

The next most medial column of cranial nerve nuclei in the adult human brain stem, **special visceral efferent,** innervates the striated muscle of branchiomeric origin and sends fibers out into trigeminal, facial, glossopharyngeal, vagus, and spinal accessory nerves. This column of nuclei really belongs to the general visceral motor column, but the majority of its component nuclei have migrated ventrally into the tegmentum, perhaps under neurobiotactic influences. The trigeminal nuclear component of this system is placed near the floor of the fourth ventricle; the others are in the ventrolateral tegmental region. This column is interrupted.

A cranial-nerve secondary sensory nucleus has about the same position, mediolaterally, as those motor nuclei just described; it is more dorsal, however, than most of them. This nucleus is a long continuous column extending throughout the length of the medulla, the **nucleus of the tractus solitarius.** Its rostral portion subserves taste, a **special visceral afferent component,** and receives fibers from the facial, glossopharyngeal, and vagus nerves. Its caudal portion subserves **general visceral afferent** innervation via glossopharyngeal and vagus nerves, especially.

Another long column of neurons, just lateral to those motor and sensory nuclei described above, extends from midbrain to rostral cervical spinal cord. It has three major components, the **mesencephalic, main sensory,** and **spinal trigeminal nuclei,** and subserves **general somatic sensation** supplied through the trigeminal nerve. The spinal nucleus also serves as a secondary station for somatic sensory fibers from the skin of the ear, entering with the facial, glossopharyngeal, and vagus nerves. The mesencephalic nucleus is an odd one in that it contains primary sensory neurons; these are usually found in ganglia on the nerve roots.

A group of nuclei quite laterally placed and extending from mid-pons level into caudal medulla constitute the **special somatic afferent** column associated with the eighth cranial-nerve divisions, **vestibular** and **cochlear.** The former transmit impulses from endings in the semicircular canals, utricle, and saccule; the latter transmit auditory impulses from the cochlea. Special somatic neurons subserving visual function are not grouped in a brain stem nucleus. In reality, the optic nerve is not a true nerve, but is composed of axons of cells derived directly from the central nervous system. The visual pathways are the subject of a later chapter. The special visceral afferent neurons and fibers of the olfactory nerves will also be described in a separate section; they are known as visceral afferent perhaps because of the intimate relationship with visceral acts, such as respiration and eating. The olfactory nerves are not compact bundles, but are composed of many scattered filaments which pass through the cribriform plate of the ethmoid bones to reach the olfactory bulbs. These filaments spring from modified epithelial cells of mesodermal origin. The nervus terminalis and the vomeronasal nerve, closely related to the olfactory nerves in the nasal cavities, are also described later.

In the following accounts the nerves will be considered as entities, and the sensory and motor components, both somatic and visceral, special and general, where they occur in a single nerve, will be discussed with each nerve separately. The third, fourth, and sixth nerves will be considered as a group; the fifth, seventh, ninth, tenth, eleventh, and twelfth, separately. The autonomic fibers will be grouped in the discussion of a nerve according to whether they innervate striated (cardiac) muscle, smooth muscle, or glandular tissue. Sensory fibers will be grouped according to supply for cutaneous surfaces and mucous membranes, muscle, viscera, and taste.

Oculomotor, Trochlear, and Abducens Nerves

The cranial nerves that supply the eye musculature can be considered together. All of them contain sensory and motor fibers, and the motor fibers in the oculomotor nerves are of two types: those subserving voluntary movements, and those subserving involuntary or autonomic function. The nuclei of these three nerves are located close to the mid-line.

NUCLEI

The **cells of origin** of the motor fibers (somatic efferent) of the **oculomotor nerves** lie

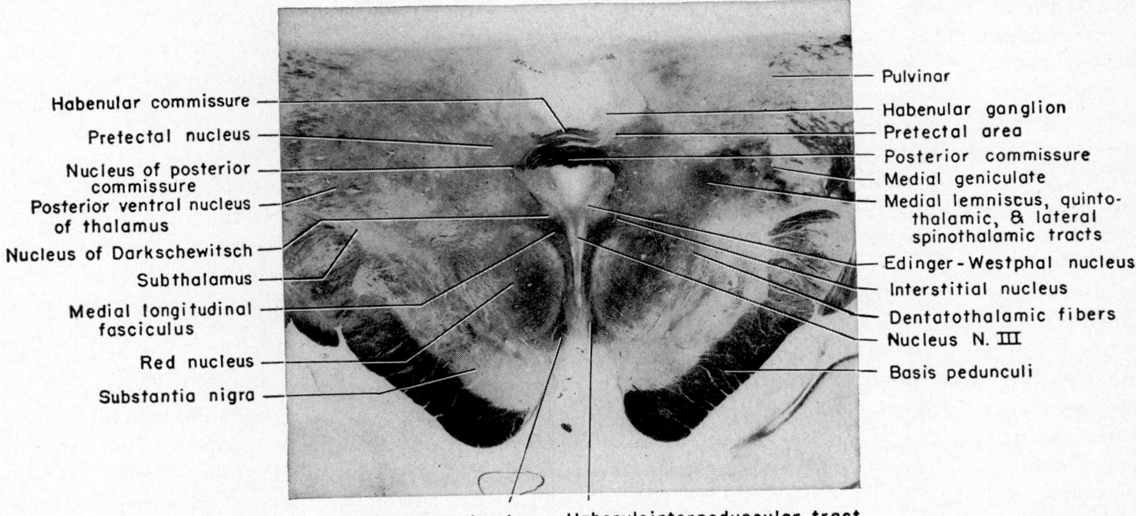

FIG. 147. Transverse section, A 1003, of human brain stem through posterior commissure. Weigert. Photograph, ×2.

below the rostral end of the cerebral aqueduct in the central gray of the midbrain, the superior colliculi serving as their external landmarks (Figs. 147–150). The cells are distributed in groups of separate nuclei in the elongated gray mass, and in a transverse section through the midbrain the contour of the nucleus is that of a V with its open end superiorly placed. The arms of the V are composed of large multipolar neurons, and these form the **lateral nuclear masses** which may be subdivided into dorsal and ventral groups. The ventral groups form a longer column than the dorsal, extending further rostrally than the latter. Ventrally placed between the lateral nuclear masses and extending across the raphe is the **paramedian**

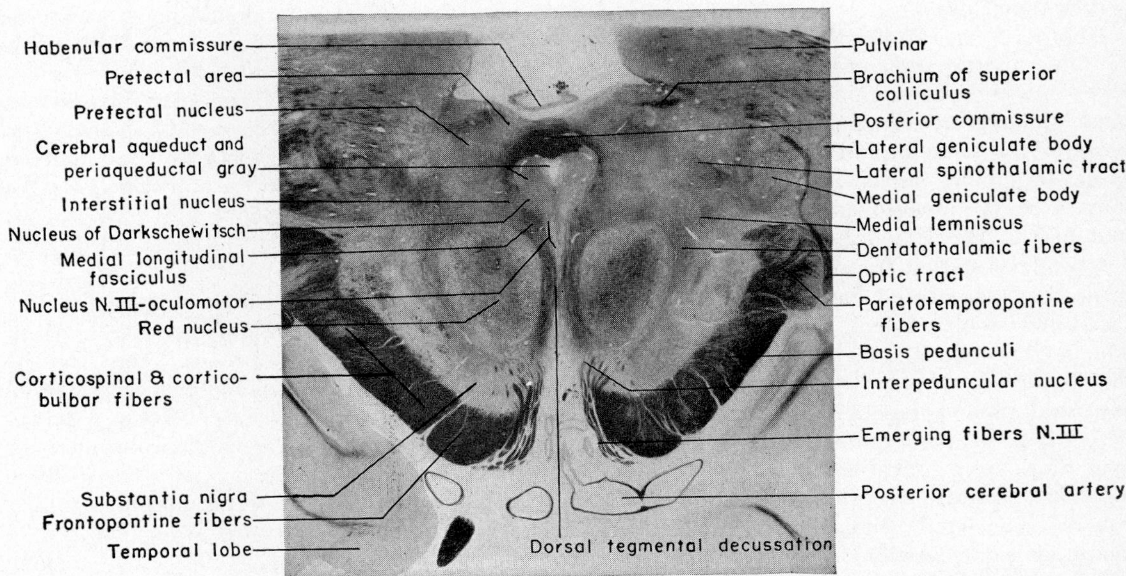

FIG. 148. Transverse section, A 973, of human brain stem through point of emergence of oculomotor nerve. Weigert. Photograph, ×2.

or **central nucleus.** Its rostrocaudal extent is not as great as that of the lateral nuclear mass, since it does not reach as far forward or caudad. The laterally placed cells of the central nucleus blend with the innermost cells of the lateral nuclei. Those neurons which occupy the raphe form the **nucleus of Perlia,** which has been considered as the nucleus subserving convergence of the eyes. It discharges through the laterally placed neurons of the central nucleus, which are thought to innervate the medial recti.

Within the lateral nuclear masses, individual cell groups have been described as innervating specific ocular muscles (196). The scheme followed by Brouwer makes the division rostrocaudally and places the cells innervating the levator palpebrae most rostral and those innervating the superior rectus, inferior obique, and inferior rectus, respectively, next in order, caudally (108) (Fig. 151). Other functional groupings have been made following the dorsal and ventral nuclear divisions, the dorsal nuclei innervating those muscles which move the eyes upward, and the ventral nuclei innervating those muscles which move the eyes downward (147).

At least two other nuclei on each side composed of small multipolar cells are associated with the oculomotor complex. These nuclei are placed medial and dorsal to the lateral nuclear masses. One, placed in relation to the rostral third of the lateral nuclear mass and extending ahead of it, constitutes the **nucleus of Edinger-Westphal.** Its most rostral and medially placed cells are occasionally designated as a separate **anterior central nucleus.** The other small-celled nucleus, placed in relation to the caudal third of the lateral nuclear mass dorsally and medially, constitutes the **caudal central nucleus.**

On the basis of their development and position it is usually considered that the small-celled nuclei are functionally related, but much disagreement exists as to this function. Without entirely conclusive evidence, some or all of the cells of the rostral part of the Edinger-Westphal nucleus are considered to send their small axons (general visceral efferent) out with the oculomotor nerves as **preganglionic parasympathetic fibers** destined to synapse in the ciliary ganglion within the orbit. The

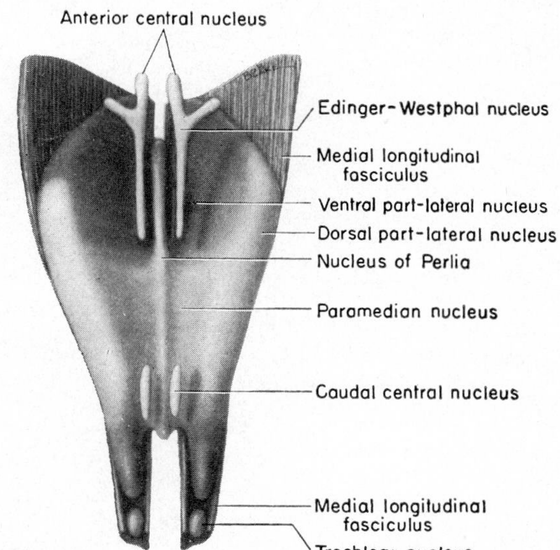

FIG. 149. Schematic representation of oculomotor and trochlear nuclei of the human.

ciliary ganglion cells give rise to **postganglionic fibers** that innervate the sphincter muscles of the iris. When the sphincter muscles contract, the pupil is constricted. Constriction can be evoked by electrical stimulation in the vicinity of the Edinger-Westphal nucleus. Constriction normally occurs when light is flashed into the eyes (light reflex), and it also occurs in association with the convergence of the eyes and the alteration of the lens diameter that are necessary for near vision. These three mechanisms—pupillary constriction, convergence, and lens-diameter alteration (increase)—constitute the act of **accommodation** for near vision. The increase in lens diameter is brought about by contraction of the ciliary muscle. It is maintained by some investigators that the ciliary muscle is innervated by neurons caudally placed in the Edinger-Westphal nucleus. Fibers from these caudal cells of the Edinger-Westphal nucleus follow in part the course of those from the rostral part of the nucleus, though they may not synapse in the ciliary ganglion. Associated with lens changes in the act of accommodation is a constriction of the pupils, as just stated. Such constriction with accommodation has been produced experimentally in animals and reported also in humans after removal or injury to the ciliary ganglion. This is the basis for the belief that these impulses

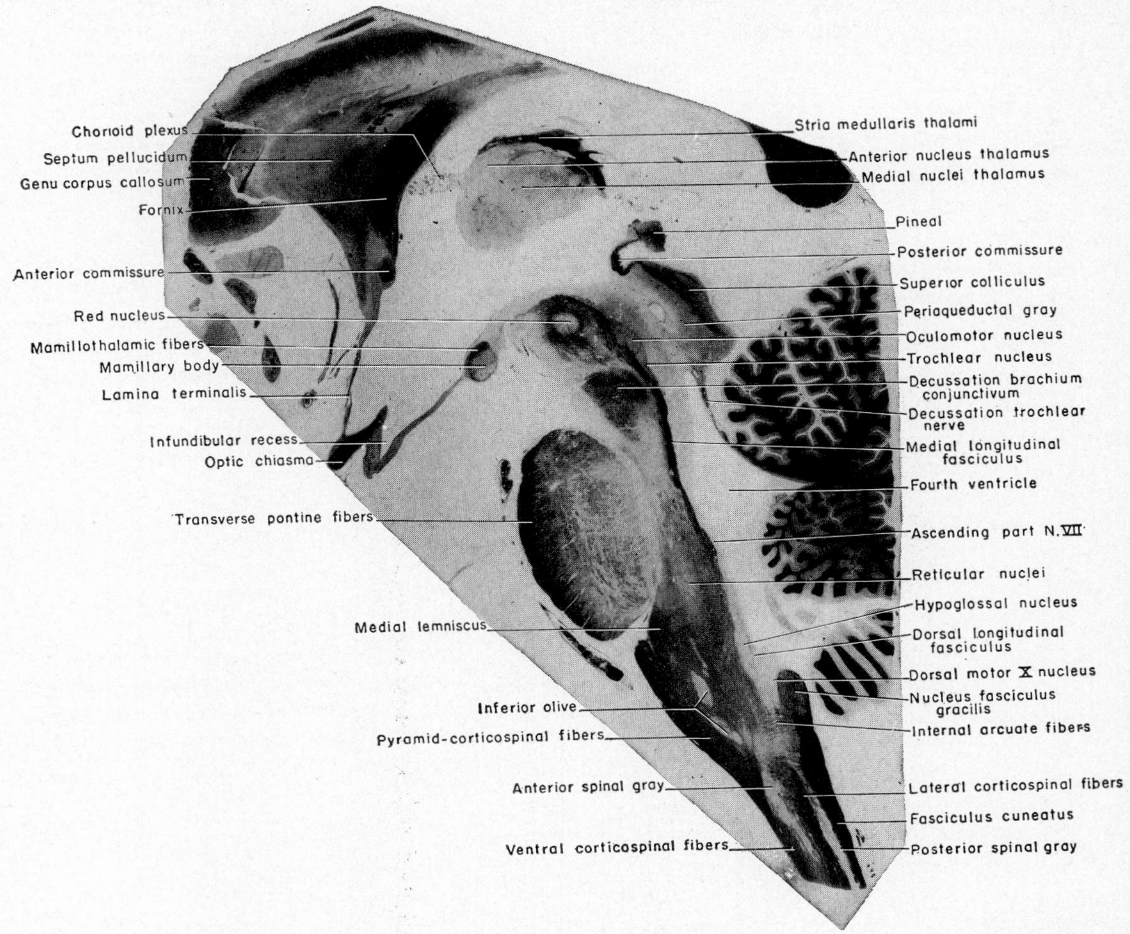

Fig. 150. Parasagittal section, A 326, of human brain, through medial edge of red nucleus. Weigert. Photograph, ×1.7.

producing constriction in association with accommodation do not traverse the ciliary ganglion but perhaps synapse in neurons found applied to the sclera, the episcleral ganglia (258, 302, 581). Two peripheral constrictor pathways may exist, therefore; one, with a ciliary-ganglion synapse, subserves pupillary constriction in response to light; the other, with episcleral-ganglia synapses, subserves constriction accompanying convergence-accommodation.

It is of interest that these schemes outlined above and diagrammed in Fig. 151 do not include the caudal central nucleus. Further, it is worthy of note that chromatolysis of Edinger-Westphal neurons does not always follow section of the oculomotor nerves and that some observers have not been able to trace axons from that nucleus into the oculomotor nerves in some species (147).

All the fibers of the oculomotor nerves curve ventrally and laterally through the tegmental portion of the midbrain, and most of them pass through the red nucleus in their course to points of emergence in the deeper part of the interpeduncular fossa, between the two cerebral peduncles. Fibers to the levator and superior rectus are uncrossed; those to the inferior rectus, crossed; and those to internal rectus and inferior oblique, mixed. It is significant that fibers to the inferior rectus are crossed ones. This muscle works most intimately with the superior oblique muscle in downward movements of the eye. The superior oblique muscle is innervated by the trochlear nerve whose fibers are entirely crossed. The Edinger-Westphal fibers are mixed.

The **trochlear** motor fibers (somatic efferent) arise from cells located in the central gray ventral to the aqueduct (Fig. 152). Externally the inferior colliculi serve as landmarks for locating the nuclei. They are frequently continuous with the ventral portion of the lateral oculomotor complex, and the cells intermingle to a certain extent with the fibers of the medial longitudinal fasciculus. The emergent fibers course dorsalward and caudalward in the aqueductal gray beneath the inferior colliculi to decussate in the anterior medullary velum (Fig. 134). The nerve supplies one muscle, the superior oblique.

Each **abducens** nucleus lies under the elevation, the facial colliculus, in the floor of the fourth ventricle, made by the genu of the facial nerve (Figs. 132, 160, 161, 210). It is for the most part ventrolateral to the fibers of the genu and lateral to the medial longitudinal fasciculus. The cells are both large and small, and not all of them undergo degenerative changes when the sixth nerve is cut, the smaller neurons escaping (423). The smaller

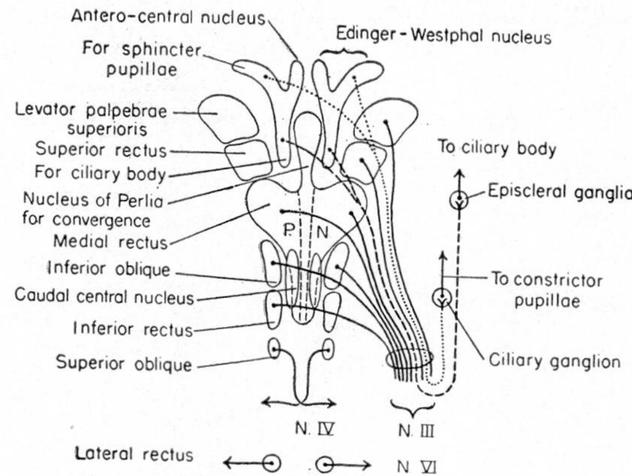

FIG. 151. Diagram of divisions of oculomotor nuclear complex. *P.N.*, paramedian nucleus.

neurons are located nearer the subependymal gray of the fourth ventricle than are the larger, degenerating ones. They have been called the **parabducens nucleus** and probably constitute the "center" for lateral conjugate gaze (see Chap. 21). Axons of the small neurons of the parabducens nucleus give collaterals to the abducens nucleus and pass via the medial longitudinal fasciculus to the oculomotor nucleus, especially to that part which

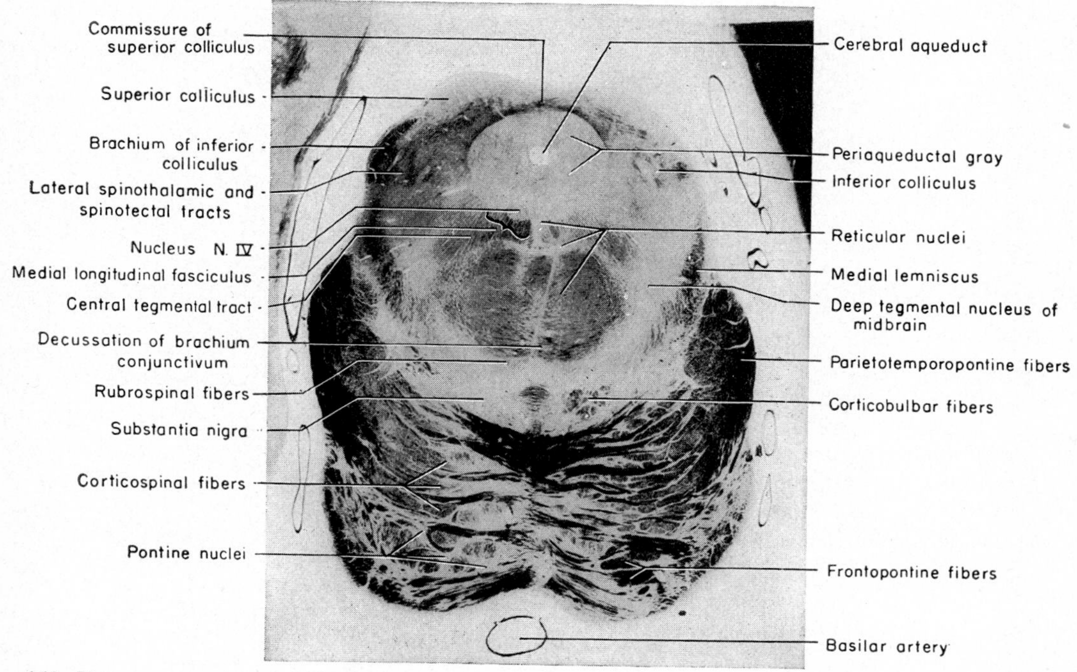

FIG. 152. Transverse section, A 836, through caudal end of superior colliculus. Human, Weigert. Photograph, ×2.5.

innervates the medial rectus. The fibers (somatic efferent) arising from the abducens nuclei course ventralward and caudalward to emerge near the mid-line at the caudal end of the pons. They supply one muscle, the external rectus.

SENSORY FIBERS OF OCULAR NERVES

In addition to the motor fibers described, sensory fibers (general somatic afferent) have been found in the eye-muscle nerves, and neuromuscular spindles have recently been redescribed in human ocular muscles (3, 172). The neuromuscular and neurotendinous spindles degenerate in the ocular muscles when their nerves are cut. These endings and their nerve fibers are thought to be proprioceptive in function, and the latter arise in part from cells scattered along the course of the third, fourth, and sixth nerves. Pearson has described ganglionlike neurons among oculomotor nucleus cells and suggests that these and the neurons along the course of the oculomotor nerves are the sources of proprioceptive fibers to ocular muscles (602). Electrical studies support this suggestion (176, 178).

CONNECTIONS OF OCULAR NUCLEI

Each of these eye-muscle motor nuclei receives fibers from a number of sources. The two eyes usually move simultaneously, and though such movements (conjugate movements) may be induced volitionally, they are more often brought about reflexly, in response to visual, vestibular, or auditory impulses. These nuclei of the ocular muscles should then receive impulses from the frontal lobe for volitional movements; from the occipital lobe for movements in response to visual impulses; from the vestibular nuclei for movements in response to alterations in head posture; and from auditory centers for movements in response to sudden sounds. It appears likely, however, that the majority of impulses from these various regions are not discharged into the ocular nuclei directly but are relayed via an intercalary neuron in tegmental reticular formation or in the tectum. These intercalary neurons constitute so-called "centers for conjugate eye movements." The superior colliculi appear to be concerned chiefly with vertical movements; the parabducens nuclei, with horizontal movements; and the nucleus of Perlia, with convergence. These "centers" discharge impulses to the ocular nuclei via tectobulbar fibers and medial longitudinal fasciculi, especially.

The flocculus of the cerebellum is thought also to send fibers via the brachium conjunctivum to the oculomotor nucleus, and probably also to those for the trochlear and abducens nerves. Fibers from the red nucleus to these nuclei, especially the oculomotor, have been described. The red nuclei may relay impulses from the basal ganglia. The ocular nuclei are interconnected via the medial longitudinal fasciculi.

The details of conjugate deviation, accommodation, convergence, and pupillomotor activities are discussed in Chap. 21. The cortical control of the eye movements is also described there.

RELATIONS OF OCULAR NERVE FIBERS

A knowledge of the peripheral course of these three nerves is useful in the diagnosis of intracranial disorders. Each nerve has important relations with the arteries at the base of the brain (Figs. 49, 51). The oculomotor and trochlear course between the superior cerebellar and posterior cerebral arteries, and as the oculomotor courses forward into the middle cranial fossa, the posterior communicating artery is medial to it. The abducens runs parallel to the basilar in its early course and crosses the vessels that arise from it to run transversely across the base of the pons. The oculomotor and trochlear run near the free edge of the tentorium cerebelli. All three nerves traverse the cavernous sinus and are in close relation with the internal carotid artery and the first two branches of the trigeminal nerve (Fig. 49). All three nerves enter the orbit through the superior orbital fissure.

ACTIONS OF OCULAR MUSCLES

Normally, the two eyes move simultaneously to the right or left lateral directions, upward or downward, or both may move inward toward the nose in convergence. In the performance of these movements certain muscles in each orbit always act together as the primary actors, certain other muscles cooperate in the movements by aiding in stabilizing the globe in certain planes, and certain other muscles

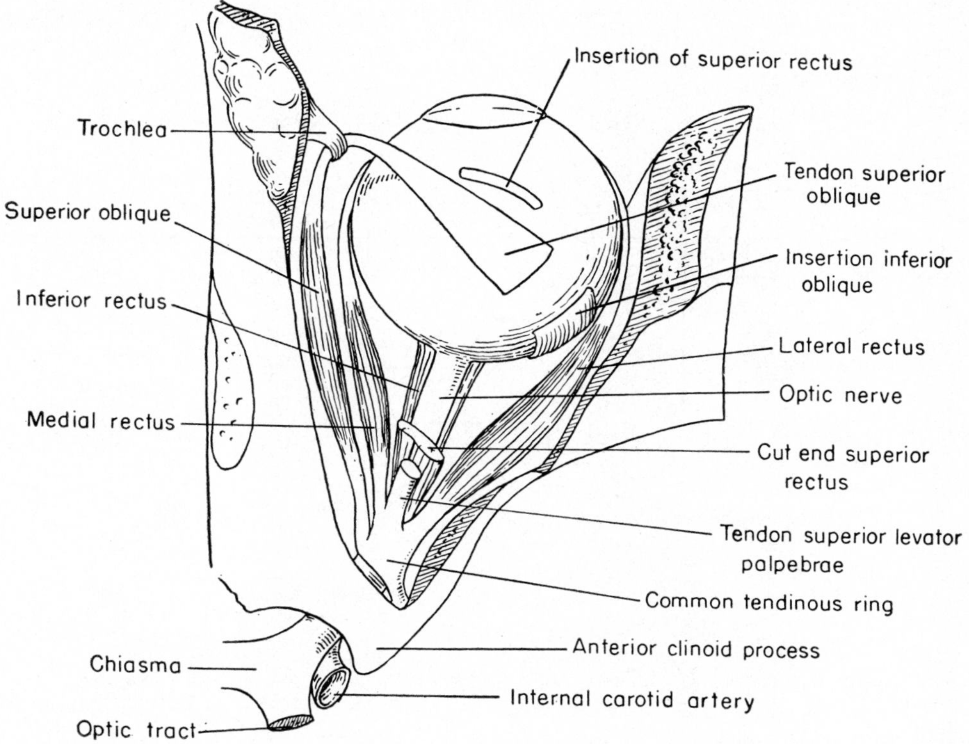

FIG. 153. The extraocular muscles.

undergo graded relaxation. Because of these conjugate movements, the light rays from objects being observed fall on homologous portions of the retinas, *e.g.*, the macular areas, and one distinct image is produced as a result of a fusion of the impulses in the visual cortex. When the two eyes are turned to the right in a right lateral gaze, for example, the principal acting muscles in this movement are the external rectus of the right eye and the internal rectus of the left eye (Fig. 154). Other muscles in each eye cooperate when the eyes are moved far to the right, in a horizontal position. In the right eye the superior and inferior obliques are

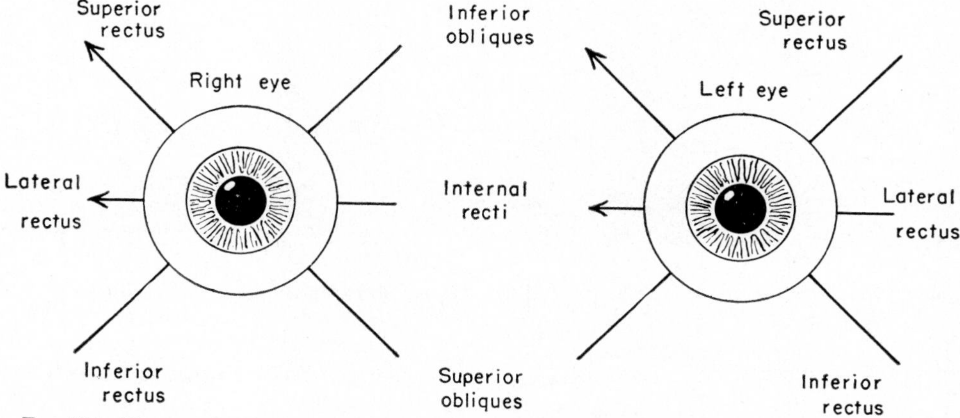

FIG. 154. Diagram for the paired action of extraocular muscles in looking up and to the right.

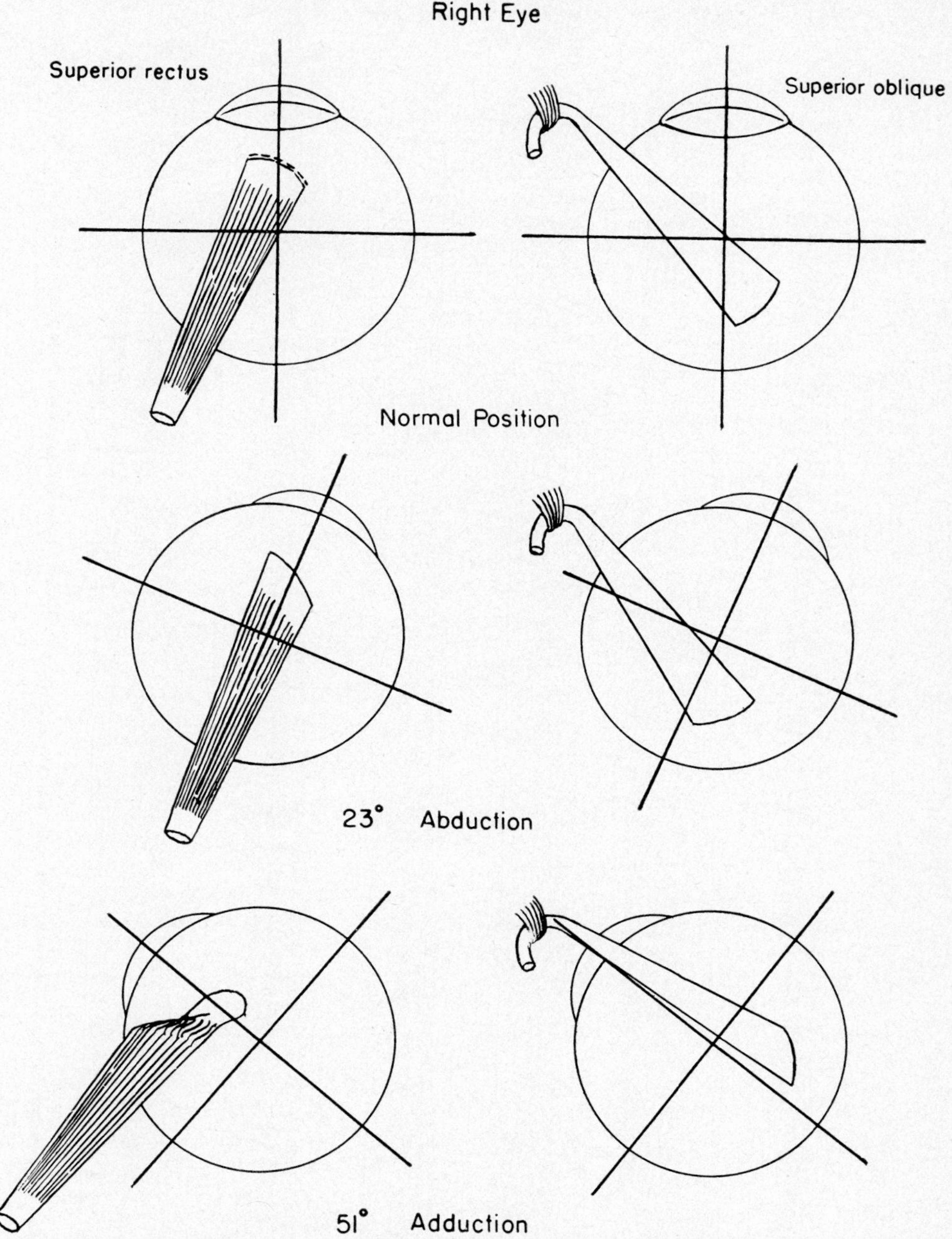

Fig. 155. Diagram of movements of the superior rectus and superior oblique muscles in various positions.

the cooperating muscles, in the left eye, the superior and inferior recti. The obliques are strong as abductors when the eye is turned out, the recti are strong as adductors when the eye is turned in, as will be noted below. The ocular muscles always act in groups, therefore, and all the muscles (excluding, of course, the levator of the upper lid) except the internal rectus and the external rectus have more than one action. Each muscle has a primary action, and all except the internal rectus and external rectus have subsidiary actions. In order to appreciate the actions of an ocular muscle, it is necessary to recall the location of its attachment to the globe and to remember that the action of a muscle at any moment will depend somewhat on the position of the globe at the time the movement is in effect (Fig. 153). An ocular muscle will usually exert its maximum primary movement when its long axis, or that of its tendon, is parallel to the long or sagittal axis of the globe. The superior rectus muscle, for example, will exert its strongest primary effect, elevation, when the globe is turned out or abducted. When the globe is in mid-position, the superior rectus will bring about adduction; when the globe is turned inward, the superior rectus will produce an inward rotation and adduction. The activities of the other ocular muscles can similarly be observed, and an outline is provided in Table 3. A simple diagram is also given (Fig. 155).

CLINICAL DISORDERS

If a paralysis of an ocular muscle in one orbit exists, the affected eye will not be able to move with the other eye in the performance of the conjugate movement of which it is normally capable. If, for example, the right external rectus is paralyzed in the right eye because of an injury to its nerve, the right eye cannot be turned toward the right (abducted) when tht left eye turns toward the right in a right conjugate movement. Because the two eyes are not moving to the same degree to the right, the light rays from an object being observed to the right will fall on asymmetric portions of the retinas. In the normally moving eye they will fall on the macula; in the other eye, they will fall to one side of the macula. The stimulation of two asymmetric retinal foci will lead to the activation of asymmetric occipital-lobe regions, and the patient will have two images of the object produced, one more distinct than the other. He will therefore "see" two objects, a condition known as **diplopia.** The diplopia is most noticeable to the patient when he attempts to look in the direction toward which the paretic muscle normally exerts its primary pull.

In addition to a subjective complaint of diplopia, a patient with a paretic ocular muscle may have a deviation of the affected eye at rest. If the right external rectus is paretic, for example, the right eye may be pulled inward by the normally acting internal rectus. The patient is said to have an internal squint, or **strabismus.** The strabismus may be pronounced, or barely noticeable. It may be produced by the unopposed pull of a normally acting muscle (its antagonist being paralyzed) or result from an imbalance in the action of two functioning muscles, agonist and antagonist.

Disturbances of the motor nerves to eye muscles can be classed as central or peripheral in type. If a complete nucleus or peripheral nerve be injured, all movements initiated by that nucleus or nerve will be lost. It is possible in certain central lesions, however, to have partial paralysis and to find a muscle to be

Table 3. Actions of Ocular Muscles

	Main action	*Subsidiary action*
Superior rectus	Moves eye up; action increases as eye is turned out; becomes nil when eye is turned in.	Adducts eye and rotates vertical meridian inward; action increases as eye is turned in. Raises upper lid.
Inferior oblique	Moves eye up; action increases as eye is turned in; becomes nil when eye is turned out.	Abducts eye and rotates vertical meridian outward; action increases as eye is turned out.
Inferior rectus	Moves eye down; action increases as eye is turned out; becomes nil when eye is turned in.	Adducts eye and rotates vertical meridian out; action increases as eye is turned in.
Superior oblique	Moves eye down; action increases as eye is turned in; becomes nil when eye is turned out.	Abducts eye and rotates vertical meridian in; action increases as eye is turned out.
External rectus	Moves eye out.	None.
Internal rectus	Moves eye in.	None.

Source: Fuchs, "Textbook of Ophthalmology," 4th ed., Philadelphia, Lippincott.

paralyzed for a certain type of movement only. The left internal rectus, for example, may contract normally in a convergence movement, whereas in conjugate lateral movements to the right it may not function at all. Why such discrepancies occur will be discussed in Chap. 21.

Peripheral **oculomotor ophthalmoplegia** resulting from complete functional blocking of the nerve is characterized not only by loss of all voluntary movement of the extraocular muscles innervated by this nerve, but also by paralysis of accommodation and of the constrictor mechanism of the pupil. The eyelid is closed and cannot be opened; the globe is rotated outwardly and cannot be moved inward, upward, or downward. The pupil is dilated and does not react to light directly or consensually (constriction of a pupil when light is flashed in the opposite eye), or during accommodation. The power of accommodation is lost and near vision is indistinct. When the trochlear nerve is injured there is a loss of downward movement of the globe when it is in adduction. When the abducens nerve is injured, there is a loss of abduction of the globe beyond the mid-line, and the affected eye is adducted (internal squint or strabismus).

The oculomotor nerve may be involved by meningitis, tumor compression or in vascular softenings involving midbrain tegmentum and the cerebral peduncles. When it is damaged with the peduncles, an ipsilateral oculomotor paralysis and a contralateral disturbance of motor power of the limbs result, the **Weber's syndrome.** If the nerve fibers are involved in a softening while coursing in the tegmentum, the red nucleus and ascending sensory tracts may be damaged also. Such a disorder might produce ipsilateral oculomotor paralysis and contralateral involuntary movements due to red-nucleus damage (**Benedikt's syndrome**). Involvement of the sensory tracts would add a contralateral anesthesia of the body to the picture. Aneurysmal dilatation of either the superior cerebellar, posterior cerebral, or posterior communicating artery could compress either the oculomotor or trochlear nerve or both; a dilatation of either the anterior inferior cerebellar or basilar artery might involve the abducens nerve. In cerebral tumors provoking displacement of the brain, with herniation of the uncus and hippocampal gyrus through the tentorium, the oculomotor nerve and the trochlear may be compressed by the free edge of the tentorium or by the herniating temporal lobe (Fig. 72) (852). Pupillomotor (constrictor) fibers apparently lie peripherally among the third nerve fibers. Frequently in cases of subarachnoid or subdural extravasation of blood, the pupil on the side of the extravasation is dilated and fixed to light. In such cases it is likely that the brain contour is displaced; the hippocampal gyrus on the side of injury is displaced through the tentorium and comes to compress the adjacent third nerve with its peripherally placed constrictor fibers. A unilaterally dilated pupil which does not react to light in a case of suspected head injury thus frequently aids in localization of the side of damage.

Within the cavernous sinus all three nerves—oculomotor, trochlear, and abducens—may be involved by cavernous-sinus thrombosis or, more commonly, by **aneurysm** of the internal carotid artery. The sympathetic fibers and the ophthalmic branch of the trigeminal may also be involved in these disorders in the sinus; involvement of sympathetic fibers leads to a Horner's syndrome, and compression of the ophthalmic fibers causes pain over the eye and forehead. An aneurysm of the internal carotid as it passes through the cavernous sinus may give variable symptoms, however, with reference to the involvement of the ocular motor nerves and the trigeminal nerve, depending on whether the aneurysm is in the anterior, middle, or posterior part of the sinus (418) (Fig. 156). Aneurysms in the posterior part, for example, may give pain and objective sensory disorder over all three divisions of the trigeminal. Bony growths about the superior orbital fissure may also compress all three nerves progressively, leading ultimately to a complete ophthalmoplegia. In some individuals a slowly **progressive ophthalmoplegia** may involve all the ocular muscles and leave the pupillary reactions intact. Its nature is obscure. Often familial, it may be a degenerative neuronal disorder or it may be a myopathy. Bilateral, or unilateral, ocular palsies may occur in myasthenia gravis.

It is important to distinguish damage of the abducens in its intramedullary course from an extramedullary injury. If the lesion is a nuclear one, the facial nerve will probably be damaged, as its fibers form the genu about the abducens nucleus (Figs. 160, 161). If the lesion is a tegmental one, the medial lemniscus, lateral spinothalamic, and secondary cochlear tracts may be damaged also, along with the seventh nerve nucleus or fibers; if the lesion is basilar, the corticospinal tracts may be involved also. The combination of unilateral external rectus and facial paralysis with contralateral hemiplegia is called **Millard-Gubler's syndrome.** Disorders in the vicinity of the abducens nucleus usually produce a paralysis of conjugate lateral movements toward the side of the lesion, as well as paralysis of the ipsilateral external rectus muscle. If, for example, the destructive process were on the right side, the patient would have paralysis of the right external rectus and an inability to look to the right with either eye. The left internal rectus, though not moving to the right in conjugate right lateral movements, may contract in convergence. Such a disturbance of ocular movement, combined with contralateral hemiplegia, constitutes **Foville's syndrome.**

Bilateral sixth-nerve palsy occasionally is seen in severe increases of intracranial pressure. The nerves in their long course along the floor of the skull are susceptible to pressure. A unilateral paralysis of the external rectus and a severe pain in the same side of the face, together with slight sensory loss, may occur in inflammatory changes in the vicinity of the tip of the petrous bone (**Gradenigo's syndrome**).

The Trigeminal Nerve

To the skin and mucous membranes of the head, and to certain of the muscles, this large nerve supplies general somatic sensory fibers in a manner similar to the spinal nerves serving the trunk and limbs. The three peripheral divisions are the **ophthalmic, maxillary,** and **mandibular.** In addition to sensory fibers the mandibular has a motor component. Because the sensory components so far outnumber the motor, they will be described first.

PERIPHERAL DISTRIBUTION

The **semilunar,** or gasserian, **ganglion,** comparable to a posterior root ganglion of a spinal

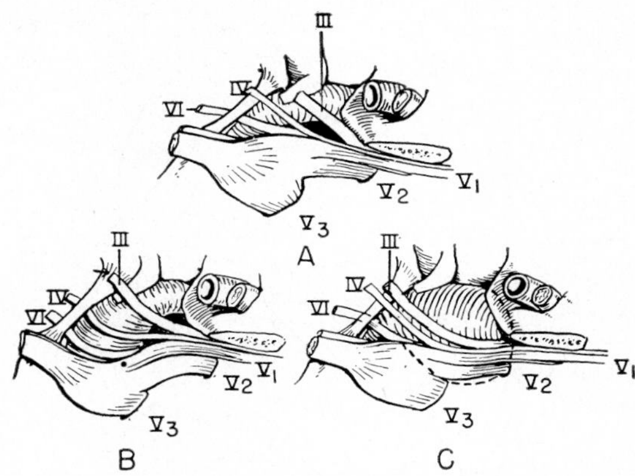

FIG. 156. Diagram of anatomical syndromes of the cavernous sinus. *A*, the normal relations of the internal carotid artery and cranial nerves in the sinus. *B*, the compression of the nerves by a carotid aneurysm in the posterior end of the cavernous sinus. *C*, the compression of the nerves by an aneurysm in the middle of the cavernous sinus. (*After Jefferson, Brit. J. Surg., vol.* 26.)

nerve, lies in a depression near the tip of the petrous portion of the temporal bone. The ganglion is concave anteriorly, and from this surface the three large peripheral divisions arise: ophthalmic, maxillary, and mandibular. The central stalk (root) of the nerve arises from the posterior surface of the ganglion. Medially the ganglion is in close relation with the cavernous sinus and internal carotid artery at the foramen lacerum (Fig. 49). The foramen ovale, through which passes the mandibular root, lies just lateral to the ganglion. The temporal lobe lies just above the ganglion, though separated from it by the dura mater. These relations are important in a consideration of disorders occurring in the middle cranial fossa and in the vicinity of the sphenoidal ridge.

The **ophthalmic division** is the smallest of the three peripheral divisions. It arises from the front of the ganglion, as noted above, in its medial part and passes forward into the lateral wall of the cavernous sinus. Just back of the superior orbital fissure, the trunk divides into three branches: frontal, lacrimal, and nasociliary. These enter the orbit through the fissure. The ophthalmic branch receives sympathetic fibers from the carotid plexus in the cavernous sinus, and sends small branches to the oculomotor, trochlear, and abducens nerves. These latter may be proprioceptive fibers, as

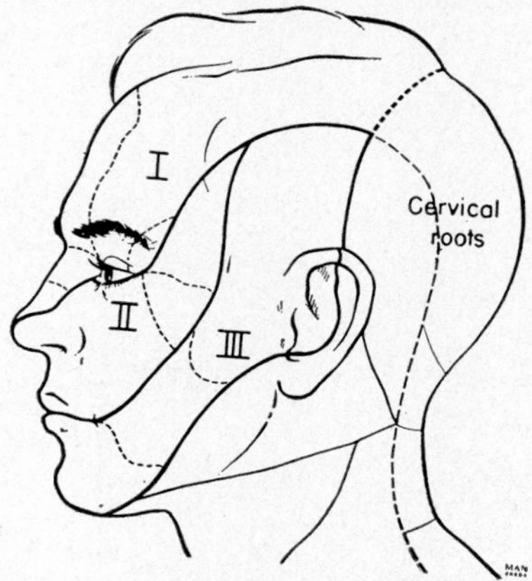

FIG. 157. A diagram of the cutaneous fields of the head and upper part of the neck. I, ophthalamic division; II, maxillary division; III, mandibular division. (*After Haymaker and Woodhall, "Peripheral Nerve Injuries," W. B. Saunders Company.*)

will be discussed later. Soon after arising from the ganglion the ophthalmic division also supplies a small sensory branch (pain fibers) to the tentorium cerebelli.

The peripheral branches of the ophthalmic division supply sensation to the ethmoid air cells, the linings of the sphenoid and frontal sinuses, the conjunctiva, the cornea (nasociliary branch) and the skin of the lids, the temporal region adjacent the eye, the skin of the forehead, and the mucous membrane and skin of the nose (Fig. 157). The distribution of the ophthalmic posteriorly over the head extends to a line connecting the apices of the ears across the vertex of the skull. The long ciliary branch of the nasociliary division supports the ciliary ganglion in the orbit. The lacrimal nerve carries sympathetic fibers to the lacrimal gland.

The **maxillary division** of the trigeminal arises from the middle part of the anterior surface of the gasserian ganglion. It also traverses the lower lateral wall of the cavernous sinus. It leaves (or enters) the skull via the foramen rotundum to enter the pterygopalatine fossa. Within the fossa it supports the sphenopalatine ganglion by several twigs. The maxillary division supplies sensation to the dura of the middle cranial fossa, the mucous membrane of the maxillary and sphenoid sinuses, the mucous membrane of the nasal septum, conchae, hard palate, and the opening of the eustachian tube, the upper teeth and gums, the skin of the face immediately below the eye, that below the nose and within the vestibule, the upper lips, and the skin of the anterior temporal region (Fig. 157).

The **mandibular division** from the gasserian ganglion joins the motor fibers. The common trunk leaves the skull through the foramen ovale. The mandibular division supplies sensory fibers (pain) to the dura; these travel with the middle meningeal artery and its branches. The lining of certain mastoid cells is also supplied with sensory fibers. Outside the skull the terminal branches supply with sensory innervation the mucous membranes over the anterior two-thirds of the tongue; the lower teeth and gums; the mucous membrane within the cheek; the skin over the lower face and chin; a small area of skin of the ear and the external auditory meatus, including a part of the tympanic membrane; and the parotid, submaxillary, and sublingual glands. The motor branches of the mandibular nerve supply the following muscles: masseter, temporal, pterygoids, tensor tympani, tensor veli palatini, mylohyoid, and anterior belly of the digastric. This motor innervation comprises the special visceral efferent component of the trigeminal, since the muscles are of branchiomeric origin (first arch).

The mandibular division supports the otic and submaxillary ganglia and also transmits peripherally the parasympathetic innervation to the salivary glands from those ganglia. Taste fibers from the anterior two-thirds of the tongue also travel with the lingual nerve and, leaving it via chorda tympani, usually join the facial.

MOTOR NUCLEUS

The motor nucleus is located at the level of the middle of the pons, in the lateral part of the tegmentum, a short distance below the floor of the fourth ventricle (Figs. 158, 159). The cells are large. The fibers from the cells of this nucleus run directly out of the pons in a ventrolateral direction, being ventral and rostral to the sensory fibers. Outside the brain stem the motor root lies medial and anterior to the sensory root and lies inferior to the gasserian ganglion, but in close contact. The close association of these fibers with the large collection of sensory fibers makes it necessary to exercise great care in operations on the sensory division, in order to spare a paralysis of the muscles of mastication.

The motor nucleus of the trigeminal receives fibers from the trigeminal sensory nuclei, from the homolateral and contralateral motor cortices via corticobulbar fibers, from the colliculi via tectobulbar fibers, from the red nucleus via rubroreticulobulbar fibers, and from the medial longitudinal fasciculus. The bilateral cortical influence appears to represent a safety device in that injury to one cortex, or to the projections therefrom, does not completely paralyze masticatory function of the contralateral muscles. In some individuals, however, the corticobulbar fibers may be completely crossed (564).

SENSORY NUCLEI

Cutaneous surfaces and mucous membranes. The fibers carrying pain, temperature, and tactile stimuli (general somatic afferent-exteroceptive) from the skin and mucous membranes of the head spring from the pseudo-unipolar cells in the semilunar (gasserian) ganglion, as described previously. Many of the central processes of the ganglion cells divide into short ascending and long descending limbs. Some fibers, however, do not bifurcate, and of these some ascend while others descend. The entering fibers are routed to various parts of the trigeminal sensory nuclei according to function and, to a certain extent, according to peripheral distribution (292, 732, 841). As they enter the reticular formation of the pons, the fibers for pain and temperature probably do not bifurcate but descend as the **spinal tract of the trigeminal** and end about cells in a long column of gray just medial to the tract, the **spinal nucleus of the trigeminal** (Figs. 158, 159, 164–166). This nucleus extends from the point of entry of the trigeminal nerve fibers to the second cervical segment of the spinal cord, and its landmark on the external medullar surface is the tuberculum cinereum.

A recent study of this long nucleus has revealed again that it can be subdivided on the basis of its cytoarchitecture into three parts (591). The **oral** part extends from near the level of entrance of the trigeminal root fibers to a level near the oral third of the inferior olivary nucleus. From this latter level to a plane just above the decussation of the pyramids, the **interpolar** nucleus is present. From a level just above the decussation of the pyramids to the second cervical spinal segment, the **caudal** nucleus is present. This last nucleus can be further subdivided into regions comparable to the marginal, gelatinosa, and dorsal spongiosa divisions of the spinal posterior gray.

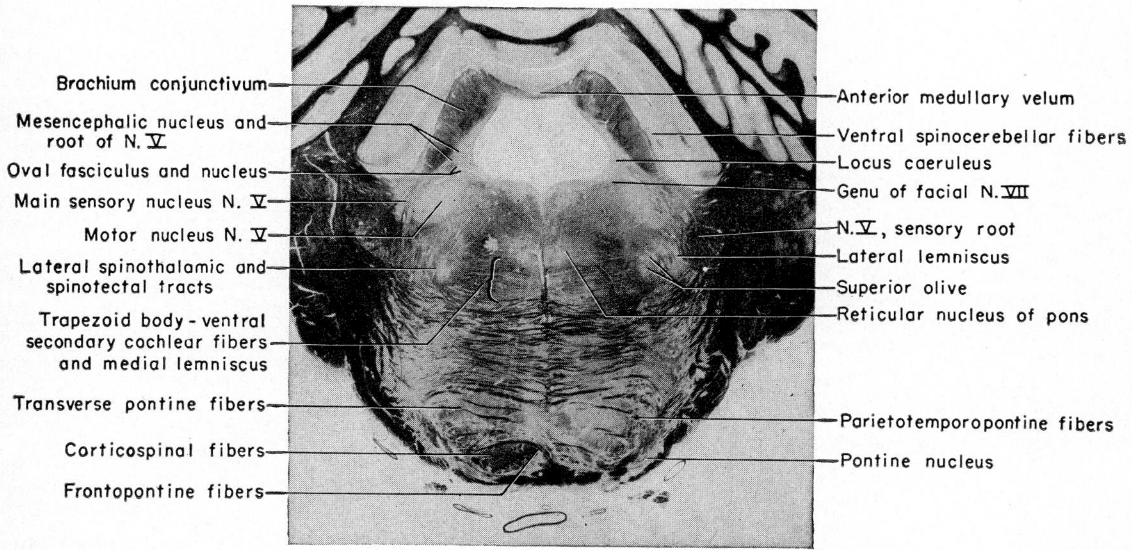

FIG. 158. Transverse section, A 560, of human brain stem through point of emergence of trigeminal nerve. Weigert. Photograph, ×2.

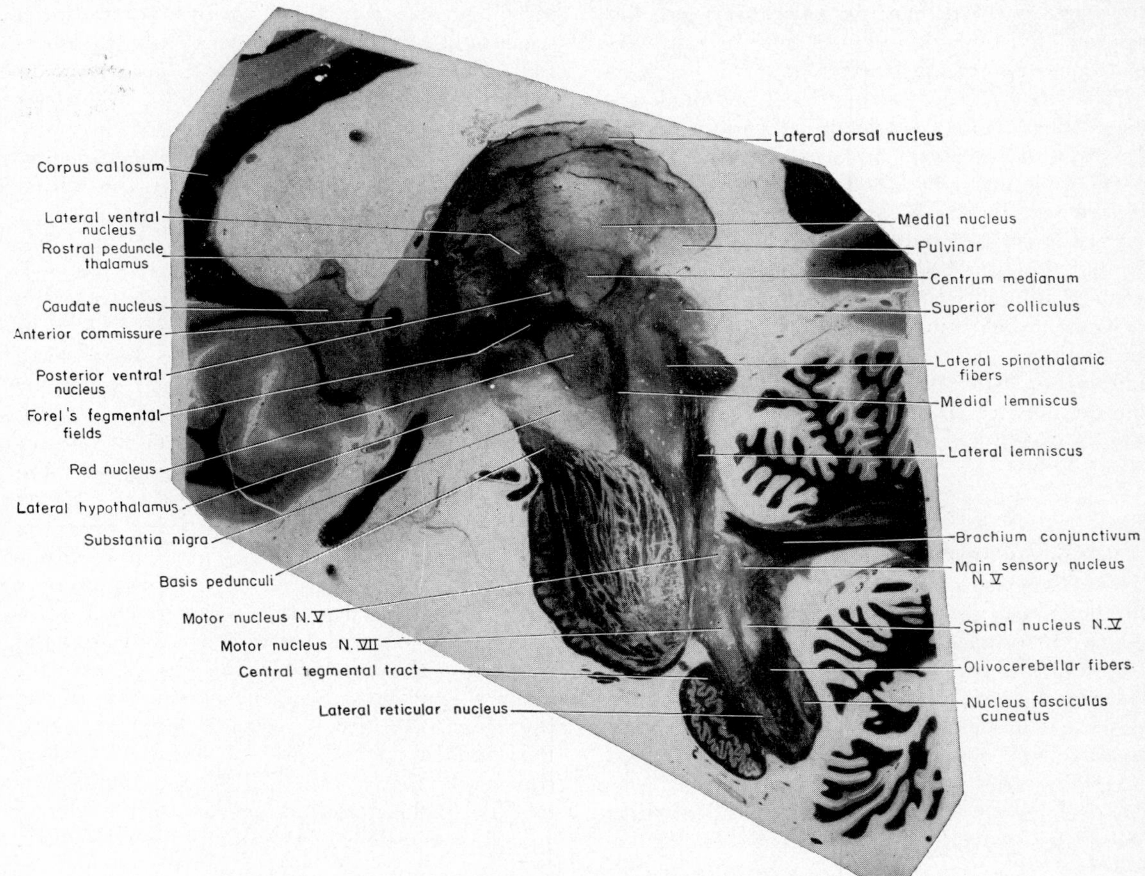

FIG. 159. Parasagittal section, A 250, of human brain stem through middle of red nucleus. Weigert. Photograph, ×1.7.

Because of this similarity in structure, it is concluded that only the caudal part of the spinal nucleus subserves conduction of painful and thermal impulses from the face. The spinal tract at this nuclear level is comparable to Lissauer's fasciculus of the spinal levels. The function of the oral and interpolar portions of the spinal nucleus is at present unknown.

Studies, subsequent to surgical procedures in which the spinal tract and nucleus have been interrupted for the relief of pain in the face, have produced much information concerning the arrangement of the fibers in the tract (311, 728). The ophthalmic-division fibers are placed most ventral in the tract; those of the mandibular division, most dorsal. As would be expected, pain and temperature impulses are transmitted over separate bundles of fibers. Pain impulses from oral mucous membranes, for example, utilize fibers medially placed in the descending tract. Further, the terminations of the fibers in the spinal nucleus are arranged in such a manner that the impulses from the ophthalmic region reach cells in the most caudal part of the gray column, especially; those from the mandibular region, cells in the upper end of the caudal nucleus, especially; and those from the maxillary region, cells in the middle third, particularly. Some overlapping of termination is present, and some impulses from all three peripheral divisions apparently reach cells in the lowest portion of the nucleus (312, 832). Complete facial analgesia has been obtained by section of the spinal tract as far caudad as 8 mm. behind the obex. This caudal part of the nucleus appears to be concerned chiefly with pain, therefore. Pain and temperature impulses from the head traveling in the facial, glossopharyngeal, and vagus nerves also pass into the spinal nucleus as will be discussed later. It should be noted that the ophthalmic "dermatome" area is adjacent the second cervical dermatome over the posterior surface of the head, and also that the part of the spinal trigeminal nucleus allocated to ophthalmic impulses is adjacent the posterior gray of the second cervical cord segment.

Some incoming trigeminal fibers carrying tactile and pressure impulses ascend without bifurcating to terminate around a large group of cells near the point of entry, the **main sensory nucleus** of the trigeminal (Figs. 158–160). This nucleus is slightly dorsal and lateral to the motor nucleus of the trigeminal and is separated from it by fibers of the nerve. Some tactile impulses appear to utilize bifurcating fibers, however, which end in the spinal and main sensory nuclei. Very careful examination of tactile sensation after surgical section of the spinal tract showed objective diminution of touch qualities even though, subjectively, the patients could feel no change. The corneal blink reflex has been obtained in some patients after section of the spinal tract, and a sensation of touch in the cornea has been reported after such a procedure (312, 690). The nature of the innervation of the cornea has long been debated. Some investigators maintain that only pain sensation is present in the central cornea, and cold and pain around the periphery. Normally any stimulus appears to evoke pain. It would seem, therefore, that the pain innervation overshadows any tactile innervation. After section of the pain fibers, tactile sense is apparent as judged by the results of the surgical procedure mentioned above. Tactile sense of the face is represented in part in some region of the spinal nucleus, therefore, and also in the main sensory nucleus. The latter nucleus perhaps is concerned with tactile discriminative faculties and deep pressure sense.

Proprioceptive. Of the remaining type of sensory fibers (general somatic afferent) carried by the trigeminal nerve, some afford a curiosity in neuroanatomy. These fibers transmit proprioceptive impulses from the muscles of mastication (stretch), and from the teeth and gums (pressure) (174). The odd thing about them is that the majority do not arise from cells in the semilunar or other peripheral ganglion but from a group of large cells, the **mesencephalic nucleus,** within the brain stem (Figs. 134, 137, 158). These cells are located between the lateral wall of the fourth ventricle

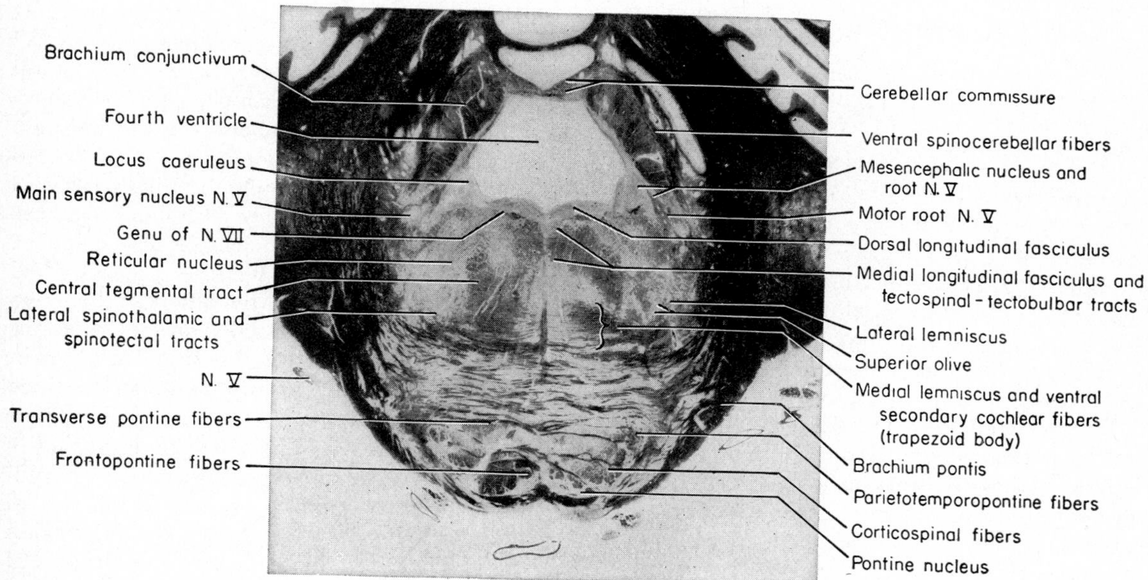

FIG. 160. Transverse section, A 530, of human brain stem at a level just caudad of point of emergence of trigeminal nerve. Weigert. Photograph, ×2.

and the fibers of the brachium conjunctivum (superior cerebellar peduncle), and they constitute a column which extends rostrally through the brain stem to the level of the posterior commissure. They mingle somewhat with the cells of the trochlear and oculomotor nuclei. Other trigeminal proprioceptive fibers apparently have primary neurons in the gasserian ganglion, and these, together with those axons springing from cells in the mesencephalic nucleus, are grouped as a distinct bundle of fibers, the **mesencephalic tract** (Figs. 134, 137, 158). The close association of the mesencephalic nucleus with that of the trochlear and oculomotor nerves has led some workers to suggest that it supplies proprioceptive innervation to ocular muscles. Pearson has found that some mesencephalic root fibers pass out with the fourth nerve and perhaps also with the third, in addition to traveling with all three divisions of the trigeminal (605). Some root fibers also pass into the cerebellum. The mesencephalic tract has also been described as descending caudally to the level of the dorsal motor nucleus of the vagus, and it has been suggested that it may contain fibers entering with the sixth, seventh, ninth, and tenth cranial nerves. Sensory neurons which may have a proprioceptive function have been found along the course of the third, fourth, fifth, sixth, seventh, eleventh, and twelfth cranial nerves.

FIBER CONNECTIONS OF THE SENSORY NUCLEI

The sensory nuclei of the trigeminal nerve contain neurons whose axons pass to neighboring motor nuclei as association fibers for the completion of reflex mechanisms, and neurons whose axons pass to the thalamus as an ascending, secondary trigeminal pathway. The main sensory nucleus also may send axons into the cerebellum in company with the ventral spinocerebellar tract.

Fibers from the spinal and main sensory nuclei pass to motor nuclei of the medulla and upper spinal cord; these association connections are chiefly crossed. Other association fibers pass to both motor trigeminal, oculomotor, facial, and hypoglossal nuclei. Through the trigeminofacial connection, the peripheral arc for the **corneal blink reflex** is completed. Afferent impulses resulting from touching the cornea with a wisp of cotton traverse the nasociliary branch of the ophthalmic and, after synapses in the main sensory or spinal nucleus, activate the facial motor nucleus to bring about contraction of the orbicularis oculi muscle.

Trigeminal lemnisci, trigeminothalamic or **quintothalamic tracts,** ascending, secondary trigeminal fibers pass to the posteromedial ventral nucleus of the thalamus. The connections and course of these secondary fibers from the trigeminal sensory nuclei in man are not well known. Information at hand is based on certain anatomical studies in humans who have had incisions into the spinal nucleus, as mentioned previously, or in whom some disease process has destroyed the nuclei and the secondary fibers. Disease is seldom limited to a single nucleus or its projections, and the anatomical studies are, as a result, difficult of evaluation. If the secondary trigeminal systems are comparable to the secondary spinal ones, the spinothalamic tracts and medial lemnisci, there should be two or more trigeminothalamic tracts arising from the main sensory, spinal, and mesencephalic nuclei, respectively.

A ventral trigeminothalamic tract is said to arise from the spinal nucleus and to be completely crossed (732). The fibers ascend through the medulla incorporated with the medial lemniscus, in its ventromedial part. At a collicular level they are immediately ventral to, and closely associated with, the lateral spinothalamic fibers, lying near the periphery of the brain stem. The fibers transmitting pain and thermal impulses are most ventrally placed in the grouping, according to studies by Earl Walker (Fig. 86). They terminate in the posteromedial ventral nucleus of the thalamus. Two dorsal trigeminal lemnisci are described by various authors, one by others. When two are described, one is usually crossed and one uncrossed. Though both the spinal and main sensory nuclei may contribute fibers to these dorsal trigeminal lemnisci, most of the fibers arise in the latter. Their course is variously described. In the monkey, crossed fibers from the main sensory nucleus run with the medial lemniscus, lying just dorsal to its medial portion (795). They terminate in the posteromedial ventral thalamic nucleus. A second group of fibers, crossed and uncrossed, passes through the dorsolateral part of the reticular formation and terminates in the pons, the midbrain, and the posteromedial ventral nucleus. From the posteromedial ventral nucleus, tertiary trigeminal impulses pass via thalamocortical fibers to the most ventral part of the postcentral gyrus. Because not all secondary trigeminal fibers cross, the peripheral areas innervated by the nerve are bilaterally represented in the cerebral cortex.

CLINICAL DISORDERS OF THE TRIGEMINAL NERVE AND NUCLEI

Because of the widespread distribution of trigeminal fibers in areas that are frequently the site of infection, such as the nose, teeth, and sinuses, these fibers are occasionally involved in inflammatory processes leading to a **neuritis,** with severe pains and sometimes other sensory disturbances in and about the area of skin or mucous membrane supplied by them. If the ophthalmic branch is the site of the disease process or compression by tumor, spontaneous pain may be felt over its distribution. If conduction in the nerve is interrupted, sensation will be lost over the peripheral distribution and the corneal blink reflex will be lost. If the maxillary nerve is diseased, pains will be experienced over the cheek and in the upper teeth, and reflex sneezing cannot be elicited on the affected side. If the mandibular division is diseased, the pain will be in the tongue, lower teeth, and face, and if the interruption involves the lingual branch, taste may be lost over the anterior two-thirds of the tongue.

A not uncommon disease, **tic doloureux** or trifacial neuralgia, is seen in middle-aged and elderly people affecting one or all of the branches of the trigeminal. Its exact cause is unknown, but it is characterized by periodic, frequently spontaneous, severe pain over the involved divisions of the nerve. The pain may be cutting, tearing, or burning in nature and may be accompanied by twitching of some of the facial muscles. The paroxysms of pain are short-lived, of 5 to 20 sec. duration, are separated by periods of freedom from pain, and may be set off by stimulation of a certain area in the distribution of the involved divisions of the nerve. This area from which a paroxysm may be initiated is clinically called a trigger zone. Rubbing against this zone, shaving, chewing, and sometimes talking or smiling may instigate an attack. Characteristically, there are no demonstrable abnormalities, such as impairment of sensation or motor strength, between the episodes of pain. Therapy, often unsuccessful, has included many forms: a medical regimen with vitamins, iron, and other drugs; alcoholic injection; some form of surgery; electric-shock therapy; and psychotherapy.

Much attention has been directed toward destroying sensitivity in the affected branch of the nerve by injection of alcohol around the gasserian ganglion or the involved branch, or by cutting the trigeminal sensory root proximal or distal to the ganglion. Partial sections of the root between the gasserian ganglion and the pons are usually done, particularly in cases in which only the maxillary and mandibular divisions are involved, and it has been considered possible to relieve the pain in most patients by cutting the inferior one-third or two-thirds of the root. In some patients this procedure is unsuccessful, because the motor root is also injured, the corneal blink reflex is sometimes lost, or corneal ulceration may occur afterward. A newer operation, an intramedullary tractotomy, has been devised by Sjöqvist for making an incision into the dorsolateral part of the medulla, in the inferior olivary region, and cutting the spinal nucleus and fibers (728). By utilizing the recently acquired information of the manner of termination of the incoming trigeminal fibers, and thus placing the incision at a definite level in the medulla, anesthesia for pain and temperature stimuli over all the areas of the peripheral trigeminal distribution can be obtained. This procedure in some hands has been useful also in relieving pain about the head resulting from cancerous growths. It has an advantage in that the corneal blink reflex is not lost in many patients, whereas root section is apt to result in such loss; furthermore, the sensation of numbness is not so common, some tactile senses remaining. The operation is best done perhaps under local anesthesia. It has a disadvantage in that facial pain may return, especially in those cases which are not typical tic pain. Another disadvantage lies in the frequent postoperative complication of ataxia, with falling toward the side of the operation.

This comes about through damage to many spinocerebellar fibers. The technical procedure has therefore been improved by Grant and Weinberger and others, who have found that the incision is best made at the level of the obex or at a point 4 to 5 mm. caudad to the obex, rather than rostral to it, as Sjöqvist advocated (312).

Cavernous-sinus thrombosis, aneurysms of the internal carotid in its intracranial portion, bony or dural tumors arising in the floor of the posterior and middle fossae, as well as temporal-lobe tumors, frequently compress the gasserian ganglion or branches of the trigeminal, giving rise to severe pains and sensory loss in the distribution of the nerve. Various combinations of ocular-muscle paralyses and sensory disorders over one or more branches of the trigeminal may occur with internal-carotid aneurysms (418).

Shingles, or **herpes zoster,** is infection, probably due to a virus, of primary sensory neurons, the ganglionic cells. The cells of the gasserian ganglion, and especially those of the ophthalmic division, are occasionally the site of the disorder. Usually, general systemic signs of illness, malaise, and fever precede the development of pain over the peripheral distribution involved. Characteristically, an increased sensibility, or hyperesthesia, occurs, and after 3 or 4 days vesicles appear over the area of the involved nerve. In ophthalmic herpes, the cornea may be the site of vesicles, and the reparative process may lead to a scar formation and thus result in impairment of vision. Occasionally, severe pains, a postherpetic neuralgia, persist over the distribution of the branch of the nerve which was the site of the inflammation. This condition is very refractory to treatment, and the mechanisms underlying its production are unknown. Perhaps a ganglionic scar serves as an irritant.

Peripheral trigeminal motor paralysis is characterized by impairment of masticatory function. On opening, the jaw deviates toward the side of the paralyzed muscles because of the opposite normally working pterygoid muscles. Central or upper-motor-neuron paralyses lead to little disturbance unless they are bilateral, as in **pseudobulbar palsy.** In this disease the corticobulbar fibers are interrupted by areas of necrosis usually resulting from cerebral vascular disease; with such bilateral **upper-motor-neuron disease** volitional movements are impaired and the jaw jerk is usually increased. This is elicited by tapping the chin gently as the patient holds the lower jaw slightly open. A reflex closure occurs. This reflex would be lost in bilateral **lower-motor-neuron disease,** such as **bulbar palsy.** In this disorder the motor neurons in the nuclei are diseased. The muscles of mastication are paralyzed for all movements, the lower jaw hangs open, and the muscles waste. The trigeminal nuclei may be damaged as a result of vascular impairment in the pons and medulla, especially in affections of the superior cerebellar and posterior inferior cerebellar arteries, respectively. **Syringobulbia,** a condition characterized by the formation of slitlike cavities in the medulla particularly, frequently involves the trigeminal spinal nucleus and thus produces loss of pain and thermal sensibility, especially, over the face.

Facial Nerve

The facial nerve contains both motor and sensory fibers. The motor fibers are destined for striated muscles under voluntary control, as well as for glandular tissues not under voluntary control and for smooth muscle of cerebral blood vessels. The sensory fibers carry impulses of taste, cutaneous sensibility from a portion of the external ear, visceral impulses of a rudimentary distribution from palatal and posterior nasal mucous membranes, and perhaps proprioceptive impulses from the muscles of facial expression. The sensory and autonomic components of the facial nerve constitute the **glossopalatine nerve** or **nervus intermedius.**

MOTOR NUCLEI AND FIBERS TO STRIATED MUSCLE

Each facial motor nucleus (special visceral efferent) lies in the ventrolateral angle of the pontine tegmentum, the chief part of the nucleus being found at a level just posterior to the facial colliculus in the floor of the fourth ventricle (Figs. 161, 162). Each nucleus is just ventromedial to the spinal nucleus and tract of the trigeminal nerve, and this might be explained because of the close relationship between the functions and distribution

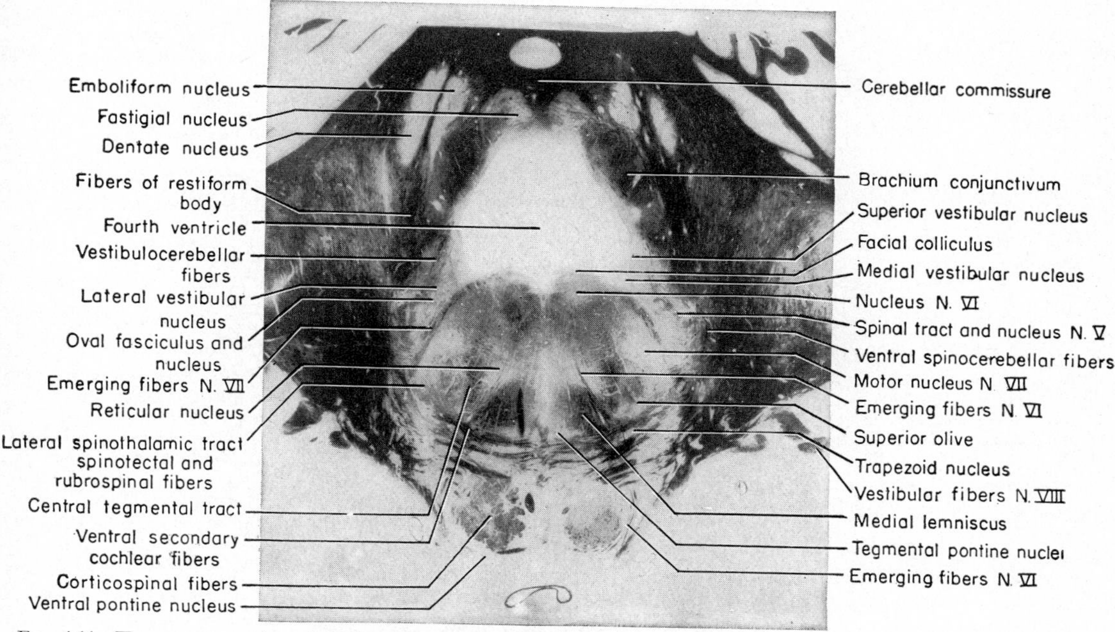

FIG. 161. Transverse section, A 495, of human brain stem at level of facial colliculus. Weigert. Photograph, ×2.

of the trigeminal and facial nerves, many of the reflex actions of the facial nerve arising through stimuli brought in by the trigeminal. The facial nuclei are dorsal to the medial lemnisci and dorsomedial to the lateral lemnisci and lateral spinothalamic tracts. The cells are moderately large and have been classified into groups according to the muscles innervated. The corrugator, frontalis, and orbicularis oculi, for example, are innervated by a particular portion of the motor nuclei.

The axons of the nuclear cells of each side pass dorsomedially and slightly rostrally, to course beneath the floor of the fourth ventricle medial and dorsal to the nucleus of the abducens, there forming the **genu** of the facial nerve (Figs. 161, 210). Thence they turn ventrolaterally and emerge from the lateral side of the brain stem into the cerebellopontine space just at the caudal end of the pons. The fibers pass then with the eighth nerve through the internal auditory meatus. Early in their passage through the meatus, the special visceral efferent fibers become associated with the glossopalatine nerve. At the distal end of the internal auditory meatus an acute turn, or another "genu," occurs, and at this point the **geniculate ganglion** is located. It is the site of the cell bodies for the sensory fibers to be described below. From the ganglion the facial fibers turn laterally and downward within the facial canal, coursing beneath the external semicircular canal. Another turn inferiorly occurs, and the nerve then pursues a nearly vertical course to make its exit at the stylomastoid foramen. Turning upward and slightly anteriorly, it then plunges into the substance of the parotid gland wherein it divides into temporal, zygomatic, buccal, mandibular, and cervical branches. These supply the muscles of expression and the buccinator, those of the scalp and external ear, the platysma, posterior belly of the digastric and the stylohyoid. A small nerve to the stapedius muscle arises from the facial as it runs in the facial canal.

MOTOR NUCLEI AND FIBERS TO GLANDULAR TISSUE

Within the adjacent reticular formation, dorsal and just medial to the main part of each facial nucleus for striated muscle, is a group of cells, the superior salivatory nucleus (general visceral efferent), whose axons pass out ventralward and laterally from the pons in close association with the special visceral efferent fibers described above. These motor

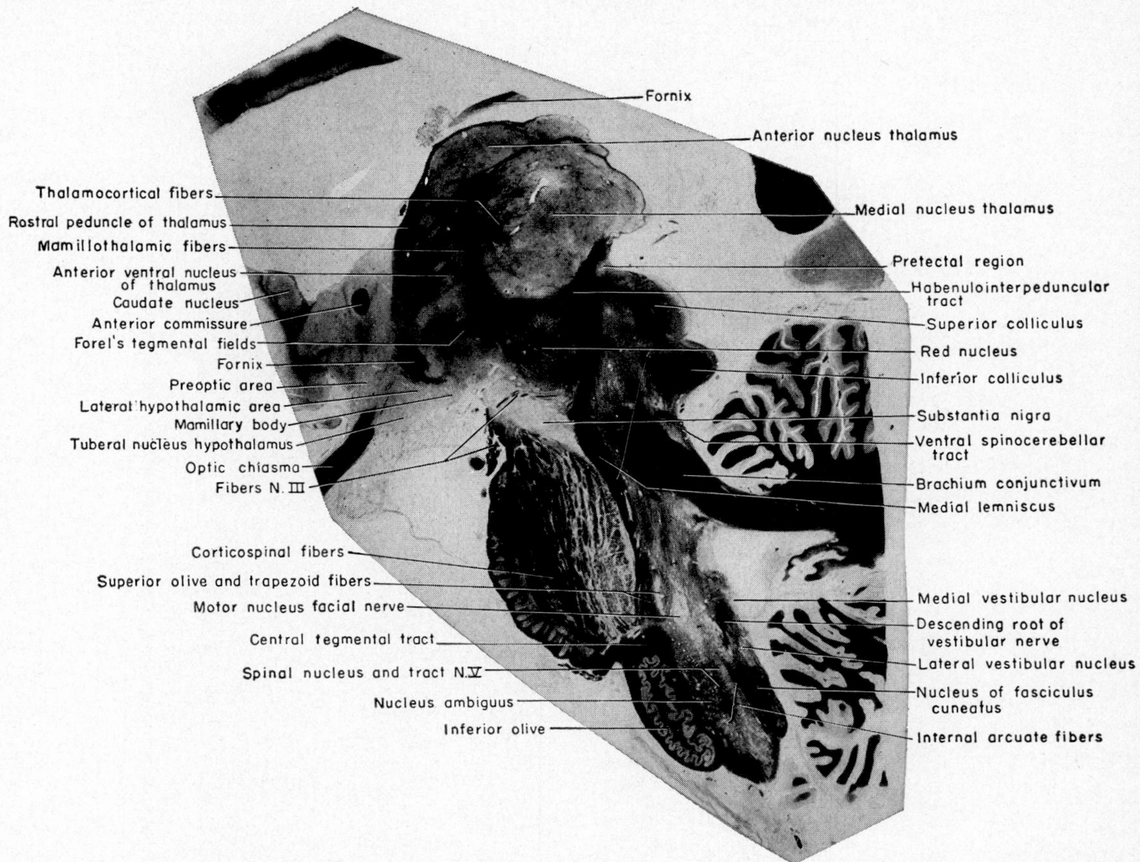

Fig. 162. Parasagittal section, A 270, of human brain stem through lateral edge of mamillary body. Weigert. Photograph, ×1.7.

fibers are **preganglionic parasympathetic.** Many of them pass through the chorda tympani nerve which leaves the facial within the facial canal and arches over the tympanic membrane on its inner surface. After traversing the tympanic cavity the chorda tympani enters the petrous bone and emerges finally into the infratemporal fossa to join the lingual nerve. With this nerve the autonomic fibers run to the vicinity of the submaxillary gland to synapse within the submaxillary ganglion. From these latter ganglionic cells, **postganglionic** axons arise to supply secretory impulses to the glandular cells in the submaxillary and sublingual glands (Fig. 163).

On the basis of experimental data obtained by others in dogs, Feiling has tentatively located the human salivatory nuclei in the reticular formation of the rostral medulla, dorsal to the inferior olive (246). Furthermore, stimulation in monkeys with the use of the Clarke-Horsley apparatus and measurement of saliva flow from cannulated ducts of parotid and submaxillary glands has "revealed an excitable region comprising the dorsal midline area between the genu of the facial nerve and the hypoglossal nucleus, and extending laterally and ventrally through the reticular formation to the exits of the 7th and 9th nerves. While overlap exists, responses of the submaxillary gland are elicited predominantly from the rostral part of the excitable area and those of the parotid gland from the caudal part." (524)

Other **preganglionic parasympathetic fibers,** the nucleus of origin of which is obscure, leave the facial nerve at the geniculate ganglion and pass through the great super-

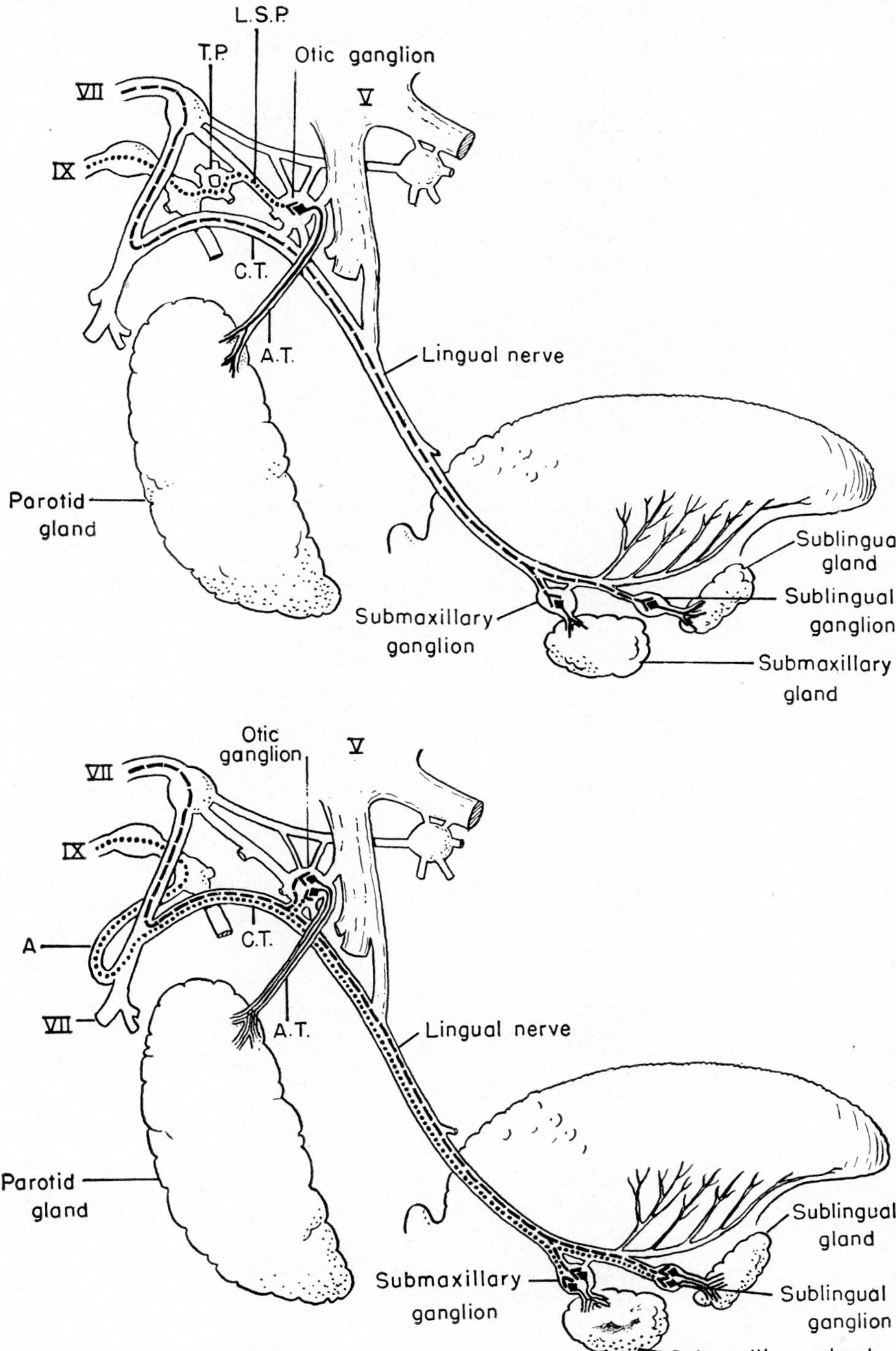

FIG. 163. Diagrams of parasympathetic innervation of salivary glands. *A*, extracranial connection between ninth and seventh nerves; *A.T.*, auriculotemporal nerve; *C.T.*, chorda tympani nerve; *L.S.P.*, lesser superficial petrosal nerve; *T.P.*, tympanic plexus. The lower figure shows "overlapping" of innervations via seventh and ninth nerve parasympathetic fibers.

ficial petrosal nerve to the sphenopalatine ganglion. From here **postganglionic fibers** arise to pass to the vessels and mucous glands of the nasal epithelium. With this group of preganglionic fibers there are others, whose definite central origin is also unknown but is suspected to be in the vicinity of the superior salivatory nucleus. These fibers also pass to the sphenopalatine ganglion through the great superficial petrosal nerve. From this ganglion **postganglionic fibers** pass to the lacrimal gland over the zygomatic nerve and the lacrimal branch of the ophthalmic division of the trigeminal.

Penfield has demonstrated a bundle of fibers leaving the medulla with these autonomic fibers above and passing through the geniculate ganglion into the great superficial petrosal nerve. Their central origin is not clear. The fibers pass from the great superficial petrosal nerve to join the internal carotid plexus. Within this are neurons which give rise to **postganglionic** fibers that pass to the cerebral arteries as vasodilator fibers (139).

SENSORY NUCLEI AND FIBERS

The sensory fibers, together with the motor fibers to glandular structures just described, constitute the **glossopalatine nerve** or **nervus intermedius.** These sensory fibers arise from cells in the **geniculate ganglion,** are distributed through several branches of the facial nerve, and carry a variety of types of impulses. One group, not nearly so large in man as in certain lower animals, carries **taste** impulses (special visceral afferent) from the taste buds on the anterior two-thirds of the tongue. These fibers arise in the geniculate ganglion and usually join the chorda tympani nerve, the course of which was described above, thence to be distributed by the lingual branch of the mandibular division of the trigeminal. Another peripheral course is possible by way of the great superficial petrosal nerve, through the otic ganglion, and thence via the distal portion of the chorda tympani (480, 712) (Fig. 275). This alternate pathway for the taste fibers from the anterior two-thirds of the tongue is of some practical importance, since it perhaps accounts for the fact that taste is not lost over this tongue area in certain patients suffering severe damage to the chorda tympani, in its tympanic part, coincident to otitis media. The central processes of these geniculate cells subserving taste sense enter the pons near the origin of the motor division of the facial nerve to synapse among cells in the rostral portion of the nucleus of the tractus solitarius (Fig. 164). Secondary fibers ascend from here to the posteromedial ventral nucleus of the thalamus or to the adjacent accessory semilunar nucleus but their upper brain stem course is at present unknown. From this thalamic nucleus, tertiary taste fibers pass to the postcentral gyrus (Chap. 20).

Exteroceptive impulses arising from the epithelium of the central area of the external ear, anteriorly about the external auditory meatus, the external auditory canal, and the tympanum, are carried by fibers (general somatic afferent) arising from the geniculate ganglion cells; similar fibers innervate also a posteromedial strip of the external ear. The fibers leave the facial nerve in the lowest part of the stylomastoid foramen, and join the auricular branch of the vagus to be distributed to the ear. Similar sensory impulses arising on the small posteromedial area of the ear travel by way of the posterior auricular branch of the facial. Central processes of these somatic sensory geniculate cells pass into the brain stem, to end in the spinal nucleus of the trigeminal. Secondary fibers run from here to the thalamus in the quintothalamic tracts.

A rudimentary innervation (general visceral afferent) of **palatal and posterior nasal mucous membranes** is also a function of the facial nerve (399, 400). The fibers arise in the geniculate ganglion and pass by way of the great superficial petrosal nerve through the sphenopalatine ganglion and into the posterior nasal and palatine branches of the ganglion for distribution. The secondary neurons for the pain fibers of the system are in the spinal nucleus of the trigeminal (100). The course of the secondary fibers would thus be with the quintothalamic tracts.

It is considered by some authors that **deep sensibility of the face,** *i.e.,* sensation of deep pressure-pain, localization of deep touch and sense of position, is carried by certain fibers (general visceral afferent) in the facial nerve. This idea has been based by Davis on his experimental work and observations in his patients that pressure and pressure-pain sensibility remained intact in the face after retrogasserian neurectomy, whereas all cutaneous touch, pain, and temperature sensibility was lost after this procedure (199). This has not been a universal experience, since other investigators have described loss of all types of facial pain sensibility to follow such a surgical procedure (126). It is probably correct that the facial nerve does not transmit deep pressure-pain impulses, unless certain of its fibers ending around blood vessels in the face are pain mediators (95).

It appears likely, however, that the facial nerve does transmit sensory impulses from the muscles of expression. These subserve a **proprioceptive** function, sense of movement and sense of contraction, in these muscles. Typical neuromuscular spindles have not been described within facial muscles, however, and another type of end organ is probable as a proprioceptive receptor there. These proprioceptive fibers of the facial nerve are thought to arise in part from neurons scattered along the course of the nerve and in part, perhaps, from the mesencephalic nucleus of the trigeminal. This latter source is postulated on the evidence that certain facial-nerve fibers within the pons join the mesencephalic root (604, 605).

CENTRAL CONNECTIONS OF THE FACIAL NUCLEI

The facial motor nucleus receives fibers from the superior olive for the completion of auditory reflexes, chiefly, the acousticostapedial, by which the tension of the stapedius is regulated according to certain sound intensities. Interconnections with the oculomotor nucleus correlate eyelid and eye movements. Closing of the eyelids is associated with an upward movement of the eyes, **Bell's phenomenon.** The facial motor nucleus receives fibers from the sensory trigeminal nuclei to complete the central arcs for the corneal blink reflex, as outlined previously. It is also interconnected with the motor nucleus of the trigeminal and with the hypoglossal nucleus, this latter probably via the medial longitudinal fasciculus, for the association of lip, masticatory, and glossal musculature. Tectobulbar fibers also end in the facial nucleus for completion of other auditory and visuofacial reflexes. An example of the latter is the blinking of the eyelids when exposure to strong light occurs. The facial nucleus also receives impulses from the basal ganglia and from the hypothalamus for the innervation of involuntary and emotional facial movements; the course these take is unknown.

Corticobulbar fibers from the face region of the precentral gyrus pass to the facial nucleus. These fibers traverse the internal capsule and cerebral peduncle in company with corticospinal fibers (Fig. 241). Some pass through the pons with the corticospinal fibers as direct corticobulbar fibers; others as aberrant corticobulbars join with the medial lemniscus and pass through the pons to the level of the facial nucleus (see Chap. 16). At this level the direct and aberrant corticobulbar fibers undergo a partial decussation to terminate in the facial nucleus. That portion of the nucleus supplying the three muscles of the upper face—frontalis, orbicularis oculi, and corrugator—receives corticobulbar fibers from the precentral gyrus of each cortex. When one corticobulbar tract is interrupted, as in an upper-motor-neuron lesion, the upper facial muscles are not completely paralyzed. The muscles of the lower face suffer more impairment. This is an important diagnostic point. When disease destroys the facial nucleus or interrupts the complete facial nerve in its peripheral course, it is customary for the entire half of the face to be paralyzed. Such would be a lower-motor-neuron lesion. This type of paralysis is frequently alluded to as a "peripheral facial paralysis"; the upper-motor-neuron type, as a "central facial paralysis."

The autonomic nuclei related to the facial nerve apparently receive fibers from the nucleus solitarius, from olfactory centers, from the trigeminal sensory nuclei, and from the hypothalamus and cortex. Such connections would underly reflex and emotional salivation, lacrimation, and nasal stuffiness.

The nucleus of the tractus solitarius and the trigeminal spinal nucleus send connecting fibers to the motor nuclei of the trigeminal, the facial, and the hypoglossal nerves and to the salivatory nuclei. Secondary connections from the nucleus solitarius pass to the nucleus intercalatus, salivatory nuclei, "respiratory centers," and motor vagal nuclei and to the spinal cord as a solitariospinal tract. The pathways by which taste impulses reach the thalamus are unknown. The secondary pathways for the cutaneous and general visceral sensory impulses are probably the trigeminal lemnisci.

CLINICAL DISORDERS INVOLVING THE FACIAL NERVE AND NUCLEI

Disturbance of the facial nerve in its nucleus or along its course in the bony canals is fairly common. Poliomyelitis and chronic bulbar palsy may involve the facial nuclei alone or in association with damage to other cranial-nerve motor nuclei. Facial nuclear lesions or damage to the fibers in their intrapontine course may be a result of tumor or vascular impairment. In such instances neighboring nuclei and tracts may also be destroyed. Other neurological signs are frequently associated with the facial paralysis, therefore, in such cases. Ipsilateral facial sensory change and contralateral disturbances of pain and thermal sensibility over the body and limbs may occur because of simultaneous damage to the trigeminal spinal tract and nucleus and the lateral spinothalamic tract, respectively. Intrapontine lesions damaging the genu of the facial nerve necessarily involve the abducens nucleus to give an ipsilateral external rectus paralysis with the facial paralysis. Massive intrapontine softening may also involve the medial lemniscus and corticospinal tracts, giving further contralateral sensory and motor disorders of the limbs. Since these motor abnormalities of the limbs are opposite to the side of facial paralysis, the condition represents a form of "crossed paralysis."

The facial nerve may be the site of injury in its course through the cerebellopontine angle, the internal auditory meatus, or the temporal bone or in the face. The resulting signs of the disorder will naturally depend on the site of the damage. Perhaps the most common disorder of the facial nerve is that condition known as **Bell's palsy.** The site of the injury, possibly caused by a local swelling, is usually along the nerve as it traverses the facial canal. The patient may awaken to find one half of his face paralyzed. Such paralysis may be complete or involve only certain muscle groups. If it be complete, he loses all movement, voluntary and emotional, on the affected side. The face is usually asymmetric, the nasolabial flold is flat, the cheek sags, and the corner of the mouth frequently droops. The patient cannot close his eye on the affected side either voluntarily or reflexly as in the corneal blink reaction; he cannot distend the cheek or purse his lips tightly, and he occasionally drools saliva from the paralyzed side of the mouth. Since he cannot close his eye and thus protect the cornea, injury to the latter is a distinct possibility. In the majority of cases of Bell's palsy, return of function gradually occurs, though frequently it does not return simultaneously in all muscle groups or to the same degree. In some individuals involuntary facial spasms occur for years after facial muscle function has returned.

Occasionally the facial nerve is involved in **infections in the middle ear** and in the mastoid cells, and occasionally it must be sacrificed during the course of operations in this region. It may be compressed by tumor arising in the cerebellopontine angle. Changes in lacrimation, in salivary secretion, and in taste may accompany some of these peripheral facial disorders, depending on the site of interruption of the nerve.

If the nerve is involved by **tumor** in the cerebellopontine angle, other cranial nerves are apt to be damaged also, the trigeminal and the eighth nerves especially. If it is damaged in the internal auditory meatus, the eighth nerve would probably also be damaged and hearing difficulty would ensue. Presumably taste would be lost over the anterior two-thirds of the tongue, and changes in quality of saliva might occur, in addition to the paralysis of all facial movement, voluntary and emotional. An occasional patient will complain of hyperacusis, since he has lost the protective mechanism of the stapedius muscle. Lacrimation might be lessened for a while because of involvement of lacrimal secretory fibers, and since the orbicularis oculi would also be paralyzed, it would be impossible for the patient to close his eyes. The cornea in such a case might become inflamed or injured, and this would serve as an irritant to produce more lacrimation, instituted through sympathetic secretory fibers. Injury to the facial nerve distal to the geniculate ganglion might produce all the signs above, excluding the changes in lacrimation. As noted above, certain patients, however, will not have a taste impairment with such lesions, since in them the taste fibers probably traverse the great superficial petrosal nerve. If the injury to the nerve is distal to the point of origin of the chorda tympani, taste function would also not be impaired. Injuries at the stylomastoid foramen or in the face may lead to complete or partial facial paralyses depending on the number of fibers severed. Meningitis and neuritis as well as head injury may involve the facial nerve.

If the cerebral facial motor area in the precentral gyrus is injured, or if interruptions occur in the corticobulbar tracts of one side coming to a facial nucleus, as often happens in **cerebral vascular accidents** or **strokes,** a noticeable loss of movement occurs in the muscles over the lower half of the face contralateral to the lesion. The upper three facial muscles escape for reasons cited above. This is an "upper-motor-neuron or central lesion" of the facial innervation, as mentioned above. Differences in the types of central facial paralysis have also been described (563). In one type, with damage to corticobulbar fibers, as mentioned previously, the lower facial muscles cannot be contracted voluntarily, but when the patient is told an amusing story, these same muscles may move quite well in laughter or in smiling. These movements on emotional reaction are apparently initiated through the basal ganglia and hypothalamic centers and their projections to the facial nuclei. These fibers are often not damaged with the corticobulbar tracts. The other types of central facial paralysis is the reverse of the above; *i.e.,* there is a loss of emotional, with a preservation of voluntary movement. This occurs when the extrapyramidal or hypothalamic centers are the sites of disease, as in paralysis agitans and chronic encephalitis (see Chap. 17).

In **geniculate neuralgia,** patients may have recurring paroxysms of severe pain over all or any part of the facial sensory distribution. It appears to the patient to be deep in the facial muscles, within the ear, or in the pharynx. Treatment for it has at times involved section of the nervus intermedius. It has been suggested that trigeminal spinal tractotomy might relieve it in some cases. Geniculate neuralgia may result from the ganglionic scarring following geniculate herpes zoster, and it was by study of acute cases of the latter that Hunt worked out the sensory distribution of the facial nerve (399, 400).

Glossopharyngeal Nerve

This nerve is commonly considered with the vagus nerve, since it shares central nuclei (of origin) with that nerve. Alone it supplies motor fibers to the stylopharyngeus muscle and, with the vagus, motor fibers to the constrictors of the pharynx. It supplies secretory fibers to gland tissue (parotid), general cutaneous sensation to a part of the external ear, general visceral sensation to the posterior one-third of the tongue, to the pharynx, and middle ear, and taste sensation to the posterior one-third of the tongue.

PERIPHERAL COURSE

The glossopharyngeal nerve leaves the medulla just dorsal to the rostral end of the inferior olive, in close association with vagus and bulbar fibers of the spinal accessory nerve. All three nerves traverse the jugular foramen to reach the neck, and only a thin bar of bone separates them from the hypoglossal as it traverses the hypoglossal canal. Within the jugular foramen or just inferior to it are one, usually two, **petrosal ganglia,** superior and inferior. Arising from the nerve trunk near the ganglia is a small branch, the tympanic nerve of Jacobson, containing visceral sensory and visceral motor fibers destined for the tympanic cavity and parotid gland, respectively. Another small branch joins the vagus, and with a branch of that nerve, the auricular, it supplies a small area of the skin of the ear. Special visceral efferent and afferent fibers and general visceral afferent fibers of the glossopharyngeal pass downward into the neck again closely associated with the vagus, spinal accessory, hypoglossal nerves, cervical sympathetic trunk, internal jugular vein, and internal carotid artery. After winding around the lower border of the stylopharyngeus which it innervates (special visceral efferent fibers), the glossopharyngeal passes forward between the internal and external carotid arteries. Fibers of the nerve join with fibers from the vagus and sympathetic trunk to form the pharyngeal plexus. A small branch of the nerve passes to the region of the carotid bulb. The terminal fibers of the glossopharyngeal supply the posterior third of the tongue with taste (special visceral afferent) and general visceral sensation.

MOTOR NUCLEI AND FIBERS

To striated muscle. The fibers carrying motor impulses (special visceral efferent) to striated muscle arise from cells in the rostral part of the nucleus ambiguus. This scattered group of cells is hard to recognize with certainty in myelin-stained sections but is located in the ventrolateral region of the medullar tegmentum just dorsal to the inferior olivary nucleus, and ventromedial to the spinal nucleus of the trigeminal (Figs. 164, 165, 166). These cells send off axons that run dorsomedialward to join others, described later, which arise near the dorsal motor nucleus of the vagus, and together the two components emerge from the lateral side of the medulla just above the inferior olivary nucleus. Their subsequent course has been described above.

Opinions vary as to the peripheral distribution of the axons which arise from the nucleus ambiguus and travel via glossopharyngeal, vagus, and bulbar fibers of the eleventh cranial nerve. Certain neurosurgeons have felt that the glossopharyngeal nerve carries the majority of the fibers to the pharynx; the vagus, fibers to the palate. Contradictions have also arisen with regard to the innervation of the muscles of the larynx, some authors asserting that they are innervated via vagus fibers, others that they are supplied by eleventh-nerve fibers distributed by the vagus. Another point of discrepancy will also be mentioned with reference to the innervation of the trapezius muscle by eleventh-cranial-nerve fibers and by cervical cord fibers. The following pattern of distribution seems most likely to be the correct one. Fibers arising in the nucleus ambiguus and traveling with the glossopharyngeal pass to the stylopharyngeus muscle alone. The constrictors of the pharynx are innervated by mixed vagus and glossopharyngeal fibers, but especially by vagal fibers. The palate muscles, with the exception of the tensor veli palatini, are supplied by vagus fibers. The muscles of the larynx are supplied by fibers leaving the nucleus ambiguus and medulla as bulbar rootlets of the eleventh nerve, but they join the vagus and are distributed through its superior laryngeal and inferior (recurrent) laryngeal branches.

To glands. In the region of the dorsal motor nucleus of the vagus, in the floor of the fourth ventricle, a group of cells, the inferior salivatory nucleus, gives rise to axons (general visceral efferent) that pass out of the medulla in company with those glossopharyngeal fibers arising from the nucleus ambiguus. These fibers are **parasympathetic preganglionic** fibers. They

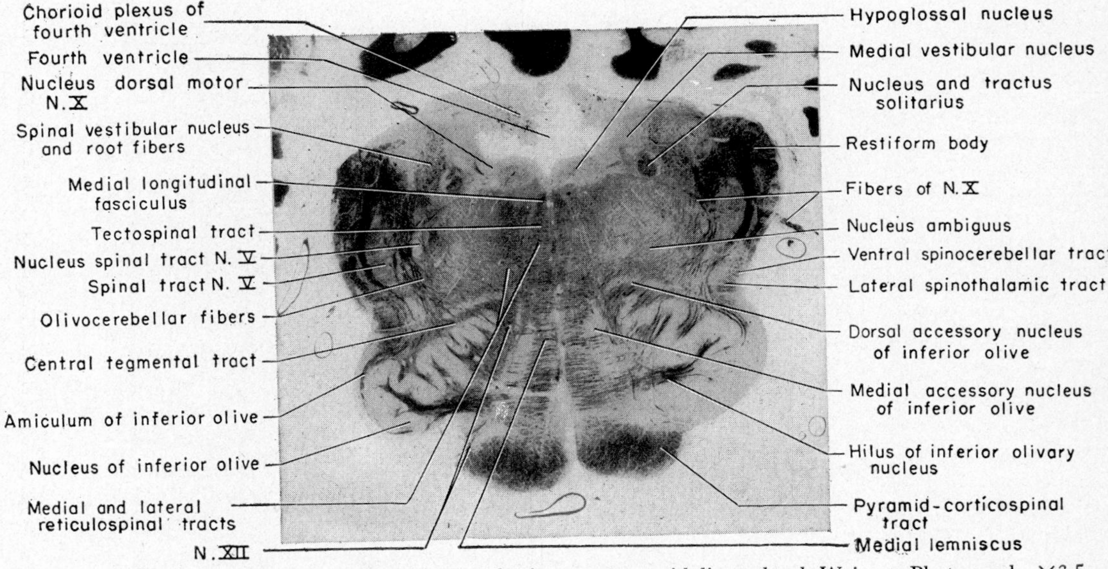

FIG. 164. Transverse section, A 333, of human brain stem at a midolivary level. Weigert. Photograph, ×3.5.

pass from the glossopharyngeal nerve by way of its tympanic branch and through the tympanic plexus into the lesser superficial petrosal nerve to the otic ganglion in which they synapse about certain of the cells. From these cells, **postganglionic fibers** pass to the parotid gland by way of the auriculotemporal branch of the trigeminal. These fibers transmit impulses which bring about secretion of saliva. In some individuals, however, these preganglionic fibers pass from the glossopharyngeal nerve high in the neck to join the facial nerve as it emerges from the stylomastoid foramen. Passing up along the facial nerve in the stylomastoid canal, the fibers join the chorda tympani with which they run for a distance. They leave this nerve and pass via a small connection to the otic ganglion (661) (Fig. 163).

SENSORY NUCLEI AND FIBERS

Taste sensation. The glossopharyngeal nerve is the most important nerve for mediation of **taste** impulses (special visceral afferent) in man. The largest taste buds in adult man are in the circumvallate papillae on the posterior one-third of the tongue. Impulses from them pass over glossopharyngeal nerve fibers which have arisen from cells in the inferior petrosal ganglion. The central processes of these petrosal ganglion cells conduct the taste impulses into the medulla in company with the other glossopharyngeal fibers. The taste fibers synapse about cells in the nucleus of the tractus solitarius in that part of the nucleus at the level of entry of the nerve. Secondary taste fibers ascend to the posteromedial ventral nucleus of the thalamus or to the adjacent accessory semilunar nucleus, and from here tertiary fibers pass to the parietal lobe, but their course is uncertain (see Chap. 20).

To skin and mucous membranes. In the superior petrosal ganglion, cells (general somatic afferent) give rise to processes that bring impulses from the **skin** of part of the concha and a small posteromedial strip of the external ear, from the posterior wall of the external auditory canal, and from the posterior part of the tympanic membrane. These fibers of the glossopharyngeal nerve join the vagus high in the neck and are distributed through the auricular branch of the latter nerve and the posterior auricular branch of the facial. The secondary neurons for these fibers are in the spinal nucleus of the trigeminal, as mentioned previously, and their axons pass to the thalamus.

From the inferior or petrosal ganglion proper, cell bodies (general visceral afferent) send out peripheral processes that carry general sensory impulses, pain and tactile especially, from the posterior one-third of the tongue and from the **mucous membrane** of the uvula, soft palate, posterior pharyngeal wall from the eustachian tube to the tip of epiglottis, the lateral pharyngeal wall, and tonsillar region to the anterior pillars (661). The central processes of these cells (at least those concerned with pain sensibility) pass into the medulla in company with the other glossopharyngeal-nerve fibers to terminate probably about cells in the spinal nucleus of the trigeminal (100). From here secondary paths pass to the thalamus, and from that center, tertiary paths pass to the postcentral gyrus.

By way of the tympanic branch of the glossopharyngeal (Jacobson's nerve) sensory fibers are supplied to the medial surface of the **ear drum,** to the tympanic cavity, to the eustachian tube in part, and to mastoid cells (400). The central processes of the neurons for Jacobson's nerve pass into the medulla in company with other glossopharyngeal fibers and are thought to synapse around cells in the spinal nucleus of the trigeminal. From here, secondary fibers pass to the thalamus.

Sensory fibers whose terminations lie in the walls of the **carotid bulb** and in the **carotid body** travel in the glossopharyngeal nerve. The terminals are pressor receptors and are important in reflex regulation of blood pressure and heart rate (**carotid sinus reflex**). Cell bodies for these fibers are in the inferior petrosal ganglion; secondary neurons are probably within, or adjacent to, the nucleus of the tractus solitarius.

CENTRAL CONNECTIONS OF GLOSSOPHARYNGEAL NUCLEI

The nucleus ambiguus receives fibers from neighboring sensory nuclei, such as the nucleus of the tractus solitarius and trigeminal spinal nucleus, for completion of reflex arcs for such acts as gagging, coughing, and swallowing.

It presumably has interconnecting fibers directly, or via internuncial neurons, with the facial and hypoglossal motor nuclei. Corticobulbar fibers from the homolateral and contralateral motor areas of the precentral gyrus reach the nucleus ambiguus also, putting it under voluntary control. Fibers from the tectum, tectobulbars, and fibers from the basal ganglia are also thought to reach the nucleus ambiguus. The inferior salivatory nucleus receives fibers from the nucleus solitarius and from the trigeminal spinal nucleus for completion of reflex arcs underlying salivary secretion. Presumably fibers reach it from the hypothalamus and also from the cortex for effecting salivation in response to emotional stimulation. The inferior and superior salivatory nuclei are apparently in close association, since salivary secretion is rather a "group affair." The nucleus of the tractus solitarius has secondary connections with the nucleus intercalatus for gustatory impulses; with the respiratory "center" neurons; with the dorsal motor nuclei of the vagus; with the salivatory nuclei; and with spinal-cord neurons via the solitariospinal tract.

CLINICAL DISTURBANCES OF THE GLOSSOPHARYNGEAL NUCLEI AND NERVE

Disturbances of the glossopharyngeal nerve alone are uncommon. There is a rare type of painful disorder of the nerve, usually of unknown cause. This condition, **glossopharyngeal neuralgia,** is characterized by sudden paroxysms of severe stabbing, boring, cutting, or burning pain over the areas of peripheral sensory distribution of the nerve in the ear, tongue, and throat (19, 417, 428, 762). There may be trigger zones in the posterior pharynx from which the paroxysms are set off, and chewing, talking, or swallowing may precipitate an attack. Each paroxysm may last from 20 sec. to 1 min. The pain may begin in the ear and radiate into the ipsilateral pharynx, but it is more common for it to begin deep in the pharynx and radiate to the ear. Section of the glossopharyngeal nerve intracranially or an avulsion of it from the jugular foramen is usually done, but Brodal recently has suggested that trigeminal spinal tractotomy might also be successful, especially if the neuralgic pains were caused by a tumor mass involving the pharynx or damaging the nerve. He thinks, as a result of his clinical studies, that the trigeminal spinal nucleus contains secondary neurons for the glossopharyngeal-nerve pain fibers (100).

Motor disturbance following isolated glossopharyngeal lesions have been differently described. Some authors describe changes in parotid secretion and paralysis of the constrictors of the pharynx on the side of the damaged nerve, and they thus feel that this nerve is motor to these muscles. More generally, only the stylopharyngeus is paralyzed, and this produces little disability. Loss of taste over the ipsilateral posterior one-third of the tongue and anesthesia over the posterior pharynx and posterior one-third of the tongue with loss of the gag reflex are the most outstanding sensory disturbances, though these are not so serious unless both nerves are at fault.

The glossopharyngeal is more often damaged along with vagus, spinal accessory, and hypoglossal, either in the vicinity of the jugular foramen or high in the neck. Some of these group disorders will be described after the last three cranial nerves are considered. The corticobulbar fibers passing to the nucleus ambiguus are frequently damaged by softenings secondary to vascular insufficiency, but again, damage of similar fibers to other cranial nerve motor nuclei is associated. The resulting clinical condition, pseudobulbar palsy, will be described later.

VAGUS NERVE

The vagus nerve contains fibers of many types, motor and sensory. Motor fibers to striated musculature; motor fibers to glands, smooth muscle, and cardiac muscle; sensory fibers from skin of the ear (cutaneous exteroceptive); sensory fibers from epithelial linings of the thoracic and abdominal viscera (interoceptive); and sensory fibers from the taste buds in the region of the epiglottis—all are united into this single nerve.

PERIPHERAL DISTRIBUTION

It is difficult to separate vagus fibers from those of the glossopharyngeal where the two nerves emerge from the medulla, since the filaments forming them are arranged in linear

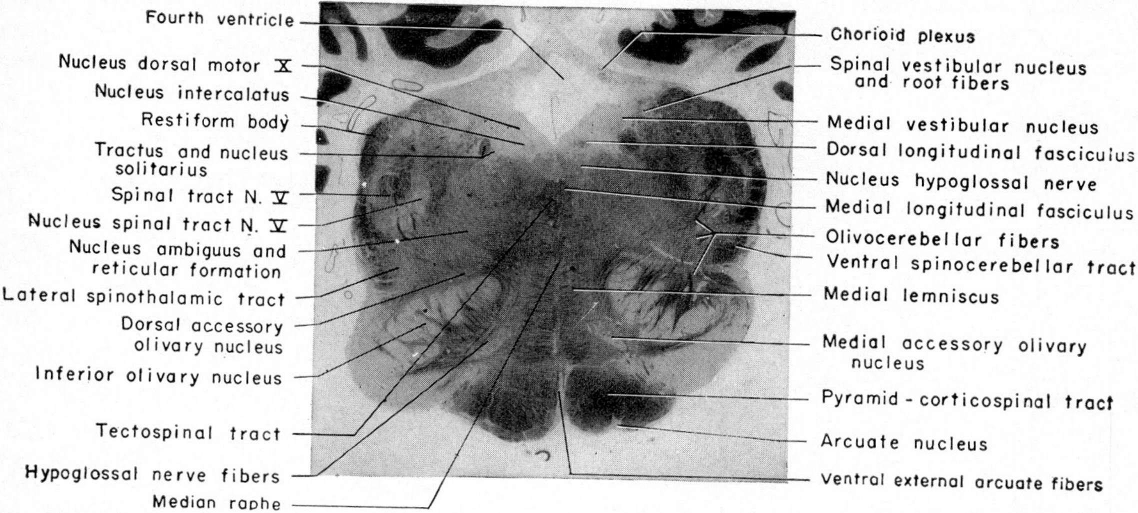

FIG. 165. Transverse section, A 288, of human brain stem, at caudal end of restiform body. Weigert. Photograph, ×3.5.

fashion in the posterolateral sulcus of the medulla dorsal to the inferior olive. By the time the jugular foramen, through which both make their exit, is reached, the nerves are separated and emerge through separate dural openings. The vagus has two ganglia also, usually within or just inferior to the jugular foramen. These are the sites of primary sensory neurons of general somatic afferent, special and visceral afferent types. The superior ganglion is the **jugular,** and it is thought to contain general somatic afferent neurons; the **inferior,** or **nodose, ganglion** contains special and general visceral afferent.

A small meningeal nerve leaves the jugular ganglion to supply the dura around the transverse venous sinus. The auricular nerve arises also from the jugular ganglion, joins with a similar branch from the glossopharyngeal, and passes through a foramen in the wall of the jugular fossa to gain the stylomastoid canal, where it communicates with the facial nerve. With the auricular nerve of the facial, these glossopharyngeal and vagus fibers are distributed to aural parts.

In the neck the vagus is closely associated with the other posterior cranial nerves and sympathetic trunk as well as the great vessels. Branches are joined with filaments from glossopharyngeal and sympathetic trunk to form a pharyngeal plexus, containing motor (special visceral efferent) and sensory (special visceral afferent) fibers. The other terminal branches of the vagus are superior and inferior laryngeal nerves with special visceral efferent and general visceral afferent fibers which, strictly speaking, belong to the eleventh cranial nerve, and the cardiac, bronchial, pulmonary, esophageal, abdominal visceral, and pericardial nerves. All except the last, which have general visceral sensory alone, include general visceral sensory and motor fibers.

MOTOR NUCLEI AND FIBERS

Since two types of motor fibers are distributed within the vagus, they arise from two nuclei. Those innervating smooth and cardiac muscle and glands will be described first.

To smooth and cardiac muscle and glands. In the dorsal motor nucleus of the vagus, situated in the floor of the fourth ventricle under the elevation known as the ala cinerea, are cells whose axons pass ventrolateralward to emerge just above the inferior olivary nucleus (Figs. 150, 164, 165, 166). These fibers are distributed as **preganglionic parasympathetic** fibers (general visceral efferent) to ganglion cells located in or near the viscera of the thorax and abdomen. The descending colon and pelvic viscera receive comparable innervation from the sacral parasympathetic fibers. Cells of Meissner's and Auerbach's plexuses serve as **postganglionic neurons** for parasympathetic innervation of the gastrointestinal tract. From the intrinsic ganglion cells, postganglionic fibers arise to run to the ultimate muscle fiber or glandular cell of termination. The nature of the impulse to each viscus is discussed in Chap. 7.

To striated muscle. In the nucleus ambiguus, located in the ventrolateral part of the medullar tegmentum, cells are present whose axons pass dorsomedialward in the medulla to join the axons of the cells located in the dorsal motor vagus nucleus (Figs. 164, 165, 166). These "ambiguus" fibers (special visceral efferent) emerge from the medulla in company with the preganglionic fibers described above, and in company with glossopharyngeal fibers in the pharyngeal plexus, they pass to striated constrictor muscles of the pharynx and esophagus; together with fibers of the spinal accessory nerve, they pass to the intrinsic muscles of the larynx. Vagus fibers alone innervate the levator palati, glossopalatinus, and salpingopharyngeus via the pharyngeal plexus.

SENSORY NUCLEI AND FIBERS

Taste sensation. Within the nodose ganglion are cells whose dendrites carry taste impulses (special visceral afferent) from the region of the epiglottis. The axons of the ganglion cells terminate in that part of the nucleus solitarius near their level of entrance. From this nucleus, secondary taste fibers pass to the posteromedial ventral nucleus of the thalamus or to adjacent accessory semilunar nucleus though the course of such fibers is not accurately known. From the thalamus tertiary taste fibers pass to the foot of the postcentral gyrus.

Cutaneous sensation. From a small posteromedial strip of skin of the external ear, from the posteroinferior area of the external auditory meatus, and from the osseous portion of the posterior part of the external auditory canal, impulses pass over fibers (general somatic afferent) in the posterior auricular branch of the vagus. These fibers arise from cells located in the jugular ganglion. The central processes of the cells pass into the medulla in company with the emergent vagal motor fibers to synapse wholly or in part in the spinal nucleus of the trigeminal. Thence, secondary fibers pass in the quintothalamic tracts to the posteromedial ventral nucleus of the thalamus.

Visceral sensation. Sensory impulses (general visceral afferent) from the posterior oropharynx, larynx, and linings of thoracic and abdominal viscera travel over fibers of the vagus. These fibers arise from cells in the nodose ganglion. Central processes of these cells pass into the medulla in company with the other vagus fibers and terminate in the postvagal portion of the nucleus solitarius, sometimes referred to as the **dorsal sensory nucleus of the vagus** (Figs. 164, 165, 166). From here ascending fibers are presumed to pass to the thalamus, though the location of such fibers is unknown.

The impulses utilizing the vagus from the larynx and upper esophagus reach central neural levels of consciousness, in contrast to the majority of impulses arising from visceral structures. The greater number of pain impulses from thoracic and abdominal viscera travel with sympathetic autonomic nerves, it is to be recalled. Impulses arising from pressure endings and those other endings activated by deformation travel in part via the vagus. Impulses underlying the sensation of nausea are transmitted by the vagus.

An important component of the vagal visceral sensory system is the aortic or depressor nerve, probably represented in man in one of the cardiac nerves. The endings of this nerve are in the wall of the aortic arch and in the aortic body in the periaortic connective tissue, and they are receptive to pressor (rises in blood pressure) and chemical stimuli. By reflex diminution of the vasoconstrictor mechanism in the aorta a lowering in blood pressure may occur. With the carotid-sinus mechanisms this reflex is important in the regulation of blood pressure. Secondary neurons of the aortic depressor nerve are in the medullar tegmentum, near, or in, the nucleus solitarius.

FIBER CONNECTIONS OF THE VAGUS NUCLEI

The nucleus ambiguus receives short connecting fibers from the neighboring sensory nuclei, the spinal nucleus of the trigeminal and the nucleus of the tractus solitarius. These complete reflexes of swallowing and correlate laryngeal mechanisms. It is to be noted that many of the motor performances of the striated muscles innervated by the vagus are involuntary or reflex. From the cortex of both precentral gyri, corticobulbar fibers reach the nucleus ambiguus for instituting voluntary control of the pharynx and larynx. The path taken by some of these in Pick's bundle is of interest (Figs. 238, 241). Fibers from the tectum, tectobulbars, end in the nucleus ambiguus as do others from the hypothalamus and basal ganglia. The nucleus solitarius has connections with many medullar and spinal neurons (solitariospinal tracts) for completing such motor acts as swallowing, retching, and coughing. Other connections of the nucleus solitarius have been described previously.

The dorsal motor nucleus receives many fibers from the nucleus of the tractus solitarius and from those neurons receiving impulses via the carotid-sinus nerve and aortic depressor nerve. Fibers, whose definite path in the reticular formation is unknown, reach this nucleus from the hypothalamus. It is also under the control of the orbital region of the prefrontal cortex directly or indirectly (52).

CLINICAL DISORDERS OF THE VAGUS NERVE AND NUCLEI

Peripheral disturbances of a vagus nerve, except as they affect speech and respiration, are difficult to recognize unless they are bilateral. The same holds true for central or upper-motor-neuron lesions. In such case of bilateral disorder severe impairment of speech, deglutition, and respiration occurs. Loss of sense of taste over the epiglottis as a result of a lesion of the peripheral vagus probably would not be noticed by the patient. Laryngeal anesthesia resulting from vagal lesions is especially serious when both nerves are involved.

Unilateral nuclear lesions in the nucleus ambiguus may be incomplete or complete. Certain of the striated muscles innervated from it may be paralyzed while others escape. In complete lesions of the vagus nerve high in the neck, there should be ipsilateral paralysis of all the palatine muscles except the tensor, ipsilateral paralysis of the constrictors of the pharynx, and ipsilateral paralysis of the muscles of the larynx. Because of the palate paralysis the patient's speech may be nasal in quality, and he may complain of nasal regurgitation of liquids, especially, since he is unable to shut off completely the nasopharynx from the buccal cavity by contracting the hemiparetic soft palate. On observation of movements of the uvula, it will be seen to be pulled toward the side of the normally contracting levator palati. Some awkwardness of swallowing, especially of small bits of food or medicine, may be encountered because of the unilateral paralysis of the constrictors of the pharynx.

The paralysis of the laryngeal muscles is possibly of more clinical interest, and certain peculiar features have been described. It is frequently characteristic of vagal paralyses that the abductors of the larynx, the posterior cricoarytenoid muscles, are first paralyzed and the adductors are spared (Semon's law). As the paralysis becomes complete, the adductors are also paralyzed. With an inability to adduct the vocal cords the patient usually demonstrates speech disorder, a **dysphonia,** his voice being husky or hoarse. Laryngoscopic examination will reveal the paretic vocal cord to be in the so-called cadaveric position midway between adduction and abduction. The patient's hoarseness may be temporary, and subsequent laryngoscopic examination will usually give the explanation. The normal vocal cord will have adapted to the situation and moved somewhat toward the paretic one. These speech and laryngoscopic findings will usually be noted in paralysis of the recurrent laryngeal nerve alone. This nerve may be compressed by lymph-node masses in the neck or mediastinum or by an aneurysm of the aorta or of the right subclavian artery. It may also be injured in operations on the thyroid and parathyroid glands. It is to be recalled that the recurrent laryngeal nerve supplies motor innervation to all the muscles of the larynx except the cricothyroid, which is innervated by the superior laryngeal nerve. The sensory fibers of this latter nerve are numerous and are of practical importance since they innervate the mucous membranes of the larynx above the level of the vocal cords. The impulses they transmit usually reach conscious levels and also invoke reflex acts such as coughing in response to foreign particles in the larynx.

Bilateral vagus lesions increase the difficulties just described to follow ipsilateral lesions.

Nasal regurgitation is more distressing and permanent, and the palate reflex is absent. **Dysphagia** is more pronounced and speech and respiratory disorder may be profound. Respiratory disorder, induced by the paralysis of the abductor muscles bilaterally, may lead to suffocation unless treated by intubation. Bilateral palate paralyses may occur early in a **diphtheritic infection,** but more often occur in the second or third week of the disorder, perhaps as a local neuritis brought on by a local diffusion of the toxin of the organisms. In certain cases of **polyneuritis** and **poliomyelitis,** cranial-nerve motor nuclei, especially, are attacked in the brain stem, and facial, masticatory, pharyngeal, laryngeal, and glossal paralyses may occur. Occasionally prolonged dysphonia may occur in **hysteria** and in certain disorders of the laryngeal cartilages, *e.g.,* ankylosis (827).

Recognizable clinical signs resulting from the associated damage to the general visceral efferent (parasympathetic) fibers are few and are not likely to develop except in bilateral paralyses. Persistent tachycardia may sometimes occur along with laryngeal paralysis and has been seen in a case of tabetic neuropathy.

The vagus, like the glossopharyngeal, is damaged along with the other posterior cranial nerves usually, especially in disorders about the base of the skull or deep in the neck. Some of these will be mentioned later. Within the medulla the nucleus ambiguus may occasionally be damaged by softenings secondary to vascular disease. Disease of the **lateral artery of the medulla,** or of the **posterior inferior cerebellar** artery, may produce the softenings. Damaged along with the nucleus ambiguus may be the lateral spinothalamic tract and the spinal nucleus of the trigeminal, spinocerebellar tracts, and descending autonomic and extrapyramidal tracts in the tegmentum. In such a lesion, the patient would have ipsilateral palatal, pharyngeal, and laryngeal paralysis; ipsilateral disorder of cutaneous sensation over the face, especially for pain and temperature; contralateral impairment of pain and temperature sensation over the body and limbs; and a Horner's syndrome and various vasomotor changes ipsilaterally. In **syringobulbia,** linear, slitlike cavities may involve the nucleus ambiguus and the spinal trigeminal nucleus.

Rarely a patient may develop a **neuralgia** of a branch of the vagus, especially of the superior laryngeal nerve (229). Usually there is a trigger zone in the pyriform sinus from which the pain paroxysm may be set off. The act of swallowing may set it off, and the pain, usually lancinating in character, radiates unilaterally from the side of the thyroid cartilage to the angle of the jaw and sometimes to the ear. The vagus, it is to be recalled, furnishes sensory innervation to certain cutaneous parts of the external ear. The paroxysms of pain may last from a few seconds to a minute, and in the intervals between paroxysms the patient is usually free of pain. Section of the superior laryngeal nerve is helpful in relieving the pain.

In elderly people, with arteriosclerotic changes which are sufficient to lead to inadequate blood flow to neural tissue, the corticobulbar fibers are occasionally damaged bilaterally, and one sees thus upper-motor-neuron disorders of trigeminal, facial, vagal, and hypoglossal mechanisms. Voluntary masticatory, facial, pharyngeal, laryngeal, and glossal movements are slowly, but progressively, impaired. Some reflex activity may remain. Such a disease is called **pseudobulbar palsy.** When the neurons of the cranial nerve motor nuclei are destroyed in the chronic **bulbar palsy,** similar disorders of all these mechanisms are encountered. In this disease, however, a lower-motor-neuron disorder, the muscles atrophy and all movements are eventually lost. A counterpart of this disease, involving spinal motor neurons, is progressive spinal muscular atrophy.

Spinal Accessory Nerve

This nerve, considered by most observers to be a pure motor nerve, has two divisions, one which arises from cells situated in the medulla, and one which springs from cells in the dorsolateral portion of the anterior gray column of cells in the upper cervical region of the spinal cord (761). It is said, then, to have bulbar and spinal components. The spinal portion emerges from a position on the lateral side of the spinal cord midway between points of entry and emergence of the cervical posterior and anterior roots, respectively. The bulbar portion arises from the medulla in close connection with the vagus nerve as described above.

The **bulbar** portion itself is of two divisions, one (general visceral efferent) distributing with the vagus to thoracic and abdominal viscera, the other (special visceral efferent) supplying the striated muscles of the larynx. The first portion, a component of the **parasympathetic** autonomic system, arises from cells in the dorsal motor nucleus of the vagus, which is dorsal and lateral to the hypoglossal nucleus. These axons arising from cells of the dorsal motor nucleus are joined in the reticular substance by axons (special visceral efferent) from cells in the caudal portion of the nucleus ambiguus (Figs. 164, 165, 166). Together, these two sets of axons form the internal or bulbar ramus of the accessory, and pass lateralward, ventral to the spinal nucleus of the trigeminal, to emerge from the surface of the medulla, in close association with the vagus-nerve rootlets. They are joined here briefly by the spinal portion of the nerve described below. Those axons arising in the dorsal motor nucleus are **preganglionic** parasympathetic and soon leave the common accessory trunk to join the vagus and to be distributed with it. They terminate about postganglionic neurons in ganglia either in or near the viscus innervated. From this latter site the **postganglionic** fibers pass directly into muscle or gland substances. Those axons from the nucleus ambiguus are likewise distributed with the vagus but go to striated muscles, the muscles of the larynx.

The **spinal** portion (special visceral efferent) of the spinal accessory nerve arises from large motor cells in the upper five or six cervical spinal-cord segments, as described above, and emerges in three or four rootlets. In the caudal end of the nucleus the cells of origin are located laterally in the anterior columns; in the rostral end, they are scattered in the medial intermediate columns. The rootlets join in the vertebral canal, and enter the skull through the foramen magnum to join briefly the bulbar portion (Figs. 42, 141). This latter portion almost immediately joins the vagus, as described above.

The axons of spinal origin pass down the neck to supply the sternocleidomastoid and trapezius muscles. In their course through the neck and beneath the edge of the trapezius they are usually joined with cervical fibers of the third and fourth roots. Fibers of the second and third cervical nerves also enter the sternocleidomastoid. These cervical contributions, in man, may be both motor and sensory or only sensory. The sensory fibers include proprioceptive-impulse transmitters from the muscles as well as cutaneous sensory fibers from the skin overlying the trapezius. Many studies regarding sensory components of the spinal accessory nerve itself have been made (175). Clusters of ganglion cells are scattered along the intracranial and extracranial portions of the nerve, and in the macaque and cat, they undergo chromatolysis when the nerve is sectioned distal to them.

The exact distribution to the trapezius of the spinal accessory and the motor cervical spinal nerve fibers is unknown. It is not possible to arrive at a uniform plan of distribution on the basis of the reported distribution of paralysis in the trapezius after spinal accessory injury. Some authors report that the cervical nerves supply chiefly the upper part of the trapezius; others report that these nerves are distributed only to the lower two-thirds or one-half of the muscle. In some individuals it would appear that the spinal accessory alone supplies the upper part of the muscle and is joined by cervical fibers in the innervation of the lower part. The reverse of this pattern may also exist, there being a dual innervation of the upper part of the muscle. In still other individuals it would appear that the cervical nerve fibers do not contribute any motor fibers to the trapezius, the motor innervation of the entire muscle being dependent on the spinal accessory nerve. A considerable individual variation in the innervation of the trapezius may very well exist. In some individuals parts of it may receive a dual motor innervation; in others, its motor innervation may be a single one.

The central connections of the dorsal motor and ambiguus nuclei have been described above with the discussions of the vagus and glossopharyngeal nerves. The spinal nucleus receives collaterals from sensory roots entering at the cervical spinal level. It also receives fibers via olivospinal, tectospinal, medial longitudinal fasciculus, rubroreticulospinal, and corticobulbar tracts. These last arise in the shoulder area of the precentral gyri of contralateral and especially ipsilateral motor cortex.

DISORDERS OF THE SPINAL ACCESSORY NUCLEI AND THEIR FIBERS

Disorders involving the dorsal motor nucleus or its axons are difficult to verify, as mentioned in the discussion of vagus symptomatology. Disorders involving the nucleus ambiguus or the spinal accessory nerve fibers arising there give some difficulty in swallowing, speech, and respiration depending on the amount of damage. These also have been described above.

Nuclear lesions of the spinal nucleus, especially if associated, as is likely, with disease of the cervical anterior gray columns, usually lead to complete paralysis of the sternocleidomastoid and trapezius muscles of the same side. If the nerve fibers are injured soon after they emerge from the jugular foramen a complete or incomplete paralysis of sternocleidomastoid and trapezius results. The spinal accessory is most often severed in its rather superficial course posterior to the sternocleidomastoid, and trapezius paralysis alone is most often seen. The trapezius paralysis, for example, may be incomplete by virtue of an undamaged cervical spinal motor innervation to the muscle. Wasting and paralysis may be more severe in the upper part of the muscle in some individuals, in the lower part in others, and of uniform degree throughout the muscle in still others.

Paralysis of the sternocleidomastoid of one side results in weakness of head rotation (face) to the opposite side. Paralysis of both sternocleidomastoids produces an inability to hold the head erect or to raise it from a recumbent position. Paralysis of the trapezius leads to a dropping of the shoulder and a displacement of the scapula downward and outward. Elevation of the shoulder is weakened, and true abduction of the arm above 90 deg. is not possible.

Disturbances interrupting the fibers (upper-motor-neuron lesion) passing to the various spinal accessory nerve nuclei from higher centers are difficult to recognize and are usually slight, unless the fibers are injured bilaterally. Various involuntary movements of the sternocleidomastoid may arise in association with movements of other axial or limb muscles as a result of damage to some of the fibers from the basal ganglia. **Torticollis** is such a condition, and in this disorder the head is repeatedly involuntarily rotated so that the face is turned to the side of the normally innervated muscle. The hyperactive muscle stands out as a large cord in the patient's neck. The awkward position may be maintained for some time. Spasmodic torticollis may be an isolated muscular dysfunction in certain patients suffering with some of the neuroses or with an extrapyramidal disorder, and the movements are usually aggravated at times of emotional stress. Steps to correct the condition have included cutting the nerve intracranially and extracranially, alone or in association with section of the upper three cervical anterior roots. The sternocleidomastoid has also been severed.

The Hypoglossal Nerve

Whereas in certain lower animals the hypoglossal nucleus is for the most part located in the cervical spinal cord, in man it has been separated from the spinal-cord region and is placed in the medulla, beneath the floor of the fourth ventricle, as a mid-line nucleus that extends as far rostral as the cephalic pole of the dorsal vagus nucleus (Figs. 128, 141, 150, 164, 165, 166). The points of emergence of the roots have also advanced rostrally. This forward shifting serves to bring the hypoglossal neurons nearer medullar nuclei, general sensory and gustatory, receiving impulses from the mouth which are responsible for certain of the reflex mechanisms of the tongue. With this forward shifting of the nucleus in man, it no longer gives rise to the descendens hypoglossi root, but these fibers arise from the cervical spinal cord and merely travel with the hypoglossal nerve a short distance within the neck. Fibers from the first and second cervical nerves compose the descendens hypoglossi. After traveling a short distance with the hypoglossal they break away, usually to unite with a descending cervical root to form a loop, the ansa hypoglossi, from which the infrahyoid muscles are supplied.

The **hypoglossal trigone** serves as a landmark for identifying the main mass of cells of the hypoglossal nuclei (Fig. 123). The axons of these large motor cells, general somatic efferent, pass ventrolaterally just medial to the inferior olives. The nerve passes through the hypoglossal foramen into the neck and thence

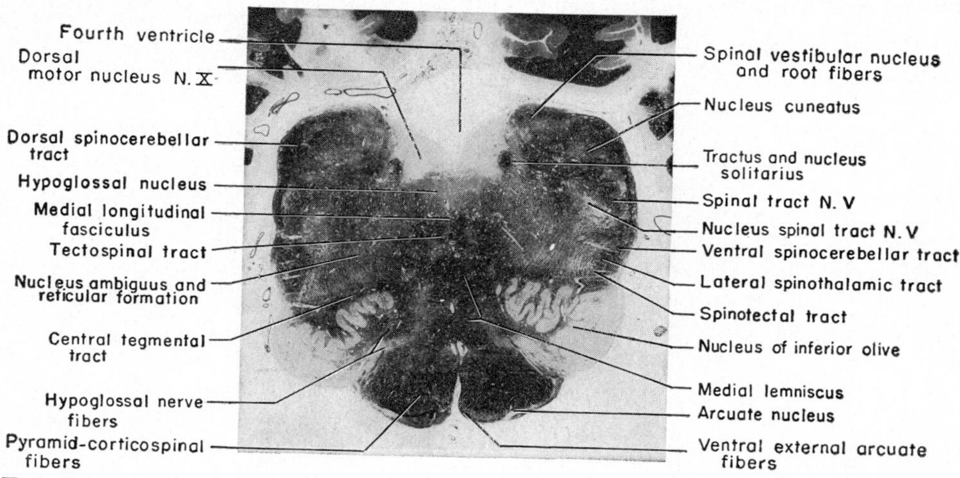

FIG. 166. Transverse section, A 245, of human brain stem, just rostral to decussation of pyramids. Weigert. Photograph, ×3.5.

to the tongue to supply the styloglossus, hyoglossus, genioglossus, geniohyoid, and the intrinsic musculature.

In its course through the neck the hypoglossal is closely related to the other posterior cranial nerves, the superior cervical sympathetic ganglion, the internal carotid artery, and internal jugular vein. Nearer its terminal distribution it is adjacent to the external carotid and lingual arteries in its course.

It is possible that not all the fibers of a hypoglossal nerve are somatic motor ones. Several other nuclei near the hypoglossal nucleus have been thought to contribute fibers to the hypoglossal nerve. One of these, lying immediately ventral to the main hypoglossal nucleus, is the **nucleus of Roller.** This nucleus has been considered to be of autonomic character because of its connections with the dorsal longitudinal fasciculus of Schütz. It seems probable that some vasomotor fibers join the hypoglossal nerve from the superior cervical sympathetic ganglion, as the two are closely associated in the neck. Vasodilator fibers to the blood vessels of the tongue appear to run in the facial nerve (177).

Whether or not **sensory** fibers are present as true components of the hypoglossal nerves themselves is a moot point. The only type of sensory fibers usually considered present are those for **proprioceptive** impulses, although the characteristic neuromuscular spindles have not been found in the extrinsic tongue muscles. A special type of flower-spray muscle spindle in the genioglossus has been described, however (828). Recent studies of newborn fetuses' and adult human brains have revealed sensory-type neurons along the intramedullary course of the hypoglossal nerve as it passes between the pyramid and inferior olivary nucleus. In the adult the majority of the cells are unipolar, and the possibility of their being proprioceptive is entertained (603). It is possible, however, that the proprioceptive sensation of the tongue is transmitted by other nerves, cranial or cervical spinal. The lingual nerve has been suggested as the transmitter from the anterior two-thirds of the tongue on the basis of clinical and physiological evidence (828). The cervical nerves may also contribute fibers via their association with the hypoglossal to form the ansa hypoglossi. Sensory fibers of cervical origin travel with the hypoglossal to supply **pain sensibility** to the posterior-fossa meninges, and irritation of them by posterior-fossa tumors gives neck pain.

FIBER CONNECTIONS FOR HYPOGLOSSAL NUCLEI

Incoming connections consist of short paths from nearby centers and longer paths from higher centers. Prominent fibers of the former type come from the nucleus of the tractus solitarius and others come from the trigeminal spinal nucleus for the completion of reflex arcs involving movements of the tongue. The medial longitudinal fasciculus gives to the nuclei, and receives from them, fibers which connect the tongue nuclei with other motor nuclei of the medulla; *e.g.,* with the facial motor nucleus. Corticobulbar fibers from each motor cortex, but especially the opposite, go to each hypoglossal nucleus, thus putting the tongue under voluntary control. Fibers from extrapyramidal nuclei also reach the hypoglossal nucleus.

CLINICAL DISORDERS OF THE HYPOGLOSSAL AND OTHER POSTERIOR CRANIAL NERVES

Peripheral, or lower-motor-neuron, hypoglossal injury may occur with nuclear or nerve damage. The hypoglossal nuclei or the nerve fibers in their intramedullary course may be involved in vascular disorders affecting the anterior spinal artery at a medullar level. Usually the medial lemniscus and pyramidal fibers are also damaged, and such a patient with a unilateral lesion would show paralysis of the ipsilateral half of the tongue, contralateral loss of deep sensibility over the body and limbs, and contralateral impairment of voluntary movement. With this lower-motor-neuron hypoglossal lesion, the tongue would demonstrate small fascicular quiverings and would subsequently atrophy on the paralyzed side. While at rest the tongue would be seen to be deviated within the mouth *toward* the *sound side* through the pull of the normal styloglossus. When protruded the tongue would *deviate to* the *paralyzed side* through the unopposed pull of the normal genioglossus. Such deviation of the tongue on protrusion to the paralyzed side, together with the atrophy and fasciculation, is frequently helpful in localizing the site of damage to the neural axis.

Bilateral nuclear lesions may occur as a result of tumor compression, in **bulbar palsy,** or in the bulbar type of **poliomyelitis.** Profound speech disorder, dysarthria, and masticatory difficulty result. The paralyzed tongue may fall back into the pharynx and produce obstruction to the respiratory passage.

The hypoglossal nerve is seldom involved alone in disease processes, though isolated hypoglossal injury may be seen as a result of trauma such as gunshot or stab wound. The hypoglossal nerve may be compressed by developmental bony anomalies in the region of the foramen magnum, such as **platybasia.** Usually the spinal accessory, some upper cervical spinal roots, spinal cord, medulla, and cerebellum may also be compressed, and many neurological signs will appear. In some patients, with or without a bony defect, the medulla and cerebellum may be displaced into the spinal canal and a kinking of medulla and upper cervical spinal cord occurs, as in the **Arnold-Chiari anomalies.** Such displacement may occur through the pull of bands of connective tissue anchored below to the vertebral canal, in which there are also occasionally anomalies of development, such as a spina bifida or a fusion of one or more vertebrae with a shortening of the neck (Klippel-Feil anomaly).

Within the neck the hypoglossal nerve may be damaged along with the other posterior cranial nerves (788). The retroparotid space, through which the nerves course, may be the site of abscess or tumor formation. This space is bounded posteriorly by the cervical spine; internally, by the pharynx; anteriorly, by the internal prolongation of the parotid and the muscles attached to the styloid process; and above, by the base of the skull in the region of the jugular foramen. In the upper part of the space the glossopharyngeal, vagus, and spinal accessory may be damaged. This would be comparable to a **jugular foramen syndrome,** and the most striking signs would be nasal regurgitation of fluids, because of palatal paralysis; dysphagia of solids, due to paralysis of pharynx; hoarseness, because of laryngeal paralysis; and drooping of the shoulder, because of trapezius paralysis.

With more inferiorly placed lesions in the retroparotid space, hypoglossal and sympathetic disorders would be added to the signs described above. Paralysis of the tongue on the side of the disorder and an ipsilateral Horner's syndrome, including ptosis of the eyelid, miosis, and anhidrosis over the face, would be observed. In addition to these cranial-nerve signs, indications of compression of the large vessels of the neck might be observed. Compression of the internal jugular vein near the foramen magnum might lead to increased intracranial pressure, depending on the anatomical arrangement of the intracranial venous sinuses.

Upper-motor-neuron paralysis of the tongue may be unilateral or bilateral, and with such disorders pathways to other cranial nerves are usually involved. **Pseudobulbar palsy** has already been described. With this bilateral upper-motor-neuron disorder, the voluntary movements of the tongue are greatly impaired. Muscle atrophy and fibrillations do not usually occur, and this serves to differentiate the type of paralysis and aids in localizing the lesion.

CHAPTER 10

THE VESTIBULAR SYSTEM

As one pursues his everyday activities in walking or sitting quietly he constantly strives, albeit to a great extent automatically, to maintain his equilibrium through all the alterations of posture. Movements of the eyes are coordinated with movements of the head, and as the latter turns from one position to another the eyes make adjustments necessary to maintain a fixation of the gaze. The alignment of the trunk naturally follows the movements of the head, as postures are smoothly altered and equilibrium maintained. Underlying these head, eye, and trunk coordinations, in the maintenance of posture, are impulses from the retinas, the muscles and joints, the body surface, and the labyrinth. The proprioceptive nerves and pathways of the spinal cord conduct these impulses to spinal, brain stem, and cortical levels from muscles and joints, and to some extent from body surface. The vestibular nerve conducts the impulses from the labyrinth. Through the central connections of this nerve the labyrinthine impulses effect many of the necessary postural adjustments for maintaining the equilibrium. The mechanics of the vestibular system may be observed in the reaction of a normal individual to being rotated and, for example, in the subjection of the steer when the cowboy secures its head and vigorously twists it. Impulses set up in the neck muscles of the steer also play a part, however.

The vestibular nerve and its central connections are therefore essential parts of the proprioceptive system. "Primary" neurons are located in the vestibular ganglion, and their peripheral processes end around hair cells in the maculae of the utricle and saccule, and in the ampullar cristae of the semicircular canals. The macular impulses arise primarily as a result of linear movement or changes in head position, the impulses from the canals chiefly through rotatory or angular acceleration. "Secondary" neurons, about which the central processes of the vestibular ganglion cells end, are located in the four vestibular nuclei in the medulla, and in certain basal parts of the cerebellum. From these neurons "secondary" fibers pass up and down the brain stem in the medial longitudinal fasciculus and in vestibuloreticular tracts principally, down into the spinal cord in the vestibulospinal tracts, medial and lateral, and some go into the cerebellum. Other "secondary" fibers probably pass to the thalamus and to certain cranial-nerve motor nuclei, the glossopharyngeal and vagus particularly. Cortical vestibular centers are thought to exist; some authors assign one to the temporal lobe, and others have evidence of vestibular representation in frontal and parietal lobes. Through the medial longitudinal fasciculus, the vestibular proprioceptive impulses can coordinate movements of the head and eyes, and through the vestibulospinal tracts, movements of the head, neck, and trunk and alterations of muscle tone.

The Labyrinth

The internal ear, or labyrinth, located within the petrous portion of the temporal bone, has two component parts, the osseous labyrinth and the membranous labyrinth (Figs. 167, 168). The membranous labyrinth rests inside the osseous, and its contour in general is similar to that of the osseous labyrinth; it is separated from the latter by a fluid-containing space, the perilymphatic space, with **perilymph,** except where the two are fused. The membranous labyrinth contains **endolymph,** and the osseous can be said to contain, therefore, perilymph.

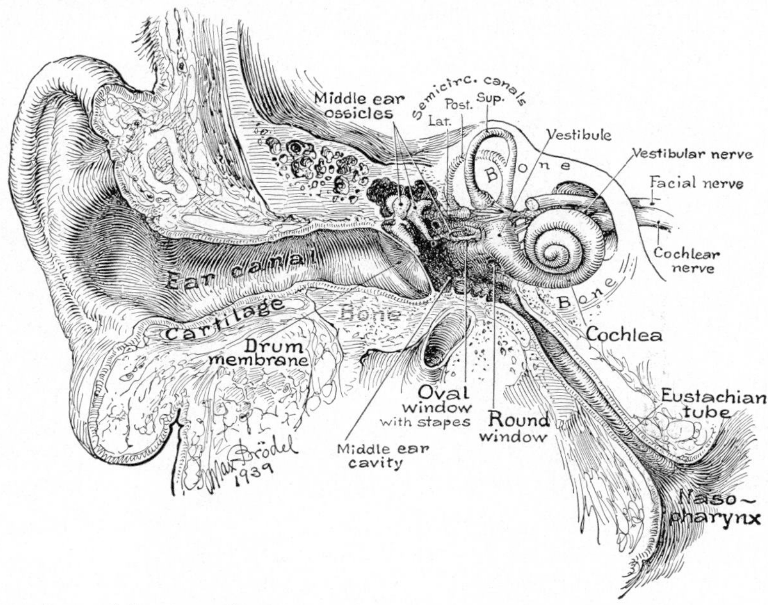

FIG. 167. The gross anatomy of the external, middle, and internal ear. (*After Brödel, courtesy of W. B. Saunders Company.*)

THE OSSEOUS LABYRINTH

This has three divisions, the **vestibule,** the **semicircular canals,** and the **cochlea** which in turn is divided into the **scala tympani** and **scala vestibuli.** It is only with the vestibule and semicircular canals and their membranous counterparts that the present discussion is concerned. The middle ear connects with the osseous vestibule by way of the oval window. Opening also into the osseous vestibule are the semicircular canals, the vestibular aqueduct, and the osseous cochlea. On the medial wall of the osseous vestibule, posteriorly and superiorly, the elliptical recess is for the utricle; anteriorly and inferiorly, the spherical recess is for the saccule. Smaller openings accommodate the nerves entering to supply the various portions of the membranous labyrinth. The bony labyrinth is lined with endosteum which encloses the perilymphatic space, filled with connective tissue trabeculae and fluid.

THE MEMBRANOUS LABYRINTH

This is suspended by the trabeculae in this space except where it is attached to bone (Fig. 168). The membranous cochlear duct and semicircular canals follow closely the outline of their bony containers; the membranous vestibular components, however, do not (Fig. 168). The latter are the **utricle,** the **saccule,** the **ductus reuniens,** and the **endolymphatic duct.** The **ductus reuniens** continues from the anteroinferior surface of the saccule to open near the blind end of the **membranous cochlear duct,** the so-called **vestibular cecum.** The **endolymphatic duct** arises from the saccule and it is also connected with the utricle by way of a very narrow channel (Fig. 168). The relationship of the wall of the utricle to the connection with the endolymphatic duct is such that a valve is produced to guard the opening (35). The endolymphatic duct shows in its course three dilatations joined by a narrow channel (Fig. 169). The second and third, or terminal, dilatations show much folding of the walls, which together with the surrounding connective tissues and blood vessels would appear to serve as absorptive devices (484). The endolymphatic duct extends through the **vestibular aqueduct** and ends in a blind sac, the **endolymphatic sac.** This sac, lined with low columnar epithelium, represents the third dilatation in the duct, and it rests on the posterior surface of the petrous bone within the layers of the dura mater. Its inner lining surface shows many folds.

Within the membranous labyrinth, a fluid,

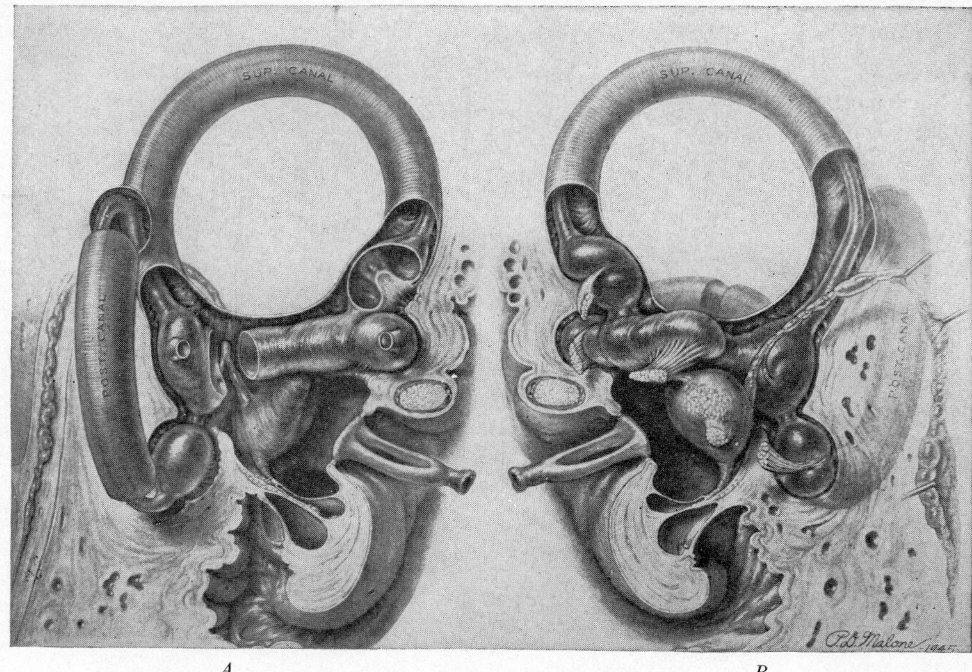

A *B*

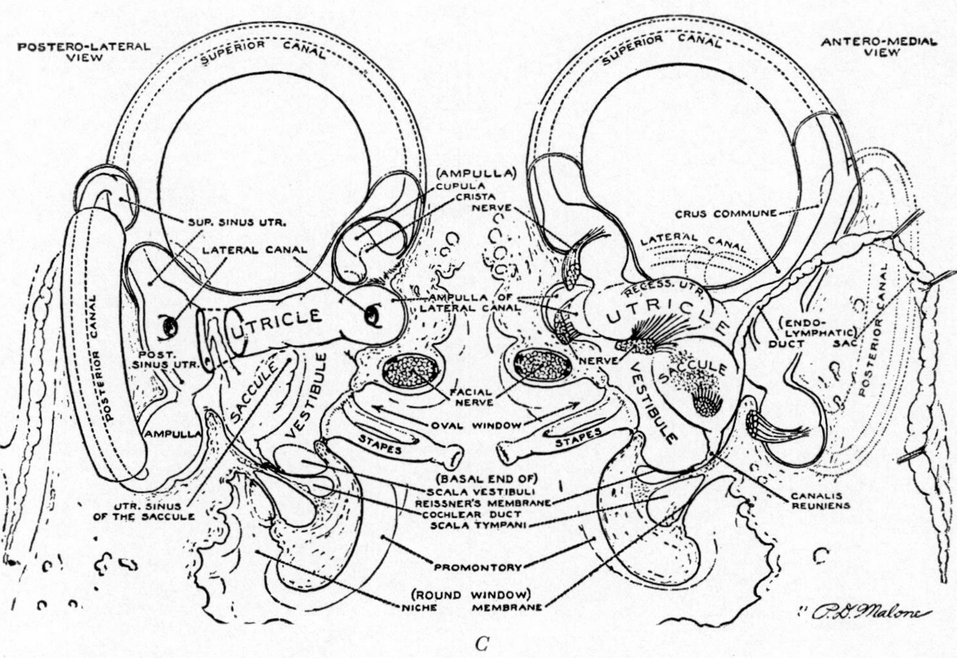

C

Fig. 168. The right membranous labyrinth of the human. *A*, postero-lateral view; *B*, antero-medial view; *C*, sketch to indicate labels of *A* and *B*. (*After Brödel and Malone, courtesy of W. B. Saunders Company.*)

endolymph, is present, as mentioned previously (Fig. 170). Guild has described endolymph formation and circulation (321). It is formed as a filtrate or transudate in the vascular layer of the membranous cochlear duct. It circulates toward the basal end of the cochlear duct and through the ductus reuniens into the saccule. From this the flow is into the endolymphatic duct and into the endolymphatic sac. It is absorbed through the walls of the dilated portions of the duct and the walls of the sac into the many small blood vessels in the surrounding connective tissue. Active circulation through the utricle (and semicircular canals) apparently takes place only at certain times. The absorption of the endolymph through the endolymphatic sac is important in the regulation of endolymphatic pressure. Increased endolymphatic pressure may cause dilation of the endolymphatic sac and absorption of fluid, whereby the pressure is reduced. Increased intracranial pressure, on the other hand, through compression of the endolymphatic sac in the dura, may cause increased pressure within the internal ear.

The perilymphatic space has been considered usually to be in open connection with the subarachnoid space through the **cochlear aqueduct,** opening from the floor of the scala tympani of the osseous cochlea and extending to the lower surface of the petrous portion of

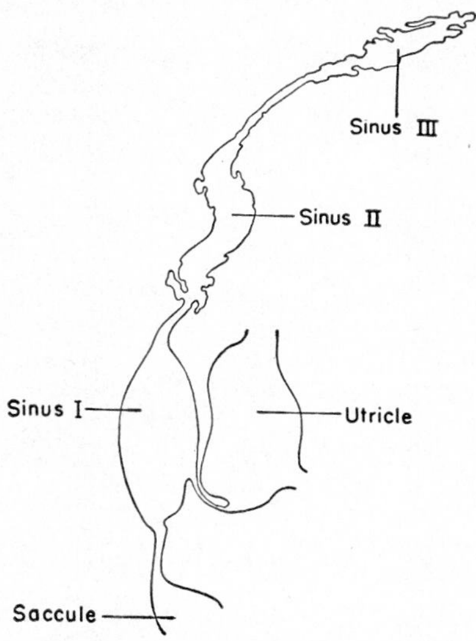

FIG. 169. Diagram of the human utriculosaccular duct. (*After Anson and Nesselrod, Arch. Otolaryng., vol.* 24.)

the temporal bone near the jugular bulb. Recent studies have served to demonstrate that a barrier membrane separates the lumen of the cochlear aqueduct from the scala tympani perilymphatic space. The presence of such a membrane will therefore prevent a free flow of cerebrospinal fluid into the perilymphatic spaces as some investigators have described. Any exchange of fluid that takes place between

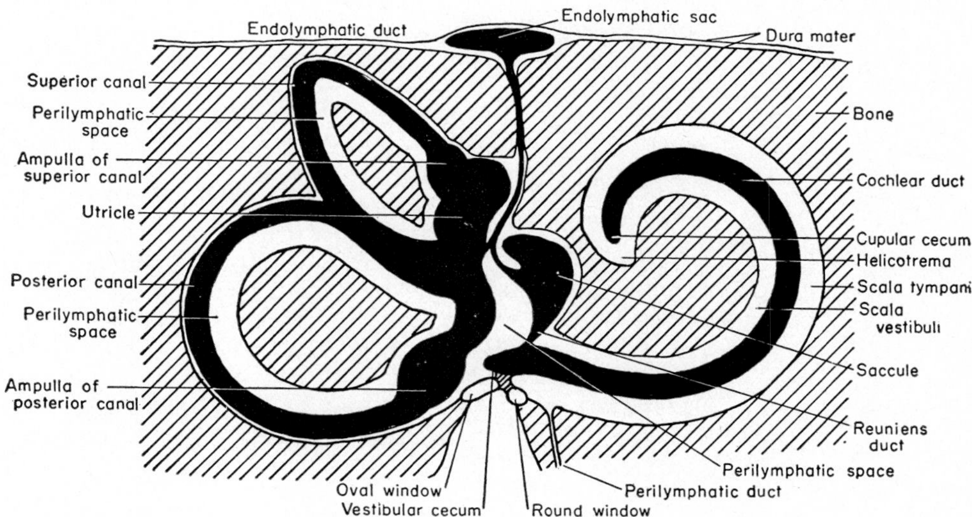

FIG. 170. Diagram of the right bony and membranous labyrinth. The endolymphatic spaces are in black. (*Redrawn after Spalteholz, "Hand Atlas of Human Anatomy," courtesy of J. B. Lippincott Company.*)

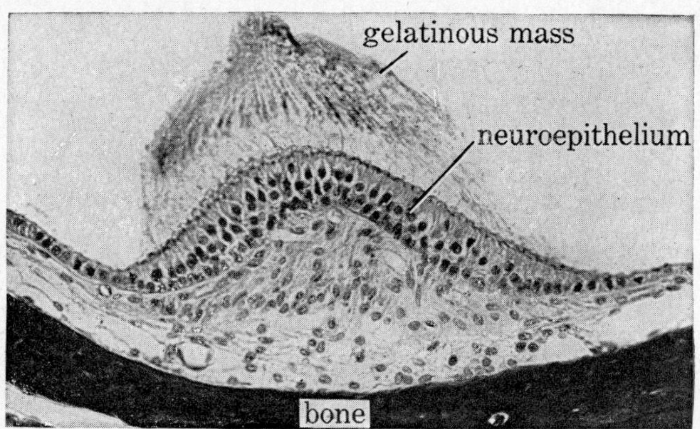

FIG. 171. Ampullary crista of the posterior semicircular canal; guinea-pig labyrinth. The gelatinous mass containing processes of hair cells has shrunk in fixation of the tissues. Photomicrograph, ×90. (*From Nonidez and Windle, "Textbook of Histology," courtesy of McGraw-Hill Book Company, Inc.*)

perilymphatic spaces and subarachnoid spaces must necessarily occur by diffusion through the barrier membrane of the cochlear aqueduct (809). The perilymph is therefore similar to, but not identical with, cerebrospinal fluid. An exchange of fluids by osmosis is thought to take place between the perilymphatic space and endolymphatic space, the fluid traversing the walls of the membranous labyrinth. Perilymph may thus be derived also from endolymph.

The three semicircular canals, located in planes perpendicular to one another, are superior (**frontal, anterior**), inferior (**sagittal, posterior**), and external (**lateral, horizontal**) (Fig. 168). The external canals of the two sides run for the most part in a similar plane, the superior canal of one side with the inferior of the other. Three physiological groups of canals result, therefore, since canals in the same plane are stimulated simultaneously. The canals show at one end a dilation, the **ampulla,** and are smooth at the other. Each ampullar end opens separately into the vestibule; the smooth ends of the superior and posterior canals have a common opening; the external, a separate one. There are, therefore, five canal connections with the vestibule. The ampullae of the superior and external canals are somewhat frontally placed; that of the inferior canal, posteriorly.

The epithelium lining the membranous semi-

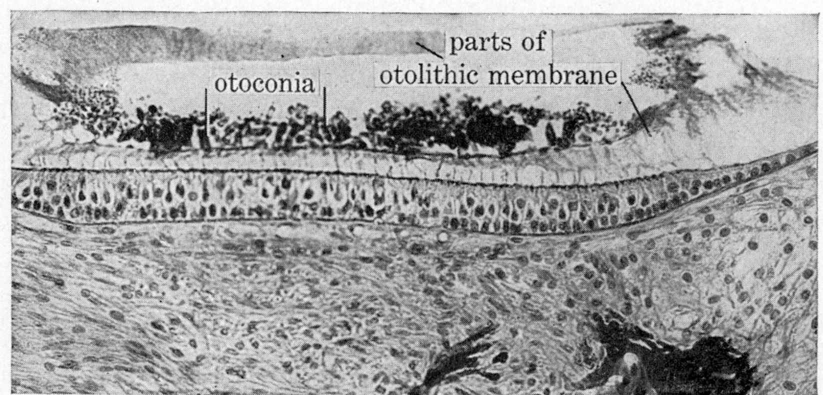

FIG. 172. Macula of the utricle; guinea-pig labyrinth. The otolithic membrane has been deformed in preservation of the tissues; otoconia are present. Photomicrograph, ×90. (*After Nonidez and Windle, "Textbook of Histology," courtesy of McGraw-Hill Book Company, Inc.*)

circular canals is low in type and rests upon a subjacent basement membrane and vascular connective-tissue layer. In the ampullae the three layers are thickened and are thrown up into a ridge, the **crista,** directed transversely across the ampullae (Fig. 171). The endings of the vestibular nerve are directed to the crista. The epithelium in the crista is columnar and is composed of two kinds of cells, slender supporting cells and flask-shaped sensory (receptor) hair cells. A gelatinous membrane, the **cupula,** rests on and between the hairs of these cells, and fluid movements of the endolymph through the ampullae cause deflections of the hairs and consequent stimulation.

The utricle and saccule are also lined by simple low epithelium (Fig. 172). Flat thickenings of their walls, the **maculae,** toward which the nerve fibers are directed, are found in each sac. The longitudinal axes of the maculae are approximately perpendicular to each other. With the head erect the longitudinal axis of the macula sacculi is about vertical, the axis of the macula utriculi, about horizontal. In the maculae, as in the cristae, the epithelium is columnar and is composed of the supporting and the sensory (receptor) hair cells. A gelatinous membrane lies over and between the hairs of the hair cells, and embedded in the gelatinous substance are the minute calcareous crystals, the **otoliths** or **otoconia.**

Vestibular Nerve and Nuclei

The vestibular nerve is composed of an inferior and a superior branch in the distal part of the internal auditory canal. These two divisions arise from bipolar neurons in the inferior and superior portions of the vestibular ganglion of Scarpa (Fig. 3*A*). The dendrites composing the peripheral inferior division terminate about hair cells in the macula sacculi and the crista of the posterior canal. Those composing the peripheral superior division end about hair cells in the macula utriculi, cristae of the superior and external canals, and macula sacculi. The axons of the bipolar cells in the two divisions of the vestibular ganglion pass centrally in the internal auditory canal, and the two branches are united into the vestibular nerve (Fig. 161). This enters the medulla medially and cephalad to the cochlear division of the eighth nerve.

As the vestibular nerve approaches the medulla there is a graded loss of the neurolemma about its component fibers. This is replaced on the various fibers at once by glial elements. At the point of change there is also a final interruption in the myelin sheath of the nerve fibers as a **node of Ranvier.** This zone of change is the **Obersteiner-Redlich zone,** and at this point the glia tends to form a septum against the connective tissue of the peripheral portion. These anatomical changes in the fibers are perhaps fundamental in the explanation of susceptibility of the eighth nerve to toxins and infections.

The vestibular-nerve fibers entering the medulla terminate for the most part in the vestibular nuclei; a few pass through the nuclei into the cerebellum directly. The vestibular nuclei are the **medial** or **Schwalbe**'s nucleus, the **superior** or **Bechterew's,** the **lateral** or **Deiters',** and the **descending** or **spinal.**

The medial vestibular nucleus lies near the floor of the fourth ventricle at the level of entrance of the vestibular root, just medial to Deiters' nucleus, which itself is medial to the inferior cerebellar peduncle (Figs. 173, 174). The medial nucleus extends rostrally to a plane through the abducens nucleus and caudally to a plane through the rostral tip of the hypoglossal nucleus. The lateral nucleus is limited rostrally by the superior nucleus and caudally by the spinal nucleus, both of which have the same general lateral position. The rostral and caudal limits of these three lateral nuclear masses are variable. Rostrally, the superior usually extends to a plane through the caudal border of the main sensory nucleus of the trigeminal, and the spinal extends caudally to about the same level (cephalic tip of the hypoglossal nucleus) as the medial nucleus.

After their entrance into the medulla most of the vestibular fibers divide into two branches, ascending and descending. From the ascending divisions a few fibers pass directly into the basal part of the cerebellum, traveling there just medial to the main body of the inferior cerebellar peduncle, in the restiform and juxtarestiform bodies. Within the cerebellum, the direct vestibular nerve fibers end in the nodulus, uvula, lingula, and fastigial nucleus. Most of the ascending vestibular fibers end in the superior and medial vestibular nuclei. Collaterals

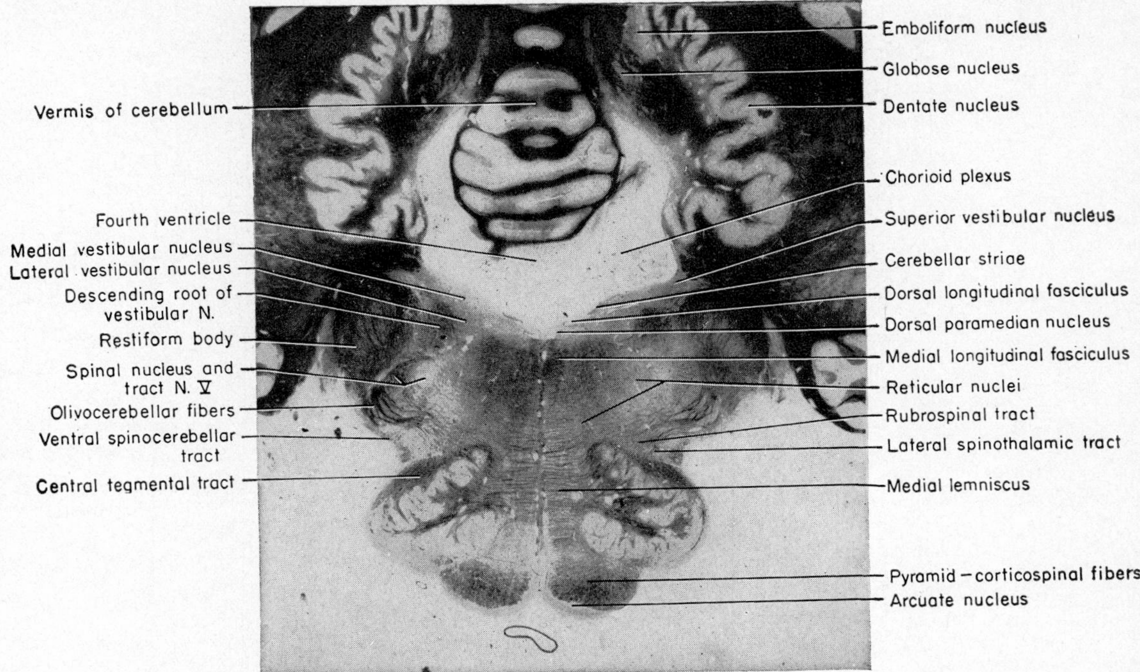

Fig. 173. Transverse section, A 418, of human brain stem through rostral end of medulla. Weigert. Photograph, ×2.5.

from ascending branches end in the lateral nucleus. Descending fibers distribute to the spinal vestibular nucleus. Some of the vestibular root fibers may cross to end in contralateral nuclei.

Secondary Vestibular Connections

DESCENDING

The lateral vestibular nucleus is the principal origin of the **lateral vestibulospinal tract,** chiefly an uncrossed tract (Fig. 93). This tract runs in the ventral funiculus of the spinal cord and terminates about anterior column cells at all cord levels. Through it the vestibular nuclei can facilitate the activity of spinal motor neurons.

The lateral nucleus probably also sends fibers into the medial longitudinal fasciculus of each side, as **medial vestibulospinal tracts.** The medial and spinal vestibular nuclei contribute crossed fibers to this tract also. Many of these fibers terminate about anterior column cells at cervical spinal-cord levels; relays from this cervical level transmit vestibular influence to thoracic and lumbar levels. These descending fibers transmit impulses useful in the organization of certain postural reflexes.

ASCENDING

Many ascending secondary vestibular fibers reach the motor nuclei of cranial nerves innervating the eye muscles, and the majority of these travel in the medial longitudinal fasciculi (Fig. 173). Fibers from the superior nucleus enter the homolateral fasciculus; those from the medial and spinal nuclei, the contralateral fasciculus. From the superior nuclei other uncrossed **vestibulomesencephalic fibers** to these ocular-muscle nuclei ascend in the dorsolateral part of the tegmentum. The superior nucleus also sends fibers into reticular nuclei adjacent to the medial longitudinal tract. Other **vestibuloreticular** fibers, to reticular nuclei of both sides of the brain stem, arise chiefly from the medial nucleus. The vagus and glossopharyngeal nuclei receive vestibular impulses via the vestibuloreticular tracts. Observation of an individual suffering with motion sickness will verify this, as indicated by the vomiting.

Secondary **vestibulocerebellar** fibers arise in

the superior, medial, and spinal nuclei. Traversing the medial part of the ipsilateral restiform body, the juxtarestiform body, they enter the cerebellum to end in the flocculus, nodulus, and fastigial nuclei.

The vestibular nuclei receive impulses from the cerebellum by way of the fastigiobulbar tract, uncinate fasciculus, and angular bundle (Fig. 174). These are derived from the fastigial nuclei of the same and opposite side, from the flocculus, nodulus, uvula, pyramis, and anterior lobe.

Higher vestibular connections are not definitely known, but many have been reported. The thalamus ("mediocaudal" part) may receive vestibular fibers directly from the medial longitudinal fasciculus; the lateral ventral nucleus of the thalamus may also receive vestibular impulses indirectly via the dentatorubrothalamic system in the brachium conjunctivum. On the basis of experimental work in cats involving measurement of cortical potentials after rotation, it has been suggested that the superior temporal gyrus (area 22) and part of the frontal lobe (area 6) receive vestibular impulses. The parietal lobe may also receive such impulses from the temporal (744, 745, 810). Subjective sensations of dizziness have resulted from cortical stimulation, especially in the temporal lobe. Further, tumors of one temporal lobe have been found to be associated with preponderant increase in nystagmus to the side of the lesion, in response to caloric stimulation (see below). One temporal lobe apparently facilitates the opposite vestibular nuclear mechanisms involved in nystagmus.

MEDIAL LONGITUDINAL FASCICULUS

This tract should be more fully described at this time because of its relation to secondary vestibular fibers. It is a large group of fibers, varying in composition from level to level, that can be traced definitely from midbrain to caudal medulla, and less distinctly into and through the spinal cord. It contains ascending as well as descending fibers.

In the brain stem the following constituents compose the tract: (*a*) ascending secondary vestibular fibers, crossed and uncrossed, to the oculomotor, trochlear, and abducens nuclei, the so-called **vestibulomesencephalic fibers;** (*b*) descending secondary vestibular fibers, crossed and uncrossed, the **medial vestibulospinal**

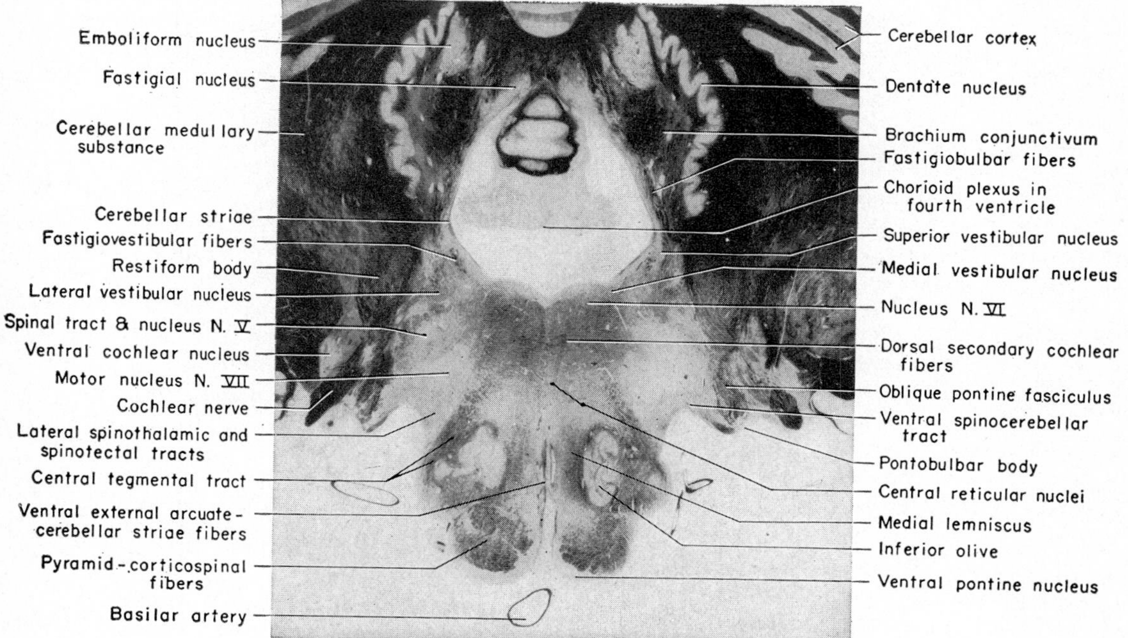

Fig. 174. Transverse section, A 455, of human brain stem, rostral medulla, at level of entry of eighth cranial nerve. Weigert. Photograph, ×2.5.

tract, mentioned above; (*c*) descending fibers from the nuclei near the posterior commissure, the interstitial nucleus of Cajal, and the nucleus of Darkschewitsch, the **interstitiospinal** and **commissurospinal** tracts, respectively, containing crossed and uncrossed fibers; (*d*) fibers from the superior olive, the **stalk of the superior olive,** which pass caudally via the medial longitudinal fasciculus to the spinal levels; other olivary fibers may relay in reticular nuclei and these send ascending axons to the various eye-muscle nuclei; (*e*) fibers which interconnect the motor nuclei innervating extraocular muscles and those spinal neurons innervating cervical musculature, for coordinating eye and head movements—corticonuclear fibers to the various centers for conjugate movements (see Chap. 21) are probably included in these; (*f*) fibers which interconnect oculomotor and facial nuclei for coordinating eye and lid movements; (*g*) fibers which interconnect hypoglossal and facial nuclei for correlating tongue and facial movements; and (*h*) possibly, vestibulothalamic fibers joining the thalamic fasciculus (Forel's field H_1) to enter the dorsal thalamus.

The interstitiospinal and commissurospinal fibers end in cranial-nerve motor nuclei and about the anterior spinal motor neurons, and they serve to coordinate head and neck movements. The nuclei of origin of these fibers receive fibers from the basal ganglia and possibly the cortex, and through such connections, these two tracts can be brought under control of the extrapyramidal motor system.

In the spinal-cord levels, medial vestibulospinal, interstitiospinal, and commissurospinal fibers are the principal constituents of the medial longitudinal fasciculus. Many of these end at cervical levels, though some fibers pass as far caudad as lumbar spinal-cord levels.

Function of Vestibular System

The labyrinth, in conjunction with retinal and proprioceptive impulses, serves to maintain equilibrium during active and passive movement of the body (head) and also at rest. In its contribution the labyrinth subserves two functions. The utricle (and possibly the saccule) serves to record the position of the head in space as well as to aid in postural adjustments through the distribution of muscle tone in response to changes in position of the head. The tone changes in the limbs in response to altering the position of the head will be described below. The semicircular canals react to the movements of the head and aid in the proper coordination of eye movements with head movements. The cristae in the semicircular canals are receptors for perception of (rotatory) movements, especially; the maculae, receptors for perception of position. Progressive linear movements result in stimulation of both receptors probably, though some workers feel such motion stimulates cristae only; others, that it stimulates maculae only (748). It is true, however, that it is the change of movement, rather than continuous movement, that stimulates the cristae, and perhaps, the maculae. Stimulation occurs with acceleration or deceleration of movement, not with the movement alone.

THE SEMICIRCULAR CANALS

The mechanism of stimulation of the vestibular nerve endings has long been debated, and these arguments hinge on whether or not a movement of the endolymph occurs through the small canals, or whether or not changing pressure relations on the utricular membrane serve as the excitant. It is perhaps easier to understand the mechanisms if it is assumed that a tendency to flow of the endolymph occurs. A flow of endolymph as the inciting stimulus in the canals, therefore, would cause a deviation of the cupula of the cristae. Such endolymph flow occurs on turning the head, at the beginning of rotation, during an increase in the velocity of turning, and at the end of turning. The flow is greater in the pair of canals the plane of which is most nearly perpendicular to the axis of rotation of the body. Because of the inertia of the fluid, the flow of the endolymph at first lags as compared to the wall of the canal, and for a short time the direction of flow, or tendency to flow, is opposite to the direction of turning. The endolymph in the canals not in the plane perpendicular to the axis of the body rotation takes little or no part. The endolymph flow, or tendency to flow, in a canal will be **ampullofugal** or **ampullopetal** depending on the direction of rotation. Ampullofugal describes movement of the fluid from ampulla toward canal;

ampullopetal, from canal toward ampulla. At the start of rotation the tendency of the flow will be in one direction as seen above; once turning is under way and the inertia of the fluid is overcome, the relative movement ceases; at cessation of rotation, the tendency of flow continues in the endolymph in the direction of rotation.

Endolymph flow causes deviation of the cupula of the cristae, and this results in a compression of the hairs of the sensory cells on one side, a pulling of the hairs on the other side. The pressure or pull serves to stimulate the nerve endings, and the impulses set up incite reflex movements of the eyes in a definite direction. If the head is turned about a vertical axis, in a normal position, there occurs, during the turning, a deviation of the eyes in the direction *opposite* to that of the turning. Such a movement of the eyes serves to maintain the image of a fixed object on the retinas. After a certain point of deviation the eyes are quickly pulled *toward* the direction of turning. These two movements of the eyes, when repeated successively, constitute **nystagmus.** The first reaction arises partly through labyrinthine impulses and partly through visual reflexes and proprioceptive reflexes arising in cervical musculature. This conjugate deviation of the eyes in the direction opposite to that of the turning of the head represents the slow component of the nystagmus. After a rotation, the eyes are seen to turn slowly in one direction and then to turn quickly in the opposite direction. Nystagmus can be defined, therefore, as a rhythmical oscillation of the eyeballs, either in a horizontal, rotary, or vertical direction, and the oscillation is composed of a slow and a fast component. The *direction* of nystagmus is clinically reported as that of the *quick component,* since this is the more striking. Postrotational nystagmus, therefore, is in a direction opposite to that of the turning. In addition to nystagmus, repetitive turning will serve to evoke other reactions after the rotation. These include an error in pointing (past pointing) with the outstretched arms, a tendency to fall or actual falling in one direction, and a sensation of continued rotation (vertigo or dizziness).

The **Bárány tests** utilize rotation of a subject 10 turns in 20 sec., after which he is suddenly stopped. He is then observed for nystagmus, past pointing, tendency to falling, and vertigo. By varying the position of the head and the direction of turning, it is possible to bring definite pairs of canals into the plane of rotation. With the head erect and inclined 15 to 30 deg. forward, the external canals are in the plane of rotation; with the head inclined forward 90 deg., the superior canals are in the plane of rotation; with the head inclined 90 deg. toward a shoulder, the two inferior canals. The induced nystagmus usually persists from 15 to 40 sec. in normal individuals; the tendency to past-point and to fall, and the sensation of vertigo, may last about the same time. Such reactions do not result when the labyrinths are dead. Exaggerated responses are found in hypersensitive or diseased labyrinths; diminished responses, in hypofunctioning labyrinths.

It appears established that an ampullopetal endolymph flow in an external canal evokes a stronger stimulus than an ampullofugally directed flow. In the other two canals the effects of an ampullofugal flow seems greater. With the normal position of the head, turning to the right results in the more effective ampullopetal flow in the right external canal at the start of the turning and in the left canal after the turning. Stated another way, at the start of rotation around a vertical axis with the head in a normal position, the external canal corresponding to the direction of rotation is relatively more excited; after cessation of rotation, the opposite canal is more excited. At the beginning of a series of turns the subject will have nystagmus in a certain direction depending on the direction of rotation. When the turning is well established and the inertia of the endolymph flow is overcome, the tendency of endolymph flow ceases and hence stimulation ceases. The nystagmus ceases. When the turning is stopped, however, the tendency of endolymph flow continues in the direction of turning, the nerve endings are again stimulated, and nystagmus is again produced. The direction of the **postrotational** nystagmus is opposite to that initiated at the beginning of turning, and it is this nystagmus that can be most easily observed.

The past pointing can be demonstrated as

follows. The subject, who continues to sit after rotation, is asked to extend his arms and index fingers horizontally in front of him. The examiner extends his fingers to touch those of the subject. The latter, with eyes closed, is then asked to swing his arms either upward or downward and to return to the starting point and touch the examiner's fingers. He usually past-points with both arms to right or left depending on the direction of rotation. When asked to stand erect he tends to fall in the same direction, and he experiences all the while a sensation of turning in that direction. If a subject with normal labyrinths is rotated to the right, with his head erect and inclined 15 to 30 deg. forward, the external canals, and especially the left, are maximally stimulated at the end of rotation. The subject will then demonstrate nystagmus (rapid phase) to the left, but will past-point and tend to fall to the right, and experience a sensation of turning (vertigo) to the right.

Syringing the external auditory canal with hot or cold water also sets up labyrinthine reactions such as nystagmus, falling, past pointing, and vertigo. This is referred to as **caloric stimulation,** and it is easier to carry out and is more selective than rotary stimulation because an elaborate rotation apparatus is unnecessary, and because it is possible to stimulate each labyrinth separately. The direction of the reactions after caloric stimulation follows definite rules. With the head tilted back 60 deg., for example, syringing an ear with cold water produces a slow phase of nystagmus, a sensation of vertigo, tendency to fall, past pointing directed toward the side of stimulation, and a quick nystagmus phase to the opposite side. Syringing the same ear with hot water results in reverse reactions. Although opinions differ as to the manner of stimulation, the temperature change with caloric stimulation is thought to set up convection currents in the endolymph which leads to stimulation of the crista. Cooling results in a sinking of endolymph; heating, in a rise. A flow of endolymph in such circumstances will occur most readily when the plane of the semicircular canal tested is vertical. Cold syringing should produce an ampullofugal flow in a canal if the ampulla is situated above the cooled portion of the canal, and an ampullopetal flow if the ampulla lies below the site of cooling. Hot syringing produces opposite conditions. On syringing of the right ear with hot water and with optimum position of the external canal (head tilted back 60 deg. and slightly inclined to the side of syringing), one would expect, since the ampulla is at the top, an endolymph pressure rise to the ampulla, horizontal nystagmus with quick component to the right. Cold syringing of the right ear under such conditions will lead to horizontal nystagmus with fast component to the left. Nystagmus induced by caloric testing usually begins 15 to 30 sec. after the start of the irrigation and may persist for 1 or 2 min., normally.

The mechanisms of **nystagmus** are of interest. Each semicircular canal is thought to have major control of that pair of ocular muscles which move the eyes in the plane of the canal (245, 516). The external canal controls lateral and medial recti muscles, the superior, the obliques, and the inferior canals, the superior and inferior recti. If both eyes deviate to the left (designated conjugate deviation to the left) on vestibular stimulation, the external rectus of the left eye and the internal rectus of the right eye must contract. The left external rectus receives its stimulation from the left abducens nucleus, the right internal, many fibers from the left oculomotor nucleus (these fibers cross on emerging from the nucleus, it is to be recalled). For left conjugate deviation to occur, therefore, a stimulation of left abducens and left oculomotor neurons must take place. Impulses stimulating these reach them from vestibular nuclei by way of the medial longitudinal fasciculus and paths through the reticular formation. With regard to horizontal eye motions the medial longitudinal fasciculus carries impulses for conjugate deviation of both eyes to its own side. Stimulation of the left medial longitudinal fasciculus, for example, produces a conjugate deviation of the eyes to the left. Through reciprocal mechanisms, innervation of the left medial longitudinal bundle in left conjugate deviation will be associated with inhibition of antagonist muscles (those producing deviation to the right) through inhibition of the right medial longitudinal fasciculus activity.

For production of both the slow phase and quick phase of nystagmus, only the following structures are necessary: the afferent fibers from the labyrinth, the efferent nerves to the eye muscles, and the part of the brain stem between these afferent and efferent structures. It seems most likely that the vestibular nuclei are the site of origin not only of the mechanisms that innervate the slow component, but also of those that excite the quick component of nystagmus (747).

Two functional types of neurons in the vestibular nuclei of one side can be postulated: those sending fibers to the reticular formation and medial longitudinal fasciculus of the same side, and those sending fibers into these structures of the opposite side (Fig. 175). Through reciprocal relationships, when one type is sending out stimulating impulses, the activity of the other is depressed or inhibited. A vestibular impulse acting on the left innervating cells and inducing left conjugate deviation produces not only excitation of the "left cells" and of the corresponding levogyric muscles, but also inhibition of the antagonistic "right cells" and the corresponding dextrogyric muscles. The relationships are then reciprocally reversed (748). One may postulate also similar mechanisms to explain the falling and past-pointing reactions. Through the lateral vestibulospinal tract, which is composed of uncrossed fibers, the vestibular nuclei on the side of the stimulated labyrinth can facilitate the extensor tone of the ipsilateral limbs. Through the crossed medial vestibulospinal fibers, the extensor tone of the contralateral limbs can be simultaneously depressed, and the patient will fall to that side. He is literally pushed over to that side by the extended opposite limb.

Stimulation of the cristae, therefore, either by caloric or rotatory means, will produce in a normal individual nystagmus, a tendency to falling, past pointing, and a subjective sensation of continued rotation, vertigo, or dizziness, as described above. In addition, there are evidences of an effect on the autonomic nervous system. The systemic blood pressure may fall and the cerebral circulation slow as a result; increased salivation appears, nausea and vomiting may occur, pupillary changes may take place, and respiration may be inhibited. The vasodepressor reaction following labyrinth stimulation results from excitation of both maculae and cristae, apparently.

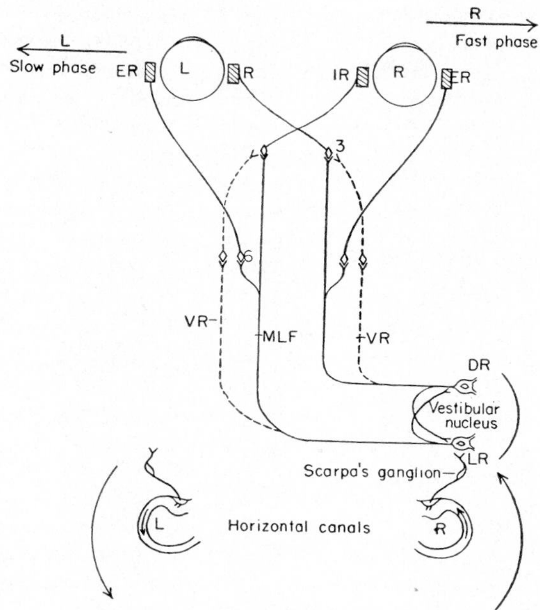

FIG. 175. Diagram of neural mechanisms of nystagmus. The rotation has been from right to left, and these are the mechanisms underlying the production of post-rotatory nystagmus (fast phase) to right. *DR*, dextrorotatory cells; *ER*, external rectus; *IR*, internal rectus; *LR*, levorotatory cells; *MLF*, medial longitudinal fasciculus; *VR*, vestibuloreticular path; 3, 6, nuclei of oculomotor and abducens nerves respectively. (*Based on studies of Spiegel and others.*)

UTRICLE AND SACCULE

The receptor endings in the maculae serve especially for reflexes that are evoked by the position of the head or by alteration of its position. The mechanism of stimulation of the macular hair cells is not clear. It is usually assumed, however, that the otoliths exert traction or pressure on the hairs, according to the position of the head. The maximum excitation is supposed to be produced on a macula when the otoliths are below the macula and thus are pulling on it; minimum excitation, when the otoliths are above the macula and are pressing on it. The maximum pull on the utricular macula will be experienced when the person is standing on his head; that on the saccular macula, when he is lying on one side or the other.

Some doubt has been cast on the function of the macula of the sacculus in the maintenance of equilibrium, since in many animals its destruction does not result in disturbances in equilibrium (514, 515). Comparative anatomic studies suggest a hearing function for the saccular macula, especially its posterior portion. One interesting assumption is that which holds that the saccule is the seat of our sense for rhythmic music. The utricle, especially, is the site of origin of static reflexes. It is doubtful, furthermore, whether the functions of the cristae of the semicircular canals and those of the maculae can be differentiated sharply. The macula of the utricle can be stimulated by rapid angular acceleration. The otolith organs are not able to check angular acceleration as quickly as are the canals, however, with rotation of moderate velocity; they are stimulated by continued and strong stimuli. It has been learned also that the semicircular canals, especially the vertical ones, participate in the mechanisms of static reflexes and in the regulation of muscle tonus. There seems to be, therefore, some interweaving of function of cristae and maculae, especially those of the utricles, and the possibility exists that changes of position and linear movements of the head may produce stimulation of the semicircular canals as well as of the utricle.

MECHANISMS UNDERLYING THE MAINTENANCE OF POSTURE

The maintenance of posture is accomplished by the steady contraction of a large group of skeletal muscles. The steady contraction in the individual muscles is described as muscle tone or tonus (see Chap. 5). It depends on a local reflex, in which the afferent organ is a proprioceptive ending in the muscle; the efferent agent, a motor neuron and its axon terminals in the muscle.

These local reflexes of muscle tonus are greatly influenced by central mechanisms; and in the maintenance of posture, in which the tonus mechanisms play such a vital part, impulses arising in the labyrinths, retinas, and proprioceptive endings in muscles and joints are essential. From the otolith organs, impulses arise as a result of alteration in the position of the head in space. These impulses bring about reflex alteration of the distribution of muscle tone. From the semicircular canals arise impulses due to movement or to rotary acceleration in space; these impulses bring about a coordination of proper eye movements with those of head and body. From proprioceptive endings in muscles and joints throughout the body impulses arise in response to stimuli of pressure or stretch. These can bring about alteration in the existing muscle tone or even in its position through activation of motor units. From the retinas arise visual impulses occasioned by changes in the position of the body with reference to its surroundings. In response to these, the movements of the eyes can be adjusted to maintain their fixation, and the movements of the limbs can be guided. In normal individuals all these sources of stimuli work together in producing their effects on posture. It is only by isolating the various components of the group that the part played by each is made clear. In the study of posture the experimental animal has been used to great advantage.

A "decerebrate" animal as first described by Sherrington was one in which the brain stem had been transected in the region beneath the free edge of the tentorium cerebelli (724, 725). The limits within which such a transection must fall are, anteriorly, the coronal plane of the inferior colliculus, and posteriorly, the plane of entrance of the eighth nerves. Following such a transection all the muscles which normally maintain an animal in its standing posture enter into a state of hypertonus, **decerebrate rigidity,** which disappears if the posterior spinal roots in the same animal are later sectioned. If the brain stem transection be below the plane of the eighth nerves, a "spinal" preparation is obtained; if anterior to the thalamus, a "thalamic" animal is obtained; and if the thalamus be above the transection and the midbrain below it, a "midbrain" animal is obtained. These animal preparations differ in their capabilities, and it has been through study of them that information regarding function of the various levels of the nervous system has been secured. Considerable caution, however, must be exercised in applying to the human the information thus obtained; in man the activity of the lower levels has come to be greatly dominated by the higher or cortical levels (804).

Passive variations in the position of the head of the "decerebrate" animal with relation to space and the position of its body will produce modifications of tone in the muscles engaged in the decerebrate rigidity (519). These modifications are expressed by changes of limb posture as well as by demonstrable modifications of the decerebrate rigidity. There are two main groups of these postural reactions, the **tonic labyrinthine reflexes** and **tonic neck reflexes.** The reactions are produced as a result of the new position imposed on the head, appear after a latent period of variable length, and endure as long as the new head position is maintained.

The otolith organs are involved in the tonic labyrinthine reactions, the adequate stimulus being a variation in the relation of the macula of the utricule and possibly also of that of the saccule, to the horizontal planes of space. To demonstrate this it is necessary either to immobilize the animal's head with relation to the body or to cut the upper three cervical posterior roots, thus excluding tonic neck reflexes. When such an animal, a cat for example, is in the supine position with snout about 45 deg. below the horizontal plane, the rigidity is minimal. The extensor tonus of all four limbs is influenced identically by the tonic labyrinthine reflexes.

By destroying the labyrinths bilaterally, modifications of extensor rigidity in the limbs can still be produced by varying the position of the head, but now the variation must be in the relation to the neck and trunk because differences in the position of the head in space are not registered. The response following changes in head position under such conditions are now tonic neck reflexes, the afferent impulses for which arise in proprioceptive endings in the deep skeletal structures of the neck. Some variation exists in the type of response of different animals, but all of them show changes in muscle tonus in response to alteration of the position of the head. Rotation of the head to the right (vertex to right) leads to increased extensor rigidity in the left limbs and diminished extensor tone in the right limbs. Lateral flexion to the right produces increased extensor tone in the right limbs, diminished in the left. Dorsal flexion in all mammals except rabbits increases tone in the forelimbs and inhibits it in the hind limbs; ventral flexion has a reverse effect. These responses can be elicited in certain patients with large lesions which practically render them "decerebrate"; *e.g.*, with massive destruction of midbrain or pons.

The tonic reflexes thus demonstrated in a decerebrate animal constitute standing reflexes. Such a decerebrate animal has no power of reflex control over the position of the head in space, or in relation to the trunk. The reactions elicited by changing the position of the head are capable of maintaining the animal in such attitudes as may be imposed upon it in this way. The decerebrate animal can stand, but it cannot change its posture without outside interference. In an intact animal there must be reactions other than the standing reflexes, and these other reactions allow for the righting of head in space and for adjusting the body to a variety of postures. These additional reflexes in the intact animal are called righting reflexes. Righting reflexes are present in an animal when the brain stem transection passes anterior to the inferior colliculi. Though the red nuclei were formerly considered essential for the righting reflexes, this has been disproved, and some other midbrain nuclei, tegmental in location, seem to be involved. "Thalamic" and "midbrain" animals as described above, therefore, show righting reflexes.

Midbrain animals differ from decerebrate animals in that the distribution and intensity of muscle tone are normal throughout and there is no rigidity. They also have righting reflexes, as mentioned. Midbrain animals are deprived of all volition, however, and their activity is purely reflex. Under appropriate stimulation they can step, run, and jump. In whatever position such an animal is placed, the head rights itself, the animal being in possession of reflex reactions which keep the head always right side up; and since the position of the head governs that of the trunk and limbs, it has reflex control over the posture of its entire body. Thalamic animals, in addition to the above characteristics, can maintain a normal body temperature and can show emotional reactions, such as sham rage (see Chap. 14).

Postural reflexes thus include a variety of mechanisms and in the intact organism these mechanisms are integrated with one another. As individual patterns there are the following: labyrinthine reflexes acting on the head;

reflexes arising in the body wall and acting upon the head; reflexes arising in the neck secondary to alterations evoked by labyrinthine reflexes; reflexes arising in and acting upon trunk and limb musculature; in the intact animal, righting reflexes arising in the retinas. These last require the integrity of the visual cortex.

Certain other postural reflexes, such as the **placing and hopping reactions,** require the cerebral cortex, especially precentral and postcentral gyri, for their integrity (55).

Some of these postural reflexes can be elicited in infants, though in incomplete patterns (268). The tonic neck reflexes, especially in so far as leg movements are concerned, can be brought out in normal infants. Otolith regulating reflexes enable an infant to maintain his head in an upright position regardless of the postion to which he is shifted. Reactions in response to linear movements include the lift and falling reactions. The **lift** reaction is demonstrated when a prone child held outstretched in the examiner's hand is suddenly lifted. The head and body are flexed forward and the arms are held downward as the movement begins. When the movement ends, the head and body are extended and the arms lifted. The falling reaction is brought out as follows. The child held in the examiner's hand is moved downward, and as this is done the head is extended and the arms lifted up. As the downward movement ceases, the child's body is inclined forward and the arms and legs are stretched out as if to break the force of the fall.

The maintenance of the extensor hypertonus in decerebrate rigidity has been attributed to the activity of the vestibular nuclei and their spinal projections, the vestibulospinal tracts. The hypertonus can be abolished by destroying vestibular nuclei or by sectioning the vestibulospinal tract in the anterior funiculus of the spinal cord. Decerebrate rigidity has been considered a release phenomenon, the activity of the vestibulospinal system having been set free from the inhibitory influences of centers rostrad the plane of section. In the light of recent studies by Magoun and others, it is more accurate to consider the extensor hypertonus of decerebrate rigidity as an expression of excitation of spinal neurons, and the vestibulospinal tract belongs to the facilitatory or excitatory group of pathways descending into the cord, others being certain reticulospinal fibers arising in the medulla, and the corticospinal tracts. In the cat, at least, the vestibulospinal tract is the chief agent whose activity maintains decerebrate rigidity, and it operates independently here of other facilitating mechanisms (41). Reticulospinal fibers contribute to the maintenance of the rigidity in other animals and also are more important in maintaining the extensor hypertonus or spasticity following cerebral lesions, a condition to which the vestibulospinal system contributes very little (815).

That the vestibular system in man has an influence on the distribution of extensor tone can easily be demonstrated by the rotatory and caloric vestibular tests described earlier. Its influence is, however, dominated normally by higher brain stem and cortical neurons, and it is only through stimulation of the labyrinth experimentally or in disease processes, or through removal of higher control by large destructions of the brain stem, that its effect on muscle tone can be demonstrated. Conversely, removal of a labyrinth has little effect on muscle tone, though some investigators have described a transient ipsilateral hypotonia.

Disorders Associated with Labyrinthine Disease

Since the maintenance of posture depends on information from the labyrinths, retinas, and sensory endings in muscles and about joints, and the correlation of such information in higher neural centers, it is natural to expect disorders in maintaining equilibrium if one of these sources of information is not functioning properly, or if the central integration is faulty. Perhaps the most common symptom of malfunction of the labyrinth is **vertigo,** the subjective sensation of discord in the postural mechanism (12). Patients often describe this sensation as dizziness and may imply that they suffer a sensation of rotation of themselves or objects in a certain direction, a feeling of falling in one direction, or a feeling of faintness, swimming, staggering, or swaying. In addition to vertigo and disorders in maintaining posture, patients with labyrinthine disorder may show nystagmus, occurring spontaneously in any position of the eyes or with gaze in a certain direction. Labyrinthine nystagmus as described above consists of two components, a slow movement in one direction and a quicker rebound in the opposite direction. Labyrinthine disease or excitation is also usually accompanied by nausea, vomiting, vasomotor reaction, facial pallor, palpitation of the heart, and perspiration. Stimulation of the labyrinth is associated with fall of blood pressure, and it is thought that the vestibular impulses are transmitted through the medial vestibular nucleus to the vasomotor center in the reticular formation of the medulla. Respiratory change following caloric stimulation of the labyrinth is reported to consist in a shortening of inspiration and a prolongation of expiration. These effects are thought to arise through action on the respiratory center itself by vestibular impulses.

Vertigo is a very common clinical complaint, and it is necessary to consider many etiological agents and topographical sites for its origin. It may arise as a psychogenic symptom, or it may arise in inflammatory, vascular, neoplastic, degenerative, or toxic disorders. It may be present because of disease in the labyrinth, vestibular nerve, vestibular nuclei, brain stem, flocculonodular portion of the cerebellum especially, cerebral cortex, or in the orbit. Vertigo arising in association with disease of the peripheral vestibular apparatus may be associated with evidence of disorder of the auditory mechanisms and indications of autonomic stimulation, nausea, vomiting, hypotension, sweating, and salivation. Nystagmus may be present spontaneously or may appear with assumption of certain positions. Vertigo arising in diseases involving the central pathways is usually associated with other signs indicative of neural disease. There may be nystagmus and this may be long-standing, vertical in type, spontaneous, or appear with change of position.

In vestibular disease, **nystagmus** may be present spontaneously, may appear with assumption of certain positions or with gaze in certain directions, or, when induced by labyrinthine stimulation, it may persist longer than normal. Nystagmus is also observed in disturbances of other neural systems, and in nystagmus of vestibular origin, it is necessary to determine whether the disorder is a peripheral one, in the labyrinth or nerve, or a central one involving the secondary vestibular connections. It is usually true that labyrinthine nystagmus is accompanied by vertigo and symptoms of autonomic stimulation as listed above. Labyrinthine nystagmus is most often horizontal or rotatory or a mixture of the two types. If the labyrinth is the site of an irritative disorder, the nystagmus is directed toward the diseased side; if the labyrinth is completely nonfunctional, the nystagmus is toward the sound labyrinth. If the vestibular nuclei or their connections with the medial longitudinal fasciculus and the reticular nuclei are the site of disease process, the nystagmus may be horizontal, vertical, or rotatory; if horizontal, it is usually directed toward the diseased side, unless the area of destruction is massive.

It is to be recalled that, with the subject's head inclined backward 60 deg., stimulation of the right labyrinth with cold water, and of the left labyrinth with hot, usually produces nystagmus to the left. In directional preponderance, nystagmus in one direction is affected whichever ear is stimulated. In temporal-lobe lesions there is said to be a directional preponderance in the nystagmus elicited by labyrinthine stimulation; *i.e.*, the nystagmus is preponderantly directed toward the side of the lesion (131, 249). The presence of directional preponderance to the right in a patient with suspected brain tumor might aid in the diagnosis. A coarse type of nystagmus, the fast and slow component movements of which are very difficult to differentiate, is seen in cerebellar disease. In this case the nystagmus is more pronounced when the patient looks toward the side of the cerebellar lesion, and it represents an inability to maintain postural fixation of the eyes. Nystagmus may also be of ocular origin, occurring in diseases of the eye. People who have complete acquired blindness are apt to show searching nystagmoid eye movements. Various other congenital and hereditary ocular disorders are associated with nystagmus.

Motion sickness such as that developed in car sickness, train sickness, air sickness, and sea sickness is usually associated with many of the symptoms just described, and it involves a prolonged stimulation of the labyrinth. It is probably true that this stimulation occurs in both maculae and cristae (786). On the basis of research during recent years, it seems likely that vertical acceleration and deceleration in the long axis of the body with the head erect is the most important factor in the production of motion sickness. The maculae of the utricles would be most susceptible to stimulation with this type of movement (569). In sea sickness also, the rolling movement of the ship, together with its pitching movement up and down, serves to stimulate the labyrinths excessively. A wide variation of susceptibility to motion sickness exists from person to person, and an individual can gradually adapt himself to the movements and not develop sickness. Optic fixation of an object that participates in all the movements of the head tends to diminish the incidence of motion sickness. The excessive stimulation of the labyrinth creates abnormal activity in the central vestibular connections and the disordered equilibrium and excessive autonomic activity results. In dogs, for example, motion sickness can be prevented by removing the pyramis, uvula, and nodulus of the cerebellum, and it seems likely that the removal of the nodulus is the essential factor (59). The flocculonodular lobe of the cerebellum, it is to be recalled, has the most extensive vestibular connections (215).

In **Ménière's "disease,"** patients are periodically subject to severe attacks of vertigo associated with the signs of disordered autonomic activity, such as nausea, vomiting, pallor, increased perspiration, and possibly hypotension. Tinnitus, or subjective ear noises, such as bells ringing or a hum, usually also is noticed as well as impairment in hearing. The mechanism of production of Ménière's "disease" is unknown, though a disorder in the formation, circulation, or absorption of endolymph has been suggested. In post-mortem examination of several cases, a hydrops of the endolymphatic system and degeneration of the sensory elements have been demonstrated (323). The disorder of endolymph circulation may be secondary to vascular disease. Ménière's "disease" can be treated by a variety of medical regimens or surgery. The vestibular nerve has been sectioned in certain individuals in order to relieve the disorder; the labyrinth has been destroyed chemically or electrically. All the vestibular fibers can be sectioned by an incision through the anterior half or five-eighths of the eighth cranial nerve; the cochlear fibers are in large measure thus spared (195). It is important to recognize a case of Ménière's disorder and to distinguish it from other conditions which might produce the same symptom complex. Labyrinthitis, intoxications with certain drugs or chemicals, and tumors growing on or about the eighth cranial nerve can produce a similar picture, though usually the symptoms do not recur periodically as they do in Ménière's "disease."

In spite of the great part the labyrinth plays in the regulation of tonus and equilibrium as seen in animals, its destruction unilaterally in man may result in only slight and short-lived disturbance. Some disturbances of equilibrium occasionally may be observed for years after unilateral labyrinthectomy, however, if detailed examination is performed. Patients with unilateral labyrinthectomies usually prefer a side position, with the operated labyrinth up. If they look at the surroundings in this position, *i.e.,* looking in the direction of the operated side, the spontaneous nystagmus in the direction of the normal side and the accompanying vertigo are reduced. In time these disorders clear, apparently through adjustments in the vestibular nuclei and central connections. Hypotonia of ipsilateral extensors persisting for a few days after unilateral labyrinthectomy has been reported. Bilateral destruction of the labyrinth is in time compensated to a great extent by other mechanisms, optical and proprioceptive, especially. Usually patients with bilateral vestibular paralysis, whether resulting from surgery or disease process, can walk without staggering in the daytime. They usually stagger in the dark, and they are unable to orient themselves in water. They are unable to maintain ocular fixation when the head is moved. As a result, if they walk rapidly or ride, they have difficulty in recognizing friends and familiar objects, apparently because of the inability to correlate eye movements with the bobbing of the head. Such persons usually do not develop motion sickness.

In this and the preceding chapter, peripheral neural mechanisms, as exemplified by cranial nerves, have been the subject of discussion. In the following sections descriptions of the central coordinating mechanisms will be undertaken. It is through these correlating systems that impulses from the periphery are integrated, neural activity thus initiated is sustained, and adjustments made as necessary, for the more effective activity of the peripheral motor neurons.

CHAPTER 11

THE RETICULAR SYSTEM

THE DESCRIPTIONS in the foregoing sections have dealt principally with receptor and effector neurons of the cerebrospinal axis that have terminal ramifications in the somatic and visceral structures of the organism. Through connections between receptor and effector neurons, simple segmental reflexes are possible, and stereotyped effector activity in response to receptor stimulation is produced. The neurons forming the subject of this present discussion are similar in function and character to the internuncial neurons described in the spinal gray. They are intercalated between receptor and effector units, and their processes do not extend without the neural axis, but end wholly within it. They are intercalated between receptor and effector units of the same level, between receptor units of one level and effector units of a more cephalic or caudal level, between collaterals of ascending systems and regional associative and effector units, and between descending systems and effector units that innervate peripheral mechanisms. Through their activities a basic continuous neural activity is maintained, a phasic one diffused and facilitated and so directed that the effector response is more variable, involves more units, and at the same time is adapted for better serving the organism.

Throughout the discussion of the intrinsic anatomy of the brain stem, reference has frequently been made to the **reticular formation,** those neurons and their short processes located for the most part within the tegmentum. In some areas of the brain stem the neurons of the reticular formation are collected into nuclei recognizable by the naked eye in sections of the neural axis. Many more are so diffusely scattered that discrete grouping is not possible. This brain stem reticular formation represents merely a rostral continuation of the reticular or associative neurons of the spinal cord. Like them, they are receptive of impulses from a variety of systems, and these impulses may be interoceptive, exteroceptive, proprioceptive, or efferent. These coordinating or associative neurons may be referred to as the reticular system. It is neither motor nor sensory in the strict sense, but serves to elaborate and coordinate the activity of those two functional systems. Discrete reticular nuclei can be found at medullar, pontine, and midbrain levels. Rostral to the midbrain level, impulses from the reticular system may be relayed through medial and intralaminar thalamic nuclei.

INFERIOR MEDULLAR RETICULAR NUCLEI

Two divisions compose the inferior medullar group. The more circumscribed and smaller portion is in the lateral region of the ventral medullar tegmentum. This is the **lateral reticular nucleus of the medulla** at the level of the vagus nerve and dorsolateral to the inferior olive (Fig. 127). It has two parts, a smaller medial and a larger lateral, and both parts are well developed in the same levels in which the olive is prominent. These nuclei are reciprocally connected with many brain stem nuclei and are also intercalaries between the spinal cord and the cerebellum through the spinoreticular tracts and reticulocerebellar tracts. The medial neurons may contribute to the medial reticulospinal tract.

The other portion of the inferior medullar group is much larger and occupies much of the central tegmentum, ventrally. It is dorsal to the inferior olive. It has gone by a variety of names; here it will be referred to as the **inferior medial reticular nucleus of the medulla.** The central tegmental tract is closely associated with it (Figs. 129, 131). Groups of reticular neurons in this general ventral tegmental position extend from a plane caudad of the inferior olivary nucleus to a plane just caudad to the entrance of the vestibular division of the eighth cranial nerve. The majority of the neurons composing this inferior medial reticular nucleus are dorsal to the inferior olivary nucleus, some being medial to the spinal nucleus of the trigeminal and others ventral to it. Many of these neurons receive impulses from the visceral sensory nuclei, *e.g.,* from the nucleus solitarius. The spinothalamic tracts give collaterals to them, as do certain of the descending extrapyramidal tracts, rubrospinal and reticulospinal.

Superior Medullar Reticular Nuclei

At the level of entrance of the eighth cranial nerve other centrally placed reticular neurons are found in the medullar tegmentum, and these can be traced rostrally in diminishing numbers to the level of the trigeminal motor nucleus. They are present along the raphe but are especially prominent lateral to it (Figs. 132, 161). These constitute medial reticular nuclei in the chain of reticular neurons and are often referred to as **central reticular nuclei of the medulla.** They receive collaterals from vestibular fibers and probably from auditory fibers. Descending fibers from hypothalamus, red nuclei, more rostrally placed reticular nuclei, perhaps from the cerebellum, from the globus pallidus, and from the cerebral cortex end about reticular neurons at this level. Certain of these neurons give rise to the medial reticulospinal fibers; others compose the inferior salivatory nucleus. Other reticular neurons, not sharply outlined into discrete nuclei, are numerous in the medullar tegmentum dorsal and dorsolateral to the central nuclei.

Pontine Reticular Nuclei

Reticular nuclei are found at all pontine levels; some are sharply outlined, others are diffuse and poorly outlined. Of this latter category the most prominent nucleus is a large one that occupies much of the lateral and central zone of the tegmentum (Figs. 135, 158, 160). It reaches from a caudal pontine level to the level of the inferior colliculus, and it is very well developed at the level of the motor nucleus of the trigeminal nerve. It is sometimes referred to as the dissipated reticular nucleus. It will be referred to here simply as the **central tegmental reticular nucleus of the pons.** The cells of this extensive nucleus are very large in its upper levels and probably relay impulses caudally as well as rostrally in the reticular formation. They are thought to receive fibers from local sensory nuclei and to give fibers to the regional motor nuclei. They may relay impulses from the lateral lemniscus and from the cerebellum. Some of the neurons contribute to medial and lateral reticulospinal tracts, according to the evidence obtained by Papez in his studies in the cat (592). More medially and ventrally placed in the pontine tegmentum is the rostral continuation of the superior medullar medial reticular nuclei. Some of these neurons probably compose the superior salivatory and lacrimal nuclei.

Circumscribed nuclei are found throughout the pontine levels in the boundary zone between tegmentum and the basal part of the brain stem. A medial column of cells is found near the raphe medial to the medial lemniscus; a lateral column of cells, at first adjacent the lateral lemniscus, gradually is displaced to the lateral edge of the brain stem (Fig. 133). Some authors consider these **medial** and **lateral ventral tegmental nuclei** as displaced pontine nuclei which receive frontopontine and temporopontine fibers; they also project axons to the neocerebellum especially.

At a level just rostral to the motor trigeminal nucleus a prominent, well-circumscribed reticular nucleus is found along the raphe. It continues rostrally to the level of the decussation of the brachium conjunctivum, and in its rostral half, it enlarges laterally into the tegmentum to replace the central tegmental reticular nucleus of the pons (Fig. 134). It receives fibers from the fascicles of the brachium conjunctivum. Tectobulbar and tectospinal fibers may relay in it. It will be referred to here as the **superior central pontine tegmental nucleus.**

Mesencephalic Reticular Nuclei

In the midbrain the **red nuclei,** the largest of the circumscribed reticular nuclei, are located. They are described in detail in Chap. 17. These give rise to the rubrospinal paths, which, upon emerging from the nuclei, cross in the ventral tegmental decussation and pass caudalward along the lateral border of the medulla in company with, and dorsal to, the lateral tectospinal tract. Possibly they are a short-chained system in man. The rubrospinal tract gives collaterals to the motor centers of the medulla and to the inferior olive, and enters the spinal cord occupying a position medial to the ventral spinocerebellar tract, ventral to the lateral corticospinal tract, and dorsal to the lateral reticulospinal tract. The red nucleus receives impulses from the cerebral cortex; from the cerebellum via the brachium conjunctivum, the striatum, pallidum, the tectum, subthalamic nucleus, zona incerta, substantia nigra, hypothalamus; and from the medial lemniscus (596). In addition to rubrospinal fibers, the red nucleus sends fibers into the dorsal thalamus and parietal cortex, into the tegmental reticular nuclei of the midbrain, pons, and medulla, and into motor nuclei of cranial nerves.

Neurons surrounding the surfaces of the posterior commissure constitute the **nucleus of the posterior commissure** (Fig. 147). Some of the neurons are in the periaqueductal gray, some are tegmental. This nucleus contributes axons to the posterior commissure and to the medial longitudinal fasciculus.

In the region of the diencephalic mesencephalon boundary, the **nucleus of Darkschewitsch** is located (Fig. 148). Its cells contribute a majority of the fibers of the posterior commissure and many fibers of the opposite medial longitudinal fasciculus (commissurospinal tract); it sends fibers into the latter tract of the same side also. Fibers are received from the vestibular nuclei, occipital and frontal cortex, and from the pallidum of the same side.

Just ventrolateral to the nucleus of Darkschewitsch, the **interstitial nucleus of Cajal** is also located in the diencephalic mesencephalon boundary region (Fig. 148). It extends more caudad than the nucleus of Darkschewitsch. Its cells contribute many axons to the ipsilateral and opposite medial longitudinal fasciculi, some of which reach the spinal cord as the interstitiospinal tract.

Other important groups of reticular nuclei of the midbrain occupy a dorsolateral tegmental position. They extend from the level of the posterior commissure caudally to the caudal end of the inferior colliculus. The component nuclei have been given various names. The entire group will be referred to here as the **deep tegmental nucleus of the midbrain** (Figs. 137, 152). The rostral components are sometimes referred to as medial and lateral mesencephalic nuclei; the caudal extension, as the pedunculopontine tegmental nucleus. These nuclei are important relays in the conduction of descending pallidal and subthalamic impulses.

At all brain stem levels below the caudal end of the oculomotor nucleus, small neurons are found in close relation to the medial longitudinal fasciculus. In the caudal midbrain levels where they are most prominent they form an arc around the dorsal, medial, and ventral borders of the fasciculus composing **dorsal, dorsal paramedian,** and **ventral tegmental nuclei,** respectively. At pontine and medullar levels the cells are present dorsal to the medial longitudinal fasciculus and are referred to as the dorsal paramedian nucleus (Fig. 133). At the rostral levels cells of these nuclei are thought to receive fibers from the habenular nuclei, the mamillary nuclei, and the interpeduncular nuclei. At more caudal levels, they probably relay impulses transmitted along the dorsal longitudinal fasciculus of Schütz.

The foregoing account obviously does not include consideration of all the nuclei which belong to the reticular system. Many small nuclei as well as large diffuse ones have been omitted. The source of the fibers ending in these reticular nuclei and the course and destination of the axons arising in them are, to a large extent, unknown. It is fairly certain, however, that many fibers pass from these nuclei to the spinal cord as reticulospinal fibers and that many other axons run rostrally or caudally to synapse around other reticular neurons.

Reticulospinal Tracts

The reticulospinal tracts, lateral and medial, arise from certain of these reticular nuclei just described (Fig. 92). Neither the exact origin of each tract nor the contribution of each nucleus to the tracts is known for man. From investigations in other mammals a few generalizations can be made, however. The **medial**

reticulospinal tract contains crossed and uncrossed fibers, the uncrossed ones appearing in the majority. The inferior medial reticular nuclei of the medulla contribute crossed fibers to this tract. The lateral reticular nucleus of the medulla may also contribute some axons to this tract. The medial reticular nuclei, or those central reticular nuclei of the medulla at the level of the eighth nerve, contribute crossed and uncrossed fibers to the medial reticulospinal tracts. The central tegmental reticular nuclei at the level of the trigeminal motor nuclei also contribute fibers to the medial reticulospinal tract of each side. Throughout its brain stem course the medial reticulospinal tract is associated with the fibers of the medial longitudinal fasciculus and is placed just ventral and lateral to this fasciculus. The **lateral reticulospinal tract** contains many fibers which arose from the central tegmental reticular nuclei at the level of, and medial to, the motor nucleus of the trigeminal nerve. Its position in its brain stem course is ventromedial to the spinal tract and nucleus of the trigeminal nerve and it contains chiefly crossed fibers. Some reticulospinal fibers probably undergo a decussation at spinal levels. In the spinal cord the medial reticulospinal is placed in the anterior funiculus. The lateral reticulospinal tract is in the lateral funiculus, near the gray, and occupies especially the ventral half of the lateral funiculus. In fact, the reticulospinal tracts are probably coextensive with the proprius fibers which ring the intermediate and anterior gray columns. On the basis of recent researches of Magoun and his coworkers the reticulospinal fibers may be better classified according to function, rather than according to anatomical location in the spinal cord and brain stem.

That reticular nuclei and their projections exert a powerful influence on the motor activities of the spinal neurons has been conclusively shown by Magoun and his associates (528). Reticular neurons, chiefly belonging to medial reticular nuclei at the rostral level of the medulla, especially, exert a powerful inhibitory effect on the motor activity of the spinal neurons, whether this activity be reflexly induced segmentally or initiated from cortical stimulation. The pronounced extensor tone present in the decerebrate preparation can be eliminated by stimulation of this reticular center. These reticular neurons constitute a **bulbar inhibitory center** for spinal motor neuronal activity. This center receives impulses from a variety of sources, including the cerebral cortex, the basal ganglia, and the anterior lobe, especially, of the cerebellum. The fibers over which the bulbar inhibitory center discharges impulses are located chiefly in the ventral part of the lateral funiculus and in the anterior funiculus and are reticulospinal fibers.

Other neurons of the reticular group of nuclei in the brain stem serve as **facilitators** of spinal-motor-neuron activity. These neurons are more widely scattered in the reticular system and are found in the midbrain, pontine, and medullar levels. In general they appear to have a position in the lateral tegmentum, at least in the pons and medulla. Their activity is reinforced by impulses from the hypothalamus, subthalamus, globus pallidus, cerebellum, and certain nuclei of the thalamus. The facilitating impulses entering the spinal cord traverse reticulospinal fibers which again are chiefly located in the ventral half of the lateral funiculus and in the anterior funiculus. In general—in the cat, at least—facilitatory fibers appear to have a spinal concentration dorsal to that of the inhibitory ones. The function of the reticulospinal fibers with reference to the innervation of skeletal muscle movement and tone is discussed more fully in Chap. 17. It should be recalled that reticulospinal fibers include certain descending autonomic fibers and fibers entering the cervical and thoracic spinal cord from the medullar respiratory center.

The Inferior Olivary Complex

A large coordinating nucleus of a somewhat different type, probably, should also be discussed here. It is the inferior olivary complex (Figs. 129, 159, 162, 164, 165). Unlike the reticular neurons just described above, which discharge spinalward to effector neurons in large measure, the majority of the neurons of the inferior olive discharge upstream, and especially to the cerebellum.

In the ventral part of the medulla a large convoluted mass of cells, saclike in contour, composes the inferior olivary nucleus. The open end of the sac, the hilus, is directed medially and affords passage for a great stream of fibers which arise from the olivary neurons. These are the olivocerebellar fibers which pass across the mid-line intermingling with the medial lemnisci, run through or around the contralateral inferior olive, turn dorsolaterally into the restiform body, and enter the cerebellum, to terminate in all its cortex except that of the flocculus. The inferior olive is connected through these fibers in a point-to-point manner with the contralateral cerebellar hemispheres and vermis. The medial portion of the olive is connected with the vermis; the other portions, with cerebellar hemisphere. Included in these fibers passing through the open end of the olive are also some transmitting impulses from cerebellum to olive (cerebello-olivary), and interconnecting fibers between the two olives.

Surrounding the olive and making a prominent group of fibers lateral to it is the **amiculum** of the inferior olive. It contains many fibers from the **central tegmental tract,** so named because of its descending course through the central tegmentum of the brain stem. In this tract are fibers coming from the striatum, red nucleus, tegmental reticular nuclei of the upper brain stem, substantia nigra, the colliculi, and possibly the thalamus. Spino-olivary fibers come from all spinal levels. In experiments in cats the electrical activity set up in the inferior olive in response to stimulation of tibial or peroneal nerve was studied. The largest and earliest response in an olive occurred from contralateral stimulation, and evidence was adduced to show that the impulses passed via the dorsal spinocerebellar fibers or a similar large-fibered bundle running in close association with it (319). Olivospinal fibers emerging into the amiculum pass to motor neurons of the cervical spinal-cord levels which activate the musculature responsible for movements of the head on the body.

Accessory olivary nuclei, more primitive than the inferior olive, are arranged around the latter. Dorsal and medial accessory olivary nuclei are present. Olivocerebellar fibers pass from these to the vermis of the cerebellum.

Interposed as it is between the various upstream nuclei of the extrapyramidal system and the cerebellum on the one hand, and the periphery and the cerebellum on the other, the inferior olive most probably has to do with movement. From the richness of its discharge to the cerebellum, it must exert a considerable influence on the activity of that structure. Removal of the inferior olive in the cat resulted in abnormal laryngeal movement, intention tremor of axial musculature, hypermetria, and extensor hypertonus of the extremities (840). Many of these same disorders also result from ablation of the cerebellum itself in carnivores. It would appear, therefore, that in the cat, at least, the cerebellum without the influence of the inferior olive is unable to exert its normal integration of posture and motion.

In summary, the reticular system is a widespread system of neurons extending from the midbrain, through pons and medulla into the spinal region. These neurons are interposed on the one hand between afferent neurons and effector systems of the same, rostral, and caudal levels; on the other, they form intercalaries between upstream motor systems and spinal neurons. The afferent systems conduct impulses of interoceptive, exteroceptive, and proprioceptive nature. The upstream motor systems include neurons located in cerebral cortex, globus pallidus, hypothalamus, subthalamus, cerebellum, and possibly the thalamus. The caudal projections from these reticular neurons, aside from those playing upon reticular nuclei themselves of lower brain stem levels, enter the spinal cord over two large systems of fibers, the lateral and medial reticulospinal tracts. Inhibitory and facilitatory influences on spinal motor neurons traverse these systems. Through the composite effect, the muscular activity initiated by the spinal (and bulbar) neurons is coordinated, correctly timed, properly directed, and properly maintained. Not all the neural activity of the reticular system is directed spinalward, however. Recent investigations have shown that many medially placed reticular neurons at medullar, pontine, and midbrain levels have an excitatory effect on the cerebral cortex, this influence being mediated in part, possibly, via the diffuse thalamocortical projections (see Chap. 13) (414, 756). Other large nuclei such as the inferior olivary complex are coordinating centers, but coordinate reticular impulses traversing brain stem levels chiefly. It discharges to the cerebellum, as will be described in more detail in the next section.

CHAPTER 12

THE CEREBELLUM

In earlier chapters the lower segmental apparatus, as exemplified by spinal and cranial nerves, has been described. These lower levels of sensory and motor activity are under the coordinating influence of more complex levels, the so-called suprasegmental apparatus of some authors. The cerebellum belongs to the latter group. It plays some part in the coordination of spinal- and cranial-nerve motor activity, is concerned also with the more complex postural mechanisms controlled by brain stem neurons, and is especially active as a coordinator in motor activity initiated volitionally at the highest, or cerebral cortical, level. With such widespread functional interests, the cerebellum should have many anatomical connections with other parts of the neural axis, in order that it might collect information from the many sources and express its effect on the motor activity of all the levels with which it cooperates.

The cerebellum has long been referred to as the head ganglion of the proprioceptive system. Anatomical studies have revealed that it receives fibers from the spinal cord, via spinocerebellar tracts, that convey impulses from muscles, tendons, and joints, and that it receives impulses from the labyrinth by way of direct and secondary vestibular fibers. In addition many fibers arise in the cerebral cortex, synapse in the pontine nuclei, and terminate in the cerebellar cortex of the opposite side. Numerous fibers enter the cerebellum via the olivocerebellar tracts. These serve to connect indirectly spinal and many brain stem centers with the cerebellum, as seen in the previous section. Impulses brought in by all these fibers are modified in the cerebellar cortex, and from cells there axons pass into the centrally placed nuclei where further modification takes place. The resultant total cerebellar response is expressed through fibers arising in these nuclei and passing into the diencephalon (and from here to cortex), midbrain, medulla, and spinal cord.

In recent years many investigators have found that these anatomically proved afferent connections are not the only such connections. Physiological studies, involving the elicitation of cerebellar-cortex action potentials in response to stimulation of afferent end organs and also cerebral cortex, have served to show that the cerebellum receives afferent impulses of many qualities including tactile, auditory, and visual. That it is not merely a proprioceptive organ is, therefore, clearly indicated.

In man it appears that the cerebellum is essentially concerned in cooperating in the performance of the skilled voluntary movements initiated by the cerebral cortex. When disease processes attack the cerebellum, the most striking and characteristic disorders are those involving voluntary movement. The cerebellum is in an admirable position for its coordinating activity, as one can judge by its connections from the peripheral receptors via spinal cord and brain stem and those coming from the motor cortex wherein the voluntary movements are initiated.

Development of the Cerebellum

Having attained such importance in man, the cerebellum should probably have started out in its development early in the animal scale. Thus, it first appears in the cyclostomes and is represented as a bridge of tissue formed by an elevation of the lateral part of the medulla oblongata, wherein lie lateral line and vestibular centers. Even in these low vertebrates the cerebellum receives fibers from the medulla, tectum, and spinal cord. In fishes, the cerebellum is differentiated into two parts, a median unpaired portion anteriorly, the corpus cerebelli, and two lateral portions posteriorly, the auricles. These latter represent the vestibular part of the cerebellum. In the larger reptiles in which appendages are well developed the corpus cerebelli is increased in size, especially its lateral parts, and the auricles are fused medially. It has been assumed that this early lateral enlargement in association with the development and use of appendages represents a forerunner of the cerebellar hemispheres as found in man. The fused auricular portion foreshadows the vestibular flocculonodular division of the higher cerebellums. The corpus cerebelli with its median and lateral parts, or hemispheres, has gradually increased in development as the mammalian scale is ascended; the auricular or vestibular portion is overshadowed, but persists. An understanding of cerebellar development helps considerably when an attempt is made to study its morphology and function in the human. The details of homology of certain portions of the human cerebellum, *e.g.*, the paraflocculus, with those of animals are still incompletely known (468).

Formerly it was customary to divide the cerebellum into a medial portion, the **vermis,** connecting two lateral portions, or **hemispheres.** Such division is incorrect morphologically and is inadequate on a functional or clinical basis. Many other divisions into various lobes have been made, and names have been given to subsidiary lobules of the lobes; unfortunately these names, although rather descriptive, are functionally meaningless. A useful organization and division of the human cerebellum is arrived at through a phylogenetic consideration of the development of its various parts, as previously noted, and of their afferent connections (410). This division, while helpful, will surely not be the last one offered, and indeed current researches indicate that even this plan may soon be revised. It is useful, however, in correlating cerebellar function with symptomatology resulting from cerebellar disorder. On the basis of development, as outlined above, Larsell has described for the human cerebellum a posterior **flocculonodular lobe** (vestibular) and a **corpus cerebelli** separated by the **posterolateral fissure** (467) (Fig. 176). This fissure is the first to be differentiated and is the most fundamental one, according to Larsell.

The corpus cerebelli is divided by the primary fissure into an **anterior** and a **posterior lobe.** The posterior lobe is in turn occasionally divided into a **middle lobe,** a part that has developed in conjunction with the cerebral

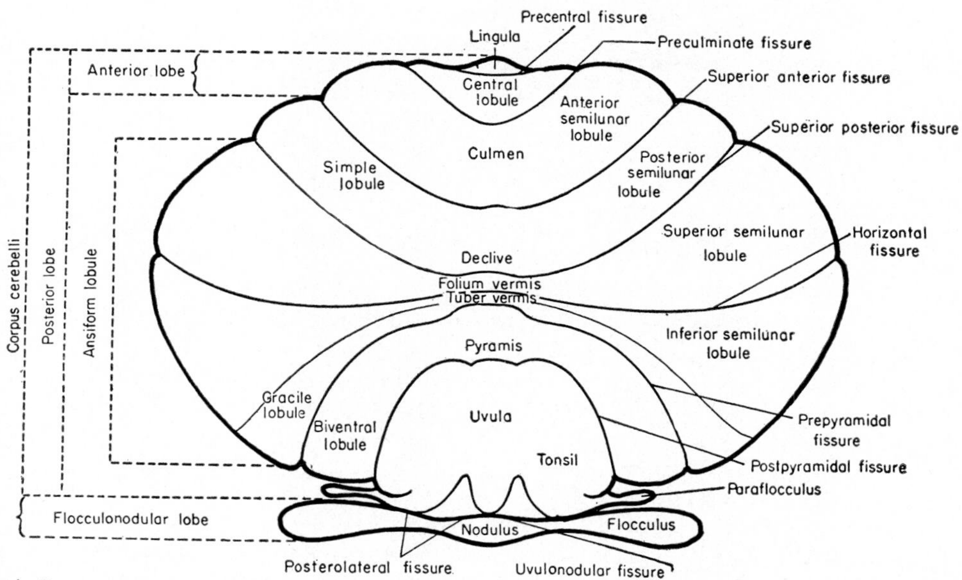

FIG. 176. A diagram of the human cerebellum. (*After Larsell, "Anatomy of the Nervous System," Appleton-Century-Crofts, Inc.*)

cortices, and a posterior division, the **posterior lobe proper.** This latter together with the anterior lobe composes the **paleocerebellum.** The flocculonodular portion is the oldest part of the cerebellum and is often called the **archicerebellum,** though, strictly speaking, some of the anterior and posterior lobes should be included in this term. Since the middle lobe develops last and in conjunction with the great development of the cerebral cortex, it is often called the **neocerebellum.**

From a study of Fig. 176, it will be seen that the anterior lobe is composed of vermian divisions: **lingula, central lobule,** and **culmen.** The lingula and central lobule have only small hemispheric extensions, while the culmen extends laterally as the **anterior semilunar lobule.** It is sometimes called the anterior quadrangular lobule. Behind the culmen medially and extending laterally into the hemispheres, the **primary fissure** separates the anterior from the medial lobe. This latter region, composing the major portion of the human cerebellum, has three vermian divisions also: the **declive, folium,** and **tuber.** These, especially the last two, have very large hemispheric extensions. The hemispheric extension of the declive is the **posterior semilunar lobule;** that of the folium, the **superior semilunar lobule;** and that of the tuber, the **inferior semilunar lobule.** The declive and its hemispheric extension are often called the **simple lobule.** The posterior semilunar lobule is sometimes called the posterior quadrangular lobule. The **prepyramidal** fissure can usually be identified just behind the tuber vermis, but it is usually overshadowed laterally by the hemispheric development. Medially, it separates middle and posterior lobe proper of the corpus cerebelli. The **gracile lobule** represents lateral hemispheric extension of tuber and pyramis folia concealed in the prepyramidal fissure. The gracile lobule is said by Larsell to correspond to the subhominid paramedian lobe (469). The posterior lobe proper

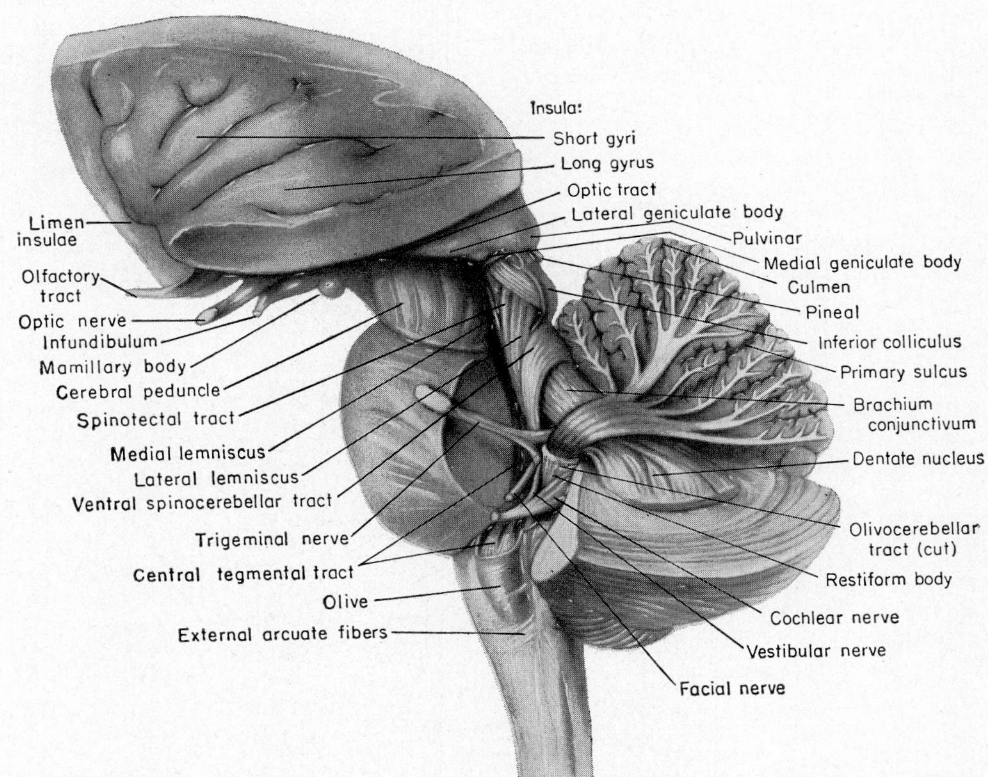

Fig. 177. A lateral view of the human brain stem with dissection to show internal structures. (*Redrawn after Büttner, Ztschr. f. Anat. u. Entwicklung., vol.* 84.)

has two vermian divisions, the **pyramis** and the **uvula.** The remaining hemispheric extension of the pyramis is the **biventral lobule;** that of the uvula, the **tonsil.** The **paraflocculus,** or accessory flocculus, is a small extension of the uvula into the tonsil (468, 469). The homologies of the paraflocculus have been the subject of much dispute. The small accessory flocculus, or human paraflocculus, is insignificant in size in comparison to the paraflocculus of some species. In fact, the subhominid paraflocculus has been divided into dorsal and ventral portions. Larsell feels that the human biventral lobule corresponds to the dorsal paraflocculus of lower mammals, and that the tonsil, in part, corresponds to the ventral paraflocculus. The superior and inferior semilunar lobules and their vermian regions are sometimes referred to as the **ansiform lobule.** The **ansoparamedian lobule** includes the biventral lobule (dorsal paraflocculus) and the ansiform lobule.

The **posterolateral fissure** can usually be identified easily behind the uvula, and it separates the corpus cerebelli from the **flocculonodular lobe.** The vermian division of this last, the **nodulus,** is connected to the hemispheric portion, the **flocculus,** by the **peduncle** of the flocculus (Fig. 130).

Structure of the Cerebellum

Roughly speaking, the cerebellum is composed of an outer layer of gray matter, the **cortex,** covering a subjacent white core. The various transverse folds of the cortex are called **folia** and are connected by **association fibers.** Deep in the cerebellar white matter are the cerebellar **nuclei,** the **dentate, interpositus** (**emboliformis** and **globosus** combined) and the **fastigial nuclei,** arranged in that order lateromedially. The fibers entering and leaving the cerebellum and serving to connect it with other parts of the neural axis are grouped into three **peduncles,** an inferior or **restiform body,** a middle or **brachium pontis,** and a superior or **brachium conjunctivum** (Figs. 177, 186). These will be analyzed in detail below.

THE CEREBELLAR CORTEX

The histological structure of the cerebellar cortex is one of only three cell layers. These three layers are the outermost, or **molecular layer;** the middle, or **Purkinje-cell layer;** and the innermost, or **granular layer.** Furthermore, the cytological arrangement throughout the cerebellar cortex appears to be everywhere the same (Fig. 178). The outermost molecular layer of the cerebellar cortex contains many nerve-cell processes of neurons located in the deeper laminae and a few stellate neurons of its own. The more deeply placed stellate neurons send their axons in the molecular layer parallel to the outer cerebellar surface, and directed in a plane parallel to the long axis of the brain and at right angles to the axis of the folia. Branches from the axons, arising at intervals, pass to many Purkinje cells of the middle layer and form arborizing networks or "baskets" as a synaptic formation about the Purkinje-cell bodies (Figs. 179, 180). These stellate cells are therefore often referred to as **basket cells.** Their axons also send collateral branches to synapse with Purkinje-cell dendrites. A single basket cell can activate many Purkinje neurons. The dendrites of the basket cells ramify in the outer part of the molecular layer.

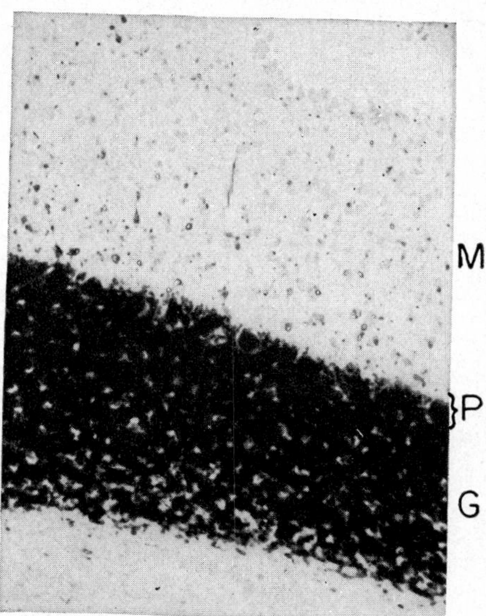

FIG. 178. Cerebellar cortex. *M*, molecular layer; *P*, Purkinje-cell layer; *G*, granule-cell layer. Macaque, thionin. Photomicrograph, ×122.

The **Purkinje-cell bodies** make up the middle or Purkinje layer of the cerebellar cortex. These cells are about 35 to 50 μ in diameter in man (Figs. 178, 180, 181). They usually

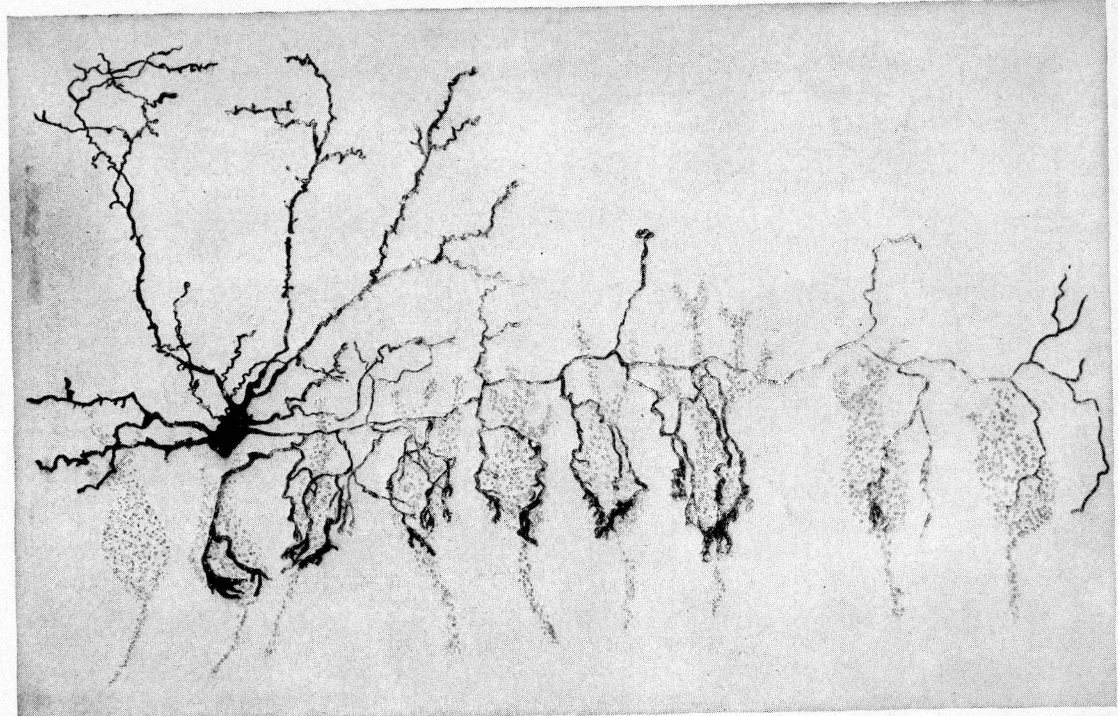

Fig. 179. A "basket" cell of the cerebellum. Collaterals of its axon form pericellular "baskets" about the bodies of Purkinje cells. (*Redrawn after Cajal, courtesy of The Williams & Wilkins Company.*)

possess two very large dendrites which are directed into the molecular layer and from which arise many branches of various sizes. The branches do not extend in all directions but are flattened laterally with respect to the contour of the brain. Because of this their full extent is seen only in sections cut longitudinally with relation to the cerebellum, or rather at right angles to the long axis of the

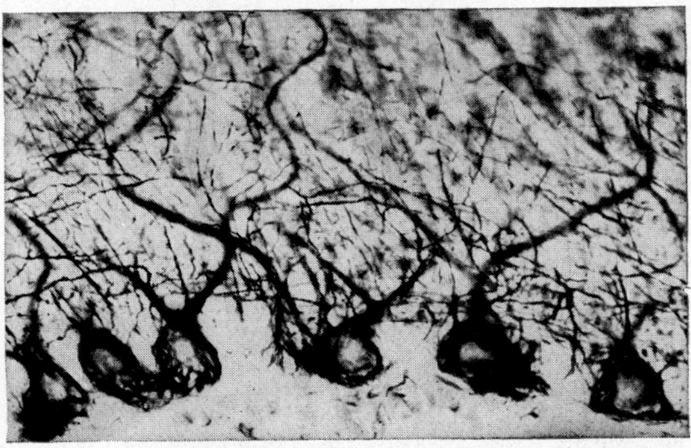

Fig. 180. Pericellular baskets about Purkinje cells. Silver, cat. Photomicrograph, ×294.

cerebellar folia. Transverse cerebellar sections, or those cut parallel to the folia axis, show the Purkinje dendritic tree on edge. The axon of the Purkinje cell is given off from the deeper pole. It passes into the central nuclei to terminate about the nuclear cells. At least, this is true for almost all the Purkinje cells. Some of those of the flocculonodular lobe, uvula, and anterior lobe apparently send axons outside the cerebellum to terminate in nuclei of the brain stem (vestibular nuclei). The Purkinje-cell axons have collateral branches, some of which return as **climbing fibers** to the molecular layer to terminate probably about other Purkinje-cell dendrites and basket-cell dendrites.

The innermost layer of the cerebellar cortex is the granular layer, so named because its most common cell type is a **granule cell** (Figs. 181, 182, 183). A typical cell has scanty cytoplasm from which arise about six short dendrites and a slightly longer axon which enters the molecular layer. Once here, the axon undergoes a T- or Y-shaped division, a branch running in either direction parallel with the long axis of the folium, or at right angles with the dendritic spread of the Purkinje cells. The axon terminals make synaptic connections with the Purkinje dendrites, many Purkinje cells thus coming to be related to one granule cell. The large Purkinje dendritic tree also accommodates axons from many granule cells. The short dendrites of the granule cells end within the vicinity of the cell body in clawlike processes. Fibers entering the cerebellum from without make synaptic contact with these. A single incoming fiber through its many terminal branches may make contact with many granule cells. Less numerous components of the granular layer are large **stellate neurons** of the Golgi type II classification (short axon). These have large dendrites which extend in all directions in the granular and molecular layers (Fig. 183). The short axon breaks up into many small terminal branches which apparently are in synaptic relation with granule-cell dendrites.

It has been customary for most authors to divide the fibers entering the cerebellar cortex from without into two types depending upon

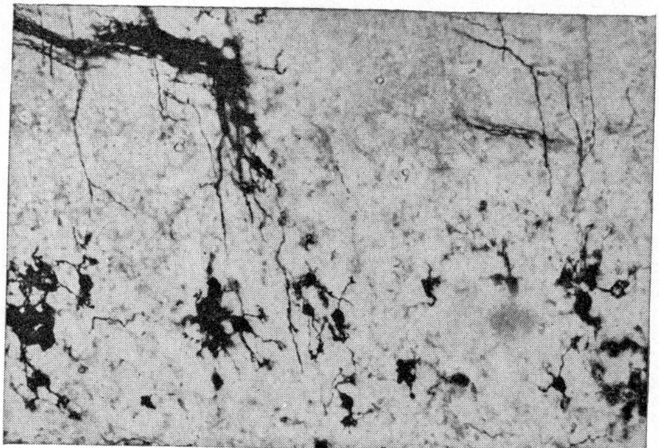

FIG. 182. Granule cells of the cerebellum. Cat, Cox-Golgi. Photomicrograph, ×189.

their mode of termination. Thus incoming fibers have been classified as **mossy** or **climbing** fibers. The mossy fibers are said to end in synaptic relation to the granule-cell dendrites, forming with them small **glomeruli.** The climbing fibers are said to "climb" into the molecular layer in which they end about dendrites of a single Purkinje cell. Actually, it is impossible at present to be accurate with regard to the manner of termination of a specific incoming fiber group. Dow, for example, feels that all incoming fibers except those of one group, the olivocerebellar, end as mossy fibers (215). Carrea and his associates think they have proof that *all* incoming fibers end as mossy fibers, and thus they confirm the opinion of others (128). It

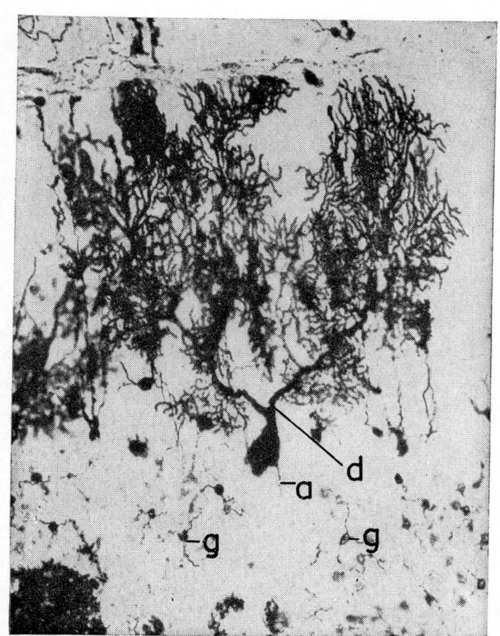

FIG. 181. Purkinje cell in cerebellum of cat. The full dendritic spread is visible. *a*, axon; *d*, a branch of the dendrite; *g*, granule cells. Silver. Photomicrograph.

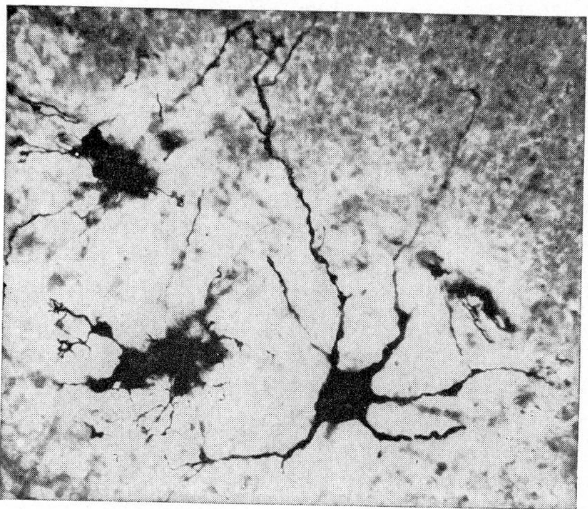

FIG. 183. A large stellate cell in the granular-cell layer of the cerebellum. The axon is not visible. Silver, cat. Photomicrograph, ×353.

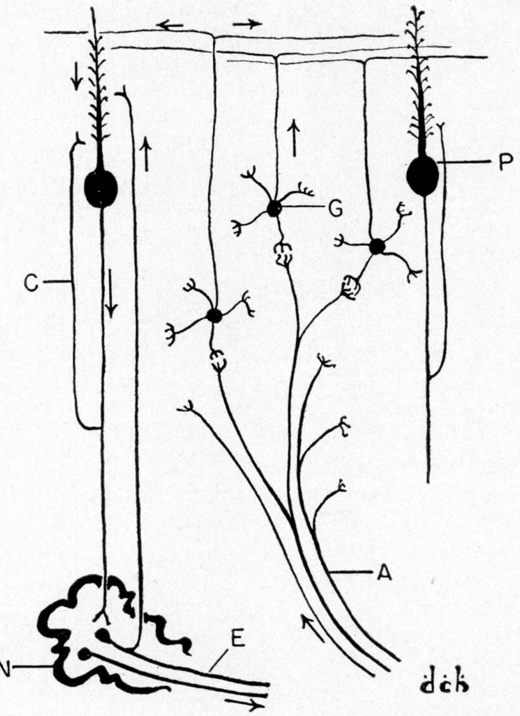

FIG. 184. A diagram of neuronal relations within the cerebellum. *A*, incoming fiber ending as "mossy" fibers about granule cells; *C*, recurrent collateral of axon of Purkinje cell; *E*, efferent fiber; *G*, granule cell; *N*, cerebellar nucleus; *P*, Purkinje cell.

is perhaps reasonable to state that the majority, if not all, of the fibers entering the cerebellum have mossy endings. Climbing fibers are probably intrinsic cerebellar association fibers, and the recurrent collaterals from Purkinje-cell and nuclear-cell axons, according to Carrea and many authors.

A review of intrinsic cerebellar cortical connections can now be attempted (Figs. 184, 185). Incoming fibers end as mossy fibers about the granule cells, a single fiber coming into synaptic relation with many of these cells. These cells in turn send impulses to the Purkinje-cell dendrites with which their axons are in contact; again, a single granule cell may come into relation with many Purkinje cells, and a single Purkinje cell receives from many granules. Stellate cells perhaps serve to maintain or to diffuse activity in granule cells, collecting from one group and passing to others, or reactivating the same group. Basket cells serve to associate many Purkinje cells and thus also to diffuse incoming impulses. Purkinje cells discharge into the cerebellar nuclei. Collaterals from the Purkinje axons may re-enter the cerebellar cortex as **association fibers** serving to coordinate and diffuse cortical activity or to complete a closed circuit for refiring Purkinje cells and thus prolong or facilitate their activity. These association fibers may be very short, ending near the parent cell, or may take a slightly longer course within the same or adjacent folia. Axons of nuclear neurons also send recurrent collaterals into the cortex, which also serve as association fibers. These association fibers may be climbing fibers according to their method of termination. These may serve to concentrate activity in certain small groups of neurons while mossy-fiber terminations serve for diffusing impulses, by activating larger groups of granule cells and, through them, many Purkinje cells.

AFFERENT CEREBELLAR FIBERS

Though all fibers entering the cerebellum may have a similar type of ending and though the cerebellar cellular cortex pattern is apparently the same everywhere, certain functional divisions can be made according to locus of termination of the fibers. Ingvar originally correlated fiber terminations with functional divisions (410).

On the basis of anatomical studies, these afferent fibers are from four chief sources: (*a*) vestibular nerve and nuclei, via direct and secondary vestibulocerebellar fibers; (*b*) spinal cord and medulla, via spinocerebellar, trigeminocerebellar, reticulocerebellar, and arcuatocerebellar tracts; (*c*) cerebral cortex, via synapses in pontine nuclei over corticopontocerebellars; (*d*) inferior olivary nuclei, via olivocerebellar fibers. The sites of termination in the human cerebellum are known for many; for others, only data from animals exist (Fig. 192). Interpretation of these is complicated by the difficulty in homologizing the various divisions of the cerebellum of animals with those of man.

Direct vestibular fibers in animals terminate in the homolateral flocculus; in the homolateral half of the nodulus, uvula, and lingula; and in the homolateral fastigial nucleus. The fibers to the flocculus traverse the lateral part of the restiform body, the others traverse the juxtarestiform body, the medial portion of the inferior cerebellar peduncle. **Secondary vestibular fibers** come from the superior and lateral vestibular nuclei, traverse the juxtarestiform body and terminate in both flocculi and fastigial nuclei (see later), and in both parts of the uvula, nodulus, and lingula (Figs. 131, 132).

Dorsal **spinocerebellar fibers** arise from the cells in Clarke's column in the spinal cord (from the eighth cervical segment to the third lumbar) and are chiefly uncrossed. They enter via the restiform body. Ventral spinocerebellar fibers are chiefly crossed and arise in all cord levels from neurons located in the medial, basal part of the spinal posterior gray columns. They enter by passing up and over the superior cerebellar peduncle. Spinocerebellar fibers end in the medial and intermediate zones of the anterior lobe, especially in the central lobule and culmen. Some fibers go to the pyramis, and the paramedian lobe, the simple lobule, and a few end in the uvula and nodulus. They end chiefly, then, in the anterior lobe of the cerebellum, the posterior lobe proper, and to a less extent in the rostral and caudolateral parts of the middle lobe. Ventral spinocerebellar fibers end almost exclusively in the anterior lobe and simple lobule; dorsal spinocerebellar fibers end anteriorly and posteriorly.

Reticulocerebellar fibers arise in the lateral reticular and arcuate nuclei of the medulla, enter via the restiform body, and may terminate in the cerebellum similarly to the spinocerebellar tracts. These fibers arising in the small-cell portion (medial portion) of the lateral reticular nucleus end in the vermis; other

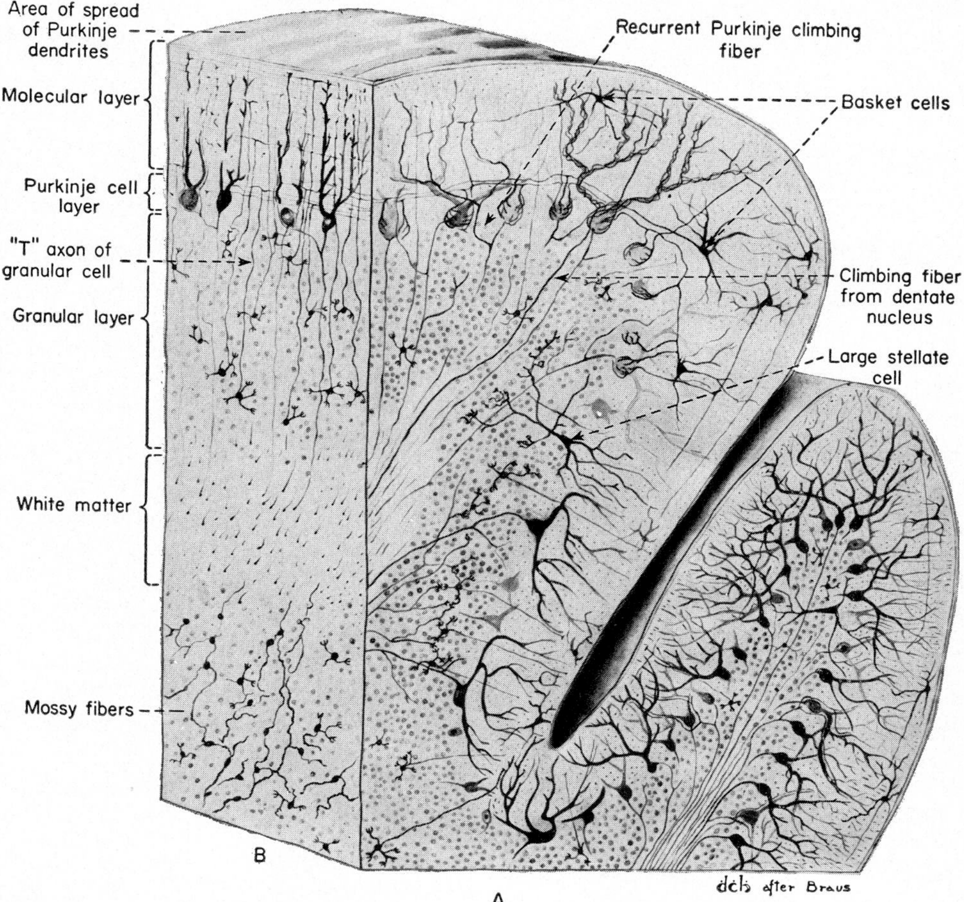

Fig. 185. Diagram of intrinsic structure of cerebellar cortex. *A*, the plane of section is at a right angle to the axis of the folium; *B*, the plane of section is along the long axis of the folium. (*Modified from Jakob.*)

reticular neurons project to the hemispheres. Some fibers from pontine reticular nuclei enter the cerebellum via the brachium pontis. **Trigeminocerebellar fibers** are thought to arise in the main sensory and mesencephalic trigeminal nuclei (468, 605). They pass with the ventral spinocerebellar fibers across the anterior medullary velum to form the cerebellar commissure. Electrical studies show them to have a termination in the simple lobule, especially. Other axons, arising in the lateral part of the cuneate nucleus, pass by way of the inferior cerebellar peduncle and end somewhat similarly to the spinocerebellar fibers. These fibers are sometimes called **dorsal external arcuate** fibers; the reticulocerebellars, **ventral external arcuates.** The lateral cuneate nucleus is thought to represent for cervical musculature a homology to Clarke's nucleus. The latter, it will be recalled, gives origin to dorsal spinocerebellar fibers. Some fibers, arising in the ventral arcuate nuclei, pass medially into and across the raphe, to pass dorsally and emerge in the floor of the fourth ventricle as striae medullares or **cerebellar striae,** which enter the cerebellum via the restiform body (Fig. 130).

Corticopontocerebellar connections develop to their greatest extent in mammals, and especially in man. Corticopontine fibers arise particularly from the precentral gyrus of the frontal lobe and, to a less extent, from more rostral gyri. Fewer corticopontine fibers arise from temporal, parietal, and occipital gyri. All terminate among cells of ipsilateral pontine nuclei (Figs. 134, 136). Frontal corticopontine fibers end most rostrally and dorsally about pontine nuclei and the parietal projections most caudally. These nuclei in turn project many pontocerebellar fibers across the basal portion of the pons and via the opposite brachium pontis into the lateral portions of the neocerebellum. A few pontocerebellar fibers enter the brachium pontis of the side of origin and thus end in the ipsilateral cerebellar cortex. The proportion of uncrossed to crossed fibers is greater in the pontocerebellar projection to the vermis than to the remaining portions receiving pontocerebellar fibers. Pontocerebellar fibers end in greater numbers in the lateral portions of the middle lobe, or neocerebellum (Fig. 192). Less extensive terminations are in the medial and vermian part of the middle lobe, in the anterior semilunar lobule of the anterior lobe, and in the pyramis and paraflocculus. In fact, it is probably true that all parts of cerebellar cortex, with the exception of that of the flocculonodular lobe, receive pontocerebellar fibers. The relationship between the pontine nuclei and the cerebellar cortex is not a point-to-point one, since pontine nuclear projections may overlap. The vermis portions of the cerebellar cortex receive projections from the paramedian pontine gray, the most ventral gray, and the dorsolateral gray of the pons. The cortex of the hemispheres receives pontine projections from the central or peduncular gray, the lateral gray, and the ventral gray. Included in these pontocerebellar projections, and especially those to the vermis, are fibers from the medial ventral reticular nucleus located near the raphe in that portion of pontine tegmentum immediately dorsal to the pontine gray (103).

Olivocerebellar fibers arise from all parts of the contralateral inferior olivary nuclei and in man are said to end in all parts of the cerebellar cortex except that of the flocculus. The olivocerebellar fibers compose a large portion of the restiform body. The lateral portions of the olive are connected with the lateral portions of the opposite side of the cerebellum (Fig. 173). The medial ends of the inferior olive, the inferior half of the medial accessory olives, and the dorsal half of the dorsal accessory olives send fibers to the vermis and the medial portions of the lateral lobes of the cerebellum (99, 390). The dorsal fold of the inferior olive is in connection chiefly with the superior surface of the cerebellum. The ventral folds of the inferior olive send fibers chiefly to the inferior part of the cerebellum. The olivocerebellar relationship is a point-to-point one, in that certain olivary neurons project to a definite cerebellar cortex area to which other olivary neurons do not project. A few olivocerebellar fibers arise from the ipsilateral olivary nuclei in the cat and rabbit. Furthermore, in these animals, and probably also in man, the cerebellar nuclei share in the olivocerebellar projection (99).

Finally, **tectocerebellar fibers** have been described in man by Riley and have been observed in human embryos by Larsell (466, 468, 675, 733). Arising in the midbrain tectum, the fibers pass through the anterior medullary velum and into the cerebellum via the medial part of the brachium conjunctivum. Their termination in the cerebellum has not been determined anatomically. Oscillographic studies have yielded some information, however (738). Action potentials have been recorded from the cerebellum in response to auditory and visual stimulation. It was shown that the auditory and visual impulses traversed inferior and superior colliculi, respectively. Tectocerebellar fibers were probably involved in the transmission of these impulses, and their site of termination can be assumed to correspond to the loci from which the action potentials were recorded. These loci are described below.

CEREBELLAR NUCLEI AND EFFERENT FIBERS

The efferent cerebellar connections may now be described, but first it is necessary to describe cerebellar cortical projections to the nuclei (212, 215). The largest and most laterally placed nucleus is the **dentate.** It is convoluted and appears something like a large draw-string purse with its mouth, or hilus, directed medially. The dentate nucleus of man apparently consists of two parts according to histological and embryological evidence (215). The older part is a smaller dorsomedial one composed of large and small cells; the newer part, and much the larger, is ventrolateral. The cells of this part are large multipolar ones with many branching dendrites. Their axons acquire myelin before they leave the nucleus proper. Axons from the cortical Purkinje cells converge on the lateral surface of the dentate nucleus. It receives Purkinje axons from all the neocerebellum, from the paraflocculus, and some few from the anterior semilunar lobule (Fig. 187).

Just medial to the dentate nucleus is the **emboliformis nucleus,** and medial to this latter one is the **globose nucleus** (Fig. 186). These two nuclei together are frequently called the **nucleus interpositus.** They contain multipolar cells of larger size than the majority of those of the dentate. They receive Purkinje axons from the lateral extensions of the central lobule and culmen, and from the intermediate por-

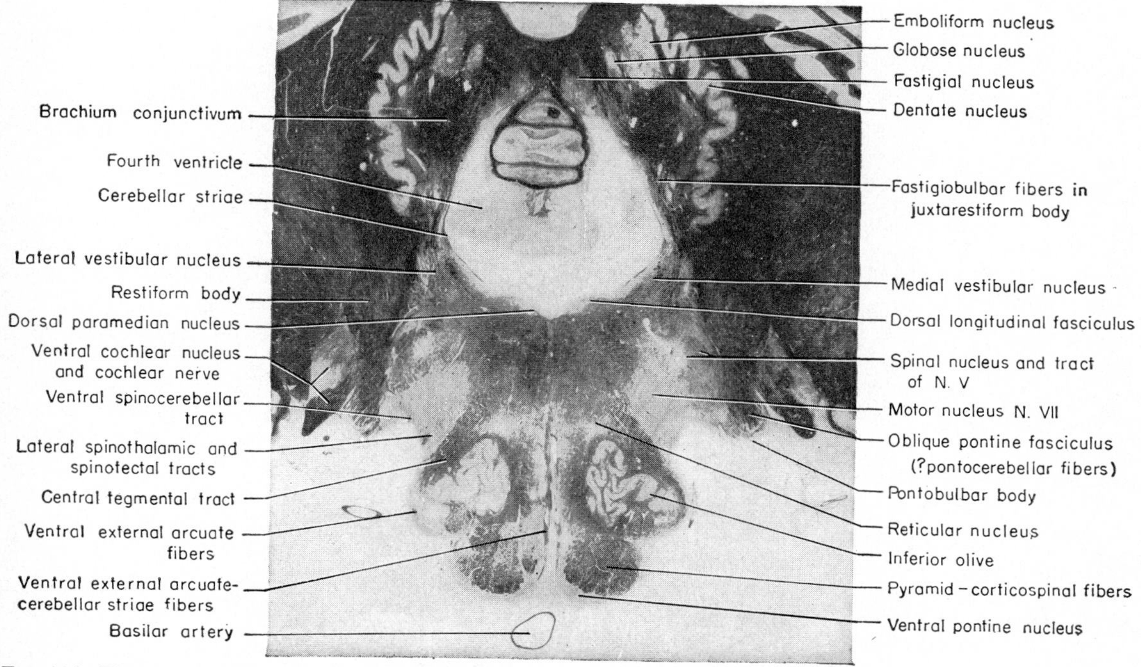

FIG. 186. Transverse section, A 450, of human brain stem at level of rostral medulla and cerebellar nuclei. Weigert. Photograph, ×2.5.

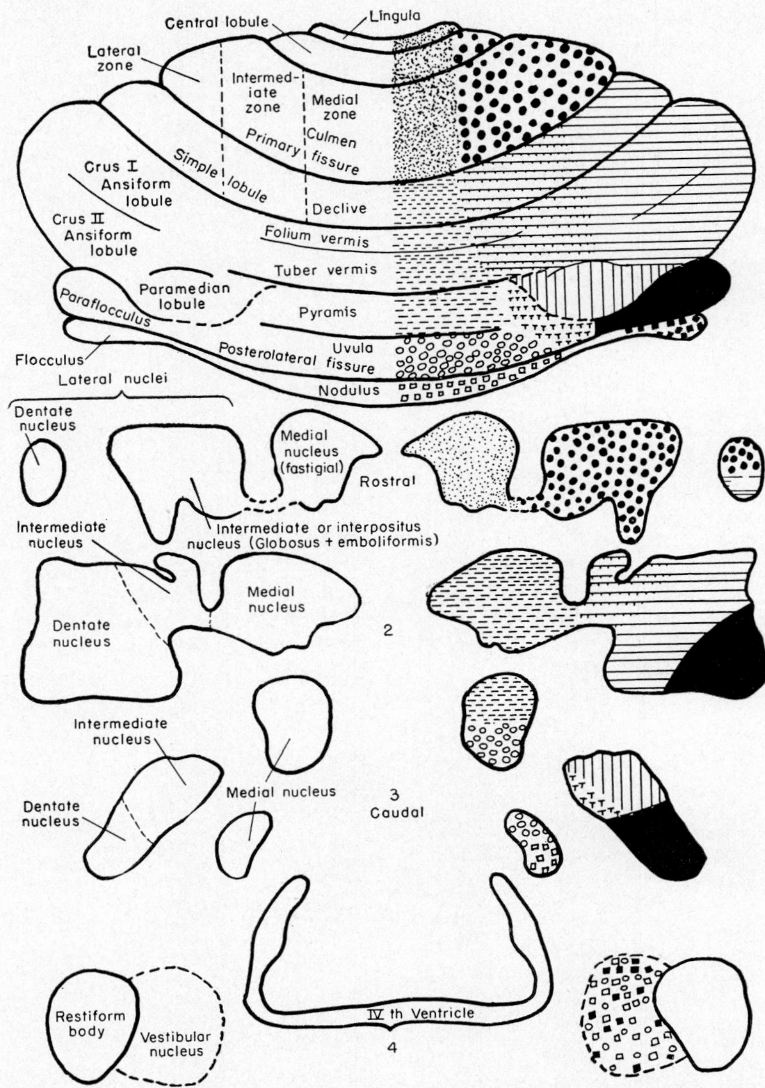

Fig. 187. The plan of the projections from the cerebellar cortex to cerebellar and vestibular nuclei. (*From Dow, Biol. Rev., vol.* 17, *based on Brodal and Jansen.*)

tions of the superior and inferior semilunar lobules (ansiform lobe) and biventral (paramedian) lobules (215, 413) (Fig. 187).

The most medial of the nuclei are the **fastigial nuclei,** sometimes called the roof or tectal nuclei, because of their position in the mid-line in that part of the cerebellum overlying the roof of the fourth ventricle. These nuclei contain large and small neurons. They receive Purkinje axons from all the vermian cortex and some axons from the vestibular nerve and nuclei. Electrical studies have suggested a wider area of reception, from the lateral parts of the anterior lobe and from the paramedian lobule (737).

The Purkinje axons of the flocculus are thought to project to the vestibular nuclei as the **angular bundle** incorporated in the juxtarestiform body, while the nodulus, uvula, pyramis, and anterior lobe send some direct fibers to the vestibular nuclei also via the inferior cerebellar peduncle (Figs. 174, 188). The

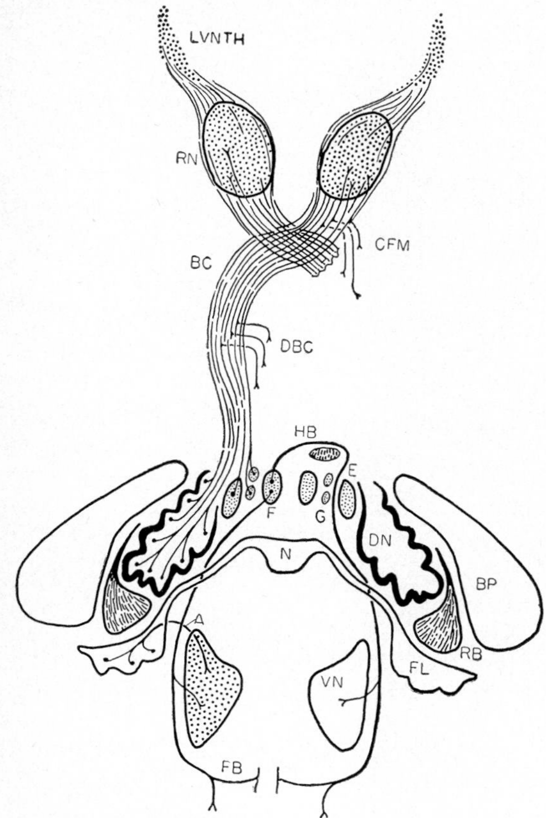

FIG. 188. Schematic diagram of efferent cerebellar fibers. *A*, angular bundle; *BC*, brachium conjunctivum; *BP*, brachium pontis; *CFM*, conjunctival fibers to mesencephalon; *DBC*, descending fibers of brachium conjunctivum; *DN*, dentate nucleus; *E*, emboliform nucleus; *F*, fastigial nucleus; *FB*, fastigiobulbar fibers; *FL*, flocculus; *G*, globose nucleus; *HB*, hook bundle (uncinate fasciculus); *LVNTH*, lateral ventral nucleus of thalamus; *N*, nodulus; *RB*, restiform body; *RN*, red nucleus; *VN*, vestibular nuclei.

flocculus also discharges fibers via the brachium conjunctivum to the oculomotor nuclei and to those of the trochlear and abducens nerves; these fibers are sometimes called Wallenberg-Klimoff fibers. The remaining **efferent cerebellar fibers** arise exclusively in the cerebellar nuclei.

The dentate and interpositus nuclei send all their projections out via the superior cerebellar peduncle, or brachium conjunctivum (Figs. 188, 189, 190). These fibers decussate and end in the contralateral red nucleus and lateral ventral nucleus of the thalamus, especially. The dentate neurons contribute the majority of the fibers to the thalamus; interpositus neurons, those to the red nuclei. A few of the crossed fibers terminate in the vicinity of the oculomotor nuclei, and some descending collaterals of the brachium conjunctivum fibers, arising before the decussation takes place, pass into the medial and ventral reticular formation of the medulla and pons. It is of considerable interest that the lateral ventral nucleus which receives these dentatorubrothalamic fibers projects to the precentral gyrus. This gyrus, it is to be recalled, sends corticopontocerebellar fibers into the cerebellum.

The fastigial nuclei project via two bundles, the direct **fastigiobulbar** tract and the crossed **uncinate fasciculus** (Figs. 186, 188). The former passes via the juxtarestiform body and terminates in all the ipsilateral vestibular nuclei, in the dorsal reticular formation of the medulla, and in the cranial nerve motor nuclei. The uncinate fasciculus arises in the fastigial nucleus, sweeps across the mid-line, loops around the superior cerebellar peduncle, and ends in the same loci as the fastigiobulbar tract but on the opposite side. It is of interest that these nuclei project to the bulbar inhibitory reticular neurons and to the vestibular nuclei.

CEREBELLAR PEDUNCLES

The afferent and efferent fibers of the cerebellum traverse the three cerebellar peduncles (Figs. 177, 189, 191). The inferior peduncle, or the **restiform body** (and including the medially placed juxtarestiform body), contains afferent fibers as follows: direct and secondary vestibulocerebellars; olivocerebellars; dorsal spinocerebellars; and external arcuates, dorsal and ventral. Efferent fibers are the cerebellovestibular fibers from the flocculus and posterior vermian cortex, and the fastigiobulbars.

The middle cerebellar peduncle, or **brachium pontis,** is composed almost entirely of pontocerebellar fibers. A few axons from pontine reticular nuclei to cerebellar cortex are also included. Some few cerebellopontine fibers may also be included, but these are insignificant. The superior cerebellar peduncle, or **brachium conjunctivum,** contains within it the efferent projections of the dentate and interpositus

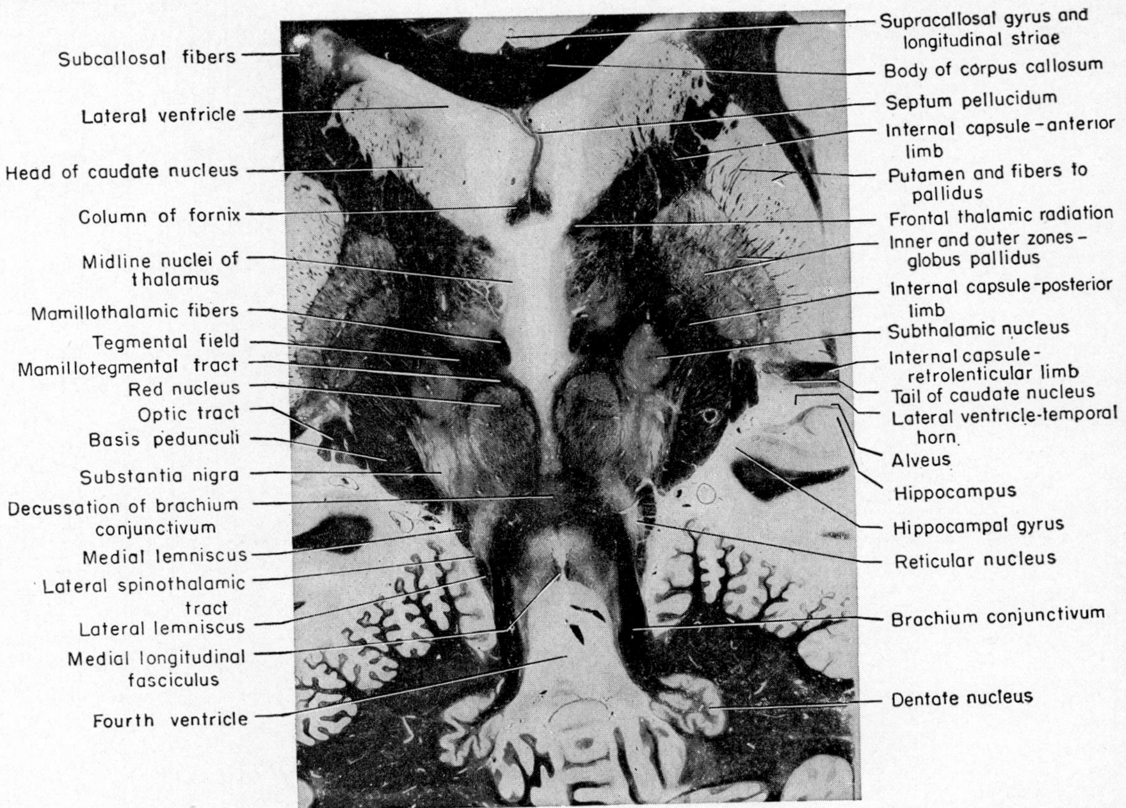

Fig. 189. Frontal section, B 440, of human brain stem, through red nuclei and brachium conjunctivum. Weigert Photograph, ×1.35.

nuclei. These pass to red nucleus, lateral ventral nucleus of the thalamus, oculomotor nuclei, and reticular nuclei of the pons and medulla. Looping around it is the uncinate fasciculus of fastigiobulbar fibers. Also passing up around it are the ventral spinocerebellar and trigeminocerebellar tracts, and running through it medially are tectocerebellar fibers.

Functional Divisions of Cerebellum

Divisions Based on Anatomical Studies

On the basis of its known fiber connections, the cerebellum has been divided into functional parts (410, 467). The divisions are not exact, however, since some overlapping of fiber terminations of certain systems exists, as seen in Fig. 192.

A simple but not exact division based upon the intensity of afferent fiber termination, shown anatomically, can be made as follows: a flocculonodular division receiving vestibulocerebellar fibers only; an anterior- and posterior-lobe-proper division receiving chiefly spinocerebellar and to less extent some pontocerebellar fibers; and a middle-lobe division receiving pontocerebellar fibers chiefly. Such a division might also follow that made by studying the order of development of the cerebellum, though again the divisions are not exact: archicerebellum or flocculonodular vestibular portion; paleocerebellum or anterior- and posterior-lobe spinocerebellar division; and a neocerebellum or pontocerebellar portion.

The archicerebellum, developed from the old lateral-line equilibratory system, is concerned through its vestibular connections with the maintenance of equilibrium or the proper orientation in space. The paleocerebellum, represented by anterior and posterior lobe

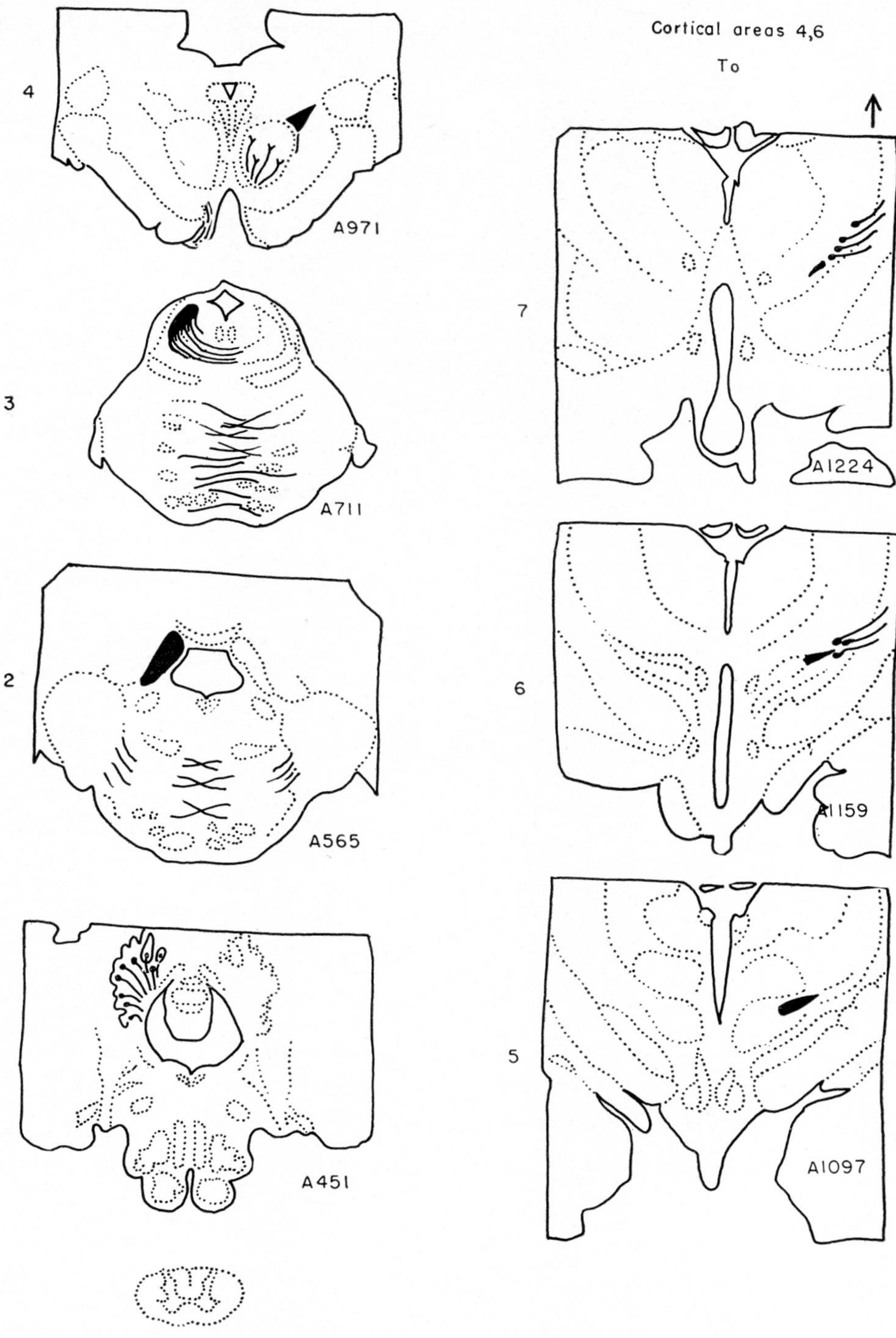

FIG. 190. Diagram of the brachium conjunctivum. The serial numbers, such as A1097, serve to orient the sections in a human brain stem series.

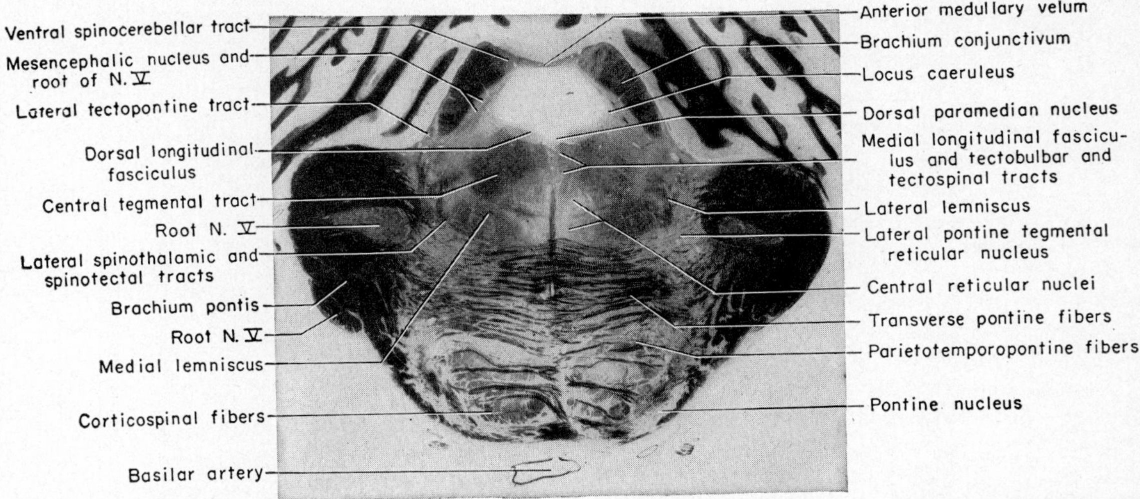

Fig. 191. Transverse section, A 595, of human brain stem through pons at a level just rostral to entry of trigeminal roots. Weigert. Photograph, ×2.

proper, is connected to the spinal cord and brain stem, develops phylogenetically with the development of the limbs, and serves to integrate postural adjustments which involve the segmental spinal, medullar, and midbrain reflexes. The neocerebellum, appearing last, develops simultaneously with the development of the cerebral cortical hemispheres, and is in intimate connection with the latter, as shown by anatomical and physiological studies. It develops also along with the development of finer, skillful, voluntary movements of limbs and cranial musculature.

DIVISIONS BASED ON ELECTROPHYSIOLOGICAL STUDIES

In recent years many electrophysiological studies in animals have served to show that the cerebellum receives impulses from sources in addition to those described in the foregoing part of this chapter (17, 214, 738). While these studies are not complete, a summary of certain results may be included. Certain of these experiments have involved either a mechanical stimulation of some peripheral sensory end organ or electrical excitation of cerebral cortical foci, and a simultaneous recording of the evoked potentials from the cerebellar cortex. Other experiments have included stimulation of the cerebellar cortex alone or in conjunction with stimulation of cerebral motor cortex, and an observation of the movement induced primarily by cerebellar activity, or by combined cerebellar and cerebral interplay. The first type of study has shown that tactile, auditory, and visual impulses evoke cerebellar potentials. Furthermore, stimulation of somatic sensory, auditory, visual, and autonomic pupillodilator areas of the cerebral cortex results in the production of cerebellar action potentials. The anatomical relations are yet to be completely established, but these physiological experiments are helpful. Tectocerebellar fibers persumably transmit auditory and visual impulses to the cerebellum. Spinocerebellar and trigeminocerebellar tracts probably transmit both tactile and proprioceptive impulses. Reticulocerebellar fibers may transmit tactile impulses. Furthermore physiologic researches indicate that a somatotopic localization of various parts of the organism exists in the cerebellum (17, 327, 328). In applying these results to the human it is essential to keep in mind the homologies at present known between the various divisions of the cerebellums of animals and man.

In the monkey and cat ipsilateral cutaneous surface is represented in the anterior cerebellar lobe and simple lobule (738). The hind limb is represented in the central lobule; the forelimb, in the culmen; the head and neck, in the simple lobule. Cutaneous surface is bilaterally represented in the paramedian lobules. In the monkey the localization is face in superior, arm in middle, and leg in inferior paramedian folia.

Two areas for representation of somatic sensibility seem to be present, therefore, in the cerebellum, as in the cerebral cortex (see later). The cerebellar auditory area in the cat is chiefly confined to the ipsilateral simple lobule and the tuber vermis, with some spread to the posterior culmen, and anterior pyramis. Auditory impulses also activate both ansiform lobes in their medial portions, and both paramedian lobules (738). The visual cerebellar area is practically coextensive with the auditory (Fig. 192). Spinocerebellar discharges from the hind limb of the cat arrive in the ipsilateral central lobule, according to Adrian (17). Discharges from the forelimb arise in the culmen, and from the snout vibrissae, in the simple lobule. Anatomical evidence has been provided for termination in the lingula of spinocerebellar impulses from the tail of the spider monkey (134). When Adrian applied strychnine to the cerebral motor area, potentials were evoked from the opposite cerebellar cortex. The leg, arm, and face areas of the motor area activated the central lobule, culmen, and simple lobule, respectively. These areas coincided with the spinocerebellar discharge areas, but extended more laterally.

It has been shown in the cat that stimulation of the cerebral somatic sensory areas also evokes cerebellar potentials. The cerebral somatic area in many species, including man, has been subdivided into so-called primary (I) and secondary (II) areas (see Chap. 19). In the primates thus far investigated, the postcentral gyrus is the cerebral somatic sensory area I; its homologue in other mammals is the primary area. The somatic sensory area II in macaque monkeys lies on the upper bank of the sylvian fissure between the auditory areas of the lower sylvian bank and the face subdivision of somatic area I in the postcentral gyrus. The face subdivision of area I is adjacent the face subdivision of area II, and the two complete areas are, in a sense, mirror images of one another. Primary and secondary auditory and visual areas have also been identified in the cerebral cortex of the cat.

These cerebral areas—somatic sensory, auditory, and visual—are related to areas of similar function in the cerebellar cortex, as shown thus far in the cat and monkey (326, 734) (Fig. 193). Somatic area I of the cerebral cortex, when stimulated, evokes responses in the opposite anterior lobe and simple lobule, especially. The various somatotopic subdivisions of the

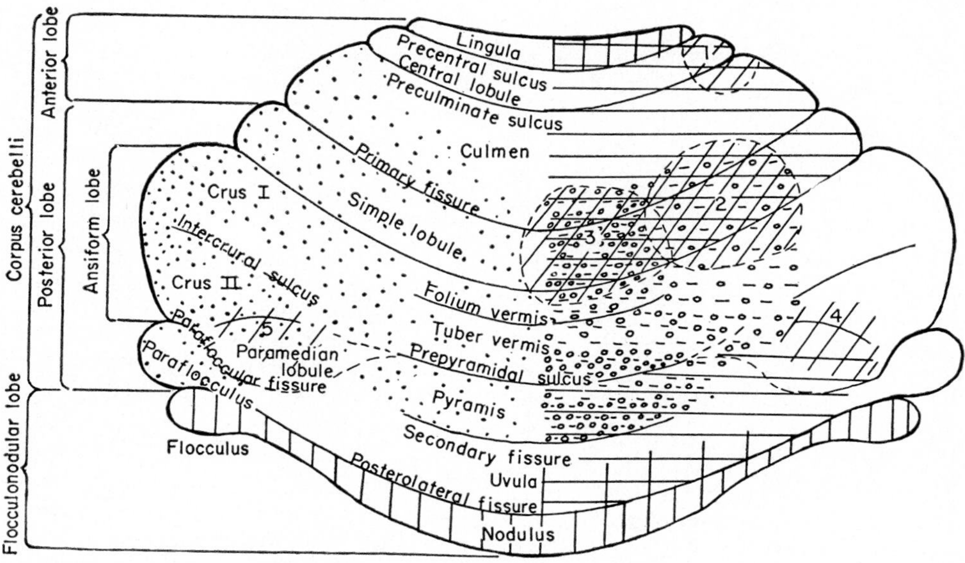

FIG. 192. Diagram of mammalian cerebellum to show the projection areas of tactile, visual, and auditory impulses. Horizontal lines indicate spinocerebellar connections. Stipple indicates corticopontocerebellar connections. Dashes indicate auditory area; circles indicate visual area; vertical lines indicate vestibular connections. Oblique lines indicate tactile areas. 1, hind foot; 2, forefoot; 3, vibrissae; 4, forefoot and hind foot; 5, forefoot and hind foot of opposite side. (*Based on studies of Snider and Stowell, Adrian, Hampson and Woolsey, from Larsell, Bull. Minn. Med. Found., vol.* 5.)

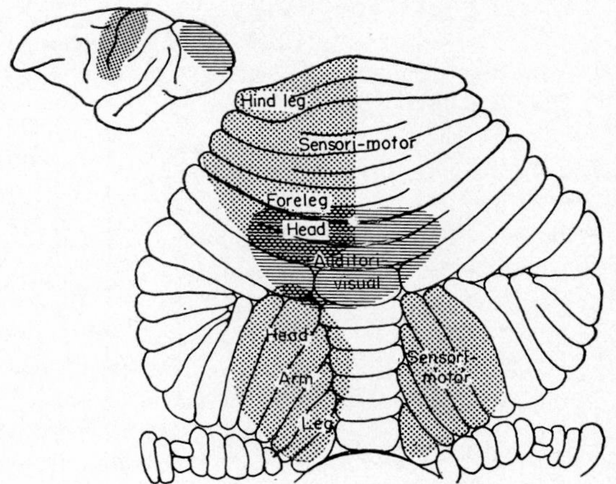

Fig. 193. A diagram of relations between cerebral and cerebellar cortices based on studies in the macaque. (*After Snider, Arch. Neurol. & Psychiat., vol.* 64.)

cerebral cortical area, face, arm, and leg, are apparently related especially to their homologous cerebellar subdivisions in the anterior lobe and simple lobule. Stimulation of cerebral somatic area II brings forth responses in the opposite paramedian lobule. The various cerebral subdivisions, face, arm, and leg, are related to their paramedian lobule homologous subdivisions.

The cerebral auditory areas I and II project to the folium and tuber of the vermis with some overlapping of termination, but with the secondary area represented in more concentrated fashion more caudally. The cerebral cortical area from which pupillodilation can be elicited in cats is related to the opposite cerebellar hemisphere, the upper folia of the adjacent paramedian lobule, and the lateral portion of the simple lobule.

By reviewing these various physiological results a new division of the cerebellum showing somatotopic localization of function is suggested. Hampson suggests that the middle lobe of the cerebellum, in the cat at least, subserves integration of cranial functions such as hearing, vision, facial expression, and somatic and autonomic control of the eyes (326). The remaining parts of the cerebellum, those which receive spinocerebellar fibers especially, are thought to serve as a dual cerebellar system for the integration of information from, and the control of, the rest of the body, the head excluded. The flocculonodular lobe remains as the vestibular division.

The cerebellar cortical surface and the central nuclei of various animals have been stimulated electrically by many investigators (132, 145, 247, 331). Clark has stimulated the cerebellum in normal, unanesthetized, unrestrained cats by using implanted electrodes. He described the resulting movements as divisible into three phases. The first phase was the movement that occurred with stimulation; the second phase, developing immediately on cessation of the stimulus, was of a rebound nature opposite from the first; the third phase was prolonged and involved various parts of the animal in a series of slow movements in a definite sequence lasting several minutes. The results from day to day were constant, and the sites stimulated showed a certain specificity for movement of a certain part of the body or limbs, thus indicating a somatotopic localization.

More recently, other electrical stimulations of cerebellar surface have also indicated a somatotopic localization for effector activity (327, 328). Flexion or extension movements can be elicited, and the representation in cat, dog, and monkey is as follows: tail (cat) in lingula; hind limbs and forelimbs in central lobule and culmen, respectively; neck, eyes, jaws, and facial muscles in the simple lobule. In the monkey, with more developed use of the extremities, stimulation of the anterior lobe laterally produced ipsilateral extension; that of the anterior lobe medially, ipsilateral flexion and extensor inhibition. Frequently, the elicited movements were followed by opposite effects, producing thus a rebound action. In some animals the stimulated movements were accompanied by reciprocal movements in the opposite limbs. A second effector center in the posterior cerebellum was also found. In the paramedian lobules a localization seems to be as follows: upper folia, face; middle folia, arm; lower folia, leg and tail. The representation, though predominantly ipsilateral, in some loci was also bilateral. Bilateral arm and leg movements were obtained from the pyramis, and conjugate eye movements toward the side stimulated, from the tuber. These studies, while incomplete, apparently indicate somatotopic localization of function in the cerebellar cortex of animals.

Electrical stimulations have shown that autonomic activity is regulated to some extent by the cerebellum. Chambers produced pupillary dilation by stimulating widely separated foci in the interior of the cerebellum of the cat; pupillary constriction was less often evoked (132). Urination resulted from stimulating an area in the region of the fastigial nuclei, the adjacent medullary substance, and buried cortex. These autonomic responses always accompanied somatic movements. Vasopressor and respiratory carotid sinus reflexes are inhibited by stimulation of the anterior lobe (570).

Some further insight into the relations between cerebral cortex and cerebellar activity has been gained by simultaneous stimulations of the two in cats, dogs, monkeys, and chimpanzees by Nulsen and his colleagues (583, 586). By varying the frequency of the stimulus, which was just over threshold in strength, the same anterior lobe cerebellar cortical focus could inhibit or facilitate ipsilateral movement induced by simultaneous stimulation of either the opposite cerebral cortex or pyramid. Thus, inhibition was elicited with low-frequency stimulation; facilitation was obtained in all animals, except the cat, with high-frequency stimulation. The foci in the anterior lobe of the cerebellum from which movement of various body parts could be influenced coincided well with the tactile representation in that lobe; the tail, hind limb, forelimb, and face musculature have an anteroposterior arrangement in the lingula, central lobule, culmen, and simple lobule, respectively. Moreover, proximal limb muscles could be activated from foci near the vermis; distal ones, from more lateral foci. By selective destruction of one cerebellar nucleus and stimulation of the remainder, he was able to demonstrate that the inhibition from the anterior lobe was transmitted through the dentate nucleus; the facilitation, through the fastigial nuclei.

It has been known since Sherrington's researches that the extensor tone of decerebrate rigidity in cats could be abolished by stimulating the anterior lobe of the cerebellum (725). Snider and his co-workers have repeated this and in addition have been able to demonstrate also that cerebellar stimulation can lead to inhibition or facilitation of cortically induced or reflex movement (735, 736, 737). Facilitation was easier to demonstrate in the monkey than in the cat, and facilitation of a cortically induced or reflex movement was more effective if the cerebellar stimulation preceded the elicitation of the movement by 5 to 15 sec. The points yielding facilitation or inhibition were found to be practically coextensive with the areas as outlined for tactile representation given above. Foci from which ipsilateral movement was altered were found in the anterior lobe; foci from which bilateral movements could be altered were present in the paramedian lobules and nearby folia. It is of interest that these workers, in contrast to Nulsen, demonstrated that the paths through which this cerebellar facilitation or inhibition was expressed traversed the fastigial nuclei, especially the ipsilateral one. From these nuclei the inhibitory influences played into the bulbar inhibitory center, the facilitatory influences into that part of the brain stem tegmentum from which facilitation of movement is most easily brought about.

Walker showed that stimulation of the cerebellar hemispheres in the cat brought about an increase in amplitude and frequency of the action potential of the cerebral cortical motor area (794). This effect was not obtained after section of the superior cerebellar peduncle. It seems likely, then, that the cerebellum can alter activity of motor centers at a cerebral level as well as at a brain stem one, as shown by Snider's results. The results of stimulation of the cerebellar surface, together with the action potentials evoked from the cerebellum, in response to somatic afferent stimuli, suggest that a similar and overlapping pattern of localization exists in the cerebellum for efferent and afferent systems.

Stimulation of the human cerebellar cortex has been reported by one neurosurgeon (633). The procedure was undertaken in the course of exposure for some other disease process and was not systematically carried out. It is of interest that stimulation of a point which was assumed to be in the rostral part of the ansiform lobe near the vermis resulted in flexion of both legs at the knees. The limbs soon returned to rest position and subsequently underwent similar flexion twice without repetition of the stimulus. Later stimulation of the same point again produced flexion of the knees, and this time abduction of the ipsilateral fingers was noted. Beyond this report, no demonstration of specific somatotopic representation in the human cerebellum has been furnished. Disease processes of the cerebellum do not long respect the divisions as made above and usually result in some impairment of movement of all parts of the body.

Ablations from the Cerebellum

Studies of animals with all or various portions of the cerebellum removed have been useful in analysis of cerebellar function. For a short time after total decerebellation cats and dogs exhibit opisthotonos, retraction of the head, extensor spasms of the forelimbs, and clonic spasms of the hind legs. These activities usually are transient. The most significant result of removal of the cerebellum in lower primates, however, is a disturbance in the control and performance of complex movements. The disturbance can be described in terms of tremor, dysmetria, asynergia, and ataxia. These terms are also encountered in the description of humans with cerebellar injury and will be elucidated below.

Removal of the flocculonodular lobe from animals results in equilibratory disorder (213). The animal falls; it shows oscillations of the head, a staggering gait with a wide base, and incoordination of the trunk movements. These signs usually are not permanent, compensation perhaps being established through medullar vestibular mechanisms.

Removal of the anterior lobe from animals results in disturbances in the postural mechanisms (171). Opisthotonos, hyperactive supporting reactions, incoordination in all extremities and the neck, hyperactive deep reflexes, and increased lengthening and shortening reactions are reported. Labyrinthine and neck tonic influences modify these disorders of posture. It appears that there is fundamentally a release of the local extensor proprioceptive mechanisms of the neck and extremities, and also a release of the labyrinthine tonic influences. In monkeys such release phenomena do not occur after ablation of the anterior lobe of the cerebellum, unless the cerebral cortical areas 4 and 6 are also ablated on the opposite side. The muscle tone is increased in those limbs opposite the cerebral cortical ablation. Carrea and Mettler report that ablation of the hemispheric part of the central lobule, culmen, and simple lobule leads to ataxia and intention tremor accompanying voluntary movement of the ipsilateral upper limb. The hemispheric portion of the culmen controls movements of the ipsilateral upper limb, the hemispheric portion of the central lobule, movements of the ipsilateral lower limb (127).

Removal of the uvula from animals results in transitory disturbance of maintaining equilibrium. Removal of the pyramis has been reported to lead to disorder in gauging distances visually. This may come about because of lack of coordination between movements of the ocular muscles and those of the limbs. The pyramis apparently is related to the control of ocular movements, and contractions of ocular muscles can be elicited by stimulation of the pyramis. Proprioceptive impulses from ocular muscles may be integrated in the pyramis and correlated with those from limb and trunk muscles in cerebellar cortex. Removal of the nodulus from dogs is effective in ridding them of a susceptibility to motion sickness, as mentioned in a previous chapter.

Removal of the neocerebellum from lower animals results in slight and transient disorder. When removals are made from chimpanzees, however, noticeable effects are produced (91). Unilateral cortical removal results in homolateral hypotonia, awkwardness in performance of voluntary learned movements, and disorders of gait. Upper and lower limbs are equally affected. These signs are apt to be transient unless the dentate and interpositus nuclei are also damaged; in the latter case, ataxia accompanies all movement also. This provokes longer lasting of the effects and adds also a tremor associated with voluntary movements. Animal experimentation thus indicates that separate types of disturbance might result from removal of each of the three divisions of the cerebellum described above.

Cerebellar Disorder in Man

The cerebellum clinically is involved by vascular disorders, tumor formation either directly within its substance or by compression by a tumor involving a neighboring brain region, by degenerative disease, by inflammatory conditions, and by direct trauma such as gunshot injuries. These disorders have certain things in common with regard to cerebellar symptomatology (383). Acute traumatic injury is frequently associated with the most pronounced signs of disordered motility. Study of humans with cerebellar disease has indicated that at least two different cerebellar syndromes can be defined, and a third can be surmised from animal experimentation. At least, adequate clinical confirmation exists for **archicerebellar** and **neocerebellar syndromes;** a **paleocerebellar** syndrome has not as yet been sharply defined. In some individuals, the first two syndromes are mixed.

THE ARCHICEREBELLAR SYNDROME

This is best observed in cases of a tumor (medulloblastoma) of the flocculonodular portion. While such a tumor is limited to this lobe it is characteristic for the patient to demonstrate a gross defect of equilibrium. The patient, most often a young child, walks on a wide base, sways from side to side, has ataxia of the trunk, and may fall or be completely unable to maintain an upright balance. Individual movements of the limbs, when the patient is lying down or when the limbs are supported, are not at all disturbed, and there is no hypotonia or change in reflexes. Maintenance of the correct upright position is most affected. Because of the relation of the flocculonodular lobe of the cerebellum to the roof of the fourth ventricle, it is common for medulloblastomas to interfere with the escape of cerebrospinal fluid from the ventricle into the subarachnoid space. This is associated with signs of increased intracranial pressure, and headache, vomiting, some impairment of vision, and a slowing of the pulse rate are seen as early signs.

THE NEOCEREBELLAR SYNDROME

This syndrome has been most completely described by Holmes in numerous studies (42, 380, 383, 803). With unilateral lesions the signs are homolateral. Usually found are atonia, disorders of muscular contraction, disorders of voluntary movement, and tremor.

One of the most important contributing factors to neocerebellar symptomatology in man is a disorder of muscle tone and thus a loss of postural fixation of muscles. This postural tone defect is most noticeable in the muscles of the limbs. Muscle tone, as described previously, arises in muscles themselves through activity of proprioceptive and effector mechanisms united at the proper segmental cord level. It is a product of the stretch reflexes. Since the purpose of tone of a single muscle is to maintain its posture, and of muscles, collectively, to maintain body posture, or rapidly alter it if necessary, muscle tone is normally more developed in those muscles that serve to maintain man in an upright position, the so-called antigravity muscles. These are the extensors of the lower limbs, trunk, and neck, and the flexors of the upper limbs.

The spinal mechanisms initiating muscle tone, and discharging other effector impulses to muscles, reflexly and volitionally induced, are under the influence of supraspinal centers in brain stem, cerebellum, and telencephalon. These supraspinal centers exert either inhibitory or facilitatory control on the spinal neurons which maintain these mechanisms. Proprioceptive pathways transmit to those upper levels the necessary information from the muscles in order that the activity of these supraspinal centers can be most effective and their coordination of the spinal effector mechanisms will be suitable for the movement pattern initiated, postural, reflex, or skilled. This may involve an enhancement of tone in certain muscle groups, a modulation of tone in others, a proper sequential distribution of tone, and a maintenance of it in proper amount in all muscles. In the cat and monkey, the anterior lobe of the cerebellum, especially, discharges facilitatory or inhibitory impulses, presumably depending on the nature of the impulses entering the cerebellum at the moment. The paramedian lobules also discharge such inhibitory or facilitatory influences. On the other hand, in man, the neocerebellum, particularly, appears to stand ready to reinforce the spinal tonic mechanisms and to maintain proper balance in tone between extensors and flexors; it thus promotes postural fixation or tone, a necessary accompaniment of the phasic, short-lived contractions of muscles, initiated at cerebral cortical level when skillful voluntary movement is performed. The tonic and phasic elements properly balanced make for correct coordination of movement. The neocerebellum as a facilitating mechanism is active in the promotion of the tonic element and cooperates with the cerebral cortical motor area when the latter initiates the phasic element. The cerebellum is also the agent through which the cerebral motor cortex in large measure coordinates postural tonic activities of spinal centers and organizes them into a performance of coordinated purposive movement (803). When the cerebellum is the site of disease process this cooperating activity is defective. The loss of facilitating influences of the neocerebellum is usually most striking in man; postural tone is deficient, and the cerebral motor cortex acts without its important coordinating ally. The cerebral motor cortex is able to initiate the phasic element of voluntary purposive movement, but the resulting act is awkward. The synergy of the muscles acting is defective; agonists, antagonists, and fixators do not cooperate properly in the performance. Timing of contraction is faulty because of the atonia, relaxation occurs too soon many times, range of movement is either too great or too little and cessation of contraction may occur too soon. All this makes for a condition characterized as asynergia.

Voluntary movements are therefore greatly impaired in the neocerebellar syndrome and these impairments are described in various terms. **Dysmetria** denotes difficulty in gauging accurately the amount of movement necessary to attain an object. The patient usually overshoots or undershoots the mark. A **decomposition of movement** is observed in the neocerebellar syndrome. A complex act involving simultaneous movement at shoulder, elbow, wrist, and fingers may be broken down into its individual parts, the shoulder adjustment performed first, the elbow next, and finally, the wrist and fingers are engaged. **Dysdiadochokinesis** is the term for a disturbance of performing rapidly repetitive movement, *e.g.*, alternate slapping of the knee with the palm and dorsum of the hand. The lack of tone and postural fixation leads to slowness of muscular contraction. The slowness, decomposition of movement, and disorder in measurement make it difficult or impossible for a patient to perform repeated movements rapidly. **Fatigability and weakness of movement** (**asthenia**) are also commonly seen. The hypotonia and faulty innervations of postural fixation make a continuous attention necessary and require a constant attempt at correction. These factors lead to fatigability, both physically and mentally.

All these disorders necessarily make for incoordination of voluntary-muscle activity. This incoordination or awkwardness is commonly described as **ataxia.** Contributing to the ataxia of voluntary movement is a **tremor** which accompanies it. To-and-fro movements or **intention tremors** of an extremity occur when a voluntary movement is performed. These appear to be due to lack of proper fixation of postural or stabilizing muscles, and to faulty timing of innervations of various muscle groups, alternate innervations of flexor and extensor patterns taking place out of normal rhythm and sequence. The tremor usually increases near the termination of the movement or near the attainment of the goal. It appears that the patient becomes more desirous and eager as the goal is approached, realizes that more skillful movement is necessary at the moment, and somewhat overcompensates in his efforts to control fixation and to initiate movement correctly in the requisite muscle groups. Tremors, comparable to the action tremors of humans, have been produced in monkeys with destructive lesions of the dentate nucleus or the brachium conjunctivum (127, 624).

In addition to the signs described above, other evidences of movement disorder are frequently described. **Nystagmus** is frequently recorded, and this especially is noted on attempts at fixation of gaze. It is slower and coarser when the patient looks to the side of the lesion. When a patient with a left-sided lesion, for example, looks to the left, a slow wandering of the eyes back to the rest point occurs, followed by a rapid movement back toward the direction of gaze (380). The nystagmus arises through the faulty postural fixation in the ocular muscles and is comparable to tremor of skeletal muscles, possibly. Similarly, disorders of speech may be seen due to lack of postural fixation and faulty sequences of innervation of glossal and laryngeal musculature. A lack of ability to check contraction is also frequently present. This can be demonstrated as follows. The examiner, attempting to extend the patient's forearm against his efforts to resist it, suddenly releases his pull. Because of the lack of proper postural tone in the triceps, its voluntary contraction is slowed and the patient is unable to check the flexion movement in time and may strike himself in the face. This is described as a **rebound** action. All these elements of the neocerebellar syndrome are worse and longer-lasting if the dentate nuclei are also damaged. A neocerebellar syndrome can be described also in lesions of the superior cerebellar peduncle. Thus far, from human cases of the neocerebellar syndrome studied, no definite somatotopical representation of arm or leg movements in the cerebellum has been proved although such has been suggested. No sensory disorder follows cerebellar injury in man.

THE PALEOCEREBELLAR SYNDROME

This syndrome, as suggested by results in animals, and especially cats, might be expected to be characterized by increased extensor tone, increased reflexes, increased supporting reactions, incoordination of the trunk, opisthotonoid postures, and perhaps "cerebellar fits" (42). These last involve retraction of the head, extensor rigidity of all four extremities, arching of the back, and irregular respiration. The symptoms would probably result primarily through a loss of the inhibitory mechanisms of the anterior cerebellum on brain stem and spinal neurons. These inhibitory effects, as shown in other sections, are expressed through the bulbar inhibitory center via certain reticulospinal tracts. A release of labyrinthine mechanisms would also be involved, and through vestibulospinal fibers facilitatory effects would be expressed. Such discrete anterior-lobe lesions clinically are necessarily rare. "Cerebellar" or so-called decerebrate fits are seen in humans with compression of, or gradually increasing destruction of, the brain stem at caudal, midbrain, and pontine levels. They are not necessarily an indication of intrinsic cerebellar disease, therefore.

VASCULAR SYNDROMES INVOLVING THE CEREBELLUM

The disorders of equilibrium and movement described above are also seen with disease of the cerebellum resulting from disorder of its blood supply. Vascular insults to the cerebellar peduncles lead to more striking disorders than do disorders of the vessels supplying only the cerebellar cortex and nuclei, because of the overlapping of blood supply to the cerebellum.

The **superior cerebellar artery** supplies the superior cerebellar peduncle and the cerebellar nuclei as well as some superior hemispheric and vermian cortex, as far posteriorly as the anterior border of the inferior semilunar lobule and tuber, respectively (Fig. 142). It sends a branch to the dorsolateral tegmentum of the pons in its course to the cerebellum. This tegmental supply may include nourishment to the lateral spinothalamic tract at the level, emerging facial nerve fibers, and lateral lemniscus. A superior-cerebellar-artery syndrome usually includes a neocerebellar syndrome plus a pontine tegmentum syndrome. The latter most commonly consists of contralateral loss of pain and temperature sense over the trunk and limbs, but it may also include facial paralysis and some impairment of hearing. Unless the tegmental disturbance is present, it is frequently impossible to separate this vascular syndrome from one arising as result of some other process in the cerebellar hemispheres.

As the **anterior inferior cerebellar artery** runs across the brachium pontis, it sends some branches into the flocculus and later divides into lateral and medial branches (Fig. 141). These supply, respectively, the lateral hemispheric region of the inferior semilunar and biventral regions and the vermian regions of pyramis, tuber, and folium. The anterior inferior cerebellar artery may overlap slightly in its distribution with that of the superior cerebellar. A syndrome of disorder in the cerebellar distribution of this vessel would probably be similar to the neocerebellar syndrome.

The **posterior inferior cerebellar artery** usually supplies dorsolateral medulla as well as posterior and inferior cerebellum including flocculonodular lobe, uvula, and posterior part of hemispheres; it also supplies the caudal portion of the cerebellar nuclei (Fig. 57). The medullar branches vary considerably, and the territory dependent on the artery or its branches may vary from only the restiform body to the entire dorsolateral medulla. It is unusual for all this lateral territory to be dependent on a single vessel, but the syndrome of the posterior inferior cerebellar artery in the classic descriptions implies such widespread medullar involvement (538). Lateral spinothalamic tracts, nucleus ambiguus, spinal trigeminal nucleus and tract, descending sympathetic tracts, and spinocerebellar tracts are those structures whose damage may be reflected clinically. Most typically the syndrome includes homolateral disorder of equilibrium due to restiform-body or archicerebellar involvement and various other signs according to amount of medullar involvement; contralateral disturbance of pain and temperature sense on the body and limbs; ipsilateral pain and temperature disturbance on the ipsilateral side of the face; paralysis of the soft palate and larynx ipsilaterally; a Horner's syndrome and varying vasomotor paralysis ipsilaterally; and often, singultus. Without striking medullar involvement, this vascular cerebellar disorder can simulate a developing archicerebellar syndrome on the basis of tumor.

Degenerations in the cerebellum or in its tracts are not uncommon and usually show varied combinations of the cerebellar syndromes, but they usually result in ataxia. Hereditary degenerations are perhaps most common and are associated with degenerative processes in brain stem, spinal cord, and cerebral cortex in some instances.

Summary

Studies of cerebellar disorder thus far have shown, therefore, that the cerebellum can be divided into at least two functional parts, neocerebellum and archicerebellum. Somatotopic representation of function has, however, not been proved for man, though an occasional hint that such may exist has been given. In cats and monkeys, however, physiological experiments are indicating that our anatomical knowledge of cerebellar connections is far from complete, that previous functional divisions interpreted on these fiber connections are not completely accurate, that a large variety of afferent impulses reach the cerebellum, and that a somatotopic localization of function, present in these animals, may yet become a proved fact in man. Recent anatomical studies, especially those concerned with pontocerebellar connections, have confirmed that this fiber system reaches all parts of the cerebellum except the flocculonodular lobe, and this fact again indicates that the present cerebellar divisions based on fiber connections are probably inaccurate. Finally, an effector system, also showing somatotopic localization of body parts, has been demonstrated physiologically in animals and hinted at in man. The complete pathway used by this effector system is only partially known. A better understanding of the mechanisms of the cerebellum is a promise of future researches.

The cerebellum is therefore of great help to the cerebral motor cortex in the integration of voluntary movement. It is normally the recipient of information from skeletal muscle spindles, from tactile endings, and from the eye and ear. It is interrelated with somatic motor and sensory areas of the cerebral cortex and with auditory and visual areas. The cerebral and cerebellar cortices are somewhat similar, therefore, in the sources of their afferent impulses. Both have large efferent systems. The cerebellum, under proper conditions of stimulation, will evoke movement, as will the cerebral cortex, though the movement patterns may be different in many respects.

The incoming impulses from muscles, tactile end organs, labyrinth, cochlea, and retina furnish the cerebellum information as to the muscular performance of the organism and its relation to the outside world. It is thus made aware of the state of contraction existing in a certain group of muscles and about joints and can use this information in its cooperation with the cerebral cortex in the activation of this muscle group for skilled movement. Through its afferent visual impulses it can aid in guiding the movement. It can work hand in hand with the cerebral cortex by virtue of its known intimate reciprocal connections with it, namely, the corticopontocerebellar system and the dentatorubrothalamocortical circuit.

Stimulation of the cerebellum lowers the threshold of the cerebral cortex to stimulation which will initiate movement. The cerebellum may thus facilitate cerebral motor-cortex activity. It may also inhibit it, under certain conditions. The two cortices, cerebral and cerebellar, can cooperate at a cerebral, brain stem, or spinal level. Through olivocerebellar connections the cerebellum is in contact with the large motor nuclei of the brain stem and the reticular nuclei of the brain stem. It can thus be guided by them and can also cooperate or influence them in their contribution to motor performance described later. In addition to the cooperation with the cerebral cortex and subcortical motor nuclei for performance of skilled skeletal movement, the cerebellum is also active in the control of normal equilibrium through its vestibular connections. Finally, it exerts some control, perhaps chiefly inhibitory, over the extensor postural mechanisms, under the management of medullar centers; *e.g.*, supporting reactions, extensor mechanisms, and tonic labyrinthine reactions are increased when the anterior cerebellar lobe of animals is removed. Its greatest contribution in man is cooperation with the cerebral cortex in the performance of voluntary skilled movements, promoting coordination of movement. Acting as intermediary in this cerebral and cerebellar cortical activity is the thalamus. This region will now be described.

CHAPTER 13

THE THALAMUS

THE DIENCEPHALON is an exceedingly complex structure, with a long and involved phylogenetic history. It may be divided into several chief parts, the exact method of division differing with the worker. Perhaps the simplest division is that used in the previous section in which its gross structure was described: the epithalamus, the thalamus proper or dorsal thalamus, the ventral or subthalamus, and the hypothalamus. The general description of them has been given in the earlier section.

THE DIVISIONS OF THE THALAMUS

The epithalamus is composed largely of the habenular ganglia and their paths; it probably serves as a complex center for correlating olfactory and somatic impulses. The habenulae are further considered in the section on olfactory paths.

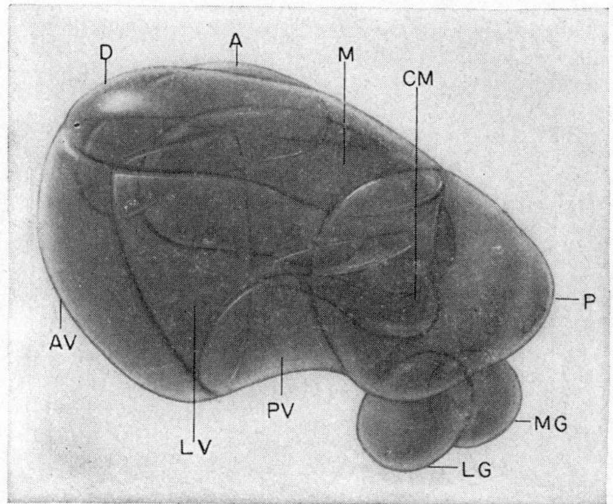

FIG. 194. A reconstruction of the left half of a human thalamus. Only the larger thalamic nuclei are shown. *A*, anterior nucleus; *AV*, anterior ventral; *CM*, centrum medianum; *D*, dorsal nuclei of lateral mass; *LG*, lateral geniculate; *LV*, lateral ventral; *M*, medial nucleus; *MG*, medial geniculate; *P*, pulvinar; *PV*, posterior ventral.

The ventral thalamus, or subthalamus, is really a continuation of the tegmentum of the midbrain, with the red nuclei and the substantiae nigrae projecting into it. In general it serves as a way station for the discharge of impulses from the corpus striatum and the extrapyramidal motor system (Chap. 17).

The hypothalamus, aside from its hippocampal and hypophyseal connections, serves as a very important visceral motor center. Among the various functional centers which it is said to contain are those which are concerned with vasomotor, temperature, sleep, and metabolic regulations. The hypothalamus is considered separately in the following chapter.

The dorsal thalamus, frequently referred to simply as "the" thalamus, is in itself so complex that in any treatment it must of necessity be subdivided (149) (Figs. 194, 195). From the standpoint of anatomy the most obvious division is into the **anterior, medial, lateral, and posterior nuclei.** The first three are separated from each other by **internal medullary laminae** of entering and connecting fibers, and each in turn consists of several subsidiary nuclei. In addition, other nuclei are enclosed

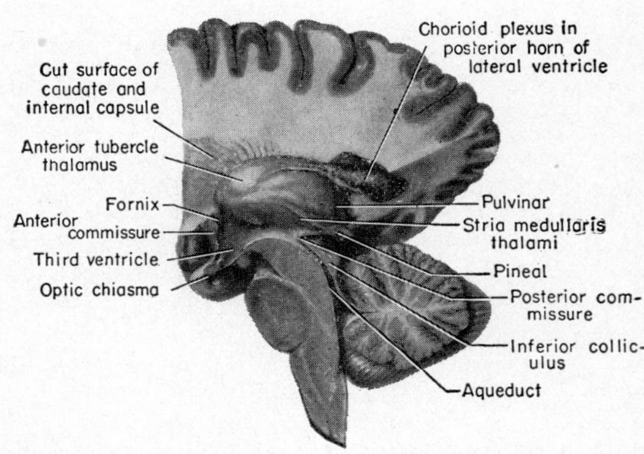

FIG. 195. The human thalamus from the medial aspect.

in the internal laminae (**intralaminar nuclei**), and still others, the **mid-line nuclei,** are topographically associated with the medial nuclei. Though the anatomy of these various dorsal thalamic nuclei and their subsidiary parts, also called nuclei, is extremely complex, Walker, in his work on the thalamus of the monkey, has made five *topographical* groups of nuclei and has indicated that each of these as a whole falls into one of three functionally distinct groups on the basis of their connections (793). Functionally, the groups are the nuclei of the mid-line and the intralaminar nuclei, which send no known direct fibers to the cerebral neocortex, but instead may project to some parts of the rhinencephalon, to the hypothalamus, and possibly to the striatum; a group composed of the ventral portion of the lateral nucleus, and the geniculate bodies, which receive ascending sensory fibers from the spinal cord and from the organs of special sense (the eye and ear), and in turn project their own fibers to their respective cortical sensory areas; a third group consisting of the anterior and medial nuclei, and dorsolateral parts of the lateral nucleus, which receive few or no direct sensory fibers, but which project to various parts of the cerebral cortex.

The Dorsal Thalamus

That the topographic divisions, made by Walker, of the dorsal thalamic nuclei in the monkey can be carried over into the human has been verified by two recent studies of the human thalamus (722, 777). With the exception of a few discrepancies in the results of these two researches, in general the same nuclei have been described by these workers. Certain differences of topographical placement of some nuclei exist, however. The following list is arranged similarly to that of Sheps:

A. Anterior nuclear group
   1. Anteromedial nucleus
   2. Anterodorsal nucleus
   3. Anteroventral nucleus

B. Nuclei of the mid-line
   1. Anterior paraventricular nucleus
   2. Posterior paraventricular nucleus
   3. Parataenial nucleus
   4. Interoanterodorsal nucleus
   5. Rhomboid nucleus } "massa intermedia"
   6. Central medial nucleus } "massa intermedia"
   7. Reuniens nucleus
   8. Periventricular gray

C. Medial nuclei
   1. Dorsomedial nucleus
   2. Centrum medianum nucleus
   3. Submedius nucleus
   4. Paracentral nucleus
   5. Central lateral nucleus
   6. Habenulointerpeduncular tract nucleus
   7. Parafascicular nucleus

D. Lateral nuclear group } ventral part
   1. Anterior ventral nucleus
   2. Lateral ventral nucleus
   3. Posterior ventral nucleus
      a. Posterolateral ventral
      b. Posteromedial ventral
      c. Posterior intermediate ventral nucleus
   4. Lateral dorsal nucleus } dorsal part
   5. Lateral posterior nucleus } dorsal part
   6. Reticular nucleus

E. Posterior nuclei
   1. Pulvinar
   2. Suprageniculate nucleus
   3. Limitans nucleus
   4. Lateral geniculate nucleus
   5. Medial geniculate nucleus

Those nuclei from the above lists located within the internal medullary laminae, and therefore designated as intralaminar, are the paracentral, central lateral, centrum medianum, and parafascicular.

The Anterior Nucleus

This is just beneath the rostral portion of the dorsal thalamic surface. It protrudes somewhat above the general level of the dorsal surface rostrally. It is easy to discern on frontal sections of the brain and consists of the three subdivisions, the **anteromedial, anterodorsal,** and **anteroventral** nuclei. The anteroventral is the most prominent in man, the others being poorly defined (Figs. 196, 197, 198, 200). It is the largest of the three nuclei, and it appears

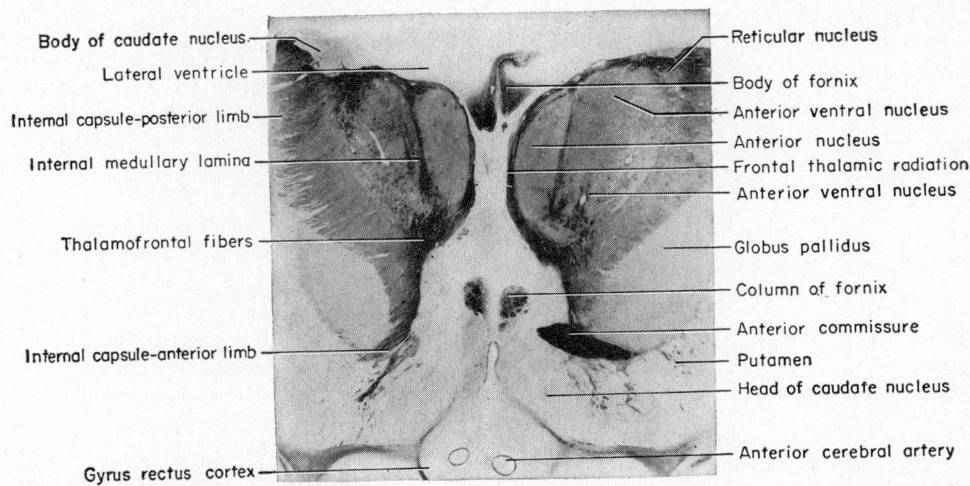

FIG. 196. Transverse section, A 1356, of a human brain stem through rostral end of thalamus and head of caudate nucleus. Weigert. Photograph, ×1.5.

in the rostral portion of the anterior tubercle and extends caudally to the massa intermedia. The anteromedial is related to the phylogenetically older nuclei of the mid-line. Large, well-staining neurons are found in all three. All three of these anterior nuclei receive fibers from the mamillary bodies by way of the mamillothalamic tracts, and each has a distinct cortical projection. In animals, the anteromedial sends fibers to the cortex of the inferior surface of the frontal pole and possibly to the anterior part of the cingular gyrus in area 32; the anteroventral projects to the cortex of the cingular gyrus on the medial surface of the hemisphere, especially to areas 23 and 24; and the anterodorsal sends fibers to the retrosplenial part of that gyrus, especially to area 29. In the human, the anteromedial projects to area 24, the anteroventral nucleus, to area 23 (149, 150, 160, 552, 687). Sheps reported that the anteroventral and anteromedial nuclei were completely degenerated after cortical degeneration (722). It has been thought that each of these nuclei may have a distinct olfactory function; *e.g.,* the anteromedial may mediate simple and poorly organized olfactory sensation, the anteroventral, more complex impulses of smell. Whether or not these nuclei are at all related to olfactory function is not definite. They receive a projection from the mamillary bodies, it is to be recalled. The chief projection to this latter nucleus is from the hippocampus, which is perhaps not directly concerned with olfaction as has formerly been assumed (101) (see Chap. 23).

THE NUCLEI OF THE MID-LINE

These, the oldest thalamic nuclei phylogenetically, are very well developed in macrosmatic animals and undergo a reduction in primates to the extent that they appear rudimentary in man (Figs. 198, 201, 203). Many investigators group them simply as central gray, but recent researches have identified a number of individual nuclei in this group. The **anterior paraventricular nucleus** extends from the rostral end of the stria medullaris thalami to the habenula. It appears to be a circumscribed collection of cells in the periventricular gray. The cells are large, are pear-shaped usually, and stain fairly well. The **posterior paraventricular nucleus,** according to Sheps, is found just caudal to the rostral end of the habenula and it gradually fades into the pretectal periventricular gray. Its cells are small and spherical or fusiform; their cytoplasm stains lightly, but contains deeply staining Nissl bodies. The **parataenial nucleus** can be found throughout the extent of the stria medullaris thalami and forms all but the medial boundary of those fibers. The cells are polygonal, of medium size, and stain deeply. The parataenial nucleus projects to the rhinencephalon apparently. The **interoanterodorsal nucleus** is a caudal continuation of the anterodorsal nucleus, is dorsal to the parataenial nucleus, and extends caudally to the level of the rostral third of the massa intermedia. The cells are small, spherical, and darkly staining.

The **rhomboid** and the **central medial nuclei** comprise the massa intermedia when it is present and the immediately adjacent thalamic area. The central medial nucleus is the largest of the mid-line nuclei, and its noncommissural portions extend in front of and behind the massa. The cells are large, flask-shaped, and deeply staining. The rhomboid nucleus lies for the most part superior to the massa intermedia. It indents the ventromedial corner of the dorsomedial nucleus through most of its extent. The gray commissural portion of the rhomboid nucleus is thin and occupies the rostral third of the massa intermedia. The nucleus contains small, poorly staining granular cells.

The **reuniens nucleus** is the most ventral of the mid-line nuclei (Fig. 198). It extends from the caudal part of the anterior tubercle to the middle part of the massa intermedia, and it is just lateral to the wall of the third ventricle. Its cells are small and of globular shape; they stain well. The **periventricular gray** is replaced by the distinct nuclei of the mid-line in the rostral thalamic levels, but in the caudal levels it is a definite thin zone of small, poorly staining cells, just about the ventricular wall. The fibers of the periventricular system are associated with these cells.

It is noteworthy that the nuclei of the mid-line show a great amount of variation in their development from one human brain to another. In any collection of human brains, several will be found to lack a massa intermedia commissure. In fact, it has been reported that the massa intermedia is absent in 28 per cent of men and 14 per cent of women (565). This should suggest several interesting questions

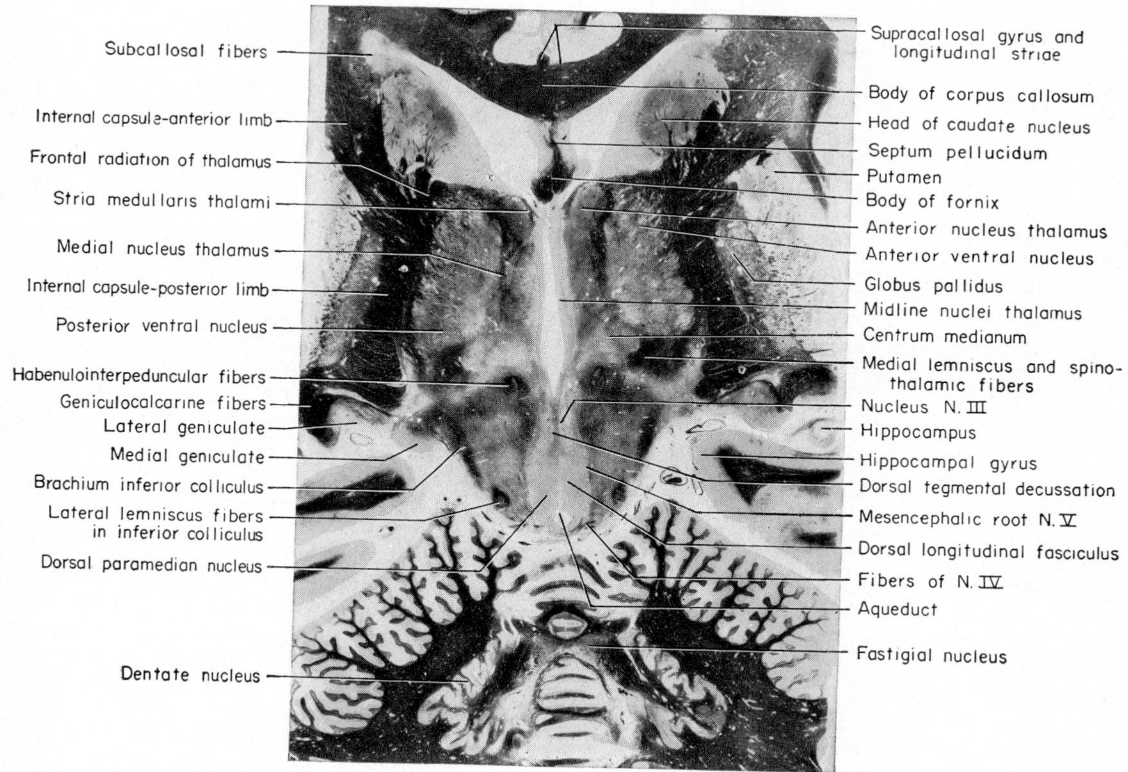

FIG. 197. Frontal section, B 539, of a human brain through head of caudate nucleus and through the dentate nucleus Weigert. Photograph, ×1.35.

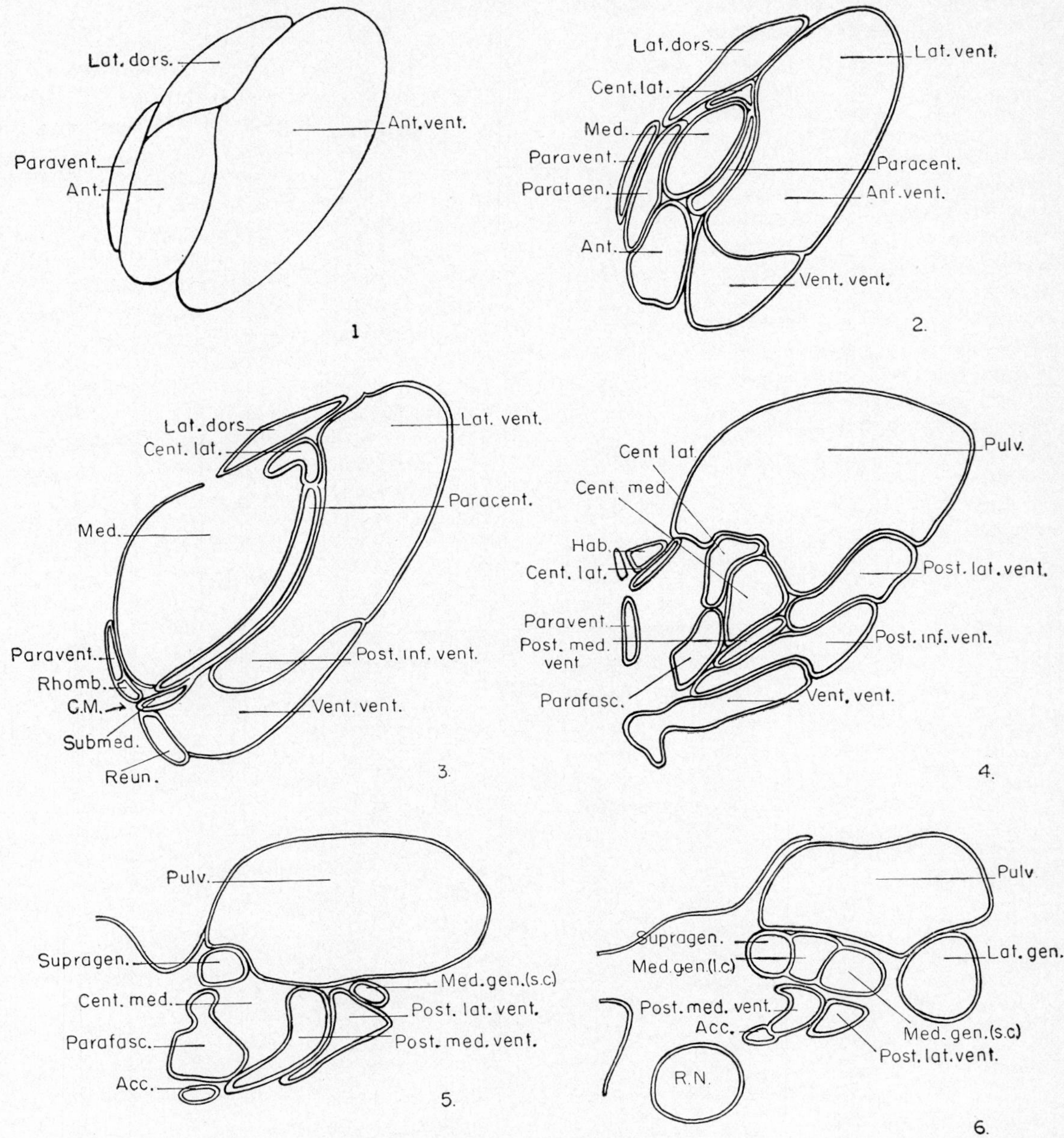

Fig. 198. The nuclear divisions of the human thalamus. 1 to 6 form a continuous reconstruction by slices of the outlines of the nuclei composing the human thalamus. They are cut in a plane perpendicular to the long axis of the brain stem. The central medial nucleus is not shown, but its location is indicated by arrow in 3. *Acc.*, accessory semilunar; *Ant.*, anterior; *Ant. vent.*, anterior ventral; *Cent. lat.*, central lateral; *C.M.*, central medial; *Cent. med.*, centrum medianum; *Hab.*, habenula; *Lat. dors.*, lateral dorsal; *Lat. gen.*, lateral geniculate; *Lat. vent.*, lateral ventral; *Med.*, medial; *Med. gen. (l.c.)*, medial geniculate (large-celled division); *Med. gen. (s.c.)*, medial geniculate (small-celled division); *Paracent.*, paracentral; *Parafasc.*, parafascicular; *Parataen.*, parataenial; *Paravent.*, paraventricular; *Post. lat. vent.*, posterolateral ventral; *Post. med. vent.*, posteromedial ventral; *Post. inf. vent.*, posterior inferior ventral; *Pulv.*, pulvinar; *R.N.*, red nucleus; *Reun.*, reuniens; *Rhomb.*, rhomboid; *Submed.*, submedius; *Supragen.*, suprageniculate; *Vent. vent.*, ventral ventral. (*Modified after Toncray and Krieg, J. Comp. Neurol., vol.* 85.)

when some of the newer ideas of the function of the mid-line and intralaminar nuclei are mentioned below. The nuclei of the mid-line receive fibers from the spinothalamic tracts, trigeminothalamic tracts, and the medial lemniscus, and they probably also receive poorly myelinated fibers from the tectum, pretectal region, and other thalamic nuclei. They send many fibers to the hypothalamus, and some also probably to the basal ganglia and to the lateral and medial nuclei of the thalamus. If the neocortex, rhinencephalon, striatum, and amygdala are removed from a rabbit's brain, the mid-line and intralaminar nuclei will degenerate. It is not known at present, however, whether these nuclei project to cortical or to subcortical regions or to both (688). Some of them, especially reuniens, may project to area 25. Walker thinks these nuclei are concerned with impulses from the axial part of the body and especially from the internal organs and viscera. He thinks that integration within them permits a limited appreciation of pain stimuli (793).

THE MEDIAL NUCLEI

Of these the best known is the prominent **dorsomedial** which is bounded laterally by the internal medullary lamina (Figs. 197, 198, 199, 200, 201, 202, 203, 204). Rostrally, it extends to the anteroventral nucleus; the centrum medianum and parafascicular nuclei replace it caudally. The dorsomedial nucleus according to the usual descriptions contains two types of cells: large, deeply staining ones and small, lightly staining ones. McLardy has also described very small neurons, ranging from two to six times the size of astrocytes, in the dorsomedial and other principal thalamic nuclei. He thinks they may be associative neurons (511). The large cells are especially prominent rostrally, medially, and dorsomedially, and they tend to form a "cortex" for the centrally placed, small cells. The dorsomedial nucleus receives fibers from the prefrontal cortex, from the hypothalamus, from the pretectal region, from the nuclei of the mid-line, from the lateral and posterior ventral nuclei and pulvinar, and from the centrum medianum. It sends fibers to the hypothalamus, pretectal region, anterior ventral thalamic nucleus, the striatum, and the prefrontal portion of the frontal lobe, areas, 8, 9, 10, 11, 12, 45, 46, and 47 (276, 511, 552, 585). The large cells of the dorsomedial nucleus are thought to project to the orbital part of the frontal lobe

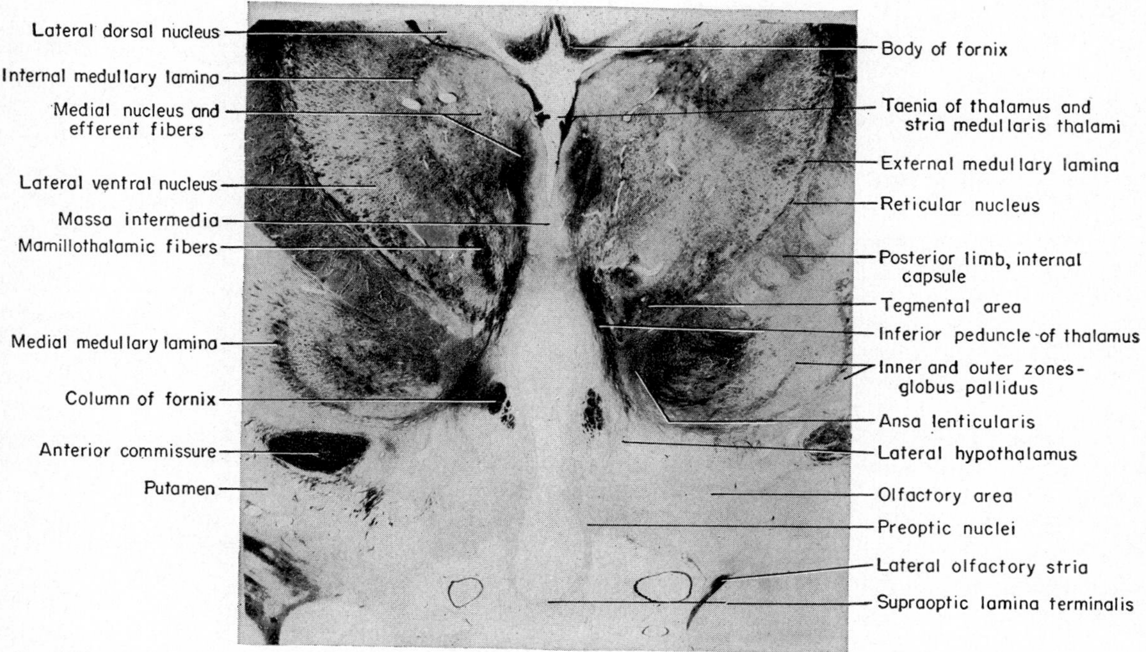

FIG. 199. Transverse section, A 1245, of human brain stem through massa intermedia. Weigert. Photograph, ×2.

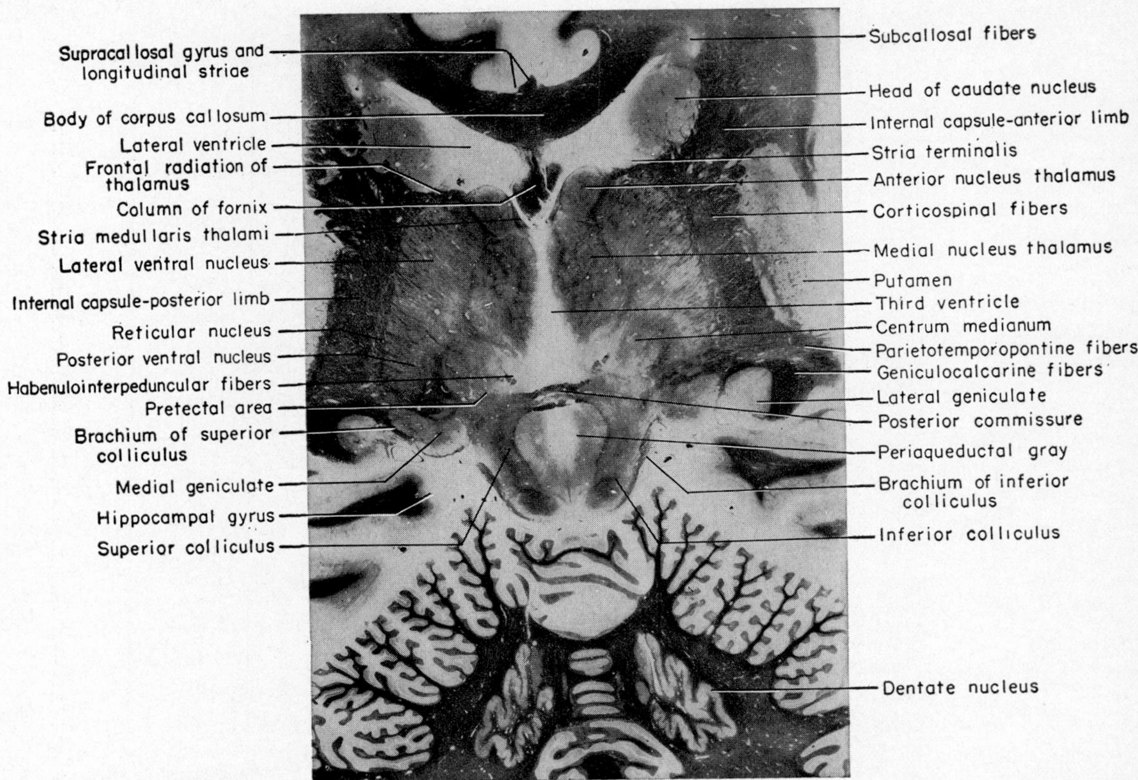

FIG. 200. Frontal section, B 610, of human brain through head of caudate nucleus and posterior commissure. Weigert. Photograph, ×1.35.

(area 11) and to the hypothalamus; the small cells, to the remaining areas of the prefrontal region. The small cells were found degenerated by Sheps after cortical degeneration. A point-to-point relation exists between dorsomedial nucleus and the prefrontal region, such that the anteroposterior axis of the nucleus projects in orderly fashion to the anteroposterior axis of the prefrontal cortex (see Chap. 18). Area 13 does not share in this thalamic projection, and areas 10 and 12 may receive only a few fibers (511). Functionally, the dorsomedial nucleus has the opportunity by means of its connections of being an integrating center for somatic and visceral sensory impulses, and presenting them to the cortex of the prefrontal region directly in a complex form as sensory concepts. Through its connection with the striatum it may influence the association of sensory and motor activity.

Another very prominent nucleus of the medial group in man is the **centrum medianum** (Figs. 201, 204). It is classed frequently simply as an intralaminar nucleus, because it is surrounded by a capsule of fibers continuous with those of the internal medullary lamina. It lies between the dorsomedial and lateral nuclei of the thalamus and the red nucleus. Its connections are practically unknown. It does not appear to receive fibers from the ascending lemniscus systems. From time to time evidence has been presented for its receiving fibers from sensory nuclei of cranial nerves (5 and 10), from the motor cortex, from the medial geniculate body, and from the dentate nucleus of the cerebellum. Similarly, it has been thought to send fibers to the dorsomedial nucleus and to the globus pallidus. A study of five human cases has indicated that the centrum medianum projects to the caudate and putamen rather than to the globus pallidus (509). It is not possible at present to be certain whether the centrum medianum projects to the cortex. In the human, Sheps found no appreciable neuron

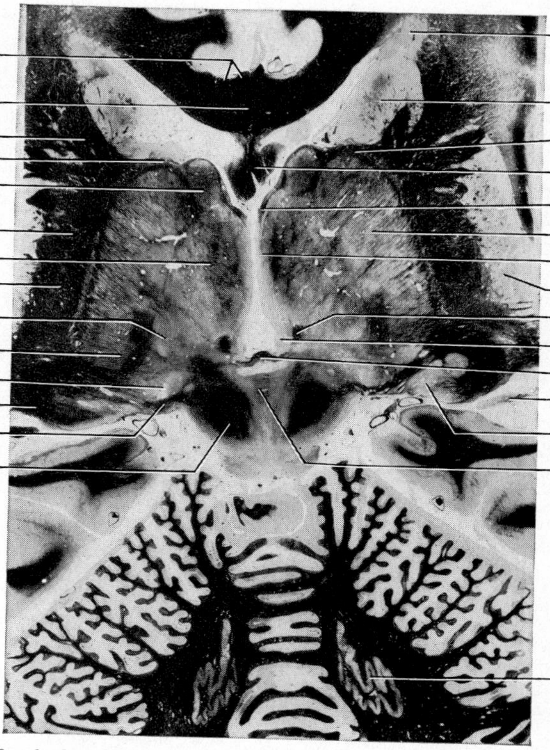

Fig. 201. Frontal section, B 650, of a human brain through the body of the fornix and the superior colliculus. Weigert. Photograph, ×1.35.

loss in this nucleus in a case of complete *cortical* degeneration, and in the monkey, no loss of neurons here follows hemidecortication.

The **submedius nucleus** (sometimes called the ventral medial) is cigar-shaped and appears to be a caudal extension of the anteromedial nucleus (Fig. 198). It reaches to the level of the caudal edge of the massa intermedia, and its caudal portion is immediately ventral to the wings of this commissure. The cells are of medium size, are flask-shaped, and stain deeply. The submedius nucleus of man has been re-

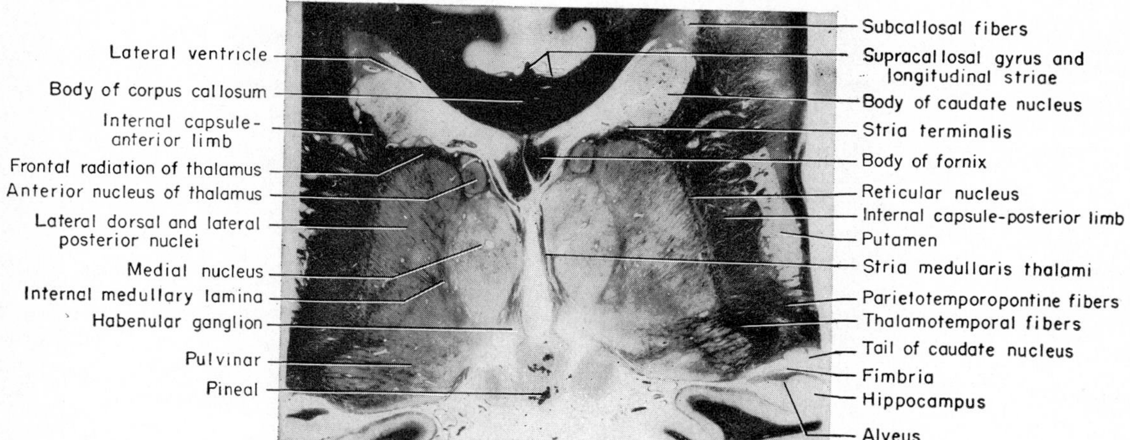

Fig. 202. Frontal section, B 690, of a human brain through the body of the fornix and pineal gland. Weigert. Photograph, ×1.35.

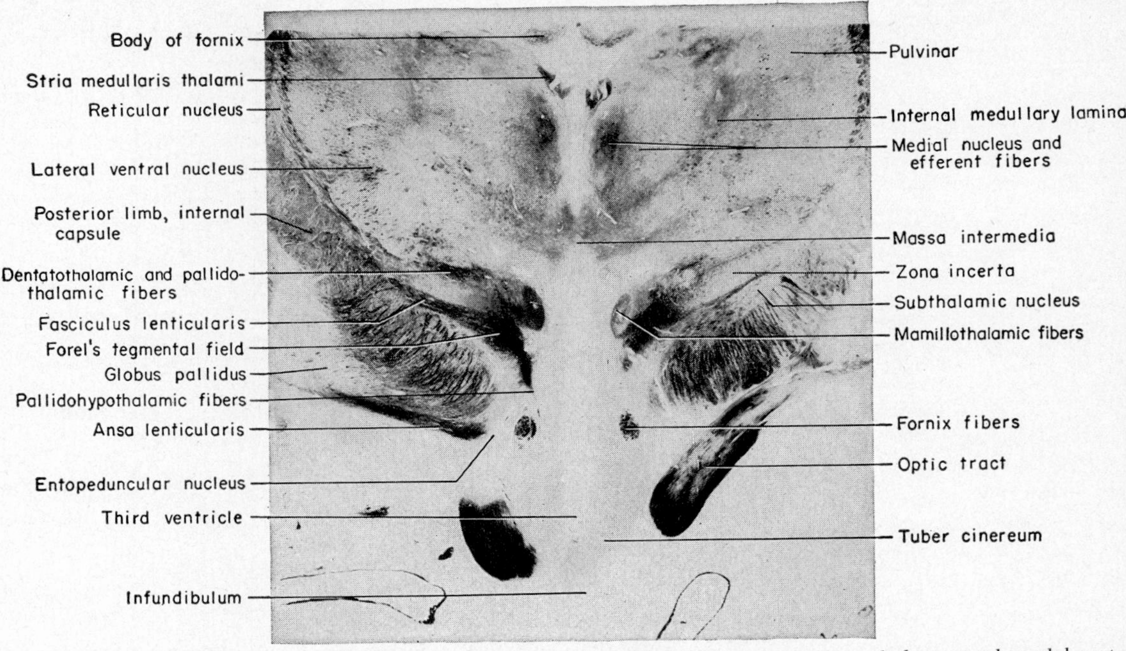

FIG. 203. Transverse section, A 1155, of a human brain stem through tuberal region of hypothalamus and caudal part of massa intermedia. Weigert. Photograph, ×2.

ported to project to area 8 and to area 46 (276, 511).

The **paracentral nucleus** lies within the internal medullary lamina (Fig. 198). Its medial edge is in contact with the central medial nucleus; its lateral edge, with the central lateral nucleus. Caudally, the paracentral nucleus is replaced by the centrum medianum. Its rostral pole appears to be an extension of the anteromedial nucleus. The cells are large, deeply staining, and goblet-shaped. The **central lateral nucleus** is crescent-shaped and lies within the fibers of the lateral part of the internal medullary lamina. It forms a cap around the dorsal half of the dorsomedial nucleus. Its cells resemble those of the paracentral nucleus but do not stain so deeply.

The **nucleus of the habenulointerpeduncular tract** lies for the most part lateral to the tract (Fig. 204). The oral pole of the nucleus extends between the habenular complex and the dorsomedial nucleus. The cells are deeply staining, large, and of polymorphic shapes. The **parafascicular nucleus** is ventral to the caudal part of the dorsomedial nucleus and medial to the caudal part of the centrum medianum. The cells are small, globular, and deeply staining. The fasciculus retroflexus of Meynert, or habenulointerpeduncular tract, passes through it. Its connections and functions are unknown.

THE LATERAL NUCLEAR GROUP

This is that part of the thalamus between the internal and external medullary laminae, anterior to the pulvinar. It also includes the reticular nucleus, a group of cells between the external medullary lamina and the internal capsule. The functions and connections of the reticular nucleus are not definitely known, but there are some interesting recent data, as will be discussed later. The lateral nucleus, exclusive of the reticular, is divided into dorsal and ventral parts. These component dorsal and ventral parts are further subdivided, as noted in the list previously given. The ventral part of the lateral nuclear mass is better known. It is divided into an anterior part and a posterior part. The anterior portion is customarily divided into the anterior ventral and the lateral ventral nuclei, though no sharp differentiation is possible on the basis of cell change. The posterior portion is divided by

Sheps into a posterolateral ventral, a posteromedial ventral, and a posterior intermediate ventral nucleus.

The **anterior ventral nucleus** with the anterior nuclei extends most rostrally of all thalamic nuclei and is the first to appear in frontal cross sections (Figs. 196, 197, 198). Its caudal boundary is considered by Sheps as being in a plane at the level of the caudal edge of the anterior commissure. Its contour is recognizable because of the grouping of its component neurons, which are large and deeply staining, into little islets. After degeneration of the human cerebral cortex, Sheps found complete degeneration of the anterior ventral nucleus. It has been reported to be interconnected with area 6 in the human (276, 511). Walker reported that the anterior ventral nucleus in the macaque did not appear to have a cortical projection. In this animal it receives fibers from the globus pallidus by way of the thalamic fasciculus or field of Forel H_1. These fibers terminate medially (652). It sends fibers to the striatum.

The **lateral ventral nucleus,** the largest of the ventral nuclei, is in front of the posterolateral ventral nucleus, and again there is no sharp line of demarcation (Figs. 198, 199, 200, 201, 203). The rostral border of the centrum medianum is near the caudal limits of the lateral ventral nucleus. Large and small neurons compose this latter nucleus. It receives fibers from the dentate nucleus of the cerebellum by way of the brachium conjunctivum. The lateral ventral nucleus sends fibers to the precentral gyrus areas 4 and 6, and has intrathalamic connections with the medial, dorsolateral, and pulvinar nuclei. A topographic localization exists in this nucleus with regard to its cortical projection fibers. Cerebral lesions in the motor foot area give a degeneration in the lateral ventral nucleus which is localized more laterally than that following a cerebral motor arm-area lesion. After degeneration of the cerebral cortex not all the neurons in the lateral ventral nucleus undergo degeneration (722).

The **posteromedial ventral nucleus** is known also as the arcuate or the semilunar (Figs. 198, 200, 201, 204). It lies next to the ventrolateral surface of the centrum medianum and has a semilunar shape. The caudal border of the posteromedial ventral nucleus is in a plane containing the greatest development of the

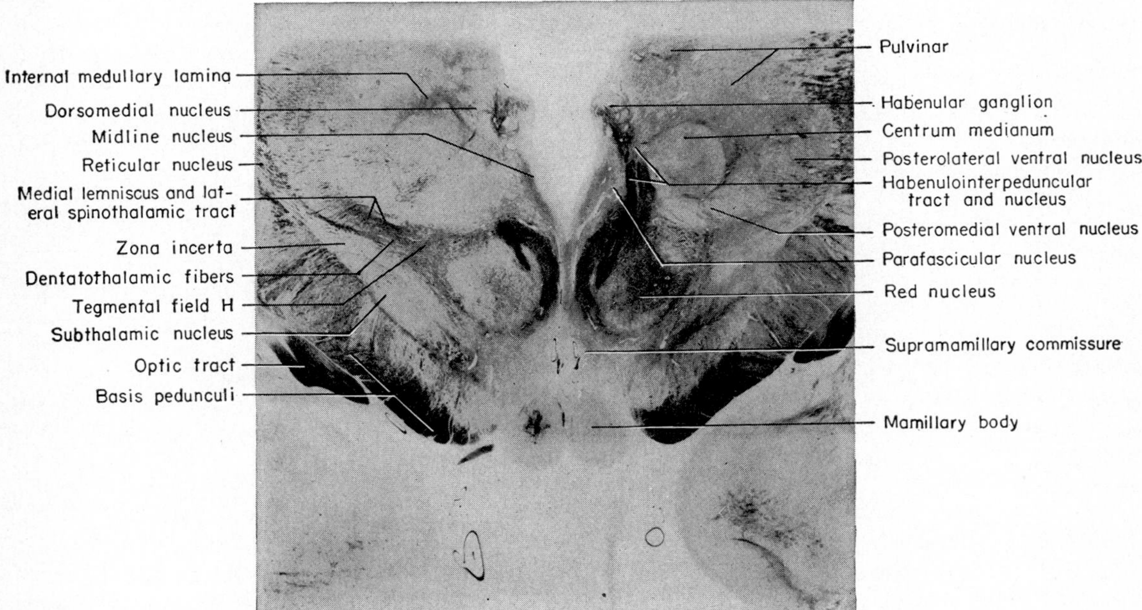

FIG. 204. Transverse section, A 1058, of a human brain stem through habenula and mamillary bodies. Weigert. Photograph, ×2.

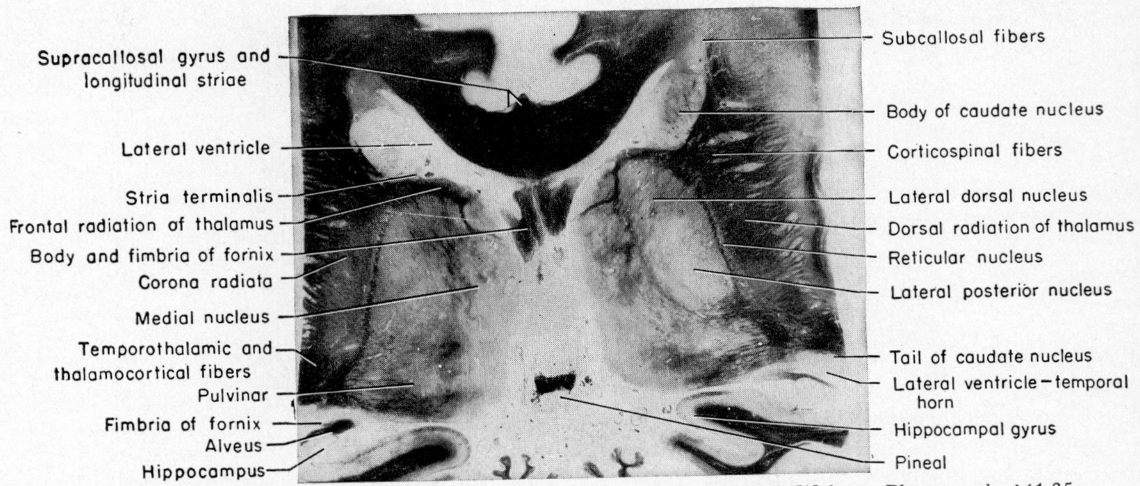

FIG. 205. Frontal section, B 750, of a human brain through pineal gland. Weigert. Photograph, ×1.35.

habenula. The nucleus contains large cells with deeply staining cytoplasm and large Nissl bodies as well as small, paler cells, the large cells being more numerous posteriorly. Within this nucleus terminate the trigeminal lemnisci of secondary trigeminal fibers and perhaps the secondary taste pathways (11). Toncray and Krieg have defined an accessory semilunar nucleus just medial to the posteromedial ventral nucleus (777). It has been suggested by others that taste fibers relay in this accessory nucleus. The posteromedial ventral nucleus sends projections to the sensory face area in the cerebral cortex, areas 3, 1, and 2 of the parietal lobe. It probably has intrathalamic connections similar to those of the lateral ventral nucleus.

The **posterolateral ventral nucleus** is just lateral to the preceding nucleus and extends more dorsally and posteriorly, to merge into the pulvinar (Figs. 198, 200, 201, 204). It contains many large neurons, especially posteriorly and ventrally. The spinothalamic tracts and medial lemniscus terminate within it. The spinothalamic fibers in the monkey terminate in the more posterior and basal parts of the nucleus; the medial lemniscus, in the more rostral and dorsal parts. It sends fibers to areas 3, 1, and 2 in the postcentral gyrus and also has intrathalamic connections similar to those of the lateral ventral nucleus. There is also topographical arrangement in this nucleus. Ascending fibers transmitting impulses from cervical spinal levels end medially with reference to those fibers transmitting impulses from thoracic, lumbar, and sacral levels. After degeneration of the cerebral cortex only the small neurons in these posterior ventral nuclei were degenerated, according to Sheps.

With the demonstration of secondary sensory cortical fields, it is of interest to learn of their thalamic relay nuclei. The thalamic relay nucleus for the secondary somatic area in the cat has been identified as a caudal extension of the posteromedial ventral nucleus. From before backward in this part of the nucleus is represented, respectively, the face, forefoot, and hind foot. The secondary-face-area relay nucleus is therefore immediately caudad to that for the primary face area. The secondary-hind-foot-area relay nucleus is just rostral to the secondary-auditory-area relay nucleus. This last is thought to be the large-cell portion of the medial geniculate nucleus or the suprageniculate nucleus (441).

The **posterior intermediate ventral nucleus** is small and contains large neurons arranged in vertical rows. The boundaries of the nucleus are indistinct, but it lies rostral to the other two posterior ventral nuclei and extends obliquely from the external medullary lamina to the dorsolateral tip of the posteromedial ventral nucleus. Its connections are not known.

The dorsally placed part of the lateral nuclear mass, the lateral nucleus, is divided into two parts, a **lateral dorsal** and a **lateral**

posterior nucleus. The lateral dorsal is more rostral and dorsal to the lateral posterior portion (Figs. 198, 199, 202, 205, 206). It extends from the magnocellular portion of the dorsomedial nucleus to the plane of the habenula. The lateral posterior nucleus extends from a plane through the middle of the massa intermedia to the level of the habenula where it becomes continuous with the pulvinar. The cells of these two nuclei are small. Both these nuclei were completely degenerated after destruction of the cerebral cortex, according to Sheps. They are probably association nuclei, since they receive fibers from other thalamic nuclei, particularly from the ventral lateral nuclei. Oscillographic studies in the cat suggest also connections with the intralaminar nuclei (756). They send fibers to the parietal lobe exclusive of the postcentral gyrus.

The **reticular nucleus** is composed of a thin line of cells which forms a cap for the most oral part of the thalamus and also lies rostral, dorsolateral, lateral, and ventral to the lateral nuclear mass (Figs. 196, 199, 200, 202, 203, 204, 205, 206). This nucleus separates the external medullary lamina of the dorsal thalamus from the internal capsule. The ventral portion of the reticular nucleus is continuous with the zona incerta. The cells are large, of varied shapes; they contain large Nissl bodies which stain deeply.

It seems likely that the reticular nucleus is interconnected with a number of cortical areas, since it will degenerate if the cortex is removed. Walker reports that the portions of the reticular nucleus project to the same cortical regions as do those parts of the lateral nucleus which they abut (793). The anterior portion degenerates following lesions in the motor area of the cortex, the ventral part after postcentral ablation, the dorsal part after posterior parietal removals, and the posterior part after damage to occipital and posterior temporal areas. They probably receive fibers from other thalamic nuclei, especially those of the mid-line and intralaminar group (see later).

THE POSTERIOR NUCLEI

Of the posterior nuclei only the **pulvinar** need concern us to any extent here (Figs. 198, 203, 204, 205, 206). It forms the posterior extremity of the thalamus and extends forward to a plane through the rostral pole of the habenula. The component neurons are small ones. The pulvinar receives fibers from the nuclei of the lateral nuclear mass, especially from those of the ventral part. Oscillographic studies indicate connections with intralaminar nuclei (756). Fibers from the geniculates to the pulvinar have been reported but seem unlikely, at least from the lateral geniculate. The pulvinar also receives fibers from the amygdaloid nucleus and from the inferior part of the temporal lobe, according to Papez. It sends fibers to the posterior part of the superior parietal lobule (area 7*b*, Brodmann), the angular (area 39) and supramarginal gyri (area 40), and the parastriate area of the oc-

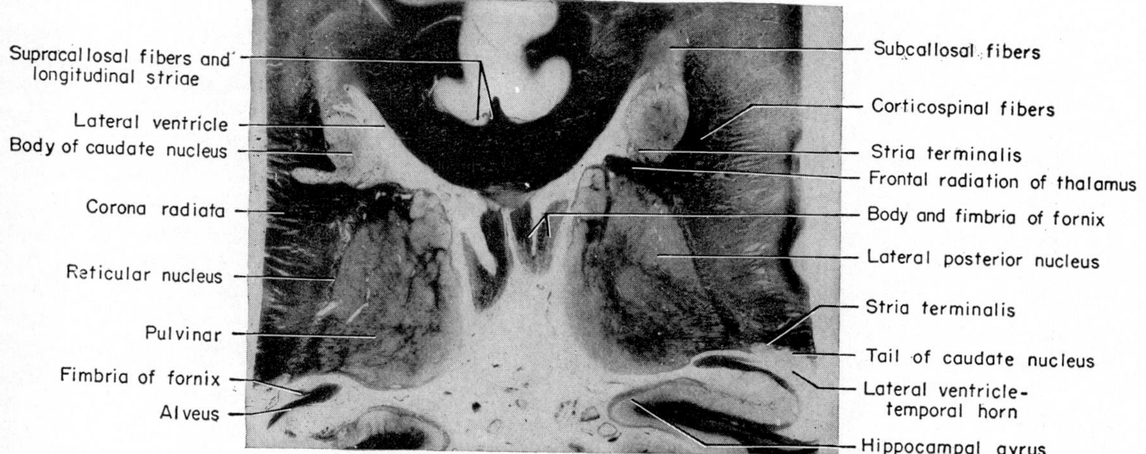

FIG. 206. Frontal section, B 800, of human brain through dorsal part of thalamus. Weigert. Photograph, ×1.35.

cipital lobe. It thus projects to the posterior parts of the parietal and temporal lobes and the middle portion of the lateral surface of the occipital lobe. It is thought to be associated with higher somatic and with visual and auditory integrations because of its connections to cortical areas adjacent to the primary cortical receptive areas for those types of impulses. The pulvinar was also found completely degenerated after degeneration of the cerebral cortex (722).

The **suprageniculate nucleus** is located along the dorsal and medial margins of the medial geniculate nucleus and is small in rostrocaudal extent (Fig. 198). It has large, darkly staining cells. Its connections are unknown. The **nucleus limitans** is a narrow band of cells placed between the posterior end of the parafascicular nucleus and the medial geniculate nucleus. Its cells are large and deeply staining. Its connections are unknown. The medial and lateral geniculate nuclei will be described in later sections. They form the most caudal portion of the thalamus, ventrally.

The differentiation of the human thalamic nuclei follows closely that observed in the higher primates. The dorsomedial nucleus, the lateral ventral, and the pulvinar, however, show a relative increase in size, as does the anteroventral nucleus. The posterior ventral nuclei and the centrum medianum retain their relative proportions, while the anterodorsal, anteromedial, and the mid-line nuclei appear to regress. The increase in size of the dorsomedial nucleus is correlated with the increase in the frontal cortical area; that of the lateral ventral, with the increase in development of the cerebellum; and that of the pulvinar, with the increasing prominence of the inferior parietal and the occipital association areas.

Thalamocortical Relations

SPECIFIC THALAMOCORTICAL SYSTEM

On the basis of presently known anatomical connections, only certain of the nuclei just described would appear to project to the cerebral cortex (688). These can be arranged into three groups (Fig. 207). One group receives impulses from ascending sensory pathways, such as the spinothalamics, medial lemniscus, quintothalamics, lateral lemniscus, and optic tracts, and it discharges impulses to the cerebral cortex, to the primary and secondary sensory areas. These thalamic nuclei serve chiefly as primary relay centers passing impulses from the periphery on to the cerebral cortex, but also to other thalamic nuclei. The primary relay nuclei are the posterior ventral, medial, and lateral geniculate bodies.

Other thalamic nuclei serve as relay nuclei of a more complex, or secondary, order. These nuclei receive impulses from other neural centers and relay them to the cerebral cortex, as well as to other thalamic nuclei perhaps. These secondary relay nuclei are the lateral and anterior ventral receiving impulses from the cerebellum and red nucleus, and striatum, respectively, and projecting to the cortical areas 4 and 6 of the precentral gyrus; the anterior nuclei which receive many impulses from the mamillary nuclei and project to the cingular gyrus; and that portion of the dorsal medial nucleus which receives impulses from the hypothalamus and projects to the orbital region of the frontal lobe.

A third group of thalamic nuclei serves a more complex function than do these first two groups. This third group receives impulses chiefly from other thalamic nuclei, integrates and elaborates them, and projects other impulses to the cerebral cortex. These nuclei include much of the dorsomedial which projects to the prefrontal region; the lateral dorsal and lateral posterior, which project to that part of the parietal lobe just posterior to the postcentral gyrus; and finally, the pulvinar, which projects to the most posterior parietal region, the most rostral occipital region, and the most posterior temporal region. These nuclei may be referred to as integrative or elaborative thalamic nuclei, receiving many impulses from the relay nuclei and projecting to associative regions of the cerebral cortex.

The anatomical connections between all these nuclei and the cerebral cortex are arranged in a point-to-point fashion. Each nucleus is related to a definite cortical region, and within that region a specific relationship exists between cortical foci and nuclear cell groups. These corticothalamic axons entering the cortical laminae constitute the so-called specific thalamic radiation fibers. When the cortex is removed all these thalamic nuclei undergo degenerative changes.

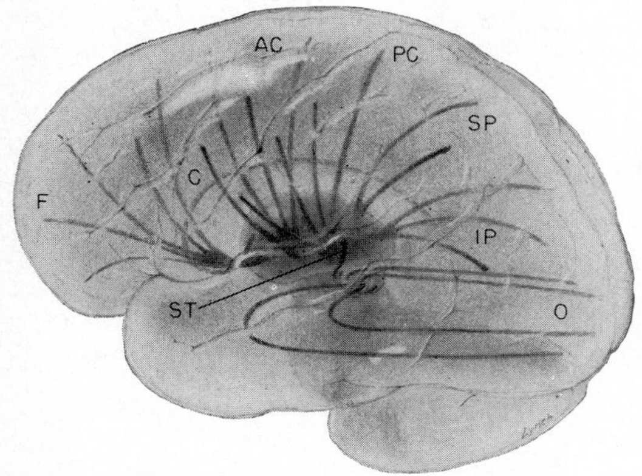

Fig. 207. Diagram of the human thalamocortical projections. *AC*, projection from anterior ventral and lateral ventral nuclei to precentral areas; *C*, from anterior nuclei to cingular gyrus; *F*, from medial nuclei to prefrontal areas; *IP*, from pulvinar to inferior parietal and rostral occipital region; *O*, from lateral geniculate to occipital area 17; *PC*, from posterior ventral nuclei to postcentral areas; *SP*, from dorsal half of lateral nucleus to superior parietal areas; *ST*, from medial geniculate to superior transverse temporal gyri.

THE "DIFFUSE" THALAMOCORTICAL SYSTEM

That thalamocortical relationships are more extensive than these just described has recently been shown by stimulating the thalamus and scanning the cortex for indications of induced electrical change. Such studies have revealed another group of nuclei which exert a strong influence on the cerebral cortex. And yet, these nuclei with an occasional exception do not degenerate when the cortex is removed. It has been suggested, therefore, that these nuclei may influence cortical activity by way of other thalamic nuclei or other subcortical relays and are not directly affected, therefore, by cortical removal. Alternatively, the thalamocortical axons from these nuclei may give off many large collateral branches to subcortical centers and these serve to prevent the parent neurons from undergoing degeneration when the cortical part of the axon only is damaged in a cortical removal. Such resistance to degenerative change is seen in other systems.

These most recently discovered thalamocortical connections have been designated as a diffuse thalamocortical system, and the nuclei concerned, as a thalamic reticular system. The pioneer investigations were carried out some years ago by Dempsey and Morison (207, 566, 568). More recently Jasper and his co-workers and Starzl and Magoun have studied this system in great detail (414, 756). The constituent nuclei identified as belonging to the diffuse thalamic reticular system by these workers are in most respects identical. Jasper includes the paracentral, central lateral, centrum medianum, rhomboid, central medial, and reticular nuclei. The anteromedial nucleus, or part of it, and the reuniens nucleus may also be included for physiological reasons. Starzl and Magoun list the centrum medianum, the other intralaminar nuclei, the anterior nuclei, the anterior ventral and only the anterior reticular. Stimulation in all these thalamic nuclei leads to a disturbance in the spontaneous electrical activity of large cortical areas, and in fact, the spontaneous cortical activity may be replaced by responses in time with the rhythm of the thalamic stimulus. These nuclei, according to Jasper, appear to have, therefore, a diffuse cortical projection to areas also having specific projections, and to areas of the cortex for which no specific thalamic projection has yet been demonstrated. Two of the nuclei listed, however, the reuniens and the anteromedial, appear to have anatomical relations with specific cortical areas, even though they give rise to a generalized cortical response when stimulated.

According to Jasper and his co-workers, a single stimulus of 1 to 2 millisec. duration and 3 to 5 volts intensity, applied to the thalamic reticular system of a cat under suitable conditions, causes a train of rhythmic waves to be set up in widespread areas of the cortex. These waves are almost identical with those of the spontaneous cortical rhythms, and it is thought that they are analogous to the alpha rhythm of the human. The induced waves were usually seen bilaterally when medial portions of the thalamic reticular system were stimulated. If the stimulus was applied within the reticular system between 3 and 4 mm. lateral to the mid-line, the induced waves were predominant in the ipsilateral hemisphere but were seen in the contralateral after a longer delay. If the stimulus was applied to the reticular *nucleus* of one side, the waves were seen throughout that hemisphere or in a restricted portion of that hemisphere. If the medial rostral portion of the reticular system was stimulated, the responses appeared first in the frontal regions, and a delay of 1 to 1½ sec. ensued before they appeared in the parieto-occipital regions. With stimulation of lateral portions, the waves might first appear in the posterior regions of the cortex and later in the frontal ones. The medial portions of the reticular system when stimulated produced leading responses in the frontal regions; the lateral portions, in the posterior cerebral regions; the posterior portion of the reticular nucleus, in the temporoparietal region. When stimulation was applied at a frequency which corresponded well with that of the existing major spontaneous rhythm, the cerebral response was gradually augmented in the nature of the "recruiting response" described some years ago by Morison and Dempsey (567). If stimulation was continued with this frequency, the responses evoked in the cortex could be seen to wax and wane.

The cortical responses to thalamic reticular system stimulation had latent periods varying from 15 to 60 millisec., depending on the portion stimulated in relation to a particular cortical area. Furthermore, the bilateral responses in the cortical areas did not depend on transmission via corpus callosum, anterior commissure, or septal region. Nor did spread from one cortical area to another depend on intracortical synapses (414, 567). Rather, the spread appeared to involve intrathalamic transmission. The latency of cortical response, plus the slow spread from one cortical region to another, indicated transmission activity by a multisynaptic relay system in the thalamus.

Certain anatomical relations of the diffuse thalamic projection system have been established by Starzl and Magoun. They found responsive cortical zones in the frontal, cingulate, orbital, parietal, and occipital association regions; none in the primary sensory receptive area. They could not find any particular dominance of frontal or posterior projections, as did Jasper. On the basis of their electrical results, they think that the radiations leave the thalamus chiefly from its rostral pole but also from its lateral region. The projection is arranged in orderly fashion to the caudate and to the cortical regions listed above. Further, they have noted that if any one of the nuclei of origin of the diffuse thalamic projection in the cat was stimulated, all became activated. They were also able to demonstrate recruiting activity in certain of the elaborative nuclei described above. These included the lateral dorsal, lateral posterior, the pulvinar, the submedius (ventral medial), the anterior thalamic nuclei, and some of the other medial nuclei.

They suggest that these nuclei may serve as relays to the cortex for the "thalamic reticular nuclei," each of the elaborative nuclei projecting to its own cortical region. They found no evidence for the reticular nucleus serving as the relay, as suggested by Jasper, except in its most rostral portion. They do not deny the possibility, however, that the thalamic reticular nuclei may project directly to the cortex, and that the axons give off many subcortical collaterals. These latter may protect the neurons from degeneration when the cortical projection sites are destroyed. It seems quite unlikely that the primary relay nuclei are involved in the diffuse thalamic projection.

The responses noted in the cerebral cortex after stimulation of the thalamic reticular system were found by Jasper to be independent of those specific responses evoked by tactile, visual, or auditory stimuli, or by stimulation of the specific primary sensory relay nuclei. Reticular stimulation had no effect on the primary evoked potentials. When the specific primary relay nuclei were destroyed so that direct stimulation of them produced no cortical response, the spontaneous rhythm which developed in the specific cortical areas, however, could still be controlled by stimulation of the appropriate portion of the thalamic reticular system. Although there appears to be no connection between primary afferent relay nuclei and the reticular system at a thalamic level, stimulation of sensory tracts before they reach the thalamus may give rise to activity in intralaminar nuclei and cause some control of cortical rhythmic activity. It seems likely that collaterals from the specific afferent pathways, such as the spinothalamics, pass into the medial intralaminar nuclei as they approach the thalamus. The medial intralaminar nuclei in turn project to other nuclei of the thalamic reticular system. The "reticular" nuclei which project then to the cortex, according to Jasper, are especially those which lie in the internal medullary and external medullary laminae bordering nuclei of specific systems; for example, the central lateral nucleus which borders the dorsomedial, and the ventral reticular which borders the posterolateral ventral nucleus. The pathways involved in this projection, however, are not definitely known, as stated above; they may be direct to the neocortex or, more likely, by way of the basal ganglia or thalamic elaborative nuclei. Recent studies have indicated that the projection may pass via cingular and orbital cortex.

Stimulation of the nucleus reuniens and of the anteromedial nucleus, each with a direct projection to a specific cortical area, frequently led to generalized control of specific cortical rhythm. Moreover, stimulation of radiations which appeared to spring from medial basal frontal and infralimbic cortex produced a generalized reticularlike response. These cortical areas are thought to be the projection sites for the reuniens and anteromedial nuclei.

OTHER RESULTS OF THALAMIC STIMULATION

Aside from the changes noted in the cortical electrical activity as a result of activating the thalamic reticular nuclei, other interesting electrical and physiologic results have been obtained (289).

A spike-and-wave pattern of response, similar to that seen in petit mal epilepsy, could be induced when certain portions of the thalamic reticular system were stimulated, especially the medial intralaminar zone, rostrally (401, 416). The stimulus frequency used was about 3 per sec. Analysis showed that the spike pattern was a reticular response, while the wave pattern was obtained at times independently of the reticular system and perhaps resulted from activation of some other thalamocortical system. Under certain conditions, however, the two patterns were combined to give the characteristic petit mal pattern.

By graded stimulation of the rostral medial intralaminar portion, various behavioral responses could be evoked in the experimental animals. In unanesthetized cats and with stimulation with low frequencies and moderate intensities, an "arrest reaction" could be produced (416). This was characterized by sudden cessation of any existing activity coincident with stimulation, and the animal was frozen in the position existing at the time. No change in muscle tone or evidence of sympathetic activity was observed, and the animal did not respond to auditory or visual stimuli.

In some animals the arrest reaction persisted beyond the time of stimulation and the pattern of behavior resembled closely a petit mal type of seizure as seen in man. Slight twitching movements about the face and eyes, comparable to those seen in humans in petit mal attacks, occurred. If more intense and rapid stimulation was applied to the reticular regions yielding the arrest reaction, a petit mal attack could usually be produced, and this would be followed by a generalized convulsion comparable to the grand mal attack seen in man. Accompanying these convulsive reactions were electrocorticograms which resemble those seen clinically with petit mal and grand mal, respectively.

Stimulation in the sensory relay nuclei never produced such reactions but did evoke behavior which appeared to be a reaction to a specific sensory stimulus, *e.g.,* to a sound or a painful stimulus. Dusser de Barenne demonstrated the reaction in response to discrete thalamic stimulation with strychnine some years ago (224, 225). The most conspicuous reactions were seen when the bit of strychnine was placed in the ventral parts of the lateral nuclear mass. The reactions consisted in hypersensitivity to all peripheral stimuli and a behavior as if a paresthetic disorder, painful in type, existed. The hypersensitivity and paresthetic reactions were observed bilaterally in the cutaneous surfaces but were stronger on the contralateral side. They were observed on the contralateral side only in the muscles and deep structures. It was possible to demonstrate by selective placement of the strychnine that a topographical arrangement within the thalamic relay nuclei into arm, leg, and face regions existed.

Corticothalamic Relations

The thalamus is also under the influence of the cortex, and generally speaking, it has been found that any thalamic nucleus that projects to a cortical region receives in turn some fibers from that cortical region. It is already definitely known, for example, that the ventral portion of the lateral nuclear mass receives fibers from cortex bordering the central fissure; the medial nuclei, from the prefrontal cortex; the lateral geniculate, from occipital cortex; the medial geniculate, from auditory temporal cortex; and the anterior nuclei, from the cingular gyrus. Cortical projections to other thalamic nuclei are less well known.

The function of the corticothalamic projections is disputed, although two chief interpretations have been offered. One assumes an inhibitory activity on the part of the cortex; the other, a modulating or sensitizing one of such a nature that certain thalamic neurons are made more susceptible at certain times to incoming impulses of a definite type, thus establishing a mechanism of sensory attention. A more highly efficient thalamus will stand ready to influence in its turn cortical activity, and that the thalamus exerts considerable influence on the cortex, and is indeed to some extent responsible for the electrical activity of the motor cortex, has been shown experimentally some years ago (219, 222).

Relation between Thalamic and Brain Stem Reticular Systems

It is not yet clear what exact relation exists between the diffuse thalamic system and the brain stem reticular system acting through the basal diencephalon (see Chap. 17) (571). Because of the generalized cortical activation in response to stimulation of the brain stem reticular system, it has been thought that the diffuse thalamic reticular system was involved in its mediation. The cortical response to stimulation of brain stem reticular system can be evoked when the intralaminar thalamic nuclei have been destroyed, however. It appears certain, therefore, that other paths of mediation of this activity of brain stem reticular systems exist. Moreover, the activity of the thalamic reticular system and that of the brain stem reticular system appear antagonistic to one another in certain activities and appear to balance one another in others.

Stimulation of the thalamic reticular system may lead to facilitation of cortically induced movement, just as stimulation of the brain stem facilitatory system may. Thalamic reticular stimulation, however, will inhibit the after-discharge seen after intense cortical stimulation. Each of these reticular systems has a strong influence on cerebral activities, therefore. And yet the spontaneous cortical rhythm does not depend for its existence on the thalamocortical or transcortical connections (94). It appears to be an intrinsic characteristic of the cerebral cortex itself. Furthermore, thalamic and cortical rhythms are not always similar, and a certain degree of independence of thalamic and cortical activity appears to exist. The thalamus may act somewhat as a clearinghouse for impulses entering from sensory receptors and lower neural levels, integrating them and bringing about adjustments without disturbing cortical activity.

Under certain conditions, however, impulses entering via specific sensory pathways and their collaterals may create sufficient activity in the diffuse thalamic system that cortical rhythmicity is brought under thalamic control. The diffuse reticular system, however, cannot block the arrival of specific afferent impulses in the cortex but can affect their elaboration through transcortical and thalamocortical circuits. The control of cortical rhythmical activity leads to regulation of local and generalized excitatory states of the cortex. The reticular systems, thalamic and brain stem, appear to serve as a regulatory medium for cortical activity, operating in the maintenance of consciousness and the focusing of the conscious activity underlying attention, as well as the gradual elimination of conscious activity in the development of sleep (798). When the basal diencephalic portion of the brain stem reticular system is destroyed, the diffuse thalamic reticular system is active in the production of wave patterns similar to those seen in sleep (522). Stimulation of the brain stem reticular system, on the other hand, gives rise to a cortical response comparable to that seen in the electroencephalogram in the arousal reaction to afferent stimulation. The mechanisms underlying the interplay of neuronal activity in these two reticular systems and in the cerebral cortex await more analysis.

Blood Supply to the Thalamus

Five principal groups of **arteries** supply the thalamus (260, 261). Two enter near the midline at the level of the interpeduncular space. One of these, anterior to the mamillary bodies,

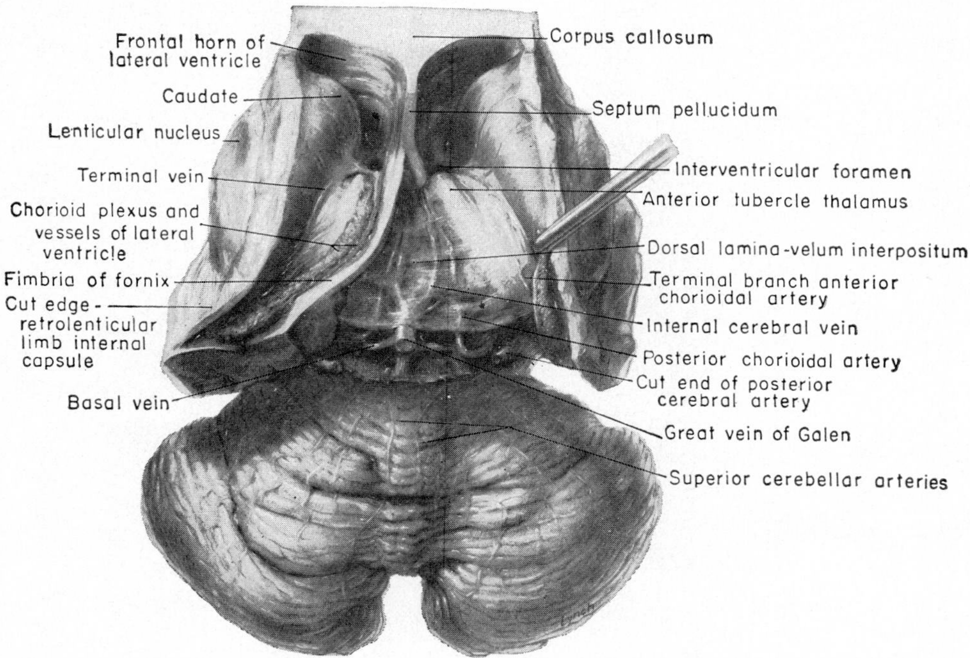

FIG. 208. Dissection to show dorsal surface of caudate and thalamus and the dorsal lamina of the pial reflection above the third ventricle.

is the **premamillary** or **thalamotuberal stalk;** the other, posterior to the mamillary bodies, is the **retromamillary** or **thalamoperforating** (Fig. 50). A third approaches the thalamus proper by its inferior lateral surface, between the two geniculates, and is called the **thalamogeniculate** (Figs. 142, 209). A fourth enters from the ventricular surface, the **chorioidal** supply. Finally, the **lenticulo-optic** (striate) arteries from the middle cerebral form a fifth superior lateral stalk. The thalamoperforating and thalamogeniculate vessels usually arise from the posterior cerebral artery; the thalamotuberal stalk, most often from the posterior communicating artery but occasionally from the posterior cerebral. The chorioidal supply is from the posterior chorioidal artery, a branch of the posterior cerebral, and from the anterior chorioidal artery, a branch of the internal carotid (Figs. 56, 208). The thalamogeniculate, thalamoperforating, and thalamotuberal supplies are composed of several vessels each. In addition to their thalamic distribution, the thalamoperforating vessels supply the cerebral peduncle, rostral end of the red nucleus, hypothalamus, and subthalamus.

Branches from the anterior chorioidal supply the subthalamus and hypothalmus, the chorioid plexus of the inferior horn of the lateral ventricle, the lateral part of the lateral geniculate, and the optic tract, and small branches nourish the ventrolateral part of the pulvinar and the superior medial portion of the thalamus. The remaining area of distribution of this artery has been described in Chap. 4. The posterior chorioidal supplies the chorioid plexus of the third ventricle, with some branches to the ventral and posterior parts of the pulvinar and many small branches to the medial nuclei from medial to lateral borders. Its other area of supply is described in Chap. 8. The lenticulo-optic supply is distributed only to the most superior and lateral parts of the lateral and anterior nuclei as well as to fibers passing into and from the thalamic nuclei.

If the blood supply to the thalamus is studied nucleus by nucleus, it is seen that the lateral nuclear group is supplied from below upward in its posterior half by the thalamogeniculate, the thalamoperforating, and the lenticulo-optic, the thalamogeniculate being the most important; its anterior half depends

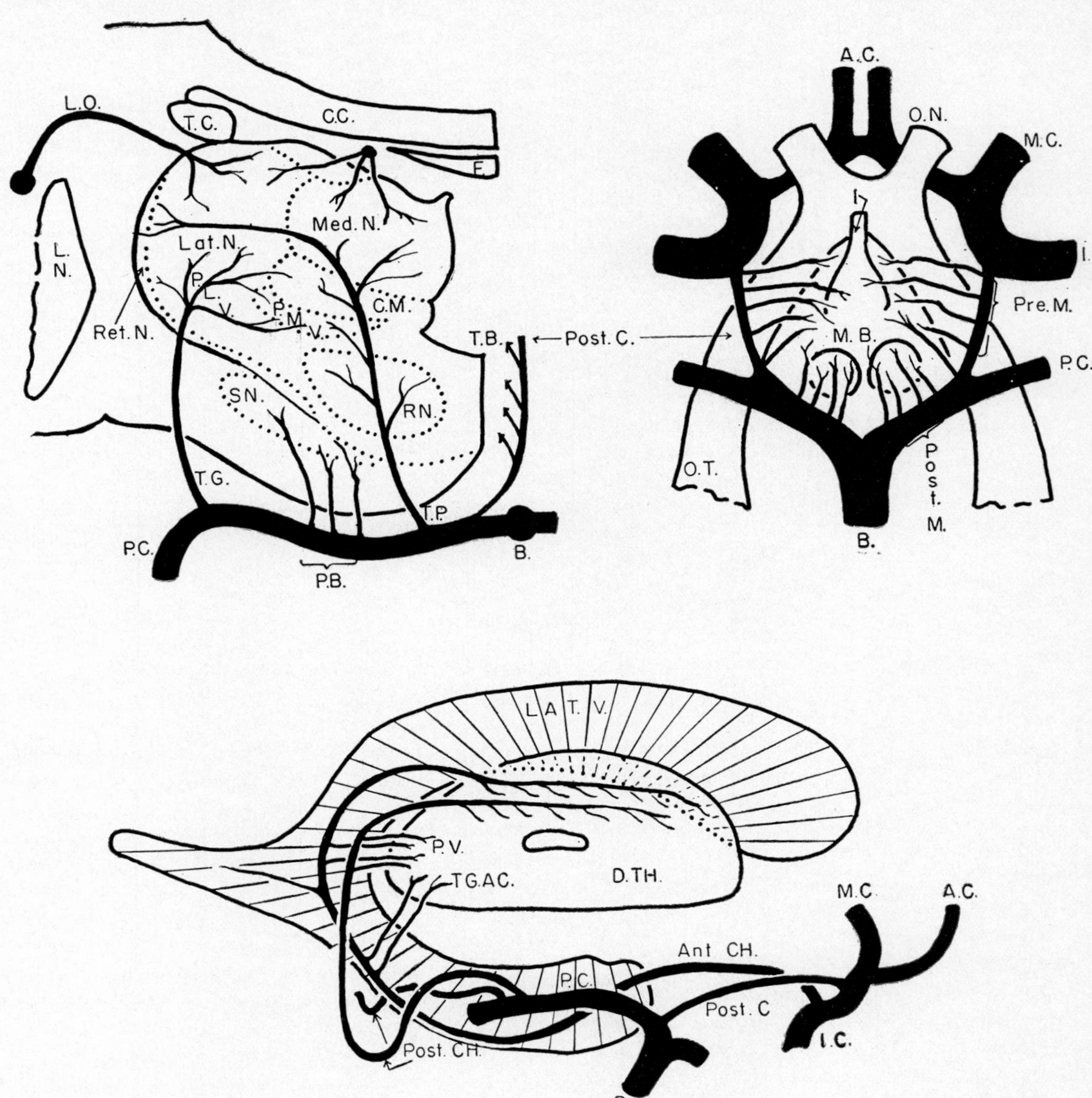

Fig. 209. Schema to illustrate the arterial supply to the thalamus. Above, left, general plan of supply; above, right, premamillary and postmamillary supply; below, chorioidal supply. *A.C.*, anterior cerebral artery; *Ant. CH.*, anterior chorioidal artery; *B.*, basilar artery; *C.C.*, corpus callosum; *C.M.*, centrum medianum; *D. TH.*, dorsal thalamus; *F.*, fornix; *I.*, infundibulum; *I.C.*, internal carotid artery; *Lat. N.*, lateral nucleus of the thalamus; *LAT. V.*, lateral ventricle; *L.N.*, lenticular nucleus; *L.O.*, lenticulo-optic artery; *M.B.*, mamillary bodies; *M. C.*, middle cerebral artery; *Med. N.*, medial nucleus of the thalamus; *O.N.*, optic nerve; *O.T.*, optic tract; *P.B.*, peduncular branches; *P.C.*, posterior cerebral artery; *P.L.V.*, posterolateral ventral nucleus of the thalamus; *P.M.V.*, posteromedial ventral nucleus of the thalamus; *Post. C.*, posterior communicating artery; *Post. CH.*, posterior chorioidal arteries; *Post. M.*, posterior mamillary arteries; *Pre. M.*, premamillary arteries; *P.V.*, pulvinar branches; *Ret. N.*, reticular nucleus of the thalamus; *R.N.*, red nucleus; *S.N.*, substantia nigra; *T.B.*, thalamotuberal arteries; *T.C.*, tail of the caudate nucleus; *T.G.*, thalamogeniculate artery; *TG. AC.*, thalamogeniculate accessory arteries; *T.P.*, thalamoperforating artery. (*Based on Foix and Hillemand, Rev. neurol.*, T. II, 1925.)

on the thalamotuberal and lenticulo-optic branches (Fig. 209). The inferior half of the medial and mid-line nuclei is supplied by the thalamoperforating branches posteriorly, by the thalamotuberal branches anteriorly; the superior half of these medial nuclei and mid-line nuclei is supplied by the chorioidal vessels. The anterior nucleus depends principally on the lenticulo-optic supply, but its most ventral portion receives branches from the thalamotuberal stalk and, rarely, branches from the internal carotid. The pulvinar is supplied by the chorioidal supply and in its anterior inferior-lateral part by the thalamogeniculate. It is on this last supply, principally, that the centrum medianum and the posteromedial ventral nuclei depend. As for the habenular complex, its principal supply is by the chorioid vessels. Finally, the subthalamus, in its more caudomedial part, bordering the rostral edge of the red nucleus, depends on the thalamoperforating supply. All its anterior medial part depends on the premamillary supply. But the majority of the subthalamus, including the corpus Luysi (subthalamic nucleus) and lenticular fasciculus, is supplied by the anterior chorioidal artery.

The **venous drainage** of the thalamus is taken care of by tributaries of the large vein of Galen. The superior and central regions of the thalamus are drained by radicles of the internal cerebral veins (small veins of Galen); some of the inferior and ventral lateral regions are drained by radicles of the basal veins (Figs. 61, 208). The basal veins and the internal cerebral veins empty into the vein of Galen. The inferior regions of the thalamus may be drained also by small veins which empty into large veins (deep middle cerebral, interpeduncular venous plexus) or sinuses (cavernous) at the base of the brain. Because of the rich anastomosis between the terminals of the internal cerebral veins and those of the veins on the cortical surface, the thalamus and other centrally placed nuclei may be drained into either channel.

The Function of the Thalamus

The thalamus stands as a prominent relay and integrative center for all types of afferent impulses. Somatic impulses from head and body pass into the posterior ventral nuclei of the lateral nuclear mass; visceral impulses especially, as well as some somatic, to the mid-line nuclei; olfactory, to the habenula, and perhaps to the mamillary bodies and thence to anterior thalamic nuclei; gustatory, to the semilunar or an adjacent nucleus; visual, to the lateral geniculate body; and auditory, to the medial geniculate body. It must be emphasized at present and it will be mentioned again in a later section that olfactory impulses do not appear to have the same relation to the thalamus as do other afferent impulses. The appreciation of an odor in the cortex does not depend on a thalamic relay, apparently. For example, there is no evidence that appreciable olfactory impulses of any order, secondary or tertiary especially, reach the thalamus. A few may reach the habenula via the stria medullaris thalami for establishing through them olfacto-somatic reflex paths.

As a result of clinical and experimental studies, it has been maintained that conscious recognition of painful, thermal, and some tactile impulses is possible at a thalamic or tectal level (348, 793). Such assumptions have arisen through studies of individuals and animals that have had removals of varying amounts of the cerebral cortex and through studies of individuals suffering destruction of the posterior ventral nuclei of the thalamus (see below). Integration in the posterior ventral nucleus or, in case of its destruction, in the mid-line thalamic nuclei and tectal regions which also receive pain, thermal, and tactile impulses from the spinal cord and trigeminal nuclei, is said to account for the simple recognition of these modalities. It will be mentioned in a later chapter that other mechanisms may be acting to underlie the perception of pain and temperature in some cases of thalamic disease of parietal-cortex removal. It is universally believed, however, that topographic and quantitative characters of these modalities require cortical and thalamic integrations. Other sensory modalities, dependent on impulse transmission by the medial lemniscus, also require cortical and thalamic integrations.

Thalamic nuclei, therefore, may serve as simple relays, as integrative centers for conscious recognition of certain impulses, and as integrative and elaborative centers which project the product of their elaboration to the cerebral cortex. Various levels of sensory activity, therefore, are found in the thalamus. The lower level or simple relay nuclei are the posterior ventral, and the lateral and medial geniculate bodies. These lower-level nuclei also relay impulses to thalamic integrative and elaborative nuclei. These latter are the lateral dorsal, lateral posterior, pulvinar, and a portion, at least, of the dorsomedial.

It is to be expected that nuclei with different levels of sensory integrating action project to different cortical areas. Simple somatosensory and visceral impulses of the lower order are relayed to cortex bounding the central fissure, areas 4, 3, 1, and 2. Certain visceral impulses from the gastrointestinal system project to the insula, according to Penfield (622). Simple visual impulses are relayed to the posterior tip of the occipital lobe, area 17; and auditory, to areas 41 and 42 on the superior posterior portion of the temporal lobe. More integrated visceral and somatic impulses are relayed to cortical areas anterior and posterior to that bounding the central fissure, the prefrontal and posterior parietal cortex; more complex visual impulses, to cortex rostral to area 17, areas 18 and 19; and auditory, to cortex bounding areas 41 and 42, area 22. These thalamocortical systems are arranged in point-to-point fashion.

The lateral ventral and the anterior ventral nuclei stand between cerebellum and cerebral cortex and between striatum and cerebral cortex, respectively. The striatum (caudate especially), under the influence of certain cortical regions, acts through one or both of these nuclei, and perhaps others, to correlate cortical and subcortical motor and sensory integrations.

The more recently described thalamic reticular system appears to have great functional significance in thalamocortical and corticothalamic regulations. Some of the activity of these nuclei has been described above. In the experimental animal they can be shown to exert a strong influence on the electrical activity of the cerebral cortex. In life they most probably exert an equally strong influence on cortical neuronal activity. This may involve simultaneous specific "tuning up" of certain cortical regions and braking of others. In such a way cortical attention may be established. They are also able to bring into play simultaneously many thalamic nuclei and large cortical areas. Such widespread thalamocortical activation probably underlies our most skillful movement patterns and our most complex concrete and abstract mental processes.

Finally, certain dorsal thalamic nuclei, midline, dorsomedial, and anterior, especially, recipients of impulses from the hypothalamus and projecting to large cortical areas, prefrontal, orbital, and cingular, participate in affective reactions.

Clinical Disorders of the Thalamus

The thalamic nuclei may be invaded by tumor or may undergo degeneration secondary to disorder in one or more of its vascular supplies. Hemorrhage from, or thrombosis in, one of the vessels may lead to striking symptoms.

In the first decade of the present century, Dejerine and his colleagues described the now classical "thalamic syndrome" (462). This results characteristically from thrombosis of the thalamogeniculate arteries, but it may arise when the thalamic nuclei they supply are destroyed from any cause. When the syndrome is complete, the signs usually seen are as follows (260).

A contralateral hemiparesis usually occurs. It often is associated with some spasticity that clears within a short time. The paresis is thought to be due to edema in the nearby posterior limb of the internal capsule, which leads to a functional blocking of corticospinal-tract transmission.

A complete contralateral hemianesthesia is usually seen at first. Later some return of superficial sensibilities of pain, temperature, and gross touch occurs, but a permanent loss, or severe impairment, of light touch and position sense together with stereoanesthesia is observed (385). This results from softening of the posterolateral ventral nucleus and possibly of the pulvinar. The face may escape sensory change, since the arcuate, or posteromedial ventral nucleus, is not completely involved in a thalamogeniculate disorder. It has been suggested that pain and temperature sensation are not more severely damaged because some of the fibers of the spinothalamic tracts and their collaterals enter the mid-line nuclei and the pretectal region wherein recognition of certain sensory stimuli is possible (796). Furthermore, a certain amount of bilateral representation of cutaneous sensibility is present in each thalamus, as has been demonstrated by selective application of strychnine to them, as has been described above. This is due to the fact, presumably, that not all spinothalamic tract fibers are crossed, and that certain crossed spinothalamic fibers may recross at posterior commissure and thalamic levels (133). A delay in the recognition of superficial stimuli usually exists, however, and an overaction or dysesthesia is produced by them. They may be excessively painful or quite pleasant. Localization of them is poor. Severe pains may occur spontaneously in the contralateral half of the body; these may be related to movement, to cutaneous stimuli, or to the emotional state.

Ataxia may be observed in the involved limbs, depending on the amount of paresis. Involuntary movements, choreo-athetoid in character, may occur in these limbs, or a to-and-fro action (or intention) tremor may accompany the movements carried out by the involved limbs, especially the upper one (see Chap. 12). The ataxia may be due in part to these involuntary movements, but in the classical syndrome it is a true sensory ataxia and arises because of the disturbance in deep sensibility, appreciation of muscle and joint movement. The choreo-athetoid movements and intention tremor arise as a result of damage to the lateral ventral nucleus or the dentatothalamic fibers which terminate in that nucleus. It has been suggested that only the intention tremor results from damage to dentatothalamic fibers, the choreo-athetoid movements resulting from damage to the pallidothalamic fibers of Forel's field H_1 (see Chap. 17).

There may be vasomotor changes with swelling and increased warmth of the extremities, fine parchmentlike skin, and trophic changes of the nails.

Contractures of the contralateral upper limb may be seen, and especially an abnormal hand posture, the so-called "thalamic hand." The fingers and hands are frequently held in a posture characterized by flexion and pronation of the wrist, flexion of the fingers at the metacarpophalangeal joints, and extension of the two distal phalangeal articulations. Muscle tone is usually reduced, and this posture can be altered passively after a few initial attempts, there being little resistance to the passive movements. The patient can move and use the fingers individually, albeit slowly.

Not all the above symptoms occur in all "thalamic syndromes." The disturbance in superficial and deep sensibilities over the contralateral limbs and trunk, the paresthesiae accompanying various stimuli, the spontaneous pains, and the ataxia resulting because of loss of joint and muscle sensibility are the features characteristic of destruction of the posterolateral ventral nuclei by tumor or secondary to a thalamogeniculate artery disorder. When the lateral ventral nucleus is the site of destruction from tumor or because of disorder in the thalamoperforating arteries, or when the dentatothalamic fibers are damaged, involuntary movements, tremor or choreo-athetoid in type, may appear. The "thalamic hand" is also observed in these cases. Any or all of these symptoms may arise in disease of the posterior cerebral artery. Other abnormal signs are apt to appear with disease of this artery, especially if its entire territory of distribution is affected. Contralateral paralysis resulting from softening in the cerebral peduncle, and homonymous hemianopsia (see Chap. 21) may be found.

Summary

The dorsal thalamus therefore serves as a relay for sensory impulses of all types, except possibly olfactory, as they are discharged from periphery to cerebral cortex. Its activity in the sensory mechanisms consists not only in a simple relay, but also in integration of sensory impulses. Recognition of stimuli as pain, as alterations of temperature, or as tactile qualities may be the result of thalamic integrations in posterior lateral nuclei and possibly mid-line nuclei as well. Other impulses arising in pain, thermal, and tactile endings, as well as many of those arising in receptors lying in muscle and tendons, relay in the thalamus, traversing and being integrated in several nuclei, and passing finally to the cerebral cortex. Herein integrations make it possible for an individual to recognize the amounts of contraction in his muscles and about his joints, so as to have a sense of position and of movement; to recognize the size, quality, and shape of objects brought into contact with tactile endings; to localize the exact point of stimulation, whether it be painful, thermal, or tactile; and to compare and differentiate stimuli. The diffuse thalamic reticular system cooperates by exercising some control on the background cortical activity. Integration of certain impulses is pointed up in order to gain for them attention; that of others may be suppressed.

Aside from its activities which are concerned primarily with the sensory system, the thalamus has functions interrelated with the motor system. It stands between cerebellum and cortex on the one hand and between basal ganglia and cortex on the other, and it facilitates or suppresses the motor activities of the cerebral cortex. Finally, it stands between the hypothalamus and that cortex of the prefrontal lobe which serves in the central integrations underlying emotional reactions. The thalamic relations to the hypothalamus, and especially the nuclei and connections of this latter brain center, will receive attention in the following section.

CHAPTER 14

THE HYPOTHALAMUS

Reference has been made previously, especially in the section concerned with the autonomic nervous system, to the hypothalamus, that region of the brain which forms the floor and lower walls of the third ventricle. Among the functions of the hypothalamus are some intimately related to the activity of the peripheral autonomic system. It is also related both anatomically and functionally with the hypophysis, and indeed, it is to be recalled that the posterior lobe of the latter structure develops as a direct extension of the floor of the third ventricle. This down-growing portion comes into intimate apposition with a diverticulum from the ectodermal lining of the primitive oral cavity which develops into the anterior and intermediate parts of the hypophysis. The hypothalamus is, phylogenetically, one of the oldest parts of the brain. In recent years its minute structure, vascular patterns, and functions have been the subjects of increasing research activity, and many details have been added to our knowledge. The regulations of water metabolism, of temperature control, of vasomotor and visceromotor activities, and of carbohydrate and fat metabolism are some of the activities of the hypothalamus. Its connections with the medial and anterior thalamic nuclei, and through them with the frontal and cingular cortex respectively, as well as its large discharge from the hippocampus, have served to stimulate both active investigation and theoretical speculations as to its role in the expression of emotion.

The rostral plane of the hypothalamus can arbitrarily be selected as one falling between the anterior commissure, dorsally, and the rostral border of the optic chiasma, ventrally. No distinct anatomical line of demarcation exists, however, between the rostral hypothalamus and the immediately adjacent tissue anteriorly, the preoptic area. The posterior boundary of the hypothalamus is also not a sharp one but is usually described as falling in a plane just behind the mamillary bodies.

In a parasagittal section of the diencephalon near the mid-line, the preoptic area and several hypothalamic nuclei can be seen, and a division of the hypothalamus into several portions can be made conveniently (Figs. 210, 211, 212). Parasagittal sections, further removed from the mid-line, are necessary for a view of the other hypothalamic areas (Figs. 213, 214, 215). These divisions (of the hypothalamus) are made more or less on geographic lines, for as yet no accurate anatomical or physiological data are available to warrant such a division (151, 159, 651).

Nuclei of Preoptic Area and Hypothalamus

The regional divisions can thus be made first and these subdivided into smaller nuclear groups. These can be listed as follows (Figs. 214, 215):

1. Preoptic area
2. Supraoptic region
   - *a.* Paraventricular nucleus, dorsally
   - *b.* Supraoptic nucleus, ventrally
3. Infundibular region
   - *a.* Dorsomedial hypothalamic nucleus } medially
   - *b.* Ventromedial hypothalamic nucleus } medially
   - *c.* Posterior hypothalamic nucleus } medially
   - *d.* Lateral hypothalamic area and tuberal nuclei } laterally

4. Mamillary region
   a. Medial mamillary nucleus
   b. Lateral mamillary nucleus
   c. Intercalatus nucleus

Though not a part of the hypothalamus developmentally, the **preoptic area** appears related to it morphologically. This telencephalic region is immediately rostral to the optic chiasma and extends to the lamina terminalis. Dorsally it extends to the anterior commissure. The preoptic area is divided into medial and lateral nuclei. The medial preoptic nucleus, composed of small cells, is placed near the ependymal lining of the third ventricle. These cells appear to have rostral connections with the parolfactory area and the nucleus of the diagonal band (see Chap. 23). Connections with the medially placed hypothalamic nuclei are also present, and some fibers of the stria terminalis end in the medial preoptic nucleus. The lateral preoptic nucleus appears to be a rostral extension of the lateral hypothalamic nuclei, and its cells are medium-sized ones, scattered among the fibers of the medial forebrain bundle. The cells of this nucleus contribute axons to this latter bundle. Both lateral and medial preoptic nuclei may be connected with the medially placed thalamic nuclei (151).

The **paraventricular nucleus** of man has been given the following dimensions by Le Gros Clark (151) (Figs. 210, 211, 214*A*, 215*A*). Its vertical extent is 7.5 mm., its sagittal, 4.5 mm., and its maximum width in transverse sections is about 1 mm. Its ventral border is 3 mm. above the optic chiasma; its upper is at the

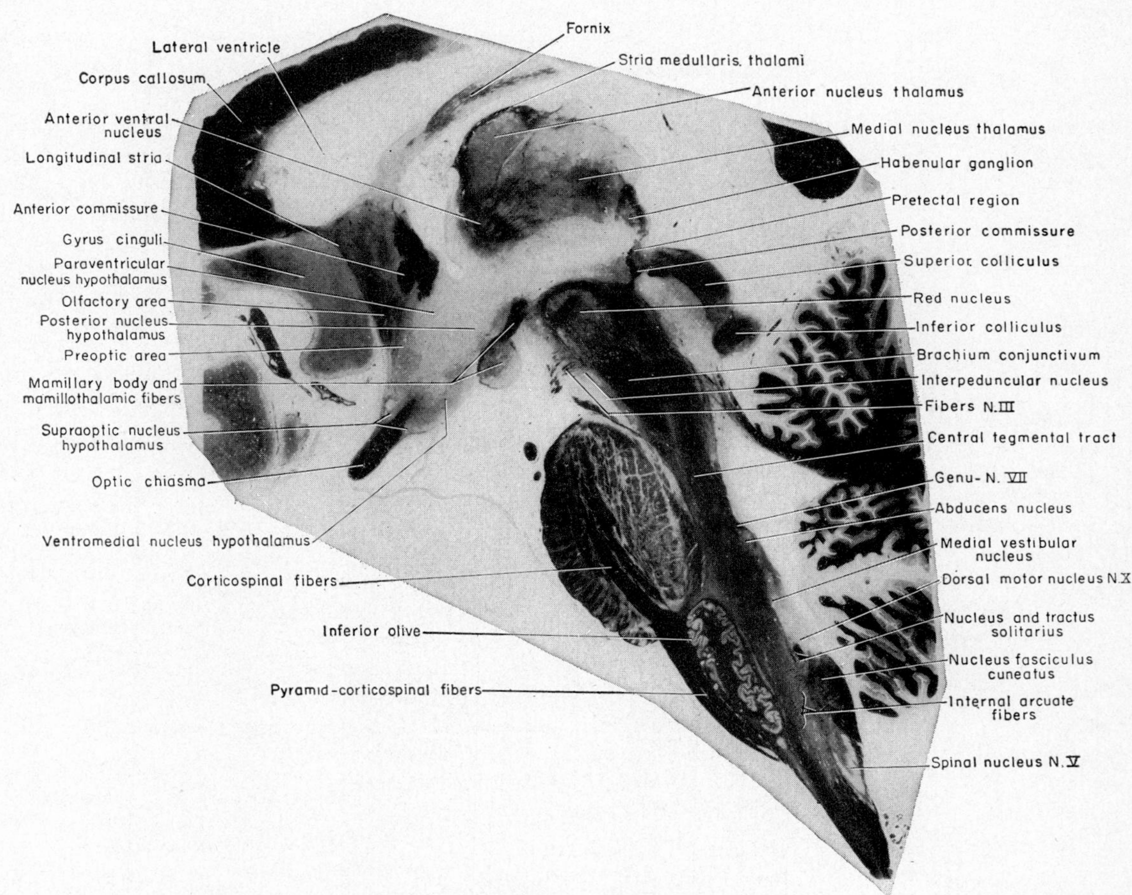

Fig. 210. Parasagittal section, A 300, of human brain stem through optic chiasma and midhypothalamus. Weigert. Photograph, ×1.65.

Preoptic
Dorsomedial
Supraoptic
Paraventricular
Posterior
Medial mamillary
Ventromedial

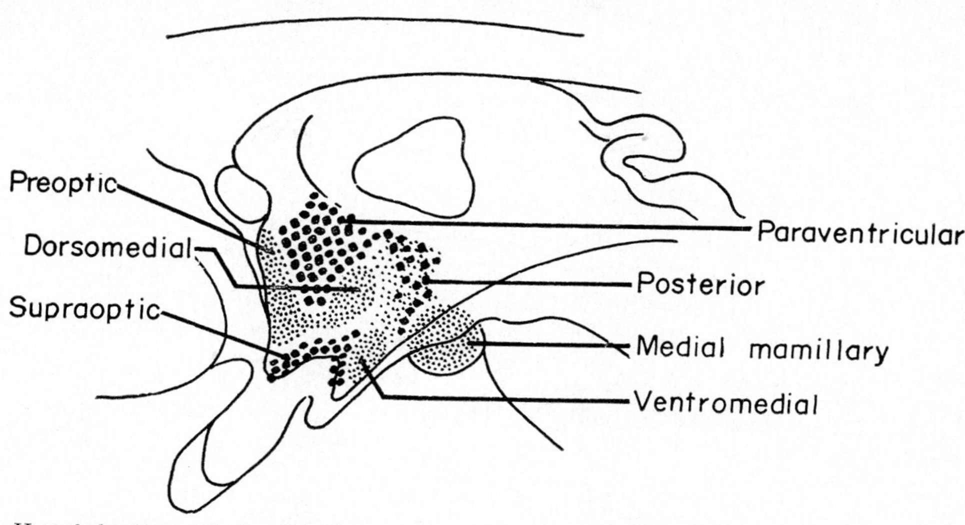

FIG. 211. Hypothalamic nuclei of man projected on the wall of the third ventricle. (*Redrawn after W. E. L. Clark, J. Anat., vol.* 70.)

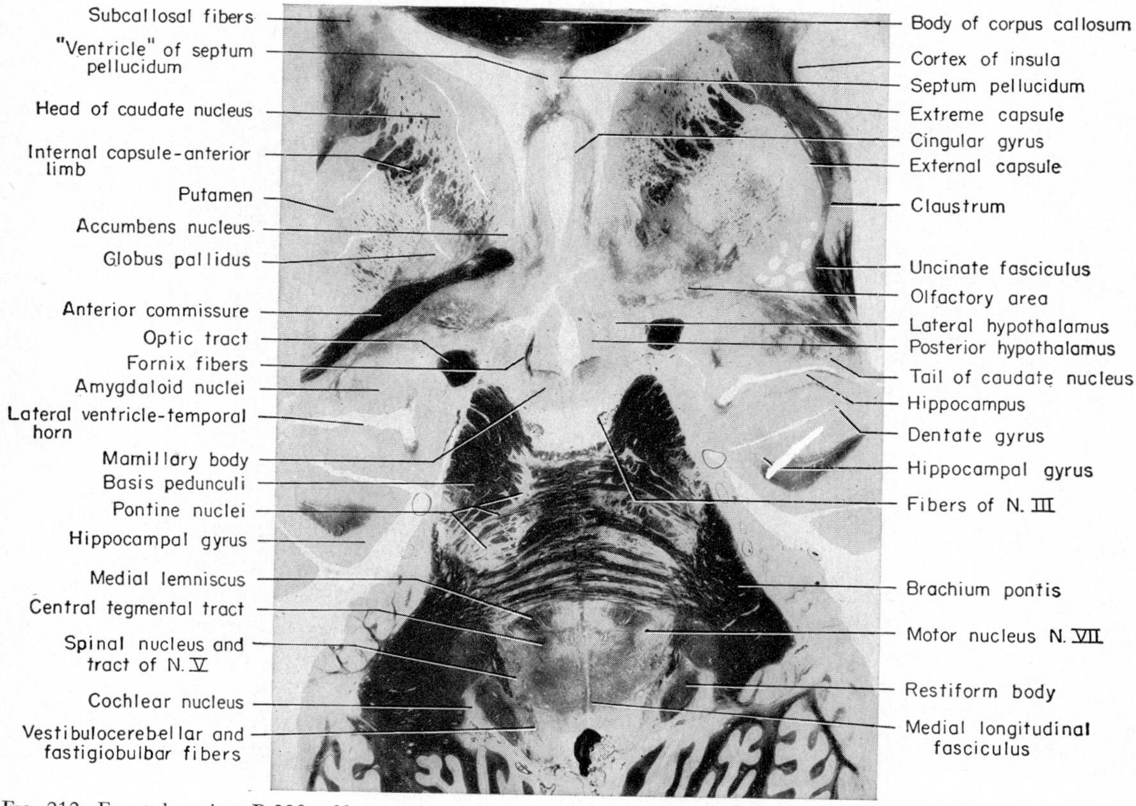

Subcallosal fibers
"Ventricle" of septum pellucidum
Head of caudate nucleus
Internal capsule-anterior limb
Putamen
Accumbens nucleus
Globus pallidus
Anterior commissure
Optic tract
Fornix fibers
Amygdaloid nuclei
Lateral ventricle-temporal horn
Mamillary body
Basis pedunculi
Pontine nuclei
Hippocampal gyrus
Medial lemniscus
Central tegmental tract
Spinal nucleus and tract of N. V
Cochlear nucleus
Vestibulocerebellar and fastigiobulbar fibers
Body of corpus callosum
Cortex of insula
Septum pellucidum
Extreme capsule
Cingular gyrus
External capsule
Claustrum
Uncinate fasciculus
Olfactory area
Lateral hypothalamus
Posterior hypothalamus
Tail of caudate nucleus
Hippocampus
Dentate gyrus
Hippocampal gyrus
Fibers of N. III
Brachium pontis
Motor nucleus N. VII
Restiform body
Medial longitudinal fasciculus

FIG. 212. Frontal section, B 280, of human brain through anterior commissure and mamillary bodies. Weigert. Photograph, ×1.4.

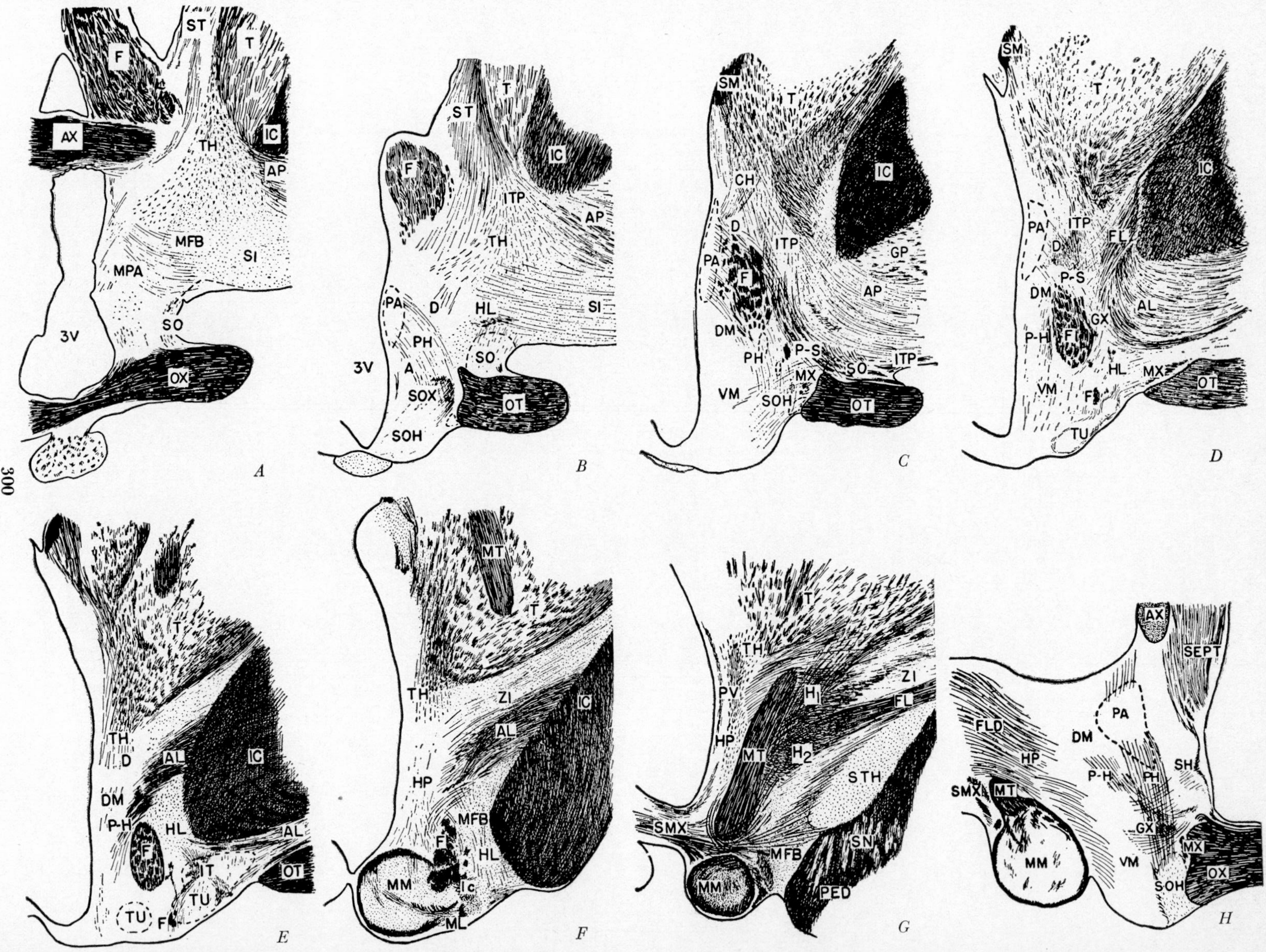
A
F
ST
T
AX
TH
IC
AP
MFB
SI
MPA
3V
SO
OX
B
ST
T
F
IC
ITP
AP
TH
PA
D
HL
SI
PH
SO
3V
A
SOX
OT
SOH
C
SM
T
CH
IC
D
ITP
GP
PA
F
AP
DM
PH
P-S
ITP
MX
SO
VM
SOH
OT
D
SM
T
IC
PA
ITP
D
FL
P-S
DM
AL
GX
P-H
F
HL
MX
VM
F
OT
TU
E
T
TH
D
AL
IC
DM
P-H
HL
AL
F
IT
OT
TU
TU
F
F
MT
T
TH
ZI
IC
AL
HP
MFB
F
HL
MM
Ic
ML
G
T
TH
PV
ZI
H1
FL
HP
MT
H2
STH
SMX
SN
MFB
MM
PED
H
AX
SEPT
PA
FLD
DM
HP
P-H
SH
PH
SMX
MT
GX
MX
MM
VM
SOH
OX

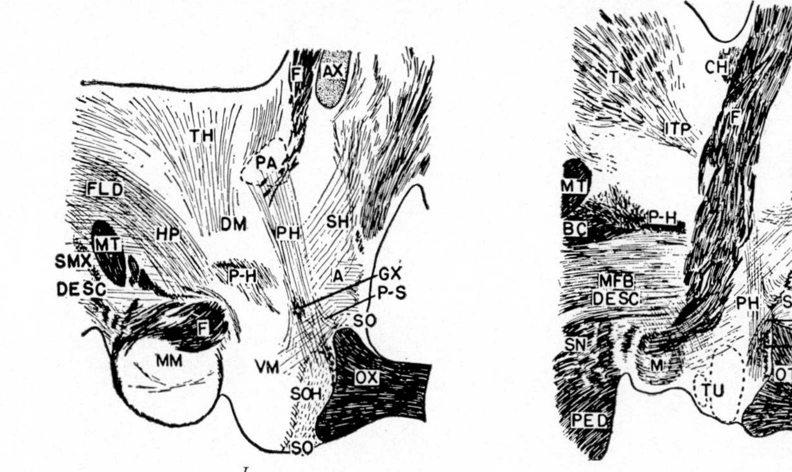

I

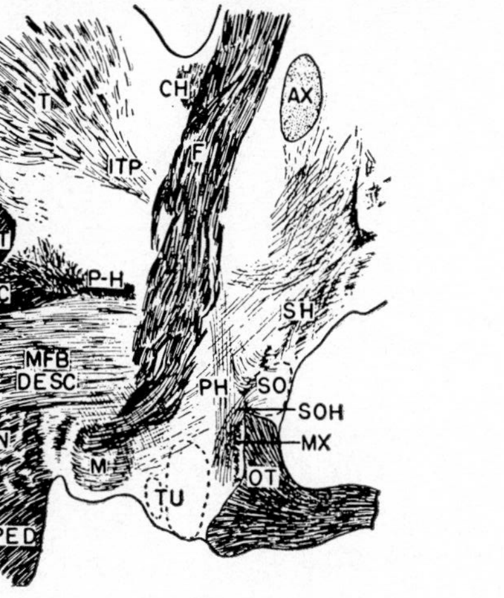

J

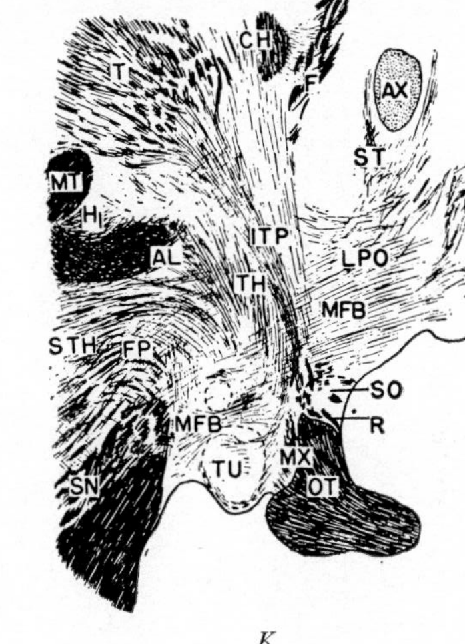

K

FIG. 213. Semischematic drawings to illustrate the nuclei and fiber patterns in the human hypothalamus. *A–G* inclusively are transverse sections of successive rostrocaudal levels through the hypothalamus. *H–K* inclusively are parasagittal sections through successive mediolateral levels, *H* being most medial. (*Courtesy of Dr. W. R. Ingram, Research Publ., A. Nerv. & Ment. Dis., vol.* 20.)

A, anterior hypothalamic area
AL, ansa lenticularis
AP, ansa peduncularis
AX, anterior commissure
BC, brachium conjunctivum
CH, corticohabenular fibers
D, dorsal hypothalamic area
DESC, fibers of the diffuse descending system
DM, dorsomedial hypothalamic nucleus
F, fornix
FL, fasciculus lenticularis
FLD, dorsal longitudinal fasciculus
FP, fibrae perforantes (lenticular)
GP, globus pallidus
Gx, dorsal supraoptic commissure, pars dorsalis
H_1, H_2, fields of Forel
HL, lateral hypothalamic area
HP, posterior hypothalamic area
IC, internal capsule
Ic, nucleus intercalatus
IT, fibers of nucleus tuberis
ITP, inferior thalamic peduncle
LPO, lateral preoptic area
M, mamillary body
MFB, medial forebrain bundle
ML, lateral mamillary nucleus
MM, medial mamillary nucleus
MPA, medial preoptic area
MT, mamillothalamic tract
MX, dorsal supraoptic commissure, pars ventralis
OT, optic tract
OX, optic chiasma
PA, paraventricular nucleus
PED, cerebral peduncle
PF, perifornical area
PH, paraventriculohypophyseal fibers
P-H, pallidohypothalamic fibers
P-S, paraventriculosupraoptic fibers
PV, periventricular system
R, fasciculus residualis
SEPT, septum pellucidum
SH, septohypothalamic fibers
SI, substantia innominata
SM, stria medullaris
SMX, supramamillary commissure
SN, substantia nigra
SO, supraoptic nucleus
SOH, supraopticohypophyseal tract
SOX, supraoptic commissures
ST, stria terminalis
STH, subthalamic nucleus
T, thalamus
TH, thalamohypothalamic fibers
TU, nucleus tuberis laterale
VM, ventromedial hypothalamic nucleus
ZI, zona incerta
3V, third ventricle

level of the hypothalamic sulcus. Its rostral border approaches the anterior commissure; its caudal border, superiorly, overhangs the dorsomedial hypothalamic nucleus while being contiguous with an extension of the posterior hypothalamic nucleus. The cells are fairly large, being rounded, oval, or somewhat triangular in shape. The Nissl granules are arranged peripherally and stain deeply, and the neurons contain a colloid substance. The neurons are densely packed, and many of their axons, very poorly myelinated, pass along the infundibulum into the posterior lobe of the hypophysis.

The **supraoptic nucleus,** composed of cells histologically similar to those of the paraventricular nucleus, lies above the rostral ends of the optic tract on both sides and its forward pole is above and lateral to the optic chiasma (Figs. 210, 211, 214*A*, 215). These neurons also send their axons into the posterior lobe of the hypophysis by way of the infundibulum.

The term tuber cinereum is usually applied to that part of the floor of the diencephalon (hypothalamus) bounded rostrally by the optic chiasma, caudally by the mamillary bodies, and laterally by the optic tract and cerebral peduncles. Suspended from its center by a peduncle is the hypophysis. This peduncle, usually bulbous at its point of origin, tapers briefly toward the hypophysis and has the shape, therefore, of a funnel. Because of this it is called the infundibulum. The median eminence of the tuber cinereum constitutes the bulbous part of the infundibulum and is functionally a part of the hypophysis. Dorsal and dorsolateral to the median eminence are the hypothalamic regions proper of the tuber cinereum. These may be divided into medial and lateral regions, as indi-

Paraventricular nucleus
Supraoptic nucleus
Optic chiasma
A

Fornix
Posterior hypothalamic nucleus
Tuberal nuclei
Lateral hypothalamic area
Ventromedial hypothalamic nucleus
Tuberal nuclei
B

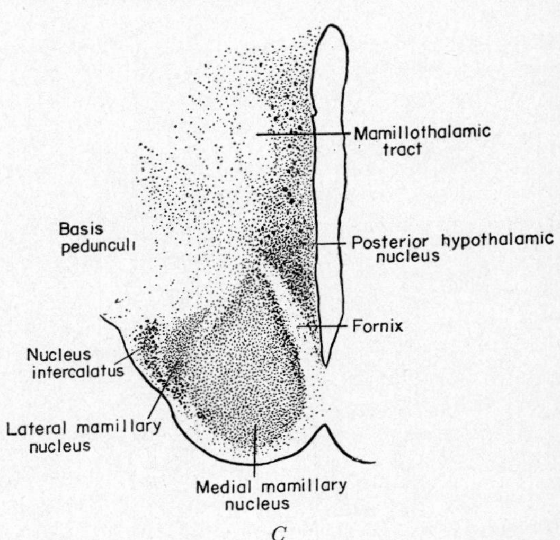

FIG. 214. Transverse sections at successive rostrocaudal levels through the human hypothalamus to show the chief nuclei. *A*, section through supraoptic region; *B*, section through the infundibular region; *C*, section through mamillary region. (*After W. E. L. Clark, J. Anat., vol.* 70, *and* "*The Hypothalamus,*" *The William Ramsay Henderson Trust, Oliver & Boyd, Ltd.*)

cated in the outline above. The medial division in man is composed almost entirely of the ventromedial and dorsomedial hypothalamic nuclei.

The **ventromedial** and **dorsomedial** hypothalamic **nuclei** lie just lateral to the ventricular cavity and extend in transverse sections 2.5 to 3 mm. (Figs. 214*B*, 215*A*). The superior extent of the dorsomedial nucleus is limited by the overhanging paraventricular nucleus. The cells are small round and oval ones that stain very poorly.

The **posterior hypothalamic nucleus** lies adjacent the ventricle wall and is fairly large (Figs. 214*C*, 215*A*). Its caudal extent is adjacent to the mamillothalamic tract, its rostral edge borders the dorsomedial and ventromedial nuclei, and it extends vertically for about 7 mm. Scattered in a dense matrix of small cells are groups of large oval or rounded cells having Nissl bodies situated peripherally. The nucleus of these latter cells is often situated eccentrically and the cells stain darkly, characteristics that have occasionally led to their being described as abnormal cells.

The **lateral hypothalamic area** lies lateral to the plane of the descending column of the fornix (Figs. 214*B*, 215*B*). It extends to the lateral edge of the hypothalamus, the ansa lenticularis and internal capsule bordering it laterally. It is composed of small cells as a matrix into which large neurons have been scattered in groups. The medial forebrain bundle passes through this area. Within this lateral hypothalamic area are several well-circumscribed nuclei, composed of small neurons, which stain lightly with Nissl techniques. These nuclei are the **tuberal nuclei,** and some of the axons from cells of these nuclei pass into the infundibulum, possibly into the posterior hypophysis.

The **medial mamillary nucleus** composes almost all the mamillary body, and its cells are small and lightly staining (Fig. 214*C*). The **lateral mamillary nucleus** located ventrolaterally to the rostral portion of the medial mamillary nucleus is quite small in comparison; its constituent cells are smaller still but are more compactly arranged. Lateral to the lateral mamillary nucleus is the **nucleus intercalatus.** Rostrally and laterally it blends with the lateral hypothalamic area. This is composed of neurons larger than those of the other two mamillary nuclei, and these are darkly staining. The cells of the medial mamillary nucleus give their axons into the mamillothalamic tract. The nucleus intercalatus and the lateral mamillary nucleus receive the terminations of the fornix.

Fiber Connections

The fiber connections of the hypothalamus of man are not well known at present, though many investigations of those of lower mammals have been carried out. It is seldom that human clinical lesions in the hypothalamus lend themselves to anatomical study, since the areas of destruction are apt to be so large that discrete fiber connections cannot be made out. Too, the nature of many of the fibers demonstrable in and about the hypothalamus prevents easy study. They are for the most part small and poorly myelinated. The résumé below represents an outline of the known fiber connections derived from comparative studies as well as from study of normal and pathological human material (409).

AFFERENT FIBERS

The hypothalamus receives fibers from the cerebral cortex, from the thalamus, from globus pallidus, from the amygdaloid nucleus, perhaps from the retina, and perhaps from the spinal cord and brain stem afferent nuclei.

The **fornix** constitutes the most prominent afferent bundle to the hypothalamus (Fig. 216). It is derived from the pyramidal cells of the hippocampus and dentate gyrus and terminates in the mamillary nuclei, especially the nucleus intercalatus and the lateral mamillary nucleus, in the rostral hypothalamic and preoptic region, and in the habenula. The **medial forebrain bundle,** though easily demonstrable in the human hypothalamus, does not lend itself well to analysis (Fig. 213). It seems likely that it carries fibers from the ventromedial rhinencephalic areas near the olfactory striae. Some of these fibers are thought to end in the preoptic area, which may in turn contribute axons to the bundle. Some others perhaps end in the lateral hypothalamic area and the lateral mamillary nucleus, but several investigators, including Krieg and Ranson and Magoun, think that many of the medial forebrain fibers pass *through* the hypothalamus to the midbrain tegmentum (444, 651). Ascending fibers may also be present in the medial forebrain bundle as

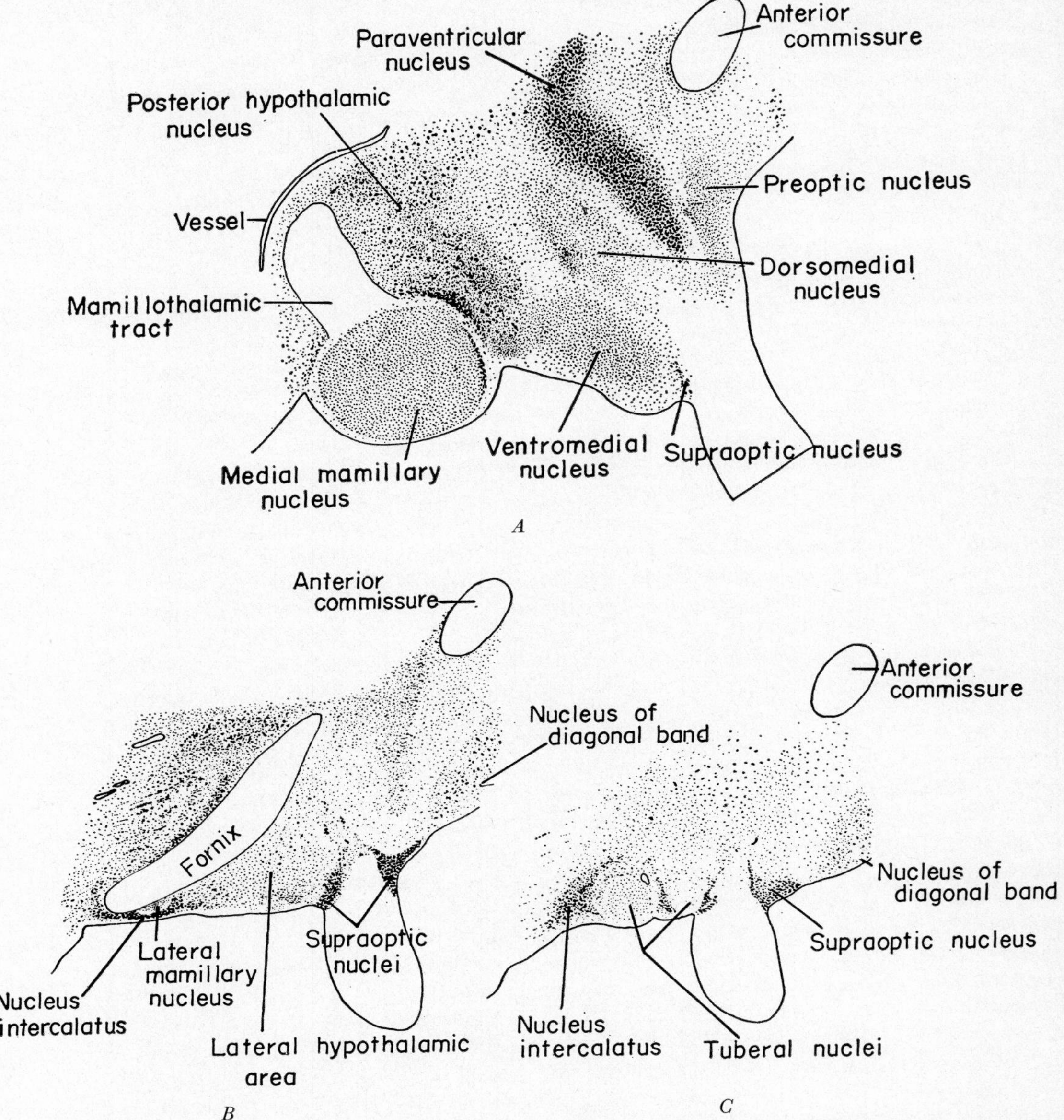

Fig. 215. Parasagittal section of the human hypothalamus at successive mediolateral planes. *A*, section near the median plane; *B*, sagittal section in the plane of the anterior column of the fornix; *C*, sagittal section near lateral margin of hypothalamus. (*After W. E. L. Clark, J. Anat., vol.* 70.)

well as descending fibers of pallidal and striatal origin.

Corticohypothalamic fibers from area 6 to the medial mamillary nucleus have been demonstrated in human material. In the monkey, fibers have been traced from the precentral gyrus to the rostral septal region. This in turn discharges into the medial forebrain bundle which gives collaterals to hypothalamic nuclei. In the monkey, corticohypothalamic fibers from the frontal pole region traverse the genu of the corpus callosum and the septum pellucidum to end in the hypothalamus (539). Fine fibers have been traced from the posterior orbital surface of the frontal lobe to the paraventricular and ventromedial nuclei in the macaque (801). Physiological experiments of Ward and McCulloch have indicated direct corticohypothalamic connections (818). They recorded electrical activity in hypothalamic nuclei following the local application of strychnine sulfate to certain cortical areas. Area 6 was found to "fire" the mamillary nuclei, the lateral hypothalamic area, and the posterior hypothalamic nuclei. Specific areas of the frontal lobe have been shown to "fire" supraoptic and paraventricular nuclei (see Chap. 18).

A pathway running from the frontal lobe to the hypothalamus via a relay in the zona incerta has been recalled by Clark (159). Other fibers from the prefrontal cortex to the dorsomedial thalamic nuclei may indirectly influence the hypothalamus, since periventricular fibers interconnect this thalamic nucleus, mid-line thalamic nuclei, and the hypothalamus. Furthermore, physiological-neuronography studies have demonstrated that fibers from the posterior part of the cingular gyrus (area 23 and possibly area 29) pass to the anterior nucleus of the thalamus (46). Anatomical studies have also revealed fibers from the cingular gyrus to the anterior thalamic nucleus (161, 308). This latter nucleus in turn is interconnected with the medial mamillary nucleus by way of the mamillothalamic tract.

The inferior thalamic peduncle derived in part from the dorsomedial thalamic nucleus appears to give off fibers to the anterior hypothalamic region (Fig. 213). The **mamillary peduncle** which contains ascending fibers chiefly is thought to arise in the midbrain tegmentum and end chiefly in the lateral mamillary nucleus (Fig. 147). Fibers from the spinal cord via the medial lemniscus may relay with the mamillary peduncle and thus may impulses of spinal origin reach the hypothalamus. Visceral afferent impulses especially may utilize this bundle (151, 159). Olfactory impulses reach the hypothalamus indirectly by way of the basal frontal olfactory centers, the olfactory tubercle and septal area, and the medial forebrain bundle, to which the septal nuclei contribute. This bundle, as noted above, gives collaterals to the hypothalamus.

The **stria terminalis** conveys fibers from the amygdaloid nuclei to the preoptic and anterior hypothalamic areas (Figs. 144, 202, 205). Fibers from the substantia innominata also seem to enter the hypothalamus (409). The globus pallidus sends fibers via the dorsal supraoptic commissure (Ganser's commissure) to the ipsilateral and contralateral hypothalamic nuclei, especially the ventromedial (Figs. 213, 255, 257). The zona incerta and the subthalamic nuclei probably also send fibers via this commissure to the hypothalamus. Fibers are said by some authors to leave the optic tract to end in the supraoptic and the ventromedial hypothalamic nuclei. It is through these nuclei, which send fibers to the hypophysis, that the latter is brought under retinal control. Some doubt has been cast on the existence of certain retinohypothalamic fibers, however.

EFFERENT FIBERS

Three chief groups of fibers compose the efferent connections of the hypothalamus (Fig. 216). These are the conspicuous bundles leaving the mamillary nuclei, the periventricular system, and the fibers passing into the hypophysis by way of the stalk.

The medial mamillary nucleus sends many fibers in the **mamillothalamic tract** into the anterior nucleus of the thalamus. The anterior thalamic nuclei project to the cingular gyrus, and a hypothalamocortical system is thus afforded. Since the anterior thalamic nuclei receive fibers from the cingular gyrus and also send fibers to the medial mamillary nucleus, a corticothalamohypothalamic relay is also present, as mentioned above. The medial mamillary nucleus also sends a prominent group of fibers into the tegmental portion of the brain stem, as a **mamillotegmental tract** (Figs. 189, 216, 258). They terminate especially in the large lateral and central reticular nuclei. Hypothalamotegmental fibers from many hypothalamic nuclei to the deep tegmental nucleus of the midbrain have been described in the macaque by Crosby and her co-workers. These are said to run in company with the medial forebrain bundle, and some cross in the midbrain tegmentum (E. C. Crosby and R. T. Woodburne, 1951).

The **periventricular fibers** arise in the posterior hypothalamic nucleus, the tuberal nuclei, and the supraoptic nucleus (Fig. 259). The fibers are either unmyelinated or finely myelinated, and they pass dorsally into the periven-

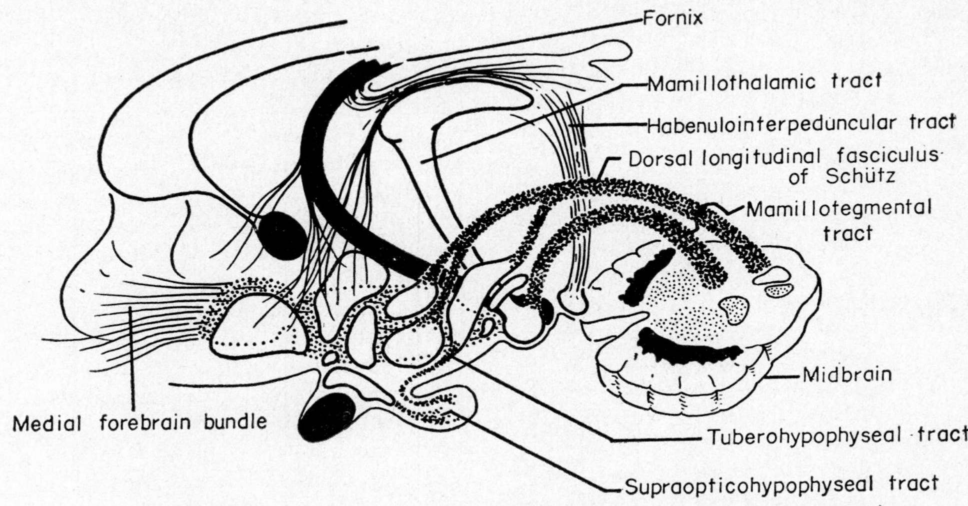

FIG. 216. Diagram of some hypothalamic connections. (*Outline in part after Clark.*)

tricular gray. Some of the fibers end in the dorsomedial and mid-line nuclei of the thalamus, both of which also send fibers to the hypothalamus. Since some of these thalamic nuclei, especially the dorsomedial, are in reciprocal connection with the prefrontal cortex, the hypothalamus is under cortical control from this region, as mentioned above.

The greater portion of periventricular fibers turn caudally and pass into the tegmentum of the brain stem. Some may end in the tectum and in midbrain tegmental reticular nuclei, but the majority continue caudalward. They are scattered throughout the lateral tegmentum especially, though some descend just ventral to the aqueduct and ventricle in the periventricular gray, as the **dorsal longitudinal fasciculus of Schütz.** There is ample clinical evidence that descending autonomic paths are dorsolateral in the medullar tegmentum as well as centrally placed. The descending autonomic fibers in the spinal cord are located in the anterior and lateral funiculi. They end in the intermediate gray column at thoracic, upper lumbar, and mid-sacral levels. Some fibers, especially pupillodilator, vasomotor, and sudomotor ones, remain uncrossed in their medulla and spinal course at least. Other descending autonomic paths contain crossed and uncrossed fibers, the decussations occurring both in the brain stem and spinal levels (71, 520). Descending autonomic fibers end about brain stem parasympathetic nuclei also.

Because of the importance of hypothalamico-hypophyseal relationships, the hypothalamic projections to the hypophysis may be discussed in some detail. A number of fibers arising in the hypothalamus enter the infundibulum to terminate in the hypophysis, especially in the neurohypophysis. The term neurohypophysis as used here refers to the neural lobe, or infundibular process, and the infundibulum, which includes the infundibular stem and the median eminence. In animals these fibers appear to have a wider origin in hypothalamic nuclei than in man. In the human, it has been estimated by Rasmussen that **hypothalamico-hypophyseal** fibers number about 100,000; these are unmyelinated and arise especially in supraoptic and paraventricular nuclei. The supraoptic nuclei, which contain an average of 60,000 neurons on a side, undergo marked degenerative changes after the infundibulum is sectioned, between 80 and 90 per cent of the neurons disappearing (653). Less striking degeneration occurs in the paraventricular nuclei, an estimated 20 per cent of the cells disappearing. It has been suggested that in man, at least, these latter nuclei contribute only a few fibers to the neural lobe of the hypophysis more of them discharging to the region of the supraoptic nuclei and to the median eminence region of the tuber cinereum. The median eminence, however, which forms the bulbous portion of the infundibulum, is functionally a part of the neurohypophysis, it is to be recalled. Scattered neurons and nuclei in the tuberal region are said to contribute some fibers to the hypophysis, and these are described as fine fibers coursing in the lateral and posterior parts of the infundibulum. Although Rasmussen considers the tuberohypophyseal tract in man as really arising from caudally placed neurons of the supraoptic nuclei, true tuberohypophyseal fibers in the human infundibulum have been described by Green (315).

The fibers arising from the supraoptic and paraventricular nuclei have a very superficial position in their course through the median eminence, but as they descend in the infundibulum they take a central position. The majority of the hypothalamicohypophyseal fibers end in the neurohypophysis, and a few apparently end in the pars tuberalis and pars intermedia. Although a few nerve fibers have been described as entering the pars distalis from the hypothalamicohypophyseal tract or from the infundibular process in many animals, a recent study of human material by Green failed to reveal any nerve fibers entering the pars distalis from the tract (314, 315). It seems probable, however, that all three parts of the neurohypophysis—median eminence, infundibular stem, and infundibular process—receive fibers from the hypothalamus.

The relative scarcity of nerve fibers in the adenohypophysis, in contrast to those in the neurohypophysis and especially in the infundibular process, has prompted investigators to search for other means through which the nervous system can control its secretory activity (313). Control via sympathetic or parasympathetic fibers entering the gland from the carotid plexus and Vidian nerve, respectively, do not appear very important in this control, although they may carry vasomotor impulses. It seems likely that a neurovascular link exists between hypothalamus and adenohypophysis. That a portal system of blood vessels is present in the infundibulum has been known for many years, but as yet universal agreement concerning the direction of blood flow in this system does not exist (635, 847). In contrast to an earlier opinion that the flow was from hypophysis to hypothalamus, the opposite direction of flow now seems the more likely one (316). Small arterial twigs from the internal carotid artery entering the pars tuberalis break up into a capillary plexus between the pars tuberalis and the median eminence. Vessels from this plexus enter the median eminence and infundibular stem to form sinusoidal loops. These loops are thought to drain into portal vessels which pass along the anterior part of the infundibulum to enter the pars distalis and to be distributed to the characteristic sinuses of this region of the hypophysis. The infundibular process apparently does not share in these portal vessels. Nerve fibers of the hypothalamicohypophyseal tract come into intimate relation with the sinusoidal loops in the median eminence and a few fibers which enter the pars tuberalis also are associated with the vascular plexus. It has been suggested that the nervous stimuli from the hypothalamus may cause the liberation of a substance into the capillary sinusoids of the median eminence. This substance transmitted via the portal vessels may excite or inhibit the pars distalis.

Blood Supply of the Hypothalamus

Small arteries arising from all the components of the circle of Willis as well as from the ophthalmic arteries nourish the hypothalamus (43, 248) (Fig. 51). The preoptic and suprachiasmatic regions and the most anterior part of the tuberal area are supplied by small vessels arising from the anterior cerebral, anterior communicating, and ophthalmic arteries. Branches from the internal carotid supply the lateral region of the tuber cinereum; from the posterior communicating arteries, branches pass to the lateral posterior region of tuber cinereum and the lateral mamillary region. Branches from the posterior cerebral artery supply the mamillary bodies. The major portion of the blood from the hypothalamus appears to drain into the vein of Galen by way of the basal vein. This latter channel receives veins draining the various hypothalamic areas outlined by arterial supply.

Function of the Hypothalamus

A knowledge of hypothalamic functions has arisen primarily through studies of experimental animals. Information gained in such a way has then been useful in correlating evidence derived from a study of patients suffering with disease of all or part of the hypothalamus. The "functions" of the hypothalamus are perhaps legion. Combinations of various lesser functions into certain major activities, expressed clinically through derangement of these activities, make it possible to ascribe certain general functions to this part of the brain.

CONTRIBUTION TO EMOTIONAL EXPRESSION

It has long been thought that the hypothalamus takes part in initiating the peripheral autonomic activities which accompany emotion. It appears likely that the cerebral cortex exerts an inhibitory influence on the hypothalamus in this activity. When the latter is freed of this inhibition by various surgical destructions, peripheral expressions of certain of its activities become unbridled and uncontrolled (54). The animals, most often cats, can be very easily provoked to demonstrate behavior usually seen in rage. Since such rage is expressed in the absence of an intact cerebral cortex, it has been called **sham rage.** Merely restraining such animals provokes violent expressions of rage during which the pupils dilate, the hair stands on end, the heart rate increases, blood pressure rises, salivation occurs, and other manifestations of sympathetic hyperactivity appear. It would appear that an intact posterior hypothalamus is necessary for expressions of rage. Mechanisms inhibiting such rage have long been thought to arise in the neocortex, in the frontal lobes especially, although the exact pathways involved have not been determined. "Sham" rage has been produced in cats by bilateral basal frontal lobe lesions just above the optic chiasma, by bilateral ablation of the orbital surfaces of the frontal lobes, by bilateral destruction of olfactory tubercles, and by bilateral destructions of the ventromedial hypothalamic nuclei (283, 431, 746, 836).

Recent studies by Bard and Mountcastle have thrown new light on the evolution of rage reactions in cats (58). They feel that a number of neural centers discharging via the hypothalamus inhibit rage and that the neocortex may also facilitate rage reactions. This facilitation, however, does not appear to be expressed by way of the hypothalamus. The problem is discussed more fully in Chap. 23. The cingular gyrus, especially the anterior portion, and the hippocampus may also be concerned with emotional experience and may act through the hypothalamus to promote or control emotional expressions. Stimulations of the human hypothalamus together with electroencephalographic records of activity of the region bear out the idea that the hypothalamus is active in the expression of emotion and is controlled in such activity by the cerebral cortex (318).

In addition to its role in the control of emotional reactions, the hypothalamus is engaged in the regulation of renal water flow, the regulation of temperature control, and the regulation of autonomic activity. It also apparently plays an important role in the regulation of sleep, of fat and carbohydrate metabolism, and of sexual behavior and reproductive processes (336, 647, 648, 651, 716, 813). Because of its intimate neural and neurovascular relations to the hypophysis the exact contribution of the hypothalamus to these processes enumerated above has been slowly realized. Such hypothalamic contribution can be made apparently directly by its neural connections with other neurons in the neural axis, or indirectly by way of its connections with the hypophysis. The mechanisms involved in this hypothalamicohypophyseal relation are not yet clear. Certainly, abundant evidence exists for fiber connections between hypothalamus and neurohypophysis, but it is not yet understood how such connections serve in the production of active substances elaborated in the infundibular process, particularly. The role of pituicytes in the elaboration of active substances in the infundibular process has been doubted; a neurosecretory mechanism seems more plausible to some investigators and in fact has been demonstrated by certain staining techniques in some species. Even more difficult to appreciate is the nature of the relation between hypothalamus and adenohypophysis. A humoral relation involving the neurovascular connections previously described between hypothalamus, neurohypophysis (median eminence), and pars distalis seems most plausible at present.

REGULATION OF RENAL WATER FLOW

Diabetes insipidus is a condition characterized by unusual thirst and water intake and greatly increased urine outflow. It has been described clinically as resulting from a disorder in the hypothalamus, and again as a sequence of tumors of the hypophysis. It can be produced experimentally by placing lesions in the proper region of either of these structures. Bilateral destructions of the supraoptic nuclei, interruption of the supraopticohypophyseal tracts, or destruction of all the neurohypophysis will result in diabetes insipidus in the experimental animal. It is thought that the hypothalamus via the supraopticohypophyseal tract regulates the secretion of an antidiuretic hormone. This substance is formed in all parts of the neurohypophysis but especially in the infundibular process. In the normal individual the antidiuretic substance is balanced usually with diuretic processes of the organism. The adenohypophysis, pars distalis especially, presumably controls these diuretic activities. Some investigators believe, therefore, that an intact pars distalis is essential for the production of a permanent diabetes insipidus, while others have been able to produce the condition in the absence of a pars distalis (354). It is possible that antidiuretic substance may also be formed in the hypothalamus, since complete separation of hypophysis from hypothalamus has in some instances failed to produce diabetes insipidus (429, 537).

Of further interest in the control of water metabolism is the demonstration that receptors for osmotic pressure change (osmoreceptors) exist within the distribution of supply of the internal carotid artery, probably within the supraoptic nuclei. The injection of hypertonic saline into the internal carotid results in an antidiuresis, and it has been suggested that osmoreceptors in the very vascular supraoptic nuclei are sensitive to the osmotic pressure changes (789). They may thus influence the activity of the supraopticohypophyseal system to regulate the release of antidiuretic substance (330). Emotional factors also appear to play a role in the liberation of substances which control urinary output. Emotional stress may inhibit water diuresis, and it has been shown that the neurohypophysis is activated to secretion of antidiuretic substances by this stress (588, 589, 789). On the other hand, other emotional reactions of nervousness and pleasure may lead to a diuresis, as is well known (29).

TEMPERATURE CONTROL

It has been shown experimentally that the anterior part of the hypothalamus, dorsal to the optic chiasma and infundibulum, is important in preventing abnormal rises in body temperature (649). If the preoptic and supraoptic regions in cats are heated experimentally by a high-frequency alternating current passing between two electrodes, the heat-loss mechanisms may be activated. Panting and sweating are part of the general reaction evoked (525). The area from which the maximum response is elicited is rather small and is placed between the anterior commissure and optic chiasma in a dorsoventral plane and extends rostral to them. The reactive area is contained in a zone within 4 mm. of the mid-line. Panting can be elicited in a cat, however, after this hypothalamic zone is destroyed. This would indicate that in temperature control the hypothalamic neurons act through neurons more caudally placed in the brain stem, perhaps through midbrain or pontine neurons. Cats and monkeys with bilateral anterior hypothalamic lesions may have a high body temperature postoperatively for a short time, but more interestingly, they cannot protect themselves from rising external temperatures. They react almost normally to external cold temperatures.

The transient hyperthermia presumably results from the irritation of the hypothalamic sympathetic centers which normally are active in heat production. Neurons within the caudal part of the lateral hypothalamus appear to be concerned with the neural mechanisms which produce heat and conserve it. The production of heat involves a variety of activities which include shivering, vasoconstriction, piloerection, increased heart rate, elevation of the basal metabolic rate, and a mobilization of carbohydrate reserve (282). All these except shivering may be evoked through hypothalamic stimulation. The mechanisms of shivering appear to be integrated at many neural levels, the highest one being rostral to the hypothalamus. Animals with posterior hypothalamic lesions run subnormal temperatures and cannot protect themselves against low external temperatures. The heat-loss mechanism may also be upset by lateral posterior hypothalamic lesions, and it is suggested that such a lesion destroys the fibers descending from the anterior hypothalamus to the lower brain stem and spinal cord centers. Large, bilateral lesions placed dorsolateral to the mamillary bodies in cats result in an inability of the animals to protect themselves against heat and cold.

SLEEP

Somnolence can be induced in cats or monkeys by hypothalamic lesions. Bilateral lesions in the lateral hypothalamic areas in monkeys caused drowsiness, somnolence, and a loss of emotional reactivity (648). Slightly more posterior lesions in cats in the region of the mamillary bodies caused somnolence. Hypothermia and a general slowing down of all bodily activities were usually also present. These animals were somnolent in spite of the fact that all sensory pathways to the thalamus and cortex were intact, as were all the motor pathways from the cortex to lower centers. Conceivably, the drowsiness and sleep in hypothalamic lesions can result from a destruction of the emotional drive furnished by the hypothalamus. The hypothalamus may contain neurons which actively drive the cerebral cortex and other rostral subcortical centers; with their destruction somnolence results. It is of interest that Hess reports the production of sleep in an animal by *stimulation* of the hypothalamus electrically (359). This might imply that the hypothalamus contains neurons which can be activated to suppress cortical activity. Other investigators repeating Hess' experiments with similar type of stimulation have reported that the current produced destruction in the hypothalamus (337).

The mechanisms underlying sleep are not yet agreed upon. A popular theory explains the onset of sleep normally as the result of decrease in flow of afferent impulses to higher centers including hypothalamus, thalamus, and cerebral cortex. This diminution in afferent impulse flow leads to an increase in synaptic resistance in the higher centers to such an extent that those incoming impulses remaining are not integrated and motor activity is gradually eliminated. The destructions in the midbrain tegmental reticular formation which result in a sleeplike state would tend to support such an idea. On the other hand, another theory of sleep involves an active inhibition of the cerebral cortex by some other neural center, presumably the hypothalamus, according to the research of Hess.

OBESITY

Obesity in rats was produced by symmetrical, bilateral lesions that destroyed the ventromedial nuclei and some immediately adjacent tissue laterally; caudal ends of ventromedial nuclei, the premamillary area, and much of the lateral hypothalamic areas adjacent; the areas in the caudal hypothalamus which lie dorsolateral to the mamillary body (360, 361). These destructions were thought to represent interruptions of paired systems at successive levels. The systems were thought to arise in the neighborhood of the ventromedial nuclei and to proceed caudally into the midbrain in the company of the medial forebrain bundle.

It is of interest, therefore, that obesity associated with hyperphagia and savagery has been produced in cats by destructions of the ventromedial hypothalamic nuclei (836). If the base of the anterior hypothalamus is superficially damaged in monkeys, or if the ventrocaudal portion of the thalamus and rostral midbrain tegmentum are destroyed, obesity also results (107, 691).

OTHER FUNCTIONS

A variety of other activities of the hypothalamus as adjudged by the results of destructive lesions or stimulation may be mentioned briefly. Hypothalamic lesions, and especially damage to the median eminence, have resulted in a loss of cyclical sexual activities and genital atrophy (210). Ovulation in the rabbit has been produced more easily by hypothalamic stimulation than by stimulation of the infundibulum or hypophysis directly (531). Hypothalamic centers presumably control the output of gonadotrophic hormones. Lesions in the central hypothalamus may result in a fall in metabolism. Hypothalamic centers which activate and inhibit the secretion of thyrotrophic hormone by the adenohypophysis have been described. Stimulation of the hypothalamus has resulted in hyperglycemia, and prolonged stimulation of the tuberal region in rabbits resulted in a decrease in sensitivity to insulin (336). Hypothalamic lesions are followed by an increased sensitivity to insulin, and such lesions may result in a reduction in the insulin requirements of pancreatectomized cats.

Many of these activities may normally be mediated through the adenohypophysis, and it is considered likely that this gland is under the regulatory control of the hypothalamus by way of a hypothalamoneurohypophyseal (median eminence) portal vessel system. The nervous impulses from the hypothalamus may lead to the liberation of a substance in the median eminence that is transmitted via the portal system to activate or inhibit the adenohypophysis, the pars distalis especially.

AUTONOMIC ACTIVITY

Stimulation of the hypothalamus causes vasoconstriction with resulting rise in blood pressure, increase in rate and depth of respiration, contraction of the bladder, alteration of tone of the gastrointestinal tract, sweating, and dilation of the pupil. These are all, in part, autonomic functions, sympathetic and parasympathetic. Furthermore, it has been shown that stimulation of the rostral hypothalamus and of the preoptic area immediately anterior to it causes in animals contraction of the bladder, occasionally a fall in blood pressure, and sometimes pupillary constriction, cardiac slowing, increased motility of the gastrointestinal tract, and increased acidity of the gastric juice. Inhibition of respiration also results. These, with the exception of the last, may be classed as parasympathetic phenomena.

Stimulation posteriorly in the hypothalamus gives increase in respiration, dilation of the pupils, increase in blood pressure, inhibition of peristalsis and diminished muscle tone in the stomach and small intestine, and increase in the mucous contents of the gastric juice together with a diminution in its rate of flow. Contraction of the bladder is also obtained, but this is thought to arise through stimulation of fibers of passage from the anterior hypothalamus and the preoptic area.

Clinical Disorders Associated with Hypothalamic Injury

The hypothalamus may be the site of inflammatory process or neoplasm, or it may suffer as result of vascular disorder or trauma. **Epidemic encephalitis** comes first to mind as a type of inflammatory disorder involving the hypothalamus, and syphilitic and tuberculous **meningitis** may also give rise to hypothalamic disorder. A variety of mid-line **tumors,** arising in the third ventricle, in its walls, or floor, in the hypophysis or infundibulum, and those arising in pineal, midbrain, and cerebellum may give rise to hypothalamic dysfunction through direct invasion of the region or through compression of it. Common symptoms arising as a result of hypothalamic disease are obesity, amenorrhea, diabetes insipidus, disorders of sleep, and glycosuria. Other disorders include disorders of thermal regulation, emaciation, ulcerations of the gastrointestinal tract, premature sexual development, autonomic epilepsy, and emotional disturbance. Several of these symptoms may be organized into a hypothalamic syndrome, and a number of these have been described by Fulton (282). A certain symptom present in the early stage of the disorder may subsequently disappear, and others usually associated with another syndrome may appear as more hypothalamic tissue is destroyed.

These hypothalamic syndromes are the hyperthermic syndrome; the diabetes insipidus and emaciation syndrome; the syndrome characterized by adiposogenital dystrophy; that characterized by somnolence and disorder of temperature regulation; and finally, diencephalic or autonomic epilepsy.

Hyperthermia in man has been correlated with destruction of the anterior hypothalamic area and ventromedial nuclei, and operative procedure carried out in this region may be followed by hyperthermia. This has been looked upon as a result of irritation of the posteriorly placed heat-production center and a disability of the damaged or temporarily inactive heat-loss mechanism.

Diabetes insipidus may occur alone as an indication of involvement of the hypothalamus, and it involves excessive thirst with increased water intake and polyuria. It appears with destruction of the supraoptic nuclei or with the interruption of their projection to the neurohypophysis. The secretion of an antidiuretic substance is under the control of this system, and this normally is balanced by the diuretic activities of the organism. The adenohypophysis plays a role in this last activity but is also under hypothalamic control. Diabetes insipidus can be produced experimentally, as seen above, in the absence of an adenohypophysis. The diuretic process working in the absence of the antidiuretic substance also appears to involve the undamaged part of the hypothalamus and its neural control over other diuretic systems; of these, the thyroid may be one. In widespread destruction of the hypothalamus, oliguria may result.

Adiposity and **genital dystrophy** (Froehlich's syndrome) may occur together or separately in humans in association with hypothalamic disease. Though the actual site of destruction associated with these symptoms is not known, it appears that the anterior and lateral tuberal area must be damaged for them to occur. The obesity with hypothalamic disorder may be a general one, but the excess fat is especially noticeable in the trunk, in the lower part of the abdomen, and in the proximal parts of the limbs. Damage to the ventromedial nuclei experimentally has led to obesity, as mentioned. Hyperphagia may play a part in the development of adiposity in the human as it does in the experimental animal. Occasionally, in widespread hypothalamic disturbance, emaciation may occur.

Amenorrhea, impotence, sexual infantilism, and general depression of sexual functions have frequently been described in hypothalamic and associated hypophyseal disorder, and there seems no doubt that they can occur as a result of disorder of either. The symptoms may be seen in cases involving destruction of anterior and tuberal regions of the hypothalamus and result in part from loss of the hypothalamic regulatory control over the release of gonadotrophic substances from the hypophysis. The type of disordered sexual function may vary depending on the age of the patient and, of course, his sex. Premature development of sexual organs and activity, in association with premature development of secondary sexual characteristics, in young children, may occur with disordered release of gonadotrophic substance either through intrinsic hypothalamic disease or as a result of compression of it by an internal hydrocephalus. It has been suggested that the hypothalamic injury interrupts the controlling influence on the secretion of gonadotrophic substance by the adenohypophysis. Thus liberated, the adenohypophysis secretes excessively, and the clinical state **pubertas praecox** results (831). Retarded development of the sexual organs and functions may also occur in children, or a regression of sexual function and a reversal of secondary sexual characters may occur in the adult—in the male, especially—as a result of hypothalamic disease acquired after puberty.

Disorders of sleep resulting from diencephalic disease were first observed in epidemic encephalitis. Inversion of the sleep rhythm, the occurrence of frequent short periods of sleep during the waking hours (narcolepsy), insomnia, as well as prolonged sleep have been seen in patients with encephalitis. The caudal portions of the hypothalamus or the transition zone between diencephalon and midbrain have frequently been found the site of disorder with the disturbances of the sleep mechanism. These disturbances of sleep may or may not be associated with disordered temperature regulation. As noted above, hyperthermia has been observed with destruction of anterior hypothalamic centers. Hypothermia, seen less often, has resulted from large destructions of the caudal parts of the hypothalamus. Poikilothermia, or the inability to maintain the body temperature, is seen rarely. Such a case has been described, and in it practically all the hypothalamic nuclei were destroyed (200, 869).

So-called **diencephalic epilepsy** was first described by Penfield in a patient who suffered from a cyst of the third ventricle (610). It was reasoned that the cyst periodically blocked the ventricular system or stimulated the thalamus, leading to headache and either one of two types of seizures. In one type, usually seen when headache was severe, the patient complained of dizziness and had a tendency to fall. In the other type her face and arms flushed, her respirations slowed, she perspired freely, and saliva ran from her mouth. The pupils dilated and the eyes appeared to bulge. Gradually the flushing would fade, and the pulse would become weak and slow. She might hiccough, and shiver. She could be roused and respond briefly to questions during the episode. Because the tumor pressed on the thalamus in the anterior nucleus of one of which there was an acute softening, Penfield believed that the thalamus was caused to discharge periodically. Since the activity produced peripherally lay chiefly in the realm of the autonomic innervations, he considered the thalamus as the highest representation of the autonomic nervous system.

Other cases involving the hypothalamus alone, however, have been described to demonstrate attacks in which some of the same and other signs were observed, especially flushing, salivation, excessive sweating, elevated blood pressure, slowing or increase of the pulse, and elevated temperature. It appears quite plausible to look upon these symptoms as expressions of periodic discharge of hypothalamic neurons which activate sympathetic or parasympathetic activity, or both, peripherally.

In many clinical conditions, inflammatory, vascular, or neoplastic in nature, **disorders of personality, mood,** and **emotional reactions** have been observed (28). Occasionally the individuals show impairment of memory and defect of judgment. Depressive reactions or maniacal outbursts associated with excitement and destructiveness may occur, and periodic, unexplained, and inappropriate attacks of weeping or laughing may take place. Anxiety attacks may occur, or the individual may be subject to episodes of apathy. Transient episodes of improper amorous behavior, or a loss of inhibitions with indecent behavior, may be seen (159).

Of course, these disorders are also encountered with disease of other parts of the nervous system and should not be looked upon as indicating that the hypothalamus is the "center" for emotional and such personality reactions. It is to be recalled that the patients who demonstrate these disorders have destructive lesions of the hypothalamus, and that the reactions expressed by the individuals represent the expression of the activity of other neural levels functioning *without* the hypothalamic integration. As has been mentioned previously, the emotional behavior and the personality reaction of an animal or a person is a result of the activity of many levels of the nervous system. That the hypothalamus takes part in such activity is certainly true, but other levels are perhaps equally important. Among these other levels are neocortex, rhinencephalic areas, and transitional cortex, such as the cingular gyrus, the orbital gyri, and the tissue in the rostral tip of the temporal lobe. These levels may act through the hypothalamus, or their activity be conditioned by it. The hypothalamus may initiate and regulate the peripheral autonomic activity that accompanies the emotional experiences.

The hypothalamus has been considered as the "timer" and the metronome of the activities of the organism (434, 612). As such it functions in controlling the rhythm of the breathing and the pulse rate, the maintenance and fluctuations of the temperature, the balance between water intake and output, and the rhythm of sleep and wakefulness, and it promotes the ebb and flow of gonadotrophic substances involved in the cyclical menstrual or estrual activity of the female and in the development and maintenance of sexual behavior and function of the male.

In carrying out the integrations which must necessarily furnish the background for this metronomic activity, the hypothalamus undoubtedly is the recipient of many impulses from other levels. It has been suggested that the mamillary peduncle, for example, serves the hypothalamus in the same relation that the ascending sensory tracts, spinothalamic, trigeminothalamic, and medial lemnisci, serve the lateral thalamic nuclei. Somatic and visceral impulses may be relayed to the hypothalamus via medial thalamic nuclei and periventricular systems, or they may relay in the neurons forming the ascending paths in the tegmental reticular formation. Other impulses reach the hypothalamus from the basal ganglia and from various regions of the cerebral cortex. Those from the frontal lobe are at present being identified, and the large fornix system from the hippocampus has long been known. Impulses from olfactory cortex probably also enter the hypothalamus, and a path from the retina has been described in certain species. The analysis and integration that exists in the hypothalamus at any one time is perhaps a product of the activity of these impulses of various origins, and it is also influenced most probably by the physical and chemical character of the blood circulating through the hypothalamic bed. It is of interest, moreover, that the nature of the response of a group of hypothalamic neurons can be altered by a variation of the frequency of stimulation. Stimulation of a locus at a frequency of 20 pulses per second may result in an increase in discharge of impulses in the inferior cardiac nerve and a rise of blood pressure; with a frequency of 2 pulses per second applied to the same spot, sympathetic activity was inhibited and the blood pressure fell (105). Once the hypothalamic analysis and integration is complete its discharge may be effected via thalamus and cerebral cortex or cortex directly, via caudal brain stem centers, and via the hypophysis. Its activity may lead to facilitation or inhibition of cortical neurons as well as of neurons of lower brain stem and spinal levels; similarly, it may excite or inhibit the liberation of humoral substances from the adenohypophysis and neurohypophysis.

In subsequent sections higher neural levels of integration for the autonomic activities and emotional expression will be described. As mentioned, these probably act via the hypothalamus.

CHAPTER 15

CORTEX AND FIBER SYSTEMS OF THE CEREBRAL HEMISPHERES

IN MAN THE cerebral cortex reaches its highest point of development. To an olfactory area and an olfactosomatic area in the brain of lower animals (archipallium or hippocampus and paleopallium or pyriform lobe, respectively) a neopallium (neocortex) has been added in the progression through the animal scale, and this new area has developed to a greater extent in man than in other forms. Intrinsic differentiation within this area proceeds more rapidly during development than in the hippocampus, though it begins earlier in the latter. And within it the cell laminations in different parts are not characterized by a difference in number but rather by a difference in distribution of neuroblasts. Differentiation also appears to proceed at different rates within the areas of the neopallium. Variety of lamination is a characteristic feature of the adult cerebral cortex. Both on the basis of cytoarchitecture and arrangement of the cells into layers and on the basis of fiber layers and fiber plexus arrange-

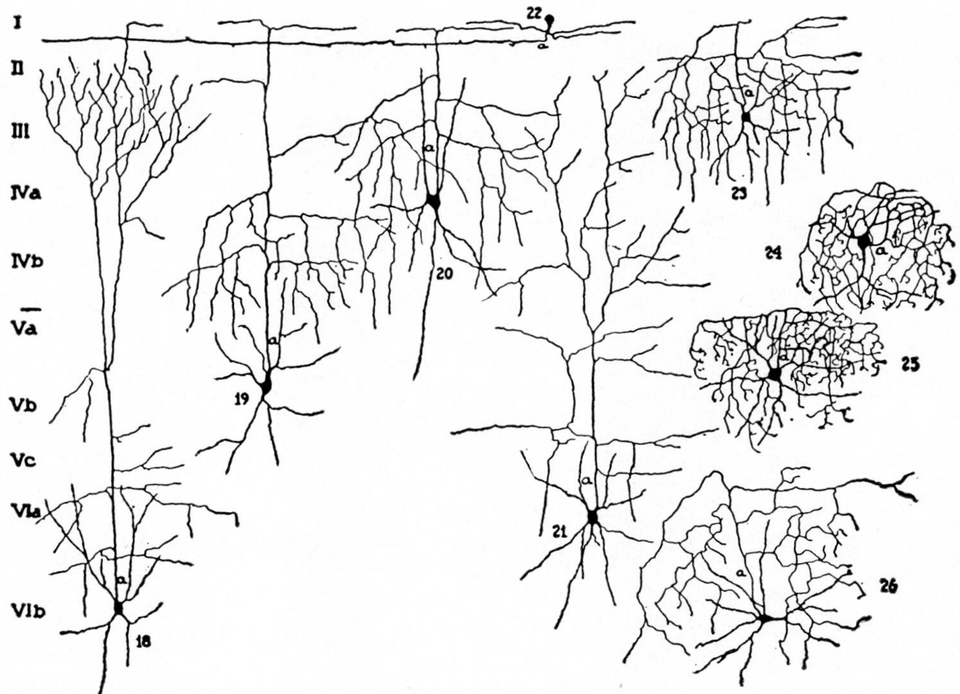

FIG. 217. Cortical neuron types with axons ending within the cortex. *a*, axon. 18, 19, 20, 21, cells with ascending axons; 22, cell with a horizontal axon; 23, 24, 25, 26, cells with short axons. (*After Lorente de Nó from Fulton, "Physiology of the Nervous System," Oxford University Press.*)

FIG. 218. Diagram of some cortical cell types and of fibers entering the cortex. At left, a diagrammatic picture of parietal cortex of adult mouse stained with Nissl technique. Cell layers are marked with Roman numerals. Except between IV*b* and V*a*, there is no sharp boundary between layers. At the center, bodies and dendrites of representative types of cells with descending axons; to avoid complication of drawing, axons have not been included. At right, the main types of cortical afferent fibers. 1, pyramids of layer II; 2 and 3, pyramids of layer III; 4, large star pyramids; 5, star cells; 6, small star pyramids; 7, 8, 9, long deep pyramids; 10, short pyramids; 11, medium pyramids; 12, 13, short pyramids of layer VI*a*; 14, long spindles; 15, medium spindles; 16, short spindles; 17, deep star cells; *a*, *b*, specific thalamic afferents; *c*, *d*, unspecific or pluriareal afferents; *e*, *f*, association fibers. (*After Lorente de Nó from Fulton, "Physiology of the Nervous System," Oxford University Press.*)

ments, an attempt has been made to divide the neopallium into smaller units. The function of the neopallium has been studied extensively, and various authors have gone to extremes in allocating function to it—some giving a general function to the cortex as a whole, others ascribing definite function to small fragments of it. Somewhere between these two extremes lies the plan of cortical function acceptable to most workers (252, 365, 615).

Cortical Neurons

It has been estimated that the total cortical area of the brain ranges between 200,000 and 248,000 sq. mm. (355). Of this amount, about two-thirds is concealed in the fissures (231). The thickness of the cortex varies between 4.5 and 1.3 mm. The total number of cells has been estimated to be about 14 billion in both cerebral hemispheres (230). The large and moderately sized cells of the third, fifth, and sixth layers total 8 billion; the small cells of all layers, 6 billion. These cortical neurons have been divided into four main types on the basis of the course taken by the axon (500). One type has an axon which descends through the cortex usually to reach the subjacent white matter, wherein it is continued as a fiber of projection to subcortical brain stem or spinal levels, or as a fiber of association to another region of the cortex. A second type has a short axon which terminates within the vicinity of the cell body. A third type, sometimes known as a cell of Martinotti, has an ascending axon which ramifies in one or several cortical layers. The fourth type has an axon which passes horizontally through the cortex (horizontal cell of Cajal) (Figs. 217, 222).

According to the contour of the perikaryon the cortical neurons may be divided into pyramidal cells, fusiform or triangular, and granule cells, and several varieties of the first and last of these types are found. Pyramid cells vary greatly in size, ranging from 10 by 5 μ to ten times that size (86, 232). Fusiform cells vary in size from 17 by 13 μ to 40 by 20 μ and are spindle-shaped or triangular, usually. The granule cells include the smallest of the cortical neurons and the majority of them belong to Golgi's type II cells in that the axons are short. Of the granule cells there are star cells, spider cells, double bush cells, and horizontal cells (of Cajal), named according to their appearance when well impregnated with metallic stains (Fig. 218). The larger star cells have certain structural features similar to those of the pyramids and have been called star pyramids. The double bush cells have bush-like collections of dendrites arising from opposite poles.

Characteristically, the pyramids and star pyramids have a long dendritic process arising from one pole, that directed toward the cortical surface, and a number of shorter dendrites arising from other parts of the perikaryon (Fig. 219). The longer process is known as the apical dendrite; the short processes, often arising from the opposite pole, as the basilar dendrites. Before branching to terminate in the outer cortical laminae the apical dendrite may give off many collaterals, in lower laminae, which run horizontally through the cortex. The direction of the basilar dendrites may be horizontal, or they may take an oblique course and descend into a deeper cortical lamina. All the dendrites of the smaller neurons may terminate near the cell body. The axonic process may ascend or descend and in its course it may give rise to a number of collateral branches. The axon, as noted above, may be very short, ending near the cell body or within the immediate cortex; it may be medium long, ending in other cortical areas; or it may be quite long, extending into subcortical and spinal levels (Fig. 220).

Cortical Laminae, Fibrous and Cellular

Studies on the architecture of the cortex have progressed from macroscopic examination of slices of it to microscopic studies of small bits of it. In such a way knowledge of the cellular make-up and arrangement of fibers in the cortex has been built up (366). Two major subdivisions of the cortex have been made by Brodmann (104). His **homogenetic** cortex

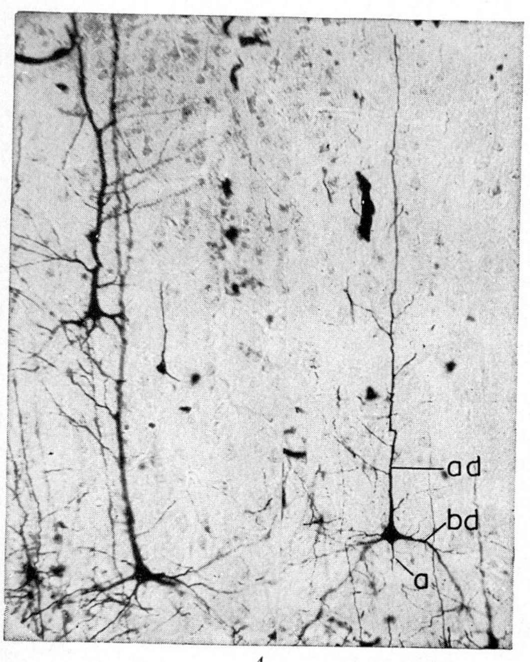

A

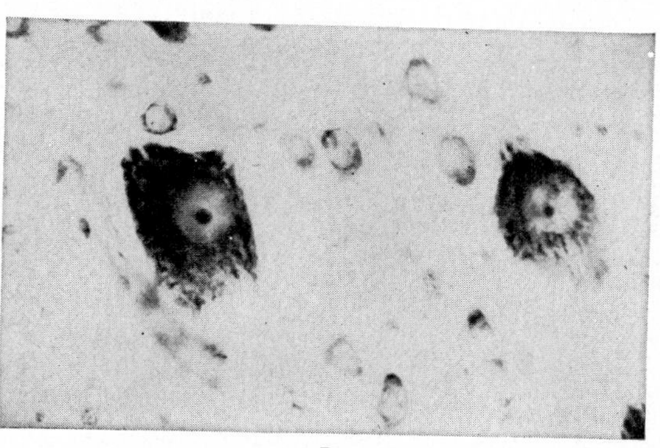

B

Fig. 219. Large pyramidal neurons of the cortex. *A*, Fox-Golgi silver, monkey; *a*, axon; *ad*, apical dendrite; *bd*, basal dendrite. ×105. *B*, thionin stain, monkey. ×387. Photomicrographs.

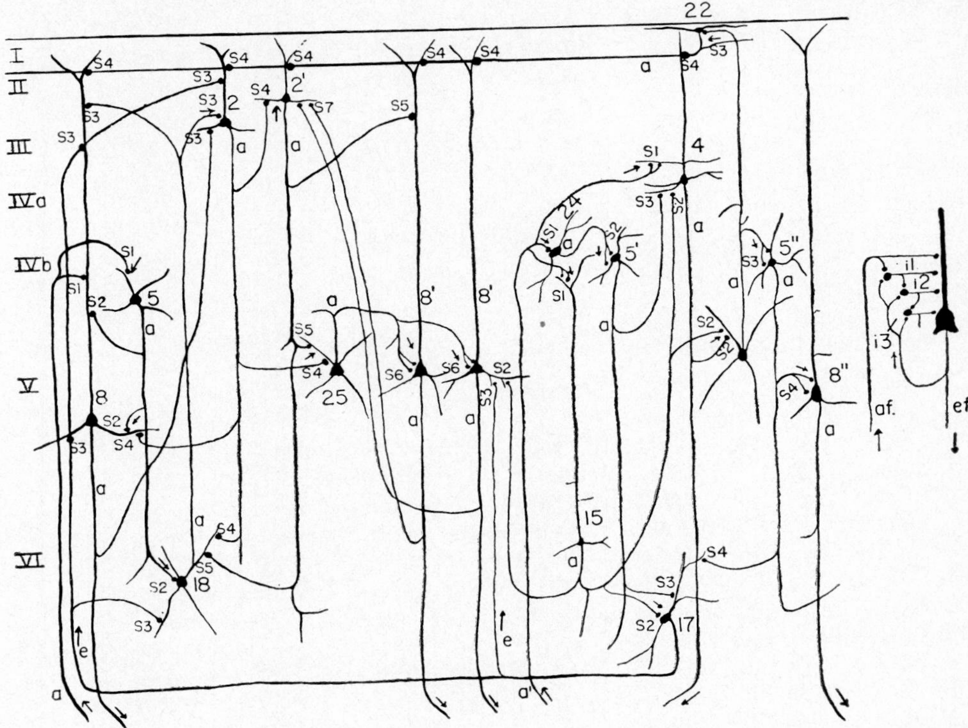

FIG. 220. Diagram of certain intracortical chains of neurons. The numbers on the neurons and the letters *a* and *e* on the fibers are the same as in Fig. 218. Synapses are indicated by *S*. On the right the small diagram is a simplification of that on the left; *i*1, *i*2, *i*3, cortical internuncial cells. Recurrent collateral of *ef*. delivers impulses again to internuncial system. (*After Lorente de Nó from Fulton, "Physiology of the Nervous System," Oxford University Press.*)

shows during its development, but not always in its adult stage, six characteristic layers. His **heterogenetic** type does not show six layers in either its developing or adult stage. Homogenetic cortex corresponds to **isocortex** in the terminology of Vogt; heterogenetic, to **allocortex.** The neopallium, or neocortex, is homogenetic; the archipallium and paleopallium are heterogenetic cortex. The fundamental six-layered plan for the neocortex, sponsored by Campbell as well as Brodmann, appears to have been more generally accepted than the eight-layered scheme of Ramón y Cajal (123) (Fig. 221).

Usually by the fifth fetal month the arrangement of neuroblasts into laminae begins (104). At first a granular layer and a subjacent pyramidal layer appear. By the sixth month the subgranular cells begin to migrate and to differentiate into the ultimate fifth and sixth layers. The cells of the primitive granular layer, the forerunner of the internal granular layer, later begin to differentiate and the layer becomes subdivided into the four outermost cell layers. By the eighth month the six layers can be recognized, and the neocortex throughout at first has a similiar appearance. Subsequently this sameness gives way, through variation in development of certain cell types and laminae, and it is possible to note regional differences in the cortical architecture (170). That the plan of stratification of the neocortex is a six-layered one has been more completely verified for the parietal, temporal, and occipital lobes than for the frontal. Certain of these basic six layers are subdivided. Fiber strata are also present in the cortex, these being formed by the axonal and protoplasmic, or dendritic, plexuses.

The **axonal plexuses** of a region contain axons which have arisen within that cortical region or have come to it from the thalamic or from other cortical regions of the same or opposite hemisphere. The **dendritic plexuses** are formed by the terminals of the apical and basal dendrites of the cortical neurons.

The fibers coming from the thalamus are often referred to as **radiation fibers** since they traverse the corona radiata. Fibers coming from other cortical regions of the same hemisphere are **association fibers,** those from regions of the opposite hemisphere, commissural association fibers. The radiation fibers from the thalamus are **specific** and **nonspecific** (500). Specific radiation fibers come from a certain region of a thalamic nucleus and terminate only in a specific part of a cortical area. They enter the cortex from the white matter, traverse the deeper cortical laminae without branching, and end by breaking up into a dense plexus, which forms the **outer stripe of Baillarger** within the fourth cellular layer (Fig. 218). A few terminals reach the second and third layers also. Nonspecific radiation fibers, as identified in the mouse, arise in certain thalamic nuclei and give rise to collaterals while still in the white matter. Through these side branches and its terminals, a nonspecific fiber may reach several different cortical regions. As these fibers enter the cortex they in turn give off collaterals within the innermost cell layer and ascend to the outermost lamina wherein they break up into terminals which run horizontally close to the cortical surface. The association and commissural association fibers behave in like fashion within the cortical layers, giving off collaterals in the lowermost strata and ascending to the outermost to terminate with horizontally running branches. The collaterals given off by these last three types of fibers in the lowermost cortical layers (V and VI) compose the **inner stripe of Baillarger;** those given off in the upper layers (II and III), the **stripe of Kaes-Bechterew.** The axons which arise within a cortical region and end within the same region may end in either of these fiber strata just described, may end just beneath the cortical surface within the tangential plexus (layer I), or may end at any level between these.

The dendritic or protoplasmic plexuses are found at several levels. Just beneath the cortical surface the tangential plexus is formed in large measure by the terminals of the ascending dendrites of neurons of the lower strata. Side branches of the apical dendrites form a dendritic plexus which is intermingled with that composing the stripe of Kaes-Bechterew. Other dendritic plexuses formed by the basal dendrites mingle with the outer and inner stripes of Baillarger.

The various laminae of the cortex can be described now with reference to their cells, especially (500) (Fig. 221).

I. Molecular or plexiform layer. This contains only a few cells, these being almost exclusively horizontal cells of Cajal. The tangential plexus occupies much of the layer and this is composed of terminals of apical dendrites and of ascending axons and ascending collaterals of descending axons. This layer usually composes about 10 per cent of the total thickness of the cortex (86).

II. External granular layer. This is a misnomer, since the predominant cell type is a small pyramid. The other cells are granules. Dendrites of these cells ascend to end in layer I or terminate within layer II; the axons of many descend to end in the lower layers, exclusive of layer IV. The stripe of Kaes-Bechterew courses through the lower part of this layer, which occupies about 9 per cent of the total cortical thickness.

III. External pyramidal layer. As the name implies, pyramid cells are the chief components of this layer which can usually be divided into three sublayers: *a, b,* and *c.* The external pyramidal layer represents almost a third of the thickness of the cortex in many regions. In the deeper subdivisions the pyramids are of larger size. Star cells and double bush cells are also found. The stripe of Kaes-Bechterew is found in the outer portion of this pyramidal layer, and many of the axon terminals in this stripe form synapses with the pyramids of layer III*a.* The basal dendrites of the pyramids of III*c* form synapses with the specific afferent fibers of the outer stripe of Baillarger. The pyramids of III*b* by means of their apical dendrites form synapses with the axon terminals of the Kaes-Bechterew stripe. Apical dendrites of pyramids within the deeper part of this layer form synapses in the intrinsic protoplasmic plexuses within the layer. The axons of neurons in layer III may end within other cortical layers above or below, or may descend into the white matter

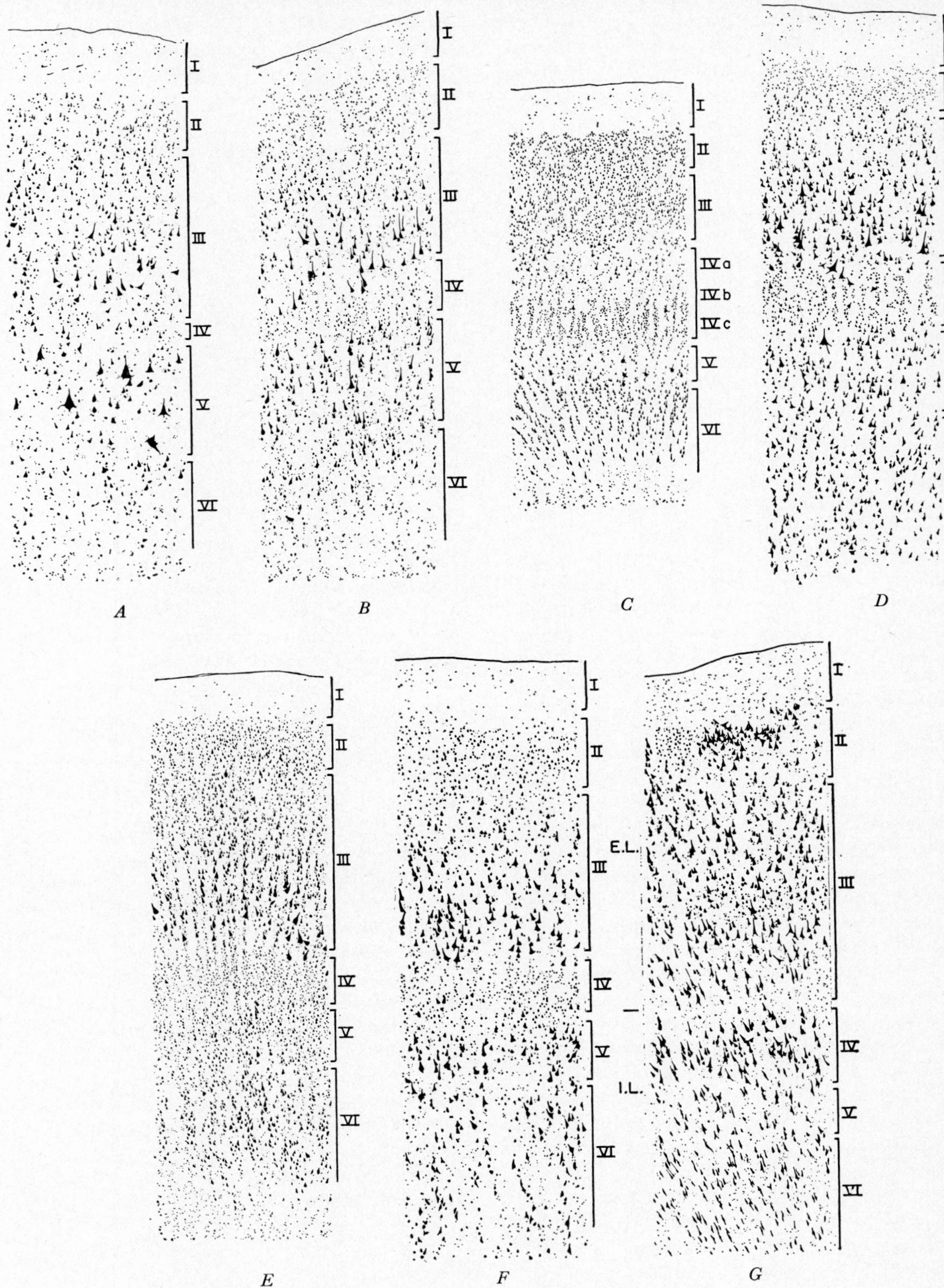

FIG. 221. For descriptive legend see opposite page.

to pass to another cortical area as an association fiber. As it descends through the lower cortical layers collateral branches are given off within layers V and VI.

IV. Internal granular layer. The two chief types of neurons are star cells and small star pyramids, and in most areas this layer shows a high cell density. The outer part of this layer, sometimes called IV*a*, contains predominantly star pyramids. The apical dendrites of these cells reach the outermost or plexiform layers of the cortex, after having given off side branches within layer IV. Basilar dendrites from these cells have chiefly a horizontal course within layer IV. The inner part of layer IV also contains small star-pyramid cells with apical dendrites reaching layer I, as well as small star cells whose dendrites end wholly within layer IV. The axons of some cells in layer IV may ascend to end in the upper layers, and those of others may descend into the lower layers or pass into the subcortical white matter as association fibers, giving off collateral branches in layers V and VI in transit. In certain cortical areas the cells in layer IV are exceedingly scarce; in such areas the outer stripe of Baillarger, present throughout the cortical mantle at this level, serves to identify the lamina. The thickness of this internal granular layer usually approximates about one-tenth of the total cortical thickness, except in regions of sensory projection.

V. Internal pyramidal, or ganglionic, layer. The predominant cells of this layer are pyramids. These are of small, medium, large, and, in certain areas, giant size. This layer is also divided into three sublayers, V*a*, V*b*, and V*c*. The largest pyramids are found in V*b* along with some granular cells. The upper and lower sublayers contain medium and small pyramids, especially. The apical dendrites of the large and giant pyramids typically end within the plexiform layer and give side branches off only within the fifth layer. The basilar dendrites of these cells also end within layer V. The apical dendrites of the medium pyramids may also reach the plexiform layer and have no side branches, or they may end within the fourth layer. The apical dendrites of the small pyramids may end within the fifth layer. The axons of the medium, large, and giant pyramids usually descend to enter the white matter as association, commissural association, or projection fibers. The giant pyramids in area 4, for example, contribute their axons to the corticospinal tracts. The axons of the small cells, especially those located in V*c*, may also descend to contribute to the commissural association fibers. All these descending axons give off collaterals; many of these end within layers V and VI, while others turn back and ascend to reach the outer three layers. Axons of some of the smaller pyramids ascend to reach the upper cortical layers. The thickness of the fifth layer approximates 20 per cent of the total cortical thickness.

VI. Fusiform layer. The predominant cell type of this layer is the fusiform or spindle cell and among these are cells of small, medium, and large size. According to the length of their dendrites they may be called short, medium, and long, respectively. The apical dendrite of the short spindle cells ends within layer V, that of the medium spindles within layer IV, and that of the long spindles gives off side branches within layer VI and ascends to reach the plexiform layer. Layer VI also contains small star cells, the dendrites of which end within the layer. The axons of these neurons within the sixth layer often descend into the white matter as long or short association fibers, and they give off side branches within the layer. Some of these end within the fusiform layer, some turn back and ascend to reach layers II, III, and even I. Some of the axons arising in the fusiform layer ascend directly, to end either within the same layer or within the outermost layers after giving off side branches to certain of the layers through which they ascend. The inner stripe of Baillarger is found in the upper part of layer VI, this lamina being occasionally divided into sublayers VI*a* and VI*b*. This fusi-

Fig. 221. Cytoarchitectural structure of representative cortical areas. *A*, precentral region, area 4; *B*, postcentral region, area 3; *C*, visual receptive area, 17; *D*, superior transverse temporal region, area 41 or 42; *E*, associative visual region, occipital area 19; *F*, a section through the middle of the second temporal gyrus, probably area 21; *G*, pyriform lobe, probably area 28. It should be noted that the cell types in the laminae of this region differ from those in the corresponding laminae of the other regions illustrated. Lamina IV here, for example, is a layer of pyramids. *E.L.*, external laminae; *I.L.*, internal laminae. ×34.5. (*After Campbell*, "*Histological Studies on the Localisation of Cerebral Function*," *Cambridge University Press*.)

Fig. 222. Diagram to illustrate intracortical distribution of branches of descending axons. Many branches have been omitted for simplification. The numbers on the cells correspond to those in Fig. 218. (*After Lorente de Nó from Fulton, "Physiology of the Nervous System," Oxford University Press.*)

form lamina composes about 20 per cent of the total cortical thickness.

In summary, the specific afferent fibers to the cortex, such as those arising in the posterior ventral nucleus of the thalamus, give no collaterals to layers V and VI, but break up into a plexus, the outer stripe of Baillarger, within layer IV. Many branches may reach layer III in some regions. The majority of the synapses then are with neurons of the fourth layer and, through their basilar dendrites, with neurons of layer III*c*. Cells of other layers, however, whose apical dendrites give collateral branches in layers III*c* and IV, also may have synapses with the specific afferent fibers. It appears true, therefore, that cells of all laminae except I and II have synapses with specific afferents. The nonspecific thalamic radiation fibers may ascend through all cortical layers and give collaterals to several layers, but especially in the sixth layer, within the inner stripe of Baillarger. The association and commissural association fibers may also have collaterals ending in the sixth layer, but their chief distribution is in layers II and III, within the stripe of Kaes-Bechterew.

The axons arising in layers V and VI enter the white matter predominantly as association fibers or projection fibers to the subcortical and spinal centers. Some axons arising in III*c* of area 4 also project to the spinal cord (750, 848). They give collaterals within layers V and VI especially, but certain collaterals turn back to ascend to the upper three laminae, wherein they ramify. Axons arising in the outer four layers end chiefly within the same cortex region, although certain of the axons of the larger pyramids may enter the white matter as association or commissural association fibers. In their descending intracortical course they give off collaterals chiefly within the fifth and sixth laminae. Certain cells of all laminae except the first have axons which reach the white matter. It is not anatomically correct, therefore, to speak of certain laminae as being only receptive, of others as being associative, and of others as serving a projectional function (500).

Interrelations of Cortical Neurons

The gray matter of the cerebral cortex may be viewed correctly as a system of chains of interrelated neurons. The simplest chain, a two-neuron arc, involves a synapse between a specific afferent fiber and a neuron whose axon becomes an efferent fiber. Superimposed within these simple chains are series of closed loops which involve internuncial neurons. The cortical chains of neurons are, therefore, not unlike chains of internuncial neurons elsewhere. A simplification of the activity of cortical neurons has been diagrammed by Lorente de Nó (Fig. 220). More complex, and yet simple, diagrams, in terms of cortical activity, can also be constructed. When the synaptic contacts of the specific afferent, the nonspecific afferent fibers, and of the association fibers are considered also, the magnitude of the interrelations involved in cortical activity can be appreciated. The activity of a certain area depends on the integration of impulses arriving from the thalamus and other cortical areas, as well as those arising within the same area.

Types of Cortex

On the basis of variation in development of cell layers and in cell type and density it is possible to classify the cortex into several types. Economo and Koskinas have described five types (233) (Figs. 223, 224).

1. The agranular pyramidal-type cortex is

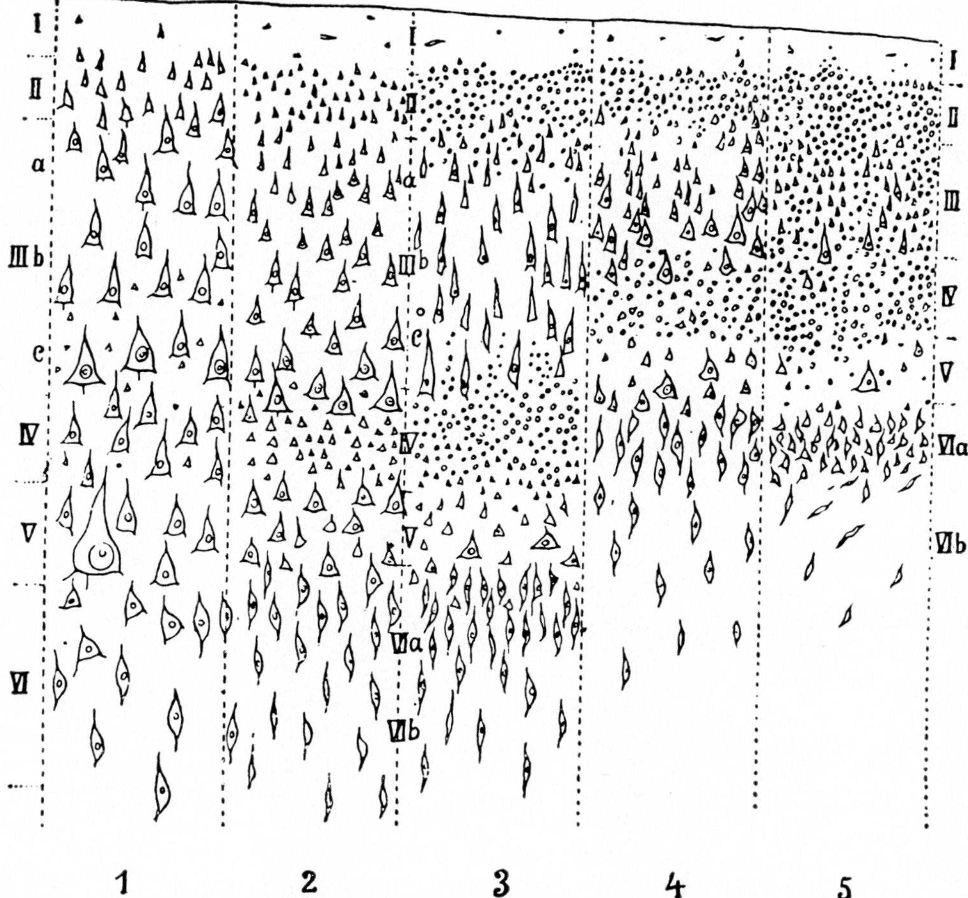

Fig. 223. The five fundamental structural types of cerebral cortex: 1, agranular; 2, frontal; 3, parietal; 4, polar; 5, granular ("koniocortex"). (*After Economo, "The Cytoarchitectonics of the Human Cerebral Cortex," Oxford University Press.*)

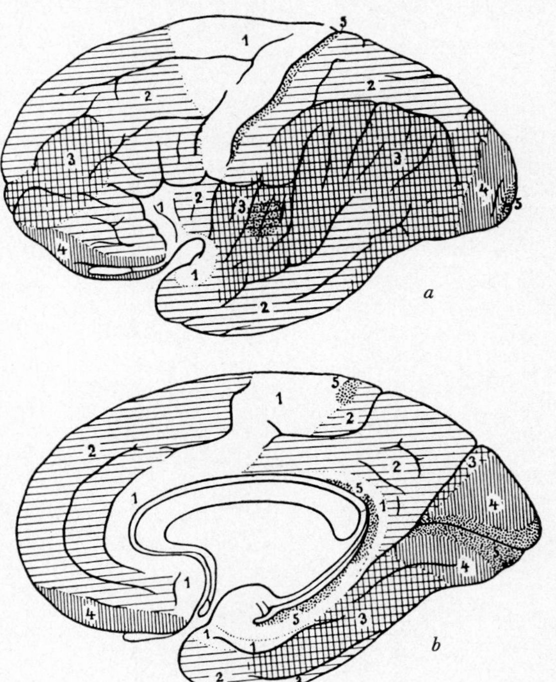

FIG. 224. The distribution of the five fundamental types of cortex: *a*, over the convexity of the hemisphere; *b*, over the medial hemispheric surface. 1, agranular; 2, frontal; 3, parietal; 4, polar; 5, granular. (*After Economo, "The Cytoarchitectonics of the Human Cerebral Cortex," Oxford University Press.*)

broad and contains many large pyramidal cells. It has either no layer IV or a negligible one. It is found in the precentral gyrus, especially, over the anterior limbic lobe, parolfactory field of Broca, and on the anterior part of the insula. Another agranular field is in the retrosplenial region of the limbic lobe, and another on the crown of the hippocampal gyrus and uncus. This last field is really composed of allocortex, not isocortex.

2. The granular pyramidal-type (frontal-type) cortex is moderately broad and contains many large pyramidal cells in layers III and V. It has a prominent granular layer IV. It is found especially in the frontal lobe rostral to type I, in the postcentral gyrus, and in the superior parietal lobule.

3. The granular parietal-type cortex is medium broad, and because of the well-developed granular layers, the lamination of this cortex is quite distinct. The pyramidal layers are thin and the pyramids are predominantly small. This type is found especially in the inferior parietal lobule, the major part of the superior temporal gyrus, and in the fusiform gyrus.

4. The polar type is a thin cortex found near the occipital and frontal poles. It is rich in granule cells, and the cell density throughout all the layers is high. Near the frontal pole, layer V shows many large pyramids, but near the occipital pole, the pyramids of this layer are smaller. This type of cortex is found in the basal and medial part of the orbital gyri of the frontal lobe and in the cuneus and lingual gyrus of the occipital lobe.

5. The granular-type cortex is a thin cortex and is characterized by granule cells in all the layers. Because of the relative scarcity of pyramids in layers III and V, the lamination of this cortex is particularly indistinct. Layer V at times appears to be absent. This type of cortex has been called **koniocortex** because the dense granule cells reminded Economo and Koskinas of clouds of dust. It is found on the posterior bank of the central fissure, in the superior transverse temporal gyri, along the bottom and banks of the calcarine fissure, in the retrosplenial region and along the dorsal wall of the hippocampal fissure. This koniocortex is the primary sensory receptive cortex.

Types 1 and 5 are classed as heterotypical since the fundamental six-layer pattern is indistinct in the adult stage. They pass through a six-layered stage in development, however. Types 2, 3, and 4 are homotypical cortex.

CORTICAL AREAS AND FIELDS

Many maps of the areal divisions of the cerebral cortex have been constructed, the majority of these based on a study of cell type variation. Some have been based on the order in which the white matter of the cortex becomes myelinated. Using cytoarchitecture as a basis, Brodmann has subdivided the human cortex into 52 areas and has used numbers to designate them, while Economo and Koskinas, chiefly through subdividing Brodmann's divisions of the old, or olfactory, cortex, have arrived at some over 100 areas and have designated them by letters (104, 233) (Figs. 225, 226, 227, 228). Other workers have made more than 200 subdivisions. Brodmann's areas

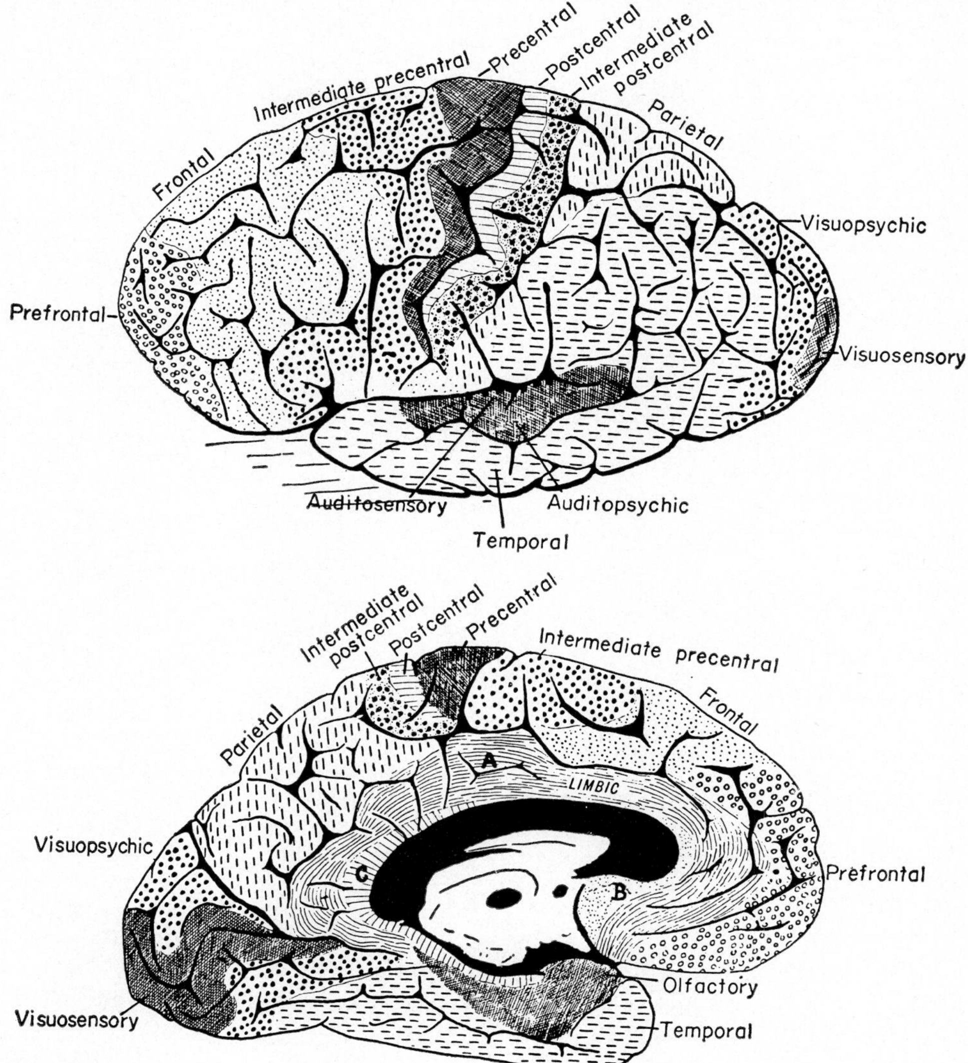

FIG. 225. Cytoarchitectural maps by Campbell of human cerebral cortex: above, over the convexity of the hemisphere; below, over the medial hemispheric surface. (*Courtesy of Cambridge University Press.*)

listed by numbers perhaps have been more generally used. Since he apparently did not publish a description of the human cortex to go with his map of the human cerebral mantle, certain contemporary schools are now favoring the lettered designations of Economo and Koskinas. It is not always easy to convert Brodmann's numbers to their exact counterparts in the Economo classification. It is seldom that the areal boundaries can be sharply defined, and it seems likely that individual variations exist in a series of brains. For these reasons minor discrepancies in various maps may be expected. Unexpected, however, is the use by some authors of different numbers to identify the same cortical area, and the failure of map makers to verify homologies in transposing from the maps of monkey to man. Naturally, much confusion exists, and there is need for a simpler division. An approach to such a division has recently been made by Bailey and Von Bonin in their 1951 monograph, "The Iso-

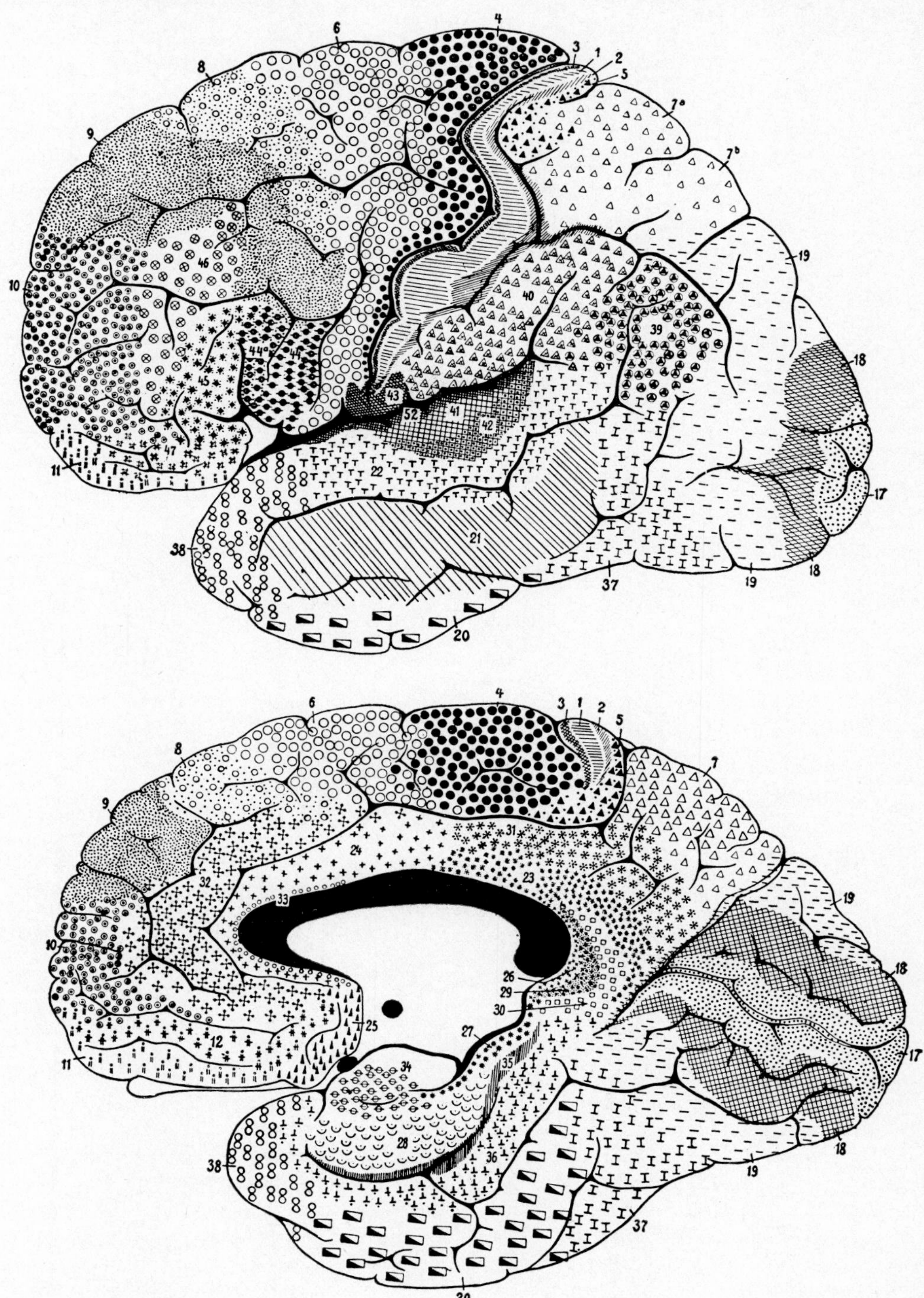

FIG. 226. Cytoarchitectural maps of human cerebral cortex by Brodmann (1914). Above, convex surface of hemisphere; below, medial surface. (*From Physiologie des Gehirns, in "Die Allgemeine Chirurgie der Gehirnkrankheiten," Neue Deutsch Chirurgie, vol.* 11, *p.* I., *Verlag. Ferdinand Enke, Stuttgart.*)

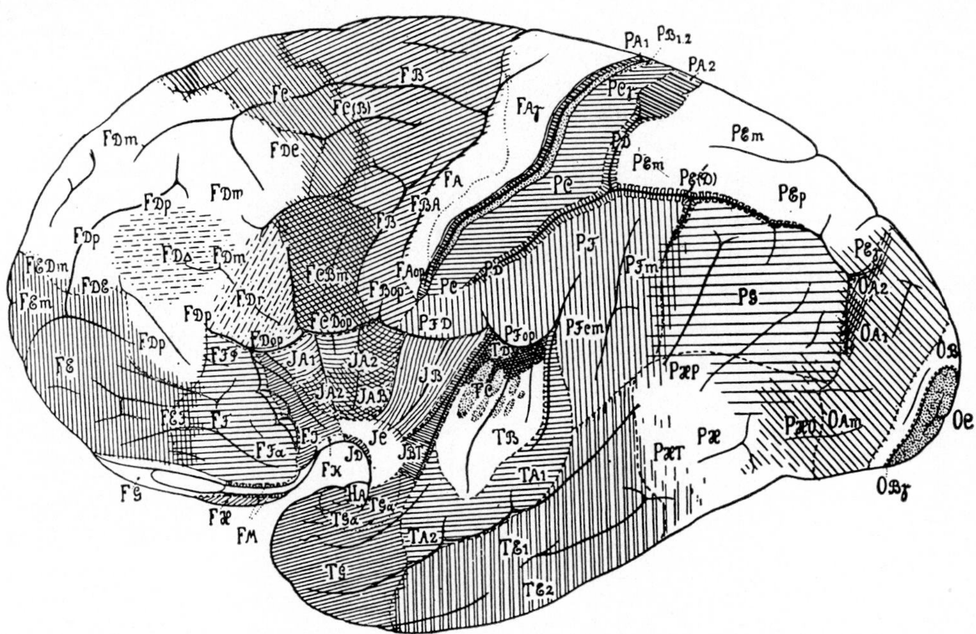

Fig. 227. Cytoarchitectural map of human cerebral cortex by Economo and Koskinas (1925). Convexity of hemisphere (*From Economo, "The Cytoarchitectonics of the Human Cerebral Cortex," Oxford University Press.*)

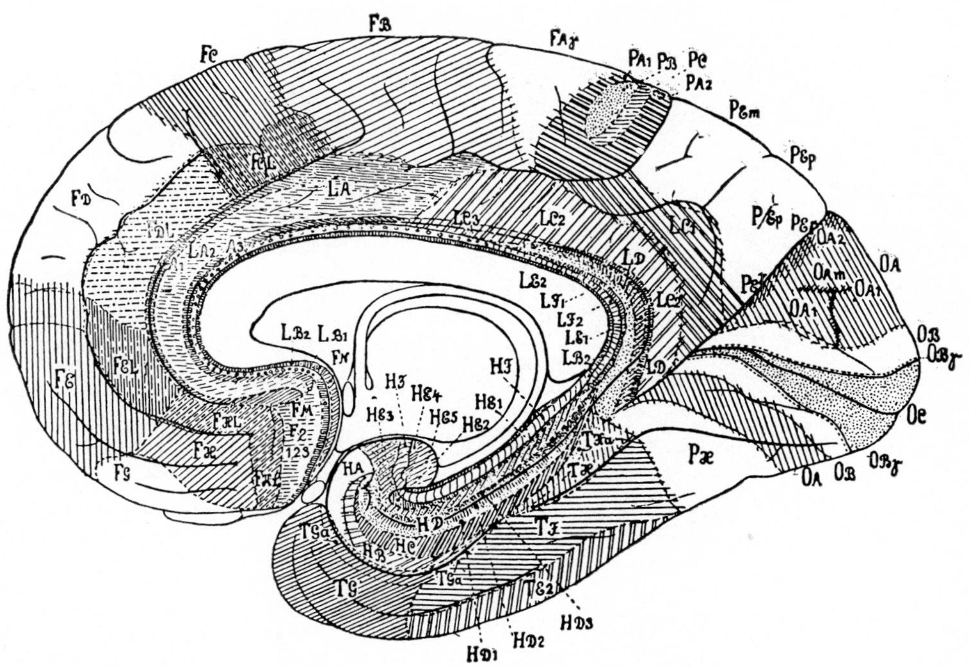

Fig. 228. Cytoarchitectural map of human cerebral cortex by Economo and Koskinas (1925). Medial hemispheric surface. (*From Economo, "The Cytoarchitectonics of the Human Cerebral Cortex," Oxford University Press.*)

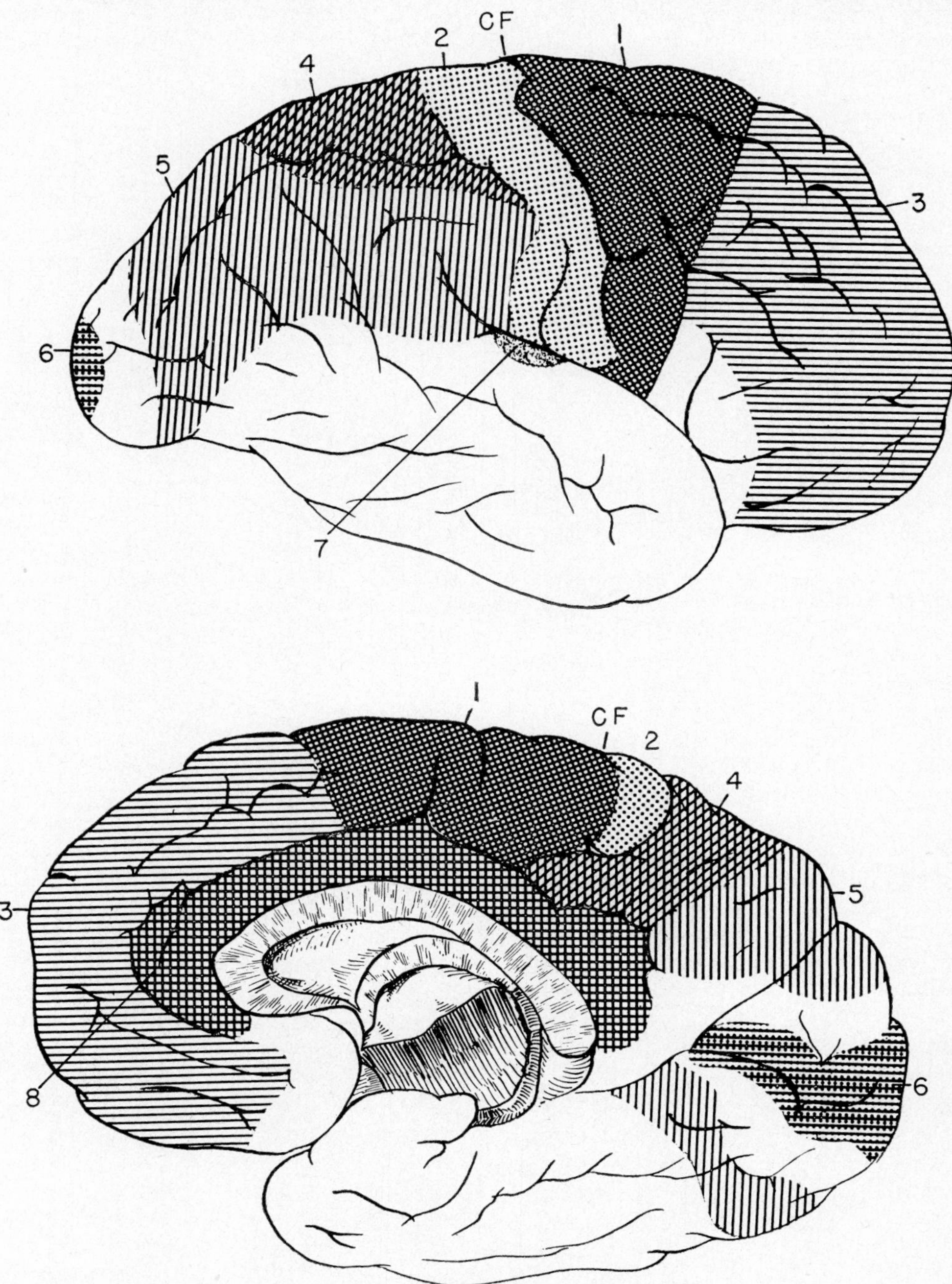

FIG. 229. Schema to show divisions of the human cerebral cortex according to thalamocortical projections. *CF*, central fissure. Above, lateral surface; below, medial hemispheric surface. 1, central region, with projections from anterior and lateral ventral nuclei; 2, central region, with projections from posterior ventral nuclei; 3, frontal region, fibers from dorsomedial nucleus; 4, parietotemporooccipital region, with fibers from lateral dorsal and lateral posterior; 5, parietotemporooccipital region, with fibers from the pulvinar; 6, an occipital region receiving fibers from the lateral geniculate; 7, a supratemporal region, with fibers from the medial geniculate; 8, a limbic region, with fibers from the anterior nuclei.

cortex of Man." They deprecate the tendency of many map makers to subdivide the cerebral mantle into many small areas on the basis of slight cytoarchitectural variations. On the basis of their recent studies, they question whether such variations are present and, if present, whether they have significance. The map of Bailey and Von Bonin has a slight resemblance to that of Campbell, although the former workers do not have as many divisions (Fig. 236*B*). Their major divisions of the cortex include the allocortex, corresponding approximately to the archipallium and paleopallium, and the isocortex, or neopallium. Within the isocortex they define a "typical" six-layered cortex or **eulaminate** variety, a **koniose** type, and an **agranular** type. Finally, they have several transitional types appearing between any two regions with well-marked structure. These include a **parakoniose** type, a **juxtallocortex** type, and a **dysgranular** variety.

In recent years, studies have indicated the rationale of dividing the cortex according to its thalamocortical relations. It has been learned from studies of thalamocortical relations in macaque and chimpanzee that the major portion of the cerebral cortex receives fibers from the thalamus. At present it is possible to verify only a few of these relations in the human, but it seems quite logical to expect that similar conditions exist in man. As noted in Chap. 13, it is possible at present to classify thalamic nuclei into those that have anatomically proved cortical projections and those that do not. And it is likely that other thalamocortical connections have not been anatomically defined thus far.

The thalamic projections thus far identified most accurately and those upon which cortical subdivisions are presently made are the specific afferents mentioned earlier. These come from a definite thalamic nucleus and pass to a specific part of the cerebral cortex, and usually within this nuclear-cortical relation there is orderly topographic arrangement. Further, each thalamic nucleus projecting to a cortical area in turn receives fibers from that cortical area. The nonspecific thalamic fibers to the cortex pass to a number of areas, and the nuclear-cortical relations have not been identified completely as yet. It seems likely that they may spring in large measure from nuclei not previously thought to have projections to the cerebral cortex (see Chap. 13). It is entirely possible that the ultimate identification of these nonspecific thalamocortical relations may alter the present simple division of the cortex into those regions which receive specific afferents and those which do not.

When such a division of the cortical gray is made, it is possible to break it down into six regions. The cortical projection areas of the lateral ventral and posterior ventral nuclei compose a central region; that of the lateral geniculate nucleus, an occipital region; that of the medial geniculate, a supratemporal region; that of the anterior nuclei, a limbic region; that of the dorsomedial nuclei, a frontal region; and that of the pulvinar, lateral dorsal, and lateral posterior nuclei, a parietotemporo-occipital region. An orbitotemporal region may be added, although its thalamic projection nucleus has not been identified. The dorsomedial nucleus appears to project to certain areas included in this region (Fig. 229).

Corticocortical Connections

ASSOCIATION FIBERS

The activity of a given cortical area depends not only on its possible thalamic connections but on its connections with other cortical areas of the same and opposite hemisphere. Such corticocortical association connections may run entirely within the gray, or they may traverse the subcortical white matter. The intracortical association fibers are quite short and are, in large measure, the myelinated axons of the horizontal cells and the horizontally coursing collaterals of the descending axons described earlier. Those association fibers traversing the white matter may interconnect adjacent regions and have a short course beneath a sulcus; these are termed U association fibers. A prominent example of these are the fibers passing beneath the central fissure to connect the precentral and postcentral gyri. Longer subcortical association fibers interconnect distant parts of a single hemisphere, others interconnect homologous regions of the two hemispheres, via one of the several commissures.

In recent years, physiological methods for demonstrating fiber connections have outdistanced the more tedious and capricious, purely anatomical techniques. Physiological

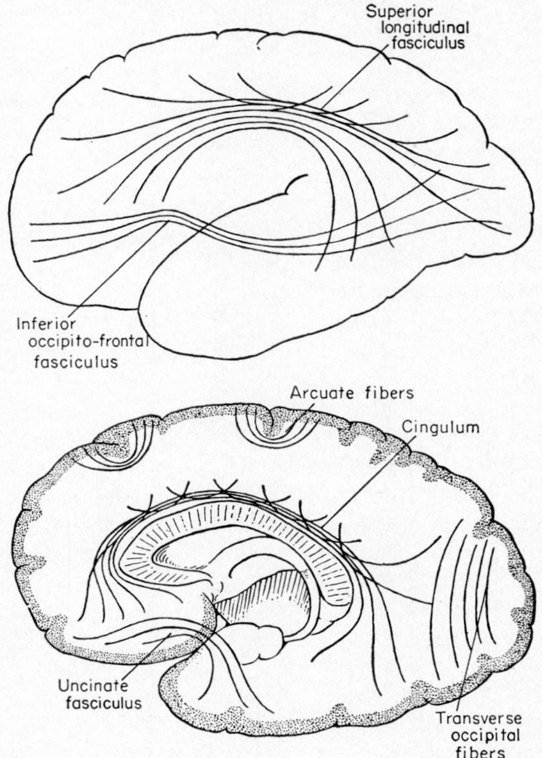

FIG. 230. Long unihemispheric association bundles, diagrammatic. Above, as seen from lateral surface; below, from medial surface.

neuronography has been used extensively for demonstrating corticocortical and corticosubcortical connections (217). The method utilizes the fact that strychnine, which acts principally at synapses, will, when placed on a minute area of nervous tissue, cause the neurons with which it comes into contact to discharge. The alkaloid activates the cell body or its dendrites and has no effect on adjacent fibers. This activity spreads along the cell axons and their collaterals, and it can be recorded electrically from the cortical areas and nuclei which the axons and collaterals "fire." Many corticocortical and corticosubcortical fibers have been postulated on the basis of studies utilizing this neuronographic technique (45, 48). A recent study of the physiological neuronography technique has shown that the method has limitations (273). The failure to obtain "firing" from a certain region does not necessarily mean absence of anatomical connections. The present discussion will be limited to gross anatomical details of corticocortical fibers.

The long unihemispheric association fibers have been grouped into five chief bundles (Fig. 230). The **cingulum** arises in the region of the anterior perforated space and in the subcallosal region ventral to the rostrum of the corpus callosum. It passes dorsally around the genu of the callosum following the course of this commissure to the splenium, around which it passes; it then extends downward and forward to the region of the temporal pole. It is composed of short fibers, predominantly, interconnecting the anterior perforated substance and the frontal region, the orbital frontal region and the anterior part of the cingular gyrus, and the hippocampus, the temporal pole, and basal occipital region.

The **superior longitudinal fasciculus** arches posteriorly from the lower portion of the frontal area, over the insula and into the temporal, parietal, and occipital regions. It is composed to a great extent of short fibers interconnecting the frontal, parietal, temporal, and occipital areas. An **inferior longitudinal fasciculus** running through the length of the occipital and temporal lobes has been considered to be an association tract by some investigators; as a part of the geniculocalcarine tract, or optic radiations, by others. It appears likely that some mixing of association and radiation fibers occurs and that the fasciculus contains fibers of each type.

The **superior occipitofrontal** or **frontooccipital fasciculus** pursues a course just beneath and at the outer border of the corpus callosum which separates it from the cingulum. It is medial to the projection fibers in the internal capsule as they pass toward the cortex. It interconnects occipital and temporal cortical areas with frontal and insular cortex. The insula-bound fibers leave the base of the fasciculus and pass beneath the fibers of the corona radiata to reach the external capsule and thence the insula.

The **inferior occipitofrontal fasciculus** passes beneath the lenticular nucleus and the external capsule; it interconnects frontal and occipital regions. The **uncinate fasciculus** is almost continuous with the inferior occipitofrontal fasciculus. It bends on itself and passes beneath the lateral fissure in its rostral third. It connects temporal pole region with the basal frontal region.

COMMISSURAL FIBERS

The commissural fibers of one cortex pass to the other by way of one of three commissures, the **anterior,** the **hippocampal** or **psalterium,** and the **corpus callosum.** The anterior commissure transverses the lamina terminalis in the median plane (Fig. 47). Laterally it divides into a small anterior portion and and a larger posterior portion. The anterior portion carries fibers interconnecting the olfactory bulbs, the posterior portion carries fibers between the pyriform and amygdaloid regions, and the middle and inferior temporal gyri of the two sides. The hippocampal commissure carries fibers interconnecting the two hippocampi and dentate gyri (Fig. 305). These fibers pass first by way of the fimbria and posterior pillars of the fornix. Beneath the splenium of the corpus callosum, the posterior pillars converge toward one another. Beneath the posterior end of the corpus callosum the commissural fibers cross. These crossing fibers and the posterior pillars of the fornix are sometimes referred to as the psalterium.

The corpus callosum is best seen on the medial side of the hemisphere of a brain sectioned through the longitudinal fissure (Fig. 47). It is then observed to be arched dorsally. Ventrally to its caudal half the fornix can be seen emerging as it runs rostrally and ventrally passing just rostral to the foramen of Monro. The rostrally arched portion of the callosum is the **genu,** the large middle portion is the **body,** and the termination is the **splenium.** The fibers traversing the rostral portion of the callosum turn in a sweeping fashion rostrally in the frontal lobe (frontal radiation), those traversing the caudal portion turn caudally (occipital radiation) and form the **anterior** and **posterior forceps,** respectively (Fig. 232). Those in the body run transversely and sweep superiorly and inferiorly within the hemispheres. As the callosal fibers swing superiorly they intermingle in the corona radiata with fibers entering or leaving the internal capsule. The occipital radiation of the corpus callosum forms a roof and lateral wall for the posterior horn of the lateral ventricle and a lateral wall for the inferior horn. These fibers are known collectively as the **tapetum.**

The distribution of the callosal fibers in the human is not accurately known. In the macaque, symmetrical areas of the neopallial cortices, predominantly, are interconnected through the callosum, although in some in-

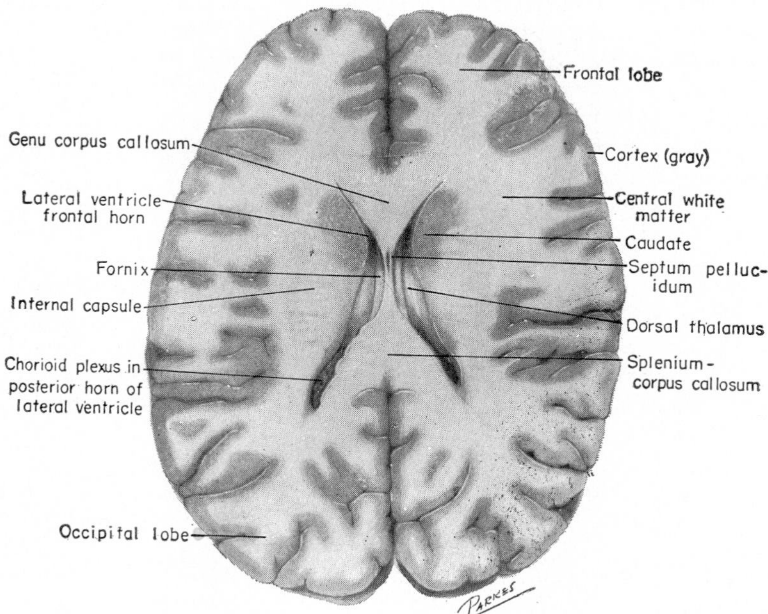

Fig. 231. Horizontal section, unstained, of whole brain, through the corpus callosum.

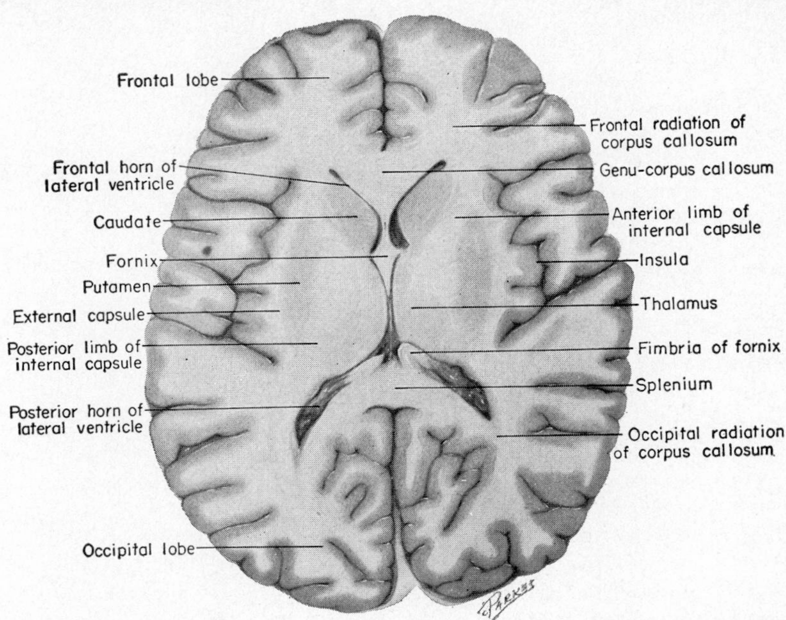

FIG. 232. Horizontal section, unstained, through whole brain at a slightly more ventral plane than Fig. 231.

stances asymmetric areas are connected (191, 506). Certain cortical areas, notably the striate cortex, area 17, do not have commissural connections. In the genu and rostral part of the callosum are connecting fibers for the frontal lobes; in the body proper are fibers for the parietal lobes and tips of the temporal lobes (area 38); in the posterior part of the body and in the splenium are fibers connecting the auditory areas (41 and 42) and occipital lobes, respectively.

Not all the corticocortical relations are exercised directly via association and commissural fibers. The caudate nucleus and the thalamus, particularly, are intermediaries for the influence of certain cortical areas on other cortical areas (220, 223, 505).

CORTICIPETAL (PROJECTION) FIBERS

Fibers arise in many areas of the cerebral cortex and pass as projection fibers to basal telencephalic nuclei, to the thalamus and many brain stem nuclei, and to the spinal cord. These projection fibers pass predominantly by way of the **internal capsule.** This is a large mass consisting of fine and large, myelinated, poorly myelinated, and "unmyelinated" fibers. Its disposition is best ascertained by study of a horizontal section of the brain taken at a level through the habenular nuclei, posteriorly, and the dorsal part of the massa intermedia, anteriorly (Fig. 233). In such a section the white matter of the capsule forms a very wide V, the apex of which is directed medially. The apex is known as the **genu;** the rostral arm of the V, as the **anterior limb;** and the caudal arm, as the **posterior** or **occipital limb of the** capsule.

The anterior limb has on its rostromedial side the caudate nucleus; on its caudolateral side, the globus pallidus and putamen (Fig. 233). Through the anterior limb travel fibers including the frontopontine tracts from frontal lobe to pontine nuclei and the anterior thalamic radiation of fibers from the dorsomedial nuclei, especially, to the frontal lobe.

The posterior or occipital limb has on its medial side the main mass of the dorsal thalamus, on its lateral side the globus pallidus (Fig. 233). The medial border of the globus pallidus is thus angular, lying against both anterior and posterior limbs and their junction, the genu. The globus pallidus is embraced laterally and rostrally by the putamen together with which it forms the lenticular nucleus (Fig. 233). The posterior limb of the capsule is divided into three portions on the basis of its relation to the lenticular nucleus, the **lenticulothalamic,** the **retrolenticular,** and **sublenticular** portions. The lenticulothalamic portion has the largest extent.

Through the most rostral part of the lenticulothalamic portion and through the genu pass the corticobulbar fibers going from the frontal lobe to cranial nerve motor nuclei in the brain stem (Fig. 235). Through the rostral

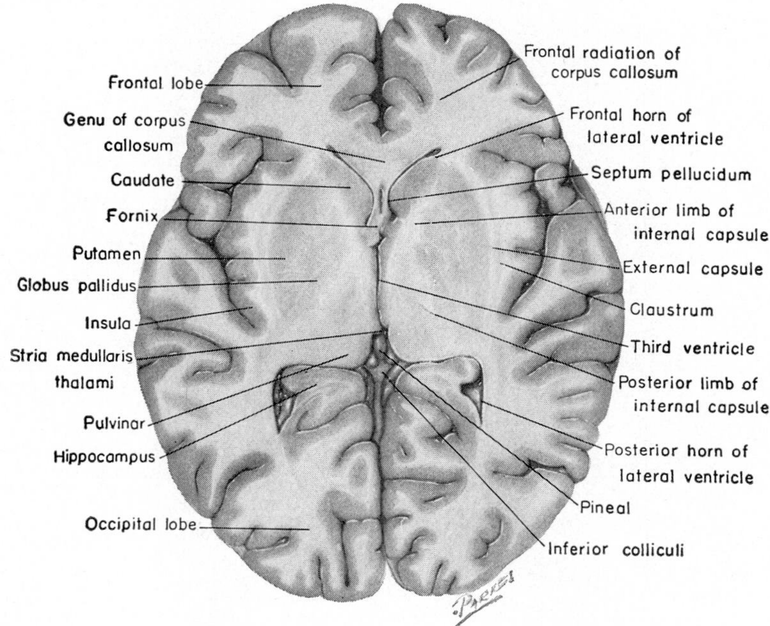

FIG. 233. Horizontal section, unstained, through whole brain at a level slightly more ventral than Fig. 232.

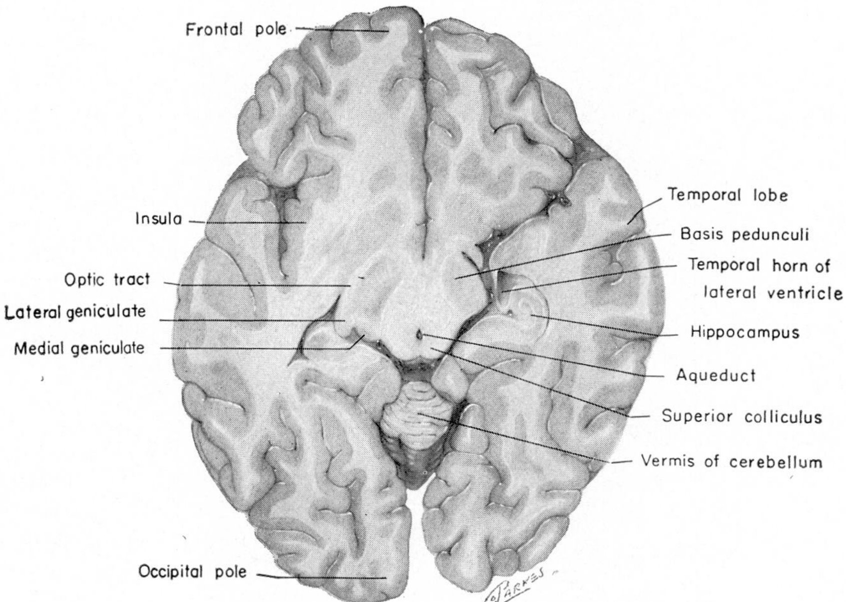

FIG. 234. Horizontal section, unstained, through whole brain at a level of the midbrain.

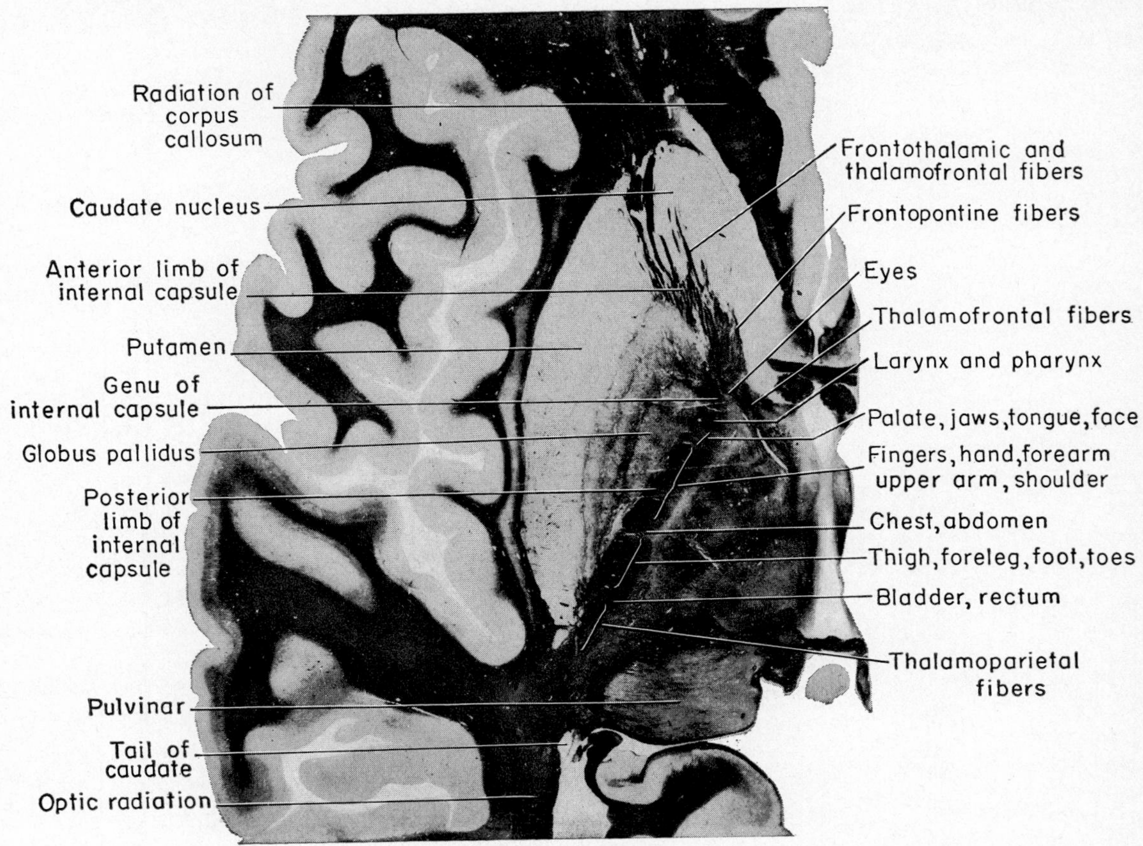

FIG. 235. Schema of the internal capsule.

half of the lenticulothalamic portion are scattered corticospinal tracts, running chiefly from the frontal lobe to the spinal cord. The fibers are so arranged that those destined for cervical cord neurons are nearer the genu than those for the lumbar cord neurons. Near the corticospinal fibers are corticorubral fibers from the frontal lobe to the red nucleus. Scattered throughout the lenticulothalamic limb are thalamocortical and corticothalamic fibers; rostrally are thalamocortical fibers to the posterior part of the frontal lobe from the lateral ventral nucleus, and corticothalamic fibers connecting the same regions; caudally are thalamocortical fibers to the rostral portion of the parietal lobe from the posterolateral and posteromedial ventral nuclei, chiefly, and corticothalamic fibers connecting the same regions.

The retrolenticular part of the posterior limb of the internal capsule is not visible completely in a single horizontal section of the brain (Fig. 208). It emerges caudal to or behind the caudal portion of the lenticular nucleus resting upon the lateral surface of the caudal part of the thalamus. Through it travel the posterior thalamic radiation, including fibers passing from lateral and posterior nuclei of the dorsal thalamus to the parietal and occipital lobes. Some of the fibers of the geniculocalcarine tracts also pass through this limb, especially those that terminate above the calcarine fissure in the occipital lobe.

The sublenticular part of the posterior limb also requires examination of several horizontal sections to be seen completely. Its position is ventral and slightly rostral to the posterior extremity of the lenticular nucleus. It contains temporopontine fibers from the temporal lobe cortex to pontine nuclei; many fibers of the geniculocalcarine tract, especially those from the lateral and ventral portion of the lateral geniculate body, terminating in the occipital lobe inferior to the calcarine fissure; occipitopontine and occipitotectal fibers; and the auditory radiation, consisting predominantly of fibers from the medial geniculate body to the superior transverse temporal gyrus and also many fibers running in the opposite direction between these two points.

Because of the fairly frequent involvement of parts of the internal capsule in vascular disorders, it will be helpful to describe the blood supply as determined by Alexander (21). Striate arterioles from anterior or middle cerebral arteries supply the anterior limb of the internal capsule, the portion dorsolateral to the genu and the dorsal part of the posterior limb. The ventral part of the posterior limb and the retrolenticular part are supplied from the anterior chorioidal artery. The genu is supplied by one or two direct branches from the carotid artery.

It might be added that on the lateral surface of the putamen there is a thin strip of white matter, the **external capsule;** the origin and destination of the fibers in it are disputed (Figs. 212, 232, 233). Lateral to this is a thin strip of gray tissue, the **claustrum,** whose mysteries likewise are debatable. Lateral to the claustrum is the **extreme capsule,** yet another thin band of white substance; its fibers, like those of the external capsule, *may,* in part, be association fibers between parietal and temporal lobes, and fibers of temporal lobe origin passing to the anterior commissure.

Electrical Activity of the Cortex

Caton in 1875 first found evidence of electrical activity in the brains of animals (130). Others subsequently observed that electrical activity was present in the visual cortex after illumination of the eyes and in the sensory cortex after a sensory nerve was stimulated. Similarly it has been learned that the human brain generates potentials which can be measured through the skull. Berger first recorded the electrical activity of the human brain in 1924, and coined the term *Elektrenkephalogram* (80). Adrian and Matthews were able to confirm Berger's results and observed that the most prominent rhythm, the alpha waves of Berger, originated in the parieto-occipital regions (18).

The changes of cortical electrical potential recorded from most humans are customarily of the order of 5 to 50 microvolts and have a duration of from 1 sec. down to 20 millisec. (300). The **alpha,** or Berger, rhythm shows a range of frequency of from 8 to 13 per sec., with 10 per sec. most common. The potential of these waves varies from zero to about 100 microvolts. Although such waves are most often recorded from the parieto-occipital regions, similar waves can be recorded from the frontal regions. The foci from which they are recorded are usually symmetrical in the two hemispheres, the rate of the waves is usually the same on the two sides, and the waves are in phase. The frequency of the alpha rhythm for an individual is remarkably constant, and electroencephalograms done at various times are usually of the same order. In early childhood the alpha waves usually show a frequency of 6 per sec.; this increases to a frequency of from 8 to 13 in adult life, and gradually regresses in old age to about 6 per sec. Much difference may be observed, however, in different adult individuals. The alpha rhythm develops when the eyes of the subject are closed and when he is physically and mentally relaxed. If the eyes are open, or if the subject is given other sensory stimulation or is asked to solve a mental problem, the rhythm is abolished. It is often suppressed or interrupted regularly every few seconds, even with the eyes closed and in the presence of mental quiet. A rise in temperature may lead to an acceleration of the alpha rhythm. Fear and nervousness may suppress the waves, and any sudden alarm may lead to their temporary depression. Drowsiness may be associated with slower and larger waves.

Another rhythm, usually of lower voltage and higher frequency of about 25 per sec. (a range from 18 to 50 per sec.), has been recorded often and is known as the **beta rhythm.** This is sometimes superimposed on the alpha rhythm, is sometimes seen in the absence of the alpha rhythm, and seems predominant in the precentral regions of the head. The beta waves as a rule are more stable than the alpha with regard to the varying physiologic conditions discussed above. **Delta** waves with a frequency of $\frac{1}{2}$ to 5 per sec. are recorded in normal subjects in deep sleep.

During sleep the alpha rhythm gradually disappears and gives way to large, slow, irregular waves (198). These latter may not be constantly present, and waves with a frequency of about 14 per sec. may appear for short periods. Unconsciousness is usually associated with larger and slower waves than the conscious state. In deep ether anesthesia also, large slow waves at a frequency of 2 to 3 per sec. appear over the cortex. Inhalation of substances which produce anoxemia leads to the appearance of slow waves. Barbiturates injected in large dosage lead to a widespread cortical discharge with a frequency of about 8 per sec. In oxygen deficiency states the cortical electrical activity slows and finally ceases. When the carbon dioxide tension is lowered by overventilation in normal subjects, occasional slow waves occur. Hypoglycemia, if severe, causes a slowing of the electrical activity.

It is of interest that the electroencephalogram in normally sleeping animals is similar to that recorded in an animal with its brain stem transected. It has been learned that the normal waking cerebral electrical activity can be abolished by destruction of certain of the brain stem reticular systems (see Chap. 17). Further, it is to be recalled that stimulation of certain thalamic nuclei leads to the appearance of cortical activity which is similar to the alpha waves. Even though these subcortical mechanisms have an influence on the cortical rhythm, and afferent impulses may modify it, the isolated cortex is capable of producing a rhythmic activity that is very similar to, if not identical with, the alpha rhythm (94, 445). If a cortical area is undercut, the rhythmic activity is abolished temporarily but later returns, and its return may be facilitated by the application of small amounts of acetylcholine preceded by local treatment with eserine. It seems likely, therefore, that the alpha rhythms, at least, are the result of inherent cortical activity, although the composition of the rhythms is at present unknown. It seems likely that they are caused by the spontaneous discharge of many cortical neurons.

Electroencephalography has become a clinical diagnostic procedure and has been utilized in experimental neurophysiology. It has been used as an aid in a diagnosis of epilepsy, especially, and as a complementary localizing aid in brain neoplasms and hemorrhages (301, 415). It is possible to make simultaneous recordings from leads placed over several cortical regions, and by the placement of the electrodes in certain loci a certain amount of localization of activity can be had. Standards of normal rhythms have been established, and it has been estimated that at least 10 per cent of the population of the United States have abnormal wave patterns and are therefore said to be dysrhythmic (476, 477). The incidence of dysrhythmia is greater than the clinical incidence of epilepsy in a ratio of 25:1. Dysrhythmia is much more common in epileptic patients and in their families than in the normal population. It appears likely that normal and abnormal electroencephalograms tend to be inherited. Clinical seizures are usually associated with a disturbance in the normal electrical activity, and some patients will demonstrate abnormalities in the electroencephalogram in the absence of a clinical seizure. The correlation between type of seizure and abnormality of the electroencephalogram is not absolute, although a very large percentage of patients with **petit mal** will show a 3-per-sec. spike-and-wave pattern from bilaterally synchronous foci, often frontal. Patients with **psychomotor attacks** also often show characteristic abnormal wave forms, in many instances having a focus in a temporal lobe tip (299). **Grand mal** does not appear to have a characteristic wave pattern associated with it, patients occasionally showing a variety of abnormal waves and frequencies. **Focal cortical seizures**, however, are very often associated with a localized abnormality in the electroencephalogram. Cerebral neoplasms are themselves usually electrically inactive, but from the adjacent injured cortex, slow delta waves are often recorded. A focal abnormality is more often to be recorded if the neoplasm is large and rapidly growing. Electroencephalography is yet an infant branch of science, and numerous mysteries are still to be solved concerning even the fundamental mechanisms which can presently be recorded.

Also, it is not possible to state with accuracy how the cerebral cortex functions. Some investigators have allocated specific function to a minute cortical region; others maintain that absolute cortical localization of function does not exist. It seems likely that localization of function is present, and that duplication of localization may exist. It also appears reasonable to suggest that large areas of the cerebral cortex function simultaneously in adjusting the organism to its environment. One cortical region can influence the activity of another in either a facilitatory or inhibitory fashion, and these influences may be expressed via direct corticocortical relations or corticosubcorticocortical relations. The brain stem activity influences the functioning of the cortex, the hypothalamus, certain thalamic nuclei, and tegmentum appearing predominant for the maintenance of basic neural integrations, continuously in play. Such basic activity is essential for the rapid integrations necessary for the performance of skilled motor acts spontaneously executed or initiated in response to an enviromental change. In the following chapters the neural mechanisms for motor activity will be discussed.

CHAPTER 16

THE PRECENTRAL CORTEX AND MOTOR PATHWAYS

THE CEREBRAL CORTEX discharges impulses for the initiation of movement to motor neurons located in brain stem and spinal-cord levels. The chief executor for the initiation of skilled movements is the precentral gyrus, its agents, the axons arising from the pyramidal neurons in its fifth cortical layer, especially, and descending into subcortical nuclei and the spinal cord. The origin of these axons, their course, their manner of termination, and their function in their contribution to movement will form the basis of the discussion of the present chapter.

Those axons which arise in the cerebral cortex and run without interruption to terminate in the spinal cord about spinal motor neurons directly, or through an internuncial, compose the **corticospinal tracts.** Those axons which end about neurons of cranial-nerve motor nuclei are **corticobulbar tracts.** The corticospinal fibers arise chiefly in the frontal lobes, pass through the corona radiata into the internal capsule, thence into the cerebral peduncle and through the basilar part of the pons to be collected in the pyramids, and later the majority cross to the opposite side before entering the spinal cord. A **lateral,** a **ventral,** and, occasionally, a **ventrolateral corticospinal** tract are known in the cord. These corticospinal tracts are often referred to as the **pyramidal tracts,** since they traverse the pyramids in their course spinalward. Other motor tracts in addition to these enter the spinal cord, but not by way of the pyramid. These others have unfortunately been called **extrapyramidal pathways.** The use of the word "extrapyramidal" has gotten somewhat out of hand, for it is also used to describe fiber bundles that do not come near the spinal cord. The extrapyramidal motor system will be discussed in the following section, and it will be found to include certain cortical areas, subcortical and brain stem nuclei, and their connecting fibers, as well as fiber tracts descending into the spinal cord from certain of these nuclei. Certain parts of the cortex, especially in Brodmann's area 4 (*FA* of Economo), which give rise to these extrapyramidal fibers, also give origin to most of the pyramidal fibers, and both systems express themselves on the common spinal motor pool, anterior column cells and their processes, directly or indirectly by means of a spinal internuncial cell. Apparently "extrapyramidal" corticobulbar fibers also are present, but knowledge of the anatomy of these is incomplete.

It should be recalled that practically any type of complex, skillful, or learned motor performance will involve the simultaneous activation of many muscles and relaxation of others. Cortical, brain stem, and spinal neurons are involved, and many pathways are therefore involved. Information concerning the activity and contribution to motor performance of each of these two systems of motor pathways, to the spinal cord particularly, has been gained through studies on man, chimpanzee, and monkey, especially. Correlations of functional disorder have been made with tissue removed by experimental ablations from, or clinical injuries to, the precentral gyrus and its projections. Electrical and chemical stimulations of the cerebral cortex have yielded information that indicates the function as well as some of the finer intricacies of anatomical detail.

Cytoarchitecture of Precentral Areas

In 1874, Betz described "giant" pyramidal cells in the precentral gyrus which he thought gave rise to corticospinal fibers. It was just about 5 years earlier than this that electrical stimulation applied over the frontal lobe, especially its posterior portion, in dogs and man, had given movements of the opposite limbs (280). The giant pyramidal cells have thus come to be called Betz cells, though the measuring standards applied and the size of a "giant" have varied from investigator to investigator. True Betz cells are practically limited to the posterior part of area 4, 4γ (*FA*γ of Economo), of the precentral gyrus of the frontal lobe and are found in the fifth cortical cell layer. The total number of giant cells in area 4γ of man has been computed as 34,370 (471, 472). The number of fibers in a human pyramid just above its decussation has been given as just over 1 million. Assuming that one giant cell gives rise to one corticospinal fiber, the so-called Betz giant cells apparently contribute some 3 per cent of the fibers of one pyramidal tract. Many of the fibers of the human pyramid are so poorly myelinated that by present staining techniques they appear as unmyelinated. Myelinated fibers account for about 61 per cent, and of these about 90 per cent are small, with a diameter of 1 to 4μ. For the human pyramidal tract 30,000 fibers with a diameter ranging from 9 to 22μ have been calculated by Lassek, and this number compares favorably with the number of giant cells as given by him. The variation in size perhaps indicates a wide variation in conduction rate, the largest Betz-cell axons transmitting more rapidly than other axons. Within a pyramidal tract, therefore, many fibers are present which arise from cells other than giant pyramids.

It has been demonstrated by several authors that cells other than Betz giant cells give rise to pyramidal corticospinal fibers (388, 479). By study of degenerating cells following spinal-cord transection, chromatolytic changes have been found not only in Betz cells but in other pyramid cells of lesser size in the third and fifth cortical layers. Such degenerating cells are not limited to area 4, but are present in areas 3, 1, 2, and 5 (Brodmann), at least in monkeys. Also degenerating axons have been found in corticospinal tracts after removal of areas, 3, 1, 2, 5, and 7 in the macaque (561, 606). It seems reasonably certain, therefore, that area 4 and parts of the parietal lobe give rise to the fibers of the pyramidal corticospinal tract in the

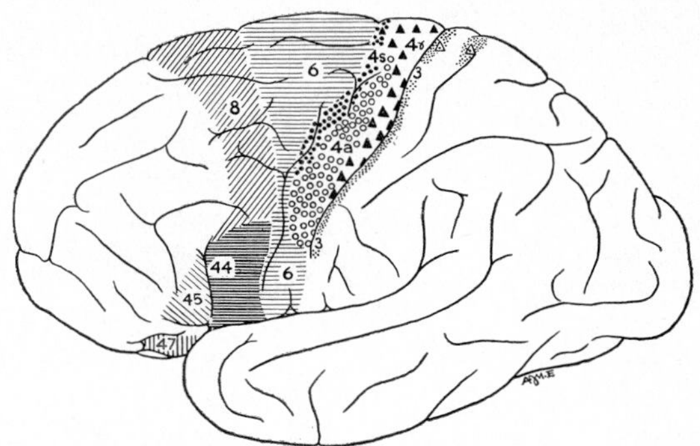

FIG. 236*A*. The human precentral and associated cortical areas on lateral hemispheric surface. (*After Von Bonin in "The Precentral Motor Cortex," University of Illinois Press.*)

human, and it seems likely that area 6 also contributes a number. Since all the fibers of the human pyramidal tract appear to arise in the cortex, and since only about 50 per cent of the fibers can be certified as arising in those areas just given, it is necessary in the future to seek the origin of the other 50 per cent. Electrical studies, in the monkey and cat, in which cortical potentials were set up antidromically, in response to stimulation of the medullar pyramid, also give evidence of origin of the fibers in a medullar pyramid from areas 4, 6, 8, 3, 1, 2, 5, and 7 (856). It was suggested that the fibers from areas 8 and 6 found at pyramid level are those conducting impulses for head-turning movements.

Several types of cortex may be defined within the frontal lobe, depending on the development of a significant internal granular (IV) layer. On this basis frontal granular, frontal agranular, and frontal dysgranular types of cortex have been described. In the last type the internal granular lamina (IV) is present but is thin and not densely populated. Within the precentral gyrus, with which the following discussion is chiefly concerned, agranular and dysgranular cortex is found. These types are also present in other regions, however. The precentral agranular cortex shows very few granule cells at all, and they are practically nonexistent in that level which corresponds to the fourth lamina elsewhere. Within this level and extending somewhat into the deep portion of layer III, the outer stripe of Baillarger, composed of terminal plexuses of specific thalamocortical fibers, can, however, be found.

When the precentral agranular region is examined histologically it is seen that it too can be subdivided into areas 4 and 6, as has been done by Brodmann, and into *FA* and *FB* by Economo and Koskinas (104, 232, 233). That these two sets of symbols do not refer to exactly the same regions, however, will be discussed later. A further division of *FA* on the basis of histological study was made by the last-mentioned investigators; they described *FA* anteriorly and *FA*γ posteriorly. A narrow strip anterior to *FA* (or immediately posterior to FB) was called *FBA* (Figs. 226, 227, 228). A similar partition of this precentral region was made by Von Bonin, who has sometimes used Brodmann's numbers, sometimes the symbols of Economo, and sometimes symbols of his own. Using the Brodmann numbers, Von Bonin had 4γ posteriorly along the anterior bank of the central fissure, 4*a* on the crest of the precentral gyrus, and 4*s* immediately anterior to 4*a* (Fig. 236*A*) (85). In his 1951 monograph,

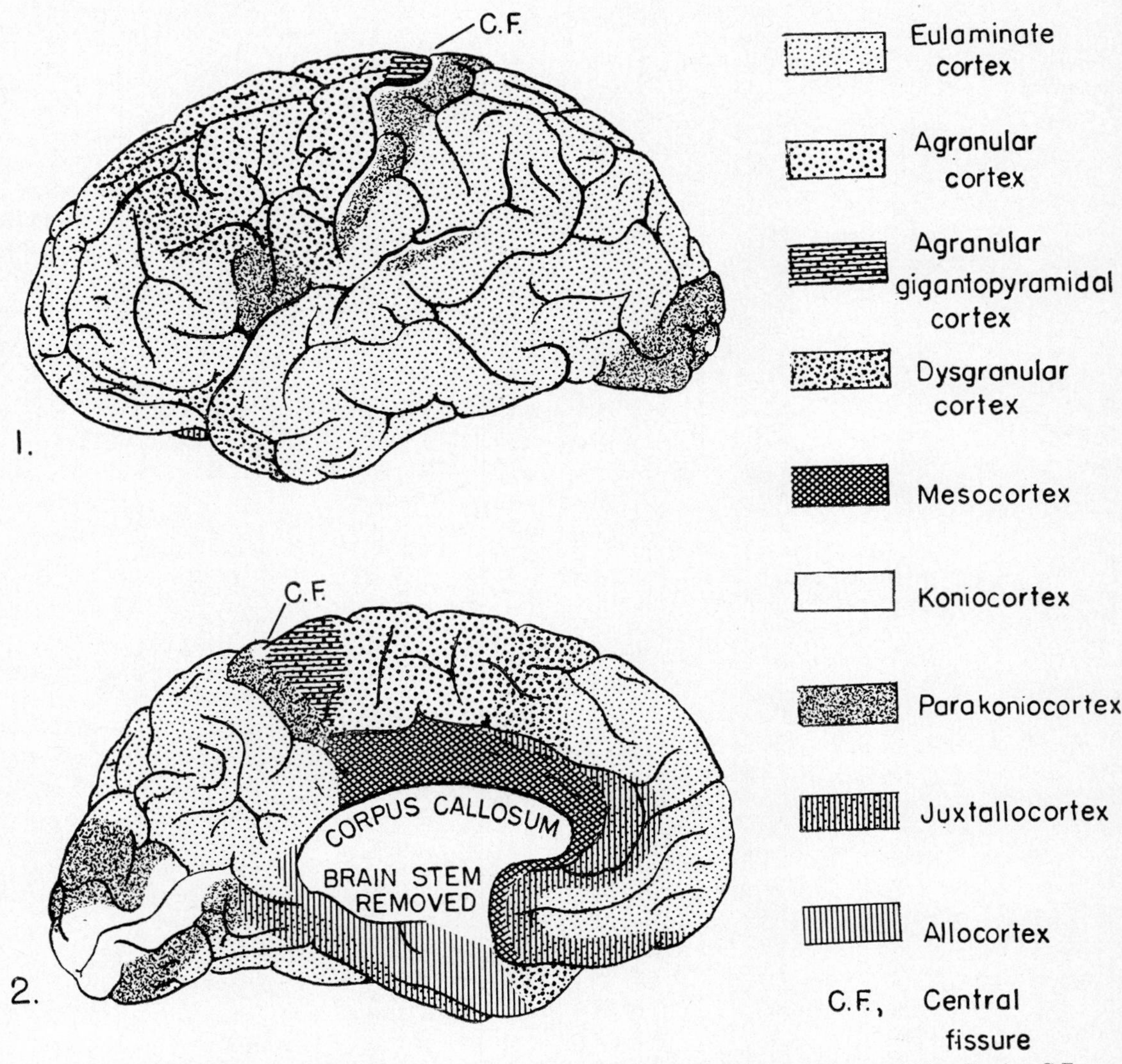

FIG. 236*B*. Cytoarchitectural map of the human cerebral cortex as defined by Bailey and Von Bonin. *C.F.*, central fissure. In their original map these investigators use colors to identify their cortical regions and by delicate shadings they indicate the lack of sharp boundaries between these regions. The present figure does not demonstrate the gradual

written with Bailey and concerned with the human isocortex, Von Bonin has revised his earlier opinions, however, regarding the division of the precentral region. He no longer recognizes an area 4*s* anatomically. His area 4γ has become an "agranular gigantopyramidal" zone, the remaining part of area 4 together with area 6 has become a simple "frontal agranular" zone (Fig. 236*B*).

Brodmann's area 4 corresponds closely to *FA*γ of Economo and the original 4γ of Von Bonin. Brodmann's area 6 included area *FA* of Economo and the original area 4*a* of Von Bonin. The area *FB* of Economo and Koskinas corresponds closely to Von Bonin's original area 6. Along the posterior edge of *FB,* Economo and Koskinas found a band of tissue of slightly different cytoarchitecture (*FBA*) from that of the rest of *FB,* as noted previously. A strip with comparable position has been identified as a physiological entity in the macaque by Hines (367, 368). Influenced by these findings, perhaps, Von Bonin identified his comparable area 4*s* in the human; it has been called also the precentral "suppressor" strip.

Following the partitions made in the cercopithecus monkey by the Vogts according to their results of electrical stimulation, Foerster and Penfield have used cortical maps showing area 6 divided into 6*a* and 6*b,* and 6*a* has

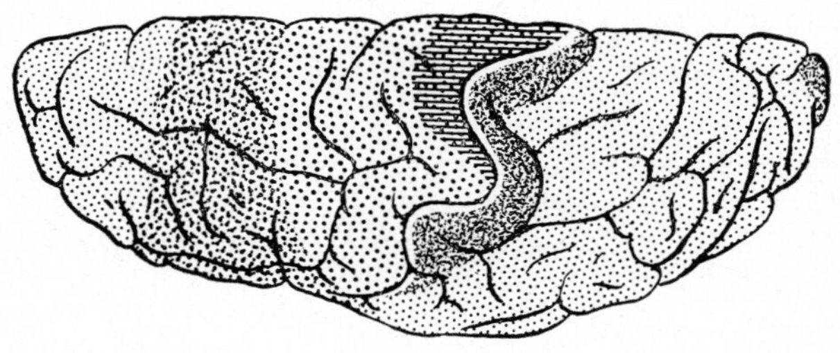

3. Superior aspect

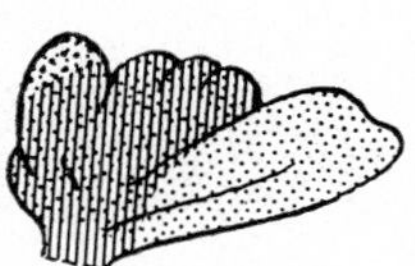

5. Insula

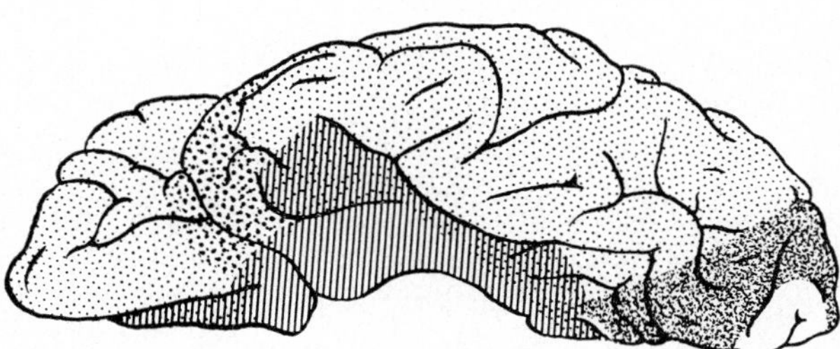

4. Inferior aspect

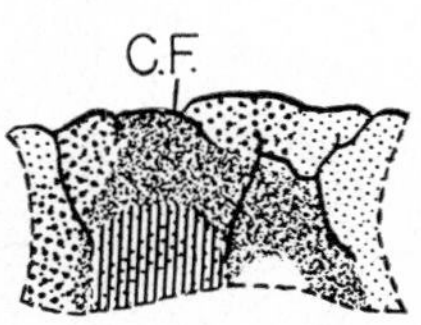

6. Parietal operculum

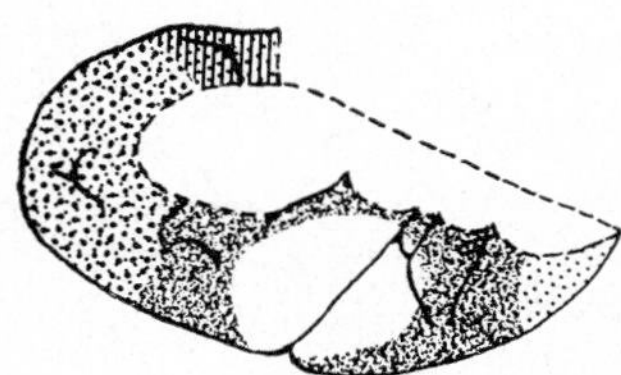

7. Superior aspect of temporal lobe

changes. 1, lateral view of hemisphere; 2, medial view of the hemisphere; 3, the hemisphere as seen from above; 4, the hemisphere as seen from below; 5, the insula; 6, the parietal operculum; 7, the superior surface of the superior temporal gyrus. (*From Bailey and Von Bonin, "The Isocortex of Man," University of Illinois Press.*)

been subdivided into $6a\alpha$ and $6a\beta$ (Fig. 237). Area $6a$ of this scheme corresponds to the earlier areas $4a$, $4s$, and 6 of Von Bonin. In so far as is feasible, hereafter, the numbers of Brodmann and Bonin will be used with the symbols of Economo given in parentheses.

Histologically, 4γ ($FA\gamma$) and $4a$ (FA) present certain similarities, in that lamination is not distinct, a columnar pattern is not clear, and the density of cells is low. Area 4γ is the thickest cortex of the entire brain. The pyramid cells of II and III show an increasing size in the deeper parts of the laminae. The fourth lamina, identified only by the presence of the outer stripe of Baillarger, contains scattered pyramids. The fifth layer, broader here than in other cortical regions, contains pyramids of all sizes including clusters of the giant pyramids, or Betz cells. The largest pyramids are present in the medial hemispheric extension of 4γ, which also shows here its widest extent. The sixth lamina shows a higher cell density than the others, and many fusiform cells are found together with the pyramids of small and medium size. Area $4a$ (FA) is quite similar to 4γ, aside from its lack of Betz cells. Area $4s$, immediately anterior to $4a$ and to 4γ in its superior extent, was originally identified by Bonin by its large pyramids in IV*a* (III*c*) and its lack of giant cells in the fifth lamina. That investigator was unable to identify $4s$ by these criteria in the human brain he has most recently studied. His present area agranularis giganto-pyramidalis corresponds to his previous 4γ. The remaining portions of his earlier area 4 are now incorporated with his earlier area 6 into an area agranularis simplex (Fig. 236). It seems safe to say that the final answer concerning parcellation of the precentral cortex in the human is not at hand. Many physiological studies in the macaque and chimpanzee and a few in man make one suspect that functional differences are present in that cortex. In view of the fact that many investigators in their researches have referred to "area $4s$" as a cortical entity, this term will be used in the discussions below.

Area 6 in Von Bonin's earlier scheme (*FB* of Economo) lay immediately anterior to the precentral "suppressor" strip, $4s$, and composed the greatest part of Brodmann's 6. This cortex occupies the anterior third of the paracentral lobule on the medial hemispheric surface, the posterior part of the frontal gyri superiorly, and the anterior part of the precentral, inferiorly, on the lateral hemispheric surface. This area also does not have true Betz cells in the fifth layer, but large pyramidal cells are present in layers II, III, and V; layer IV contains pyramidal cells and is practically indistinct as a separate layer, hence this area has been included in the agranular frontal division. The cells of the outer three layers are arranged in a characteristic radial columnar pattern.

A small area of cortex anterior to the most ventral part of area 6, has been called area 44 by Von Bonin (*FCBm*) (Figs. 226, 227, 236*A*). It corresponds to area 44 of Brodmann and has also been called Broca's area (see Chap. 22). This cortex contains a faint, but distinct, internal granular layer. This layer contains medium and large pyramidal cells in addition to its small granules. Because the cells of this layer tend to be arranged in columns, leaving gaps between groups of granules, this cortex has been called dysgranular. This area shows a more distinct lamination than the areas described above. Columnization of the cells is also evident in layers other than IV.

Just anterior to area 6 (*FB*), in the upper two-thirds of its extent, is a band of cortex overlying the posterior end of the superior and middle frontal convolutions. This in its upper portion is designated area 8 (*FC*). The lower, most lateral portion, occupying the triangular part of the opercular area, has been called 45 by Von Bonin and apparently represents the $FD\gamma$ and anterior portion of area *FCBm* of Economo and Koskinas (Figs. 226, 227, 236*A*). It seems to correspond to Brodmann's area 45 and a small strip from the caudal edge of his area 9. Cytoarchitecturally, the pyramid cells, the most numerous elements of area 8 (*FC*), are smaller in general than those of area 6 (*FB*). Granule elements are found mixed with small pyramids in layers II and IV which, although distinct, are narrow and frequently interrupted. Layer III shows progressive increase in size of the pyramids in its depths. Layer V is rather thick and can be subdivided. The largest pyramids are in its middle level, medium-sized ones being scattered above and below. The sixth layer contains many spindles. The thickness of this area 8 cortex is not as great as that of the areas just caudal to it. This region has been called transition cortex between the frontal granular and agranular types. Area 8 seems closely related in activity to the precentral areas. It is the frontal "suppressor" area, and from that part of it overlying the end of the middle frontal gyrus it is possible to stimulate eye movements.

Area 45 ($FD\gamma$) is narrow cortex and shows clearly a radial columnization of the cells. The lamination is distinct also, with layers II and IV prominent. These contain many granules. Layer III shows pyramids approaching giant size in its lower depths. Layer V is rather pale and contains scattered small pyramids, and layer VI, well demarcated from the white matter, shows many spindles and small pyramids.

The Corticospinal Tracts

It appears likely that the corticospinal tracts arise principally from pyramidal cells, including the large Betz cells, in the fifth cortical cell layer (218). As described above, these fibers spring most abundantly from the posterior part of the precentral gyrus 4γ ($FA\gamma$) and from the postcentral gyrus, but also probably from areas $4a$ (FA), $4s$, and 6 (FB). Areas 8 (FC) and 6 (FB) also contribute fibers to the corticobulbar tract. Some large pyramid cells in the third cell layer (the external pyramidal) also possibly contribute axons to the corticospinal tracts. The giant cells of Betz are largest in the superior (or dorsal) part of area 4γ ($FA\gamma$), and they decrease in size gradually in the inferior (or ventral) part. It is known that the fibers destined for spinal-cord neurons innervating muscles of the legs arise higher and more medially in area 4γ than those for the arm, and those for the arm higher than those for the fingers. There is, therefore, a difference in size in the cells giving rise to the various parts of the voluntary motor pathways. Generally speaking, the length of the axon determines the size of the cell in this system. Those cortical cells giving rise to fibers which pass into the motor nuclei of the cranial nerves, the corticobulbar tracts, are smaller than those giving rise to the corticospinal or pyramidal fibers. In the internal capsule the corticobulbar and corticospinal fibers are grouped closely together in its genu and the posterior limb, respectively (Fig. 238).

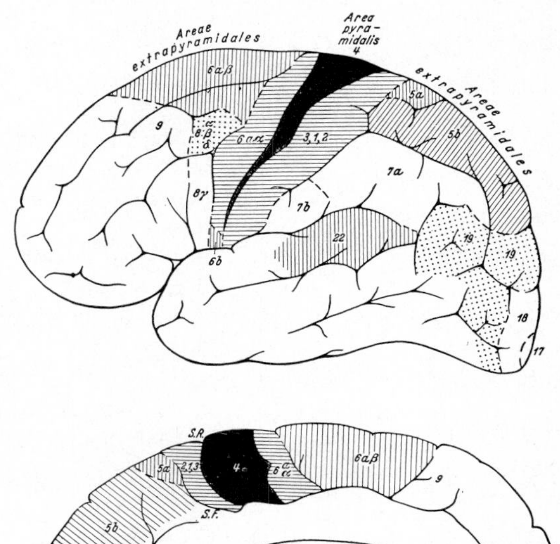

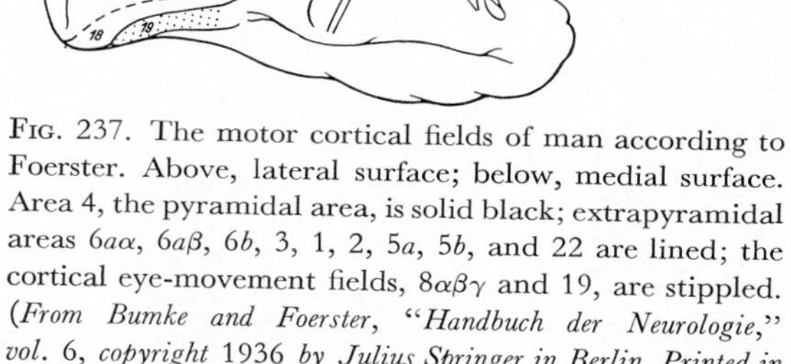

Fig. 237. The motor cortical fields of man according to Foerster. Above, lateral surface; below, medial surface. Area 4, the pyramidal area, is solid black; extrapyramidal areas $6a\alpha$, $6a\beta$, $6b$, 3, 1, 2, $5a$, $5b$, and 22 are lined; the cortical eye-movement fields, $8\alpha\beta\gamma$ and 19, are stippled. (*From Bumke and Foerster, "Handbuch der Neurologie," vol.* 6, *copyright* 1936 *by Julius Springer in Berlin. Printed in Germany. Vested in the U.S. Attorney General.*)

From the internal capsule the corticospinal fibers pass into the basis pedunculi, of which they occupy the middle three-fifths. In the basilar part of the pons the fibers are scattered into irregular, isolated bundles, but as they enter the medulla they are grouped into the pyramids. At the caudal end of the medulla a decussation takes place, but not all the fibers cross (285) (Fig. 125).

Much variation of decussation pattern in man has been described, and several cases in which no decussation occurred have also been reported. In certain decussations the arm, trunk, and leg fibers destined for one side may cross before any of those for the other do so; or the left arm fibers may cross, then the right, the left trunk fibers, then the right, and finally the left leg fibers and then the right. Cus-

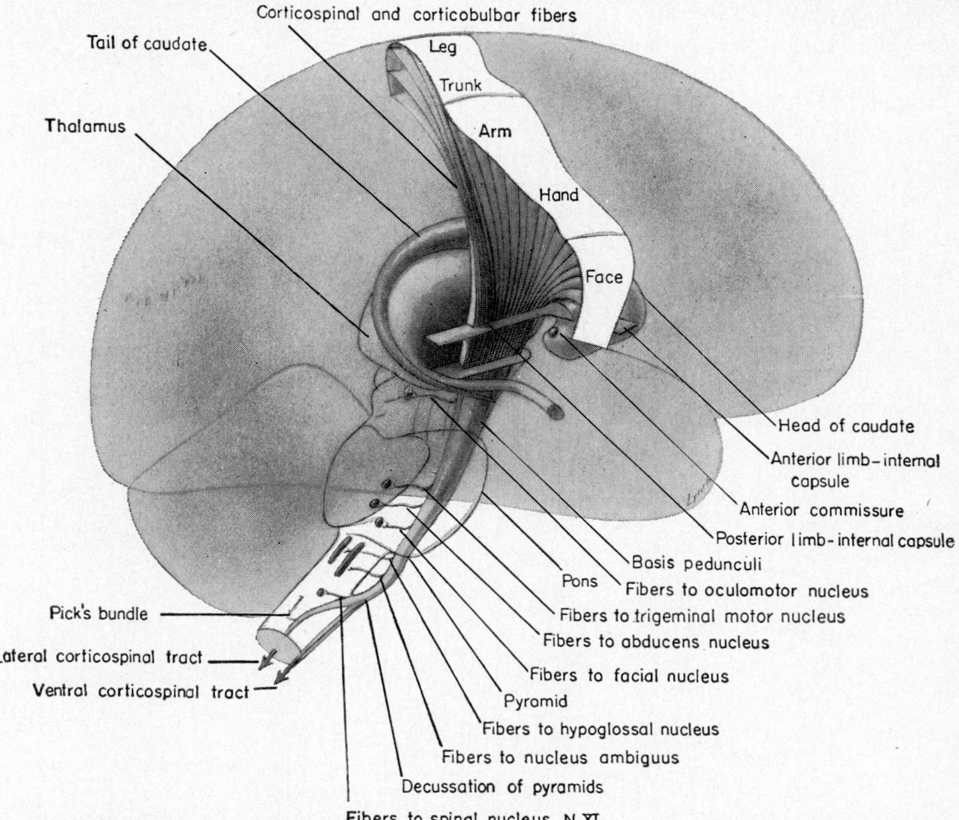

FIG. 238. Diagram of the course of corticospinal and corticobulbar fibers. The lenticular nucleus has been removed. The "leg" area continues on the medial hemispheric surface. The finer divisions of these major areas are not shown for purposes of simplification. The "wavy" contour of the corticobulbar fibers passing to cranial-nerve motor nuclei denotes decussation. (*General outline modified from Tandler.*)

tomarily, about 70 to 90 per cent of the fibers of a pyramid cross and pass dorsally to be continued in the spinal cord as a lateral corticospinal tract; the remaining fibers remain uncrossed. Of these, some pass dorsally to join the lateral corticospinal tract of that side; others continue in a ventral position as a ventral corticospinal tract. The crossed and uncrossed lateral corticospinal fibers are distributed to all spinal levels, while the ventral ones terminate without crossing at cervical and thoracic spinal levels. A ventrolateral corticospinal tract of uncrossed fibers, Barnes' tract, is occasionally present in the human (60). These fibers terminate uncrossed at cervical levels. More accurate data are at hand concerning the situation in the chimpanzee (285).

In this animal, for example, three divisions of corticospinal fibers can be recognized in the decussation: the large majority cross to the opposite side to run down as the **lateral corticospinal tract;** about one-tenth that number pass dorsally into the **lateral corticospinal tract on the same side;** a few fibers remain in a ventral location and continue down the cord on the same side as the **ventral corticospinal tract.** Many of the nondecussating fibers remain on the ipsilateral side throughout the length of the cord. In the spinal cord the corticospinal fibers may terminate in one of two ways: they end either directly about a large anterior column cell or about an intercalary neuron. The intercalary neuron may be located either in the anterior portion of posterior gray columns, in the intermediate, or in the anterior gray columns. In monkeys such intercalary endings

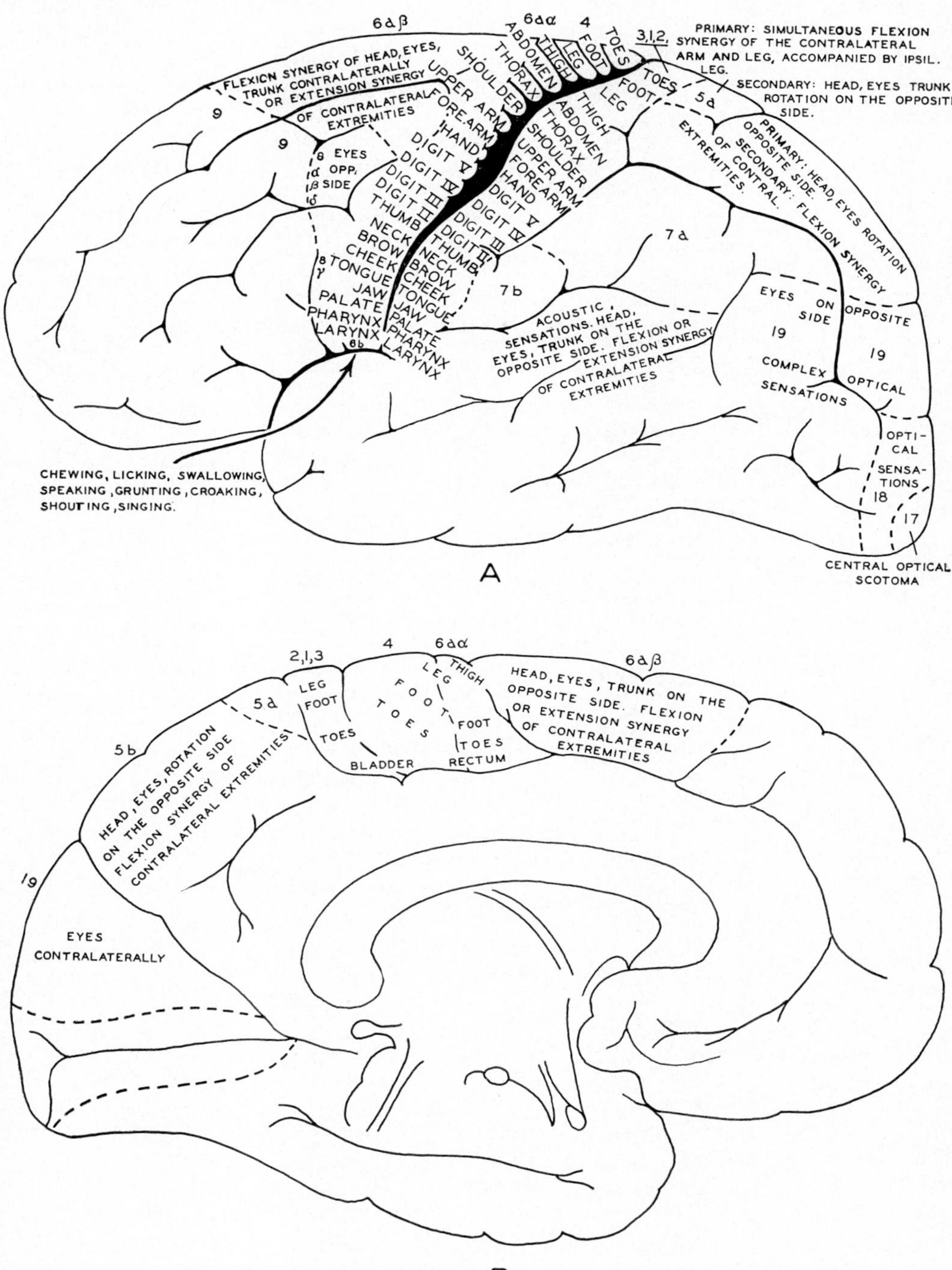

FIG. 239. Diagrams to show representation of movements, simple and complex, in the cerebral cortex of man, as determined through electrical stimulation by Foerster. *A*, lateral cortical surface; *B*, medial cortical surface. (*From Bumke and Foerster, "Handbuch der Neurologie," vol.* 6, *copyright* 1936 *by Julius Springer in Berlin. Printed in Germany. Vested in the U.S. Attorney General.*)

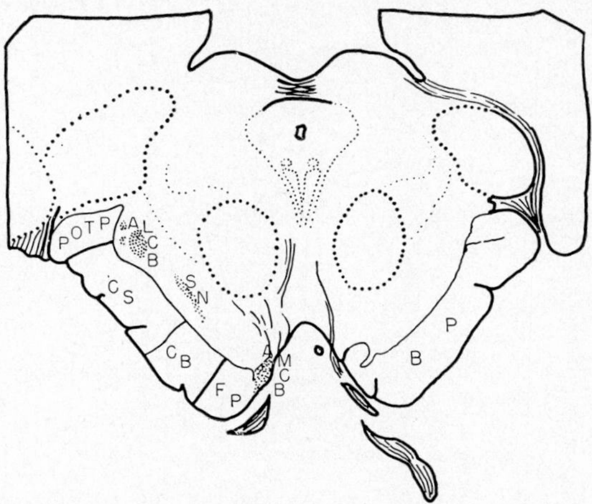

Fig. 240. Diagram of arrangement of fibers in the basis pedunculi. *ALCB*, aberrant lateral corticobulbar; *AMCB*, aberrant medial corticobulbar; *BP*, basis pedunculi; *CB*, corticobulbar; *CS*, corticospinal; *FP*, frontopontine; *POTP*, parieto-occipito-temporo-pontine. Corticoreticular fibers from area 4*s* are probably intermingled with corticospinal fibers.

are predominant, and in cats many pyramidal fiber mechanisms in the spinal cord involve such neurons intercalated between fibers and anterior column cells (490). The reticular nucleus, occupying the lateral and most anterior part of the posterior gray columns, is possibly the site of termination of many corticospinal fibers. It is not possible at present to make a definite statement as to the site of termination of corticospinal fibers in the spinal cord gray of man.

A definite topographical arrangement of the corticospinal fibers exists in the upper parts of their course. Those fibers destined for lumbar spinal levels, for example, arise from one part of the precentral gyrus; those destined for cervical levels, from another; and those passing to cranial motor nuclei, from another. In fact, electrical stimulations of the precentral gyrus of monkey and chimpanzee have revealed precise representation in that gyrus of individual muscles (or the movements of individual muscles). Though such studies in man have naturally not been carried out so painstakingly, evidence is plentiful that a definite somatotopic representation of motor performance or muscles is to be found in the human precentral gyrus, and area 4γ ($FA\gamma$) has yielded more excitable points than areas 4*a* (*FA*) and 6 (*FB*). The cortical maps of Penfield and Foerster are illustrated in Figs 237, 239, and 242.

Within the internal capsule a definite arrangement of the fibers is also to be found. Corticobulbar fibers occupy the genu; the corticospinal fibers destined for cervical spinal levels, though in the posterior limb, are nearer the genu than those passing to lumbar and sacral levels (Fig. 235). Within the basis pedunculi the corticobulbar and corticospinal fibers again have a definite arrangement. These two groups occupy the middle three-fifths of the basis pedunculi. Within this collection, the "leg" fibers are lateral; the "face" fibers, medial; and "arm" fibers, intermediate (Fig. 240). No definite data are known for topographical arrangement of the fibers below the peduncular level. In the macaque, the "corticospinal" fibers arising in the parietal areas occupy the posterior limb of the internal capsule, the lateral portion of the basis pedunculi, and the ventrolateral portion of the pyramid. A few of these fibers end at all spinal levels (606).

Corticobulbar Fibers

The motor nuclei of the cranial nerves also receive impulses from the cerebral cortex. The fibers over which such impulses pass are called **corticobulbars.** They have their origin from cells in the precentral gyrus (4γ), near its foot, and also from areas 8 and 44. Through electrical stimulations in humans, it has been learned that movement is represented in the following order in the inferior part of the precentral gyrus proceeding inferiorly: neck, brow, eyelid and eyeball, upper face, lower face, lips, jaw, tongue, palate, pharynx and larynx. Vocalization, salivation, and mastication mechanisms are also arranged in overlapping position (621). Lateral movement of the eyes is also located in the caudal part of the middle frontal gyrus; this is probably area 8 (see below).

At present no universal agreement or apparently unquestioned data exist concerning the course these corticobulbar fibers follow below the level of the internal capsule. The present discussion follows the descriptions of Dejerine, based on human material. The corticobulbar fibers are divided into several groups, some running to their termination closely associated with corticospinal (pyramidal) fibers, as **direct**

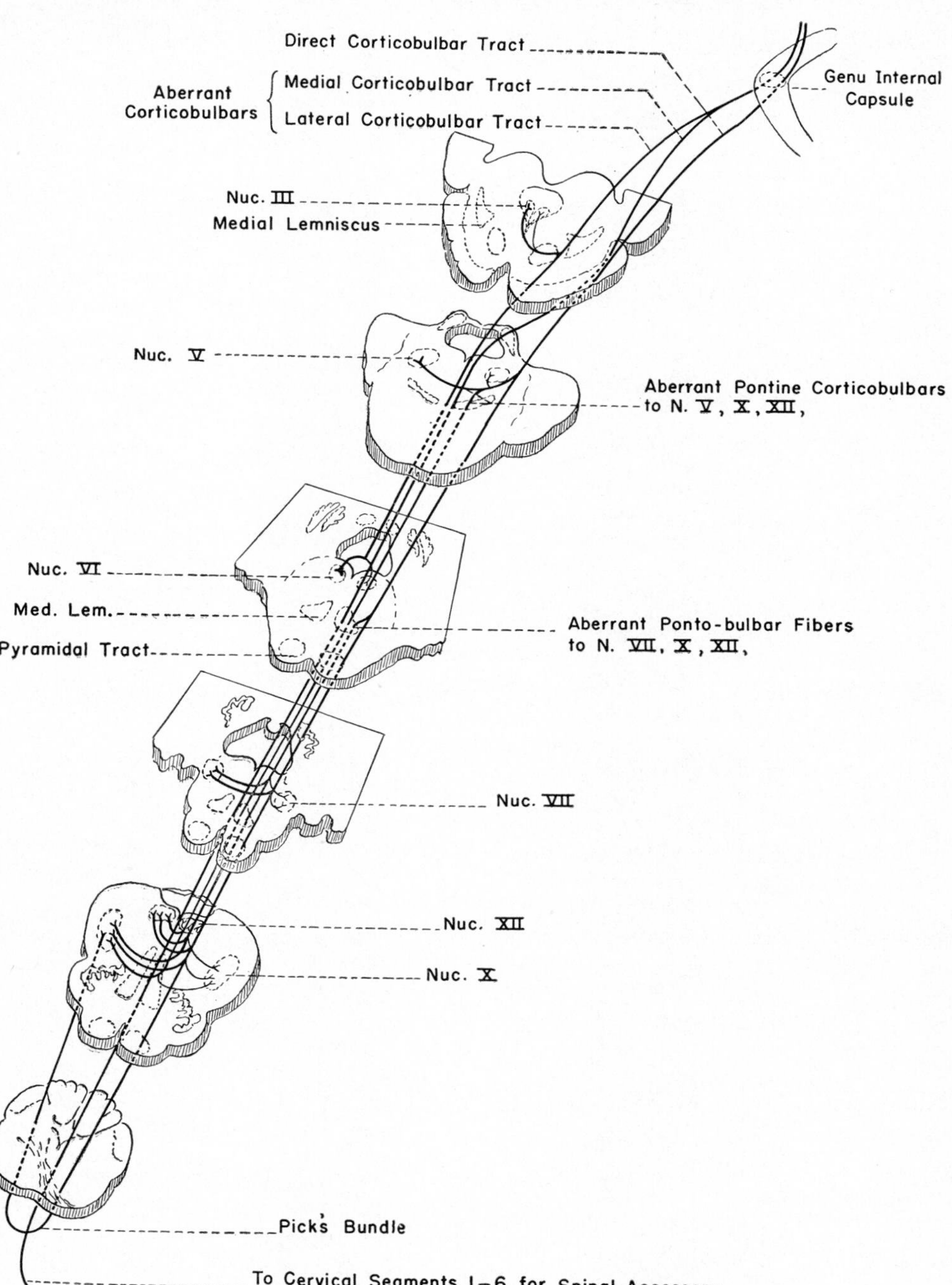

FIG. 241. Diagram of the corticobulbar tracts.

corticobulbars, others leaving the corticospinal fibers at various levels in the midbrain and pons and passing to cranial motor nuclei by other routes (204, 753, 845). These latter groups of fibers are called **aberrant cortico-bulbars** and the several divisions are named according to the level at which they separate (become aberrant) from the corticospinal fibers (Fig. 241). Obviously, all corticobulbar fibers become "aberrant" ultimately, and certain of them, especially those which will cross and end in the facial and hypoglossal nuclei, are the last to become "aberrant." Corticobulbar fibers decussate in part near the level of the cranial motor nucleus for which they are destined. This decussation is not complete, and movements of the majority of the striated muscles of the head are accordingly represented in each precentral gyrus. Since many of the homologous striated muscles of the two sides of the head necessarily work in unison, such a bilateral cortical representation is useful. The upper part of the face, the pharyngeal muscles, laryngeal muscles, and muscles for closing the jaw have the greatest bilateral representation. The sternocleidomastoid and external pterygoid muscles are represented to a greater extent ipsilaterally, according to results of electrical stimulation (see later).

The **direct** corticobulbar fibers arise in the precentral gyrus and in the caudal portion of the middle and inferior prefrontal gyri. They pass into the internal capsule and run through it near its genu (Figs. 235, 241). They pass through the basis pedunculi in the middle three-fifths, in association with the corticospinal fibers, and enter the pons. Near the level of the seventh motor nucleus a group breaks away and passes dorsally into the tegmentum. Some of these decussate to terminate in the contralateral facial motor muscles, especially in that part which innervates the muscles of the lower face. Very few decussating fibers end about cells that innervate frontalis, orbicularis oculi, and corrugator supercilii. Nondecussating fibers end in the ipsilateral facial motor nucleus about the cells which innervate these upper three muscles especially. Other fibers of this direct group continue caudalward to the level of the hypoglossal nuclei; then they pass dorsally into the tegmentum, and some decussate to end in the contralateral hypoglossal nucleus, especially around those cells which innervate the genioglossus. Nondecussating fibers pass to the neurons which innervate the other muscles of the tongue, intrinsic and extrinsic. These direct corticobulbar fibers may synapse first about an intercalary neuron, which in turn activates the final common neuron in the cranial-nerve nucleus.

The **aberrant** fibers, of similar cortical origin as the direct, are a bit more complex in their course, and some fibers may relay through intercalary neurons in the mesencephalic, pontine, and medullary gray before getting to their ultimate cranial motor nuclei (Fig. 241). There is not universal agreement on this, but clinical studies tend to show that those fibers for eye-muscle nuclei, at least, synapse around intercalary cells. This is particularly true of fibers carrying impulses which bring about conjugate eye movements. The aberrant corticobulbars apparently remain in company with the direct ones until the rostral end of the cerebral peduncle is reached. At this level and caudal to this, the following divisions have been described by various investigators after the observations of Dejerine.

Two aberrant bundles are present at the rostral peduncle level, a superficial and a deep. The superficial one is described as dorsomedial to the frontopontocerebellar fibers, the deep, medial to the temporopontocerebellar fibers (Fig. 240). These are then described as passing dorsally in the reticular formation to approach the medial lemniscus and to be distributed to the nuclei or internuncials of the third, fourth, sixth, and eleventh nerves (spinal portion), only part of the fibers decussating before terminating. The majority of the fibers for the spinal portion of the eleventh nerve may not decussate. Those fibers going to the oculomotor nuclei and trochlear nuclei pass dorsally into the mesencephalic tegmentum.

In the pons a second group of fibers leaves the company of the direct bundles, passes dorsally, joins the medial lemniscus group above, decussates partly at the level of the corresponding nuclei, and distributes to the nuclei of the fifth, twelfth, and tenth (ambiguus) nerves.

At the level of junction of pons and medulla a third bundle of fibers leaves the direct group, passes dorsally to the region of the medial lemniscus, decussates partly, and goes to the seventh, tenth (ambiguus), and twelfth nuclei.

Pick's bundle is composed of fibers which arise from the crossed pyramidal (lateral corticospinal) tract, turn sharply rostrally just after the decussation, and terminate about neurons in the nucleus ambiguus (60) (Figs. 241, 244*A*).

Certain investigators have come to the conclusion that the majority of Dejerine's several "aberrant" corticobulbar fibers are in reality bundles of corticopontine elements. In their descriptions, corticobulbar fibers are constantly leaving the company of corticospinal fibers below midbrain levels and thus do not form discrete fascicles (701). They pass dorsally into the tegmentum, some decussate, others remain uncrossed. Some fibers destined for a certain nucleus break away from the corticospinal fibers a short distance rostral to the level of the nucleus, enter the tegmentum and approach the nucleus from its frontal pole; others do not leave the corticospinal tracts until the nuclear level is reached.

It will be seen after study of the above scheme that the facial and hypoglossal nuclei receive fibers from both corticobulbar systems, direct and aberrant. The other nuclei are innervated by the aberrant bundles and some of them receive fibers from two "aberrant" groups, some of which decussate, and others of which do not. These overlappings of innervation provide a margin of safety from injury except through widespread lesions.

Other Projection Fibers from the Precentral Gyrus

Other pathways, in addition to corticospinal and corticobulbar fibers, arise in the precentral gyrus. They also contribute to motor performance. These other pathways project to subcortical brain stem centers, some of which in turn project to the spinal cord by way of several pathways. These latter, however, do not traverse the medullar pyramid and are therefore known as extrapyramidal tracts. Arising in the precentral gyri, from neurons in the fifth and sixth cortical layers especially, and perhaps also in the third, are axons which pass to the caudate nucleus, putamen, globus pallidus, thalamus, red nucleus, substantia nigra, subthalamus, hypothalamus, and tegmental reticular nuclei as well as basal pontine nuclei. These pathways will be dealt with in more detail in the following chapters. Suffice it to say at this point that they are activated simultaneously with the corticospinal and corticobulbar mechanisms in the motor activities of the organism.

Associative Connections of the Precentral Gyrus

The identification of corticocortical connections, even in experimental animals, has not kept pace, until recently, with the demonstration of cortical projections to subcortical levels. Some association fibers have long been identified anatomically, and many more have now been observed with the use of the physiological-neuronographic technique (217). By anatomical studies, the whole precentral gyrus has been found to receive association fibers from the homolateral areas 3, 1, 2, and 5 of the parietal lobe, and from 21 and 22 of the temporal lobe (371). Area 4 receives fibers from areas 7, 8, 9, and 10. The upper part of area 6 receives fibers from area 4, and the lower part of area 6, from area 10. Commissural fibers from contralateral cortical areas come to each of the divisions of the precentral gyrus from areas 4, 6, 1, 5, and 7.

Certain of these have been verified, and others demonstrated anew, by physiological neuronography in macaques and chimpanzees (85, 505). Area 4, considered as a whole, sends ipsilateral association axons to areas 1, 5, and 7, to the secondary motor area, and to part of the inferior parietal lobule, area 39. Area 4*s* projects to area 32. Area 4 receives axons from areas 1, 5, 7, 39, 40, and 6, and from the secondary motor area (see later). Area 6 sends fibers to areas 4, 1, and 39; it receives axons from areas 5, 40, 41, 42, and 46. Areas 44 and 8 are considered in Chap. 18.

Commissural fibers are sent from the posterior part of area 4 to the symmetrical contralateral region. Commissural fibers are received by the posterior part of 4 also from areas 5 and 6. Area 6 sends commissural fibers to contralateral areas 6, posterior 4, 1, 5, and 39; it receives fibers from the contralateral 6 only (505).

Thalamocortical Fibers to the Precentral Gyrus

Specific thalamocortical fibers reach areas 4 and 6, especially, from the lateral and anterior ventral nuclei of the thalamus (276, 797). These fibers to 4 and 6 probably arise from different parts of the nuclei. Further, it is likely that a somatotopic organization exists in these connections in man, as has been demonstrated in the macaque and chimpanzee (797). The "face" area of the precentral gyrus, for example, receives axons from the more medial neurons in the lateral ventral nucleus; "arm" and "leg" areas, from successively more laterally placed neurons. Whether or not area 44 receives specific thalamocortical fibers is not known; area 8 receives fibers from the dorsomedial and submedius nuclei.

Electrical Stimulation of Movement from the Human Cortex

Several neurosurgeons have made reports of stimulations of the human cerebral mantle, usually in association with efforts to delimit an irritable cerebral focus in patients who suffer from convulsive disorders. Among these have been Foerster, Penfield and his co-workers, and Scarff (255, 615, 616, 706). The conditions existing during stimulations have varied with the experimental investigators and the neurosurgeon. Faradic, direct, and galvanic currents have been used, as well as that delivered by the Thyratron, and a 60-c.p.s. sine-wave current. Conscious patients as well as patients under general anesthesia have been used. For the most part, the animals have been anesthetized, though several important researches have been carried out on unanesthetized animals with the use of implanted, fixed electrodes (144, 146).

In man, the stimulations have resulted in the construction of several maps which show the motor representation of body parts, as mentioned previously (Figs. 239, 242). Close observation of these maps will reveal differences, and these differences may be the result not only of varying conditions of stimulation, but also of individual characteristics of representation. Foerster stimulated many cortical areas and produced various types of movement. The loci from which he evoked movement are found chiefly in his areas 4, 6*aa*, 6*aβ*, 6*b*, 3, 1, 2, 5*a*, 5*b*, 7, 8*aβδ*, and 22. Stimuli of lesser intensity were more successful in evoking movement from area 4 than from the others, some of which required stimuli of great intensity (252, 255). Obviously, the majority of these areas are not in the precentral gyrus, but for sake of comparison it is best to describe the results of their stimulation here.

The movements produced varied in character. They involved contractions of individual muscles of the limbs, or of single groups of limb muscles, movements which have frequently

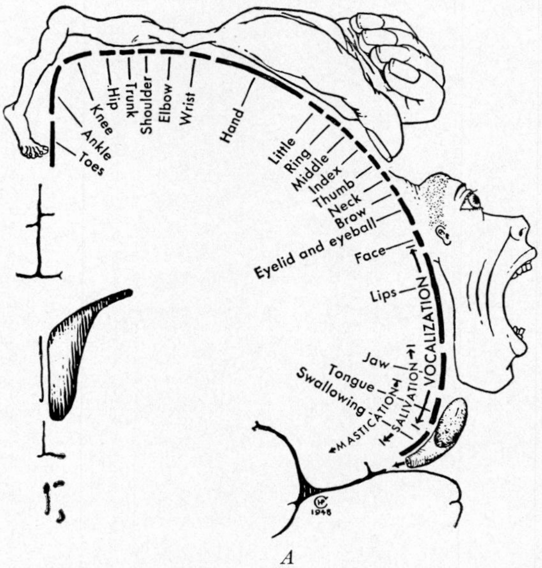

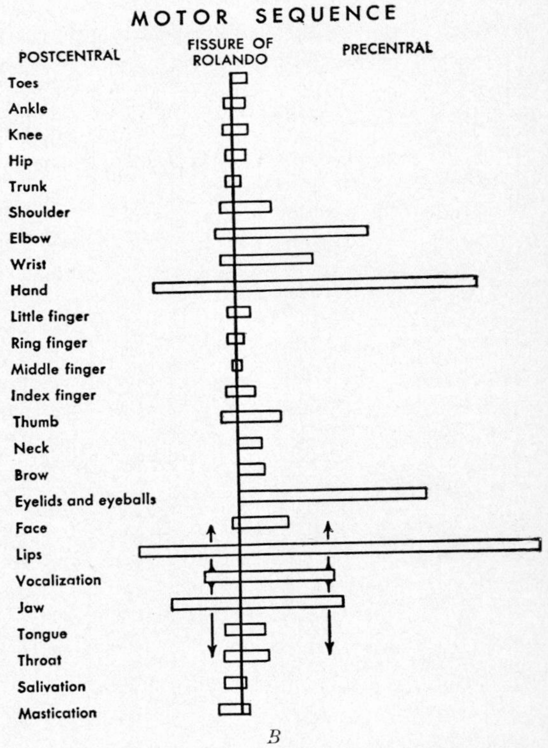

Fig. 242. The representation of motor activity in the central region of the human cerebral cortex. *A*, motor homunculus to diagram representation; *B*, the extension of the motor representation into the postcentral gyrus. (*Both after Penfield and Rasmussen, "The Cerebral Cortex of Man," The Macmillan Company.*)

been referred to as "isolated" or "discrete." More widespread contractions resulted in so-called mass movements, adversive movements in which head, eyes, and limbs were turned to a side, and synergic movements of flexor or extensor patterns in a limb. Since Foerster used an areal map slightly different from that of Brodmann and from that proposed recently by Von Bonin, it is necessary to note the correlations of the areas stimulated. In the following discussion the cytoarchitectural area number used by Foerster will be given first, followed by the Bonin or Brodmann number in parentheses.

Stimulation over area 4 (4γ Bonin) gave isolated movement; stimulations over area 6*aa* (4*a*), 3, 1, and 2 gave isolated movements when area 4 and its pyramidal projection were intact, and "mass" movements when 4 was removed. Areas 6$a\beta$ (6), 5*a* and 5*b* (5 and 7), and 22 gave mass movements characterized by rotation of head, eyes, and trunk to the opposite side, and synergic patterns of flexion or of extension of the contralateral arm and leg. These were obtained whether or not area 4 was intact, and occasionally ipsilateral as well as contralateral movements were obtained from area 5. Foerster is the only neurosurgeon to have elicited such movements from area 6, and he used quite strong stimuli. Area 7 sometimes gave turning of the head and eyes to the opposite side (area 7 here is area 39 in Brodmann's plan) and areas 8$a\beta\delta$ (8) and 19 gave contralateral turning of the eyes alone. Stimulation over area 6*b* (area 44) by Foerster produced rhythmic coordinated movements of musculature innervated by the fifth, seventh, ninth, tenth, and twelfth cranial nerves.

The mass movements elicitable electrically in man consisted either of flexor or extensor synergies of the limbs and turning of the eyes, head, and trunk to the contralateral side. Most commonly the arm was raised and abducted, the forearm was flexed, the hand was pronated, and the fist was opened or closed, those actions composing a flexor synergy. Less frequently the extensor synergy appeared, but with it the hand was also usually pronated. The leg usually was simultaneously flexed at the hip and knee, with dorsal flexion at the foot and toes, thus producing a flexor synergy; or an extensor synergy might occur in which there was extension of the hip and knee, with plantar flexion of the foot. The turnings of the eyes, head, and trunk to one side were called **adversive** movements by Foerster.

Though the anatomical connections of all these areas above are not known, it is believed that movement elicitable from all except area 4 (4γ) depends on extrapyramidal connections. Foerster designated those areas from which impulses for mass movements go spinalward by extrapyramidal paths as **extrapyramidal** areas and included in this category 6*aa* (4*a*), 1, 3, 2, 5 (Brodmann's 5 and 7), 7 (Brodmann's 39), 6$a\beta$ (6), 8, 19, and 22; area 4 (4γ) he designated **pyramidal** and in it alone were discrete movements represented for him (Fig. 237).

Movement of individual muscles and of small related groups was obtained from area 4 (Fig. 239). Foerster's stimulations also showed that certain foci of the precentral gyrus responded with bilateral movements even with the lowest stimulating current. This was particularly true of larynx and palate muscles (area 44), and to a certain extent it was true for the muscles moving the mandible. Bilateral proximal muscle groups in general responded to unilateral stimulation with small stimuli more often. Distal groups and especially the fingers very infrequently responded bilaterally to a stimulus, but the requisite stimulus was always strong. The studies also showed overlapping of representation of movements of small muscle groups, certain groups being most easily stimulated from a single spot, but other related groups being also stimulated from the same focus.

Penfield and his colleagues have not been able to reproduce all the movement patterns defined by Foerster, though they have found evidence of topographical representation of body parts (613, 616, 622). They have elicited movements almost exclusively from the precentral and postcentral gyri, and the majority of them have been evoked from the precentral gyrus and especially from area 4 (4γ) (Fig. 242). Similar current strengths were successful over precentral and postcentral gyri. They have not found evidence for all Foerster's extrapyramidal areas, nor have they found significant ipsilateral contractions of the extremities, except in one patient.

Variation in the relative size of the motor "face," "arm," and "leg" areas has been found.

In some individuals the "face" area was found to extend to within 4 cm. of the longitudinal fissure, and in others it was very small and confined to the most inferior strip of precentral gyrus. The "leg" area was found completely in the medial hemispheric surface in some cases, and in others it extended several centimeters on the lateral surface. Certain minor differences in the sequence of representation have been brought out (Fig. 242).

Vocalization has been elicited throughout the "face" area of both hemispheres. Mastication, in contrast to other cranial muscle movements, was found to have chiefly a postcentral-gyrus location, and in this gyrus it was found in the sensory tongue area and below. Salivation was also found in this postcentral location. Gastrointestinal motility and sensation are probably represented in the insula. Eyeball movements were evoked frequently from the precentral gyrus and were found between loci for face and thumb movements. Close association of the representation cortically of flexors and extensors of the limb joints seems to be the usual case in man, in contrast to widely separate representation as described in animals.

Simultaneous movements of all fingers and toes were most often elicited from "arm" and "leg" areas, respectively. Flexion or extension of the thumb or of the great toe and of individual fingers or toes was less frequently obtained. Flexion and extension of the wrist and elbow alone were frequently elicited, as were flexion or extension of the ankle, knee, or hip. Flexion movements were more often obtained than were extensions.

Conjugate deviations of the eye were obtained from loci in the anterior part of the precentral gyrus and also further anteriorly, approaching area 8 ($8\alpha\beta\delta$ for Penfield). Stimulation of these loci most often resulted in turning of the eyes to the opposite side, together with an occasional instance of upward or downward movement. Eyeball movements could also be elicited from the cortical tissue immediately anterior to the central fissure, and these were as often deviations toward the same side as to the opposite. Upward rotation and convergence were also occasionally elicited here.

Closure of the lids was most often noted, and this was usually bilateral, though it was remarked that the patients most often held their eyes open while the procedure was being carried out. This may have accounted for the failure to produce opening of the lids. Lip movements were most common in the facial field, though in some patients other facial movements were obtained. These were usually contralateral movements, though occasionally bilateral movements were seen. Opening of the jaw, retraction or protraction of the tongue, swallowing or gagging, and masticatory movements were also elicited. These last were frequently associated with sensation in the tongue, roof of the mouth, or throat. Bilateral activation of jaw, larynx, pharynx, and palatal movements was the rule. Turning of the head (face) toward the opposite side was nearly always associated with conjugate deviation of the eyes to the opposite side, and the loci from which the head rotation was elicited were in the anterior half of the precentral gyrus or in the caudal portion of the middle and inferior frontal gyri, in contrast to the localization of other neck movements in cortex immediately anterior to the central fissure.

Indications that a **secondary** motor area is present in man have come from Penfield's stimulation studies (622) (Fig. 243*B*). This area is located at the foot of the precentral gyrus along the upper border of the fissure of Sylvius. Representation of both ipsilateral and contralateral upper and lower limbs seems present here, but representation of cranial structures has not been found. Stimulation has evoked movement, desire for movement, and inability to perform movement. Penfield also describes a **supplementary** motor area located on the medial hemispheric surface in a region that appears to be area 6 (Fig. 243*A*). Extended on the lateral hemispheric surface, it would perhaps correspond to the region from which Foerster elicited turning movements of head and eyes and flexion or extension synergies of the limbs, the so-called adversive movements. From this medially placed supplementary area Penfield elicited a raising of the opposite arm and a turning of the head and eyes as though the patient were looking at the outstretched hand. Pupillary change (dilation usually), acceleration of heart rate, and vocalization or arrest of speech have also been elicited here. It would appear that this brain region has both somatic and visceral functions and that the somatic control over the skeletal muscles, at least, is concerned chiefly with postural activity.

An interesting finding that demonstrates variation of response with variation of stimulus frequency has been mentioned briefly by McCulloch (503). According to him Bailey has found that over a certain part of the "face" area impulses at a frequency of 12 per sec. regularly evoked contraction of the facial muscles. With impulses at a rate of 10 per sec., this same focus elicited movements of the tongue only. It was suggested that subcortical filters were important in the differentiation.

Subjective sensations of numbness, tingling, and electricity were elicited by stimulating the precentral gyrus, and the topographical localization here was similar to that found postcentrally (see Chap. 19). By stimulating that part of the human precentral gyrus presumed to be 4*s*, Bucy has been able to inhibit the resistance to passive manipulation of the contralateral extremity. He was able to abolish the after-discharge in the contralateral upper extremity which was produced by stimulating the "arm" area of area 4γ with a stimulus of greater than threshold intensity (287). It will be seen in the following discussion that this dual control of muscular activity, contraction and relaxation, demonstrated in the precentral gyrus of man, has been observed many times in animals.

Stimulation and Ablation of the Precentral Gyrus in the Monkey

Analysis of the results of stimulation of the precentral gyrus of the macaque and the chimpanzee indicates that the organization of the human motor mechanisms is basically different from that of those primates or, perhaps better, that the studies on humans are quite incomplete. In spite of the many experimental investigations in the monkey, especially, there is wide divergence of views as to the fundamental plan of cortical representation and action (140, 208, 808). It has been found, for example, that a discrete somatotopic localization of muscles and of their movement can be predicted for those animals when liminal stimuli are used in anesthetized animals. Larger "leg," "arm," and "face" areas have been partitioned into limb and face parts, and the experimental work in the "leg" area seems more advanced. The representation in the pre-

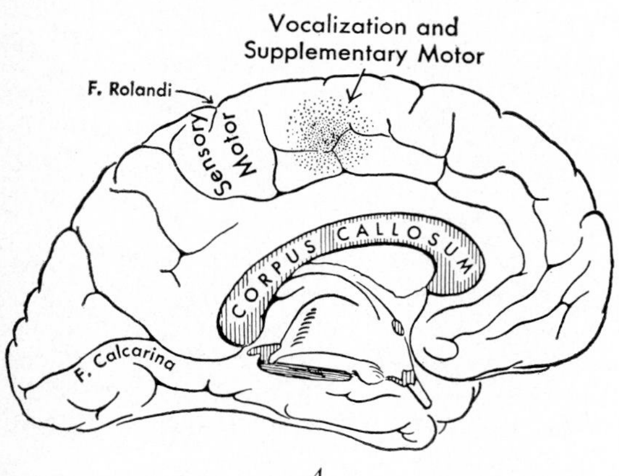

A

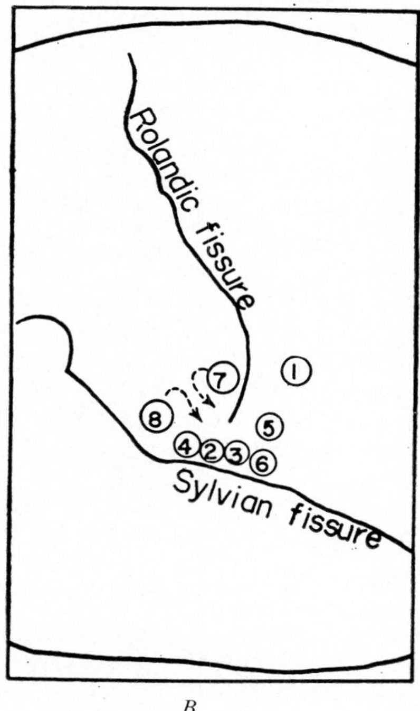

B

Fig. 243. Supplementary and secondary motor areas in the human cerebral cortex. *A*, vocalization and supplementary motor area on the medial surface. *B*, the secondary motor area in the central opercular region. Stimulation at 1 produced movement of the contralateral hand; at 2, desire to move contralateral hand; at 3, movement of contralateral hand and foot; at 4, desire to move ipsilateral hand; at 5, desire to move and paralysis in contralateral hand; at 6, desire to move and paralysis in contralateral foot. *Subcortical* stimulation at 7 produced movement of ipsilateral toe; at 8, movement of contralateral hand. (*After Penfield and Rasmussen, "The Cerebral Cortex of Man," The Macmillan Company.*)

central "leg" area duplicates that analyzed for the spinal cord motor mechanisms (371). Extensors and abductors were found to have a representation on the medial hemispheric surface; flexors and adductors, on the dorsolateral surface (854). Further, intrinsic hand muscles were found to be represented not only in a hand area but also in various loci of the area for the trunk and shoulder. Close correlations have been found to exist in the representation of contracting muscles in the precentral gyrus with the dermatomic pattern of representation of skin sensibility in the postcentral gyri. A secondary motor area has been found in the precentral gyrus of the monkey (765). This area is located in the frontal opercular and insular tissue. The second somatic sensory area is just posterior (see Chap. 19). The representation of body parts in this second motor area is in the reverse order from that established for the so-called primary somatic motor area occupying the major part of the precentral gyrus. When this secondary area is stimulated in the absence of the first, contralateral movements of the distal parts of the limbs, especially, were obtained. This fact and other electrical and anatomical studies have indicated that in the monkey, at least, this second motor area contributes fibers to the pyramidal tract.

An analysis of cortical representation of the muscles acting about the ankle joint by Chang, Ruch, and Ward has indicated that each of the eight muscles has its own area of cortical representation. A discrete cortical focus was found for each muscle from which that muscle only could be selectively stimulated. Each muscle had only a single optimum focus, and no two muscles were activated with equal ease from the one focus. Points from which flexor muscles could be activated were less active than extensor points, and they responded only to stimuli near threshold strength. Stronger stimuli applied to a flexor point evoked extension, perhaps through an inhibition of flexor neurons by the surrounding extensor points which were activated. This would represent reciprocal innervation, it was emphasized. Threshold stimulation of cortical points of area 4 in the chimpanzee has also resulted in the elicitation of movement in single muscles (135).

Stronger stimuli applied to the precentral cortical surface may yield different results. In the rabbit, cat, and macaque, Murphy and Gellhorn have used strong stimuli over a stimulation period of 10 sec. and have found evidence of multiple cortical foci from which a certain movement could be evoked. The cortical areas from which movements of various joints of the leg, for example, were obtained were coextensive in the "leg" area, and in fact, arm and leg movements were elicited from adjacent foci. The multiplicity of representation of a movement was less in the monkey than in the other animals, however.

By varying the intensity and the duration of stimulations over a single point of the motor cortex of cats and monkeys, Bosma and Gellhorn have been able to evoke varied muscular responses (90). The responses elicited with weak stimuli were relaxation of flexor and extensor muscles, if tonic activity existed in the muscles prior to stimulation; with stronger stimulation, reciprocal innervation of agonist and antagonist muscles; and with stronger stimuli, coinnervation of flexor and extensor muscles. With adequate stimuli of long duration, reciprocal innervation appeared early in the stimulation period; coinnervation, later.

The character of the response from the precentral gyrus depends on the activity of other neural levels. In researches on the monkey, Gellhorn studied the effect of the position of a joint just before cortical stimulation on the reactions produced in the muscles which move the joint (290). He observed the movement induced by cortical stimulation and also recorded the activity in the muscles in an electromyogram. It was found that when the length of a muscle was increased by stretch the amplitude of its cortically induced electromyogram was increased. It was believed that the increasing numbers of proprioceptive impulses, induced in the muscles by stretching them, served to facilitate the response. It is to be recalled that the afferent endings in striated muscles are activated by the increase in length of the muscle fibers. It has also been demonstrated that nociceptive stimuli applied peripherally can alter the cortical motor response (291).

It has been known for years that the activity of an area 4 focus may be facilitated by previous stimulation of a corresponding postcentral gyrus focus. It has been reported in recent years that stimulation of other cortical areas, 4*s*, 8, 2, 24, and 19, leads to suppression of the motor response from area 4γ. Although mechanical and electrical stimulation of these areas could induce the suppression of 4γ, strychnine stimulation was most often used in these studies (222, 505). Because of their suppressive effect on the motor response of area 4, these areas have been designated as "suppressor" areas. They will be discussed further in the following chapter. Cortically induced motor responses can be facilitated by simultaneous stimulation of the posterior hypothalamus (576, 587). This hypothalamic facilitation of cortically induced movements was most marked in the ipsilateral motor area but was also noticeable bilaterally. A suppressive effect on pyramidal tract discharge has been produced by stimulation of medial reticular formation in the upper brain stem (571).

It has been mentioned earlier that simultaneous stimulation of the cerebellar cortex and the cerebral motor area may result in a facilitation or inhibition of the cortically induced movement. It will be noted in the next chapter that simultaneous stimulation of basal ganglia and motor cortex will produce motor effects unlike those produced by cerebral cortex stimulation alone.

Stimulation of the cerebral cortex of unanesthetized monkeys and cats has been carried out by several investigators (144, 146). A method was devised whereby electrodes could be implanted in the skull in such a fashion that they would remain fixed and repeated stimulations could be carried out. The response evoked from a fixed point depended to a great extent on the existing pattern of activity in the nervous system. For example, in the cat flexion would be produced in a limb that was extended at the time of the stimulus, and extension in a flexed limb, from a single point. The threshold for the production of movement varied insignificantly over the cortical area between area 8 and the postcentral gyrus, inclusively, and this was considered further proof for a wide origin of corticospinal fibers. It was impossible to distinguish the responses obtained from area 4 from those induced from area 6, and no predominance was found in the frequency of response of proximal or distal parts of the limb. After a weaker stimulus over a point had induced a response of one group of muscles, a stronger stimulus often produced a stronger movement involving several groups of muscles, and with this larger pattern the previous small group contraction did not appear. With stimuli under the threshold value for motor response, it was possible on several occasions to produce relaxation of the tension existing in the muscles of a limb.

When the anterior part of 4, 4*s*, and the posterior part of area 6 were stimulated in a macaque, with both pyramids sectioned, diagonal movements were elicited from each. These involved simultaneous contraction of one arm and the contralateral leg. Synergic movements of flexors and extensors were also elicited from these areas. Stimulation of the anterior part of area 6 resulted in flexor synergies with grasping and conjugate deviation of the eyes, head, and trunk to the opposite side (371). Stimulation of area 6 of the chimpanzee has not produced the adversive movements described as resulting from stimulation of this area in man (369, 371). Rather, movements which resembled the flexor synergies described above were obtained.

Experimental studies of the results of ablations from the precentral gyrus or section of the pyramid, and of stimulation of the precentral gyrus with its corresponding pyramid sectioned, have indicated that this gyrus contains not only pyramidal but extrapyramidal mechanisms. In ablation studies it is well to remember that the signs arising as a result of the removal of cortical tissue are of two types, signs of *deficit,* and signs of *release.* The latter arise through activity of some other cortical or subcortical mechanism deprived of the control normally exerted upon it by the tissue removed. Examples of signs of release in motor-system disturbances are increased deep reflexes, clonus, and increased muscle tone in the opposite limbs, especially in the antigravity muscles. This triad of signs is known clinically as **spasticity.** In addition, with forceful movements of the normal limbs, there occur in the paralyzed limbs slight but definite movements, somewhat mirroring those of the normal limbs. These are referred to as associated movements. Signs of deficit are the losses of voluntary movement in individual muscles or muscle groups as well as difficulty in the initiation and integration of the movements of such groups into various patterns. Atrophy of certain contralateral muscles also occurs. Signs of deficit and signs of release are usually seen together in man in the condition called spastic hemiplegia following a "stroke," such a disorder resulting from a disturbance in the blood supply to the precentral cortex or its projections. That both groups of signs do not result from damage to the pyramidal motor fibers alone has been shown quite nicely in monkeys.

With various partial ablations of the precentral gyrus of monkeys, Hines has demonstrated a difference of activity in the different areal parts (368). She has found that lesions involving the posterior portion of area 4 (corresponding to 4γ in man) are followed by effects different from those resulting from a lesion of the anterior portion. She has also shown that results of a lesion of area 4, partial or complete, differ from those following an area 6 lesion. In the anterior part of area 4 she has described a strip of tissue, the "strip" area, cytoarchitecturally area 4, but showing fewer large pyramidal and Betz cells in the internal pyramidal layer, V. The removal of this "strip" led to temporary and rapidly clearing loss of voluntary isolated movements, but also produced signs of release which were permanent (especially increased tone in antigravity muscle groups). This "strip" area corresponds to 4*s* in man (Fig. 236*A*).

When that part of area 4 *posterior* to the "strip" area was removed there was loss of voluntary isolated movement, with either fleeting or late minimal spasticity. In area 6 ablations Hines found no paralysis, and no signs of release, but a temporary grasp reflex was found. This latter consisted of a rapid flexor movement of the forearm and hand muscles in response to the slightest stimulus in the palm.

Ablations from area 6 and the "strip" area combined resulted in increase in muscle tone in protagonists as well as in antagonists, rather than merely in antigravity muscles as in "strip" area ablations; clonus and brisk deep reflexes were also present. The results of such ablations indicate that the anterior part of area 4 in the macaque contains projection systems which inhibit tonic extension, and area 6, those which inhibit the grasp. Ablations of the "strip" area alone demonstrate that in the anterior part of area 4 of the monkey at least two projections exist, one which initiates isolated discrete movements, the other which inhibits the appearance of hypertonus, clonus, and brisk irradiating deep reflexes. Ablations of the posterior part of area 4 indicate that chiefly a projection arises there which initiates isolated discrete movements in contralateral muscles or small-muscle groups, and also initiates simultaneous cooperation of other synergic muscles with the prime contractor when complex or skilled performance is desired.

A very interesting corollary of these experiments is the work of Tower and Hines involving sectioning of the pyramid in the medulla with subsequent electrical stimulation of the motor cortex of the same side (783). In lesions of the pyramids in animals, corticospinal (pyramidal) fibers are interrupted. The result of such a lesion has been a deficit of voluntary isolated movement without the development of spasticity and the usual signs of release (124, 780, 781). On the contrary the muscle tone appeared diminished. Gross voluntary movements of the limbs were present, however, the limb moving more as a unit. When the motor cortex was stimulated in an animal with the ipsilateral pyramid cut, Tower and Hines observed an inhibition of any movement previously present in the animal's contralateral limbs. If a sufficiently strong current was used, mass movements were elicited. If the total motor cortex was subsequently removed, with the ipsilateral pyramid also cut, the usual signs of release were superimposed on the pyramid movement deficit. These experiments again indicate the existence in area 4 of the monkey of two components of a motor system, initiative and suppressor, pyramidal and extrapyramidal.

To Tower, who has studied in detail the results of pyramid section in monkey and chimpanzee, the pyramidal system shows both spatial and temporal organization (781, 782). The spatial organization is underlined by the discrete somatotopic representation of muscular contraction in the cortical areas from which many pyramidal fibers spring, and the ability of pyramidal impulses to initiate contraction in any muscle or in any groups of muscles. The temporal organization shows two phases, one continuous, the other intermittent. The former continuous phase is represented by a tonic function fully operative during the entire waking state and diminishing during sleep. This tonic function is considered by Tower to be a contribution to the central excitatory state of the segmental motor mechanism, and with such contribution a facilitation is given to whatever action is taking place at that segmental level by virtue of incoming segmental or other suprasegmental impulses. The resultant effect is a reinforcement of muscle tone and a maintenance of superficial and deep reflexes at a low threshold. It is to be recalled that the corticospinal tract is listed as a powerful facilitating mechanism in the classification of motor systems as devised by Magoun.

The phasic function of the corticospinal tract is that which initiates contractions in individual muscles or in cooperating groups of muscles in an extremity in the performance of some complex, skilled act. The tonic mechanism provides an ever-ready and efficient foundation for rapid and forceful contractions which the phasic mechanism activates. Though the more striking activity of the phasic mechanism is one of excitation of agonists and synergists, a relaxation or inhibition of antagonists in the reciprocal innervations is also its function.

In numerous studies involving stimulation of the precentral gyrus of the infant, young adult, and adult monkeys, Hines and Boynton have observed the development of motor functions in the cortex, and the part played in motor mechanisms by the pyramidal and extrapyramidal components, resident in the precentral gyrus (373). The pyramidal component again has been found to play an important part in the maintenance of normal muscle tone and is the sole initiator of isolated (individual) voluntary movement of discrete parts. The extrapyramidal system initiates mass movements and also inhibits movement and tonic states. It will be seen in the next section that this system also controls postural and associative movements. The initiation of flexor movement patterns and the inhibition of tonic flexor states are concentrated in area 6; the initiation of diagonal movements, the movement pattern of quadrupeds, and the inhibition of tonic extensor states are concentrated posteriorly to area 6 in the anterior border of area 4, the "strip" area. In their animal experiments Tower has ascribed the reduction of movement of small-muscle groups to interruption of the pyramidal corticospinal tract, and Hines has allocated the signs of release to interruption of the extrapyramidal tracts which are closely associated in the cortical space.

Inhibitory and excitatory activity thus reside in area 4 of the monkey. The pathways over which these influences are exerted take different courses in their descent to the spinal cord, in which they terminate about anterior column cells, directly or after synapse about an intercalary neuron. Those fibers over which travel impulses for voluntary movement of individual muscles or small muscle groups pass by way of the pyramid; those fibers through which inhibitory or suppressor activity is exerted and mass postural movements initiated do not pass by way of the pyramids and are called extrapyramidal. That the extrapyramidal fibers subserve similar activity is likely in man, though not as yet definitely proved.

Ablation of Precentral Motor Areas in Man

Some difficulty arises in attempts to apply directly information derived from animal experiments to the motor mechanisms in man. Destructive lesions of the nervous tissue in man are very infrequently distinct and isolated with regard to the nucleus or pathway they damage. Much information has been gained through surgical ablation of parts of area 4 or area 6 or both, but the demarcation of 4 into several functional parts as in monkeys has not as yet been conclusively shown. Discrete removal of area 4*s* in man, for example, is unlikely. The results of removal of parts or all of the precentral gyrus has been described by Foerster, Bucy, and Walshe among others (117, 257, 806).

In the hands of Foerster small destructive lesions within the precentral gyrus involving only 4 (4γ) or both it and 6*aa* (4*a*) resulted in paralysis limited ultimately to distinct parts of the body. In addition to a deficit of movement in such cases there appeared, after varying periods of time, certain of the signs of release. If, for example, the "leg" area of the precentral convolution were removed, there were immediate sequelae, some of which were altered with the passage of time. Immediately after the ablation all voluntary and reflex movement of the contralateral lower limb was lost, and it was hypotonic—this last itself an indication of suppression of, or loss of facilitation of, the segmental stretch reflexes. Deep reflexes at knee and ankle were lost, and no plantar response was obtained at first. Within 5 to 10 hr., however, stimulation of the plantar surface of the foot resulted in an extension of the great toe and a fanning movement of the small ones, the Babinski phenomenon. Deep reflexes gradually returned in 8 to 10 days and became increased in briskness and excursion; muscle tone became increased, and the paralysis of the leg was characterized as "spastic." Such a result appeared in man, according to Foerster, whether the ablation involved area 4 (4γ) or areas 4 and 6*aa* (4*a*) combined.

The initial effect of such a lesion of the "leg" area of the precentral gyrus is loss of isolated movements of the toes, of the foot, of the leg, and of the thigh. Later, some activity of the leg returns and it is initiated by other cortical areas, the extrapyramidal areas, according to Foerster. Such activity consists of compound simultaneous movements of all segments of the leg, flexor, and extensor synergies, and such movements represent the only voluntary movements the patient is able to perform for a time. These are the same types of movement that are elicited electrically from the extrapyramidal areas, as seen earlier. Later, by a further process of compensation, the ability to innervate single muscle groups is restored, and it is possible to modify somewhat the stereotyped extrapyramidal synergies. For example, it is then possible for the patient to raise the thigh without associated movements of the leg and foot taking place. Isolated movements of the toes never return, however. Lesions of the arm area are similar in their results, but the compensation practically never reaches a point where movements of single fingers are possible. It is generally true that those muscles showing the greatest deficit of movement are the ones showing the greatest increase in tone. The more extensive the destructive lesion, the more severe the degree of paralysis and the less chance there is for restitution of function by compensation. The larger a lesion is which includes also the precentral gyrus, the more the deficit will be with regard to movements which are least specialized and least voluntary. The ultimate effect of lesions limited to area 4γ or to areas 4 and 6*aa* (4*a*) in man, as determined by Foerster, is that small isolated distal muscle groups suffer most in the deprivation of movement.

Destructive lesions of 6*aβ* (6), 22, 7 (Brodmann's 39), 8, and 19 show little or no motor effect; with those of area 5 (Brodmann's 5 and 7), some ataxia is most notable. There have been few if any ablations in man limited to areas 6*aa* (4*a*) and 6*aβ* (6 of Von Bonin), and most of the patients in whom these have been done were suffering varying amounts of paralysis before operation. Nearly always area 4γ has also been damaged in such procedures. The nearest approach to such an ablation is that done originally by Bucy for the relief of athetoid movements, and this patient had some damage to 4γ (119). Such movements have been diminished after ablations of 6*aa* (4*a*) and 6*aβ* (6), and a resulting spastic paralysis has been described.

Foerster reported ablations of 6 which would probably include the areas 4*a*, 4*s*, and 6 of Von Bonin. He described difficulty in turning the head and trunk to the opposite side as well as difficulty in stopping movement. The movements of the contralateral limbs were slow, and there was faulty performance of sequential movements as well as of rapidly alternating movements. After ablation of area 6 in man, Kennard, Viets, and Fulton reported spasticity in the contralateral limbs (433). This ablation included the anterior border of area 4, or 4*s*, as these precentral divisions are now made.

Bucy summarizes the results of removal of both areas 4 and 6 from the human as follows (117). A flaccid paralysis ensued at once, but this was temporary in that recovery of movement began in 4 to 16 days. No definite order of recovery has been noted by him, but once started, it progressed most rapidly in the proximal muscles of the limb. The ultimate loss of movement was always greater in the distal muscles of the limbs, and certain of these remained permanently paralyzed. If only the "arm" or "leg" area were removed, the ultimate recovery of that limb was more complete than when both the "arm" and "leg" areas were removed. In the upper limb the flexor muscles showed more recovery; the extensors of the wrists and fingers sometimes never recovered. Supination was more defective than pronation. In the lower limb the extensors showed more recovery than did the flexors. Movements of the toes often remained feeble or absent, and dorsiflexion of the foot was weaker than plantar flexion.

The ultimate result of ablation from the precentral gyrus is never as severe as that impairment observed soon after the removal. In other words, motor performance improves as time goes on. The mechanisms underlying this improvement are not definitely known, but several neural systems are thought to contribute. Foerster suggested that the undamaged opposite precentral gyrus contributed to the improvement through its uncrossed corticospinal fibers. In his stimulations he found evidence of more widespread bilateral cortical representation of movement than have others to date, and he also used stimuli of greater intensity. That some bilateral representation of movement is present is true, however, from the more carefully controlled stimulations of Penfield and his colleagues (120, 616). The undamaged parts of the ipsilateral precentral gyrus and the postcentral gyri also contribute to the improvement that develops after partial precentral gyrus ablation (307). The precentral gyrus contributes not only by means of undamaged corticospinal fibers, but by means of extrapyramidal fibers and connections in subcortical neural levels, especially. It has been demonstrated that the postcentral gyrus is essential to the partial restitution and improvement of motor performance in the monkey, following removal of the precentral gyrus (9). This effect is probably brought about by parietothalamic, parietospinal, and other parietal projections to subcortical centers.

Thus far in this discussion the effect of ablations from the precentral gyrus on movements of the cranial-nerve musculature has not been described, and in fact, few clinical reports are available. It is necessary to observe the effects of disease processes in order to evaluate the precentral control of cranial musculature. Studies of patients who have suffered vascular, neoplastic, or traumatic disorders to the frontal-lobe motor areas or to the motor pathways in internal capsule, basis pedunculi, and lower brain stem have verified differences in the distributions of the corticobulbar systems. With injuries at any of these levels the patients nearly always present evidence of impairment of voluntary movements of the contralateral lower half of the face and contralateral half of the tongue. At least, movements of the contralateral facial muscles about the mouth and contractions of the contralateral genioglossus are more impaired than movements of ocular, masticatory, palatal, pharyngeal, and laryngeal muscles. It is usually the case that some impairment of voluntary movement in all these groups can be demonstrated contralateral to a frontal lobe or capsular lesion, but lower face and tongue movements are more handicapped. A maintained deviation of the eyes toward the side of the lesion and an inability to deviate the two eyes voluntarily in the opposite direction are usually observed for several days after the capsular lesions or frontal disorders which damage cortical tissue in the vicinity of area 8.

Two anatomical interpretations for these discrepancies are possible. The corticobulbar fibers for that part of the facial nucleus innervating the lower face and for that part of the hypoglossal nucleus innervating the genioglossus remain throughout the major part of their course with corticospinal fibers; or those two nuclei receive corticobulbar fibers chiefly from one, the opposite, frontal lobe, whereas all the other cranial-nerve motor nuclei receive corticobulbar fibers from both frontal lobes. In the latter case, unilateral lesions would result in only minimal and transitory impairment of voluntary movements activated through these nuclei. This latter interpretation seems more plausible, even though anatomical proof is at present lacking. It is also possible that both occur.

General Discussion of Results of Stimulation of the Precentral Gyrus

The experimental data previously presented have served to indicate that electrical stimulation of the precentral gyrus, especially its posterior part, in the anesthetized monkey, can produce contraction of single contralateral muscles, that extensors and flexors can be activated individually in reciprocal innervation pattern, or in coinnervation patterns. Frequently, the coinnervations produced have resembled the pattern of movements of which the animal is capable. When the anterior part of the precentral gyrus (areas 6 and 4*s*) is stimulated, after a section of the corresponding medullar pyramid, diagonal movements, flexor and extensor synergies, and conjugate deviations of the eyes, head, and trunk to the opposite side are produced. Furthermore, in animals under light anesthesia as well as in those unanesthetized, it has been possible to demonstrate an inhibition or suppression of existing skeletal muscle tone and movement from the precentral gyrus. This inhibition in the lightly anesthetized animal is topical and limited to certain muscles if the pyramids are intact, and is nontopical after their section. Stimulation of 4*s*, however, relaxes standing tone; that of the posterior part of area 6, flexor tone (371). When the precentral gyrus of an unanesthetized monkey is stimulated with adequate stimuli, movements are evoked from a wide area of cortical tissue between area 8 and the postcentral gyrus, inclusively, and in fact, little difference was noted in the stimulation threshold of points scattered throughout this area. In conscious human patients no difference in threshold was found between stimulations of areas 4 and 6, and the postcentral gyrus was more easily excitable than either (615).

It appears likely that the electrical elicitation of movement from the cortex of the monkey and man is possible over a wide cortical area including area 8, the precentral gyrus, and the postcentral gyrus, and that corticospinal, or pyramidal, fibers arise from areas 8, 6, 4, 3, 1, 2, 5, and 7 in the monkey. Within this cortical tissue, and especially within the confines of area 4, it is possible to demonstrate in anesthetized monkeys that a concentration of a single muscle can be evoked by stimulation of a certain point under optimum conditions of stimulation and with weak stimuli. If stronger stimuli are used, the contraction of the same muscle together with inhibition and relaxation of its antagonist can be produced. Other muscles can be activated by stimulation of immediately adjacent points, and in fact, from the same point, by varying the conditions of the stimulation. It seems to be true that a muscle or its contraction is represented at several cortical foci, but that one cortical focus serves as the prime focus and several other foci serve as secondary points for this muscle. That these secondary points may be dispersed through the cortical tissue has been shown by the use of supraliminal stimuli, and it may be true that the dispersal pattern coincides with the peripheral grouping of muscles into movement patterns, in such fashion that muscles usually acting together about a joint in performance of a complex movement will have neighboring or adjacent cortical foci.

Under certain conditions the response from a cortical point will vary, however. Leyton and Sherrington learned that repetitive stimulation of a single cortical point did not always induce the same response, and they therefore spoke of instability of cortical points (482). They believed that this instability was due to varying physiological states, and they described the various expressions of these transient physiological states as **facilitation, deviation of response,** and **reversal of response.** Facilitation denoted an increase in the amount of movement produced by a second similar stimulus. The initial stimulus had produced, for example, a certain degree of flexion of the elbow, from a point, and a second stimulus of equal strength produced flexion of greater degree and occasionally other movements. Facilitation was also said to occur when a second stimulus evoked movement from a cortical point from which a similar, earlier stimulus had not evoked a response. Deviation of response to repetitive similar stimuli was characterized by the appearance of movement about a joint other than that which was displaced by the initial stimulus. Reversal of response was said to appear when the initial stimulus evoked flexion from the cortical point and a second evoked extension from the same point. Since these fundamental researches were carried out with the use of an inductorium, these characteristics of the cortical mantle have been demonstrated repeatedly and other features have been described with more carefully controlled methods of stimulation (93, 370).

It is to be realized that the stimulating electrode in the anesthetized animal can bring about only fragments of the movement patterns in use by the normal, intact animal and can only indicate the type of movements of which the animal is capable. The electrode cannot replace all the various impulses which in the normal animal play upon the cortical foci. The results of electrical stimulation will vary with the type of stimulus, its strength and duration, as well as the conditions during the stimulation and just prior to it. Varying conditions as well as varying neural activity in other neurons will affect the response. The posture of a limb or the influx of nociceptive stimuli from it will alter the response induced in it by cortical stimulation. The impulses entering the spinal cord may influence internuncial pools or anterior gray neurons, or may travel centrally to express their effect at a higher level, tegmentum, thalamus, or hypothalamus. Further, the response evoked by the cortical electrode can be altered by simultaneous stimulation of cerebellum, basal ganglia, tegmentum, thalamus, or hypothalamus. The response induced through an electrode can be suppressed, or the cortex beneath the electrode can be made nonexcitable by activity of another cortical area, acting through subcortical centers, basal ganglia, thalamus, and brain stem tegmentum. The presence of tonic activity in muscles of a limb, prior to stimulation of a cortical point from which these muscles can be activated, will alter the response.

Cortical response to the stimulating electrode will vary with certain chemical conditions. Anesthesia depresses the excitability of certain cortical areas, and barbiturates, for example, almost completely depress area 6, and only mildly depress area 4. Stimulation in the unanesthetized monkey fails to differentiate areas 4 and 6, and little true differences in their excitability is found in stimulations in conscious humans. Increasing the pH (alkalinity) of the blood, as can be done in hyperventilation, increases the excitability of nerve cells, cortical neurons included. Under satisfactory experimental conditions acetylcholine is an exciter of cortical neurons. It serves as an excitant of the sensorimotor cortex as well as of the suppressor neurons. It increases the sensitivity of receptive areas to afferent stimulation. Eserine has similar effects, while cholinesterase usually depresses the cortical neuronal activity (75, 403, 559).

The stimulating electrode over an area cannot reproduce the normal neural activity within that cortical area or in the other cerebral cortical areas which send association fibers to that area being stimulated. It has not been determined as yet how these association mechanisms contribute to the motor performance, but it seems likely that the majority of the cortical functions as demonstrated by the electrical stimulus depend on the transmission of impulses via fiber systems which pass well into the white matter and into subcortical centers. Some of these cortical functions have been referred to above.

It is probable that the neurons of varying size which contribute to the pyramidal tracts have varying stimulation thresholds, and that the smaller neurons, by far the majority, cannot be activated alone. Under conditions in which they may be activated the response is widespread and develops into large convulsive movement patterns. The extrapyramidal neurons are also activated in such diffuse discharge.

The Influence of the Precentral Gyrus on Certain Reflexes

Other impulses than those for initiating voluntary innervation of individual muscle or small muscle group movement utilize the pyramidal tracts. Pyramidal impulses acting continuously in the waking state maintain certain superficial and the deep reflexes at low threshold, and they maintain a continuous facilitation of segmental tonic mechanisms, as has been indicated. When these pathways are interrupted, therefore, certain alterations of reflex movement patterns and tone patterns ensue.

In the monkey and chimpanzee with a pyramid sectioned, a state of muscular hypotonia exists contralaterally. The threshold of the *deep* reflexes is increased to such an extent that they become slow and difficult to obtain. Once obtained, however, their excursion is full because the response is unopposed by antagonist contraction. The threshold for *superficial* reflexes is increased, often to such an extent that they are completely abolished or reversed. The superficial reflexes usually tested during the course of a neurological examination are the corneal, the superficial abdominal, the cremasteric, and the plantar. The corneal reflex is elicited by stroking the cornea with a wisp of cotton, and it consists of a reflex blinking of the eyelids. The superficial abdominals are elicited by lightly stroking the skin of the abdomen toward the umbilicus, and a reflex contraction of the underlying abdominal muscles of that side occurs. The cremasteric reflex is elicited by stroking lightly the inner surface of the upper thigh, and the cremaster muscle reflexly contracts and elevates the testis. The plantar reflex is elicited by stroking the lateral part of the plantar surface of the foot from the heel to the ball of the foot, and the five toes reflexly plantar-flex. Though each of these superficial reflex patterns has a segmental reflex arc, they depend also on the integrity of the corticospinal tracts. When these are damaged, the corneal reflex (fifth and seventh cranial nerves), the superficial abdominals (seventh to twelfth thoracic spinal segments), and the cremasteric reflexes (first and second lumbar segments) are usually diminished or abolished The plantar-flexor response (fifth lumbar segment to second sacral) is replaced by an extension or, better, a dorsiflexion of the great toe and usually an abduction and dorsiflexion of the other toes. This abnormal plantar response is known as the Babinski phenomenon, and it is occasionally associated with a withdrawal of the foot and leg from the stimulus through a flexion at knee and hip. This pattern of movement is interpreted as a return of a primitive spinal withdrawal reflex of the foot in response to potentially harmful stimuli. With intact pyramidal systems this primitive response is suppressed, and the toes normally flex in response to plantar stimulation as though to dig into or "grasp" the object. Some authors maintain that the extension of the large toe is the pure sign of pyramidal-tract injury, the extension and abduction of the small toes an extrapyramidal component. In some disorders of corticospinal fibers the superficial abdominal reflexes are not lost. They are frequently present in that peculiar degenerative disease, amyotrophic lateral sclerosis, which has a predilection for motor neurons and pathways, and they usually return in cases of injury of the motor pathways in children.

Clinical Disorders of the Precentral Gyrus or of Its Projections

This present discussion of motor function has been concerned chiefly with the role the corticospinal and corticobulbar fibers, the pyramidal systems, play. Actually, it is impossible to separate sharply the contributions pyramidal and extrapyramidal systems make, and even in this "pyramidal" discussion it has been necessary to refer, from time to time, to extrapyramidal activities. The extrapyramidal motor system will be considered in greater detail in the next chapter, but it is necessary to refer to certain general features of its anatomy and its function here, in order to describe more clearly the results of disease process in the precentral gyrus or in its projections.

The extrapyramidal system is dispersed through a number of neural levels or arcs, and these various levels are interconnected. Many cortical areas have been called extrapyramidal by Foerster, since he was able to elicit movements from them, and he suspected that the impulses evoking this movement traveled by fibers not contained in the medullar pyramid. It has been shown repeatedly that many extrapyramidal projections arise from all divisions of the precentral gyrus, and this evidence is anatomical as well as physiological. It has been seen that these extrapyramidal projections, in Foerster's experience, can initiate contractions of large groups of muscles, the movement patterns thus produced being somewhat stereotyped flexor and extensor synergies. That these extrapyramidal projections springing from the anterior portion of area 4 also probably suppress tone in the human has been demonstrated in stimulations several times, and involuntary tremor has also been suppressed (287, 353). Furthermore, when extrapyramidal mechanisms suffer destruction by disease process tonic mechanisms are released, certain other involuntary movements are released, and certain innate associated and emotional movement patterns are lost. In the monkey it has been possible more clearly to observe the contribution each of these motor systems offers to movement performance. In the human definite evidence is lacking, though certain inferences and indications are extant that contributions similar to those in the monkey are offered by pyramidal and extrapyramidal systems.

Disease process in man seldom restricts its damage to single neural systems, and obviously therefore disease limited to the pyramidal system is very rare. Destruction of the precentral gyrus or of its projections in their subcortical and brain stem course is fairly common as a result of vascular disease (Fig. 244). This may involve a bleeding from or a plugging of cerebral vessels as in cerebral

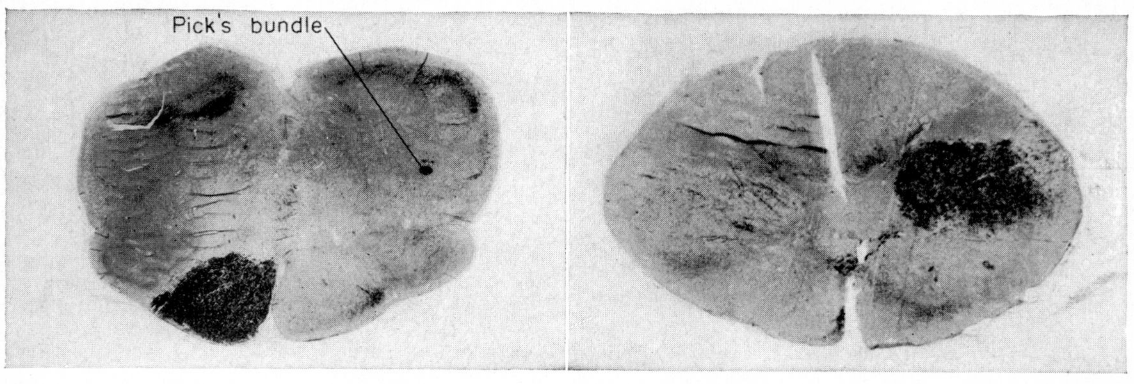

A

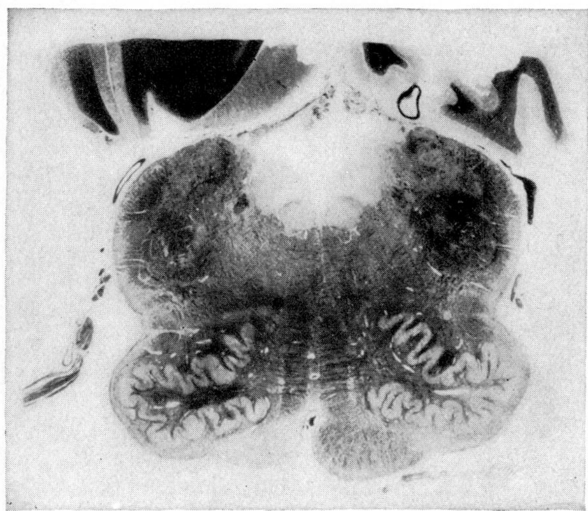

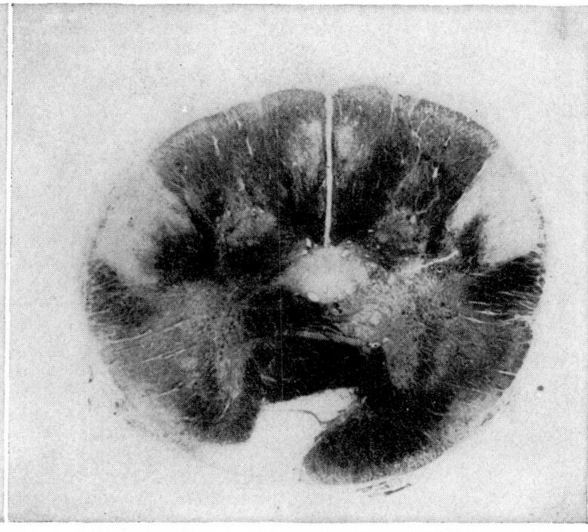

B

FIG. 244. Corticospinal injury caused by cerebrovascular accidents, demonstrated histologically. *A*, the Marchi technique with degenerating corticospinal fibers stained black at medullar (left) and cervical spinal (right) levels. *B*, the Weigert technique, showing a failure to stain degenerated corticospinal fibers at midmedullar (left) and caudal medullar (right) levels. Human. (*Courtesy of Dr. George Margolis.*)

hemorrhage, cerebral thrombosis, and cerebral embolism. Tumors arising primarily in the brain or spreading there secondarily from other organs also may destroy the precentral gyrus or its projections or both. A degenerative disease, amyotrophic lateral sclerosis, has a particular affinity for motor systems. In these various types of disease process, destroying precentral gyrus or its projections in the upper part of their course, both pyramidal and extrapyramidal systems are damaged, with the result that certain motor performance is no longer possible (deficit reaction) or is severely handicapped, and other features of motor performance are exaggerated (release reaction). It has long been the custom to refer to these symptoms of deficit and symptoms of release as a composite **upper-motor-neuron syndrome,** implying as the upper motor neuron those cerebral pyramidal neurons and their axons which compose the corticospinal tracts. It is readily apparent, however, that corticospinal or pyramidal upper motor neurons are not the only ones resident in the precentral gyrus. Other precentral-gyrus neurons send their axons through the subcortical white matter and into the internal capsule in company with the corticospinal fibers, and these axons synapse in various subcortical nuclei. These have been called extrapyramidal. The "upper motor neuron" therefore includes not only pyramidal neurons, but also extrapyramidal, and it is most likely that the fully developed syndrome results from simultaneous damage to both these groups of neurons. It is not fully agreed as yet which of these signs in the upper-motor-neuron syndrome in man appear because of pyramidal damage and which appear because of extrapyramidal damage, but it is likely that these components can be allocated in man as has been clearly proved in the monkey.

The classical **spastic hemiplegia** characterized by the upper-motor neuron syndrome nearly always develops with an injury to the posterior limb of the internal capsule and a consequent damage to the pyramidal and extrapyramidal projection systems traversing it. It will be assumed, for purpose of description, that all corticobulbar and corticospinal fibers in the one internal capsule are injured as well as many extrapyramidal fibers. Some one of the major cerebral arteries or their branches supplying the internal capsule and adjacent basal ganglia is usually involved, its disease resulting in a leakage from or an occlusion of the vessel, and when this hemorrhage or thrombosis or embolism occurs, the patient is said to have had cerebral apoplexy, or to have suffered a "stroke." Clinically, the condition is frequently referred to as a **cerebrovascular accident.** If the patient survives the initial injury, the full complement of the upper-motor-neuron syndrome usually develops in a few days. Immediately after the "accident" the patient may be unconscious, and examination will reveal a complete loss of all movement of the face and limbs of the opposite side, together with complete loss of all reflexes and muscle tone of that side. The eyes and sometimes the head are usually deviated toward the side of the lesion. The patient may be breathing slowly and deeply, and the paralyzed side may be warmer than the other, with some dryness of the skin. Urinary retention may be noted.

Consciousness may be regained within a few minutes or after several hours in favorable cases, and the loss of movement is noticeable through the simple observation that the patient does not move the paralyzed limbs. Within 8 to 10 hr., however, some slight movement may return to shoulder and pelvic girdles, the muscles of the trunk may have some movement, the plantar response may be extensor (Babinski phenomenon), and the bladder may be emptied normally. Within a day or so, in favorable cases, the deep reflexes may begin to return and, in fact, will be found increased as compared to those of the opposite normal side. An increased resistance to passive stretch may be demonstrated in certain muscles, especially in the adductors of the shoulder, flexors of elbow, wrist, and fingers, adductors and extensors of the thigh, knee, and ankle. The superficial abdominal and cremasteric reflexes are absent on the paralyzed side. The palpebral fissure opposite the lesion may be wider than the other, the nasolabial fold is usually flatter than its opposite partner, the corner of the mouth may droop slightly, and a deviation of the jaw and tongue may be demonstrable. The jaw deviates toward the side of the paretic muscles through the action of the normal pterygoids, and the protruded tongue deviates toward the side of the weakness because of the unopposed action of the normal genioglossus. Impairment of movement of the upper face, pharynx, and larynx is usually not so noticeable, presumably because of the more developed bilateral cortical representation of these movements.

As time goes by, the patient usually continues to improve in his mobility, as increase in muscle tone and deep reflexes persists, and he may be able to walk about. Examination will reveal normal movement in the eyes, the width of the palpebral fissure will be normal, and the corneal response may be normal. Volitional facial movement will usually be about normal except for minor weakness about the mouth, and the nasolabial groove may be a little deeper than the normal one. Some exaggeration of facial movement with emotional response may be observed. Jaw movement will usually be normal, and if the tongue deviates at all on protrusion, it will do so very slightly. Other movements such as those of the pharynx, palate, larynx, and neck will usually be quite normal. Movements of the trunk are usually normal.

In the limbs a different state of affairs will usually be found, however. A differential distribution of maximal paralysis will be evident. In the upper limb, the abductors, elevators, and protractors of the upper arm, the extensors of the elbow and fingers, the supinator of the forearm, and the opponens of the thumb will show more paralysis. In the lower limb the flexors of the thigh and knee, the abductors and external rotators of the thigh, and the dorsiflexors of the foot and toes will be more paralyzed. Moreover, the maximal distribution of increased muscle tone will be differential. The upper limb usually shows greater increase of tone in the adductors, retractors, and internal rotators of the upper arm, in the flexors of the elbow, pronators and flexors of the wrist, and flexors of the fingers. In the lower limb the extensors of the hip, the adductors of the thigh, the extensors of the knee, the extensors (plantar flexors) of the ankle, inverters of the foot, and flexors of the toes show greatest increase in muscle tone. The differential increase in muscle tone determines the posture of the individual. The deep reflexes are hyperactive, showing a lowered threshold, an increase in briskness, and a tendency to radiate. The superficial abdominal reflexes are absent; the plantar response continues to be one of extension. The deep reflexes usually tested clinically are the triceps, biceps, brachioradialis, quadriceps, and gastrocnemius. Increased tone in finger and toe flexors is usually demonstrated by passively stretching them and observing the exaggerated contraction (Hoffmann reflex in fingers, Rossolimo in toes). When a sudden stretch is put on the gastrocnemius-soleus complex, these muscles reflexly contract vigorously and so stretch their antagonists, the dorsiflexors of the ankle, which in turn reflexly contract. The contraction of the dorsiflexors stretches the gastrocnemius-soleus, and they again reflexly contract, and so on. These alternating contractions constitute clonus, and this is most easily demonstrated at the wrist and ankle and at the knee. The increased muscle tone, hyperreflexia, and clonus are signs of release and constitute **spasticity,** as mentioned earler. Occasionally, associated movements may be demonstrated in the paretic limbs. When the patient performs quite forceful movement of the normal limbs, for example, as in strong flexion of the fingers in grasping an object, the paretic arm will occasionally demonstrate a feeble flexor synergy.

The voluntary movements present in the affected upper limb are usually in the nature of the flexor synergies described by Foerster. The contractions of individual muscles and small groups of muscles and the individual usage of one or more fingers are impossible. In the lower limb little movement is possible at the ankle and in the toes, but usually flexion movements at the thigh and knee are better. Because of the increased tone in the extensors of hip and knee and the movement possible in them, the patient can use the lower limb as a prop, and as he walks the leg is circumducted in order to compensate for the loss of ankle movement and the increased tone in the plantar flexors of ankle and toes. As the months pass, a patient can regain more motility through a process of compensation by other cortical and subcortical motor mechanisms and a training program in which he learns to use other muscles. He always will show impairment of individual finger movements, however. After a considerable time atrophy will occur in certain of the paretic muscles, and contractures will develop in these and the hypertonic ones, especially if rehabilitation is poor.

The picture just described has arbitrarily been a maximal one with reference to the subcortical capsular fibers of the pyramidal and extrapyramidal motor fibers. The area of destruction will also involve sensory pathways passing between thalamus and parietal lobe with a consequent impairment of sensibility contralateral to the lesion. The nature of the sensory loss is described in Chap. 19. Because of the close association of the fibers from the precentral gyrus in the relatively small space of the internal capsule, small areas of destruction here will result in widespread motor and sensory impairment, and a **hemiplegia** as described above is common, although with damage of one of the small arteries supplying the internal capsule the area of softening is more discrete and paralysis of less wide distribution will sometimes be observed. It is possible to have involvement of corticobulbar fibers alone or in conjunction with a few cervical corticospinal ones, or it is possible to damage corticospinals only and leave relatively unharmed the corticobulbar fibers. A review of the arrangement of the pyramidal fibers in the internal capsule together with the blood supply of the capsule parts will demonstrate why this is so.

With vascular disorder of the precentral gyrus it is again usually the case that the patient will have partial paralysis, or a **monoplegia.** For example, if an anterior cerebral artery is diseased and a softening occurs in the motor areas it supplies, the patient will suffer especially a monoplegia of the contralateral lower limb, since it is the superomedial parts of the precentral gyrus that are damaged. If the cortical portion of the middle cerebral artery is diseased, the inferolateral portion of the precentral gyrus, the "arm" and "face" areas, will be damaged and the paralysis will be limited to arm, face, and tongue. Occasionally ocular movements away from the side of the lesion are impossible. With massive destruction of the precentral gyrus by tumor or trauma, hemiplegia may result. It is usually true that the disorders of muscle tone and deep reflexes are not as noticeable with precentral gyrus destruction, as are the increases in them consequent to capsule destruction. With capsule interruptions, conceivably, more extrapyramidal fibers and certain of the extrapyramidal nuclei, caudate and globus pallidus, may be damaged.

If the corticospinal and corticobulbar fibers are damaged at the level of the basis pedunculi because of tumor or vascular disease in a peduncular artery, a hemiplegia may ensue. The distribution of motor impairment in such instance is similar to that consequent to capsule lesion with the exception that the eyes may not be involved. The corticobulbar fibers to the eye muscle nuclei, it is to be recalled, have left the motor projection systems above the peduncle. It is occasionally true, however, that destruction of the peduncle will involve the emerging third-nerve fibers and the patient will have a paralysis of those ocular muscles in the ipsilateral eye that are supplied by the nerve. These include intrinsic as well as extrinsic muscles, it is to be recalled. Such a paralysis of a cranial-nerve mechanism on one side and a paralysis of limbs of the opposite side constitutes a **crossed paralysis,** as mentioned previously. Such involvements can include face and limbs, jaw and limbs, tongue and limbs, the sites of destruction being at the level of emergence of the cranial nerves involved, facial, trigeminal, and hypoglossal.

The paralysis that ensues with damage of corticospinal mechanisms at spinal-cord levels has been referred to in Chap. 5. It is usually true, with interruptions of the corticospinal tracts at the levels described, that extrapyramidal fibers will be damaged also, though in varying amounts. Fewer extrapyramidal paths may be damaged with basal pontine and basal medullar (pyramid) lesions than with higher interruptions, since the majority of the extrapyramidal fibers have already passed into the tegmentum in pons and medulla. It may be possible that the human medullar pyramid, for example, represents a "pure culture" of pyramidal fibers, as it appears in the monkey. A human case of suspected pure pyramid damage that tends to verify this is under observation. The neurological symptoms in the patient are similar to those described in the monkey after pyramid section. Signs of deficit are more prominent than the signs of release (345).

It is a clinical fact that the so-called upper-motor-neuron syndromes in a series of patients, and consequent to supposed damage at similar levels, are frequently dissimilar in the presence and development of the signs of release, *i.e.,* spasticity. The variation in the clinical pictures probably is a product of the damage of variable amounts of extrapyramidal fibers. Stated another way, the upper-motor-neuron syndrome, which involves pyramidal and extrapyramidal systems—or facilitating and suppressing mechanisms, in the terminology of Magoun—will depend, in its quality and quantity of development, on the relative amounts of damage to facilitating and suppressing mechanisms. This will be referred to again in the next chapter, in which also the nature of movement patterns, stereotyped and postural, will be further analyzed.

In the previous discussion of disorders of the motor cortex and its projections, only those symptoms which follow ablation or destruction of neural tissue have been described. And yet, other symptoms are frequently seen in disease process, especially when the disease process serves as an irritant. Intracranial neoplasms, especially if situated near the cortical surface, are apt to lead to sensitization or facilitation of cortical neurons. Similarly, vascular disease of cerebral vessels may lead to conditions which serve to increase the excitability of cortical neurons. This excitability of cortical neurons can be so widespread and of such intensity that they are brought to discharge and peripheral musculature is activated in a convulsive or epileptic movement.

Small neoplastic nodules, scars, tuberculomata, or gummata located within the precentral gyrus can set off a movement pattern in a muscle or group of muscles in a contralateral limb. Under certain conditions the clonic convulsive movements (alternating excitation of agonist and antagonist) may spread to encompass other muscles, and the order of involvement of other muscles follows a definite pattern. This pattern is reflected by the topographical representation in the motor cortex. A convulsive pattern that begins in the toes may spread to calf, thigh, trunk, shoulder, upper arm, forearm, fingers, and finally face. Such a convulsive pattern following a definite sequence was first believed by Hughlings Jackson to indicate the order of representation of movement in the motor area. Since the order of representation has been amply verified, these patterned convulsions are known as **jacksonian convulsions** or as jacksonian epilepsy. It is of great diagnostic aid to observe the development and spread of such a convulsion in a patient, since in many of them surgery will be of value. The muscles which are first involved in the convulsive movements usually indicate the site of the irritable focus. It is most common perhaps to see jacksonian convulsions begin in the great toe, the thumb, or the index finger or about the mouth, and this fact may be related not only to the larger cortical area allocated to these parts but also to a possible lower threshold of excitation. If the patterned convulsions are limited always to the same muscles of the upper or lower limb, or those of the face, it is customary to refer to them as **focal fits,** or focal epilepsy. The determination of these focal points of cortical irritation may be made by observation of the fits and the surgical approach may be dictated. In fact much of the information gained thus far concerning the function of the human precentral gyrus has been gained through stimulation of the cortex during the operative procedure for removal of an irritant neoplasm or scar. Depending on the site of irritation in the cerebral mantle, focal seizures may be motor, somatic sensory, visual, or auditory in type. In many patients who suffer jacksonian or focal attacks, it is customary to find a postconvulsive paralysis, usually flaccid, of those muscles involved in the convulsion. These paralyses may indicate a profound depression of the motor mechanism for the duration of their existence.

Convulsions of a different type occur occasionally with other systemic disease process or in the absence of known disease, and these do not appear to follow a jacksonian march as outlined above. They frequently involve all the limbs, the head, and face simultaneously, and they are associated with loss of consciousness. The movements may be clonic or they may be tonic, representing widespread coinnervations of agonist and antagonist muscles. Such generalized convulsions, recurring in an individual without known structural disease of the cortex, and in the absence of systemic disease, are classed as **idiopathic grand mal** convulsions. They perhaps reflect widespread cerebral-cortex discharge. Certain other convulsions which begin as deviation of eyes and head to one side, with or without simultaneous extension-adduction of the limbs of the side to which the eyes and head are deviated, have been called **adversive seizures** and have been thought to represent discharge from certain of Foerster's so-called extrapyramidal areas especially from area 8. Adversive seizures may or may not be associated with loss of consciousness. They are also "focal" in that they spread from a definite cortical area (622).

It has been observed that other convulsions are characterized by momentary loss of consciousness alone or together with some minor contraction of a group of muscles. These are called **petit mal;** they have been referred to in the previous discussions of the thalamus and cerebral cortex. In still others, the patient may suffer a period of amnesia and during this carry out some pattern of behavior, a stereotyped movement, a complex, skilled movement, or some inappropriate motor act; these are called **psychomotor seizures.** They are considered focal by some investigators, the point of irritation considered to be located in the tip of the temporal lobe (51, 300, 317).

The mechanisms of neural activity underlying such convulsive patterns are not understood. As described in the previous chapter, certain types of electrocortical activity are associated with the seizures, and the seizures are prone to occur during certain times and under conditions of emotional stress. They frequently come soon after the patient goes to sleep or awakes. They can frequently be induced by hyperventilation, by hydration, or by the use of certain drugs, *e.g.,* Metrazol. As more is learned concerning the mechanisms underlying cortical excitation and inhibition, facilitation and suppression, the neural mechanisms underlying convulsive disorders will gradually be elucidated.

Summary

That the precentral gyrus is the chief agent for the execution of movement has been seen, but that other cerebral areas, notably the postcentral gyrus, contribute to this has also been seen. Within the posterior part of the precentral gyrus, especially, there appears to be an orderly arrangement of neurons, whose axons pass to certain subcortical and spinal neurons. It is possible to activate single muscles by stimulation of certain foci and to construct patterns reflecting the representation of these muscles or of their contraction in the cerebral mantle. It is possible to activate an agonist and at the same time inhibit its antagonist, or it is possible to activate simultaneously agonist and antagonist. It is not possible to reproduce skilled movement patterns, however, and the researchers have only served to demonstrate some of the fragments that go into such a movement. It is probably true that the anterior part of the precentral gyrus normally is the organizer of the complex skilled movement patterns, though stimulation of this region does not elicit skilled movement, but evokes muscular synergies. It has been possible to differentiate two motor mechanisms springing from the precentral gyrus. One, the pyramidal, seems to be responsible for the activation of movement in individual muscles and the inhibition, or graded relaxation, of the antagonists of these muscles, and for the combination of these with contractions of certain other muscles and with inhibition of their antagonists. In such fashion a skilled act is compounded. The other, the extrapyramidal mechanism, activates large groups of muscles at once and suppresses the activity of others in the production of stereotyped movement patterns. The pyramidal facilitates mechanisms underlying muscle tone; the extrapyramidal suppresses them. The pyramidal system maintains deep reflexes at low threshold; the extrapyramidal tends to keep their threshold high.

Any skillful movement of a limb involves activity of many muscles. Usually the distal muscles of the limb, those moving the fingers, especially, serve as the **prime movers** in the performance. As they contract, whether they be flexors or extensors, adductors or abductors, their **antagonists** must relax in orderly fashion and in proper timing. Muscles acting about the wrist must contract to stabilize that joint in order that the muscles moving the fingers will have a sound structure on which to perform. These wrist fixators are **synergists.** Similarly, other muscles about the elbow and shoulder cooperate by fixing or allowing necessary mobility of those joints. In many skilled movements the patterns are more complex and involve also the trunk, lower limbs, and opposite limb. Rapid alterations of posture are required, as well as rapid alterations in contractions and relaxations of those muscles of the acting limb. In order that such complex movement be properly performed, pyramidal and extrapyramidal systems are working together.

The pyramidal system enables the individual to select a prime mover and to coordinate its activity with that of synergists and antagonists. Alternate prime movers may be activated quickly, their contractions slowed or speeded up, and the rapid alterations of activity in synergists and antagonist coordinated. The extrapyramidal system activates and correlates the postural adjustments necessary to the easy and rapid performance of the active limb, and holds tonic mechanisms at the proper level for easy and labile motor adjustments. In fact, the extrapyramidal mechanism may set the stage for action, arrange all the "props," so to speak, and the pyramidal system selects the correct "props" and activates them phasically in orderly fashion for the smooth motor performance. The pyramidal system is a facilitator of the segmental motor mechanisms, probably acting in segmental internuncial pools directly, and it enhances any neural activity that may be taking place at that site as a result of other impulses arriving there from the periphery or from supraspinal (extrapyramidal) levels. The segmental mechanisms underlying muscle tone are thus facilitated by the pyramidal system. Extrapyramidal activity is controlled and adapted for the moment to the motor performance of the pyramidal system, when a group of muscles are to be activated into a simple movement or as part of a skilled movement pattern.

The successful performance of the pyramidal system, however, depends on the proper cooperation by the cerebellum, the thalamus, the basal ganglia, and the reticular neurons of the tegmentum of the brain stem. Impulses arising in the peripheral muscles also play a part in determining the success of the movement. These impulses, passing into spinal internuncial pools as well as into the supraspinal neural levels just listed, may facilitate the excitability of certain neurons and inhibit that of others. Similarly, impulses arising centrally in certain of these neural levels can facilitate the activity of some regions and inhibit that of others. Successful movement will result when the neural integrations result in the proper balance of facilitating and inhibiting mechanisms, these ultimately expressed through spinal internuncial pools on anterior column neurons, the axons of which end in striated muscle. Perhaps certain anterior column neurons initiate phasic muscular contraction, others activate tonic mechanisms continuously (322, 446, 447, 448).

When a patient suffers destruction in a pyramidal system arising in one cerebral cortex, he loses the ability to select the prime movers of the opposite limbs and to correlate their action with that of synergists and antagonists. He is no longer able to carry out discrete movements of the distal parts of his contralateral extremities. Through the activity of undamaged extrapyramidal units and, perhaps, of uncrossed pyramidal units, he may be able to move the extremities as a single unit in crude flexor or extensor synergies, adapting the upper extremity to a crude prehensile pincer and the lower to a substantial prop. The establishment of this latter depends on increased tone in the extensor, or antigravity, muscles, which results from associated damage to certain extrapyramidal systems which normally suppress these tone mechanisms. Pyramidal and extrapyramidal systems are nearly always damaged simultaneously. The losses of movement (paralysis) result from pyramidal injury; the hypertonia, hyperreflexia, and clonus, from extrapyramidal disturbance.

The details of extrapyramidal connections, further appraisal of their function, and a review of other movement disorders resulting from their disease will form the basis of the next chapter.

CHAPTER 17

THE EXTRAPYRAMIDAL MOTOR SYSTEM

THE PYRAMIDAL motor system, discussed in the previous chapter, is present only in mammals. It is relatively slow in its development in a given species in comparison to other motor mechanisms. The earliest movements in a developing animal are integrated and initiated by fiber systems which are not a part of the pyramidal motor system. Brain stem tegmental systems and short-chained associative fiber systems in the spinal cord are involved. When the pyramidal motor system is destroyed in a number of mammals, they can continue to right themselves to a proper position, to stand, and to make progression movements. In the past chapter it has also been noted that much restoration of motor activity is possible in a human with injury to the pyramidal motor system. When it is injured in man, the patient can walk and grasp in crude fashion with the affected limbs. Those motor mechanisms maturing before, taking over in the absence of, or in the presence of injury to, the pyramidal system, as well as cooperating with it normally, constitute the extrapyramidal motor system. This system, spread through all neural levels from cerebral cortex to spinal cord, naturally encompasses a number of cortical areas and many nuclei and their fibers. Nor is all of it necessarily old phylogenetically, since parts of it reach their greatest development in man.

It seems wise to discuss first those large basal telencephalic nuclei belonging to the extrapyramidal motor system, namely, the caudate, putamen, and globus pallidus, and then to describe those diencephalic, mesencephalic, pontine, and medullar nuclei associated with them. After this, the cerebral cortical areas contributing fibers to these subcortical extrapyramidal nuclei will be briefly recalled.

Because of their anatomical position, the caudate, putamen, globus pallidus, and amygdaloid nuclei are sometimes referred to as the **basal ganglia.** The amygdaloid nuclei, within the rostral tip of the temporal lobe, are functionally a part of the olfactory system and will therefore be described elsewhere. The contour of the putamen and globus pallidus together is similar to a lens, and together these two nuclei are frequently referred to as the **lenticular nucleus,** or nuclei. The caudate and putamen are closely associated gray masses ventrally with a few fibers of the anterior limb of the internal capsule and interconnecting fibers separating them. On cut surface here they have a striated appearance because of the intervening fibers. The term **corpus striatum** is therefore occasionally used to denote the caudate and lenticular nucleus. Since the caudate and putamen are newer structures, phylogenetically, than the globus pallidus, and since they also have similar cell structure, they are sometimes called the **neostriatum,** and the globus pallidus, the **paleostriatum.** At other times the globus pallidus alone is referred to simply as the **pallidum** (Figs. 245, 246, 247).

Other nuclei, related to the caudate, putamen, and globus pallidus, functionally, are found in the diencephalon, midbrain, pons, and medulla, but only some of these will be discussed here. These include the subthalamus, red nucleus, substantia nigra, and certain nuclei of the brain tegmentum and reticular formation (Figs. 248, 249). The anterior ventral, lateral ventral, and medial thalamic nuclei, and certain hypothalamic nuclei also have connections with parts of the extrapyramidal system but will be mentioned here only in passing, since they are discussed elsewhere. Similarly, the tectum, the nuclei associated with the posterior commissure, the vestibular

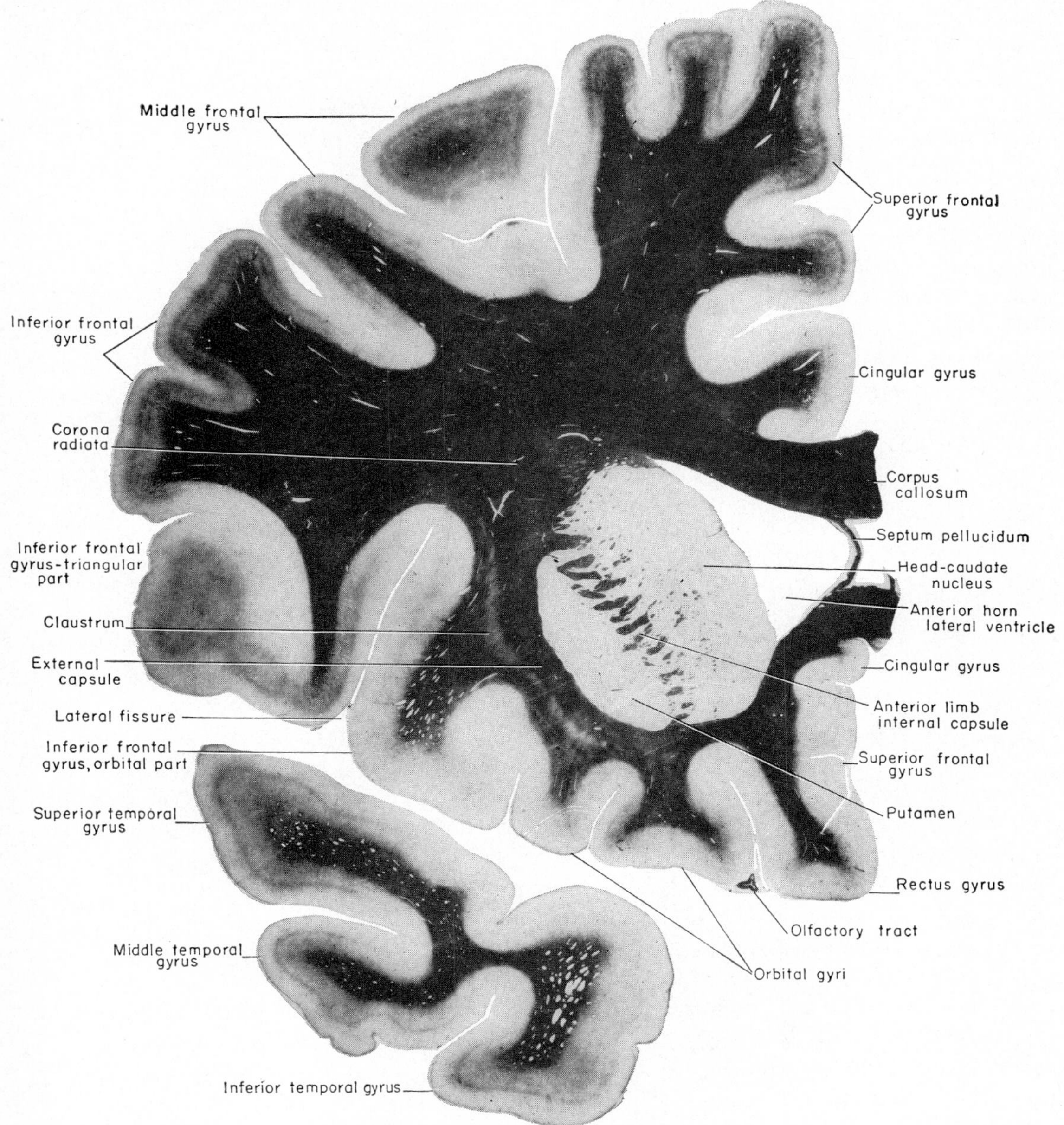

FIG. 245. Frontal section through cerebral hemisphere of human. (*From Jelgersma, "Atlas Anatomicum Cerebri Humani," Amsterdam, Scheltema and Holkema.*)

nuclei, the inferior olivary nuclei, and parts of the cerebellum are related to the extrapyramidal motor system but will not be described in detail here since they have been considered elsewhere. Many areas of the human cerebral cortex have been called extrapyramidal motor areas by Foerster because he has been able to elicit movements of a gross type from them even in the absence of integrity of pyramidal mechanisms. The anatomical verification of their extrapyramidal connections is not yet available for all of these, but physiological

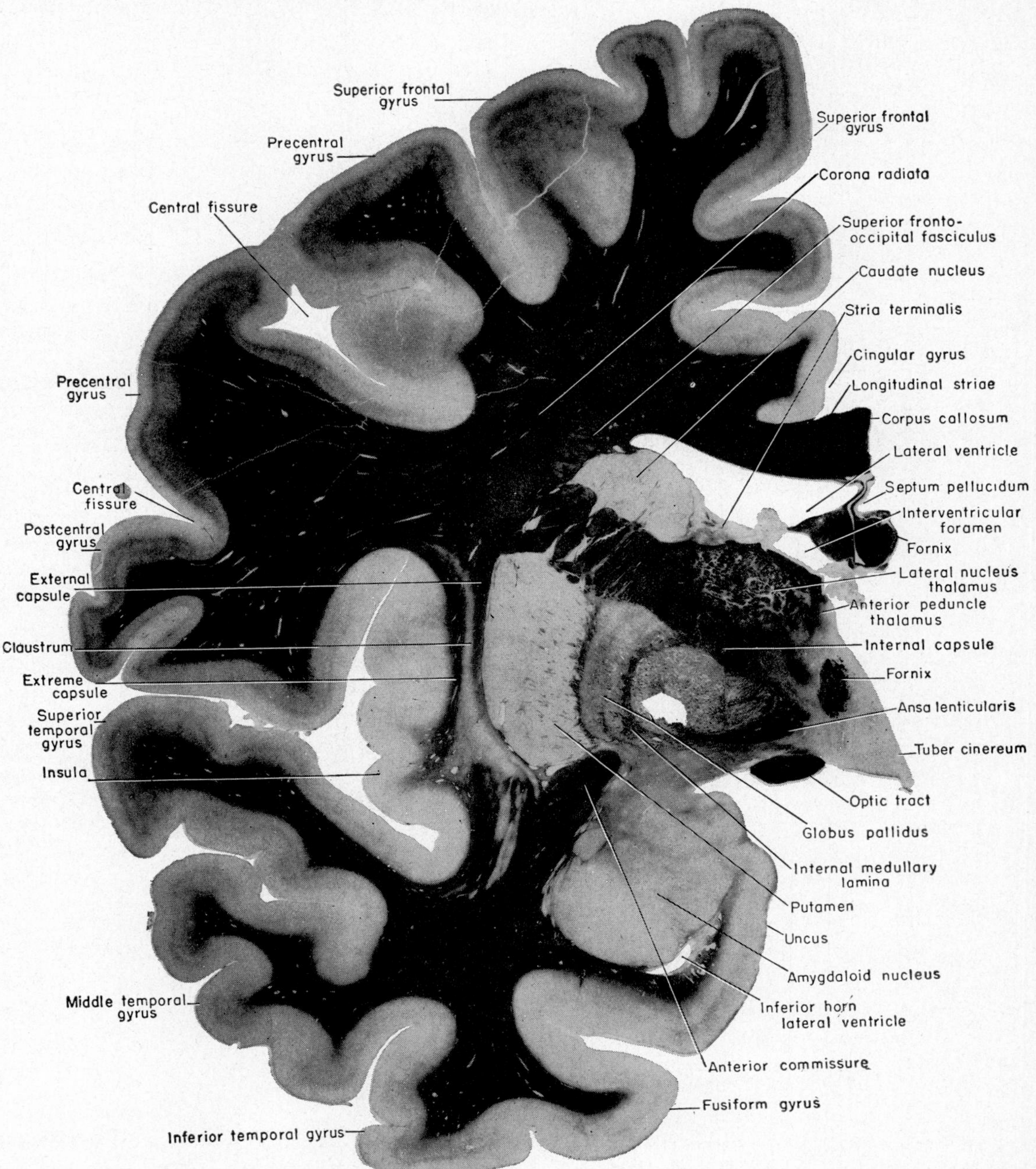

Fig. 246. Frontal section through cerebral hemisphere of human at level of tuber cinereum. (*From Jelgersma, "Atlas Anatomicum Cerebri Humani," Amsterdam, Scheltema and Holkema.*)

electrical stimulations have indicated that many cerebral cortical areas are probably associated in part with extrapyramidal activity.

Since many of these nuclei are so closely associated anatomically, it is difficult to carry out anatomical investigation into their discrete connections, but both ascending and descending connections seem to exist. These latter end chiefly about neurons in reticular formation in midbrain, pontine, and medullar tegmentum.

These neurons in turn send axons spinalward which pass dorsal to the medullar pyramid, and are outside it; they are therefore called extrapyramidal fibers. The most numerous of these are the reticulospinal tracts. Other extrapyramidal projections, less dense and less important perhaps in man, are the rubrospinal, vestibulospinal, and tectospinal tracts, the component bundles of the medial longitudinal fasciculus, and certain autonomic pathways. These descending extrapyramidal motor fibers end about intercalary neuron pools as well as about anterior gray neurons, and the axons of the latter compose the anterior spinal roots. Many of the descending extrapyramidal fibers are short-chained systems of relays and are therefore difficult to study anatomically. The present description follows to a great extent that given by Papez and is based on his anatomical researches in the human brain chiefly (594). Reference will be made, however, to the researches of Mettler, Glees, and Woodburne, Crosby, and McCotter, especially, in the monkey.

The Caudate and Putamen

It is difficult to visualize the shape of the caudate nucleus from its appearance in cross sections of the brain. When its full contour is realized, it may be divided into a head, body, and tail (Fig. 250). The head lies in relation to the floor of the anterior horn of the lateral ventricle (Figs. 251, 252, 253, 254). The tail lies in the roof of the inferior horn of the same ventricle, while the body makes a curve in following the lateral wall of the ventricle. In such manner, the tail terminates just ventral to the lateral border of the head. In transverse frontal sections of the human brain, the head of the caudate is continuous with the ventral and rostral portion of the putamen, but in more caudad sections the putamen and globus pallidus lie lateral to the body and tail of the caudate (Figs. 245, 246, 247, 248). Medial to the putamen and embraced by its caudal portion is the globus pallidus. This last separates the caudal part of the putamen from the internal capsule. The caudate and putamen are considered newer nuclei developmentally than the globus pallidus, and all three are generally thought to be alar-plate derivatives. The caudate and putamen receive fibers from neighboring regions. The globus pallidus, which receives fibers from these two nuclear masses, in turn sends out a large collection of fibers to the neighboring and more caudal brain stem nuclei.

The caudate and putamen are composed of large and small cells, the latter being more numerous, in a ratio of about 20:1. The small cells stain poorly and their contours are difficult to make out. They are considered to be the receptive cells of the two nuclei. Their dendrites receive impulses from the neighboring region and from the cortex, and their axons pass them on to the large cells of the two nuclei. Each large cell has many short dendrites; its axon passes into the group of fibers which radiate through these nuclei and separate them from the globus pallidus. Most of the axons of the large cells terminate in the globus pallidus, though some have been described to pass through it and to terminate in the substantia nigra and subthalamus. The axons become myelinated while within the substance of the caudate and putamen, and they form prominent radiating bundles which give these nuclei a striated appearance.

The striatum is thought to *receive* a few unmyelinated fibers from the cerebral cortex as collaterals of corticothalamic and corticospinal fibers. In addition, the **subcallosal bundle,** a group of fine fibers occupying the ventricular surface of the angle made by the corpus callosum and the internal capsule, is thought to contain corticocaudate fibers from the frontal lobe from areas 4, 6, 8, and possibly from 9 (594) (Fig. 247). Areas 6 and 4*s* are said to contribute corticocaudate fibers via the internal capsule and, in the cat, areas 2 and 19 as well (304). The posterior part of area 4 is said to project to the putamen. That these areas in the monkey project to the striatum has been learned also by physiological studies (220). The orbital area 13 also projects to the striatum (700). Physiological-neuronographic technique has shown that areas 4, 6, 8, 2, 24, and 19 project to these nuclei. Areas 4*s*, 8, 24, 2, and 19 project to the caudate; area 6 and that part of 4 exclusive of 4*s* project to the putamen, and area 6, to the globus pallidus. Fibers to the striatum from the medial nucleus of the thalamus, from the centrum medianum, and from other intralaminar thalamic nuclei have

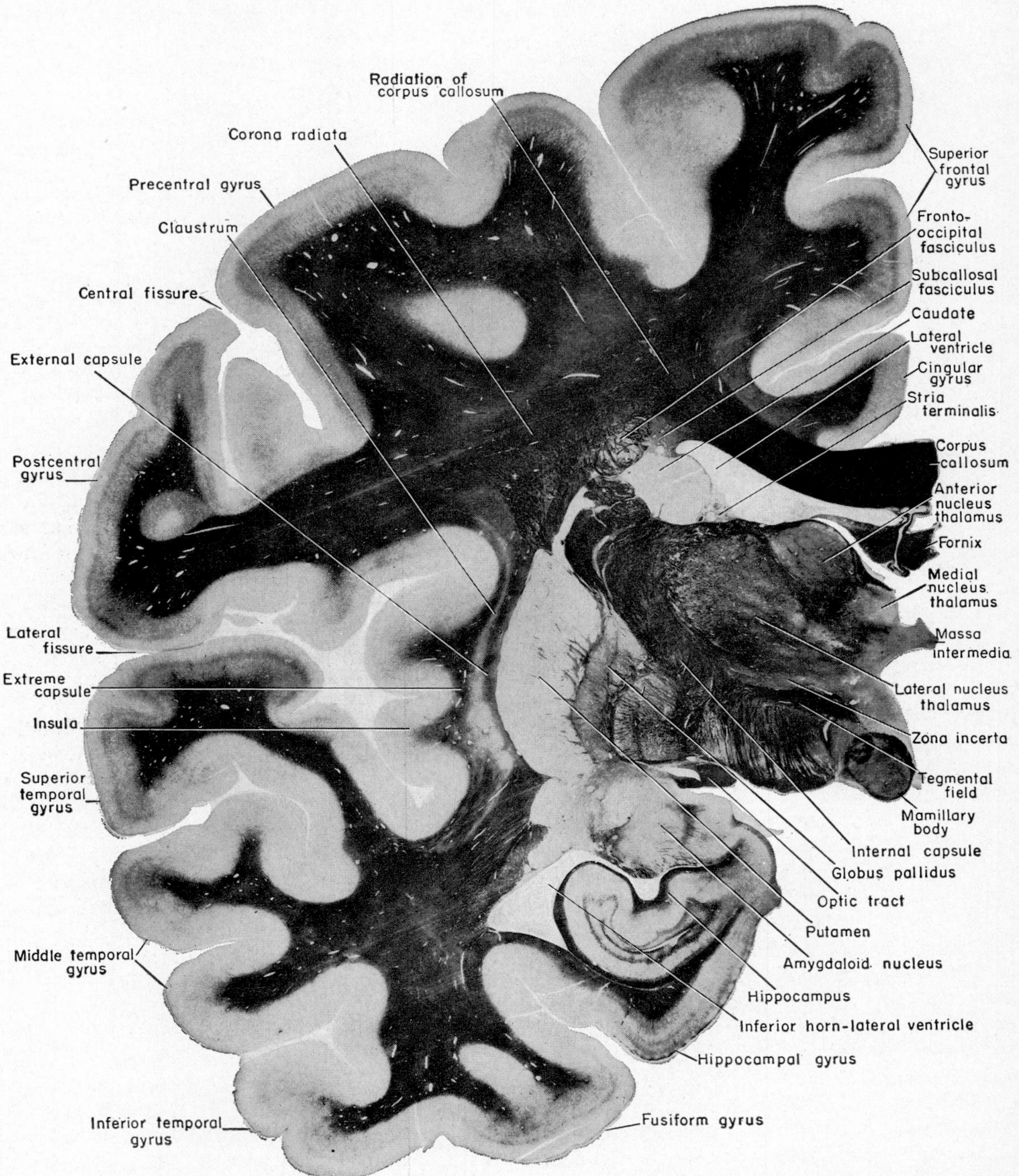

FIG. 247. Frontal section through cerebral hemisphere of human at level of mamillary bodies. (*From Jelgersma, "Atlas Anatomicum Cerebri Humani," Amsterdam, Scheltema and Holkema.*)

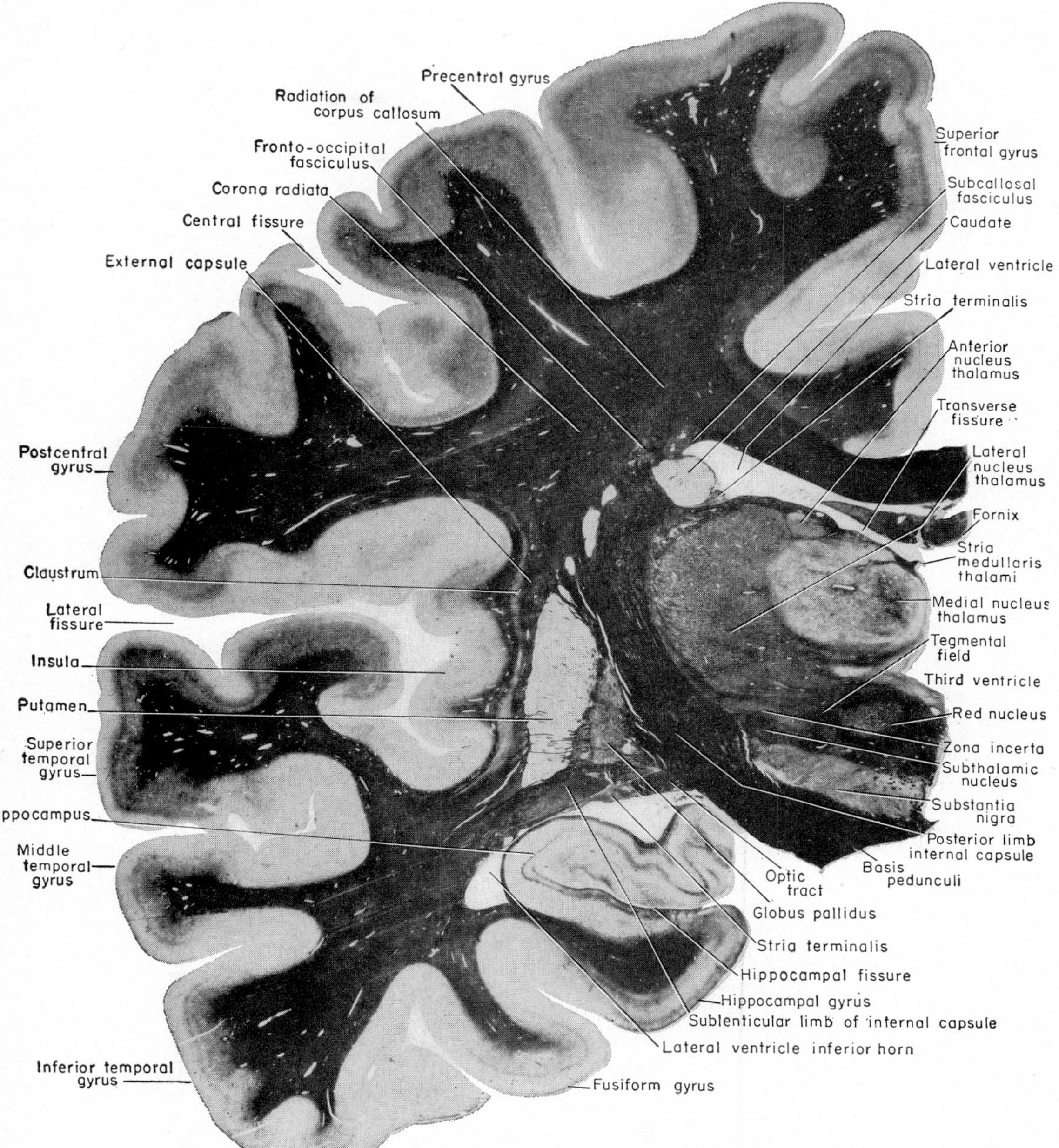

FIG. 248. Frontal section through cerebral hemisphere of human at plane of rostral end of red nucleus. (*From Jelgersma, "Atlas Anatomicum Cerebri Humani," Amsterdam, Scheltema and Holkema.*)

been described (509, 594). These run with the inferior thalamic peduncle which is described below.

Efferent fibers of the striatum of man, according to Papez, include striopallidal, striosubthalamic, and strionigral fibers. The last pass through the globus pallidus, emerging from its posterior end into the lateral border of the cerebral peduncle to enter the reticular portion of the substantia nigra. It will be noticed in

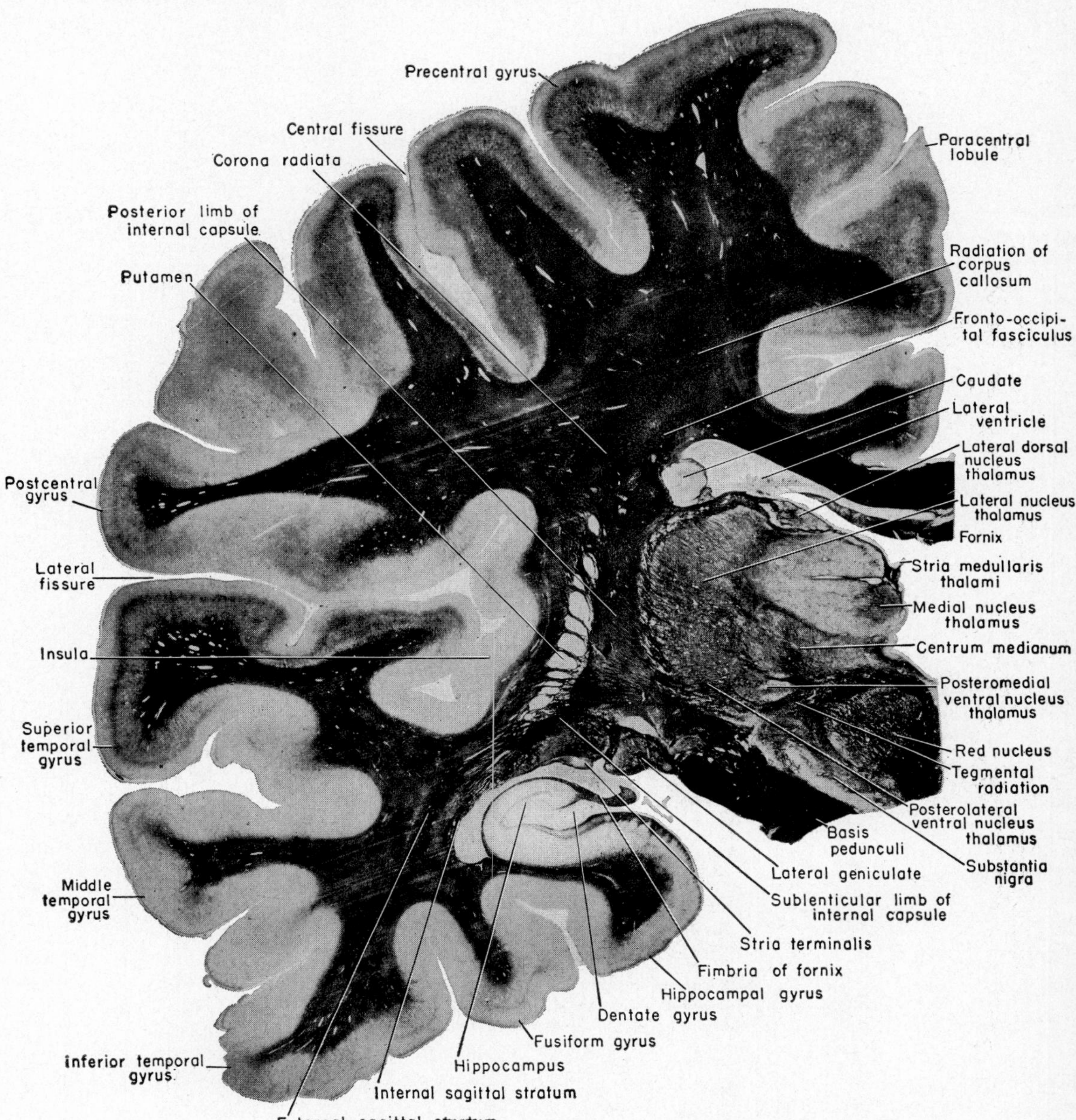

Fig. 249. Frontal section through cerebral hemisphere of human at plane of middle of red nucleus. (*From Jelgersma, "Atlas Anatomicum Cerebri Humani," Amsterdam, Scheltema and Holkema.*)

sections that the caudal end of the globus pallidus and the substantia nigra are practically continuous. Ranson has described similar fibers in the monkey but wondered if they were not nigropallidal instead, since lesions of the nigra were followed by degenerating fibers ascending from the nigra and passing into the inner division of the pallidus beyond which they could not be traced (652). Fibers probably pass in each direction.

The Globus Pallidus

The globus pallidus is enclosed on its lateral and frontal surfaces by the putamen, and its mediodorsal surface is adjacent to the internal capsule (Figs. 247, 255, 256). The ventral surface is covered by the preoptic region. It consists of two divisions, an outer and an inner, the former being larger and extending more anteriorly. The histological structure is uniform. Many multipolar neurons of medium size are embedded in an abundance of myelinated neuropil which is permeated by many myelinated fiber bundles, afferent and efferent in type. The globus pallidus contains much iron.

The fiber connections of the globus pallidus are numerous. Its *afferent* connections will be mentioned first. These include corticopallidal, thalamopallidal, striopallidal, subthalamopallidal, nigropallidal fibers, and perhaps some collaterals from the medial lemniscus, although a recent investigation failed to reveal any of these last (656). The corticopallidal fibers have been demonstrated both by physiological-neuronography technique and by anatomical study. They appear to come directly from area 6, especially, via the internal capsule. They end chiefly in the inner segment of the globus pallidus. The thalamopallidal fibers arise from the medial part of the dorsomedial nucleus, perhaps from the medial part of anterior ventral nucleus, and from the centrum medianum. These fibers pass by way of the inferior thalamic peduncle, and this can usually be recognized in myelin preparations, as a group of fine, myelinated fibers just medial to the genu of the internal capsule (Figs. 255, 256, 257). The thalamopallidal fibers enter the medial edge of the pallidum all along the extent of the inner segment, and they are distributed to both segments. A majority of those fibers from the centrum medianum appear to end in the striatum.

The striopallidal fibers are dense and arise in caudate and putamen. These can be seen, arranged in radiating pattern in the putamen and converging on the pallidum (Figs. 189, 255). They form a noticeable band of fibers which indicate the separation of putamen from pallidum, and they terminate in both segments of the pallidum. A definite order of termination seems to be lacking; *i.e.,* a discrete part of the striatum does not appear to project on a discrete part of the pallidum. Nigropallidal fibers travel with nigrostriatal fibers and have been identified anatomically (542). Numerous subthalamopallidal fibers, leaving the lateral part of the subthalamic nucleus, in the macaque, pierce the internal capsule and end in the inner segment, especially, of the pallidum (309, 837).

The *efferent* fibers of the globus pallidus arise from both segments of the nucleus, but chiefly in the inner division. They emerge from this division by way of three streams and in-

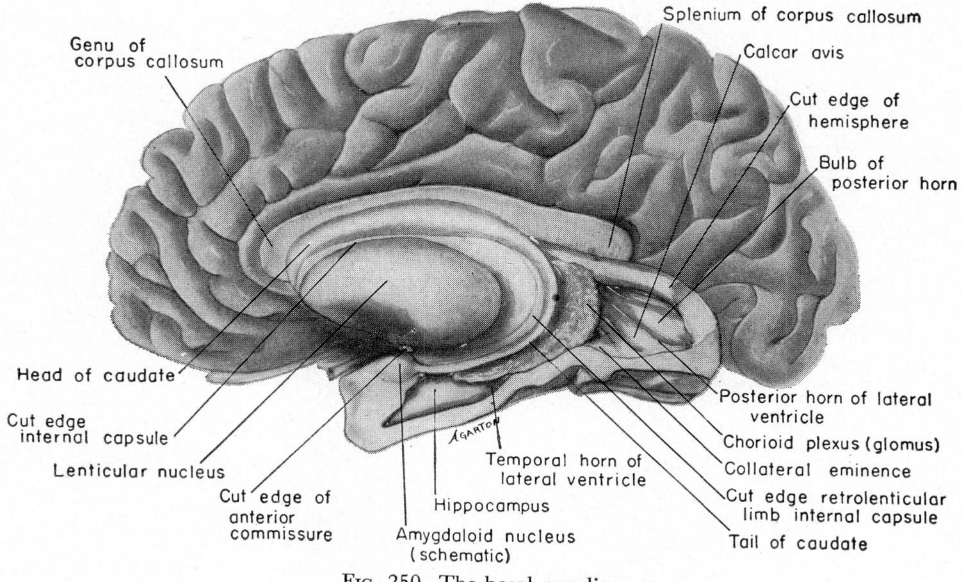

FIG. 250. The basal ganglia.

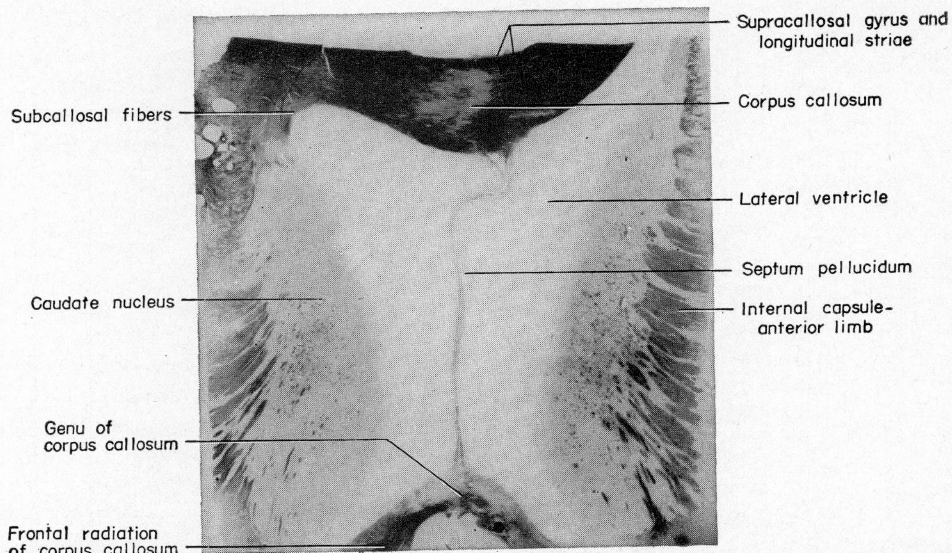

Fig. 251. Transverse section, A 1560, of human brain stem through head of caudate nucleus. Weigert. Photograph, ×1.8.

clude pallidothalamic, pallidosubthalamic, pallidohypothalamic, and pallidoprerubral and pallidorubral fibers.

The fibers issuing from the ventral part of the pallidum constitute the **ansa lenticularis;** those from the dorsal surface, throughout its extent, the **fasciculus lenticularis** (Figs. 246, 255, 257, 258). Fibers which emerge in an intermediate position and which pass through, and ventral to, the internal capsule pass directly into the subthalamus. They are sometimes referred to as the **subthalamic fasciculus.** Some authors consider all three of these divisions as parts of one large ansa lenticularis. They have been

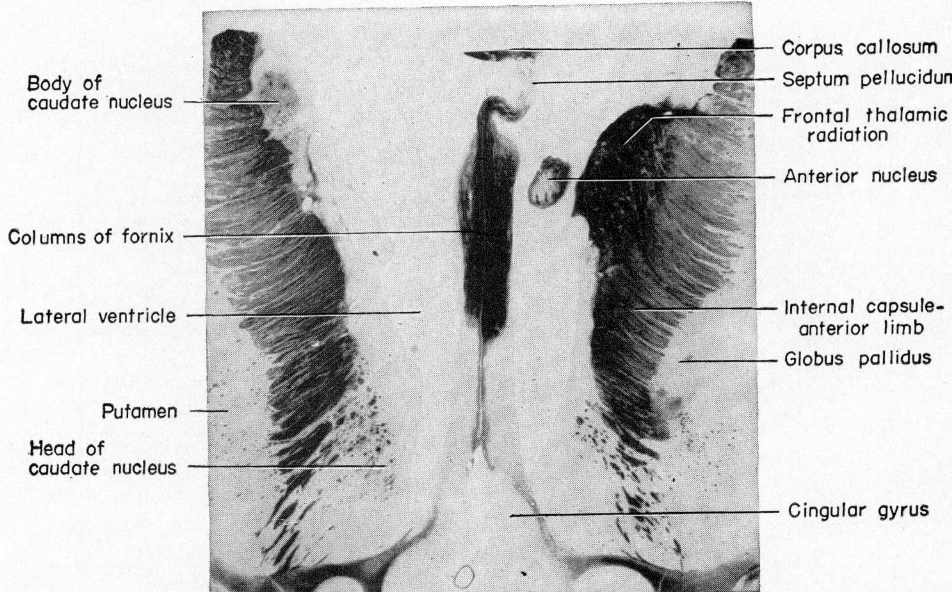

Fig. 252. Transverse section, A 1430, of human brain stem through frontal edge of columns of the fornix. Weigert. Photograph, ×1.9.

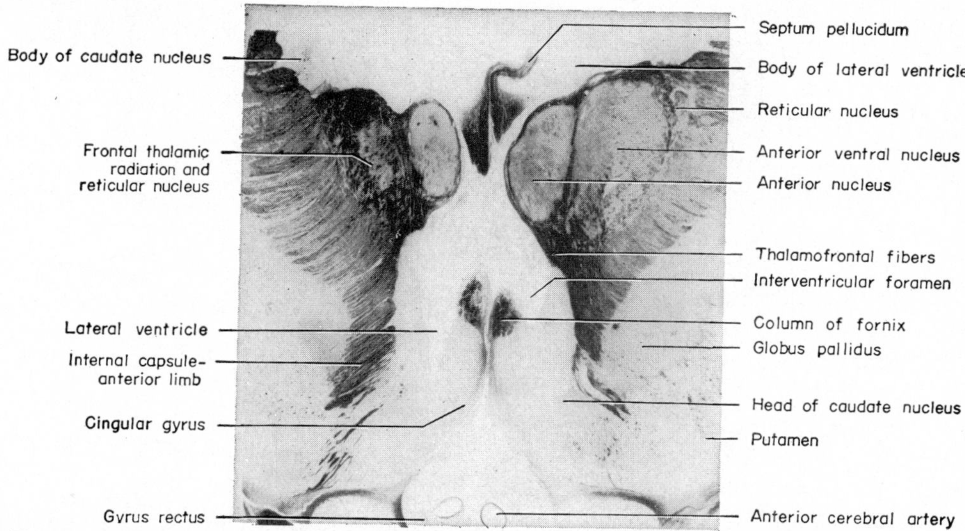

FIG. 253. Transverse section, A 1383, of human brain stem through rostral pole of thalamus. Weigert. Photograph, ×1.7.

described in detail in man by Papez, and in the monkey by Ranson, Mettler, Glees, Woodburne, and others (305, 309, 542, 594, 595, 596, 652, 850).

The nomenclature of these efferent fibers from the globus pallidus has been unnecessarily confused by the introduction of repetitive eponymous terms. The name of Forel, who studied these fibers, has been attached to them, and since he used the German word *Haube* (crest, cap) to designate the tegmentum at this level, the letter H is also used, and certain of the masses of fibers are frequently referred to as Forel's tegmental fields H, H_1, H_2. The fasciculus lenticularis is called by most workers Forel's field H_2, though Papez appears to use H_2 for the common mass of ansa and fasciculus fibers. The fasciculus lenticularis will here be referred to as H_2.

The fibers of the ansa lenticularis arise chiefly from the inner segment of the pallidum, emerge from its ventral surface, turn medially, and then bend dorsally around the anteromedial border of the internal capsule to reach the tegmental field of Forel in the subthalamus, in which they meet the fasciculus lenticularis (Figs. 159, 162, 246, 257). This latter bundle of fibers arises from both divisions of the pallidum, but the majority of the fibers arise from the inner division. These fibers emerge from the dorsal surface of the pallidum, collect along the lateral edge of the internal capsule, and penetrate the latter in a dorsomedial direction to enter the subthalamus (Figs. 203, 247, 258). They continue medially with the zona incerta nucleus of the subthalamus above them and the subthalamic nucleus below them, to reach the medial tegmental area, the field of Forel (Figs. 189, 257). Some fibers are given off to the zona incerta, but the main bulk of them reach the tegmental field of Forel. In this area they are joined by the fibers of the ansa. Having combined, the large mass of fibers turns caudally and passes into the area of the prerubral field, Forel's field H, rostral to the red nucleus (Figs. 159, 162, 248, 259).

At the point of union of the fibers of the ansa and fasciculus, a small bundle of the fibers runs into the hypothalamus (Figs. 255, 257). They pass over and around the columns of the fornix to gain their destination. They appear to end in the paraventricular and dorsomedial nuclei of the hypothalamus. Some pallidohypothalamic fibers cross in the anterior hypothalamic commissure to end in the opposite hypothalamus. Pallidohypothalamic fibers are said to end in the supraoptic, ventromedial, and mamillary nuclei in the monkey, and to leave the pallidum with both ansa and fasciculus fibers (305, 542).

As the combined ansa and fasciculus fibers start their caudal course in the subthalamus, many fibers break away, turning dorsally and swinging laterally to form the **thalamic fascic-**

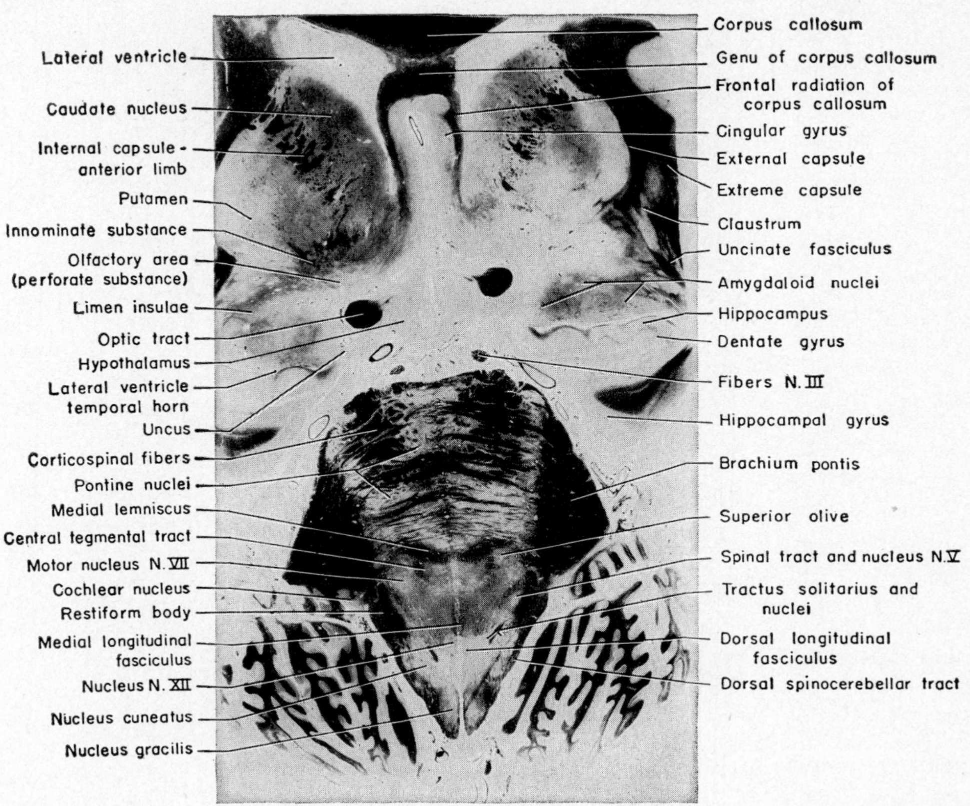

FIG. 254. Frontal section, B 230, of human brain through basal hypothalamus and the nucleus gracilis. Weigert. Photograph, ×1.2.

ulus, or Forel's field H_1 (Figs, 203, 257). Pallidothalamic fibers traveling in the thalamic fasciculus end in both the lateral ventral and anterior ventral nuclei (542, 594). It should be recalled that the lateral ventral nucleus receives the dentatothalamic tract and discharges to the precentral gyrus of the frontal lobe, areas 4 and 6, wherein arise many of the pyramidal motor fibers. The lateral ventral nucleus is then an intermediary between extrapyramidal and pyramidal systems. The anterior ventral nucleus also projects to area 6.

The majority of the descending pallidofugal fibers which remain in the combined ansa and fasciculus group, after the pallidothalamic fibers are given off, are thought by Papez to terminate about small neurons in the **prerubral field,** H. This field forms an area about 2.5 mm. thick and is curved over the frontal pole and lateral surface of the red nucleus. The neurons in the prerubral field which have received pallidoprerubral fibers in turn give rise to the **prerubral tract** which surrounds the rostral pole of the red nucleus and forms especially the dorsomedial part of its capsule (Figs. 162, 189, 248, 259). Some of the prerubral-tract fibers pierce the red nucleus and terminate therein, and some of the descending pallidofugal fibers apparently pass into the red nucleus without synapsing among prerubral field neurons. Papez and Woodburne and co-workers feel that many prerubral-tract fibers pass beyond the red nucleus to end in tegmental nuclei and, especially, in the deep tegmental nucleus of the midbrain, in its ventral and lateral portions. Some may end in the nuclei associated with the posterior commissure and in the oculomotor complex. A certain number of the prerubral fibers also cross in the subthalamic decussation to end in the contralateral red nucleus.

The pallidosubthalamic fibers are thought to

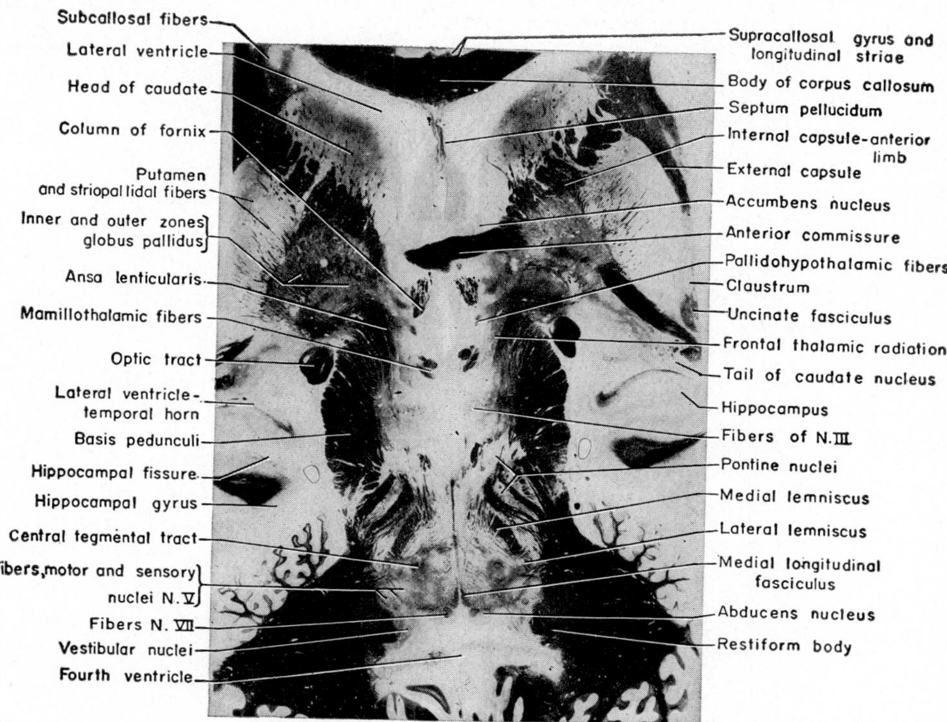

FIG. 255. Frontal section, B 340, of human brain through anterior commissure and facial colliculus. Weigert. Photograph, ×1.2.

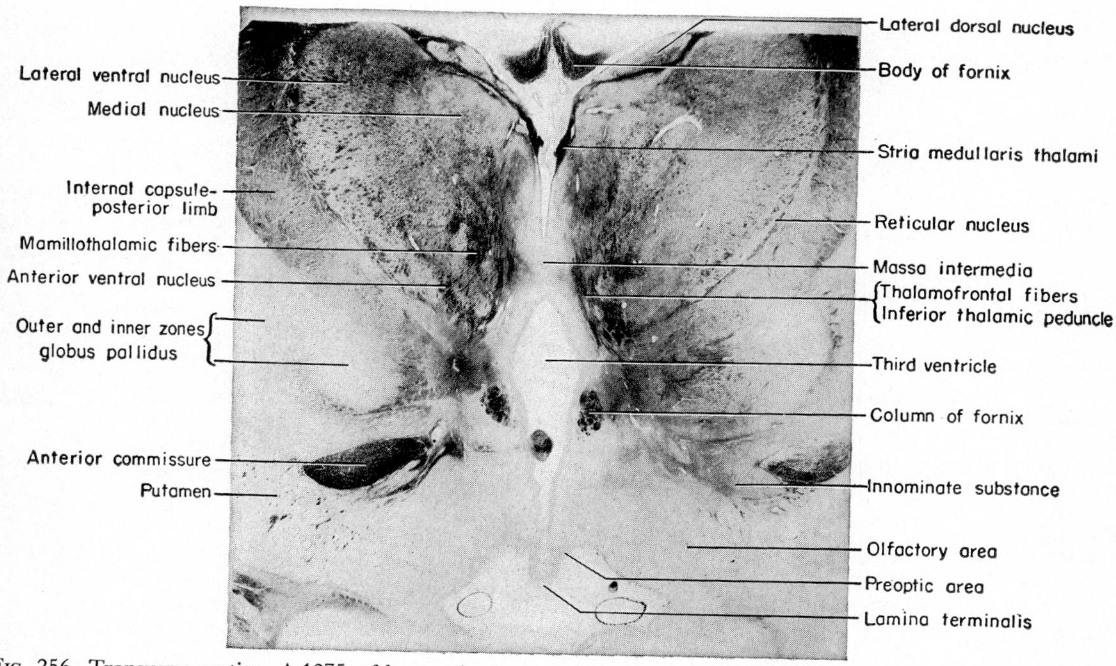

FIG. 256. Transverse section, A 1275, of human brain stem through rostral edge of massa intermedia. Weigert. Photograph, ×2.

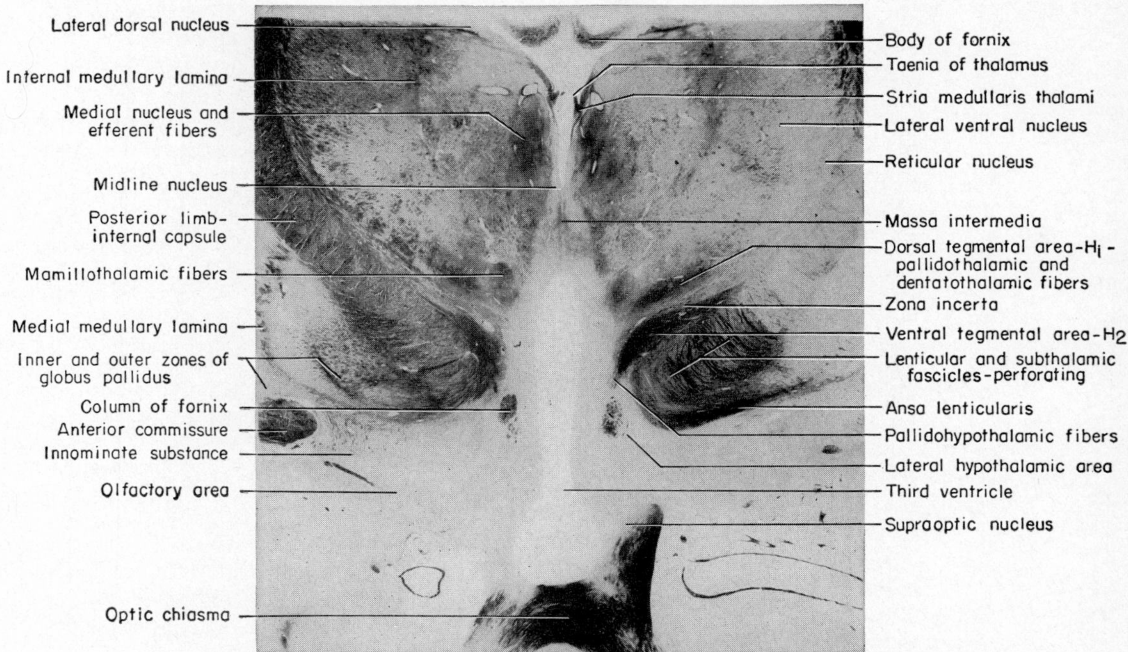

Fig. 257. Transverse section, A 1198, of human brain stem through massa intermedia. Weigert. Photograph, ×2.

arise chiefly in the outer segment of the globus pallidus. A few striosubthalamic fibers are included in the monkey also (850). Some of the fibers perforate the internal capsule, others pass ventrally and loop around it, and others emerge from the pallidum with fasciculus lenticularis fibers (Figs. 189, 257). These last form a dorsal capsule for the subthalamic nucleus, while other pallidosubthalamic fibers form a ventral capsule. Both groups appear to end in the subthalamus.

Mettler describes efferent pallidal fibers which arise in the outer division of the pallidum and enter the anterior commissure as this latter structure traverses the pallidum (542). The caudate and putamen may also contribute fibers to the anterior commissure. He considers these contributions to the anterior commissure as fibers which interconnect the pallida and striata of the two sides. He also described pallido-interpeduncular fibers which traversed the descending mass of pallidal efferents. Other points of difference are also mentioned in his papers. He describes no direct pallidoprerubral fibers, for example, and feels that Forel's field *H*, the prerubral field, is composed of fibers of the brachium conjunctivum. Forel's field H_1 is a rostral continuation of part of these.

In their studies in the monkey, Woodburne and co-workers described individual distribution of the three large bundles of pallidofugal fibers. The fasciculus lenticularis and closely allied fibers contained contributions to the hypothalamus, the anterior ventral and lateral ventral thalamic nuclei, the zona incerta, the neurons of the field of Forel, the nuclei associated with the posterior commissure, the interstitial nucleus of Cajal, the nucleus of Darkschewitsch, the red nucleus, and the various divisions of the deep tegmental nucleus of the midbrain. The ansa lenticularis contained fascicles from the putamen, both pallidal segments, and from the substantia innominata (Figs. 254, 256, 257). Contributions from this bundle were given off to the neurons of the field of Forel, to periventricular hypothalamic gray, and to the deep tegmental nucleus of the midbrain.

The subthalamic fasciculus, in their studies, arose in external and internal pallidal segments and also in the putamen. Most of these fibers ended in the subthalamic nucleus directly from its lateral surface, or indirectly after forming dorsal and ventral capsules about the nucleus. A small bundle of fibers, closely associated with the subthalamic fasciculus, passed beyond the subthalamic nucleus to end in the lateral part of the substantia nigra. This pallidonigral bundle was joined by subthalamonigral fibers. It is easily apparent that this description of pallidofugal fibers in the macaque closely resembles that given by Papez for man.

In summary, then, the caudate receives fibers from the cerebral cortex, areas 4*s*, 6, 8, 9, 24, 2, and 19; from the dorsomedial and centrum medianum nuclei of the thalamus. It discharges into the putamen, the globus pallidus, the substantia nigra, and perhaps the subthalamus. The putamen receives fibers from areas 6 and 4 and from the caudate, and it may share in the thalamostriate and nigrostriate fibers. It projects to the pallidum, the substantia nigra, and the subthalamus. The globus pallidus receives fibers from area 6 of the cerebral cortex, from the caudate and putamen, from the dorsomedial and centrum medianum nucleus, from the substantia nigra, and perhaps from the medial lemniscus. It projects to the anterior ventral and lateral ventral thalamic nuclei, the subthalamus, the hypothalamus, the prerubral field, and midbrain tegmental nuclei.

BLOOD SUPPLY OF THE BASAL GANGLIA

The following description of the blood supply of the caudate, putamen, and pallidum is based on the reports of cases by Alexander (21). **Striate arterioles** arising from the anterior and middle cerebral arteries supplied all the striatum (putamen and caudate) with the exception of the posteroventral recurved part of the tail of the caudate nucleus and of the adjoining posteroventral crest of the putamen (Fig. 51). These portions were usually supplied by the anterior chorioidal artery. In two-thirds of the cases the anteromedioventral tip of the head of the caudate and of the putamen were supplied by striate arterioles from the anterior cerebral artery; the remaining portion of the caudate and putamen, by vessels from the middle cerebral artery. In one-third of the cases all the striate arterioles arose from the middle cerebral artery.

The anterior chorioidal artery supplied the medial segment of the globus pallidus. In one-fourth of the cases this artery also supplied the lateral segment of the pallidus, with the exception of its anteroventral tip; in another one-fourth of the cases striate arterioles from the middle cerebral supplied this; and in one-half of the cases striate arterioles from the middle cerebral artery supplied its lateral part and arterioles from the anterior chorioidal artery supplied its medial part. In about two-thirds of the cases striate arterioles of the anterior cerebral supplied the anteroventral tip of the lateral segment of the globus pallidus; in one-third of the cases this was supplied by arterioles from the middle cerebral artery.

Veins draining the striatum and pallidum empty both into the vein of Galen and into the cavernous venous system.

In searching for the cause of the frequent involvement of the pallidum in circulatory disorders, Alexander reported that the anterior chorioidal artery, which more often supplies it, is longer and has less branches and anastomoses than any other cerebral artery. Thromboses easily form in this artery in carbon monoxide poisoning and circulatory disturbances. Further, the capillary bed of the pallidum is less dense than that of any other part of the cerebral cortex, while that of the striatum is more dense than that of any other part.

The Substantia Nigra

The substantia nigra will be discussed next, because it is interconnected with the striatum by numerous fibers. It is embedded in the dorsal surface of the basis pedunculi (Figs. 147, 159, 189, 258). Its caudal limit reaches the pontine nuclei; its rostral limit is at the level of the subthalamic nucleus. The rostral end of the substantia nigra appears to be continuous with the ventral portion of the caudal end of the globus pallidus. The substantia nigra is divided into two portions, a **compact** and a **reticular** one. The compact portion is the more dorsal and contains numerous medium-sized cells, some arranged in definite groups and many containing a brownish pigment, melanin. The reticular portion, intermingled with the most dorsal peduncular fibers, has fewer cells, some of which contain little pigment and some none at all. Phylogenetically, the substantia nigra can be divided into an older caudal portion and a newer cephalic portion. *Afferent*

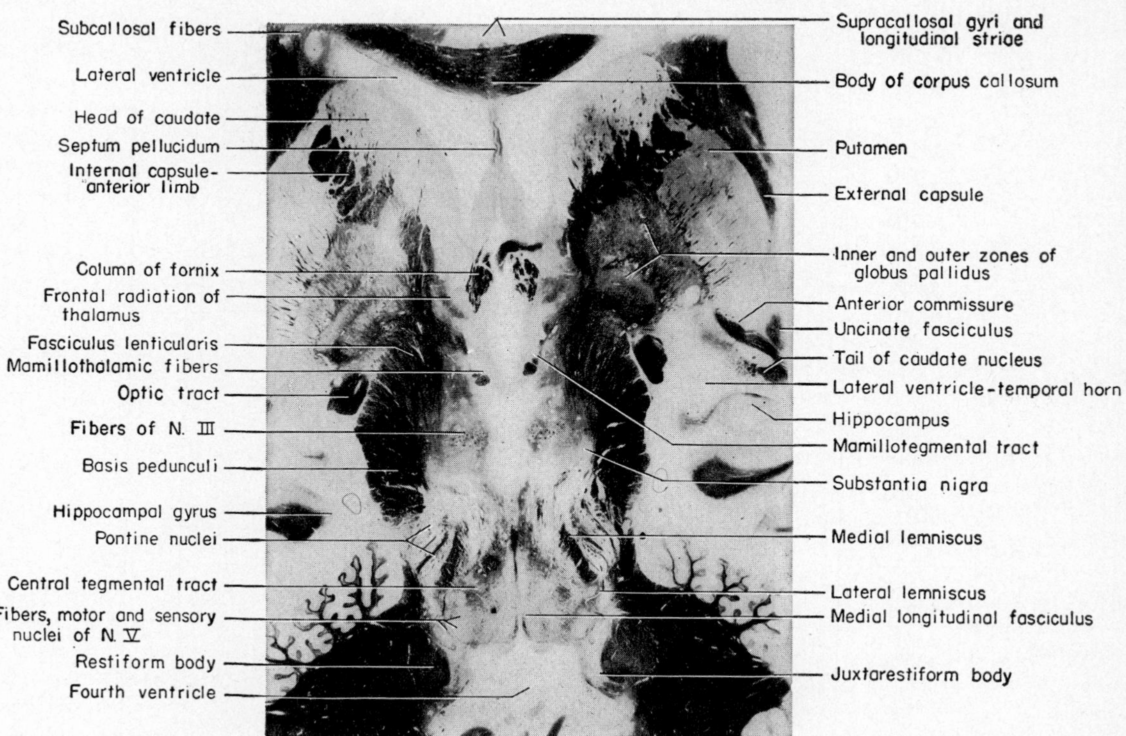

FIG. 258. Frontal section, B 360, of human brain through head of caudate and the basis pedunculi. Weigert. Photograph, ×1.3.

connections include strionigral, pallidonigral, and subthalamonigral fibers which end in the caudal and cephalic portions, and corticonigral fibers from areas 4γ, 4*s*, and 6 which end in the reticular portion of the cephalic zone. Fibers from the cortex about the central fissure, from the opercular region of the precentral and postcentral gyri, and from contiguous regions of the frontal and parietal lobes are said to end in the nigra in the human. The nigra is thought to receive also many other afferent impulses: some, from the mamillary body; optic impulses, via the tectum; proprioceptive, via collaterals from the medial lemniscus; and general cutaneous sensibility, via collaterals from the spinothalamics. These end in the caudal nigra, especially. Many *efferent* fibers arising in the compact portion of the nigra pass dorsally to end in the deep tegmental nucleus of the midbrain near the decussation of the brachium conjunctivum (437). Other fibers from the nigra pass into the two segments of the pallidum and to the striatum. In the monkey fibers are said to end in addition in centrum medianum, the subthalamus, and the superior colliculus (309).

THE SUBTHALAMUS

The subthalamus or ventral thalamus is closely related functionally to the nuclei of this discussion. It is ventral to the dorsal thalamus and dorsal and dorsolateral to the hypothalamus (Figs. 203, 204, 259). It lies between the rostral end of the red nucleus and the internal capsule in a coronal plane.

Several distinct nuclei compose the subthalamus, and many nerve fibers traverse it, interconnecting the striatum and pallidum, subthalamus, thalamus and lower brain stem. The subthalamic nucleus, or corpus luysi, is the most prominent nucleus; it is situated along the dorsal surface of the rostral part of the basis pedunculi. It has an oval or biconvex shape, and it is lateral to the cephalic tip of the substantia nigra (Figs. 203, 204, 248). A dense capsule of fibers is present about it, and many of them terminate within the nucleus. The zona incerta is a wedge-shaped nucleus, lying rostral and dorsal to the subthalamic nucleus and separated from it by the fibers of the fasciculus lenticularis (Figs. 135, 203, 259). Dorsal to the zona incerta is the thalamic fasciculus. The entopeduncular nucleus appears in the course of the ansa lenticularis medial to the basis pedunculi (Figs. 203, 259). The more medial portion of the subthalamus contains Forel's tegmental field *H,* and mamillotegmental and mamillothalamic fibers traverse this region. Forel's tegmental field is composed of fibers of passage, with small and medium-sized neurons scattered among them. The prerubral field is a part of it.

The subthalamic nucleus consists of closely packed multipolar cells of medium size. It *receives* many fibers from the globus pallidus, especially from the outer division, and a lesser number from the putamen. These compose the subthalamic fasciculus and emerge intermediate to fasciculus lenticularis and ansa lenticularis. Many form dorsal and ventral portions of the capsule of the subthalamic nucleus, while others pass into the lateral surface of the nucleus directly. Pallido-incertal fibers are also included in the pallidofugal fibers to the subthalamus, and some of the ansa lenticularis fibers give collaterals to the entopeduncular nucleus. Corticosubthalamic fibers have been described as arising in areas 4γ, 4*s*, and 6 in the monkey, and such fibers are also present in man (554). Glees reports that fibers from the substantia nigra converge at the ventral surface of the subthalamic nucleus and that some of them terminate therein (309).

The subthalamic nucleus *discharges* fibers from its dorsal and caudal surfaces which pass especially to various parts of the deep tegmental nucleus of the midbrain, and to other reticular nuclei of the upper brain stem, as a subthalamotegmental tract. Other subthalamic projections have been described to the dorsomedial region of the substantia nigra, to the prerubral field, to the ventral thalamic nuclei and the centrum medianum, and to the globus pallidus. Recent studies in the macaque have failed to verify a subthalamotegmental tract (837). A subthalamonigral tract and numerous subthalamopallidal fibers were described, however.

The zona incerta contributes many fibers as a component of a pallido-incertotegmental tract. These with the subthalamotegmental fibers serve to interconnect pallidum, subthalamus, and reticular nuclei of the upper and lower brain stem. The pallido-incertotegmental tract is augmented by additions from the deep tegmental nucleus of the midbrain, and from the red nucleus and other tegmental reticular nuclei of the brain stem. The composite bundle forms a component of the central tegmental tract, and many of its fibers reach the inferior olivary nucleus. The descending projections of the subthalamus appear most numerous and perhaps are of more significance. The incerta also sends axons into the hypothalamus.

The Red Nucleus

The human red nucleus is about $\frac{1}{2}$ cm. in diameter and is almost spherical in shape (Figs. 135, 148, 159, 189, 204, 210, 259). It is prominent in sections through the midbrain at the level of the superior colliculus, has a reddish appearance in the fresh state, and appears almost completely encircled with a dense capsule of fibers in myelin-stained preparations. The majority of the component cells are small and medium-sized, multipolar ones, although some large, deeply staining multipolar cells stand out prominently along its lateral and caudal poles, especially. These represent in man all that remains of the larger, magnocellular portion of the red nucleus of lower mammals. On the other hand, the small-celled portion in man is larger than in any other species, and it has increased progressively as the mammalian scale is ascended.

Papez divides the human red nucleus into three parts—the caudal, lateral, and medial (596). The fibers of the brachium conjunctivum, dentatorubral elements, pierce the caudal pole of the nucleus and the large neurons partially encircle these fibers. These large cells give rise to a portion of the rubrospinal tract. The small and medium-sized neurons of the lateral division of the red nucleus give rise to the bulk of the rubroreticular fibers and the remaining portion of the rubrospinal tract. The medial division of the red nucleus forms the dorsomedial portion of the rostral end of the nucleus and, according to Papez, gives rise to fibers entering the medial longi-

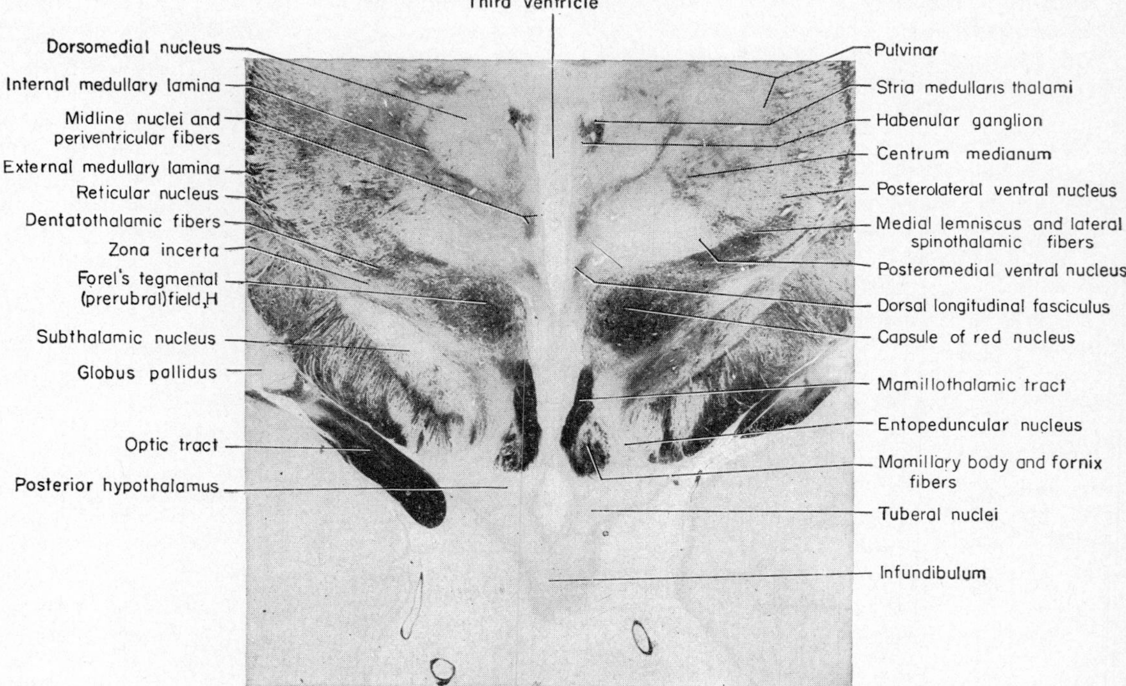

FIG. 259. Transverse section, A 1105, of human brain stem through rostral pole of red nucleus. Weigert. Photograph, ×2.

tudinal fasciculus and passing to the nuclei of the third, fourth, and sixth cranial nerves (rubro-oculomotor tract).

Incoming and outgoing fibers form a dense capsule about the red nucleus, as mentioned previously. In front of the nucleus is the tegmental field *H* of Forel composed of fine fibers and scattered medium and small-sized nerve cells which form the **nucleus of the field *H* of Forel.** Many fibers from the pallidum by way of Forel's field end among neurons in field *H;* some pass into the red nucleus (pallidorubral tract) directly without a prerubral synapse. From the cells in the nucleus of Forel's field *H* short axons join the pallidorubral fibers and spread over the frontal surface of the red nucleus before entering it to terminate (prerubralrubral tract). The brachium conjunctivum (dentatorubral tract) enters caudally and centrally, as noted previously. The pallidorubral, prerubralrubral, and dentatorubral fibers end principally about the neurons of the lateral division. Fibers from the subthalamus enter ventrally; their exact site of termination is not clear. Tectorubral fibers perhaps enter dorsomedially. The red nucleus is said to receive fibers also from the substantia nigra and hypothalamus and possibly from the spinal cord by way of the medial lemniscus.

It is not clear whether the red nucleus receives fibers from the cerebral cortex in man, though some investigators have reported corticorubral fibers arising from the orbital gyri, the precentral and postcentral gyri, and the anterior part of the superior and middle frontal gyri. In the monkey corticorubral fibers have been described as arising from areas 4 and 6, though other reports deny such. Certainly, if corticorubral fibers exist, they are not numerous, or they are of such histological character that they do not readily lend themselves to anatomical study.

The red nucleus sends the majority of its fibers caudalward. The rubro-oculomotor fibers to the third, fourth, and sixth cranial-nerve nuclei leave the lateral side of the medial segment of the nucleus and form the most mediodorsal part of the capsule of the red nucleus.

The rubrospinal tract emerges posteriorly for the most part from the posterior and lateral segments. It crosses very soon in the ventral tegmental decussation. The rubroreticulo-olivary tracts emerge dorsally from the anterior end of the lateral segment, descend through the reticular formation, and synapse about reticular cells that give rise to the reticulospinal tracts and also about cells that project to the inferior olive (reticulo-olivary tract). Fibers to other cranial-nerve motor nuclei, a rubrobulbar tract, are probably included in the rubral outflow. From the rostral end of the red nucleus, fibers are thought to pass into the centrum medianum and lateral ventral thalamic nuclei. Rubrofrontal and rubroparietal fibers are described as leaving the dorsolateral surface of the nucleus and passing by way of the internal capsule to frontal and parietal lobes.

In summary, the red nucleus *receives* fibers from the globus pallidus directly and by way of the prerubral field, *H*; from the subthalamus and nigra; from the tectum and hypothalamus; from the cerebellum, via dentatorubral tract or brachium conjunctivum; possibly from the spinal cord; possibly from areas 4 and 6, especially, of the frontal lobe; and from the post-central gyrus. It *sends* fibers to the ocular muscle nuclei (3, 4, and 6), to other cranial nerve nuclei, to reticular nuclei, and to the inferior olive and thence to the cerebellum, to the centrum medianum and lateral ventral thalamic nuclei, and to the frontal and parietal lobes of the cerebral cortex. The rubrospinal tract is the only projection that crosses soon after its origin. In comparison to the rubroreticular outflow it is an insignificant projection system in man. Rubroreticular fibers may remain uncrossed for varying distances. They are joined by components from tegmental reticular nuclei and relay in caudal reticular nuclei of the brain stem, including the inferior olivary nuclei. Certain of these reticular nuclei relay reticulospinal fibers to the spinal gray.

The Tegmental Reticular Formation and Tegmental Nuclei

The deep tegmental nucleus of the midbrain includes many neurons, large and small. Some of these are scattered; others are collected into discrete nuclear groups (Figs. 135, 136, 137, 152). The complete nucleus extends from the level of the posterior commissure to the caudal end of the inferior colliculus. With reference to its relation to the red nucleus, the rostral part of the deep tegmental nucleus is divided into medial, lateral, and ventral parts. The caudal portion beneath the inferior colliculus is sometimes called the pedunculopontine tegmental nucleus. It is situated in the concavity formed by the medial lemniscus and spinothalamic fibers, and it extends caudally through the decussating fibers of the brachium conjunctivum. Caudal to this level numerous other reticular nuclei are found in the brain stem tegmentum. Some of these too are outlined as discrete cellular masses, but many are so interspersed with nerve fibers that their contour is indistinct. Some have been mentioned in Chap. 11. The deep tegmental nucleus of the midbrain represents a very important relay center in the discharge of pallidofugal, subthalamofugal, and hypothalamofugal fibers. Some fibers from the pallidum enter the tegmental nucleus without previous synapse. Many pallidal fibers are relayed by way of the prerubral field, subthalamus, and, to less extent, via substantia nigra, as seen in the previous discussions. Fibers from areas 4, 4*s*, and 6 of the cerebral cortex reach the deep tegmental nucleus of the midbrain, and projections from 4*s*, 8, 2, 19, and 24 to the medial reticular nuclei of the medullar tegmentum have been demonstrated by physiological neuronography (507, 816). Collaterals from ascending sensory pathways from spinal and brain stem levels terminate within the tegmental nucleus of the midbrain and other reticular nuclei, and tectotegmental fibers have been described. Collaterals from the brachium conjunctivum also end in the tegmental nuclei of pons and medulla.

The tegmental nucleus of the midbrain discharges to more caudal tegmental reticular nuclei and also to the inferior olive. Reticulospinal fibers may arise from some midbrain reticular nuclei as well as from more caudally placed ones. Papez feels that the caudal portion of the midbrain deep tegmental nucleus gives rise to tegmento-olivary fibers. Rubroreticulo-olivary tracts lie medial to the caudal portion of the nucleus, and some of those fibers arise within it. Most of the fibers of these two tracts end in the chief inferior olivary nucleus,

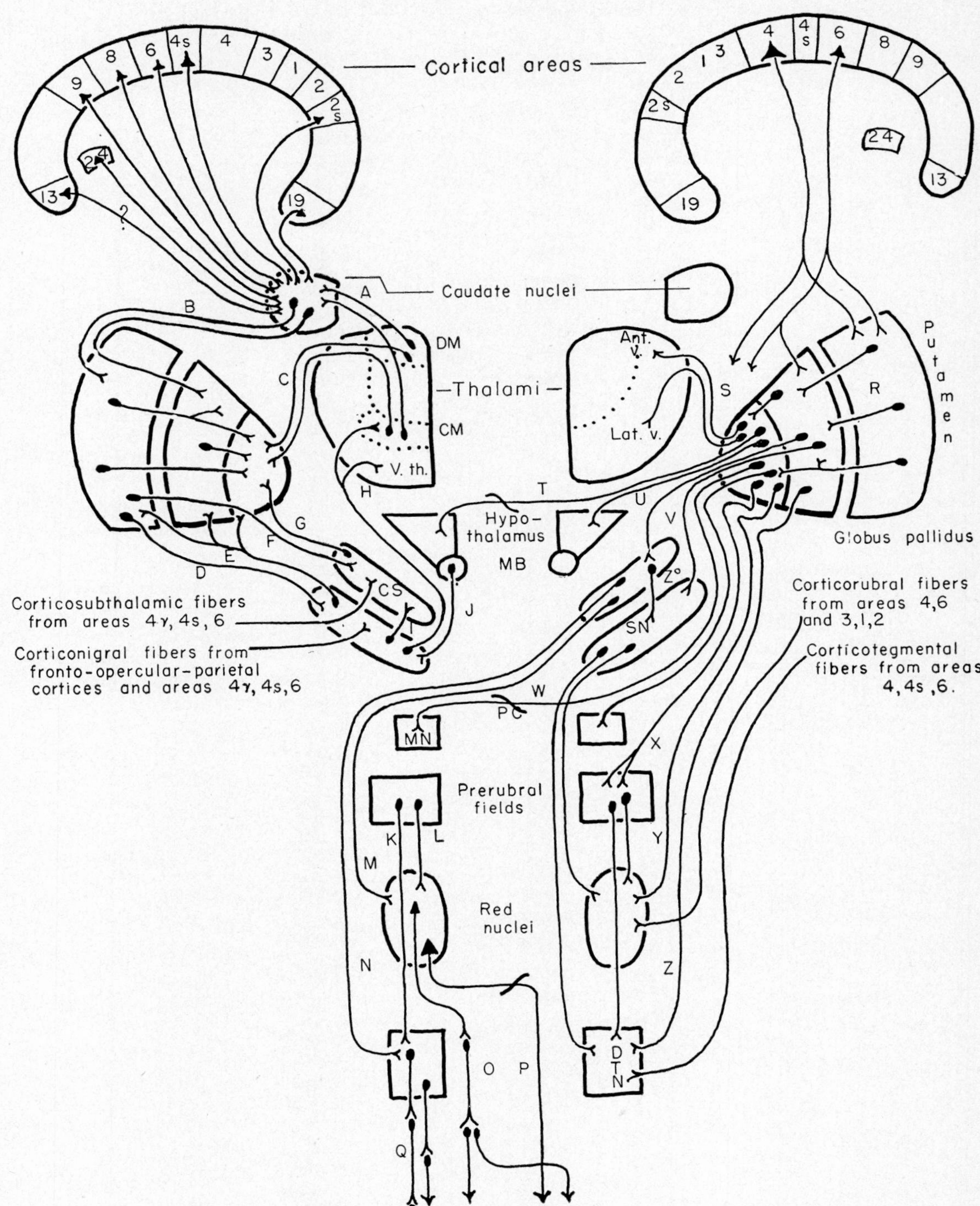

Fig. 260. Schematic representation of some extrapyramidal pathways.

though a few terminate in the dorsal accessory olivary nucleus. From the inferior olivary nucleus, fibers pass into the lateral parts of the cerebellar cortex, while from the dorsal accessory olive, fibers pass into the cortex of the vermis.

If transverse sections of the human brain stem between midbrain and caudal medulla are stained with a Weigert technique, many myelinated fibers, large and small, can be observed in the tegmentum. These are in addition to the long, ascending sensory and descending motor pathways, and a large number of them occupy the central tegmental area as a fairly discrete bundle (Figs. 128, 129, 131, 133, 160, 162, 210, 212). At rostral midbrain levels fiber elements of this bundle are found dorsal and dorsolateral to the red nucleus; at pontine levels, the large bundle is in the central tegmentum; at medullar levels it is ventrolateral in the tegmentum, and many fibers can be traced into the amiculum of the olive placed around the lateral border of the inferior olive. Many of the fibers end in this nuclear mass (787). This large, fairly compact bundle has been called the **central tegmental tract.** In addition to it there are, as mentioned, other fiber bundles, not nearly so compact in arrangement, because of the interspersing of neurons among them. The origin and destination of these tegmental fibers are not definitely known, although some descend and others ascend. Many of these fibers *within* the central tegmental bundle as well as *outside* it are short and are the axons of reticular neurons. They terminate about other reticular neurons. Some of the fibers may run from midbrain to medullar levels without interruption, but these appear to be in the minority. Some of these constitute the tegmento-olivary tract previously mentioned as arising in the deep tegmental nucleus of the midbrain. Other long fibers arise in the gray about the aqueduct and constitute the anulo-olivary tract, according to Mettler (544). Thalamo-olivary fibers have long been described as a component tract, apparently without adequate justification. Many of the myelinated fibers in this large tegmental area are ascending relays of reticuloreticular and reticulothalamic systems (571).

On the basis of recent studies it seems likely that many of these myelinated fibers in the tegmentum represent discharge pathways for the basal ganglia to caudal brain stem tegmental nuclei and to the inferior olive (Figs. 260, 261). Pallidoprerubral, pallidorubral, strionigral, pallidotegmental, and pallidosubthalamic fibers are the most rostral elements in the system. Rubroreticular, nigrotegmental, subthalamotegmental are relays of the next order. Tegmentoreticular, reticuloreticular, tegmento-olivary, anulo-olivary links are next, and olivocerebellar, olivospinal, and, especially, reticulospinal tracts would be final links in the projections of the ganglia caudalward. Certainly on the basis of recent investigations reticulospinal fibers compose the most important extrapyramidal projection. Rubrospinal fibers are not numerous in the human. Vestibulospinal, tectospinal, medial longitudinal fasciculus components, and dorsal longitudinal fasciculus of Schütz represent other extrapyramidal projections. The last-mentioned fasciculus, together with other less discrete tracts, constitute descending autonomic motor tracts. The descending components of the upper part of the medial longitudinal fasciculus represent a discharge pathway from the basal ganglia. The tectospinal and tectobulbar tracts correlate head, eye, pupil, and trunk movements in re-

---

A, thalamostriate fibers
B, caudatoputamen-pallidal fibers
C, thalamopallidal fibers
D, strionigral fibers
E, nigropallidostriate fibers
F, striosubthalamic fibers
G, subthalamicopallidal fibers
H, nigrothalamic fibers
I, nigrosubthalamic fibers
J, mamillonigral fibers
K, prerubrotegmental fibers
L, prerubrorubral fibers
M, subthalamicorubral fibers
N, subthalamicoreticular fibers
O, rubroreticular fibers
P, rubrospinal fibers
Q, reticulospinal fibers
R, striopallidal fibers
S, pallidothalamic fibers
T, pallidohypothalamic fibers
U, pallidosubthalamic fibers
V, pallidonigral fibers
W, pallidomesencephalic fibers
X, pallidoprerubral fibers
Y, pallidorubral fibers
Z, pallidotegmental fibers
Z^0, subthalamiconigral fibers
Ant. v., anterior ventral thalamic nucleus
DM, dorsomedial thalamic nucleus
CM, centrum medianum
Lat. v., lateral ventral thalamic nucleus
V. th., ventral thalamic nucleus
CS, corpus subthalamicum
DTN, deep tegmental nucleus
MN, mesencephalic nucleus
PC, posterior commissure
SN, substantia nigra.

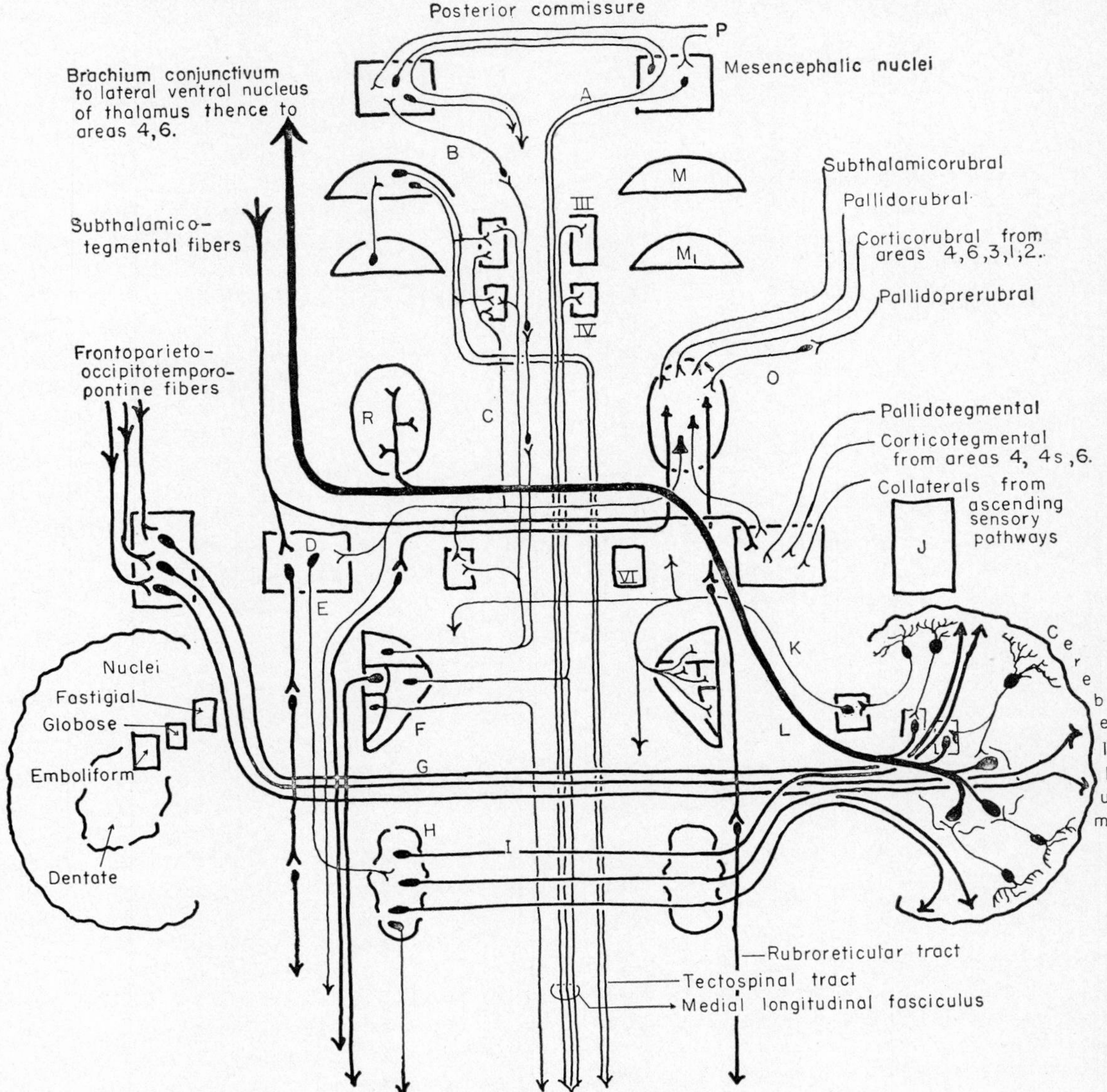

FIG. 261. Schematic representation of other extrapyramidal pathways.

A, interstitiospinal tract
B, vestibulomesencephalic fibers
C, rubrobulbar fibers
D, deep tegmental nucleus
E, tegmento-olivary
F, vestibular nuclei
G, pontocerebellar fibers
H, nucleus of inferior olive
I, olivocerebellar fibers
J, pontine nuclei
K, fastigiobulbar fibers
L, brachium conjunctivum
M, Superior colliculus
M_1, inferior colliculus
O, prerubrorubral fibers
P, pallidomesencephalic fibers
R, red nucleus.

sponse to visual and auditory impulses, whether the responses are integrated at midbrain or cortical levels. The vestibulospinal and vestibulomesencephalic tracts fundamentally correlate head, eye, trunk, and limb movements in response to labyrinthine impulses and underlie the tonic labyrinthine reflexes and labyrinthine righting reflexes described in Chap. 10. The function of reticulospinal projections will be discussed below. Spinospinal, or propriospinal, tracts fundamentally correlate limb-and-limb or limb-and-trunk movements in response to incoming sensory impulses, especially proprioceptive, and underlie the so-called body-righting reflexes, the mark-time reflexes, and also certain features of reciprocal innervations.

Cortical Extrapyramidal Projections

From time to time in the preceding discussion concerning the connections of the subcortical extrapyramidal motor nuclei, cortical projections to these nuclei have been mentioned. The majority of these projections probably arise in the precentral gyrus, in areas 4, 4*s*, and 6, and anatomical and physiological proof of them has been furnished, especially in the monkey. Either by anatomical or physiological research in the monkey, areas 4*s*, 8, 9, 24, 2, and 19 have been shown to discharge to the caudate; area 6 and that part of 4, exclusive of 4*s*, project to the putamen; area 6 projects to the globus pallidus. Areas 4, 4*s*, and 6 project to the substantia nigra, to the subthalamus, and to the tegmental nucleus of the midbrain. Areas 4 and 6 have been said to project to the red nucleus, on the basis of degeneration in these nuclei after frontal-lobotomy incisions which included section of projections from these areas (554). Area 19 discharges to the tectum. Areas 4*s*, 8, 24, 2, and 19 discharge to medullar reticular nuclei, especially to that medial part which constitutes the bulbar inhibitory center of Magoun and Rhines. Corticothalamic projections appear to have a wide origin. As a result of physiological-neuronography studies, corticohypothalamic fibers in the monkey have been described as arising from many of the frontal-lobe areas. In addition to area 4, areas 8, 6, 4*s*, 3, 1, 2, 5, and 7 have been found to discharge to the brain stem and spinal-cord motor nuclei via corticobulbar and corticospinal tracts, the pyramidal motor system.

Another large system of cortical extrapyramidal fibers is composed of the several corticopontocerebellar fiber groups, named according to their origin in the cortex (73, 769).

Frontopontocerebellar fibers arise from cells in the posterior part of the frontal lobe, areas 6 and 4, as well as from area 10. This tract is also called Arnold's bundle. It passes into the anterior limb of the internal capsule and enters the pons through the middle one-fifth of the cerebral peduncle (Figs. 160, 240). In the pons it synapses about cells in the homolateral pontine nuclei. These cells in turn give rise to axons that cross the mid-line as the transverse pontine fibers and pass into the cerebellar cortex by way of the brachium pontis (middle cerebellar peduncle).

Temporopontocerebellar fibers arise from cells in the caudal part of the second and third temporal gyri and pass ventral to the lenticular nuclei into the posterior limb of the internal capsule. They enter the pons by way of the lateral one-fifth of the cerebral peduncle (Figs. 160, 191, 240). These fibers are also called Turck's bundle, and once in the pons, they behave similarly to the frontopontocerebellar fibers.

Occipitopontocerebellar fibers are thought to be associated with the temporopontocerebellar group, and though their exact origin in the occipital lobe is unknown, area 19 contributes some of the fibers.

In addition to the groups above, a parietopontocerebellar system arising from the superior parietal lobule is described. In the monkey these corticopontocerebellar fibers terminate in the rostral two-thirds of the pontine nuclei, in the ventrolateral and lateral cell groups, and the parietopontine group terminates caudally to the other divisions listed above.

Through these extrapyramidal cortical projection systems the cerebral cortex can exert an influence on the pontine nuclei and cerebellar cortical cells. These latter in turn may exert effect on cerebral cortex activity by means of the projection system from the cerebellar dentate nuclei to the thalamus. The dentatothalamic system terminates in the lateral ventral nucleus of the thalamus, which in turn projects to the cortex of areas 6 and 4. It is to be recalled that the rostral part of this thalamic nucleus and the anterior ventral are important links in another circuit of the extrapyramidal system, the corticocaudatothalamic system. The activity of the corticopontocerebellar extrapyramidal system is related primarily to voluntary motor activity, and interruptions of the dentatothalamocortical limb of it are said to be found in many patients having tremors associated with voluntary motor action (see later).

Function of the Extrapyramidal System Based on Experimental and Clinical Study

Foerster was able to evoke massive movement patterns from certain areas of the cerebral cortex when area 4 or its projection was damaged (Fig. 239). These have been described in the preceding chapter. He used very strong stimuli. Since the movement was produced in the absence of a large part of the pyramidal system, he felt that the impulses evoking it traversed extrapyramidal areas, and these were 6*aa* and 6*aβ* (4*a* and 6, respectively, of Von Bonin's map), 3, 1, 2, 5 (Brodmann's 5 and 7), 7 (Brodmann's 39), 8, 19, and 22. These mass movements consisted of either flexor or extensor synergies of the limbs and turning of the head, eyes, and trunk to the contralateral side.

That stimulation of cerebral cortical areas with appropriate stimuli does not always produce movement has also been noted from time to time in the previous discussions. Electrical stimulation of the anterior lip of the precentral sulcus (area 4*s*?) in the human has resulted in the abolition of the resistance to passive movement in the muscles of the contralateral upper limb. The clonic after-discharge movements resulting from suprathreshold stimulation of area 4γ could also be suppressed by such stimulation of this area (287, 353). Stimulation of area 4*s* in the macaque has led to relaxation of standing (extensor) tone, while flexor tone can be relaxed through stimulation of 4*s* and 6, when the medullar pyramids are sectioned. In an animal with pyramidal mechanisms intact and under light ether anesthesia, tonic innervation could be inhibited by stimulation of any part of the whole of area 4. This inhibition was exerted contralaterally, and it could be selectively produced by stimulating fixed points in the cortical area; in other words, a somatotopical arrangement appeared to be present. This topical inhibition transmitted via pyramidal elements may underlie in part reciprocal innervations. After section of the pyramids, stimulation of area 4 in the monkey could not evoke topical inhibition. An inhibition effective bilaterally and without topical localization was obtained. Further, any movement present spontaneously was stopped.

The "Suppressor" Areas

With use of their physiological-neuronography technique in the macaque, Dusser de Barenne and McCulloch reported that the application of strychnine to a small precentral area led to the suppression of the spontaneous electrical activity of area 4γ behind it. They also observed that strychninization of this small precentral area resulted in the suppression of the motor response from any point within area 4γ (221, 222, 223). Their precentral strip was thought to correspond to the anterior strip of area 4 defined physiologically by Hines. It was designated by Dusser de Barenne and McCulloch the precentral "suppressor" area, 4*s*. They later found other "suppressor" areas, 8*s*, 2*s*, 19*s*, and 24*s*, in the cerebral cortex of macaque and chimpanzee. Stimulation of any one of these areas was said to be capable of suppressing the motor response elicited by stimulation of any focus of area 4; of causing a rise in threshold of the motor cortex; of holding in abeyance motor after-discharge; and of relaxing any existing muscular tension (505). These activities were included in suppression of motor response. The suppression of spontaneous cortical electrical activity was found to be more widespread than at first reported. It was found that the application of strychnine to any one of these "suppressor" areas led to suppression of cortical electrical activity not only in area 4γ but throughout the cerebral mantle. The suppression was described as appearing after a latent period and spreading slowly in wavelike fashion from the point strychninized throughout the cortex. As long as 30 min. was required for the wave to spread to remote cortical foci (502, 505). Electrical and mechanical stimulation of these "suppressor" areas was also reported effective in the production of the suppressive activities.

With the demonstration by physiological neuronography of corticostriate fibers from these "suppressor" areas and the knowledge that the thalamus exerts a strong influence on the electrical activity of the cortex, a corticocaudatothalamocortical circuit was postulated as underlying the general suppressive phenomena. The suppression of cortical electrical activity resulted from a blocking at a thalamic level of the thalamocortical activity. The demonstration of the bulbar inhibitory center by Magoun and subsequently, by physiological neuronography, of the corticobulboreticular projection to it from area 4*s* led naturally to the suggestion that the suppression of motor response from area 4γ by 4*s* involved these circuits. Later similar projections from the other "suppressor" areas to the bulbar inhibitory center were demonstrated physiologically. Finally, all "suppressor" areas were found to have corticocortical connections with area 32. Area 24*s* was reported as the most powerful of the "suppressor" areas (816). Muscular contraction existing at the time of stimulation of area 24 was relaxed. Motor activity induced by stimulating the precentral gyrus was suppressed; motor after-discharge was prevented; deep reflexes were abolished. Normal walking has also been suppressed in the unanesthetized cat by stimulation of area 24 (822).

Certain concepts concerning this suppressive system and indeed the existence of specific "suppressor" areas have been questioned recently (141, 142, 534, 535, 729, 730). Evidence has been obtained to support these doubts. Stimulation of the "suppressor" areas in the unanesthetized monkey and dog failed to elicit suppression of motor activity. On the other hand, motor facilitation and bilateral tonic movements have been produced. The wave of spreading suppression attributable to stimulation of specific "suppressor" areas in the anesthetized animal has been evoked at times from any area of the cortex in cat and monkey under certain conditions of stimulation. The wave of suppression of cortical electrical activity produced by stimulation of the "suppressor" or "nonsuppressor" areas in anesthetized animals has been reported as identical to the spreading depression of Leão (473, 474, 535, 730). This latter reaction was first demonstrated in the cortex of rabbits, and it was described as a slowly spreading wave of depression of electrical activity moving through the cortex at a rate of 2 to 3 mm. per min. The depression wave could be set off by mechanical, chemical, or electrical stimulation applied at any focus to the pia-arachnoid membrane. It persisted at any point for 2 to 6 min. A corticocortical mechanism has been suspected as underlying the spreading depression, and in fact mere neural contiguity rather than continuity appears sufficient for its extension (729). The reported suppression of thalamocortical activity at a thalamic level by the suppression wave has not been substantiated (730, 846). In fact, it has been demonstrated that the thalamic suppression is secondary to the reduced cortical activity of its projection areas. As the wave of suppression spreads from one cortical area to another, the thalamic nuclei of projection are affected successively.

Sloan and Jasper have stimulated the anterior limbic area, 24*s*, in lightly anesthetized cats and macaques and have elicited three types of immediate, widespread changes in cortical electrical activity (730). They have described these types of response as attenuation, augmentation, and activation and have produced evidence to support their belief that these responses are produced via corticosubcortical mechanisms. To them the anterior limbic area appears more as a "regulatory" area of cortical activity than a "suppressor." They have suggested that this area is closely related in its activities with the diffuse thalamic reticular system and the brain stem reticular system. It seems fitting to say, then, that the suppression of cortical electrical activity is not a capacity peculiar to "suppressor" areas. Suppression by the cortex of motor activity of subcortical levels is no doubt possible, however.

RESULTS OF STIMULATION AND ABLATION

It can be said that the striatum and pallidum in higher mammals probably have no definite motor function that is independent of cortical action. Electrical stimulation of these nuclei alone, in so far as is possible, has given negative results. Suspecting the close relation between pyramidal and extrapyramidal function, Mettler and his colleagues performed ingenious experiments in cats (540, 541, 547). They found that when a phasic flexion movement had been induced by stimulating area 4, stimulation then of the ipsilateral globus pallidus caused an inhibition of the cortically induced movement, by converting it into a state of plastic tone. The limb muscles then showed no evidence of rigidity or tremor, and the limb was held in a position somewhere between the extremes of the phasic movement. Its position could be altered passively, and the limb would remain equally well in the altered position. Similar findings were true with stimulation of the caudate except that it exerted its influence on movements subcortically as well as cortically induced.

Cats and monkeys with unilateral striatal lesions have shown no definite dysfunction, nor have monkeys or chimpanzees with unilateral lesions of either the caudate or putamen alone. Bilateral lesions of caudate *or* putamen in monkeys and chimpanzees also have been followed by no visible effect on motor performance (430, 432). Bilateral striate injuries in cats, usually made in connection with bilateral removal of frontal cortex, were followed by increased movement and by tardy defense reactions which, when once aroused, resulted in a continuous activity regardless of danger or obstacles obstructing progress (541, 549). Increased movement usually followed bilateral removal of frontal cortex alone. Similar findings have been reported if the striate removals were made without previous cortical ablation (350). Such cats also bumped into stationary objects. They appeared disoriented and out of contact with their environment. They showed no interest in food and were refractory to vestibular, auditory, and visual stimuli. They did not withdraw from painful stimulation. Most interesting, perhaps, was the fact that the cats died in 3 to 5 days if the bilateral striate removal was carried out at one stage. It was reasoned that the striatum has a specific influence on metabolic function. Unilateral lesions of the globus pallidus in monkeys gave no permanent defect except a failure to use the hand opposite the lesion as well as the other. Bilateral pallidal lesions were followed by some motor weakness, difficulty in fine prehension, increase in resistance to passive movement, and pronounced tremor, the tremor being worse when the musculature was under tension or during voluntary movement (430, 432). These monkeys, however, necessarily had bilateral injuries to the motor cortex, particularly to the face areas, and such an injury may have contributed to the postoperative behavior.

Electrical stimulation of the subthalamus in cats has given alternating movements of the legs similar to those of normal walking and running (802). The locomotor point in the subthalamus seemed to be in Forel's field *H* at the level of the subthalamic nucleus of Luys. This activity of the subthalamus was apparently expressed by impulses descending through the tegmentum dorsolateral to the red nucleus and relayed in reticular nuclei.

Selective, discrete electrolytic lesions of a subthalamic nucleus in macaques have been followed by involuntary choreiform movements in a contralateral extremity (837). In some instances the movements approached the violence of the ballistic movements seen in humans coincident to injury in the vicinity of the subthalamic nucleus. Occasionally, when a customarily provocative subthalamic destruction was combined with damage to the ipsilateral lenticular fasciculus, thalamic fasciculus, or pallidum, the hyperkinetic phenomena did not appear. The involuntary movements resulting from subthalamic injury are perhaps then an expression of disordered neural activity of the pallidum caused by the loss of the controlling or suppressive subthalamic influence.

Electrical stimulation of the substantia nigra, in normal cats as well as in cats with motor cortex removed and in cats with pyramid section, has resulted usually in extension of both forelegs, but particularly of the one opposite the side stimulated. In normal cats in which cortical stimulation was followed by stimulation of the nigra, a reduction in the amplitude of the cortically induced phasic reaction occurred and a tremor developed (541).

Cats with bilateral lesions of the red nuclei retain their righting reactions but show dysmetria of gait, with overstepping and skating movements of the limbs, and retarded and hypermetric hopping reactions. They also demonstrate consistent increases in extensor tonus, as shown by extension of the limbs when the cats are suspended and by clear-cut resistance to passive flexion. Although no alteration in extensor tonus follows rubrospinal lesions in monkeys, a transient ataxia and tremor are present, signs attributable to the interruption of the dentatorubrothalamic connections. In man, red-nucleus lesions are said to be followed by hypotonia. In the human, the red nucleus contains fewer of the large cells, the destruction of which in cats is thought to lead to the hypertonia. Electrical stimulation of the red nuclei in cats and monkeys has been described as causing ipsilateral forelimb flexion and contralateral forelimb extension, with curvature of the head, body, and tail, the concavity being toward the side of stimulation. Stimulation in the tegmentum near the red nucleus has resulted in bending of the rostral and caudal parts of the body toward the stimulated side, and the curvature of the trunk is maintained for the duration of the stimulus (541).

In studies to determine the anatomical and functional relations of brain stem extrapyramidal mechanisms in the monkey. Magoun and his co-workers have destroyed various nuclei and pathways (624, 819). When the subthalamus or midbrain tegmentum was injured, the motor activity, somatic and visceral, was substantially reduced, occasionally to the state of complete akinesia. After an area of destruction involving the medial thalamic nucleus, centrum medianum, and mesencephalic tegmentum and periaqueductal gray, stupor or coma was added to the akinesia. When the rostral midbrain tegmentum was destroyed, spasticity was produced. This was interpreted as resulting from destruction of suppressor relays traversing this tegmental region and transmitting impulses from the basal ganglia to the bulbar inhibitory center. The cerebral suppressor inflows to the center traversing the basis pedunculi and the cerebellar suppressor inflows more caudal in the tegmentum were not damaged. When the fibers of the superior cerebellar peduncle were damaged, the animals demonstrated **action tremors** accompanying voluntary movement. This was similar to the tremor which follows destruction of the human neocerebellum or its discharge path. With destruction of the ventromedial midbrain tegmentum, dorsal to the central part of the substantia nigra, a **postural tremor** was produced. This was characterized by alternating contractions in agonists and antagonists at a rate of 6 to 8 per sec., and it was thought to be comparable to the so-called static or alternating tremor seen in humans in parkinsonism (see later). The mechanisms underlying the production of action and postural or alternating tremors are not understood. It is at present unknown how the anterior horn cells which discharge to agonist and antagonist muscle groups are brought to the stage of constant regularly alternating volleys, in contrast to the irregular stream of volleys which subserve normal posture.

The effect of **extirpation** of various extrapyramidal cortical areas has been more widely investigated in animals than man. Few ablations of the human cerebrum have been limited to a single area, and disease processes are seldom limited to single regions. Following Foerster's classification, areas 6, 8, 3, 1, 2, 5, 7, 19, and 22 may be listed as extrapyramidal cortical areas. It was from these that he evoked complex movement patterns. To these area 24 may be added as a result of experiences in macaques. Foerster has described the result of removal of area 6 and in the Von Bonin terminology this would have probably involved the areas *4a*, *4s*, and 6. After such extirpation, slowness of movement of the contralateral extremities was observed, together with difficulty in turning the head and trunk to the opposite side. The patient was unable to perform well rapidly alternating movements and complex sequential acts, but his ability to carry out isolated single movements was judged normal. Though Foerster made no mention of such a sign, other clinical reporters of disease process in the vicinity of area 6 have described a **grasp reflex** with such disorder. This reflex is characterized by strong flexion of the fingers in response to gentle stimulation of the palmar skin. If the examiner lightly places one of his own fingers, or a long object such as a tongue blade, into contact with the skin of the palm contralateral to the damaged area 6, the patient's fingers quickly flex about the object and are relaxed with difficulty. If the patient lies on his side with the affected limb uppermost, the reflex is exaggerated, and if the affected limb is below the reflex is diminshed. Young infants normally demonstrate the grasp reflex in response to cutaneous and proprioceptive stimulation. It normally disappears with the acquisition of voluntary motor activity. It should be noted that a grasp reflex can be demonstrated in patients with diffuse cerebral disease, especially when they are in a stuporous condition.

Ablations from area 8 in the human might be expected to result acutely in deviation of the eyes toward the side of the lesion together with an inability to move the eyes toward the normal side. Such ocular disorder is observed early in vascular destruction of this frontal region or of its projections. Further, extirpation of area 8 in the macaque is followed by deviation of the eyes toward the side of the lesion. The result of ablation of the postcentral region is discussed more fully in a later section, but certain features may be mentioned here. Atrophy, or rather, failure to develop occurs in the contralateral extremities when a human suffers damage to his parietal areas in early life (623, 844). It has not been observed in several monkeys from which the major part of the parietal lobe has been removed bilaterally in infancy. Removal of the postcentral gyri in the adult monkey gives rise to certain disorders of movement in the contralateral limbs as well as of sensation (607). Sensory ataxia is present in the contralateral limbs when the animal does not watch his performance, abnormal postures are not corrected, hypotonia and diminished deep reflexes are found, movement is slow, and atrophy of the muscles may occur. Ablation of area 19 in humans by Foerster was followed by a deviation of the eyes to the side of the removal and an inability to turn the eyes to the opposite side (252). Removal of temporal areas including area 22 in the monkey does not result in motor deficit. Ablation of area 24 in the monkey results in a loss of mimetic activity and grooming procedures. A loss of fear of man, a loss of signs of affection, and a development of indifference to fellow monkeys have been described (817). Disorder of muscle tone or of complex learned movement was not reported.

EXTRAPYRAMIDAL INHIBITORY AND FACILITATORY MECHANISMS

Numerous experimental studies by Magoun, Rhines, McCulloch, and their colleagues have indicated that two fundamental mechanisms which influence segmental motor activities are demonstrable in the tegmentum of the brain stem (528). These have been referred to previously from time to time in the text. The mechanisms include one of *suppressor* character and another of *facilitatory* character (Fig. 262). The investigations began with the demonstration that it was possible in cats to suppress movement, cortically or reflexly induced, by stimulating the ventromedial medullar tegmental reticular formation. Subsequent studies, and researches by other workers as well, have served to show that this **bulbar inhibitory** or suppressor **region** receives impulses from area 4*s* and other "suppressor" areas of the cortex, from loci in the cerebellum, especially its anterior lobe, fastigial and perhaps interpositus nuclei, and from the basal ganglia, especially caudate and putamen. Cortical suppressor fibers have been definitely identified as springing from area 4*s*. In the experimental animals, they accompany the corticospinal fibers at least to the level of basis pedunculi but become divergent below that level. The cerebellar suppressor fibers are included apparently in fastigiobulbar systems traversing the juxtarestiform body to reach the bulbar inhibitory center. The suppressor path from the basal ganglia may be a relay system. The caudate discharges to the pallidus and nigra, which in turn have relays to the midbrain tegmental areas. These last discharge to the bulbar inhibitory center. It is thought that the rubrospinal system is not involved in these relays, but a decussation of the basal ganglia suppressor system apparently takes place at the level of the red nuclei. From this bulbar inhibitory center reticulospinal fibers pass into the spinal cord and presumably to segmental (cranial-nerve) motor mechanisms in the brain stem. If all the incoming impulses to the bulbar inhibitory center are cut off, the center itself is incapable of maintaining suppressor activity.

The anatomy of the facilitatory mechanism is gradually evolving also. During the initial studies leading to the recognition of the bulbar inhibitory center, it was learned that it was possible to increase the excursion of the patellar reflex, for example, by stimulating points in the lateral region of the medulla and in the periphery of the inhibitory zone. It was suspected that the increased excursion of the patellar reflex resulted from the stimulation of facilitatory mechanisms resident in, or traversing, the lateral medullar tegmentum. Subsequent studies by Magoun and Rhines, as well as by Murphy and Gellhorn, served to show that cortically induced movement could be facilitated by simultaneous hypothalamic stimulation (576, 665). It has been learned, moreover, that facilitation of cortically induced movement can be produced by stimulating the subthalamus, hypothalamus, central gray and tegmentum of the midbrain, the pontile tegmentum, and the medullar reticular formation.

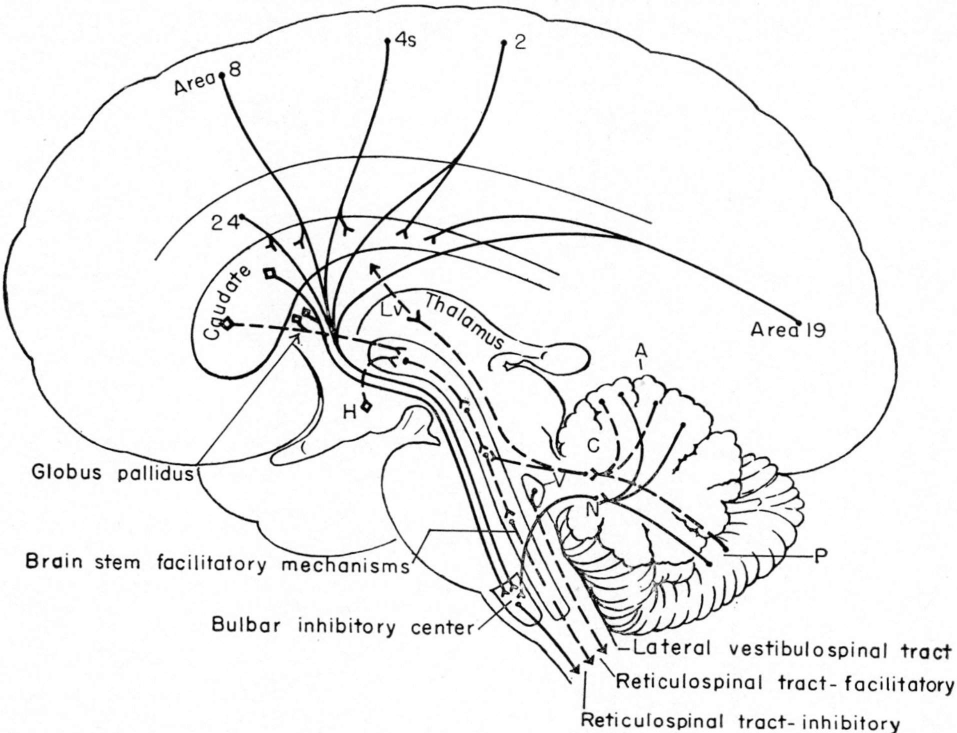

FIG. 262. Schema of certain suppressor mechanisms. Based on experimental data in macaque, adapted to human. Solid lines, inhibitory mechanisms; broken lines, facilitatory mechanisms. *A*, anterior lobe, cerebellum; *CN*, cerebellar nuclei; *H*, hypothalamus; *Lv*, lateral ventral nucleus of thalamus; *P*, paramedian lobe, cerebellum; *V*, vestibular nuclei.

This facilitating mechanism also relays into the spinal cord by reticulospinal fibers (547, 548, 582). A series of tegmental relays compose this brain stem facilitatory system, and the more cephalad ones can be destroyed without impairing the activity of those more caudally situated. The critical level of destruction, in cats at least, seems to be at the pontomedullar junction, since reticulospinal facilitation was greatly diminished, though not abolished, when the system was interrupted at and just below that level. Some lesser facilitatory elements are apparently present in the medullar reticular formation (582). In the cat, facilitatory reticulospinal tracts were found to arise from each level of the brain stem. This, it will be recalled, is in contrast to the arrangement of suppressor reticulospinal tracts, which arise only in the medulla. Furthermore, the facilitation expressed by one side of the brain stem, like the inhibition, is exerted on both sides of the spinal cord. Brain stem and spinal decussations exist in the facilitating reticulospinal systems, only spinal crossings in the suppressor ones. Both systems of reticulospinal fibers are present in the lateral and ventral funiculi, especially in the ventral part of the lateral.

It is the opinion of Magoun that the facilitation mechanism of cortically induced movement is not only an ascending one acting at the cortical level but certainly also a descending one, expressing facilitation at spinal levels. Facilitation of movement produced by stimulation of the medullar pyramid, in an animal with cortex ablated, appeared to indicate that the process did not always occur at cortical levels.

In addition to this tegmental reticulospinal facilitating system, there are others. It has long been known that the corticospinal system belongs in this category, maintaining both tonic and phasic facilitatory effects on spinal and brain stem segmental motor units. Both the frontal and parietal lobes give rise to facilitatory impulses. The cerebellum, moreover, also is included in the facilitatory systems, its middle lobe, especially, in man. When the middle lobe, or neocerebellum, is destroyed acutely, a condition of hypotonia exists. It seems to be true that this facilitating influence on spinal activity, in animals at least, is exerted over fastigiobulbar paths also. It may play into the tegmental facilitatory system. Finally, the vestibular nuclei and vestibulospinal tracts are facilitatory mechanisms for brain stem and spinal motor neurons.

Normally, a balance is thought to exist in the activities of the suppressor and facilitatory mechanisms at rest, and such adjustments as are necessary for phasic movement as well as for postural activity are smoothly arranged. When the balance is upset by disease process or by experimentally induced lesions, varied symptomatology presents itself, most often in the nature of involuntary movements, loss of certain normal movements, and the presence of abnormal states of muscle tone, spasticity, rigidity, or hypotonia, with or without increased deep reflexes. For example, spasticity can be produced by destruction of one or more of the suppressor inflows to the bulbar inhibitory center. Characteristically it is seen in its mildest form with disorder in area 4*s*; it increases in amount with larger disturbance of the precentral gyrus, or with destruction of precentral gyrus projections at a capsular level, or at the level of basis pedunculi. Destructions at these last two levels perhaps also cause damage to the basal ganglia suppressor flow in addition to the corticoreticular outflow. In such instances the undamaged facilitatory mechanisms and the tegmental reticulospinal and vestibulospinal systems maintain the spasticity (486, 711). Decerebrate rigidity, as noted previously, is similarly maintained by both reticulospinal and vestibulospinal impulses. The postural tremor, produced experimentally as described, may be maintained by activity generated in facilitating reticulospinal systems. It may be dependent to a certain extent on the continuous tonic corticospinal activity, since the tremor can be abolished, temporarily at least, by severing the corticospinal tracts, or damaging the cortical area from which they arise in greatest number. Damage to the tegmental facilitatory system, especially at its rostral levels, results in a hypokinetic condition in the monkey that has been compared to that present in human cases of parkinsonism (665, 819).

More recent studies of the brain stem tegmentum have been concerned with its relation to cortical activity (485, 571). It has been learned that stimulation of the reticular formation in animals produces changes in the electroencephalogram. These changes consisted in the abolition of synchronized cortical discharge and the introduction in its place of low-voltage, fast activity. The "resting or relaxed" electroencephalogram was converted to one similar to that produced by any type of afferent stimulus that arouses the subject to alertness. The effect on cortical activity was most pronounced in the ipsilateral hemisphere, especially the anterior part, but it was also observed in both hemispheres. The effect was produced by stimulating the medial tegmental area at medullar, pontine, and mesencephalic levels, as well as by stimulating dorsal hypothalamic and subthalamic levels. An ascending system of reticuloreticular relays present in the central tegmentum apparently underlies this activity, and the diffuse thalamic projection system to the cerebral cortex may be the intermediary between reticular formation and cerebral mantle. When this ascending reticular activating system was selectively destroyed, or interrupted, at mesencephalic or basal diencephalic levels, the resulting electroencephalogram was comparable to that seen in normal sleep or in a condition of anesthesia induced by barbiturates. It has been suggested that the continuous influence of this brain stem activating system underlies wakefulness, while absence of the influence results in the production of sleep. Collateral fibers from the ascending sensory pathways, the spinothalamics, medial lemnisci, and lateral lemnisci, transmit afferent impulses into this reticular system, in which they are maintained. Perhaps visual impulses enter via the tectum. Certainly, investigations into the activity of this larger tegmental system of neurons and fibers give promise of further elucidating the mechanisms of central neural integrations.

Electrostriatograms have been recorded from the human in the course of operative procedures (346). The putamen, head of the caudate, globus pallidus, and subcallosal bundle were investigated. The frequency of the electrostriatogram exceeded that of the electroencephalogram recorded from the scalp. As is characteristic of the latter, however, individual variations were also found in the rhythms recorded from the basal ganglia. The activity in the head of the caudate or the putamen or both had almost continuously an electric sign opposite to that of the surrounding zones. It was suggested that this region may serve as a pacemaker. Neither the performance of voluntary movements nor the stimulation with a pinprick caused a noticeable alteration in the basal ganglion activity. It was possible to follow electrical activity from the hypothalamus successively through thalamus, basal ganglia, and cortex in patients who became drowsy spontaneously or as a result of Seconal medication. The basal ganglia are no doubt significantly involved in the neural mechanisms underlying the sleeping and waking states as well as in the maintenance of attentiveness and general well-being.

Symptomatology Associated with Extrapyramidal Motor Disorder

Two basic disorders underlie the symptomatology usually seen in diseases of the extrapyramidal motor system. These are disorders of muscle tone and involuntary movements (412). The disorders of muscle tone may be so severe, *i.e.,* such hypertonia may exist, that volitional and emotional movements are suppressed or lacking to such an extent that the patient appears paralyzed. He does not alter facial expressions easily or frequently, he does not often blink, he does not swing his arms while walking, he does not make the rapid postural movements which accompany the assumption of erect posture from a sitting position, and he frequently remains quiet for long intervals without any volitional movement. Some of this poverty of movement is due to increased muscle tone; some is due to a suppression of certain associated postural movements that accompany voluntary movements of the limbs. It can be easily demonstrated, however, that the patient is not paralyzed.

The disorder of muscle tone is most often one of increased muscle tone. Fundamentally it is due to disorder similar to that which underlies spasticity described before; *i.e.,* the stretch reflexes are heightened as a result of a lowering of their threshold or a facilitation of their activity. In **spasticity,** the heightened reflexes and the increased tone are seen especially in the muscles the contractions of which usually oppose the pull of gravity. It has been stated earlier that spasticity occurs when certain of the extrapyramidal projections to the bulbar inhibitory center are interrupted, and it is seen in its mildest and most characteristic form when those projections from the area 4*s,* especially, to the bulbar inhibitory center, are interrupted. The increased muscle tone which accompanies widespread frontal-lobe disease or disorder of the subcortical members of the extrapyramidal system is not topically distributed and is observed in all muscle groups except possibly those of the eyes. Such generalized heightening in stretch-reflex mechanisms, or widespread disorder of muscle tone, is clinically referred to as **rigidity.** This may be of two types, a plastic rigidity and a cogwheel rigidity. In the former condition, the hypertonia in the muscles can be demonstrated by passive stretching, a smooth, continuous resistance being felt throughout the arc of the passive stretch. In cogwheel rigidity, the resistance is not continuous but is frequently and transiently abolished and then reestablished. These diverse manifestations of increased muscle tone are varying degrees of the same physiologic disorder, and are thought to depend on the varying amounts of damage to extrapyramidal mechanisms. The greater the disturbance of suppressing mechanisms, or the more the balance of power swings toward facilitating mechanisms, the greater the influx of facilitating impulses from supraspinal centers to segmental motor arcs, and the more intense and more widespread is the increased activity of stretch reflexes, or hypertonia. In certain disorders of the extrapyramidal motor systems, the facilitating mechanisms are presumably more damaged, and the patients have hypotonia. In other cases, rapid alterations of muscle tone are found, hypotonia or normal tone giving way to hypertonia, temporarily.

The involuntary movements which are usually seen in diseases of the extrapyramidal motor system are of various types. These include **tremors,** postural or static, and action or intention; **choreiform movements; athetosis; hemiballism;** and **dystonia.** The mechanisms by which these various movements are produced and sustained are not clear, although underlying all of them may be a similar fundamental disturbance of motor performance.

The tremors that occur at rest are referred to as postural, static, or alternating tremors. They characteristically can be seen to be alternating activity in agonist and antagonist muscles, at a rate of alternations of about 5 per sec. Alternate flexion-extension, supination-pronation, or adduction-abduction movements can be seen. In the hands, for example, the so-called "pill-rolling" tremor is seen in the involuntary movements performed by the thumb and other fingers. In reality, the tremor is seen in muscles that are engaged in the maintenance of a posture by a semivoluntary effort, and the term postural tremor seems more fitting.

The postural tremor is usually suppressed during voluntary activity; on the other hand, it may be intensified. It is more severe at times of emotional stress; it may disappear at complete rest, and it disappears in sleep. The action or intention tremor always accompanies voluntary movements. The frequency of these tremors increases as the ultimate goal of the voluntary movement is approached. At times of rest these are not present in mild cases; in severe cases the long continued maintenance of a posture of head or limb may result in the initiation of these tremors.

Choreiform movements are rapid, jerky movements that may appear to be somewhat purposive in character. Rapid, isolated flexion of a finger, abduction of an arm, elevation of a shoulder, a grimace about the lips, or a twitch of a facial muscle are patterns frequently seen. These movements may occur at rest or may accompany voluntary movements. They are frequently associated with hypotonia. Athetosis is a slow, involuntary movement pattern. It may occur at rest or may be particularly noticeable in association with voluntary movement. It is not usually of a purposive character. The athetoid movements develop slowly and, as seen in the hands, may consist in alternating hyperextension and flexion postures of the fingers, usually with associated abductions. The wrist is frequently slowly flexed and pronated as the fingers flex, and the arm may be retracted. Because of their slow, writhing character, they appear serpentine. Grimaces about the face may accompany the limb movements. Athetosis is associated with hypertonia but the muscles are hypotonic when quiet. Occasionally mixed types of involuntary movements may occur such as choreo-athetosis. Dystonic movements involve especially the axial and proximal limb muscles and lead to severe twisting or rotational movements involving cervicothoracic or lumbar spine. Muscle tone is increased during the movements and diminished in the intervals of relaxation. Hemiballism is characterized by severe involuntary movements of an entire limb, the movements appearing to begin proximally, to move distally, and to involve wide arcs of wild swinging, especially of the arms. Twisting or rolling, wavelike patterns appear to flow down the arm at times.

The correlation of destruction of a particular extrapyramidal nucleus with the appearance of a specific form of involuntary movement clinically can seldom be made. All the movements perhaps represent the overactivity of certain parts of the motor system in the absence of the supportive or controlling influence of the diseased nucleus or nuclei. They may appear as signs of release or as a result of excessive facilitation when normal suppression is lacking. Currently, however, the mechanisms underlying the production and maintenance of involuntary movements are not known. Bucy has compiled some interesting diagrams which combine certain known anatomical facts and other supposed ones that might serve to explain the disorders (116, 118).

Disease Processes Involving the Extrapyramidal System

With the exception of hemiballism, which is most often of sudden onset in association with disease of the vascular supply to the subthalamus, the symptomatology of the diseases of the extrapyramidal system evolves gradually and is usually the result of chronic, progressive disorder. One of the most common diseases of the extrapyramidal motor system is **paralysis agitans**, or **Parkinson's disease.** This disorder most often has its clinical onset between the ages of forty-five and fifty-five and is associated with degeneration of the neuronal elements of the globus pallidus and substantia nigra, especially, and to a less extent, of the putamen and caudate. The cause of the degeneration is unknown. Characteristically, the patients have muscular rigidity and postural tremor. The rigidity, plastic or cogwheel in type, involves all the muscles, especially those of the trunk, and leads to the assumption of a flexed posture. The tremors involve particularly the distal muscles of the extremities, occur at the rate of about 5 per sec., occur at rest, and frequently disappear with voluntary movement, although this may occasionally make them worse.

A similar rigidity-tremor syndrome is seen with the disease **epidemic encephalitis,** or encephalitis lethargica. The syndrome occurs in some cases as a manifestation of the acute phase of the disease. More often, it is a later developing complication or progressive residuum (77). Encephalitic parkinsonism may be seen at any age, but is most common in young adults. The tremors are frequently of a more rapidly alternating type of about 8 per sec., and the rigidity may be more pronounced than that seen with paralysis agitans. Various disorders of the autonomic nervous system are also occasionally seen; these perhaps indicate involvement of hypothalamic centers. In patients between fifty-five and sixty-five and older, parkinsonlike syndromes may occur in association with widespread cerebral arteriosclerosis. These cases are more apt to show rigidity as the striking manifestation, and less often do the patients have involuntary movements. Because of the rigidity the erect and sitting postures are altered, usually an attitude of flexion is assumed, and gait disturbances characterized by short, rapid steps and loss of balance with rapid turning are prominent. The Parkinson symptom complex may be seen in patients after carbon monoxide or manganese intoxications. On the basis of his post-mortem pathological studies, Davison has reported that when rigidity was the outstanding symptom in parkinsonism, the globus pallidus and reticular portion of the substantia nigra were most often found severely damaged (201). When tremor was an outstanding symptom, the compact zone of the substantia nigra was frequently damaged and the pallidum was less involved.

In **hepatolenticular degeneration,** or **Wilson's disease,** severe disorder of muscle tone and a variety of involuntary movements, especially action tremors, are seen. A hepatitis is often recognized early in the disease. Later, the hepatitis is followed by cirrhosis and signs of obstruction to the portal circulation occur. The disease is associated with a disordered copper metabolism, increased amounts of the metal being present in the urine. Emotional instability, with frequent crying or spontaneous laughter, is prominent. Rigidity may be very incapacitating, leading to disorder of posture, of gait, and of complex movement. Choreic, athetoid, and dystonic movements may be seen. In many of the cases a ring of golden brown pigmentation, the Kayser-Fleischer ring, is noted near the outer margin of the cornea; this is considered pathognomonic of the disorder. Though degenerative changes are found especially in the putamen, in which softening and cavitation may be grossly visible, they are widespread throughout the nervous system.

Choreic movements are seen notably in **Sydenham's** and **Huntington's chorea.** The former characteristically is a disease of childhood, occurring as a feature of rheumatic fever. It is characterized by the rapid involuntary movements, the incoordination of voluntary movement they produce, and some muscular weakness. Inflammatory changes are diffusely spread through the nuclear centers in cerebral cortex, basal ganglia, brain stem, and cerebellum. Huntington's chorea occurs always in adults and usually has its onset between ages thirty-five and forty. It has a strong heredofamilial incidence and is characterized by moderate or severe involuntary choreiform movements and progressive mental deterioration. Degenerations, as expected, are found in cerebral cortex and basal ganglia. Choreiform movements may be seen also as a manifestation of the Parkinson syndrome, in Wilson's disease, in certain inflammatory diseases and intoxications, and occasionally as a complication of toxemia of pregnancy.

Athetosis and dystonic movements may also be seen as variants of the Parkinson syndrome, particularly the encephalitic variety, and dystonia is common in Wilson's disease. Athetosis may be seen in children in a variety of pathological conditions characterized by degenerative and fibrotic or anomalous developmental changes in the putamen and globus pallidus. Infantile hemiplegia with disorder of the pyramidal system may be seen. **Dystonia musculorum deformans,** or torsion spasm, is a progressive disease beginning most often in the first or second decade. It is characterized by the frequent, maintained tonic contractions of axial muscles which lead to the bizarre twisting postures. Degenerations have been found in putamen, globus pallidus, subthalamic nucleus, and dentate nucleus. **Hemiballism** is associated with destruction of the subthalamic nucleus (562). Tumor and tuberculoma may occasionally destroy the nucleus and lead to the production of the severe movements, but softening resulting from vascular disease is most often found.

Some Physiologic Interpretations of Extrapyramidal Disorder

Some help in the elucidation of the mechanisms underlying the symptoms of the various diseases of the extrapyramidal system has been obtained from study of muscle activity in these disorders and from comparing it with that found in normally acting muscles. Such activity may be studied by placing electrodes on the skin over the muscle or by implanting them within the muscle itself. Muscle action potentials then can be recorded as an electromyogram. Simultaneous recording of action potentials of synergistic and antagonistic muscles may be made. By using several electrodes in the same muscle, the distribution of activity of the motor units (the spinal anterior gray column cell, its axon, and the muscle fibers which it innervates) of a single muscle has been learned (376). Such studies have revealed that normal muscle at rest shows no measurable action potentials, though it is under constant mechanical tension. During active voluntary movement it has been found that the motor impulses were out of phase. While one group of units showed activity, others were inactive. Such nonsynchronization of impulses was characteristic of normal muscle activity, but the action of the entire muscle was smooth because there was smooth alternation in the activity of the various units. In spastic muscles there was synchronization of the motor impulses with simultaneous activation of many units giving spurts of activity. The myotatic, or stretch, reflexes were found increased, but balanced in protagonist and antagonist muscles. Strong contraction in a protagonist set up stretch reflexes in the antagonist, which then contracted, setting up similar impulses in the protagonist. In such a way an alternating contraction and relaxation may be produced, resulting in the condition known as clonus. In spastic muscles no measurable action potentials were found at rest. In rigidity, however, a basic activity was always seen in resting muscles. With voluntary movement of rigid muscles there was again synchronization of impulses, increased myotatic reflexes, and thus much activity in both protagonists and antagonists. Tremor was found to have central mechanisms similar to those of rigidity. The muscles involved by tremor showed rhythmic bursts of synchronized motor-unit discharges. In athetosis and chorea there was no activity in the muscles at rest, and as in normal muscles, voluntary activity showed asynchronization of motor impulses. The fact that there was similar irregular simultaneous innervation of antagonist muscles caused irregular movements. Fundamentally, disturbance in the timing of the nerve impulses to the muscles characterized disorders of the extrapyramidal system. This was true not only in individual muscles but also in the relations between agonist and antagonist muscles.

The electrical activity in the skeletal muscles which are the site of hypertonia or hypotonia, and of various involuntary movements, is to a great extent an immediate expression of the neuronal activity in the spinal (and cranial-nerve) motor neurons. These last are played upon by impulses coming from the periphery as well as from intrinsic spinal and supraspinal neurons. The supraspinal neurons exert their effect by way of long and short, or relay, paths, and certain of these paths end directly about the discharging anterior horn neuron. Others end about an intercalary neuron, the activity of which in turn influences the motor neurons whose axons pass out to the muscles. It has been demonstrated experimentally that the two-neuron spinal reflex, the type to which the stretch reflex underlying muscle tone belongs, can be facilitated by supraspinal influences. Combined stimulation of the dorsal root involved in the reflex and facilitatory reticulospinal fibers was carried out. When the reticulospinal stimulus was introduced sufficiently far in advance of that applied to the dorsal root so that the activity of relay and internuncial neurons in its path could be also expressed, the facilitation of the stretch reflex was greatest (489, 490). Suppressor activity can similarly influence spinal motor activity. The discharge of these motor neurons then will depend on the summative effects of supraspinal, spinal, and peripheral facilitatory and inhibitory impulses. The experimental studies of Magoun and his co-workers are beginning to elucidate the nature of the activity of supraspinal neurons, especially those of the tegmental reticular formation. Strong facilitatory and inhibitory regions have been defined as described previously. These receive impulses from cortical areas directly, as well as indirectly through basal ganglia. They are also recipient of cerebellar impulses, and the cerebellum receives impulses from the cerebral cortex via the corticopontine systems, and from the basal ganglia via the tegmento-olivary relays. Cerebral cortex, cerebellum, tegmental reticular formation, and, probably, basal ganglia and allied neurons, all receive afferent impulses from the peripheral receptors. The tectum and nuclei associated with the posterior commissure, which receive impulses from the cortex and periphery, also discharge to reticular formation as well as to spinal and cranial nerve nuclear motor neurons. Vestibular nuclei in contact with the labyrinth also receive impulses from the cerebellum, and perhaps also from the cerebral cortex. They discharge to segmental neurons at spinal and brain stem levels. And finally, the precentral gyrus and certain other cerebral cortex regions which project to the numerous subcortical extrapyramidal centers also send impulses via corticospinal and corticobulbar tracts to the segmental motor neurons directly, and indirectly through neighboring internuncial neurons. Voluntary, skillful motor performance is therefore an expression of the interrelated activity of the total motor apparatus, a summation of facilitatory and inhibitory effects, exerted continuously but subject to rapid alterations with the initiation of phasic activity.

When a member of this motor apparatus is destroyed, the resulting movement, voluntary and involuntary, and the resulting state of muscle tone are a product of the actvity of the remaining, undamaged members of the motor apparatus. Resident in all the members normally are certain neurons engaged in facilitatory activities and others engaged in inhibitory activities. Disease processes can affect the motor performance by destroying facilitatory influences. A deficit of performance results thereby, because of lack of influx influences supplied to the segmental motor apparatus, together with an unchecked suppressor system also playing on them. On the other hand, disease processes can affect motor performance by damaging primarily the inhibitory influences and rendering thereby overactive the segmental motor apparatus, because it is "released" from the inhibition, and at the same time the influence on it of the facilitatory mechanisms is unchecked. Normal motor performance was originally considered by Hughlings Jackson to result from a sum of influx and suppression integrated through several levels of neural activity and discharged to spinal motor neurons, which activated certain muscles and inhibited others. Disordered motor performance results from loss of influx and excessive suppression in some instances, release from suppression and preservation of influx in others. It is generally true that facilitatory and inhibitory systems are damaged simultaneously clinically, and the resulting motor performance will depend on the product of facilitatory and inhibitory activity left undamaged.

Certain interpretations of the mechanisms at work in the production of abnormal motor performance have come from Magoun and his colleagues. Persisting, increased muscle tone, resulting from disease processes, depends chiefly for its production on the activity of facilitatory reticulospinal and vestibulospinal centers exerted on the stretch reflexes. Increased deep reflexes and clonus presumably result from similar activity. When suppressor mechanisms only are destroyed, the spinal stretch reflex underlying muscle tone is not intrinsically capable of exaggeration. The exaggeration resulting from experimental damage to suppressor mechanisms was transient, but it was more pronounced and enduring after combined lesions of both cerebral and cerebellar suppressor systems. In fact, a condition resembling rigidity has been produced experimentally by combined ablation of anterior lobe of the cerebellum and cerebral motor area (739). After a period of time, however, some reduction of hypertonia usually occurs, especially in the flexor muscles (711). Postural tremor, experimentally induced by destroying ventral mesencephalic tegmentum, depends for its maintenance on alternating discharges most probably arising in undamaged caudal reticulospinal neurons, facilitatory and inhibitory. These discharges play upon spinal motor neurons that are simultaneously being activated by vestibulospinal and corticospinal paths. The spinal neurons are thus brought to discharge to agonist and antagonist muscle, repetitively. Action tremors, induced experimentally by interruptions of the superior cerebellar peduncle, are conceivably the result of facilitatory impulses arising at a cerebral cortex level and acting in the presence of imbalance in cerebellar inhibitory and facilitatory mechanisms.

Surgery in Extrapyramidal Disorders

Surgical procedures have been devised for the relief of the involuntary movements of extrapyramidal disease in humans. Many of these have not been successful, and the reason for the lack of success probably is to be found in analyses of the experimental results of Magoun and colleagues. Spasticity has been attacked by a ventromedial chordotomy by which vestibulospinal fibers, especially, were to be sectioned (114). This was not successful, presumably because reticulospinal facilitatory mechanisms were left undamaged in the ventrolateral and lateral regions of the spinal white matter. Section of the lateral funiculus in man has also not reduced spasticity (640). Bilateral anterolateral chordotomy has been somewhat successful in relieving extensor spasm (405, 406). A patient who had unilateral tremor at rest, as well as with voluntary movement, most noticeable in the arm, was relieved of his tremors permanently (and of some voluntary movement also) by extirpation of the contralateral precentral "arm" area (areas 4 and 6) (119). This result, together with the fact that patients with tremor at rest who subsequently suffer capsular hemiplegia lose the tremor when the hemiplegia occurs, indicates that certain of the impulses, at least, which maintain tremor at rest arise at a cortical level and travel via the pyramidal tract (642). It has been shown experimentally, however, that postural tremor recurs as the animal gradually regains the voluntary movement, lost as a result of precentral-gyrus ablation that was performed in an effort to abolish the tremor. This fact, together with the report that the experimentally induced postural tremor could not be correlated with rhythmic alteration in the electroencephalogram of cerebral motor areas, lends support to the idea that the reticulospinal systems, chiefly, maintain the tremor, even though pyramidal impulses contribute. That pyramidal fibers do contribute to the maintenance of the postural tremor in man seems apparent from the reports of Putnam and others that lateral corticospinal-tract section at a cervical level has considerably relieved such tremor (226, 641). Surgical lesions which interrupt pallidofugal fibers near their point of origin from the globus pallidus have been reported also to abolish postural tremor (556, 557). In such instances the rostral tegmental facilitatory system may have been damaged. Involuntary movements characterized as choreo-athetosis have been abolished by extirpations from the precentral motor area and have been lessened by anterolateral chordotomy. Because of these results, it is the opinion of Bucy that the choreo-athetoid movements are produced by nervous impulses arising in the precentral motor cortex and traveling thence through certain subcortical centers. These latter in turn discharge spinalward via extrapyramidal fibers traveling predominantly in the anterior funiculus (118). It has been mentioned previously that inhibitory and facilitatory reticulospinal fibers are dispersed throughout both the anterior and lateral funiculus. Hemiballism has recently yielded to a surgical procedure in which an incision, roughly parallel to the central fissure, was made sufficiently deep into the precentral gyrus to sever U-association fibers passing between areas 4 and 6 (558). Walker has reported that section of the outer two-thirds of the basis pedunculi is successful in diminishing hemiballistic and other forms of involuntary movement (799). Ligation of the anterior chorioidal artery may be of value in relieving the rigidity and involuntary movements of parkinsonism (I. S. Cooper, 1953).

Summary

The extrapyramidal motor system stretches throughout the various "levels" of the neural axis. It has agents dispersed in the outer telencephalic mantle as well as in the basal nuclei of the telencephalon; others are present in diencephalon, mesencephalon, metencephalon, and myelencephalon. Certain of its components are the oldest members of the motor apparatus phylogenetically and ontogenetically, and certain are among the youngest, appearing in their greatest development in the human brain. The earliest motor activity of the organism, a mass performance, is initiated by certain of its neurons. Fragments of the total performance are developed and separated from the total pattern finally to become capable of individual expression. And yet this early individual performance initiated by extrapyramidal neurons is one involving an entire segment or limb or at least two limbs of the organism, an altogether gross form of movement when compared to the later usage of one or several muscles made possible via pyramidal mechanisms. The extrapyramidal motor system, however, serves the individual well, before and while the pyramidal is developing. Furthermore, when the pyramidal mechanism is damaged by disease process, the extrapyramidal system can bestow sufficient mobility on the organism that posture, ambulation, prehension, crude though it may be, and emotional reaction may be maintained.

An oversimplification of motor performance can be sketched as follows. The spinal segmental motor units are capable of simple reflex performance such as flexor withdrawal alone or in combination with crossed extension to simulate maintenance of stance. Intersegmental connections make possible a correlation of upper-limb activity with that of the lower limb. Upper cervical spinal and medullar motor units bestow postural regulations on the other spinal units through utilization of neck and labyrinthine reflexes. Tegmental reticular units throughout the brain stem coordinate segmental neurons and prime them for discharge to initiate movement and increase muscle tone, or hold them in abeyance. Later, they also will facilitate the activity of cortical neurons through the diencephalon. Midbrain motor units alone, or with assistance from cerebellar neurons, contribute additional postural regulation in the nature of righting reflexes. Progression movements are bestowed by diencephalic neurons which initiate and coordinate them out of caudal motor mechanisms. Grasping is also now acquired, and emotional expression is possible. The basal ganglia modify and increase the flexibility of the gross postural movements and add certain "automatic" movements such as arm swinging. They also make it possible for flexor and extensor synergies to be developed in the limbs. The cerebral cortex in turn further correlates postural patterns, develops further the flexor and extensor synergies, fragments them, and utilizes the units to develop individual usage of digits. Prime movers, or agonists, are developed for selecting an object, and with the activation of the agonist, the graded relaxation of the antagonist and the activation of the fixator are developed via pyramidal mechanisms. The organization of these individual agonist-antagonist-fixator patterns into complex, sequential movement, in order that the object may be skillfully used, is contributed no doubt by the cortical extrapyramidal units in the rostral precentral tissue. The cerebellum cooperates in the movements by being intimately associated in the coordination of these agonist-antagonist-fixator relations, and it expresses its influence by way of the thalamus. The thalamus, recipient of suppressive impulses from the caudate and of facilitatory impulses from spinal cord, tegmentum, and hypothalamus, thus balances corticocortical contributions.

In the performance of movements certain cerebral cortical areas through their activity contribute regulation by modulating and suppressing the excitation of the executors at cortical and tegmental levels. Directional guidance of the motor performance is contributed by certain cortical regions, into which impulses from general and special somatic receptors are sent. Other cerebral regions, especially the left inferior parietal lobule and the two prefrontal regions, lend "planning" and significance to the motor acts. Still other cerebral regions, acting possibly through diencephalic agents, cooperate by contributing vasomotor regulations, balancing somatic and visceral discharge, and offering emotional coloring to the motor performance. Certain of these last cerebral regions may now be considered in more detail.

CHAPTER 18

THE PREFRONTAL REGION OF THE FRONTAL LOBES

IN THE TWO immediately preceding chapters consideration has been given especially to that part of the frontal lobes from which motor responses can be initiated with electrical stimuli. The motor responses emphasized particularly include the initiation of contraction in skeletal muscles or the relaxation of such existing contraction as might be present in the muscles at the time of stimulation. Those frontal areas from which muscular contractions can be elicited include 4γ, 6, 8, 24, 44, and certain parts of the orbital surface; those frontal areas from which motor response can be suppressed are 4*s*, 8, and 24. Stimulation of some of these areas, 4, 6, 8, 24, and certain orbital surface loci, will also elicit alteration in peripheral autonomic activity. Thus far, the remaining portion of the frontal lobes has not yielded somatic motor response on stimulation, and this portion has been divided into the following areas by Brodmann in his 1914 map of the human cerebral mantle: 9, 10, 11, 12, 25, 32, 33, 45, 46, and 47. This division was apparently made by him on the basis of his studies of brains of animals, since he has no published description of these areas in the human (44). Economo and Koskinas have made subdivisions in the Brodmann areas on the basis of their cytoarchitectural studies (Figs. 226, 227, 228). It is not possible to homologize completely and accurately Brodmann's numbers with the symbols of Economo and Koskinas. Area 9 would correspond to *FDm,* area 10 to *FE,* 25 in part to *FH,* 32 to *FDL,* 45 to *FD*γ in part, 46 to *FD*Δ, 47 to *FF*.

An inspection of the cortical maps of Brodmann and Economo and Koskinas, respectively, will reveal a difference in the parcellation of the orbital surface of the frontal lobe. Exclusive of the parolfactory area 25, Brodmann divides this orbital region into two large areas, 47 and 11. Areas 45 and 46 merge onto this surface from the lateral hemispheric surface; area 10, from the frontal polar region. Economo and Koskinas have *FF* (which has subdivisions), *FG, FH,* and overlapping parts of *FD* and *FE.* Much interest has recently centered on the orbital surface, and stimulations in macaque, chimpanzee, and man have yielded striking autonomic and less striking somatic activity. Sufficient attention to minute architectural detail and differentiation has not yet been given, and one finds some reports which list area 47 (or *FF*) as the excitable region and others which list an area 13 as the excitable region in the macaque, especially. Area 13 in the macaque has been considered as homologous to area 47 in man. Beck has recently restudied the human orbital cortex (72). She has found generally that the rostral part of the orbital surface is covered by a granular-type cortex, the posterior part by an agranular-type cortex, and that these two parts are separated by a transitional or dysgranular-type cortex. Exclusive of the gyrus rectus, she finds areas 11, 13, 47 anterior, and 47 posterior, with transitional zones between 11 and 13 and 47 anterior and 47 posterior, respectively (Figs. 42, 263). The gyrus rectus, included in Brodmann's area 11, has been separated from that area by Beck into an anterior rectus area and a posterior rectus area, homologizing with *FG* and *FH,* respectively, of Economo and Koskinas. Area 47 anterior occupies the forward portion of the middle and lateral orbital gyri as well as much of the orbital portion of the inferior frontal gyrus. Beck feels that her area 13 corresponds to area 13 of the macaque described by Walker. Von Bonin has criticized the designation of a frontal-lobe area as 13 because Brodmann

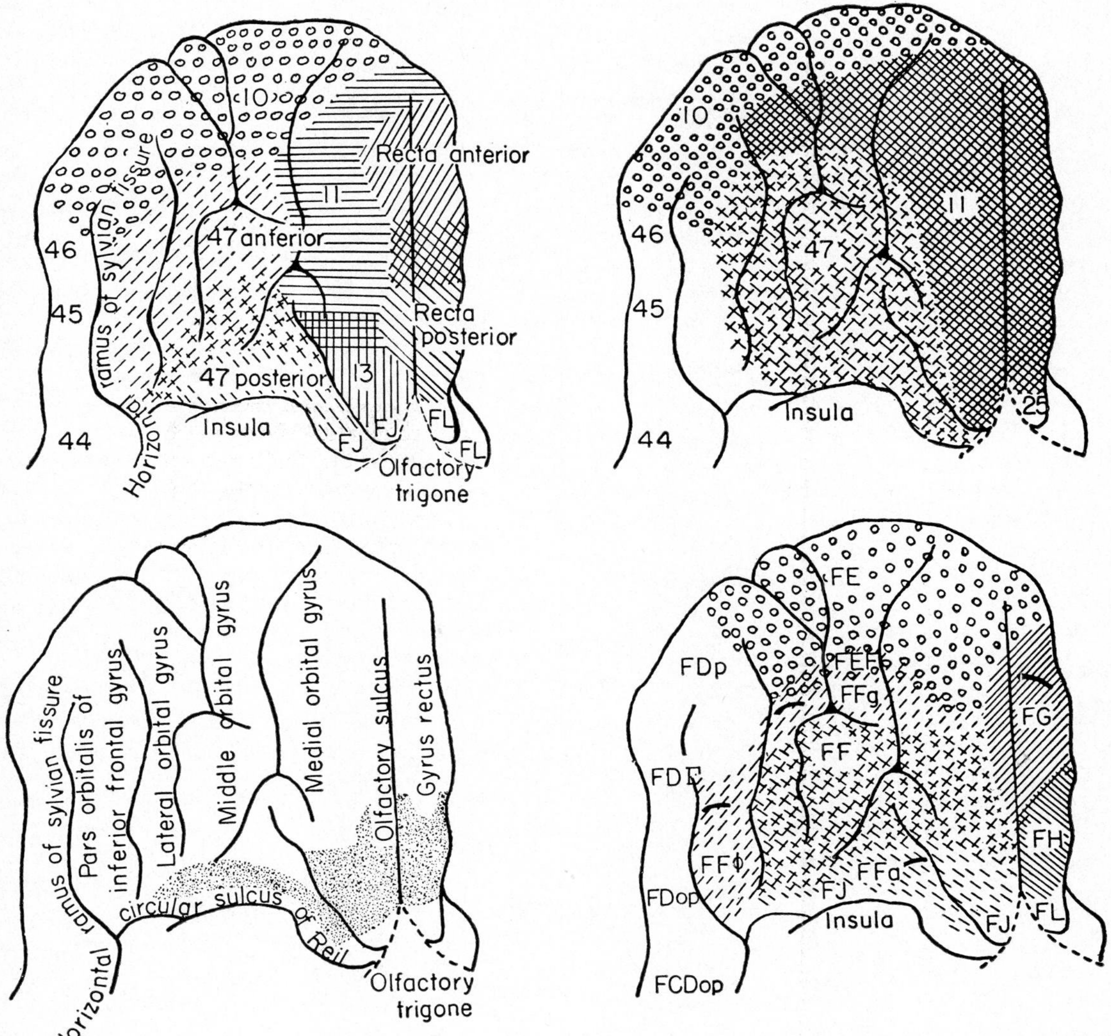

FIG. 263. The orbital region of the human cerebral cortex. The curvature of the brain has been flattened. Left, above, the parcellation of the orbital areas according to Beck; left, below, gyri and sulci of the orbital region; the stippled portion is agranular cortex; right, above, the orbital areas, according to Brodmann; right, below, the orbital areas according to Economo and Koskinas. (*After Beck, J. Anat., vol.* 83.)

used that number for a division in the insula. It is most significant at present that the most posterior part of the lateral, middle, and medial orbital gyri and of the gyrus rectus is an agranular-type cortex. Whether or not this agranular zone can accurately be subdivided on the basis of differences in function, as well as in cytoarchitectural variation as Beck has found, remains for future study.

A recent report on the cytoarchitecture of the frontal lobe of the chimpanzee has listed three primary subdivisions—the precentral agranular, the anterior limbic, and the frontal cortex proper—and several transition zones (44). The precentral agranular would include Brodmann's areas 4 and 6; the anterior limbic, Brodmann's 24 especially, and perhaps 25; the frontal cortex proper, Brodmann's 9, 10, 12, 45, and 46; the transition zones, Brodmann's 8, 11, 32, 44, and 47. When the recent studies of Beck are considered, Brodmann's areas 11 and 47 yield subdivisions, some agranular, some granular. Area 11 has been sudivided into a granular 11 and an agranular 13, and the gyrus rectus has been taken from it and also divided into a forward granular portion and a posterior agranular portion. Area 47 has been divided into a granular rostrolateral portion and a posterior agranular portion. Transition zones exist between 11 and 13, anterior and posterior rectus areas, and rostrolateral and posterior parts of 47.

Cytoarchitecture of Prefrontal Areas

A brief description of the cytoarchitecture of certain of these regions has been given in the earlier chapters. Only the basic pattern of the frontal cortex proper will be mentioned here. This region is characterized by a continuous inner granular layer IV, and a thinner lamina of the same type, in the external granular layer II. The external molecular layer I is poor in cells and shows approximately the same thickness in the frontal area proper as in the other divisions. The external granular layer II is not sharply delimited from layer III and contains granules and small pyramids. The density of the cells in the external pyramidal layer III is less than that found in other regions, and the component pyramid cells increase in size in the deeper parts of the layer, but even there they are only of moderate size. The internal granular layer IV, though quite prominent, is not so distinct as in the parietal lobe. The cells are predominantly small granules with an admixture of small pyramids and polymorphous cells. The internal pyramidal layer V is especially rich in cells in its upper part, and in this region the component pyramids are larger than in the deeper part. The largest of them, however, are of only moderate size when compared to the large pyramids found in the internal pyramidal layer of area 4. The fusiform layer VI is thin, its cells of small size, and of irregular shape, many being fusiform in contour.

Variations in this general pattern have led to the division of this frontal area proper into its several subsectors. In some, for example, area 45, the pyramids in layers III and V are larger than in others, and in area 46 the cell density throughout its layers appears greater, chiefly through the increase in smaller cells. On the orbital surface of the frontal area proper the pyramids of the external pyramidal layer III tend to be smaller, and as the frontal pole is approached all the component cells become smaller and the internal granular layer IV becomes relatively thicker (44). Transition zones between the frontal area proper and the precentral and anterior limbic agranular zones are characterized by minor differences in the external and internal pyramidal layers, and by the gradual appearance of the internal granular layer as one passes rostrally from area 6.

Area 24, or *LA* of Economo and Koskinas, occupies much of the anterior part of the cingular gyrus. On the basis of its architecture it is an agranular cortex like the areas 4 and 6. The outer two layers are similar to those layers in other cortex. The third layer, while rather broad, shows predominantly pyramids of about equal size throughout. They are not densely arranged, but scattered. The fourth cell layer is absent. The fifth, or internal pyramidal, layer is broad and contains many moderately large pyramids, closely packed. The sixth, or fusiform, layer is also broad and contains many medium-sized spindle cells. The outer stripe of Baillarger appears in the fifth cell layer.

Association and Commissural Connections of the Prefrontal Areas

Anatomical studies of the distribution of thalamocortical fibers and physiological-neuronographic studies of corticocortical connections have indicated a basis for differentiation of cerebral cortical areas. It is quite likely that similar studies already reported, and others under way, with respect to the frontal area proper will justify the divisions listed above on a cytoarchitectural standard. As yet, the data for this region of the human brain are relatively scarce, but a map of corticocortical connections in the chimpanzee has been constructed, and reports of similar connections in the macaque appear from time to time (86). Furthermore, anatomical studies concerning the fiber connections of the frontal area proper are now appearing. Association fibers, passing from one cortical area to another in the same hemisphere, as mentioned previously, may be intracortical or subcortical, the latter being short U fibers as well as long subcortical bundles. Commissural fibers from the frontal area proper to areas of the opposite hemisphere pass by way of the corpus callosum, although it is possible that commissural fibers from area 47 may utilize the anterior commissure.

Physiological neuronographic studies have demonstrated many corticocortical fibers in chimpanzees and monkeys (216, 279, 504, 766, 767, 820). These are listed in Table 4. It should be noted that those areas having an auditory function are associated with the frontal areas concerned with the production of speech, that the temporal pole region and olfactory associative cortex are associated with the orbital cortex, and that the nonauditory temporal cortex, presumably serving as a complex associative area, is richly connected with the frontal areas.

Table 4. Corticocortical Connections of Prefrontal Areas as Determined by Physiological Neuronography

Afferent	*Efferent*
8 ← 18, 22, 37, 41, 42	8 → 18
9 ← 23	10 → 22
10 ← 22, 37, 38	46 → 6, 37, 39
44 ← 41, 42, 22, inferior frontal and parietal opercula	47 → 38
	24 → 31, 32
45 ← 21, 22, 37, 38	
46 ← 20, 21, 23, 37, 41, 42	
47 ← 36, 38	

Utilizing the Marchi technique in the macaque, Mettler has described many myelinated fibers passing from a typical area (9) of the frontal area proper to the precentral and postcentral gyri, to posterior parietal area, to anterior insula, superior temporal gyrus, and to the orbital and cingular gyri. Association fibers have been described from areas 8, 9, 10, 11, 12, and 13 (545, 700). Preliminary anatomical studies in humans have indicated possible connections between the inferior frontal gyrus and the temporal lobe, as well as some association fibers passing into the cingulum from the frontal area proper and the anterior limbic area (552).

Anatomical studies have indicated numerous callosal fibers from areas 8, 9, 10, 11, and 12, especially to symmetrical areas but also to others. Physiological-neuronography studies are as yet incomplete, but they have failed to bear out these results completely. Area 8, for example, sends callosal fibers only to the opposite area 18 and is the only one of the "suppressor" areas to discharge callosal fibers. Areas 31 and 32 appear to have symmetrical callosal connections, and this seems to be true for the other frontal areas.

Thalamic Projections to the Prefrontal Areas

Several reports have indicated a profuse thalamic projection from the dorsomedial nucleus to the frontal area proper, and in fact a point-to-point relationship has been described (Fig. 264). The large-cell portion of the dorsomedial nucleus projects to the medial half of the orbital region and particularly to area 11. The more extensive small-cell portion of the dorsomedial nucleus is divided into medial, dorsolateral, ventrolateral, and central parts. The medial part projects to area 11 and to area 47; the dorsolateral, to areas 45 and 46; the ventrolateral part, to area 8; and the central part, to areas 46, 9, and possibly 10 (511, 552, 554, 686). The results of Freeman and Watts are fairly similar; they have shown further a projection from the submedius thalamic nucleus to area 46 (276). The

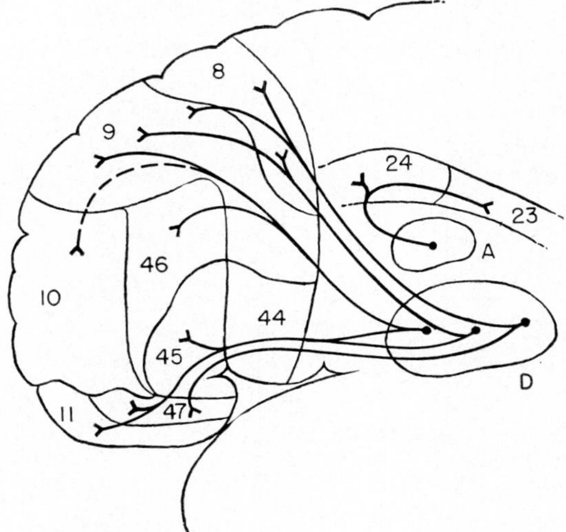

Fig. 264. The relations of the dorsomedial and anterior thalamic nuclei to the prefrontal and cingulate cortex. The "point-to-point" relations are indicated. The broken line indicates few or questionable connections. *A*, Anterior nucleus of the thalamus; *D*, dorsomedial nucleus of the thalamus.

anteroposterior axis of the dorsomedial nucleus is related to the anteroposterior axis of the frontal lobe in a general way. It is to be recalled that this scheme appears consistent for other thalamocortical projections. Area 13, as delineated by Beck, does not appear to share in the dorsomedial projection. The projections to areas 10 and 12 are small.

Certain of the frontal areas under discussion, particularly area 24 and its posterior cingular neighbor 23, receive fibers from the anterior thalamic nuclei. The anteromedial nucleus projects to area 24, and the anteroventral to area 23 in the human (552). Slightly different projections have been reported in animals (see Chap. 13). The thalamocortical fibers leave the thalamus via the inferior thalamic peduncle and are distributed through the anterior limb of the internal capsule to the cortical areas concerned.

The Corticifugal Projections of the Prefrontal Areas

The corticifugal projection fibers of the frontal area proper are gradually being analyzed. They are divided by Le Gros Clark into four groups: **corticostriate, corticothalamic, corticohypothalamic** projections, and descending **connections to the brain stem** (158) (Fig. 265).

Corticostriate fibers from this frontal cortical region include those from suppressor areas 8 and 24 to the caudate nucleus, demonstrated in the chimpanzee. Area 4*s* also discharges corticostriate fibers. These have been described as

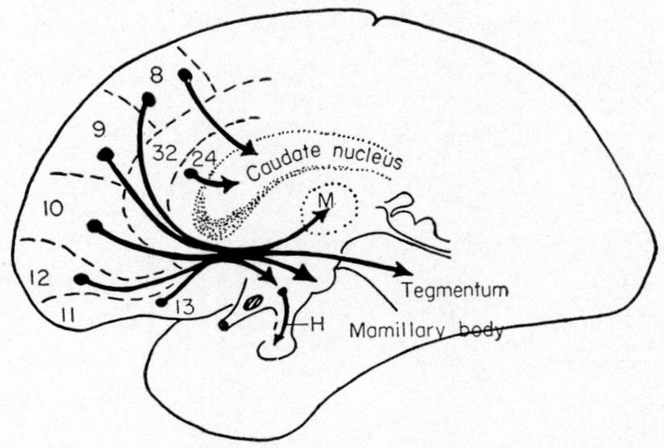

Fig. 265. Diagram of projections from the prefrontal region. *H*, hypothalamohypophyseal tract; *M*, dorsomedial nucleus of thalamus. (*After W. E. L. Clark, Lancet,* **1**, 1948.)

collaterals of fibers passing from the "suppressor" areas to the medullar tegmental inhibitory center. Recent studies by Sachs and co-workers have indicated a projection from area 13 in the macaque (homologous to Beck's area 13 of the human) to the ipsilateral and contralateral putamen, to the contralateral caudate, and to ipsilateral field *H* of Forel (700). Corticothalamic fibers from the frontal area proper pass to the dorsomedial thalamic nucleus, according to studies in macaque and man (158, 554, 577). A cortical projection to the submedius nucleus is also indicated in the human (554). All these projection fibers traverse the anterior limb of the internal capsule. In the human studies the degenerated corticothalamic fibers were not sufficiently numerous to establish a point-to-point relationship between specific frontal area and specific part of the thalamic nucleus. No projection from the rostral part of the cingular gyrus to the anterior thalamic nuclei could be demonstrated (554).

Corticohypothalamic fibers have been studied with physiological neuronography in the macaque (819). The lateral and inferior surfaces of the frontal lobes have been most studied. The connections are chiefly homolateral ones, and they can be summarized as follows (Fig. 266). The supraoptic nucleus receives fibers from areas 8 and 10; the paraventricular, from areas 10 and 47 and the posterior and medial parts of the orbital surface; the periventricular region receives fibers from area 45 and inferior frontal tissue just posterior to it; the posterior hypothalamic nucleus receives fibers from areas 47 and 45 and posterior orbital cortex. Area 13 of the macaque fires the lateral preoptic area and the region of the median forebrain bundle (700). In addition to these connections, areas 4*s* and 6 discharge to the mamillary nuclei, 6 to the lateral hypothalamic and posterior hypothalamic, and questionably to the dorsomedial hypothalamic nucleus. Anatomical confirmation of direct corticohypothalamic fibers from area 6 to the medial mamillary nucleus in the human has been given (554). On the basis of results of electrical stimulation, the orbital region of the frontal lobe, as well as the anterior part of the cingular gyrus, would be expected to have corticohypothalamic connections (see later). Indirect ones via the thalamus exist.

The projections from the frontal areas under

consideration to the brain stem include corticopontine and corticotegmental fibers. Area 10 is thought to give rise to a group of prefrontopontine fibers that join the frontopontine projection from areas 4 and 6 to the pontine nuclei (73, 552, 554). The orbital portion of the frontal lobe may also contribute to the corticopontine system. It has been demonstrated physiologically in monkeys that areas 8 and 24 send fibers to the medullar tegmentum, especially medially, into the so-called bulbar inhibitory area. Anatomical proof has been offered for such fibers from area 24 (816). It is to be recalled that areas 4*s*, 2, and 19 have a similar projection and that all these corticotegmental fibers have unmyelinated collaterals that end in the caudate. There is no conclusive anatomical evidence, according to Mettler, that any of the "suppressor" areas send any *myelinated* fibers to the striatum, pallidum, substantia nigra, nuclei of the pons, or to the inferior olives (545). In fact, he finds that there is no anatomical evidence that any cortex rostral to area 9 sends any myelinated fibers caudal to the thalamus. Unmyelinated or very thinly myelinated projections have not yet been disproved.

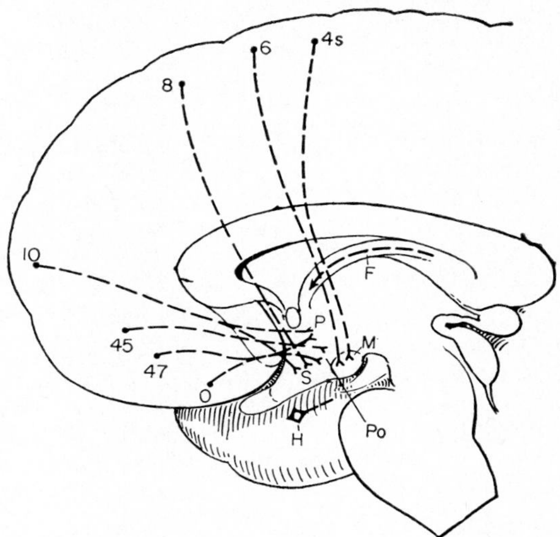

FIG. 266. Corticohypothalamic connections. Based in part on data from the macaque, adapted to the human. The cortical areas are numbered according to Brodmann, and *O* is posterior orbital region. *F*, fornix arising from *H*, the hippocampus; *M*, mamillary nuclei; *P*, paraventricular hypothalamic nucleus; *Po*, posterior hypothalamic nuclei; *S*, supraoptic hypothalamic nuclei.

The orbital gyri and the anterior part of the superior and middle frontal gyri have been said to contribute fibers to a corticorubral system in humans. Corticonigral fibers have been said to arise in part from the inferior frontal and orbital gyri. These statements have been based principally on studies of degenerations secondary to destructions in the frontal lobes. It is perhaps wise to consider that anatomical evidence for many possible projections from the frontal lobes is quite incomplete.

Results of Stimulations of the Prefrontal and Anterior Limbic Cortex

Of the areas within these regions investigated thus far, somatic or autonomic motor activity has been elicited in response to electrical stimulation of areas 24 and 46 and of certain loci on the orbital surface. The results have been most striking perhaps from area 24, from which either suppressor or excitatory effects have been elicited (731, 816, 822). The suppressor activity has been described in the preceding chapter. The excitatory effects include both somatic and autonomic activity. The activity produced varies with the conditions of stimulation and state of anesthesia. Long stimulation has produced slow, extensor postural movements of the extremities in the anesthetized animal. Vocalization with or without facial grimaces has been produced in the anesthetized monkey and unanesthetized cat. The autonomic responses have been interpreted as belonging to both sympathetic and parasympathetic mechanisms (443, 731, 816). Pupillary dilation, considered a result of active sympathetic discharge, and piloerection have been reported. Vagal-type slowing of the heart, cardiac arrest, and usually a marked blood-pressure fall have been recorded. From the rostral, deeper portions of the area, respiratory slowing and arrest maintained up to 25 sec. have also been described. Simultaneous bilateral stimulation of the anterior part of the cingular gyrus in 12 humans has resulted most often in a significant elevation of both systolic and diastolic blood-pressure levels, and the elevation usually persisted as long as did the stimulation (634). A fall in pulse rate occurred in seven cases; an increase, in three. An increase in respiratory rate was observed in two cases; a decrease, in two. This decrease led to complete apnea persisting for about 30 sec. after cessation of stimulation. It was admitted that with accurate form of stimu'ation and attention to stimulus wave type and frequency, more significant results may have been obtained. Other autonomic activities were not observed.

Respiratory and blood-pressure alterations can be produced by stimulating orbital gyri. That part of the orbital surface which yields alteration of respiratory activity in the macaque has usually been described as area 13, area 11, or orea 47. To Von Bonin, area 13 of the macaque is homologous with his human area 47; to Beck, it is homologous to her area 13 in the human (Fig. 263). It was noted as long ago as 1894 that stimulation of the posterior part of the orbital surface in lightly anesthetized rabbit, cat, dog, and monkey elicited prompt and complete arrest of respiration in an expiratory position (743). These findings have since been repeated by a number of investigators (52, 206, 487, 488, 700). Respiratory movements have been almost instantaneously arrested regardless of the phase of respiration existing at the time of stimulation. The arrest has usually persisted for the duration of the stimulus, or until an "escape" occurred, usually after 10 to 30 sec. A slow, moderate rise in blood pressure or an instantaneous fall has also been obtained from discrete foci of the orbital area, and some of these foci are indentical with those from which respiratory movements were obtained. Respiratory and vascular responses have been obtained independently. In monkeys with bilateral vagus section and the two adrenals excised, and in monkeys with only the two adrenals removed, the respiratory and vascular responses to orbital stimulation have not been altered. The elicitation of responses has varied with the nature of the stimulation, and a relatively slow frequency of pulses seems essential to the stimulation of the orbital gyri. Decreased tonus of gastric musculature has also been produced by stimulation of orbital gyri as well as of rostral cingular region (40, 52). Another interesting report has mentioned a rise in temperature of all the extremities of the animal when a cold saline "patty" has been applied to the posterior orbital region (area 13), or when repeated electrical excitation or slight mechanical disturbance of the area has taken place (206). A shunting of renal blood flow, such that a renal cortical ischemia with resultant anuria occurred, has also been elicited by stimulating the posterior orbital surface of the cat, but this effect can be produced also by stimulation of other neural centers and certain peripheral nerves (784, 785). It is of interest that excitation of the vagus nerve in the cat results in an increase in the cortical potentials in the orbital cortex only. Alteration of respiratory activity can also be produced by stimulating the frontal lobe of the monkey in the vicinity of the principal sulcus (area 46?) (205). This region is considered to be a very strong respiratory "center."

The orbital cortex of humans has also been stimulated through electrodes introduced transcortically, preliminary to prefrontal lobotomy (487). The result of such stimulation, with a stimulus frequency of between 10 to 40 c.p.s., has been a prompt and usually complete arrest of respiration with the chest assuming an expiratory position, and a gradual rise in blood pressure, after a latent period of 2 to 4 seconds, to a maximum point of increase of 18 to 20 mm. Hg in the diastolic level. In some of the human cases, stimulation after lobotomy has not produced vascular or respiratory responses. The active area in the human has thus far been identified only as the lateral half of the posterior orbital region.

Results of Removal of Prefrontal and Anterior Limbic Cortex

When area 13 has been ablated bilaterally in monkeys, hyperactivity, in the nature of movement or walking, has been observed repeatedly, this increased activity being 8 to 16 times that of normal monkeys (488, 693). In addition to the hyperactivity, the extremities of the animals have shown increased temperature and an increased reflex vasodilation. This effect has been considered to be independent of the hyperactivity. Unilateral ablation of area 13 in the macaque and chimpanzee has resulted in moderate hyperactivity, and the temperature changes of the extremities were most marked in the contralateral ones. The general behavior of the animals with bilateral removal of area 13 has not been remarkable, and the animals have been described as being easily tamed and without excessive fear or anger (488). Richter and Hines, studying hyperactivity resulting from bilateral prefrontal ablations from the macaque, have considered it to result particularly from damage to area 9 (670). In their experience, the subsequent ablation of the head of the striatum resulted in a great increase in activity in animals from which the ipsilateral prefrontal cortex had been removed previously without noticeable effect. When area 24 has been removed unilaterally or from both hemispheres of monkeys, a change in personality has been described to result. The animal loses its shyness, is less fearful of man, but is more inquisitive. Grooming behavior or acts of affection toward its cage companions are lost, and it becomes indifferent to the other animals. Its behavior has been characterized as a loss of "social conscience" (817). In a human with destruction of the cingular gyrus, there was a lack of affect with development of indifference and finally complete apathy (791).

A number of studies have been made concerning the behavior and learning ability of animals after bilateral prefrontal lobectomy. Aside from the hyperactivity mentioned above, no sign of paralysis, no increase in tone or alteration of deep reflexes has been observed (371). If, on the other hand, the prefrontal removals are combined with bilateral removal of areas 4 and 6 in the monkey, the abilities of the animal to maintain posture, initiate quadrupedal progression, and feed himself are lost—abilities which can be carried out, albeit in abnormal fashion, after removals of areas 4 and 6 alone. This would appear to indicate a definite contribution to motor performance by these prefrontal areas.

Monkeys with bilateral removals of the prefrontal cortex were inferior to normal animals in their performance of learning problems (332). Chimpanzees, tested both before and after removal of the prefrontal cortex, in their ability to meet certain problem situations, have been described in great detail (180, 411). The problems have entailed the ability to remember certain physical characteristics of the test objects used, as well as the necessary sequential use of them for a successful test. Another test of delayed response entailed simply the ability to remember. Bilateral prefrontal removal caused a greater deficit than did unilateral. It took the animals longer to perform tests after operation, and in certain tests they failed completely to relearn how to carry out the test successfully. The performance, if successful, was frequently not repeated regularly, and the animals appeared to lack insight as to the organization of the performance. The delayed-response test was failed completely by one animal if the delay was longer than 2 sec. It has been observed in monkeys that the failure of the delayed response was not necessarily a failure of memory alone, but rather an inability to maintain attention to the test against incoming, distracting impulses from the environment (529). Distractibility of attention has been observed repeatedly in monkeys with both prefrontal lobes removed, and they shift quickly and aimlessly from one activity to another. As time went on in postoperative testing of the lobectomized chimpanzees, some marked improvement in performance of certain tests occurred; in other tests, improvement was minimal. Erratic and variable character of performance was outstanding in their postoperative periods. It was observed in one of the chimpanzees that she had mild temper tantrums preoperatively whenever she failed a test. These increased to such a degree that she developed an experimental neurosis. After bilateral removal of prefrontal lobes, she no longer showed temper tantrums or reacted to frustration when she failed the tests.

In animals, then, bilateral prefrontal lobectomy leads to an impairment of learning ability, a distractibilty, variable and erratic performance, a lack of development or organization or plan of action, and a failure to react to frustrations. The results of bilateral removal or of isolation of these prefrontal areas in humans will be discussed later.

Frontal-lobe Syndrome in Man

In 1868 a report appeared describing the behavior of a man who lived for 12 years after he had had an iron bar forced through his skull. The bar had entered below the left orbit and had come out of the top of his head in the mid-line anterior to the coronal suture (333, 334). Before the injury he had been an efficient foreman, but after it he had become incapable of such work. He became irreverent and profane and showed no deference to his companions. He was impatient of restraint or of advice and became exceedingly obstinate. He became quite capricious and vacillating and flitted from one plan of operation to another without ever completing one.

Since this report a human "frontal-lobe syndrome" has been defined, and occasionally this has been done without a strict consideration of the conditions prevailing during its observation. Humans who have suffered trauma to their frontal lobes and those who have neoplasms of the frontal lobes have been used, the latter both before and after surgery. Obviously, the conditions are not the same, and the "syndrome" should and does vary accordingly.

Aside from the presence of convulsions, paralysis, speech disorder, or other somatic motor disturbance, due to extension of the injury or neoplasm to the posterior part of the frontal lobes, the syndrome includes indications of behavioral alteration (697). Certain cases of traumatic disorder have been analyzed after healing of the injury. The patients have demonstrated a slowness in motor performance and slowness in formulation of ideas. They have frequently been irritable. Occasionally they have shown a disturbance as to temporal relations and have been disoriented as to spatial relations, losing directions easily and failing to distinguish right from left. In one well-described case, the patient was quite irritable and was not at all dependable. He did not carry through with what he set out to do and took too long in the performance of the things done. He took pleasure in frightening and threatening other people, and he required confinement. One year after the damaged neural tissue was removed the patient was said to be normal (352).

In patients with frontal-lobe tumors one frequently sees personality changes with disorderly and inappropriate conduct, facetiousness, and jocularity. There is again disorientation as to space and time. An inability to deal with hypothetical situations in contrast to familiar ones is apparent. A task demanding a simple type of reaction is usually well performed but a task involving one of several solutions is usually failed. A deficit of synthesis and an inability for organizing several related items into a single pattern may be noted. An inability to prepare a two- or three-course meal, a performance which had formerly been done with ease, characterized a patient with one prefrontal lobe removed because of neoplasm (618). In another well-authenticated case, with bilateral prefrontal lobe removal because of neoplasm, the patient demonstrated boastfulness, self-aggrandizement, distractibility, hostility toward other members of his family, poor memory for recent events, poor orientation as to time, and an incapability for logical thinking (97). Personality changes are usually not present after unilateral removal, but a defect of perception is frequently demonstrable (861). The nature of this defect includes a longer time required for perceiving a stimulus, a lesser number of situations perceived in a stimulus, an inability to shift readily from one stimulus to another, and distortion of normal perceptions. As a result of the perception defect the responses on certain specific tests were grossly altered. The separating of objects into classes of color, use, size, and shape was poorly done; figures with reversible perspective were not handled well, and responses to a Rorschach test were altered. Some alteration was present in emotional responses, this alteration being in the direction of euphoria or depression. No impairment of ability was noted as based on intelligence tests.

A prolonged analysis is available of the deficit demonstrated by an individual with a surgically verified bilateral frontal-lobe defect, congenital in origin or present since very early age (4). The patient has been described as suffering a "primary social defect." He has never demonstrated any anxiety in dealing with any of the problems of living. Things distasteful are forgotten, avoided, or blamed on another. He resents change from one task to another and makes the adjustment slowly. He is unable to plan ahead. He has never demonstrated noticeable swings of mood but maintains an evenness of mood. He does not daydream but responds to stimuli quickly. He may react quite normally to a situation at the moment, but he cannot elaborate this reaction into an experience that may serve him later. He cannot deal with the abstract. He is rather boastful in childlike fashion. He may win a friend one day and lose him the next without any obvious satisfaction in either result. He has never demonstrated any love dependence on his mother, has never had a permanent friend, and has never been in love, nor has he ever shown persistent hostility toward anyone. He apparently has social feeling but cannot amplify it. Psychological tests have demonstrated an average intelligence level.

Prefrontal Lobotomy

It was mentioned earlier that a chimpanzee with bilateral removal of prefrontal tissue did not react to failure of test problems with temper tantrums. In other words, she did not develop a frustration neurosis. This fact, plus others, apparently spurred the Portuguese neurosurgeon, Moniz, to devise a method of severing the white matter within the prefrontal portion of the human frontal lobes in certain types of mental disorder. From this beginning a variety of surgical procedures has been devised for removing or isolating bilaterally symmetrical portions of the frontal lobes proper. The greater part of the central white matter of the prefrontal area is severed in a prefrontal lobotomy or leucotomy (275, 278, 636, 824). Such a transection passes just rostral to the anterior horn of the lateral ventricle and interrupts especially the interconnections between prefrontal cortex and dorsomedial nuclei of the thalamus. In a transorbital lobotomy, a strong, sharp instrument is forced through the roof of the orbit and with sweeps medially, laterally, and, in some cases, inferiorly in the frontal lobe, the major part of the ventral central white matter is sectioned (274). In topectomy symmetrical cortical tissue, usually from areas 9 and 10 especially, is removed bilaterally; in gyrectomy, symmetrical gyri, especially the superior frontals, are removed (122, 351, 614). In another procedure various prefrontal cortical areas are undercut; in still another, thalamotomy, the dorsomedial nuclei, the source of the major projection to the prefrontal areas, are selectively destroyed (713, 749).

These procedures have been devised especially for the treatment of certain types of mental disorder and in cases of intractable pain (244, 277, 823). They have been most helpful in the relief of involutional depressions, schizophrenia, and obsessive tension states. It is not clear why the severing of frontothalamic and thalamofrontal fibers should be of benefit, but it is reasoned that their interruption prevents the flow of many complex sensory impulses, especially of visceral origin, from reaching cortical levels in which they may be further integrated, and in which they may set into activity many other neuron circuits created as a result of the elaboration of past experience. The activity of these frontal "association" areas cannot thus be brought into play, and engrams are not recalled. Introspection is lessened, and a comparison of the present with the remembered past and the possibilities of the future does not obtain. The patient who suffers from intolerable pain does not lose pain perception as a result of the leucotomy, but he is rid of the suffering associated with the pain. He still experiences pain, but since he no longer ruminates over its consequences it no longer bothers him or causes him to suffer. Even though the patient is happier with his freedom from suffering as a result of losing the anticipatory element with regard to his pain, he usually shows a lowered threshold to somatic pain such as pinprick or radiant heat. He consequently overreacts to a painful stimulus (138).

The relief from intractable pain most often involves a relief from the effects of visceral pain. It has been suggested that many visceral impulses normally reach hypothalamus, midline and dorsomedial thalamic nuclei, from which they are projected to the prefrontal cerebral cortex. The leucotomy interrupts this flow to those cortical areas in which conscious integration occurs. Similarly, the patient loses his emotional tensions, and this may lead to an alteration of his behavior. It is impossible, however, to find agreement as to the extent of this alteration of behavior and the extent of change in the intellect. Many patients exhibit tactlessness, extrovertness, and euphoria; they have a noticeable lability of emotions, with a tendency to outbursts (680, 698, 699). Some patients become relatively sluggish and torpid, rather than euphoric. Many of the patients have shown a complete reversal of their likes and dislikes. Some observers report no loss of ability by their patients in performing standard intelligence tests; others note a definitely lowered ability and find an intellectual impairment. Nearly all agree that the capacity for abstract thinking is lessened and that the patient develops a more concrete attitude. There is a noticeable distractibility in the majority of the patients, they being unable to maintain attention and set attitude. They are unable to plan and their judgment is often defective. Even with these alterations, many patients have been able to be freed from confinement; many have been able to return to their former business and professional positions. The results of the operations will necessarily depend on the nature of the patient before his psychosis, on the severity of his mental alteration, and particularly on the extent of the operative procedure. It is quite true that this psychosurgery has proved of benefit to many individuals in that their postoperative behavioral alteration and intellectual deficit does not outweigh the loss of their mental instability. In some patients the reverse may be true.

Aside from the failure sometimes to relieve the mental disorder, psychosurgery occasionally leads to several unwelcome results. About 10 to 12 per cent of the patients have grand mal convulsions postoperatively. Many have temporary urinary incontinence; a few, more persistent incontinence. Postoperative bleeding or infection occasionally results, but these may intervene following any neurosurgical procedure.

Efforts have been made to correlate sequelae of leucotomy with the plane of section, in order to appreciate more fully the varied type of change in certain cases. It has been observed that personality changes tend to be most severe when the posterior orbital gyri are damaged. General restlessness, the presence of vasomotor and trophic changes (cyanosis of extremities, edema, and vesicles of skin) was also thought to result from posterior orbital and/or striatal damage. It is worth recalling that restlessness can be produced in monkeys by bilateral destruction of area 13 with or without damage to the caudate nucleus. A higher incidence of uremia as a possible cause of delayed postoperative death may also be correlated with posterior orbital damage. The development of nutritional deficiency leading to general trophic deterioration and death has been correlated with damage to the subcallosal fasciculus region at a level underlying premotor cortex (510). As yet, however, evidence for these correlations is inadequate. Persistent urinary incontinence has been found to occur most often when the premotor region has been damaged, and indeed, it appears likely that the majority of the undesirable sequelae may be correlated with damage to agranular or dysgranular cortex (74, 553). The desirable results, with reference to improvement in the psychosis, may not specifically be related to removal or isolation of any particular part of the frontal lobe, but seem to vary directly with the amount of cortex removed or isolated, without damage to the agranular and dysgranular regions (551). It is of interest that recent studies tend to indicate that removal from, or isolation of, orbital cortex (not including posterior orbital tissue) may be more important in obtaining an improvement (512).

Several intensive investigations have been carried out with regard to the physiologic effects of leucotomy and topectomy, especially (356, 546, 721, 770). Some patients show persistent abnormalities in the electroencephalogram after leucotomy. Alterations in sugar metabolism may occur; a diabetic type of sugar-tolerance curve may revert to normal temporarily, or it may become more abnormal. Carotid-sinus reflex irritability may be increased postoperatively and other signs of vasomotor instability occur. The change in functional capacity of the urinary bladder occurs, and with this limitation of capacity comes a heightened irritabilty. Usually temporary, occasionally the effect is permanent. Topectomy has been found to lead to no definite, enduring physiologic changes, aside from alteration in the electroencephalogram in certain cases.

Other operative procedures are being attempted in a search for relief of mental disorder. A few patients have had a cingular gyrus removed with some improvement in their psychosis. This line of attack was based on the fact that cingulate ablation in the macaque appears to lead to a loss of fear. The tip of the temporal lobe and the hippocampus have also been removed in an effort to convert an aggressive patient to one who will be placid and calm (329, 839). Again there is an experimental hint that such a result might occur (see Chap. 23). These various surgical procedures, together with accurate preoperative and postoperative evaluation as to physiologic and psychologic changes resulting from the removal of neural tissue, may in time lead to a better understanding of the cerebral functioning.

Summary

The posterior portions of the frontal lobes are concerned primarily with the organization and initiation of contractions of skeletal muscle. To a less extent, autonomic activity may be initiated there. The prefrontal portion of the frontal lobes, while contributing to the elaborateness of movement, bestows upon an individual an ability to plan and to look ahead; a capacity for perceiving a stimulus or a problem not only as an event of the present but in relation to past experience and anticipation of future possibilities; an ability to maintain a steadfastness of purpose in the face of distractions; and an ability to adjust himself agreeably to his neighbors and to control his emotional reactions. Toward this last, prefrontal and limbic cortex take part in autonomic control acting through hypothalamus and other brain stem centers. They contribute to this control, presumably, by integrating impulses from those same visceral structures, the contractile and secretory activities of which they are capable of altering. Within the frontal lobe also certain mechanisms of speech are carried out, especially in the posterior portion of the inferior frontal gyri. Speech is a function of many cortical areas, including cortex of temporal and occipital lobes. It will be discussed later after these regions are described.

CHAPTER 19

THE SENSORY PATHWAYS AND THE PARIETAL CORTEX

THE INITIATION of movement, and especially the successful attainment of a goal or object sought through the performance of the movement, depends in large measure on the normal functioning of sensory mechanisms. Sensory impulses integrated at various levels of the neural axis are of great influence in the initiation and guidance of motor mechanisms at the various levels. Not all sensory impulses gain recognition in consciousness; in fact, relatively few of the total number entering the neural axis do gain such recognition. Many sensory impulses bring about activity at spinal and brain stem levels only; others pass to the thalamus and cerebral cortex directly. As noted in earlier sections, certain impulses from posterior spinal roots pass through associative neuronal arcs at spinal levels, and others gain the spinothalamic tracts and medial lemnisci. Not all impulses traversing spinothalamic tracts and medial lemnisci, however, reach the thalamus and cerebral cortex directly, for fibers of these tracts give off collaterals at various levels to nuclei of the reticular system, and their impulses may pass to these brain stem reticular levels. The activity in these brain stem reticular centers, however, may strongly influence cortical activity. Sensory impulses reaching the cerebral cortex, then, may utilize express highways such as spinothalamic tracts and medial lemnisci with few synapses. Or they may reach the cerebral cortex, or at least influence its activity, after traversing a system of relays. Sensory impulses traverse the express highways episodically, while activity in the relay mechanisms is continuous during the waking hours and is only partially depressed in sleep (571).

Those impulses reaching thalamus and cortex directly and thus gaining conscious recognition and those which end in spinal and lower brain stem levels come from the periphery of the organism as a result of environmental change, or they come from within the organism as a result of change within it. The organism is constantly exposed to changes within its environment and to changes within itself. These changes may activate sensory end organs scattered throughout the organism, especially within the integument, within the muscles and tendons, within the walls of viscera and of blood vessels, and within the mesothelial linings of the various body cavities.

SENSORY RECEPTORS

Sensory receptors have been classified by Sherrington into three types according to their distribution. **Exteroceptors** include receptors in the skin and its appendages, in the organs of special sense, in the eye and ear (hearing), and in certain specialized epithelial surfaces such as the olfactory mucous membrane and the taste buds. They include, therefore, cutaneous, distance, and chemical receptors, respectively. **Interoceptors** were originally intended to include those receptors found within the inner surfaces of the body—within the walls of the gastrointestinal tract, for example, and within the walls of blood vessels and within visceral structures. These may also be called visceroceptors. They include tension receptors and perhaps chemical receptors. **Proprioceptors** include the end organs within the muscles, tendons, deep and muscular fasciae, and joints. These are tension or pressure receptors. The proprioceptors also include end organs within the semicircular canals, the utricle, and saccule of the labyrinth. Both visceroceptors and proprioceptors are, in a sense, interoceptors in that they are *within* the deeper parts of the organism and are stimulated by changes within the organism.

In the present discussion the receptors and nerve fibers of the organs of special sense and of the labyrinth will not be included. It is the receptors and their fibers in the skin, subcutaneous tissue, muscles, and tendons with which we will be primarily concerned, and especially the somatic impulses arising in these receptors which reach the thalamus and cerebral cortex directly and are thus recognized consciously. The impulses arising within the viscera in large measure do not gain recognition in consciousness, except as they underlie sensations of hunger, thirst, sexual desire, and desire for excretory function. Impulses of visceral and blood-vessel origin chiefly bring about local changes through spinal and peripheral neural mechanisms, without their being recognized consciously. They utilize sensory endings and nerve fibers, however, that are similar to the somatic sensory endings and fibers in origin (posterior root ganglia) and appearance. Nor have distinct secondary visceral tracts been adequately demonstrated.

In life, impulses normally pass over sensory fibers after having arisen through stimulation of the sensory end organ, or receptor. The finer branches of the sensory fibers may end as naked endings among the epithelial cells of the cutaneous (or visceral) surfaces. In some instances the endings may penetrate the cells. They may end as naked endings in the subcutaneous connective tissues and in perivascular tissues. Some naked endings are composed of a specialized epithelial cell which rests in a cuplike expansion of a terminal nerve fiber. The tactile corpuscles of Merkel are of this type (Fig. 267). They are found among the epithelial cells covering the finger tips and the glans penis and in the mucous membranes of the lips and mouth. Free nerve endings also form spiral or basketlike processes about the base of hairs to serve as tactile endings (Fig. 267). Free nerve endings are found in the cornea, in the epidermis and dermis layers of the skin, in the stratified squamous epithelium of the oral cavity, and among and within the lining cells of the mucous and serous membranes. Free nerve endings arise from unmyelinated or very thinly myelinated nerve fibers. Pain endings are naked ones (Fig. 267).

Other terminals of sensory fibers may end in a specialized form of receptor within an intricate capsule. Some sensory endings are therefore free, naked, or unencapsulated, and some are encapsulated.

Encapsulated nerve endings are numerous, and the principal differences in individual types may lie in the thickness of the capsule or in the manner of termination of the fibers within the capsules. Meissner's corpuscles are found in the skin of the hands and fingers. Each corpuscle is made up of a connective-tissue capsule surrounding cells whose elongated nuclei are arranged transversely to the long axis of the capsule. The myelinated nerve fiber enters the corpuscle, losing its myelin as it enters, and branches about among the cells within (Fig. 267). It is thought that this type of ending is for tactile sensations. An encapsulated ending with a thicker capsule is the Vater-Pacini corpuscle (Fig. 267). A nerve fiber enters one end, loses its myelin, and proceeds, branching at times within a central core, surrounded by a lamellated connective-tissue capsule, the outer layer of which is in contact with the neurolemmal sheath of the nerve. These endings are found in the subcutaneous tissue, in tendon sheaths, in muscle fasciae, in the periosteum, and in the peritoneum, pleura, and pericardium. They are thought to be pressure endings and are classed as proprioceptors. Similar, but simpler and smaller encapsulated endings are the end bulbs of Krause, the endings of Ruffini, and the corpuscles of Golgi-Mazzoni (Fig. 267). These are thought to be receptors for cold, warmth, and pressure, respectively. They are present in the skin and are exteroceptors.

Complex encapsulated endings, neuromuscular and neurotendinous spindles, are found in striated muscles and tendons. Only certain muscle fibers and tendon components receive such endings. These muscle fibers, known as intrafusal fibers, are of smaller caliber and contain more sarcoplasm, relatively, than the others. They are enclosed in a thin-walled connective-tissue capsule. A myelinated nerve fiber pierces the capsule, and its terminals spiral about the intrafusal fibers. These receptors,

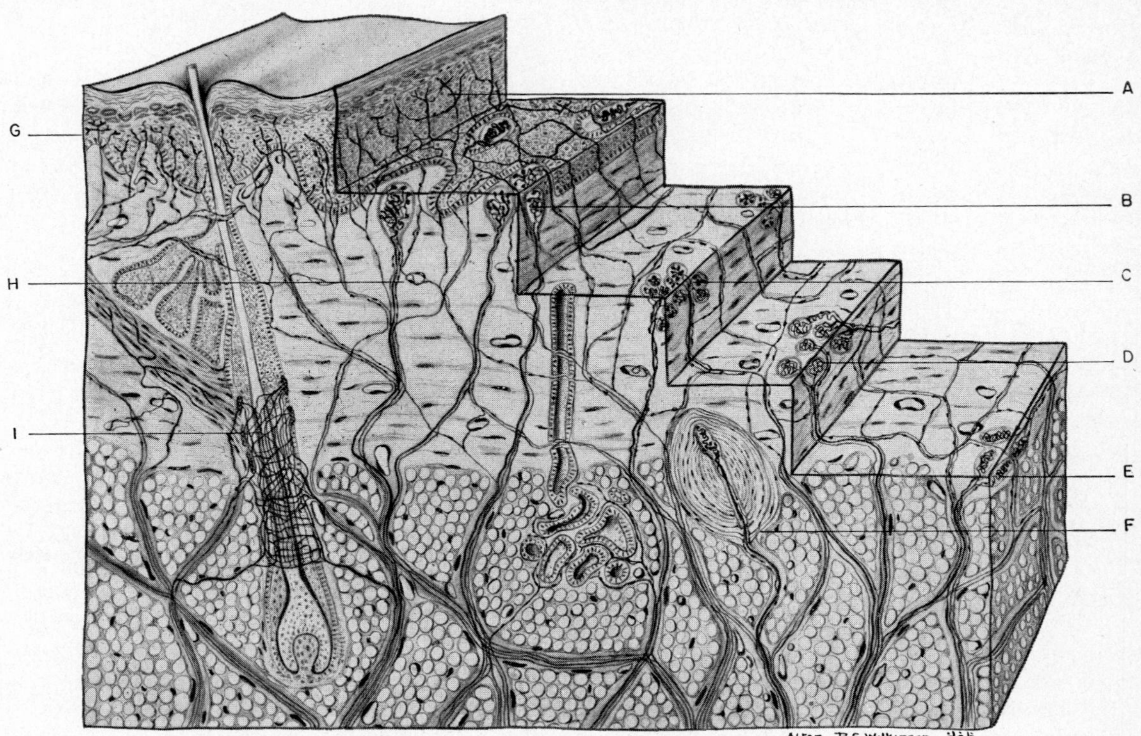

Fig. 267. Diagram of the cutaneous innervation. *A*, beaded nerve nets subserving pain (probably fast pain); *B*, Meissner's corpuscle, subserving touch; *C* and *D*, groups of Krause's end bulbs, subserving cold (these lie at variable depths beneath the skin surface); *E*, group of Ruffini endings, subserving warmth; *F*, pacinian corpuscle, subserving pressure; *G*, Merkel's disks, subserving touch; *H*, beaded nerve fibers derived from nerve nets, subserving pain and associated with blood vessels (probably slow pain); *I*, nerve terminals about the sheath of a hair, subserving touch. (*Redrawn, courtesy of Dr. G. Weddell, Brit. M. Bull.*, **3**.)

arranged "in parallel" with the muscle fibers, are activated by the elongation of the intrafusal fibers in passive stretching of the muscle during relaxation. The intrafusal fibers also receive flower-spray endings, within the connective-tissue capsule. These are formed by fine myelinated nerve fibers spiraling about the muscle fibers. The neuromuscular spindles and flower-spray endings are not present in all striated muscles and vary in appearance and size from muscle to muscle. The spindles are found in greater number in the muscles of the limbs than in those of the trunk. They are numerous in the "antigravity" muscles and in the muscles subserving posture. They are present in greatest numbers in the intrinsic muscles of the hands (364). Neurotendinous spindles are usually present near the musculotendinous junction. They too have a connective-tissue capsule in which fine myelinated nerve terminals spiral about the tendon bundle. These endings are also stretch or tension receptors, and unlike the neuromuscular spindles, they are activated by the tension created by active muscular contraction as well as by passive stretch. Naked endings are also present in the perivascular tissue throughout muscles. The neuromuscular relations of striated muscles are diagrammed (Fig. 114). All these endings in muscles are proprioceptors.

The Pattern of Cutaneous Innervation

Weddell and his co-workers, following Woollard, have provided much of the information concerning the arrangement of sensory nerves and end organs in the skin (825, 826, 853). Beneath the skin, sensory nerve bundles give off many branches which pass in all directions to enter the skin (Fig. 267). In the skin two main plexuses are formed, a deep and a superficial. Both plexuses are composed of thick and thin fibers, myelinated and unmyelinated, though the deeper plexus in general is composed of larger fibers. Fine fibers of the superficial plexus shed their myelin sheaths, become varicose, and branch to form arborizations of naked and beaded terminals which lie below and between epidermal cells. The fine branches enter the stratum mucosum and stratum granulosum, branch and provide the network of beaded terminals. The fine fibers from each parent nerve fiber interlock with those of other fibers, but there is no continuity between overlapping arborizations. Fibers from the deep plexus ramify among the connective tissue, immediately below the epithelium, supplying end organs there, and about hair follicles, sweat, and sebaceous glands. The arborizations of a single parent fiber innervate an area of skin that is roughly circular, the dimensions of the area varying from one body region to another. The end organs on all terminals of a single sensory nerve fiber are of the same type.

In any given skin area a grouping of end organs of similar type occurs, each group being composed of two to three end organs. Several such groups are known to the physiologist as a "spot," a touch "spot," for example, being several groups of Merkel's or Meissner's corpuscles. Each "spot" is innervated by at least two main fibers. In addition, each encapsulated end organ in the "spot" receives an accessory fine fiber which is similar to the branches of the superficial plexus fibers, subserving pain.

The investigators cited above assign specific function to the various types of nerve endings similar to that already given, and they ascribe the reception of pain to free nerve endings alone. These latter are a prominent feature of the superficial cutaneous plexus but are found also in the deep plexus. A single parent pain fiber may supply branches to each plexus, in such a way as to give the functional pain unit depth as well as width in its disposition. Other endings are similarly organized. The functional sensory unit thus consists of a single posterior root ganglion cell with its dendrite and all the latter's branchings and endings (780).

The dual, principal innervation of each "spot" by at least two parent stem fibers and the overlapping arborization of free endings afford a certain margin of safety. Such overlapping of supply to areas by larger nerves is a characteristic feature of cutaneous innervation. With this arrangement in mind the mechanisms of hypoesthesia, or diminished sensation, in any skin area can be appreciated. After section of a cutaneous nerve, a given group of nerve endings would have less than their normal complement of innervation, and stimulation of such spots would thus set up less than the normal amount of neural disturbance. In similar fashion, there would be a lesser number of arborizations of fine fibers subserving pain for a given area, and a diminished pain response would be noted. Another interesting point brought out by Woollard and his coworkers is the fact that into an area surgically deprived of one of its cutaneous nerves he found growing, advancing pain fibers from adjacent intact nerves. This finding is of great importance and serves to explain the early apparent return of pain sensation to a partially denervated skin area.

These newer findings in the arrangement of cutaneous innervation help explain some long-disputed ideas concerning the state of affairs existing after section of superficial nerves. A brief review of these ideas may be given (347, 760). On the basis of observations in himself, Head postulated that cutaneous nerves contain two types of nerve fibers subserving two types of sensibility, the **protopathic** and **epicritic** (347). Under protopathic he included pain sensibility of a vivid, radiating, nonlocalizable type, extremes of temperature, and sensation from hairs. Under epicritic he classed the recognition of light touch, thermal sensations between 25 and 40°C., localization of sensations, and two-point discrimination, the appreciation of all these characters involving a discriminative faculty.

After severance of a cutaneous nerve of the forearm, a zone of skin was outlined by Head in which superficial sensibility was completely abolished (autonomous or absolute zone of nerve). Immediately around this zone was a narrow strip wherein pain sensibility was preserved and extremes of temperature were also recognized (intermediate zone). In this narrow strip, however, touch, discrimination, and differentiation of slight variations of temperature were absent. The pain recognized in this narrow strip was a diffuse, intense one, and the subject was incapable of localizing it. The sensation present in this narrow zone was the protopathic type, and it was the first type to return in the absolute zone during regeneration. The epicritic sensibility returned much later. Head thought that these two types of sensation were carried by two types of nerve fibers having different speeds of regeneration. It is well recognized that an intermediate zone of altered sensation is present around the zone of complete anesthesia after cutaneous nerve section. This zone in which pain is appreciated and touch sensation is diminished or absent corresponds to the area of overlapping distributions of pain fibers in two adjacent cutaneous nerves. The diffuse intense pain in the intermediate zone is subserved by a fewer number than the usual quota of pain endings. In fact it has been maintained that the dysesthesiae demonstrable after incomplete nerve sections result from a lessened number of sensory impulses passing into the higher sensory centers and their imperfect integration (829). The apparent rapid, early shrinkage in the size of the zone of anesthesia after cutaneous nerve section appears due to the taking over of its innervation by adjacent nerve fibers normally present in the fringes of the zone or growing into it as mentioned above. It is not necessary to postulate two types of sensory fibers of different regeneration rates.

Other features of Head's thesis are made less tenable by Woollard's and Weddell's findings (807). The ability of localization is inherent in all sensory functional units. As mentioned previously, a sensory unit has been defined as a single posterior root fiber with all its branches and endings which are disposed in area as well as in depth. When any one part of this unit is stimulated there is widespread activity throughout the unit and a modification of the activities of all the other similar endings in the unit. Further, each sensory spot has at least a dual innervation by two parent fibers. Since this is so, spatial summation of impulses from the two fibers activated allows for localization of the stimulus. Discrimination—at least as far as the recognition of two successive pinpricks is concerned—is brought about when the pricks are so placed as to set up separate impulses in two afferent fibers. Further, deep pain and superficial pain are subserved by a single neural mechanism. Deep pain is of greater intensity and of a diffuse character; in eliciting it a prick necessarily passes through the disposition of a single unit in its superficial and deep arborizations, thus stimulating not only superficial arborizations but also deep fiber branches. The mechanisms of end organs other than those for pain are thought to be similar. The massed arrangement of the individual end organs and the multiple innervation of each group help to achieve localization. When part of the innervation is reduced through nerve injury, discriminative abilities are lost.

The fact that the fine accessory fibers to each specialized encapsulated ending resemble a pain fiber led to the suggestion that, by their presence in such endings, they served as a sort of burglar alarm to signal the advent of supramaximal and potentially harmful stimuli. Their presence also might account for the wide range of stimuli capable of yielding a sensation of pain, and at the same time be compatible with the specificity of each type of end organ.

For reasons of simplicity four modalities of sense are usually recognized in cutaneous sensation, and these are pain, touch, cool, and warm, each subserved by a specific type of end organ. The recent correlation by Weddell and coworkers of a particular type of sensory ending with particular modality fits in well with the old doctrine of Müller of specific nerve energies: that, however a sensory pathway was excited, the activity produced gave rise to a sensation characteristic of the pathway and its central connection and to that sensation alone (572). Sensory experience is broader, however, than a strict adherence to the concept of these specific modalities will allow. The nerve impulses underlying the modality are not specific. Specificity is derived from the total sensory mechanism, peripheral and central. More types of cutaneous end organs exist than the types of modalities listed above. An argument against specificity of end organs has been raised, since several sensations can be elicited by experimental stimulation of a single type of ending. If a pain ending is stimulated electrically, for example, it is possible, by varying the rate of stimulation, to produce in order contact sense, itch, prick, bright pain, and ache (82). According to Weddell, however, it is not possible to elicit these various sensations from a cutaneous area in which *only* pain endings are present. Within the "touch" modality are included two types of endings, each selective for a different aspect of contact, touch, and pressure. The sensations of simple contact, moving contact or rubbing, repetitive contact or vibration, all have the common basic factor of contact and arise from stimulation of tactile endings. Other sensations such as wetness, smoothness, clamminess result from multiple stimulations of several types of end organs.

Sensory end organs can be regarded as modified nerve fibers, since they demonstrate characteristics of nerve fibers. An "all-or-none" relation holds between the stimulus and the activity excited in the nerve fiber, and the impulse for a fiber in question is of constant and unvarying value (potential). A stimulus can determine the total activity of the nerve impulse by controlling the number and frequency of the impulses set up. This determination is subject to the limitations imposed upon the nerve fiber by its refractory state and by its rate of adaptation. A stimulus of progressively increasing strength is more potent than a constant stimulus in eliciting impulses in a nerve fiber. A stimulus of constant strength applied directly to a nerve rarely sets up in the nerve more than a single impulse, for the fiber rapidly becomes adapted, the stimulus falls below threshold value in consequence, so that by the time the refractory phase following the initial impulse has passed off, the stimulus has become inadequate. In the study of sensory end organs in skin, cutaneous, and muscular tissues, however, Adrian found that, when a nerve fiber is stimulated physiologically through the normal channels, a sequence or volley of impulses is commonly set up in the fiber (13). A sensory nerve is able to conduct from the sense organ a series of discrete impulses of a constant and definite frequency which is determined by the strength of the stimulus. The factors of fatigue and adaptation by the nerve fiber must be taken into consideration, however.

That the sensory end organs also show the feature of adaptation is a common experience. Adaptation in the response of a sensory receptor is characterized by a decrease in frequency of impulses starting from the beginning of stimulation. Adaptation in a sense organ is similar to the failure in the exciting effect of a constant stimulus to a nerve. Marked differences in the rate and degree of adaptation exist in different types of end organs. It occurs rapidly in the tactile receptors, slowly in the muscle receptors. The slower rate of adaptation of the end organ allows it to set up sequences of impulses, as Adrian found. Muscle spindles adapt so slowly that they set up a sequence of impulses of relatively long duration, while rapidly adapting tactile end organs may upon minimal stimulation adapt so rapidly that only a single impulse is set up. Pressure end organs adapt less rapidly than those subserving purely tactile sensibility. A steadily increasing pressure on the skin sets up in the nerve fiber a sequence of impulses of waxing and waning frequency. Pain receptors show little or no adaptation.

Various types of stimuli are necessary for activating the various end organs. Tactile, pressure, and postural end organs require a stimulus of mechanical deformation. This probably acts by stretching the terminal part of the sensory nerve fiber in the end organ. Heat and cold spots respond to exchanges of heat at the body surface—the heat spots to additions of heat, the cold spots to subtractions of it—and not to temperature-scale variations as such. The pain receptors respond to mechanical, chemical, and thermal stimuli. Radiant heat is a most effective stimulus for pain endings in experimental study. The warm endings are the only ones that cannot be excited electrically (82).

Mechanisms by which vibratory stimuli are perceived are not agreed upon but are described by four theories (113). These are briefly as follows: Vibration sensibility is perception of repetitive mechanical stimuli delivered to the deep receptors, the pressure receptors of skin and subcutaneous tissues as well as those sense organs which respond to mechanical stimulation and lie in the fascia, muscles, tendons, and periosteum. Vibration is perceived by means of repetitive mechanical stimulation to the tactile receptors located in the skin and not by any other sense organs. Vibration is perceived by means of an independent group of sense organs, the sole function of which is to subserve the vibration sense. Vibration is perceived through the stimulation of either pressure receptors or tactile end organs or both.

In summary, the cutaneous sensory end organs vary in morphology, have preferential forms of stimulation, and vary in their adaptability to stimulation. When they are stimulated individually, the activity set up in the central sensory mechanism leads to a definite and specific sensation. The sensory unit is a posterior root ganglion cell, its dendrite and branches, and all the sensory receptors on these branches. These end organs are all similar, and they are scattered over an area of skin that may have macroscopic proportions. Stimulation of any one ending of a unit leads to a modification of the activity of the others. Through overlappings of distribution, and through concentration of sensory organs of a similar type, sensory "spots" for the various modalities are formed, and each spot is innervated by at least two fibers. The arrangements of the end organs in a pattern of depth as well as width and the dual innervation of the "spots" make it possible for temporal and spatial summation of impulses created in the "spot" to occur centrally. Localization and discrimination may be inherent qualities of the peripheral sensory mechanism therefore. Normal sensation in so far as the peripheral mechanism is concerned depends on the presence of the normal and full quota of sensory endings and fibers, and on the most suitable conditions of the skin. The activity set up in the nerve fiber follows the "all-or-none" law. Increasing the intensity of the stimulus and, consequently, activating more end organs lead to activity in more nerve fibers and transmission of more impulses centrally.

Sensory Nerve Fibers

A certain amount of specificity is also seen in the arrangement and caliber of the sensory fibers (13, 242, 288). Peripheral nerves are collections of nerve fibers of varying size and varying amounts of myelination. Variations of fiber size parallel to a certain extent the various sensory modalities. In a study of compound potentials from a nerve such as the sciatic, for example, it has been found that variations in fiber size, in amplitude of potential, and in rate of conduction of the component nerve fibers influence also the character of the nerve impulse. Compound potentials resulting from stimulation of a nerve show three main waves *A*, *B*, and *C*. *A* is largest and most rapid and has four components: α, β, γ, and δ. The *B* wave is smaller and of longer duration. After an interval a long-drawn-out wave, *C*, is seen. *A*-wave fibers are largest in diameter and most rapidly conducting, and from the place they occupy in the record they must have the lowest threshold of excitability. *C*-wave fibers are small, least excitable, and most slowly conducting. *B*-wave fibers are intermediate. Wide differences exist in the rates of conduction by the various sensory fibers, and the range may extend from 0.5 to 100 m. per sec. In meters per second the conduction rates have been given as follows for the various fiber sizes subserving sensory impulses: *A* fibers, α, 100; β, 60; γ, 40; and δ, 25; *B* fibers, 10; *C* fibers, 2.

Other facts regarding variation in activity in nerve fibers are brought out by observing the effect of a cocaine block on a nerve. After such blocking the fibers go out of action progressively in the inverse order of size: *C*, *B*, *A*. With regard to function the different modes are said to go out as follows: pain, cold, warmth, and touch (288). Vibration sense is abolished before light touch; then pressure follows. It is not absolutely certain, however, that pain is lost before thermal sensibility. When a nerve is compressed, sensibility in the area of supply is lost in the following order: pressure, touch, cold, warmth, and pain.

With regard to size, fibers subserving pressure are among the largest of the sensory components of the nerve, those subserving postural sensibility being of the same order. Afferent fibers stimulated by deformation of their end organs (touch, pressure, and posture) are widely distributed through the *A* range and are the last to be blocked by cocaine, as has been shown. Probably the fibers subserving vibration and light touch are of larger average diameter than those subserving pressure. Warmth and pain are subserved by fibers slightly larger than those for cold, and also by the small *C* fibers. Pain is served by a large range of fiber sizes, especially the δ fibers of *A*, some *B* fibers, and some pain (delayed) is conducted by *C* fibers which remain active when all other fibers have been blocked. Cold is subserved by the narrowest range of fiber sizes. On the whole, however, the fibers associated with each different modality of sensation are of characteristic size ranges, although the ranges for the various modalities overlap at their margins. Fastest conducting fibers are those that respond to mechanical deformation, those responding to thermal and other modes of stimulation being slower.

Sensory Nerve Roots

Roots and peripheral nerves carry all the modalities of sensation, but the cutaneous nerves do not carry sensations of deep or postural sensibility. The receptors underlying this form of sensibility are in muscles and tendons, especially, and the nerve fibers run with the motor nerves. The various sensory nerves distributed to the body and limbs are made up of dendrites arising from pseudo-unipolar cells in the posterior root ganglia. The axons of the pseudo-unipolar cells constitute the posterior roots. A peripheral nerve innervating the extremities contains fibers that will enter the spinal cord over several posterior roots, but in the trunk region the individual spinal intercostal nerves usually contain all the sensory fibers entering by any one root. Each root contains fibers from a definite part of the skin of the body, a **dermatome.**

The dermatomes over the trunk have the appearance of wide circular belts arranged in the original metameric pattern. Since certain groups of metameres migrate into the limb buds, the dermatomes of the limbs have also shown the effects of this migration. Each limb shows axial lines anteriorly and posteriorly except in the distal portion. In the upper limb the axial lines are fairly straight. Because of the rotation of the lower limbs the axial lines are semispiral. The migrating dermatomes are arranged parallel to the long axis of the limb except in the distal portion where they are in semicircular fashion (Fig. 268). The dermatomes of the higher segments supplying each limb are arranged along the preaxial border of the limb; those of the lower segments, along the postaxial border.

How the dermatome arrangements have been determined clinically has been described earlier. Some individual variation of arrangement of particular dermatomes exists, and of more general significance is the fact that a considerable area of distribution overlap is present between adjacent dermatomes. This overlap is apparent in the dermatome map illustrated in Fig. 268 but is not shown in Figs. 105 to 107.

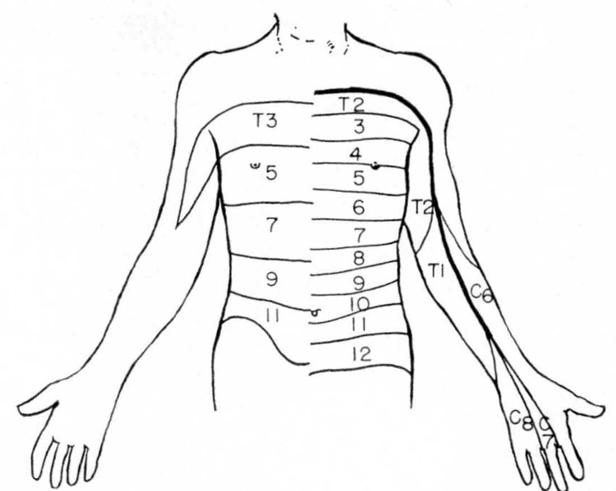

Fig. 268. Diagram to show the relation of the dermatomes of the upper extremity to the ventral axial line, and also the overlapping of the thoracic dermatomes. The ventral axial line of the upper extremity is shown on the right-hand side of the figure only. On the left-hand side of the figure, the thoracic dermatomes are shown in their full extent; on the right side, as they are usually diagrammed.

A knowledge of the dermatomes and their relation to certain roots is essential (253, 425, 426).

Sensory Mechanisms in the Spinal Cord, Brain Stem, and Thalamus

The range of fiber sizes in the posterior roots is from 2 to 20 μ. Large fibers with thick myelin sheaths are not as numerous as small poorly myelinated ("unmyelinated") fibers. The posterior roots enter the spinal cord as a linear series of filaments passing into the segments. The fibers of each filament approaching the spinal cord undergo a sorting out such that the smaller fibers and the majority of the medium-sized ones are placed in the lateral division of the posterior root. The larger, more heavily myelinated fibers are collected into the medial division of the posterior root. The rearrangement of the posterior root fibers appears to be in most respects one of convenience in order to bring the fibers in close association with the neurons about which they will synapse.

The **lateral division** root fibers transmit pain and thermal impulses. As these fibers enter the marginal zone of the posterior gray they divide into short ascending and descending limbs, each of which has several small collateral branches. Some fibers synapse about larger neurons in the marginal zone and other fibers traverse the gelatinosa to end in the proper sensory nucleus of the spongiosa about large cells. These latter cells contribute their axons to the crossed lateral spinothalamic tracts. Collaterals of the root fibers and other short axons from Lissauer's fasciculus synapse about small cells in the marginal zone and in the gelatinosa. These small cells in turn may send their axons rostrally in Lissauer's fasciculus for several segments to contribute to an uncrossed, short-chained pain and temperature pathway. Alternatively, the small cells may serve as internuncials between the root fibers and the larger neurons of the proper sensory nucleus, or between root fibers and spinal motor mechanisms.

The **medial division** dorsal root fibers enter the spinal cord just medial to the posterior gray, and on reaching the posterior funiculus, they divide into ascending and descending branches. The descending limbs are short and after descending through several segments enter the posterior gray for synapse. Many of the ascending limbs are quite long and reach the nucleus gracilis or cuneatus, depending on their level of entry into the spinal cord. Other ascending limbs are short and, after passing through one or several segments, they end about neurons in the posterior gray, especially in Clarke's column, Stilling's column, and among neurons in the proper sensory nucleus. Collaterals arising from incoming medial division posterior root fibers as well as from ascending and descending limbs also pass into the gray of posterior, intermediate, and anterior columns to synapse for completion of reflex circuits.

Impulses arising in tactile and subcutaneous pressure end organs may pass via long ascending-limb fibers in cuneatus and gracilis fasciculi, or they may pass via short ascending limbs or collaterals into the gray to synapse about cells within the proper sensory nucleus. These neurons send their axons across the spinal cord into the opposite anterior funiculus as the ventral spinothalamic tract. Two tactile and subcutaneous pressure tracts are present in each half of the spinal cord, therefore: an uncrossed one in the fasciculi cuneatus and gracilis, a crossed one in the ventral spinothalamic tract. After having gained the synapse in nucleus cuneatus or gracilis, the uncrossed tactile impulses are discharged by way of the crossing medial lemniscus fibers. Other tactile impulses may pass only via associative circuits for reflex activity in spinal levels.

Impulses arising in receptors in muscles and tendons may pass via long ascending-limb branches to reach nucleus cuneatus or gracilis, thence to gain the crossing medial lemniscus fibers and pass to the thalamus. Others may pass via short ascending limbs or collaterals into the posterior gray to synapse and gain the spinocerebellar tracts, crossed or uncrossed, and reach the cerebellum thereby. Other impulses of muscular and tendinous origin may bombard anterior gray motor neurons directly, or utilize other reflex circuits.

Many impulses entering the spinal cord activate associative neurons and complete reflex circuits. Only a comparative few of the total number gain the long ascending spinal tracts. When sufficient receptors are stimulated simultaneously, and temporal and spatial summation is of sufficient magnitude to fire an appreciable number of projection neurons, the impulses will gain the long ascending tracts. Those pain and thermal impulses entering over the fibers of any one posterior root and gaining the lateral spinothalamic tract will have become crossed within the extent of one spinal segment. The extent of several segments appears necessary for tactile impulses entering via a single posterior root to gain the crossed ventral spinothalamic tract. The arrangement of the fibers in these tracts is to be recalled. Fibers which first enter the tracts at caudal spinal levels are gradually pushed nearer the periphery by subsequently incoming fibers. In such a way the impulses from sacral dermatomes utilize peripherally placed fibers, impulses from cervical dermatomes utilize medially placed fibers. Furthermore, within the lateral spinothalamic tracts the thermal impulse-bearing fibers are collected more posteriorly in the tracts (Figs. 84, 85).

Within the medulla and pons, crossed and uncrossed trigeminothalamic fibers become associated with the long ascending spinal sensory tracts. Those bearing pain and thermal impulses have arisen in the spinal trigeminal nuclei; those transmitting touch and pressure impulses, especially, from the main sensory;

and those transmitting impulses of muscular origin, from secondary neurons within the mesencephalic nuclei. In midbrain levels the spinothalamic, trigeminothalamic, and medial lemniscus fibers are quite closely associated. A somatotopic arrangment of the fibers continues to hold; "leg" fibers being most dorsal, "arm" fibers next, and "face" fibers most ventral, and they end in particular thalamic nuclei (Fig. 86). Fibers transmitting impulses from the face and head end in the posteromedial ventral nucleus; those from the arm, trunk, and leg, in the posterolateral ventral nucleus, the "leg" fibers ending most laterally in this nucleus. The medial lemniscus ends more anteriorly than the spinothalamic fibers.

Collaterals may pass from these sensory tracts into brain stem reticular nuclei and into the mid-line "reticular" thalamic nuclei. Impulses using such arcs are of importance in maintaining constant neural activity in the brain stem reticular formation. Such activity seems of great importance in facilitating cortical activity and maintaining the waking state (see Chap. 13). Spinotectal tracts carry impulses of spinal origin into the tectum. Conscious recognition of pain and thermal impulses may be possible at this level in the presence of destruction of thalamus and postcentral gyrus. Pain and thermal impulses and tactile impulses subserving gross contact sense under normal circumstances may gain conscious recognition in the thalamus. Discriminatory relations of pain and the differentiation of finer grades of temperature change depend on the transmission of certain pain and thermal impulses to the parietal cortex wherein they are integrated. Tactile impulses, subcutaneous pressure, and muscular and tendon sense impulses are integrated in the parietal cortex, and the individual gains thereby the ability to recognize amounts of contraction about, and the postural relations of, the joints of the limbs; to recognize repetitive vibratory stimuli or two simultaneous tactile stimuli; and to appreciate the shape, size, and quality of objects.

Certain thalamic neurons, therefore, in the posteromedial ventral and posterolateral ventral nuclei send their axons into the posterior limb of the internal capsule and thence into the postcentral gyrus. Other thalamic neurons in these nuclei relay somatic sensory impulses to the medial, lateral dorsal, lateral posterior, and pulvinar nuclei. Within these various nuclei some integration occurs, and the product of this activity is discharged into other cortical regions. From the medial nuclei the projection is to the prefrontal and orbital region, from the lateral dorsal and lateral posterior nuclei to the posterior parietal regions, and from the pulvinar, to the cortical region wherein parietal, temporal, and occipital lobes join.

The Parietal Lobe

Four large regions compose the parietal lobe in man. These are the postcentral region, the superior and inferior parietal regions, and the basal region. The postcentral region is equivalent to the postcentral gyrus. The superior parietal region is the superior parietal lobule; the inferior parietal region includes the angular and supramarginal gyri. The basal region is a strip of parietal cortex extending inferiorly between the posterior limit of the temporal gyri and the anterior edge of the occipital lobe.

The areal subdivisions of the parietal lobe as made by Brodmann and Economo and Koskinas correspond fairly well (Figs. 226, 227). Brodmann has areas 3, 1, 2, and 5 in the postcentral gyrus, *7a* and *7b* in the superior parietal lobule, 39 and 40 in the inferior parietal region, and area 37 in the basal region. These correspond respectively with *PB, PC, PD, PE* (5 and 7), *PG, PF,* and *PH* of Economo and Koskinas.

Through the electrical stimulation studies of the Vogts primarily, the parietal lobe is subdivided somewhat differently and their maps have been used often in the publications of neurosurgeons, especially by Penfield (616, 622, 790). The numbering of the areas in this scheme of subdivision, which includes three regions, is as follows: The postcentral gyrus includes areas 3, 1, and 2; the superior parietal lobule includes areas *5a* and *5b*; the inferior parietal lobule includes areas *7a* and *7b* (Figs. 237, 271). Numbers 39 and 40 do not appear on such maps, these being included in area 7 of the Vogts.

The cortex of the anterior portion of the postcentral gyrus is rather thin in comparison to that of the precentral. Area 3 is the postcentral koniocortex and is the thinnest of the parietal areas; area 5 is next thinnest. The

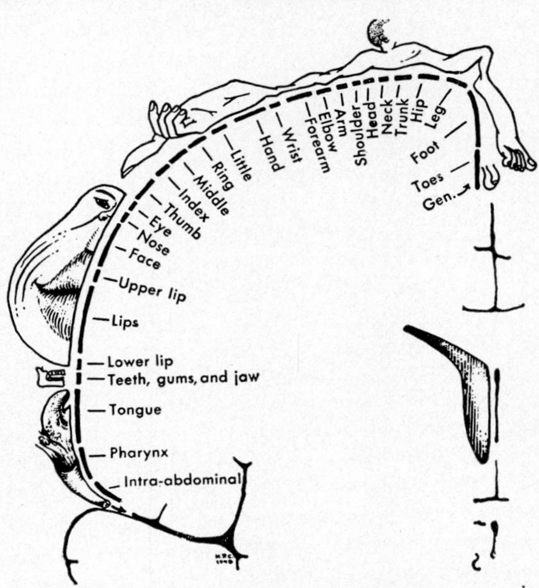

FIG. 269. A sensory homunculus laid upon a cross section of the hemisphere and drawn somewhat in proportion to the extent of sensory cortex devoted to its component parts. The length of the black lines within the cortex surface more accurately indicates the comparative extent of each representation. (*After Penfield and Rasmussen, "The Cerebral Cortex of Man," The Macmillan Company.*)

lamination of area 3 is rather indistinct, and columnization of the cells is not at all evident (Fig. 221*B*). These features, lamination and columnization, become more evident in the posterior portion of the postcentral gyrus and in the other parietal regions. All the parietal areas have a broad layer IV, and it can be subdivided into two sublayers. The upper sublayer contains some medium-sized pyramids, while the lower sublayer has densely packed small granules. In all the parietal areas large pyramids are found in the deeper portion, especially, of layer III. In areas 1, 5, 7, 39, and 40 the pyramids in this layer show a gradual increase in size as their distance from the cortical surface increases. The superior parietal areas perhaps have the largest cells in this lamina. The internal pyramidal layer V shows only a few cells in the postcentral areas, and these are small pyramids. Area 5 contains quite large pyramids in this lamina, however, and area 7 has many pyramids of medium size here. Areas 39, 40, and 37 show small cells in the fifth layer. Layer VI is more dense in the postcentral areas and more easily separated from V. In the other parietal areas the fusiform cells of VI are sparse and this lamina is not easily separated from V. The outer stripe of Baillarger is broad in areas 3 and 1, especially, and it can be divided into two zones. The upper zone contains finer fibers which arborize in layer IV*a*. Area 39 shows also a prominent stripe of Kaes-Bechterew as well as a prominent outer stripe of Baillarger.

Thalamocortical Connections of Parietal Areas

Fiber connections between thalamus and cortex of these parietal areas are not well known in man but are inferred from the situation that exists in monkeys and chimpanzees. Areas 3, 1, and 2 receive a specific projection from the posteromedial and posterolateral ventral nuclei of the thalamus; areas 5, 7, and 40 receive fibers from the lateral dorsal and lateral posterior nuclei; areas 37, 39, and posterior part of 7 receive fibers from the pulvinar. On the above basis, the nuclei of the thalamus receiving the majority of the fibers of the ascending lemniscus systems (spinothalamic tracts, medial lemniscus, and trigeminal lemniscus) project to the postcentral gyrus. Those nuclei receiving collaterals from the lemniscus systems as well as intrathalamic connections send fibers to the superior parietal lobule, the inferior parietal lobule, and the basal parietal area.

The termination of the specific afferent fibers in the postcentral gyrus is such that the somatotopical arrangement of the sensory systems is complete (56, 256, 855, 858). The lateral portion ("leg region") of the posterolateral ventral thalamic nucleus projects to the superior region of the postcentral gyrus and to its continuation on the medial hemispheric surface, the paracentral lobule. These cortical zones constitute the "leg" field. The medial portion of the posterolateral ventral nucleus projects to the middle zone ("arm" field) of the postcentral gyrus, and the posteromedial ventral nucleus projects to the lower end ("face" field) of the gyrus. A topographical sensory representation of the contralateral body surface is present therefore in the postcentral gyrus, and this agrees well in its disposition with the motor representation in the precentral gyrus (Figs. 269, 270, 271). Electrical stimulations in humans, chimpanzees, and macaques have given verification of this sensory representation. The postcentral gyrus, especially areas 3 and 1, is the primary somatesthetic area. On the basis of electrical stimulations, a secondary somatesthetic area is present in the infraparietal plane or parietal opercular region. This will be described below. The superior and inferior parietal lobules do not have a detailed focal representation of body parts apparently.

Association Connections of Parietal Areas

The knowledge of the associative connections of the human parietal areas is incomplete. Area 3, buried as it is in the depths of the central fissure, is difficult to study in isolation. For the other parietal areas physiologic-neuronographic technique in the chimpanzee has indicated associative connections shown in Table 5 (49, 86, 502, 505).

Table 5. Associative Connections of the Parietal Areas, Exclusive of Area 3, as Demonstrated by Physiologic Neuronography

Afferent	*Efferent*
1 ← 4, 6, 39, 40, 5, 7	1 → 4, 5, 7, 39
2 ← ?	2 → 31, 32
5, 7, ← 4γ, 6, 44, 1, 40	5 → 4γ, 6 ("leg" field), 1, 7, 40
39 ← 4, 6, 1, 7, 40, 19	7 → 1, 5, 39, 8 (superior part), 19
40 ← 1, 5, 39, 37, 42	
37 ← 18, 19, 20, 21, 39, 40	39 → 4, 46, 40, 19
	40 → 4, 6 ("arm" field), 1, 5, 37, 39
	37 → 18, 19, 20, 21, 39, 40

Physiologic-neuronographic studies in the macaque have shown that the cortex buried in the intraparietal sulcus has a two-way connection with that frontal cortex about the principal sulcus, area 46 (767). Cortex along the inferior bank of the intraparietal sulcus, area 7 in the macaque, projects to all the occipital areas, to the frontal pole, especially to that cortex near and in the principal sulcus, and to the posterior end of the superior temporal gyrus, area 22. The cortex along the superior bank of the sulcus discharges to the dorsal half of the precentral region and to the frontal intermediate region, areas 8 and 9 especially. Anatomical studies utilizing the Marchi technique after parietal ablations from the macaque cortex have shown many short intraparietal association fibers, as well as connections between parietal regions and frontal, temporal, and occipital regions (539, 606).

In general, then, the parietal areas are interconnected with one another, the postcentral areas also with corresponding regions of the precentral gyrus, the superior parietal lobule with the precentral "leg" field, the inferior parietal lobule with the precentral "arm" and, perhaps, "face" field. The posterior part of the inferior parietal lobule has connections with the occipital cortex, especially the associative regions; the anterior part, with the superior temporal and basal parietal cortex. The basal parietal region is densely connected with associative visual areas and with that temporal cortex outside the auditory field. The afferent connections of area 2 are perhaps similar to those of the other postcentral areas, but it projects to areas 31 and 32 as do the other cortical "suppressor" areas.

Physiologic-neuronographic technique has failed to reveal callosal fibers for symmetric parietal regions except for areas 5 and 40, and that cortex buried in the intraparietal sulcus. The parietal areas 1, 5, and 39 receive callosal fibers from area 6; and the superior parietal lobule sends fibers to area 4γ. The cortex about the inferior bank of the intraparietal sulcus also sends callosal fibers to the frontal tip. Other methods involving electrical stimulation indicated more extensive connections, however, all parietal areas appearing symmetrically interconnected (191). Area 7 discharges fibers also to areas 1, 2, 4, and 5; area 5, to 2 and 1; area 2, to 4 and 7; and area 1, to 4, 5, and 7. After removal of parietal areas in the macaque, degenerating callosal fibers have also been demonstrated with the Marchi technique. Area 3 sends axons to areas 3, 1, 2, and 4; areas 1 and 2, to 1, 2, 3, and 4; area 5, to 5, 3, 2, 1, and 4; area 7, to 7, 5, 2, and 1 (606).

Corticifugal Projections from Parietal Areas

Projection fibers from the parietal areas in the macaque have been described as passing to several subcortical levels. Areas 3, 1, 2, 5, and 7 contribute axons to thalamic nuclei, especially to those nuclei from which they receive a projection. These same areas also contribute axons to the spinal levels via the medullar pyramid. Area 2 has been shown to project to the caudate nucleus and to the medullar reticular inhibitory center (304, 507). This area is the parietal "suppressor" area. Numerous corticopontine fibers have been described as arising in the parietal areas (606, 769). Corticosubthalamic, corticorubral, corticonigral, corticogeniculate, corticoolivary, corticobulbar, corticotectal, and corticohypothalamic fibers have also been reported from various of the parietal areas.

Results of Stimulation of Parietal Areas

Stimulation over the parietal lobe as done by Foerster served to differentiate the various areas in man (256). Motor and sensory activities were induced (Figs. 239, 271). Areas 3, 1, and 2 responded with isolated movement of single muscle groups or of a single muscle contralaterally, if area 4 were intact. If area 4 were damaged, they responded with complex movement involving turning of the eyes, head, and trunk to the opposite side, and flexor or extensor synergies of the limbs. The superior parietal lobule (this would be, for Foerster, Brodmann's 5 and 7) responded with turning movement of the head, trunk, and extremities contralaterally, whether or not area 4 was intact; occasionally there would be turning of the eyes also. The inferior parietal lobule in its posterior part (this would be Brodmann's 39) responded with turning of the eyes contralaterally, and occasionally, turning of the head. Stimulation over the postcentral gyrus (3, 1, and 2) and over the superior parietal lobule (Brodmann's 5 and 7) gave rise to sensations of various types of stimuli, referred to contralateral body regions. In cases of postcentral-gyrus stimulation, the sensations were more focally experienced and progressed to adjacent body regions; in cases of superior-parietal-lobule stimulation, paresthesiae involved larger body regions. There was, as a rule, no sensory effect resulting from stimulation of the inferior parietal lobule (Brodmann's 39 and 40, Vogts' 7).

Penfield and his colleagues have also reported both motor and sensory responses as a result of postcentral-gyrus stimulation. The motor responses were similar in many instances to those elicited from precentral stimulation, and in fact, they were obtained after removal of

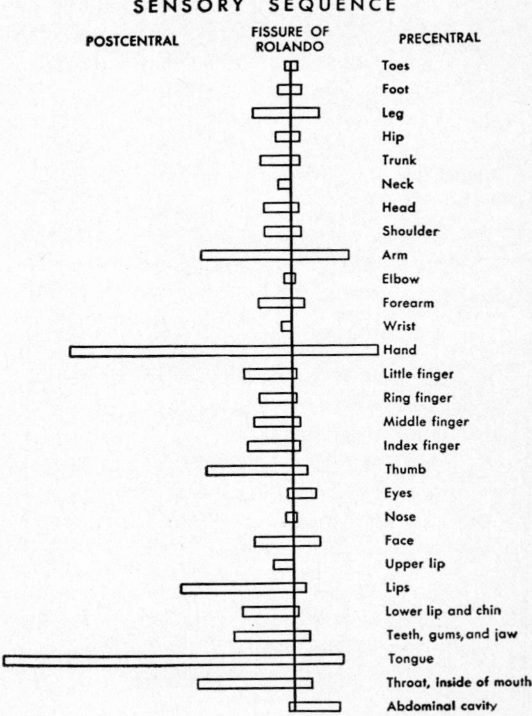

FIG. 270. A diagram of the sensory sequence to show the extension of sensory representation into the precentral gyrus. The horizontal bars represent the proportional number of responses elicited anterior and posterior to the central fissure. The latter is represented by the solid vertical line. (*After Penfield and Rasmussen, "The Cerebral Cortex of Man," The Macmillan Company.*)

the precentral gyrus (Fig. 242*B*). They apparently depend on direct parietospinal projections, therefore. In similar fashion, Penfield reports sensory responses from precentral stimulation (Fig. 270) with or without postcentral gyrus being intact. He feels, however, that the major cortical representation of somatic sensation, proprioceptive and discriminative, is in the postcentral gyrus (622).

The subjective sensations produced by stimulating the precentral and postcentral gyri were usually reported by the patients as being a numbness, tingling, or feeling of electricity. Less often the patient reported a sensation of movement although no movement occurred. A desire to move and a feeling of being unable to move were sensations also reported occasionally. The sequence of sensory responses in a series of patients has been found to be almost invariable, and it reflects the order of termination of the

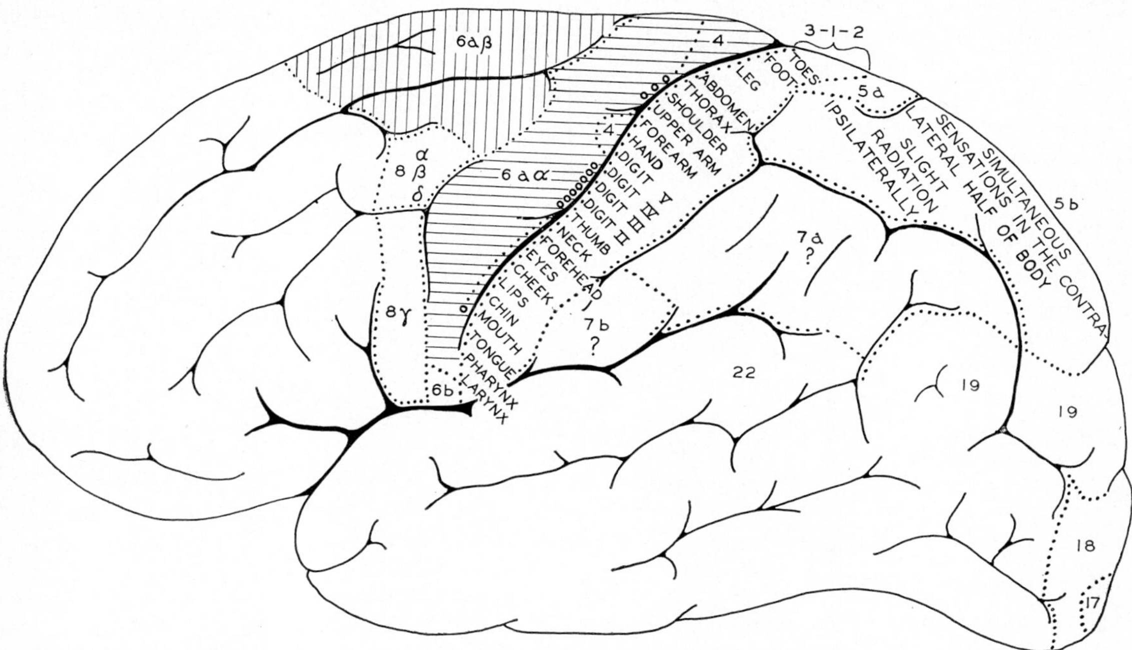

Fig. 271. Topographical cortical sensory representation in man, according to experiences of Foerster. Areas 3, 1, 2, and 5 are the chief sensory areas; 4, $6a\alpha$, and $6a\beta$ are subsidiary sensory areas; $7a$ and $7b$ are questionable. Note the difference in the numbering of the parietal areas from the plan of Brodmann. (*From Foerster in Bumke and Foerster, "Handbuch der Neurologie," vol.* 6, *copyright* 1936 *by Julius Springer in Berlin. Printed in Germany. Vested in the U.S. Attorney General.*)

thalamocortical fibers in the postcentral gyrus. It is diagrammed in Figs. 269 and 270. The relative extent of postcentral cortex given to the representation of any one structure varied from patient to patient, however. Only contralateral representation of structures was found except in the case of the face and tongue, for which bilateral representation was sometimes found. Several points have been emphasized by Penfield. The representation of the rectum, the buttock, and possibly the nipple seems to be closely associated with that of the genitalia and is contralateral. Intra-abdominal sensation is represented in the insular cortex, as might be judged, since sensory representation of tongue, throat, and inside of mouth is located in the cortex along the superior bank of the sylvian fissure. The intra-abdominal sensation was more often obtained from a precentral insular focus; the tongue, throat, and buccal sensation, from postcentral foci.

Penfield has not been able to verify that the sensory representation in the human postcentral gyrus follows closely a dermatomal plan as reported in the chimpanzee and macaque (622, 858, 859). The dermatomal sequence in these animals was discovered by Bard and his colleagues, by recording the cortical electrical potentials set up in response to tactile stimulation of skin surface (Fig. 272). An interesting observation by these investigators is the reversal of the arrangement of the cervical dermatomes, such that the eighth cervical dermatome is adjacent the upper margin of the "face" area, which is the representation of the chin.

Penfield observed that the human face representation is reversed so that the parts appear in erect fashion (Fig. 269). He found further that the representation of the neck and head (second cervical dermatome) appeared as an extension of the trunk and shoulder and was placed above the representation of the arm. The responses in the extremities were referred to individual fingers or toes or to the hand or foot as a whole. The representation of the hand and all the fingers is above that for the individual fingers, the representation of the thumb lowest of all. In similar fashion, the lips have a representation between the individual upper lip and lower lip.

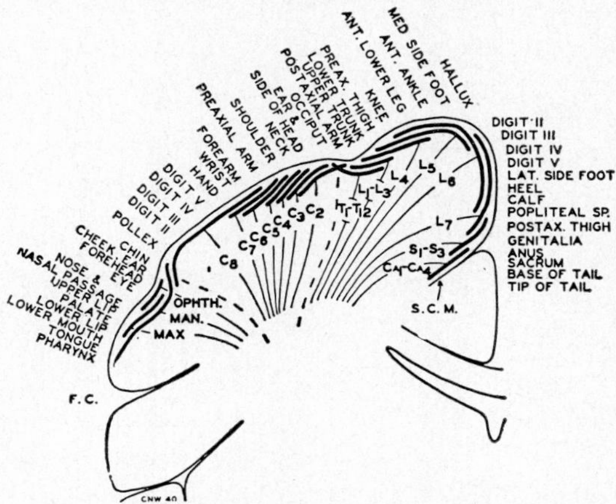

FIG. 272. Schematic frontal section through the post-central gyrus of the macaque to illustrate the dermatomal projection to the parietal lobe and the overlap of successive dermatomes as represented within that lobe. *F.C.*, central fissure; *S.C.M.*, callosomarginal sulcus. (*After Woolsey, Marshall, and Bard, Bull. Johns Hopkins Hosp., vol.* 70.)

That a *secondary* somatesthetic area is present in the cortex is well proved in animals (15, 857). This area was defined by recording the cortical potentials in response to peripheral stimulation. It is located on the infraparietal plane in a region not thus defined as a cytoarchitectural entity. The representation here is in reverse order to that in the primary somatic sensory area, with face area II adjacent face area I (Fig. 273). Bilateral representation of structures is present here, although the contralateral appears more dense. Penfield has been able to verify a secondary somatic sensory area in the human in the infraparietal plane adjacent the foot of the central fissure (Fig. 274). This secondary sensory area borders the secondary motor region. The face, tongue, mouth, and throat, however, do not have a secondary representation in Penfield's experience. The arm and leg representation is chiefly contralateral, although ipsilateral representation is also present. With stimulation of this region, the patients reported subjective sensations similar to those elicited by stimulation of the primary somatic sensory area. Penfield also noted sensory sensation as a result of stimulation of his **supplementary** motor area (see Chap. 16) (Fig. 243*A*). The phenomena reported were abdominal sensation, head sensation, and a sense of palpitation.

In Penfield's experience, stimulation of the

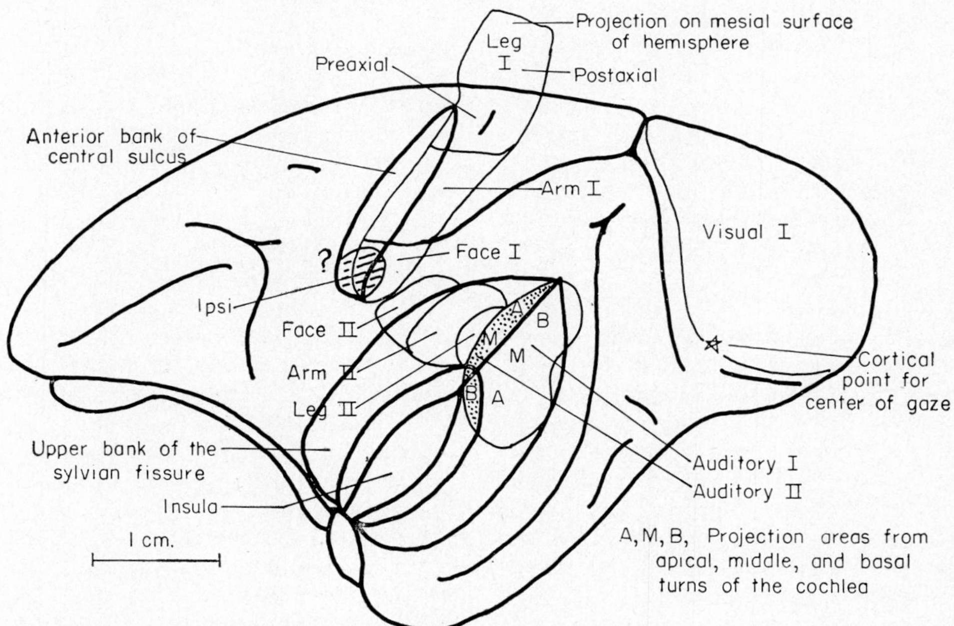

FIG. 273. Diagrammatic representation of somatic sensory areas I and II in the macaque. Monkey brain represented with the rolandic and the sylvian fissures widely spread apart. *?*, probably the ipsilateral face area may extend onto the anterior bank of the central fissure. (*After Woolsey and Fairman, Surgery, vol.* 19.)

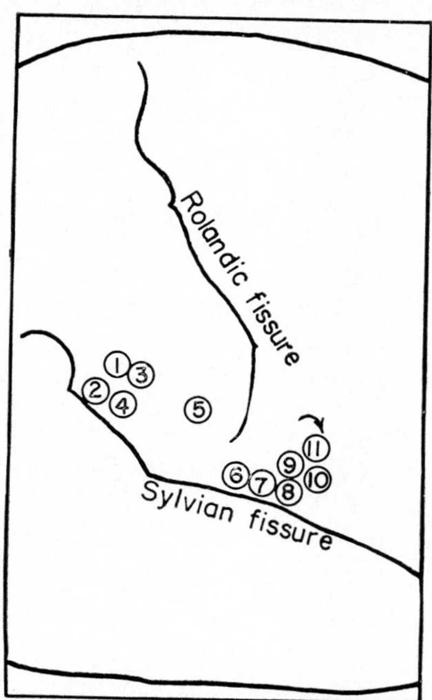

FIG. 274. The secondary somatic sensory area of man. Stimulation at 1 produced sensation in the contralateral foot; at 2, in the contralateral hand; at 3, in the contralateral arm; at 4, in the contralateral hand; at 5, in the contralateral thumb; at 6, in the contralateral arm; at 7, in the contralateral foot; at 8, in the contralateral foot; at 9, in the contralateral hand; at 10, in the contralateral fingers; at 11, in the contralateral fingers. (*After Penfield and Rasmussen, "The Cerebral Cortex of Man," The Macmillan Company.*)

parietal cortex behind the postcentral gyrus does not induce sensory responses. He reasons that a patient might be unable to perform a problem with contralateral hand or foot, if asked to do so while a superior parietal lobule is stimulated. Such an inability would correspond to the patient's inability to find a word when the left inferior parietal lobule was stimulated. This is described below. Furthermore, simple cortical stimulation over this upper parietal region did not produce the adversive movements reported by Foerster from the superior parietal lobule, especially.

Stimulation of the left inferior parietal lobule, or the dominant one, has led to arrest of speech present during the time of stimulation (621, 622). A patient who was counting backward was stopped immediately. He also had difficulty in finding the correct names for familiar objects presented to him during stimulation. When he misnamed them, he recognized his error. Other cortical areas from which speech arrest may be induced are in the vicinity of area 44 and in the posterior temporal region, in the dominant hemisphere. All three of these regions are concerned with the production of speech, as will be indicated in a later chapter.

Parietal Lobe Integrations

Within the parietal lobe, wherein somatic sensation finds cortical representation, it is customary to identify two levels of sensory integration. The postcentral gyrus contains the somatic sensory **receptive** cortex; the remaining parietal portion, the somatic sensory **associative** areas. The simpler sensory impulses from tactile, pressure, and proprioceptive endings are integrated in the postcentral gyrus and the localization of the stimuli peripherally can be completed and comparisons be made with previous sensory experiences. In fact, accurate localization and comparison of painful and thermal stimuli are also completed at a cortical level. The appreciation of position and the movement of a body part are gained also through postcentral integration.

Further integrations are available in the posterior parietal lobe, and in certain thalamic nuclei also perhaps, which enable the individual to combine tactile, pressure, and proprioceptive impulses from an object into concepts of texture, size, and form. This integration underlies **gnosis** or gnostic ability. The appreciation of the form of an object by an integration of sensory impulses is known as **stereognosis**, although this term is broadly used to imply the ability to recognize not only the form but also the size and texture. The recognition of such qualities and the recalling of previous similar sensory experience may be sufficient to identify an object. It may be necessary, however, that the concepts resulting from somatic sensory experience be combined with visual concepts, before the object is recognized accurately. Such recognition may also set in action other neuronal patterns established by previous experience, and the appreciation of the uses of the object is gained. Through a combination of somatic sensory concepts with those resulting from visual, auditory, and perhaps olfactory and gustatory experience, the individual comes to have a knowledge of his relations to the world about him. He can identify the object by a name, and he can build and recall patterns of motor activity which he adopts for the usage of the objects.

These cortical sensory activities are carried on in each hemisphere and especially in the dominant one, usually the left. The exact parietal localization is not clear. Integration in the superior parietal lobule may underlie stereognostic ability. The appreciation of the uses of objects, the skillful uses of tools, and the concept of the plan and sequence of motor activity in the performance of complex movement are perhaps products of cortical integration in the left posterior parietal tissue (Fig. 301). Such ability is known as **eupraxia.** Integration of proprioceptive concepts and elaboration of plans for motor skills involving the leg perhaps occur in the upper and medial areas of the superior parietal lobule. Elaboration of plans for the arm occurs in the lower portion of the superior parietal lobule, or that part posterior to the primary sensory arm field in the postcentral gyrus. Elaboration of motor skills for the tongue, lips, and face in the production of speech occurs in the inferior parietal lobule. These activities occur in each parietal lobe; those in the left, or dominant lobe, appear more advanced.

A concept of the body image is also gained through integrations in the posterior portion of the parietal lobe. As a result of integration of tactile and proprioceptive impulses in this parietal tissue the individual develops a body scheme for himself and he carries the image of this scheme in his consciousness. He becomes aware of the relation of parts of his own body to the environment. Although the representation of body scheme is a contralateral one—left side of body in right hemisphere, and vice versa—the representation in the left, or dominant, hemisphere is more elaborate and involves the total body plan.

The Character of the Sensory Defects Resulting From Disorder at Various Levels of the Sensory Paths

Given a patient with disorder of his sensory mechanism, it behooves the examiner to ascertain the nature of the sensory defect, the modalities involved, as well as the distribution of the sensory loss. One wishes to learn if the defect involves the perception of all the sensory modalities or only some of them, and whether the sensory defect results from injury to the sensory mechanism at the level of peripheral nerve, posterior root, intrinsic spinal gray, secondary sensory tracts, thalamus, or parietal cortex. The performance of the sensory examination requires patience and cooperation on the part of both patient and examiner. It is difficult to evaluate since it not only involves somatic aspects but also intrudes into the psychic and emotional reactions the patient has developed with respect to pain. The threshold of stimulation will vary from individual to individual, just as it varies in different skin areas.

In general, sensory disorder, especially if it develops chronically, involves two types of symptoms, positive and negative. The positive symptoms may occur because the disease process is serving as an irritant, and the patient experiences certain subjective sensations. These may be subjective, spontaneous pain, periodic or continuous in character, or other sensations of tingling, numbness, or electricity. The negative symptoms are those of loss of sensation.

If the disorder involves a **cutaneous peripheral nerve,** the patient may have partial or complete loss of pain, thermal, and tactile sensibility in the distribution of that nerve. If the nerve is not completely blocked, he may have the subjective sensations mentioned above. The deeper sensibility of muscles and tendons will not be involved in the sensory loss, since the sensory-nerve fibers, serving the deeply placed receptors in muscles and tendons, travel in company with the motor nerves to the muscles. The autonomic nerve fibers traveling in the cutaneous nerve may be damaged, however, and the patient will have sweating and vasomotor change in the skin. The areas of impaired cutaneous sensibility will not be exactly the same for pain and touch. It will be possible to demonstrate the autonomous zone of sensory loss, the zone in which all the cutaneous modalities are lost, and the surrounding narrow intermediate zone, in which some pain and thermal sensibility is present and touch is lost. The pain and thermal fibers of two adjacent nerves overlap to a greater extent, it is to be recalled, and this fact, in large measure, accounts for the presence of sensibility in the intermediate zone. If the site of damage occurs in the mixed spinal nerve or in the brachial plexus, for example, the patient will have combined motor and sensory disorder. The sensory loss may involve all the sensory modalities: pain, thermal, tactile, pressure, and muscle and tendon sensibility. The distribution of the sensory loss will follow the distribution of the peripheral nerve if the nerve is completely blocked.

If the site of damage involves **posterior root,** the distribution of sensory loss will follow the dermatomal pattern. A neoplasm growing about the root and a bony spur or a herniated intervertebral disk compressing the root are frequent disorders damaging roots. Again, all the sensory modalities may be lost over the dermatome area, but the dermatome for touch is somewhat larger than that for pain and thermal sensibility. If only a single posterior root is damaged, it is usually very difficult to demonstrate the area of sensory loss because of the extensive overlapping of adjacent dermatomes. If the patient has also positive symptoms such as pain, this will be felt by him along the course of distribution of the fibers of the damaged root. Since this pain follows along the entire course of distribution of the root fibers, it is called root pain or radicular pain. Root pain over the thoracic dermatomes is frequently referred to as girdle pain, since it follows an encircling pattern about the trunk. The root pain may not be continuous with the same intensity. It may be accentuated by movement, by straining, stooping, coughing, or any maneuver which serves to increase the pressure on the damaged root or to stretch it. Posterior and anterior roots may be compressed simultaneously, and the patient will have paralysis of muscles innervated by the anterior-root fibers and subsequent wasting of them. In the early stages of anterior-root compression he may have such positive motor symptoms as involuntary muscular twitches and fasciculations, or contractions of individual fascicles of muscle fibers. If the anterior root contains autonomic nerve fibers also, additional visceral disorders may be added to somatic motor and sensory disturbance. These will vary in accordance with the functional type of autonomic fibers compressed.

The degree of sensory loss and whether or not all modalities are disturbed in root lesions will depend on the extent of compression or damage of the roots. It is possible to have loss of only certain modalities. In **tabes dorsalis,** for example, the medial-division posterior-root fibers appear most susceptible to damage, and the patient usually has impairment of touch, pressure, vibratory, and muscular sensibility. The lateral-division root fibers are less subject to damage, usually, and pain and temperature sensibility may be preserved. Such selective involvement of sensory modalities is referred to as **dissociation of sensation.** It is more commonly observed in sensory disorders involving the secondary sensory paths and the higher sensory levels.

Destruction of the **gray matter** in the **posterior horn** will lead also to a segmental or dematomal pattern of sensory loss, and pain and temperature sensation will be lost, especially. Tactile sensibility will also be found impaired if tested for by careful methods, this impairment being characterized especially by a diminution in the number of touch spots. Since the long ascending limbs of the large medial division posterior root fibers do not synapse in the spinal posterior gray, the postural, vibratory, and tactile discriminative sensibilities will not be impaired. **Syringomyelia,** which characteristically is associated with areas of softening about the central canal, has been discussed in Chap. 5.

When the destructive process in syringomyelia or in **intraspinal neoplasms** spreads from gray to **anterolateral white matter** of one side, the pattern of sensory loss will be altered. Those fibers of the spinothalamic tracts which will be damaged first are those most recently added to the tracts, and they transmit impulses from dermatomal areas just caudad of those affected by the central gray destruction. The enlargement of the area of pain and temperature loss, especially, will occur on the side opposite that of the tract destruction. As the area of spinal destruction enlarges and destroys more spinothalamic fibers, the area of contralateral loss of pain and thermal sensation will enlarge, finally to involve all the caudal dermatomes. Tactile sensibility will be less disturbed than pain and thermal.

The pattern of development of sensory loss consequent to intramedullary destruction of spinothalamic fibers is just the reverse of that which sometimes follows destruction of spinothalamic fibers by **extramedullary spinal compression,** *e.g.,* by a meningeal neoplasm. If such a neoplasm is placed on the lateral surface of the spinal cord, it may compress a posterior root and lead to positive and deficiency signs of sensory disturbances, involving all modalities, over the area of distribution of the compressed root or roots. As spinothalamic-tract fibers are compressed the patient develops disturbance of pain and thermal sensibility, especially, on the opposite side and the area of sensory loss occurs first over the sacral dermatomes. The most peripherally placed spinothalamic tract fibers, it is to be recalled, transmit impulses from sacral dermatomes. As the compression of the spinal cord increases and more and more medially placed spinothalamic fibers are destroyed, the level of sensory loss will rise and gradually will approach the level of the compression. In such a case of compression at the right fifth cervical segment and root, for example, the patient will have lost sensation of all modalities over the right fifth cervical dermatome; on the left side, he will have impaired pain and thermal sensibility, especially, over all the dermatomes from the sixth cervical, caudally. Occasionally with progressive destruction of spinothalamic tract fibers, it is possible to demonstrate the arrangement of the fibers according to function. Tactile and pressure fibers are most anteriorly placed, thermal fibers most posteriorly, and pain fibers intermediate.

When a **posterior funiculus** is the site of disease process the area of sensory loss is on the same side as the lesion. If the fasciculus gracilis is destroyed, the sensory loss will be present over the lower half of the trunk and lower limb; if fasciculus cuneatus is selectively destroyed, the sensory loss will be present over the upper trunk and upper limb only. If both fasciculi of the right side are destroyed at the level of the fourth cervical segment, the patient will have a loss of his discriminative sensory faculties below that level on the right. He will have loss of ability to appreciate two tactile stimuli simultaneously applied, to appreciate vibratory sensibility, to recognize figures and letters drawn on his skin, to recognize the texture of an object placed in his hand, and finally, to appreciate changes in position of his extremities. Recognition of touch stimuli will usually be possible, but with finer methods of testing, the number of touch spots will be found reduced and their threshold will be increased. Because of the defect in the sense of joint position and muscle sense, the patient will have sensory ataxia. This will be especially noticeable when he performs movement in the dark or with eyes closed. He will be unable to stand with the eyes closed and the feet placed together. Such a disability is referred to clinically as a positive **Romberg's sign.**

Finally, the type and distribution of sensory defects present in the Brown-Séquard (**spinal-hemisection**) and **anterior-spinal-artery-thrombosis syndromes** should be mentioned. In the former, the discriminative sensibilities are impaired on the same side as the area of destruction; the sensibilities of pain and temperature, on the opposite side beginning at a level of one dermatome below. Tactile sensibility, found not noticeably impaired by ordinary tests, will be found defective bilaterally when finer methods of testing are used. In the syndrome due to thrombosis of the anterior spinal artery, the patient has impairment of pain and temperature sensibilities especially, and less of tactile. The disturbance is usually present bilaterally, and the levels are asymmetric. It is customarily true that the nutrition of the central gray is more defective than is that of the white matter, since the latter is supplied by penetrating branches from vessels encircling the spinal cord. A segmental pattern of sensory loss will be more striking and common, therefore. Discriminative sensory faculties are not disturbed in thrombosis of the anterior spinal artery at spinal levels. Thrombosis of paramedian branches arising from the anterior spinal artery at a medullar level, however, will usually be associated with softening of the central medulla, and the pyramids, medial lemnisci, and hypoglossal nuclei and nerves will be destroyed. Such a patient will therefore suffer paralysis of the tongue and extremities, together with a loss of discriminative sensibilites. Paramedian softening at lower pontine levels usually damages medial lemnisci and corticospinal tracts together.

Destructions of the sensory tracts at lower **pontine and medullar levels** may be followed by a dissociated type of sensory loss, therefore, since the medial lemnisci and spinothalamic tracts are not adjacent. In upper pontine and mesencephalic levels they are closely associated and are usually destroyed simultaneously. In addition, the secondary trigeminal tracts are grouped with them at these levels and will also be damaged. In lower pontine and at all medullar levels, it is more customary, with laterally placed lesions, especially, to have associated destruction of the lateral spinothalamic tract and the spinal tract and nucleus of the trigeminal nerve. A patient with such a lesion would accordingly have loss of pain and thermal sensibility over the ipsilateral half of the face and buccal cavity and a loss of the same sensibilities, especially, over the contralateral extremities and trunk. Such a type of sensory disturbance, associated with ipsilateral palatal, pharyngeal, and laryngeal paralysis and a variable amount of cerebellar ataxia, is seen in the so-called **lateral medullar syndrome.** It follows a thrombosis of the posterior inferior cerebellar artery as a rule, and sometimes that of the lateral artery of the medulla.

A **lateral pontine tegmental syndrome** may include destruction of the spinothalamic tract and associated secondary trigeminal fibers, secondary auditory tracts, the trigeminal nuclei, and facial nucleus and nerve, especially. Such an area of softening may follow thrombosis of the superior cerebellar artery which usually also supplies anterior superior cerebellar cortex and superior cerebellar peduncle. A patient with a complete syndrome would therefore show ipsilateral disturbance of facial sensibility and motility, loss of pain and thermal sensibility over contralateral extremities and trunk, especially, and less so, over the face. Cerebellar ataxia in the ipsilateral extremities, and mild impairment of hearing bilaterally, usually demonstrable by audiometer test only, will complete the picture.

The nature of sensory disorder consequent to destruction of sensory tracts at a **lateral thalamic level** has been previously described in Chap. 13 and will not be discussed here. Suffice it to say that pain and thermal sensibilities usually suffer less, and in fact, a patient with a thalamic syndrome usually can recognize pain and thermal stimuli. The recognition of sensibilities dependent on medial-lemnisci transmission will be abolished. Such dissociated sensory disturbance results presumably because pain and thermal stimuli may be recognized by tectal and mid-line thalamic nuclei, or because the medial lemniscus fibers are completely crossed whereas not all spinothalamic fibers are. The uncrossed lateral spinothalamic fibers may transmit adequate impulses for recognition of pain and temperature sensations by the undamaged lateral thalamic nuclei and parietal cortex.

Ablations from, neoplasms in, or injuries to the **sensory cerebral cortex** result in contralateral sensory disturbances, but there may also be slight ipsilateral disturbances. The severest changes resulting from disorders in the parietal lobe are in the distal parts of the limbs, with the fingers and toes suffering most, for example, in the "arm" and "leg" area injuries. After injuries to the "face" field, however, the sensory loss over the face is not as severe (622).

It is the nature of the sensory loss, rather than the distribution peripherally, that is so interesting in parietal cortical injuries (381). The discriminative sensory functions, sometimes referred to as "cortical sensibilities," are involved more than the others, and variation exists in the extent to which the various modalities are disturbed. A patient may have only an inability to localize stimuli and to distinguish two tactile stimuli applied simultaneously. Sense of position may be present, and stereognostic ability may be lost. Associated with a loss of proprioceptive sensibility, there is at times incoordination and hypotonus in the muscles of the opposite side of the body. When sensory examinations are made in a patient with a postcentral gyrus lesion, his responses are variable, it is difficult to ascertain a threshold for a stimulus, and the patient soon wearies or is unable to keep his attention on the affected part.

Foerster has described many patients with lesions in the postcentral gyrus and he has given detailed description of the type of sensory loss and the pattern of return of ability to recognize sensory stimuli (256). After an acute lesion a loss of all types of sensation might be found at first. Pain returned first, *i.e.*, the simple recognition of painful stimuli as such. An increase in the threshold for pain was noted, and the duration of the stimulus had to be increased. Discrete localization of the pain was not possible, and there was radiation of the pain from the point stimulated; the sensation created by the stimulus outlasted the stimulus.

The recognition of pressure and touch returned next, but the localization of them remained impaired. Similarly, there persisted usually an inability to recognize as separate, and to discriminate between, two simultaneous touch stimuli. The ability to differentiate the superficial quality and form of objects (stereognosis) and to name the object usually did not return, since the stream of impulses, the integration of which was necessary for such ability, was interrupted. Differentiation in the amounts of pressure (weight discrimination) was also impaired for a long time or permanently.

The recognition of temperature returned next after simple recognition of touch and pressure, warmth before cold. Before recognition of cold returned, cold stimuli were expressed as warm. While both cold and warmth recognition were still absent, some patients described very warm, or very cold, stimuli as pain.

Position sense and recognition of passive movement were impaired longer than those qualities described above, and the ability to describe the direction and extent of passive movement was even longer in returning, if indeed it did return. Similarly, the ability to recognize the *amount* of active muscle contraction was slow to return. Bone-vibration sense was among the last to return. It is obvious, therefore, that discriminative faculties in these patients were most severely damaged in the cortical lesions and were slower in returning, if they returned at all.

Several explanations have been offered to account for the early return of the ability to recognize painful, tactile, and thermal stimuli in these and other patients. In an earlier chapter it was mentioned that many investigators believe that the simple recognition of pain, temperature, and gross sense of contact is possible as a result of thalamic and tectal integrations. Foerster believed, however, that the early return of pain, touch, and temperature recognition contralateral to his parietal removals depended on integration in the undamaged or ipsilateral parietal lobe. He was able to elicit subjective sensory phenomena bilaterally by stimulating a parietal lobe. Furthermore, Dusser de Barenne elicited sensory reactions bilaterally in his animals as a result of strychninization of the thalamus of one side. Finally, it is recognized also that not all fibers of the spinothalamic tracts are crossed. It is therefore likely that the undamaged thalamus and parietal cortex contralateral to a parietal removal may be responsible for the early return of perception of pain, gross touch, and temperature. In incomplete parietal removals, furthermore, and especially in those sparing the secondary somatic sensory area, this latter region may also play a role in the recognition of these sensibilities.

The contralateral recognition of pain stimuli has been repeatedly recorded, however, in individuals from whom an entire cerebral cortex has been removed (76, 194, 533, 870). Some of the patients have also been able to localize a painful stimulus grossly and to recognize gross touch (76). Pain and touch sensibilities have been reported as less disturbed over the trigeminal area than elsewhere. Some of the patients have been able to recognize thermal stimuli; others have perceived them as pain. Vibratory sensibility has been reported present but impaired in some patients. Position sense, sense of passive movement, two-point discrimination, accurate localization and quantitative differentiation of all stimuli, and stereognostic ability have always been lost in these patients with wide cortical removals. It is not possible at present to give a final answer concerning the apparent dissociated sensory loss with thalamic and parietal cortex lesions. While both affective and discriminative faculties of somatic sensation are disturbed, the latter suffer the more severe impairment. It is an interesting paradox that small parietal lesions may be associated with disturbance of pain sensibility, while large ones are not.

With partial lesions in the postcentral gyrus, Foerster described localized disturbances in the contralateral body part, the cortical representation of which was damaged. There was never as much recovery in hand or foot as in proximal parts of the limbs, and there was never as much return in the hand as in the foot.

In the experience of Foerster, destructive processes involving the superior parietal lobule were followed by sensory disturbances similar to those resulting from postcentral-gyrus lesions, as far as type of loss was concerned. The degree was usually worse. The entire contralateral half of the body was affected in complete lesions, and sometimes slight ipsilateral involvement was also seen. Improvement occurred first in parts of the trunk and in the proximal parts of the limbs. A complete return of sensation never occurred. Sensation of passive movement, recognition of amount of active contraction, pressure differentiation, tactile discrimination, and vibratory sense were somewhat impaired permanently. It was thus usually a more severe lesion than one in the postcentral gyrus, in Foerster's experience.

As a result of lesions limited to the inferior parietal lobule, Foerster did not observe any sort of somatic sensory disturbance. This result is in direct opposition to results obtained in several cases by Evans (243). He reported extensive and permanent loss of somesthetic sensation. In the light of subsequent reports it seems likely that such sensory defects resulted from damage not only to cortex but also to subjacent white matter. If the excision is limited to cortex, sensory defect is not produced, but the patient will demonstrate a change in the usage of the limbs. For example, Penfield does not report somatic sensory defect following excision of the major part of the superior and inferior parietal lobules of the right hemisphere (622). A particular patient after such an excision did have disability, however, in that he appeared to forget his left hand. He seemed to have difficulty in anticipating and formulating what the limb was to do. The patient had difficulty in performing complex acts with the left hand and, therefore, tended to use the right instead. This disability was not permanent, presumably because the left limb had a secondary representation in the left hemisphere, and this hemisphere assumed the organization of proprioceptive activities of the limb. Within each superior lobule, therefore, Penfield feels there is representation of neuronal patterns which underly the elaboration of manual acts performed by the opposite extremities. The superior parietal lobule correlates the simple sensory impulses of the postcentral arm and leg fields. In the inferior parietal lobule of the dominant hemisphere, cortex which is just posterior to the postcentral and precentral representation of tongue and lips, the elaboration of simple actions of these structures into the mechanism underlying speech takes place.

Apraxia

It is pertinent at this point to mention a disorder of movement known as apraxia. This condition represents an inability to carry out complex learned or skilled movement, in the absence of paralysis, sensory loss, ataxia, or dementia. It appears likely, however, that the performance of complex skilled movement involves elaborative neural activity in frontal and parietal lobes.

Several forms of apraxia have been described. **Kinetic,** or **motor, apraxia** is characterized by an inability to carry out movement well on command. The patient performs as though he were carrying out an act for the first time. He is unable to perform fine movements such as writing (agraphia), threading a needle, or sewing, and grosser movements are poorly performed. Such apraxia may be observed in patients with tumors, especially, in the region of area 6. If the tumor be present in the dominant motor region, the patient usually has apraxia in the left hand. The usually present right-handed paralysis masks the apraxia in that extremity. It is assumed that the kinetic eupraxic center in the left hemisphere controls the movements of the right limbs and through association fibers traversing the corpus callosum controls a right-hemispheric eupraxic center that in turn is responsible for organization of movement in the left limbs.

Ideational apraxia is characterized by motor activity that one typically observes in an "absent-minded" individual. The movements themselves are well performed, but they are not carried out in proper sequence to serve correctly the purpose intended. For example, a patient who wishes to light a cigarette and smoke may put both match and cigarette in his lips without striking the match. Ideational apraxia is seen in diffuse disorders of the brain, *e.g.,* in cases with multiple areas of softening due to vascular insufficiency. It may be seen during the post-epileptic confused state. It therefore usually does not have localizing value.

In **ideomotor apraxia** simple motor acts may be normally performed. Complicated acts, such as would involve the use of tools, or even acts such as saluting, are incorrectly performed. The plan of the act appears to be defective or completely absent. Instead of saluting, for example, the patient might stand, handle his ear, or merely raise an arm. This type of apraxia seems to imply that complicated acts are performed by a plan or engram of the sequence of motor events which the patient has developed through previous performance. This form of apraxia is usually seen in destructions of the left or dominant supramarginal gyrus or in the corpus callosum. It would appear that an ideational area is present in the left supramarginal parietal region and that through association fibers this center guides the motor organization necessary for the performance of the complicated acts. Interruptions of the association fibers passing from this parietal region to the dominant motor center, or destructions of the parietal area itself, would be associated with ideomotor apraxia. This is usually demonstrable bilaterally when a parietal lesion is present, and such a form of apraxia has some localizing value. It is of interest that uncomplicated surgical section of the corpus callosum is not followed by apraxia (20).

After destructions of the left inferior parietal lobule and adjacent occipital tissue, patients may have a disturbance in their orientation of their own body scheme. They may have difficulty in recognizing right from left, and may be unable to differentiate fingers, name individual fingers, or show them on request. They usually also cannot write, and they have difficulty in arithmetical calculations. Such a symptom complex constitutes the **Gerstmann syndrome** and involves both agnosia and apraxic disorder of fingers. With disturbance in the right inferior parietal lobule, the patient has difficulty with his left limbs only. He may deny that they are a part of him or that they may be the site of a paralysis which in reality exists in them.

Occasionally in the course of neoplastic, degenerative, or posttraumatic cicatricial disorder of the postcentral parietal cortex, especially, a patient will demonstrate certain positive sensory symptoms. He may have **sensory seizures,** characterized by a sensation of numbness, tingling, rushing of blood, or electricity. The sensation usually begins in a certain skin region and spreads in a characteristic pattern which mirrors the topical representation in the postcentral gyrus. If the area of cortical discharge spreads to involve the precentral cortex, the patient may have convulsive movements. The skin of the face (especially about the mouth), the thumb, and the toes are sites in which sensory seizures are prone to occur, perhaps because these regions have relatively such a large cortical area of representation.

The limits of the cortical sensory fields have been described as more extensive by some workers, on the basis of thalamocortical connections, sensory phenomena occurring in animals after strychninization of the cortex, and in man with electrical stimulation, as well as because of results of operations in man. Areas 4 and 6 have been included as accessory sensory areas, and they receive fibers from the lateral ventral nucleus of the thalamus. Return of sensation following parietal-lobe lesions has been attributed to the secondary sensory functions of these areas as well as to the activity of the contralateral parietal areas. In the experience of Foerster, tactile discrimination was most often impaired in cases of ablation from the hand and finger region of the precentral gyrus. Improvement was the rule, with no permanent deficiency. Bucy, however, reports no demonstrable sensory deficit in his patients following ablation from the precentral gyrus, when the sensory examination was performed several hours after operation (117). If the examination were delayed beyond 24 hr. postoperatively, sensory defect was invariably found, involving all modalities, but unequally. This delayed defect was interpreted as being produced by the edema and vascular alterations which developed in the postcentral gyrus consequent to the surgical removal from the precentral. These sensory defects were usually not permanent.

There is no exact information as to the manner in which the various sensibilities are located in the parietal cortex. It appears most likely that the postcentral gyrus and, perhaps, the infraparietal or opercular plane receive the majority of the simple sensory impulses from the thalamus. The other parietal tissue serves as a somatic sensory associative region. It receives association fibers from the postcentral gyrus and projections from those higher-level thalamic nuclei in which sensory integrations occur. It is probably true that these latter connections are of more importance in the initiation of cortical integrations subserving sensory association.

Summary

The sensory system is organized on a number of interconnected levels. Each part of the path from lowest level to highest bestows upon the sensory impulses, originating in the periphery and transmitted centrally, some characteristic of its own. A variety of receptors, susceptible to different forms of stimulation, and reacting characteristically in terms of adaptation when activated, set up impulses in various types of sensory nerve fibers. Some of these last transmit rapidly, some quite slowly, others at intermediate speeds. Receptors of similar type are grouped into sensory spots, served by at least two fibers, and fibers arising from similar spots are grouped together in spinal nerves and end about common spinal neurons. Possibility for mutual interaction is given, spatial and temporal summation may result, and the first steps of stimulus localization be set in operation. As they enter the neural axis, posterior root fibers are grouped for convenience of termination in posterior gray, and within the gray facilities are at hand both for projection of impulses to higher levels and for discharging them into various spinal reflex paths. Secondary sensory fibers are grouped according to the character of receptors from which their impulses sprang. The fibers in the sensory bundles are also arranged in a pattern that reflects the site of the peripheral receptor. These projection paths serve not only to bring impulses to thalamic levels but also, through their collaterals, to discharge impulses into brain stem reticular nuclei and tectal gray. The secondary sensory tracts end somatotopically within relay thalamic nuclei which in turn relay the impulses in orderly fashion to the postcentral gyrus and to other thalamic nuclei.

Thalamic integration may contribute to the conscious recognition of pain, tactile, and thermal impulses, and it interrelates all types of somatic impulses with their kind and with those of visceral, visual, and auditory character. Two orders of sensory impulses are thus discharged to the cerebral cortex. The posterior ventral nuclei discharge simple tactile, pressure, and proprioceptive impulses to the postcentral gyrus, within which a somatotopic representation is also maintained. The lateral dorsal, lateral posterior, and pulvinar nuclei relay more complex sensory concepts to the posterior parietal region; the medial thalamic nuclei, to the prefrontal region.

The postcentral gyrus gives accurate localization to peripheral sensory activity and completes identification of modality. The posterior parietal region shows somatotopic representation in that the superior parietal lobule serves for integration of sensory activities of arm and leg; the inferior parietal, for face, lips, and tongue, especially (622). Posterior parietal integration combines sensory concepts, *e.g.*, of touch, to give recognition of roughness or smoothness, and of pressure to give concept of size and shape to objects. Integrations in left posterior parietal, posterior temporal, and rostral occipital regions bring forth a symbol, a name of an object with these characters and an appreciation of its uses.

The body scheme is represented in posterior parietal tissue consequent to integration of proprioceptive, tactile, and visual impulses. The elaboration of proprioceptive impulses from a body part, necessary for the skillful use of that body part in movements, occurs in posterior parietal tissue. The localization of this elaboration in man, at least, seems to be as previously given: arm and leg uses in superior parietal lobule; face, lips, and tongue, in inferior parietal (622). The elaboration of movements of the tongue and lips in speech would occur in this latter region of the left hemisphere, especially.

The associative connections of the parietal cortex, thus far identified, serve to give some indication of the functions of its various regions. The superior parietal lobule, especially, is related to leg region of precentral tissue and would serve to guide motor uses of that limb. The inferior parietal lobule is associated with precentral arm and face fields and guides the movements of these regions. These experimental findings in the macaque and chimpanzee correlate well with the clinical impression of parietal representation of sensory elaboration. The posterior portions of the superior and inferior parietal lobules and the basal parietal area are related to visual associative areas; the posterior part of the inferior parietal lobule and the basal parietal region are also related with the middle and inferior temporal gyri, which in turn are also related to visual associative areas. These interrelations subserve speech and memory patterns, which will be further discussed in a later section.

CHAPTER 20

TASTE AND TASTE PATHWAYS

Man depends very little for his existence on the sense of taste, and structures subserving that sense apparently make up only a small part of the nervous system. Little is known, furthermore, of the anatomy of these taste pathways. Taste buds are scattered over the tongue in adult man, but those in the circumvallate papillae are most important. Nerve fibers terminate about special cells (chemoreceptors) in the taste buds, and the sense of taste depends on their stimulation by a fluid medium. In the taste system the primary neurons are in the ganglia of certain cranial nerves—the seventh, ninth, and tenth, especially—in man. The secondary neurons are located in the nucleus of the tractus solitarius in the medulla, and particularly in the cephalic end of this nucleus. The tertiary and higher neurons are in the thalamus and cerebral cortex, respectively, but their exact locations are not certain. Cortical representation of taste is perhaps bilateral and it has been thought to be either in the temporal or parietal lobe. Evidence obtained in recent years favors the latter site.

In adult man taste impulses arise from the dorsal surface of the tongue, the region of the epiglottis, and sometimes also from the mucous membranes of the cheeks, lips, and larynx. It is said that the middle dorsal surface of the tongue is not excitable, and the rest of the tongue is divisible into the tip, border, and base when taste function is tested, experimentally. Clinically, a simpler division is used, anterior two-thirds of tongue and posterior one-third.

The four qualities of taste are sweet, salty, bitter, and sour, and materials for testing taste should include a representative of each of these qualities. The latent period before perception of taste and the concentration of the test material should be taken into consideration in testing taste. There is individual variation in the location of taste perception for these substances, as well as difference in individual appreciation and interpretation. The tip of the tongue is usually sensitive to all, but most sensitive to sweet and salt. The borders of the tongue are usually most sensitive to sour, and the base most sensitive to bitter.

Peripheral Taste Paths

From a neuroanatomical standpoint, the cranial nerves bringing in taste impulses are the seventh, ninth, and tenth. Argument still persists as to whether the trigeminal is also a taste carrier, and in some individuals it perhaps is. The seventh nerve is responsible for taste over the anterior two-thirds of the tongue, and the fibers can pass over a variety of paths in reaching the geniculate ganglion (Fig. 275). In some individuals, for example, the taste impulses from the anterior two-thirds of the tongue may travel along fibers, consecutively a part of the lingual nerve, the chorda tympani, and its connection with the otic ganglion, a branch from this ganglion to the great superficial petrosal nerve, and finally along this last nerve to the geniculate ganglion (480, 712). In the majority of individuals, however, the course seems to be lingual nerve, chorda tympani, and facial nerve to geniculate ganglion. The glossopharyngeal is responsible for taste impulses from the posterior one-third of the tongue, and the vagus for the region about the epiglottis.

The primary neurons for taste impulses are then in the geniculate ganglion of the seventh nerve, the superior petrosal ganglion (when there are two) of the ninth nerve, and the nodose ganglion of the tenth. The central processes of these various ganglionic cells pass into the medulla by way of the three individual nerves, and synapse about secondary cells in the

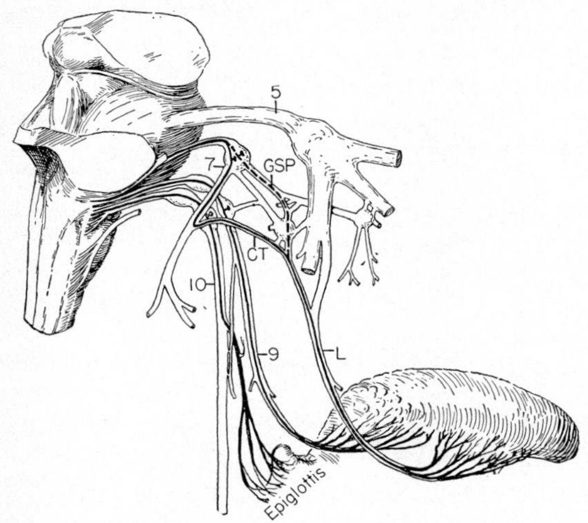

FIG. 275. The peripheral pathways for taste impulses. 5, 7, 9, and 10 are the trigeminal, facial, glossopharyngeal, and vagus nerves, respectively; *CT*, the chorda tympani; *L*, lingual branch of trigeminal nerve; *GSP*, greater superficial petrosal nerve. Solid black lines are the usual paths; the broken line, an alternate path for taste impulses from the anterior two-thirds of the tongue.

rostral part of the nucleus solitarius. Some authors, however, insist that some or all of the secondary neurons for taste are in the nucleus intercalatus, a collection of cells situated in the medulla just between the hypoglossal nucleus and the dorsal motor nucleus of the vagus. This seems unlikely.

Central Taste Paths

The course of the pathways arising from these secondary neurons is at present unknown. It seems most likely that the secondary solitario-thalamic fibers travel in company with the other secondary sensory systems, either with the quintothalamic, spinothalamic, or medial lemniscus fibers. These secondary taste fibers presumably synapse within the medial portion of the posteromedial ventral thalamic nucleus or in an accessory semilunar nucleus, adjacent medially (Fig. 276). At least, experimental destruction of these nuclei in the macaque leads to a loss of taste (83, 599). Furthermore, some clinical evidence tends to support this. A patient suffering with loss of taste on one side of the tongue was found at post-mortem examination to have a circumscribed tumor involving the posteromedial ventral and centrum medianum nuclei of the thalamus (11).

Cortical Representation of Taste

Conscious recognition of taste, or at least discrimination of taste qualities, would appear to require cortical integration. The cortical representation of gustatory function, however, has not been universally agreed upon, and three cortical loci have been suggested. Such suggestions have been based on subjective disturbance of taste sensibility in patients suffering with neoplasms or degenerative disorder sec-

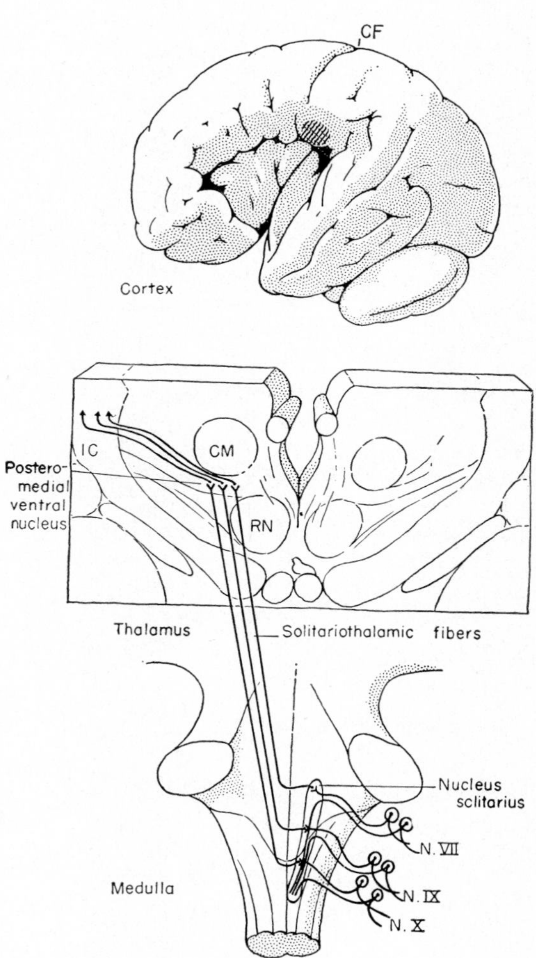

FIG. 276. The central taste paths. Schematic. It is improbable that all the secondary taste paths via solitario-thalamic fibers are crossed as indicated. The cortical taste field is represented as the crosshatched area on the parietal opercular region. The sylvian fissure has been retracted widely to expose the deep opercular region and insula. *CF*, central fissure; *CM*, centrum medianum; *IC*, internal capsule; *RN*, red nucleus.

ondary to vascular disease. The three cortical regions are the uncus or some other part of the temporal lobe, the anterior part of the insula, and the opercular part of the postcentral gyrus. It is recognized at once that these areas are closely associated, spatially, and that a neoplasm might cause compression of all three simultaneously.

Taste hallucinations are described as a feature of "uncinate fits," attacks occasionally arising in disease of the uncus or adjacent temporal lobe. Such attacks are characterized by olfactory or gustatory hallucinations, or both, associated frequently with chewing or smacking movements, and a peculiar form of mental confusion, or dreamy state (see Chap. 22). Practically no post mortem evidence has been offered in such cases that the uncus alone was involved, and it is primarily through clinical examinations of such patients that the cortical taste area has been placed in the uncus or other part of the temporal lobe. A secondary reason for placing taste in the uncus along with olfaction is the functional similarity of the two senses, both being stimulated through chemical agents and both being peripherally so closely associated, subjectively. Little good evidence has been given for a discrete insular cortex location of the taste sense.

Clinical and experimental evidence, however, has recently been collected which favors a parietal opercular location for taste sense (89) (Fig. 276). That the posteromedial ventral thalamic nuclei project to the cortex about the foot of the central fissure has been well substantiated. This fact, together with the fact that destruction of that thalamic nucleus in macaques resulted in taste loss, directed attention to this cortical area. Extirpation from the opercular part of the precentral and postcentral gyri, especially, in that region adjacent the insula, has led to taste loss in the macaque and chimpanzee (598). Furthermore, stimulation in humans of sensorimotor cortex where it joins the insular cortex, deep within the fissure of Sylvius, has elicited taste sensations (622). This region would appear to lie in Brodmann's area 43. Finally, Shenkin and Lewey reported a patient who experienced a taste aura prior to his epileptic attacks (720). He also was unable to recognize sweetness on one side of his tongue. At operation he was found to have a vascular anomaly of the middle cerebral vessels which compressed the postcentral opercular region, especially. This anomaly was contralateral to the tongue area in which taste was defective.

The location of taste in the parietal operculum would place it adjacent to the center for sensory representation of the tongue and near the cortical motor centers for mastication and tongue movements. Such a cortical locus for taste seems more plausible than one in the uncus. Neoplasms growing within the basal temporal region or within the vicinity of the inferior horn of the lateral ventricle would be likely to lead to compression of this frontoparietal opercular region, and this has undoubtedly led to the misinterpretation of a temporal focus for taste representation.

A person with a loss of taste is said to have **ageusia,** a diminished amount of taste is **hypogeusia,** and when there are misinterpretations or hallucinations of taste, the condition is called **parageusia.** It is well to keep in mind that taste is impaired through changes in the peripheral olfactory apparatus, as well as in local disorders of the mouth, and that a disturbed taste function is not always indicative of diseases of the taste pathways.

CHAPTER 21

THE VISUAL PATHWAYS AND OCCIPITAL LOBE

THAT AREA from which the retinas receive light impulses at any particular time is called the visual field or fields. By mapping out the visual field of an eye, information is obtained regarding the functioning of the retina and the visual pathways. Objects in the upper fields stimulate photic cells in the lower portions of the retinas, and objects in the nasal half of a field stimulate sensitive cells in the temporal half of the retina. In the conscious visual perception of an object a chain of neurons is involved; they are located in the retina, in the lateral geniculate body of the thalamus, and in the cerebral cortex adjacent the calcarine fissure of the occipital lobe, successively. A partial decussation of optic-nerve fibers in the optic chiasma occurs, and as a result impulses from the nasal half of each retina (hence from temporal fields) cross to pass to the opposite lateral geniculate body and occipital lobe. Such a partial decussation is presumed to have arisen with the development of binocular vision in animals with frontally placed eyes. Simultaneous movements of the two eyes in the same direction, or conjugate deviations, in response to a variety of stimuli are possible through cortical and brain stem mechanisms.

In this chapter the optic pathways will be considered neuron by neuron, beginning with the retina, and concluding with the occipital-lobe cortex. Information about the paths has been gained through neuroanatomical studies in man and monkey, and only minor disagreement now exists concerning the topical arrangement of this system. At first glance, it would seem to be difficult experimentally to learn some of the connections of the optic fibers that are buried within the central nervous system, *e.g.*, in the lateral geniculate body. In most cases of degeneration of axons, the degenerative process proceeds to the end of the axon and stops. In the optic system, however, injuries of neurons in the retina will bring about changes not only in their axons, but also in the cells of the geniculate body around which they synapse, a transneuronal degeneration. Ablations in the occipital cortex likewise produce degenerative changes in the cells of the lateral geniculate body of the same side. Combining the results of the two "peripheral" methods of approach will give some knowledge of the middle connections, and such has been done in the study of the optic system. In the following discussion, the neuronal links composing the visual tracts will be described in some detail. Some of the light- and visual-reflex mechanisms and certain mechanisms controlling movements of the eyes will also be described.

ANATOMY

THE RETINA

The retina develops from the central nervous system, and in its component layers of nerve cells and fibers it resembles the architecture of the cerebral cortex. As many as 9 or 10 layers or divisions can be depicted in microscopic sections, but for present purposes, it can be assumed that there are three chief layers of nerve cells and their fibers (Fig. 277). The deepest layer of the retina and the most distant from the light is composed of two types of cells, **rods** and **cones.** This layer of cells composes the light-sensitive part of the retina. Not all the retina, however, is light-sensitive. That part of it through which the optic nerves run is not sensitive, nor is that within the anterior part of the globe, anterior to the ora serrata

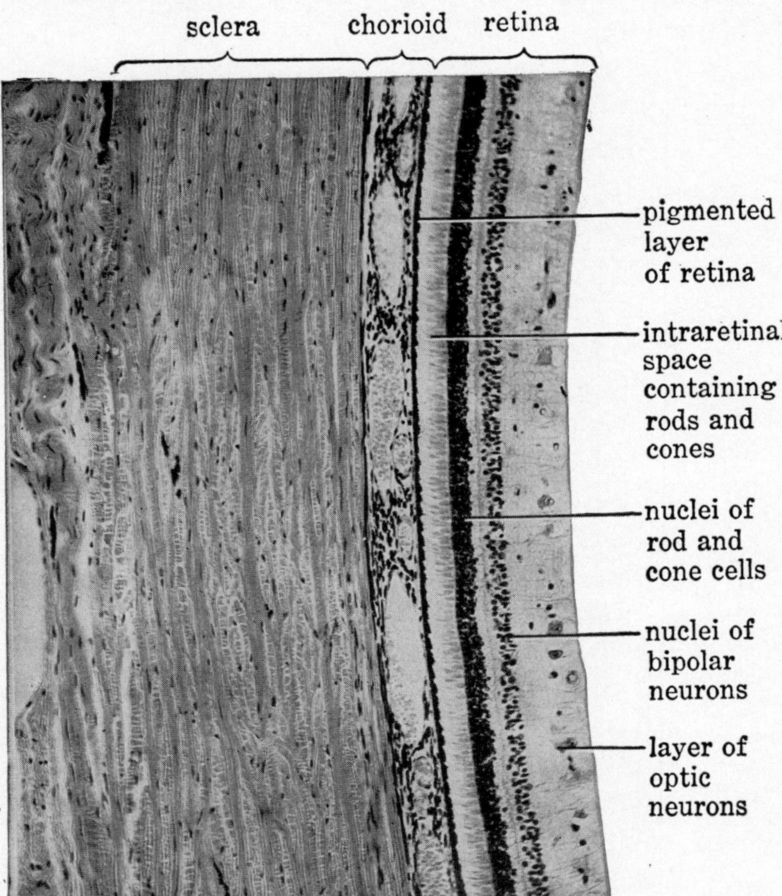

FIG. 277. Human eyeball. The section passes through all coats about 5 mm. behind the ora serrata; exterior is toward the left. Specimen in the Piersol collection. Photomicrograph, ×125. (*After Nonidez and Windle, "Textbook of Histology," courtesy of McGraw-Hill Book Company, Inc.*)

and just behind the iris. In the central part of the retina which lies within the visual axis of the eye is a small yellowish area, the **macula lutea;** a small depression in the center of the macula is the **fovea centralis** (Fig. 278).

THE RODS AND CONES

The rods and cones are not equally distributed in the sensitive portion of the retina. The cones are concentrated in the fovea, and outside it they diminish in number fairly rapidly as the peripheral part of sensitive retina is approached; no rods are present in the central part of the fovea. In order for an object to be in the line of distinct vision the light impulses from it must fall on the fovea. Since only cones are present in the fovea, they are considered to be the elements necessary for distinct vision. Outside the fovea both rods and cones are found except near the periphery of the sensitive retina, where apparently only rods exist.

It has been estimated that the human retina contains 110 to 125 million rods, and from 6.3 to 6.8 million cones (96, 343). Both are somewhat slender columnar cells, but the cones are bulkier (Fig. 279). The nucleus of the cone is more within the mid-region of the cell proper rather than near one end as in the rod. Deep to the layer of rods and cones, or peripherally placed with regard to them, is a pigmented epithelial layer, the cells of which send processes in between the rods and cones. The pigment inclusions within these processes change their position with changes of illumination. They surround the rods and cones of a retina exposed to light and perhaps serve as a sheath to prevent diffusion of light from one rod or cone to another.

The rods contain a substance, rhodopsin or **visual purple,** which is thought to be concerned with their visual function. When the retina is exposed to light, this visual purple bleaches white. Other pigments formed in this process have been described. Xanthopsin, or visual yellow, is identified at an intermediate stage; leucopsin, or visual white, at the end stage. Visual white has been identified as vitamin A; visual yellow is probably vitamin A aldehyde coupled to protein (this is sometimes identified as retinene, a carotinoid). Visual purple is considered to be a polymerization product of retinene. With exposure to light, visual purple is converted to retinene, in darkness this process is reversible. As the cycle is repeated many times, some loss of visual purple may occur. This is replaced through the union of vitamin A with protein to form retinene, which is converted to visual purple. Whether or not the cones contain a photosensitive substance comparable or similar to visual purple has long been debated, but not proved.

The rods are in that part of the retina not essential to distinct vision and are thought to subserve dim vision (*i.e.,* night vision). It is recognized that night blindness is a symptom of vitamin-A deficiency. The rods are also concerned with peripheral vision and perception of movement. To the cones, on the other hand, in addition to being responsible for bright or distinct vision, some authors attribute color vision. Many theories of color vision exist, and a brief summary of some is given below.

The relations of the rods and cones to the bipolar cells, the secondary visual neurons, are of interest (631) (Figs. 279, 280). Groups of rods are related to a single bipolar cell which also is in synaptic contact with several cones. A certain amount of overlap also exists between the dendritic territories of two such bipolar cells. In the fovea and macular areas, especially, a single cone is in synaptic relation with a single bipolar cell, and there is no overlap between the dendritic spreads of adjoining bipolars of this type. Rod and cone "party" lines and cone "private" lines exist, therefore.

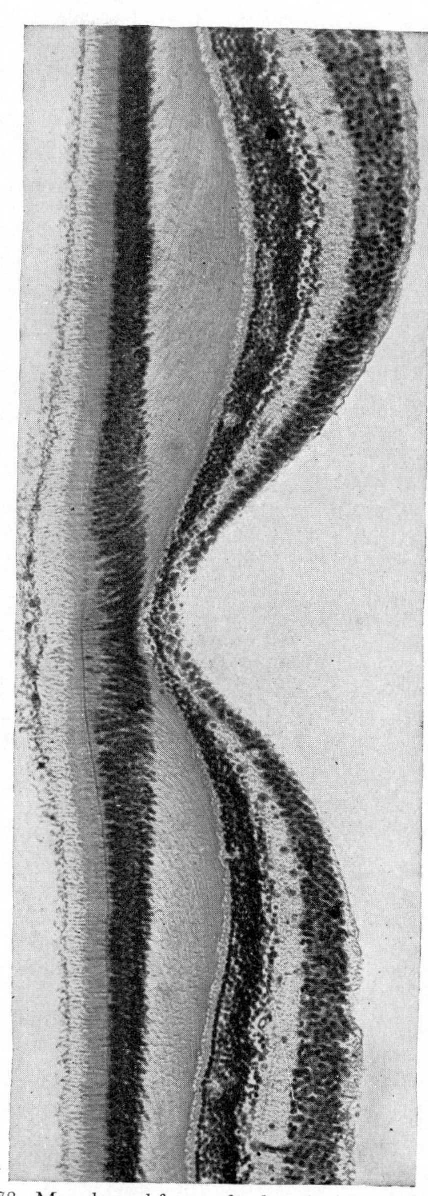

FIG. 278. Macula and fovea of a detached human retina. The cones have pulled away from the pigmented epithelium, cleavage taking place in the intraretinal space. Compare the thickness of each layer in the macula with the same layers in Fig. 277. Specimen by Dr. L. L. Caulkins. Photomicrograph, ×125. (*Courtesy of McGraw-Hill Book Company, Inc. After Nonidez and Windle, "Textbook of Histology."*)

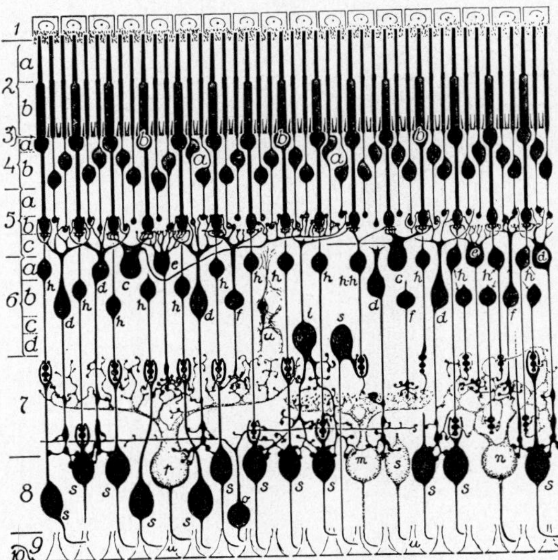

Fig. 279. Scheme of the structures of the primate retina as revealed by the method of Golgi. The designation of the layers, the zones, and the cells also applies to Fig. 280. 1, pigment layer; 2*a*, outer zone; 2*b*, inner zone of the rod and cone layer; 3, outer limiting membrane; 4*a*, outer zone; 4*b*, inner zone of the outer nuclear layer; 5*a*, outer zone; 5*b*, middle zone; 5*c*, inner zone of the outer plexiform layer; 6, inner nuclear layer with its four zones; 7, inner plexiform layer; 8, layer of the ganglion cells; 9, layer of the optic nerve fibers; 10, inner limiting membrane. The designation of the nerve cells: *a*, rods; *b*, cones; *c*, horizontal cells; *d*, *e*, *f*, *h*, bipolar cells; *i*, *l*, so-called "amacrine cells"; *m*, *n*, *o*, *p*, *s*, ganglion cells; *u*, "radial fibers" of Müller. In this scheme the nervous elements are reduced to their essentials, with, however, the characteristic features of each variety preserved—the location of the bodies, the size, the shape, and the spreading of the dendrites and of the axis cylinders—and with the synaptical contacts presented accurately. (*Courtesy of the University of Chicago Press. After Polyak, "The Retina."*)

Horizontal cells whose cell bodies are located in the outer part of the bipolar cell layer are found throughout the retina but are most numerous in the macula and fovea (Figs. 279, 280). They receive impulses from cone cells of one region and discharge via horizontally running axons to distantly placed rods and cones.

BIPOLAR CELLS

Two chief types of bipolar cells are described, **centripetal** and **centrifugal.** The centripetal bipolars are those conducting impulses from rods and cones to ganglion cells, and it has been observed above that these are of two orders (Fig. 280). Some of these bipolars are **polysynaptic** in that they have dendritic relation with many rods and cones; others are **monosynaptic** and have relation with only a single cone. These monosynaptic bipolars are sometimes referred to as midget bipolars. Polysynaptic bipolars are of several morphological varieties, and in general they are found throughout the retina. Certain varieties are less numerous or absent in the fovea. Monosynaptic bipolars are especially numerous in the fovea and macular regions, where the cone population is most dense. They are less numerous in peripheral regions of the retina.

The centrifugal bipolars appear to be in dendritic relation with the bodies of ganglion cells and possibly with axons of centripetal bipolars. Their axons pass outward to split and come into contact with rods and cones (Fig. 280). These centrifugal cells have sometimes been included in the group of "amacrine" cells. The term "amacrine" has been applied to both nervous and neuroglial elements, and the "amacrine" neurons have been thought to be devoid of an axis cylinder. Neuroglial ele-

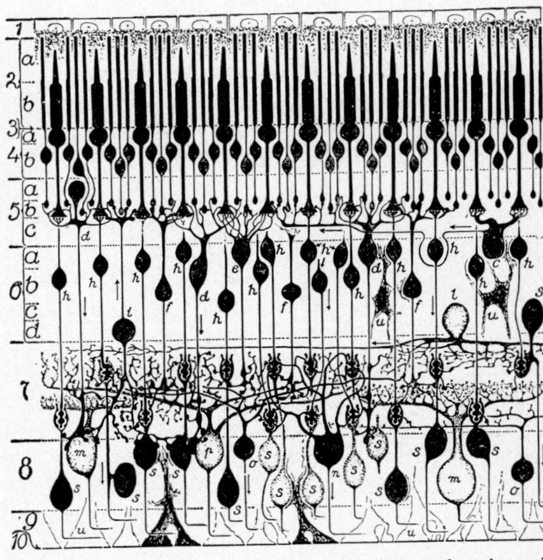

Fig. 280. Scheme of the primate retina, showing the types of the neurons and their synaptical relationships, so far revealed by means of the method of Golgi. The designation of the layers, zones, and cells is the same as in Fig. 279. The probable direction of the propagation of the nervous impulses is indicated by arrows. (*Courtesy of the University of Chicago Press. After Polyak, "The Retina."*)

ments perhaps should not be included in the "amacrine" group (631). The centrifugal bipolar neurons, however, do have axonal and dendritic processes, as just described, and the designation of "amacrine" for them should be dropped. Other cells in the lower parts of the bipolar or inner nuclear layer may be association cells since their axons pass in a horizontal direction through the retina. Some of these neurons have also been included in the "amacrine" group, although since axonic processes can be seen, they should not be called "amacrine" cells. "Amacrine" cells are more fully discussed by Polyak (631).

GANGLION CELLS

These retinal constituents present the customary appearance of neurons seen elsewhere in the nervous tissue better than do the retinal neurons heretofore described. Small, medium-sized, and large ganglion cells are present (Figs. 279, 280). Two varieties of ganglion cells have been described, according to their synaptic relationships: **diffuse** or polysynaptic, and **individual** or monosynaptic. The diffuse ganglionic cells come into contact with many of the centripetal bipolars, and some overlapping exists in the contacts made with the bipolars by several diffuse ganglion cells. The individual ganglion cells are in general smaller neurons. Their dendritic spread is sufficiently small that it is in contact with one bipolar cell only, and this is a monosynaptic or midget bipolar. The "private line" one-to-one relationship of one cone, one bipolar, and one ganglion cell is extended therefore. Certain individual ganglion cells, however, are also related to the bipolar cells of the polysynaptic type.

As might be expected from the variation in ganglion cell size, their axis cylinders are of variable size. The largest ganglion cells in general have the largest axons, and the largest axons may be five times the thickness of the small ones. In man all the ganglion-cell axons, or all the fibers of the optic nerves which they constitute, are myelinated (96). The ganglion-cell axons do not give off collaterals or divide, as has sometimes been related. On the basis of fiber counts in the optic nerves, and assuming a 1:1 ratio with respect to fibers and ganglion cells, the ganglion cells of the human retina total between 565,000 and 1,140,000 (38).

In addition to the neural elements just described, the retina contains neuroglial cells and fibers of several varieties. It is doubtful that oligodendrocytes are present, however.

Optic Nerve

The axons of the ganglion cells make up the optic nerve. The axons may be looked upon as running from each of four quadrants of a circle (the retina) to a central collecting point, the **optic papilla.** The papilla is also called the **optic disk,** and it is situated medially to the posterior pole, or **visual axis,** of the eye. It has a depressed center, the **physiologic cup,** and a slightly elevated circumference (Fig. 281). No retinal layers other than the nerve fibers are present in the papilla, and it is therefore a blind spot. Where the optic-nerve fibers pierce the sclera, a sievelike plate exists, the **lamina cribrosa.** As the fibers in man collect and pass outward from the retina through the cribriform area they become myelinated.

The optic-nerve fibers have no neurolemma but have glial cells scattered among them. Lack of neurolemma may play a role in the failure of the optic nerve to show regeneration after injury. Estimates calculated from counting 5 per cent of the total fiber content in silver-stained sections of 10 human optic nerves showed an average of 1,010,000 fibers (96). Proportionately more fibers arise from the macular region than from the other regions of the retina. These nerve fibers, judging from the connections between cones, bipolars, and ganglion cells, may be so-called "private" or "party" lines for visual impulses.

Each optic nerve is covered by the meninges, between which are the usual intermeningeal spaces. The meninges fuse with the sclera of the globe. The **central artery** and **vein** of the retina reach (or leave) the globe through the optic nerve, penetrating the lower side of the latter at a distance of 7 to 12 mm. from the globe. The central artery and vein of the retina are branches of the ophthalmic artery and vein, respectively. As the central artery enters the optic nerve, it gives off small branches to the meninges. Running along with the nerve fibers, the artery approaches the lamina cribrosa, and at this level and also at a chorioidal level it gives off small branches which form anastomoses with branches of the

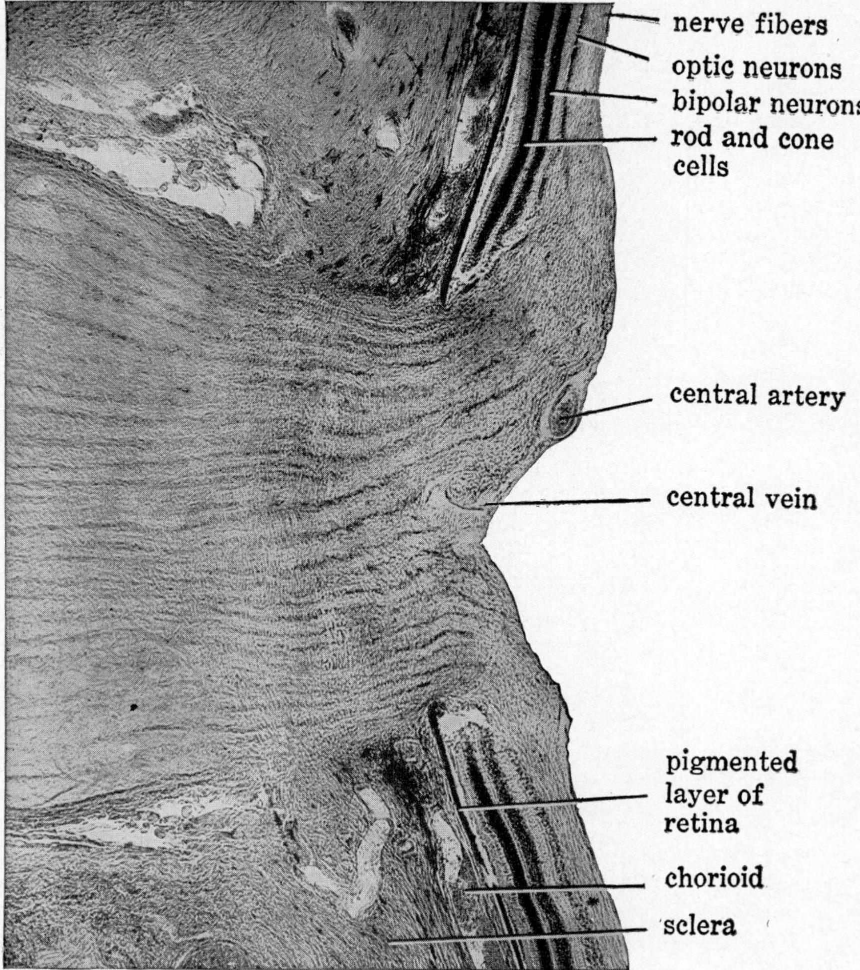

FIG. 281. Optic papilla and optic nerve of a human eye. Specimen in the Piersol collection. Photomicrograph, ×40. (*After Nonidez and Windle, "Textbook of Histology," courtesy of McGraw-Hill Book Company, Inc.*)

ciliary vessels which supply the chorioid. Beyond the level of the chorioid the central retinal arteries are end arteries. At or near the level of the lamina cribrosa, the central arteries divide into upper and lower branches. These appear usually in the center of the optic papilla and in turn divide, respectively, into large upper and lower nasal and temporal vessels. Smaller nasal and temporal branches may spring from the four major trunks. The retinal arteries and their branches become progressively smaller until they are the size of capillaries. These penetrate the retinal layers, extending only to the outer surface of the inner nuclear layer and no farther. The central arteries do not supply, therefore, the rod-and-cone layer and the pigmented epithelial layer. These are nourished via the choriocapillary plexuses derived from the ciliary arteries. The very center of the fovea is avascular, and in the immediate region about the fovea the retinal capillaries are very small. In some individuals a **cilioretinal artery,** a branch of the ciliary supply, passes through the temporal margin of the optic nerve and into the retina. When present this vessel practically always supplies either the macular area or a small portion of the retina adjacent it. This is of some practical importance, since macular vision may be spared in certain instances after thrombosis of the central artery of the retina. The central vein of the retina collects corresponding nasal and temporal retinal veins near the center of the optic papilla.

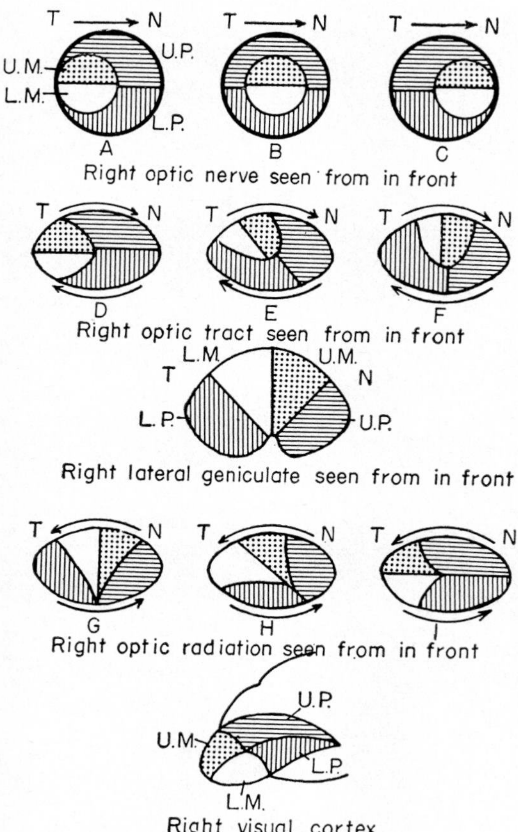

FIG. 282. Diagrams to show shifting of the optic fibers within the optic nerve and the rotations of the fibers in the optic tract and optic radiation (geniculocalcarine tract). *A*, transverse section of the right optic nerve near the eyeball; *B*, near the middle of the nerve; *C*, near the chiasma; *D*, *E*, *F*, transverse sections of right optic tract at successive levels approaching the lateral geniculate; *G*, *H*, *I*, transverse sections of the right optic radiation at successive levels approaching the calcarine area. The right visual cortex is drawn as seen from within. *T*, temporal side; *N*, nasal side; *U.M.*, upper macular fibers; *L.M.*, lower macular fibers; *U.P.*, upper peripheral retinal fibers; *L.P.*, lower peripheral retinal fibers. These four groups of fibers are indicated in identical fashion throughout the diagram. The arrows indicate the directions of rotations of the fibers. (*Modified slightly from Hartridge, "Recent Advances in the Physiology of Vision," J. & A. Churchill, Ltd.*)

Since the general cranial subarachnoid space is continuous with that surrounding the optic nerve, increase in intracranial pressure is transmitted through the spinal fluid to the optic subarachnoid space. This may result in distention of the latter space and compression especially of the central vein of the retina. This causes engorgement of the intraocular veins and subsequent swelling of the optic papilla, or **"choked disk"** (597).

Within the optic nerve the component fibers are arranged in a pattern that reflects their site of origin in the retina. The fibers from the upper half of the extramacular retina are dorsally placed in the nerve; those from the lower half, ventrally placed. Nasal fibers are medially placed, and fibers of temporal origin are grouped laterally. The fibers arising in the macular and foveal area are at first placed on the lateral side of the nerve. The macular fibers gradually move to a central position, and as the chiasma is approached, they are on the medial side of the nerve (Fig. 282).

As noted above, the optic-nerve fibers vary in size. They also vary in rates of conduction. It seems unlikely that the human optic nerves contain any centrifugally directed fibers.

OPTIC CHIASMA

A partial decussation of the optic-nerve fibers takes place at the chiasma. If it is imagined that a vertical axis passes through the center of the macula and the peripheral retinas, those fibers arising on the temporal side of this axis will be found to enter the ipsilateral optic tract. Those fibers arising on the nasal side of this axis cross to enter the optic tract of the opposite side. The ventral or lower peripheral nasal fibers cross ventrally and in the rostral part of the chiasma, while those from the dorsal peripheral nasal area cross dorsally in the middle part of the chiasma. The nasal macular fibers, dorsal and ventral, cross in a manner similar to those from the periphery but occupy more central and posterior positions in the chiasma.

Fibers from the lower nasal quadrant of the retina, in crossing, do not enter the opposite optic tract directly, but may form a short loop in the most medial part of the contralateral optic nerve (Fig. 283). The crossing fibers from

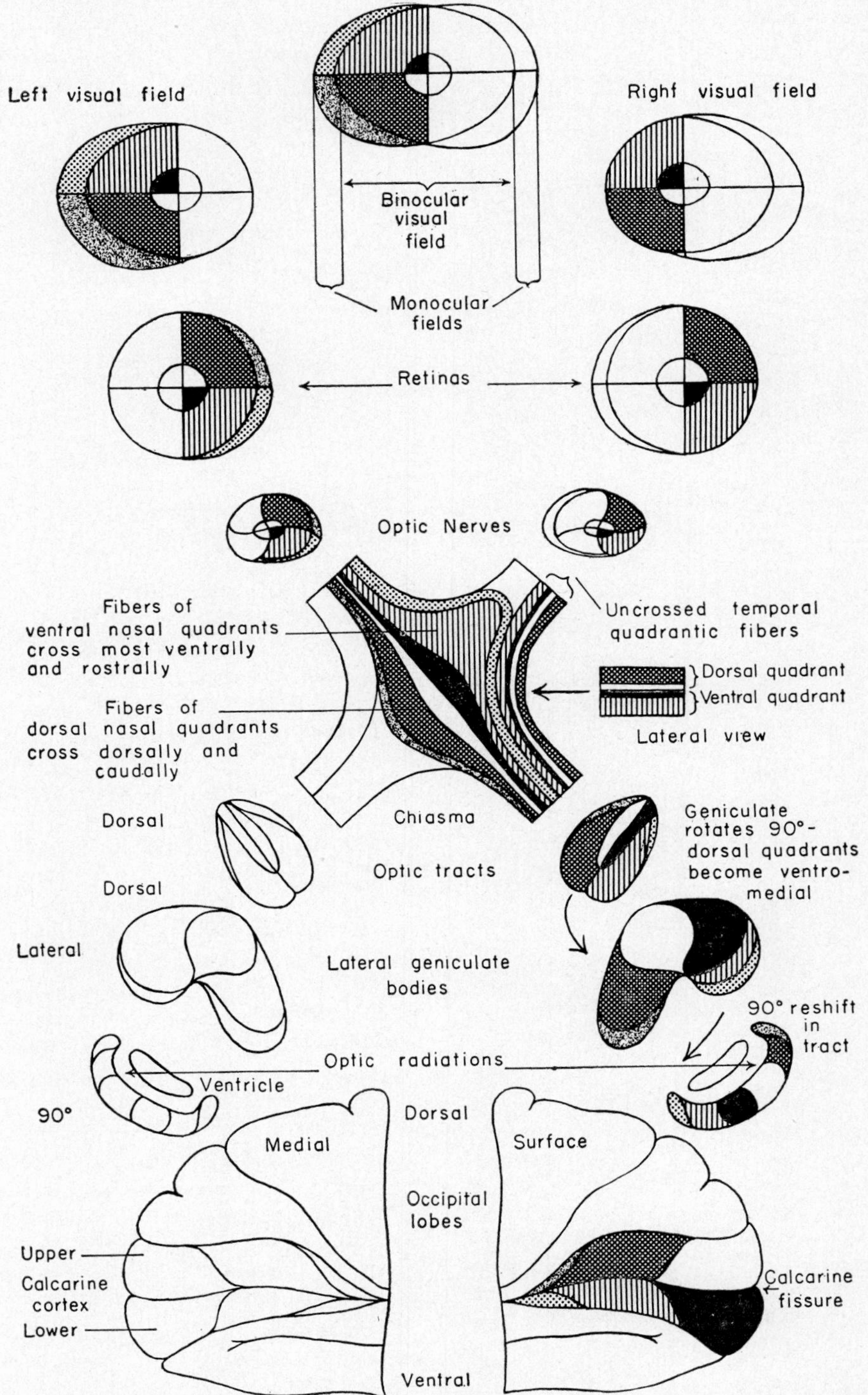

FIG. 283. Schema of the visual pathways. (*Slightly modified from Bender and Kanzer, Brain, vol.* 62.)

the upper nasal quadrant may also form a loop in the rostral end of the ipsilateral optic tract before entering the opposite tract.

Dorsal to the chiasma are several **supraoptic commissures.** The crossing fibers are fine. The largest bundle of fibers, the dorsal supraoptic decussation, is the **commissure of Meynert.** Fibers from the globus pallidus to the subthalamic nucleus and zona incerta cross by way of this commissure. The **commissure of Ganser,** or the anterior hypothalamic decussation, is composed in part of crossing pallidohypothalamic fibers, and probably of interconnecting hypothalamic fibers. The **commissure of Gudden,** formerly referred to as the medial division of the optic tract because of the intimate relations between the two, is very insignificant in man. In the monkey this tract arises in the lateral tegmentum of midbrain and pons and passes through the cerebral peduncle to reach the dorsal surface of the optic tract (526). After crossing within and above the chiasma, the fibers terminate in the ventrolateral part of the midbrain, the pretectal region, and possibly, in the medial geniculate body.

It has been reported occasionally that fibers leave the optic nerves at the chiasma to pass into the hypothalamus (see Chap. 14) (419). Some doubt concerning such fibers has been expressed by Clark, who feels that the reported observations may have resulted from a misinterpretation of the occasional aberrant course of the optic fibers themselves within the chiasma (157).

The relation of the optic chiasma to the sella turcica and hypophysis is a variable one because of the differences in lengths of the optic nerves in various humans. It is most often situated a little behind the tubercle of the sella. It may be rostral to this or some distance behind it (Fig. 284).

Optic Tract

As a result of the rearrangement of fibers in the chiasma, an optic tract contains fibers from the temporal retinal quadrants of the ipsilateral eye and fibers from the nasal retinal quadrants of the opposite eye. The two groups of crossed and uncrossed fibers are intimately intermingled. That is, no stratification of crossed and uncrossed upper retinal fibers exists in the optic tract, although such a separation occurs with respect to their termination in the lateral geniculate nucleus. It is true, however, that all the upper peripheral retinal fibers, crossed and uncrossed, are at first placed dorsomedially in the tract; all lower peripheral retinal fibers, ventromedially. The macular fibers are at first laterally placed. The optic tracts rotate slightly about their long axis, the macular fibers gradually moving dorsally, with lower macular fibers arranged laterally and upper macular fibers medially (Fig. 283). The upper peripheral retinal fibers gradually gain a ventromedial position; the lower ones, a ventrolateral position. Approximately 80 per cent of the fibers in the optic tract go to the lateral geniculate body directly. The remaining fibers pass into the pretectal area, the superior colliculus, and possibly into the pulvinar.

The Superior Colliculus

The structure of this nucleus has been described before (see Chap. 8) (Fig. 138). The retinal fibers entering the colliculus and pre-

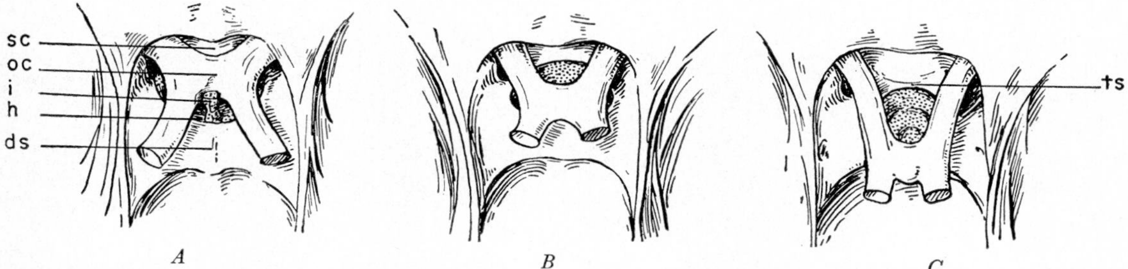

Fig. 284. Diagrams to show variable relations between optic chiasma and infundibulum due to varying length of optic nerves. *A*, relations found in 5 per cent of 124 cases studied by Parsons Schaeffer; *B*, relations in 79 per cent of 124 cases; *C*, relations in 4 per cent. Other variation not shown. *ds*, dorsum sellae; *h*, hypophysis; *i*, infundibulum; *oc*, optic chiasma; *sc*, chiasmatic sulcus; *ts*, tuberculum sellae. (*Modified from de Schweinitz*, 1923.)

tectal area leave the optic tract, pass medial to the lateral geniculate body and dorsal to the medial geniculate body, and gain the brachium of the superior colliculus. They form the layer of white matter designated the stratum opticum within the colliculus, and they terminate in all that part of the colliculus superficial to this layer.

In addition to these fibers coming to the superior colliculus from the optic nerve, a number of other fibers may be mentioned. Spinotectal and probably accompanying trigeminotectal fibers, bringing pain and thermal impulses, enter the superior colliculus to occupy the layer designated the stratum lemnisci. The inferior colliculus sends acoustico-optic fibers into the superior colliculus. The frontal and precentral cortex appear to discharge to the superior colliculus, and fascicles from the pallidum and other associated extrapyramidal motor nuclei may reach it. A considerable projection from the occipital lobe, and especially from area 19, also reaches the superior colliculus. These are concerned with automatic eye movements (see later).

The superior colliculus discharges fibers to the habenula, to the cerebellum, to the oculomotor and trochlear nuclei, and to the spinal cord, especially cervical levels, via the tectospinal tracts.

The smaller fibers of the optic tracts terminate in the superior colliculus and the pretectal region. The latter region appears to be a relay center concerned with the pupillary light reflex. The fibers ending in the superior colliculus are probably concerned with eye-movement patterns. The arrangement of the fibers terminating in the colliculus reflects their retinal origin. The rostromedial portions of the colliculus appear to receive impulses from the lower retinal quadrants; the caudolateral portions, from the upper retinal quadrants (36, 37, 182). The relation of the superior colliculi to eye movements will be discussed below.

Lateral Geniculate Body

The structure of the lateral geniculate nucleus is characterized by alternating layers of cells and fibers (Fig. 285). Six cell laminae are present in the lateral geniculate of man. This lamination of cell layers is related to the manner of termination of the optic fibers. The

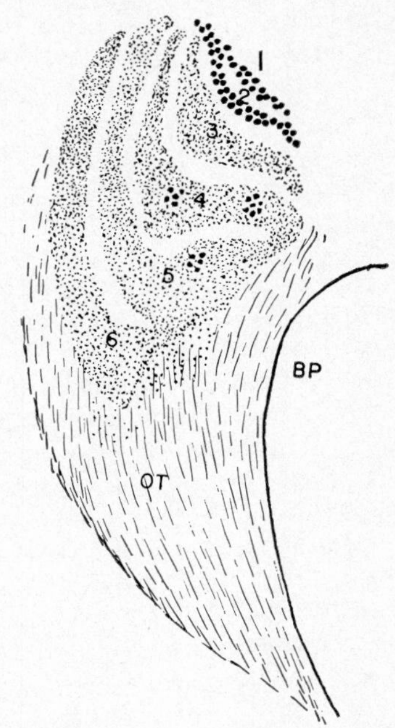

Fig. 285. Camera-lucida drawing of horizontal section through human lateral geniculate (dorsal nucleus). The large-celled laminae are most superficial. *BP*, basis pedunculi; *OT*, optic-tract fibers approaching the geniculate.

cell laminae are numbered from 1 to 6 from the surface inward. The two most superficial (ventral) laminae (1 and 2) are composed of large neurons; the other four, of small or medium-sized cells densely packed. The crossed fibers of an optic tract end in laminae 1, 4, and 6; the uncrossed, in laminae 2, 3, and 5 (148, 155, 163, 560.) The macular fibers end in the caudal two-thirds of the nucleus (632). In the most caudad portions this macular representation area occupies the full width of the nucleus; in the more rostrad portion, it is flanked by the peripheral retinal representation fields. The superior peripheral retinal fibers end ventromedially in the cephalic end of the lateral geniculate; the inferior peripheral retinal fibers end ventrolaterally. This manner of termination correlates very well with the relative positions of these fibers in the posterior portion of the optic tracts.

The retinal-geniculate relations are quite precise and approach a point-to-point character. The smallest area of retinal injury, experimentally produced, leads to a measurable change in the lateral geniculate body through transneuronal degeneration. This change is a discrete, bandlike zone of atrophy extending through all the three corresponding cell laminae. The lateral geniculate can be viewed as an orderly collection of many such bands of cells, each band related to tiny retinal areas, and thus representing the receptive unit of the geniculate.

Each optic-nerve fiber in the monkey appears to end about cells in only one lamina, and it would seem therefore that these small bands of atrophy result from damage to at least three separate ganglion cells (306). Glees and Clark observed in the macaque that each optic-nerve fiber terminated in a spray of five or six branches, each branch equipped with a single terminal button. Each terminal button made synaptic contact with the cell body of only one geniculate cell. Each optic-nerve fiber then appears to make contact with five or six geniculate cells, and all these are in a single lamina.

The lateral geniculate in man may receive a few collateral fibers from those optic axons entering the mesencephalic regions, although such collaterals are probably few in number. The cells of the lateral geniculate project only to occipital cortex, and all the cells are probably projection cells. In other words, geniculocollicular fibers do not appear to exist, and no geniculate neurons appear to serve an intrageniculate associative function. Furthermore, all the geniculate neurons send their axons to occipital cortex of the same hemisphere. Removal of the visual receptive area 17 results in total retrograde degeneration of the ipsilateral lateral geniculate nucleus.

Geniculocalcarine Tract

From the large and small cells of the lateral geniculate nucleus the axons composing the geniculocalcarine tract pass out in a fan-shaped manner, but in a definite order, in their course to that cortex of the occipital lobe about the walls of the calcarine fissure. This radiation from the lateral geniculate traverses the retrolenticular and sublenticular divisions of the posterior limb of the internal capsule. An orderly arrangement of the geniculocalcarine fibers exists, and this arrangement again reflects the site of origin of the axons in the geniculate (Figs. 282, 283). It was noted previously that the fibers in the optic tracts undergo a partial rotation in their course to the lateral geniculate body. The fibers of the optic radiation likewise make a compensatory rotation in their course to the occipital cortex.

Those axons arising from the superior retinal fields were observed above to be in a medial position in the terminal part of the tract. They ended ventromedially in the lateral geniculate. The neurons in this geniculate region send their axons at first superiorly and then almost directly caudally. They come thus to compose the dorsal or superior strata of the optic radiations. The ventrolateral geniculate neurons, receptive of inferior peripheral retinal fibers, discharge their axons in a frontal and ventral direction. These axons continue forward and ventrally for a short distance before arching caudally about the anterior portion of the temporal horn of the lateral ventricle (550) (Fig. 207). They compose the inferior or ventral strata of the optic radiations. Those fibers arising from the "macular" zone of the geniculate pass superiorly and turn caudally to occupy the intermediate strata of the radiations (157, 343, 639).

All the fibers passing into the calcarine cortex from the lateral geniculate compose the **external sagittal stratum** of the optic radiation. They run near the lateral wall of the inferior and posterior horns of the lateral ventricle. They are separated from the ventricular wall by the **internal sagittal stratum** and fibers of the corpus callosum often referred to as the tapetum. The former are corticifugal fibers from the occipital lobe to the superior colliculus and other brain stem centers for conjugate deviations of the eyes. These will be described below.

The Visual Receptive and Associative Cortex

The geniculocalcarine fibers terminate in a definite order in that cortex in the banks of the calcarine fissure. This cortex composes Brodmann's area 17, the so-called striate cortex. This name characterizes this cortex in that a definite striation is clearly visible within it to the unaided eye. The striation is formed by a dense plexus of fibers. It was observed first by Gennari and is sometimes referred to as the stripe of Gennari (281). In reality, the fiber plexus constitutes a particularly well-developed outer stripe of Baillarger.

The relations between lateral geniculate and visual cortex are quite specific and serve to complete the exact topographic relations characteristic of the visual system (629). These relations between geniculate and cortex can be determined by making cortical lesions and studying the retrograde degeneration of the geniculate. The smallest cortical lesion which results in noticeable changes in the lateral geniculate always leads to atrophy in adjacent and corresponding zones of all six cellular laminae in the geniculate (630). The projection unit of the lateral geniculate is therefore a thin band of cells extending in radiate fashion through the dorsoventral axis of the geniculate. Crossed and uncrossed retinal impulses end in very close association in the striate cortex. The lateral geniculate in the macaque is thought to have approximately 1.8 million cells. Each square millimeter of visual cortex in this monkey is presumed to receive axons from 1,350 cells (155).

The **striate area** 17 (Economo's *OC*) is characterized cytoarchitecturally by a broad internal granular layer IV, separated into two sublayers by the heavy outer stripe of Baillarger, or the stripe of Gennari (Fig. 221*C*). The cell population in the inner of these two sublayers is greater than that of the outer, and the cells are predominantly small granules, although some medium-sized pyramids are present also. The outer sublayer contains moderately large star pyramids. Laminae II and III are composed of quite small cells, granules and pyramids. The cell type of the deeper part of III and the relative density of this zone have led to its being mistaken for a part of layer IV. The internal pyramidal layer V is rather light. Scattered among its typical small pyramids are occasional rather large pyramids, the solitary cells of Meynert. Lamina VI is dense.

The optic radiation fibers enter the outer stripe of Baillarger but their terminals apparently do not form all this plexus. The actual site of termination of the optic fibers is not known, although some evidence points to the deeper sublayer of IV. The general plan of topical localization of retinal areas within the striate area has been accurately worked out in the macaque, and clinical studies indicate that the cortical representation of the retina in man follows a similar scheme (109, 110, 112, 384, 387). Those geniculocalcarine fibers carrying impulses from the upper retinas end dorsally to the calcarine fissure; those from the lower retinas end ventrally to the fissure (Fig. 283). The peripheral retinal fibers end more anteriorly in the occipital lobe about the fissure. The macular fibers end posteriorly, extending to the very tip of the occipital lobe medially and onto the lateral hemispheric surface. In the striate cortex on the lips of the fissure, the retinal sectors adjacent to the vertical meridian are represented; in the depths of the fissure, the retinal sectors adjacent to the horizontal meridian are represented. Each macular area is represented in only one cortex, in contrast to the belief of some authors that the macula has a double cortical representation.

The remaining part of the occipital lobe is made up of two areas, according to Brodmann's numbering. Area 18 (*OB*), the **parastriate area,** is adjacent to 17, and area 19 (*OA*), the **preoccipital** or **peristriate area,** is most anterior in the occipital lobe. These last two have generally been called visual associative areas. The internal granular layer IV is much more developed in area 17 than in the other two areas. The cytoarchitecture of areas 18 and 19 is not particularly distinctive (Fig. 221*E*). Area 18 shows, in its posterior portions especially, some rather large pyramids in the deeper part of layer III. The cells of area 19 are in general smaller throughout than those of 18. Both areas have a prominent laminar development and columnar pattern.

FIBER CONNECTIONS OF VISUAL AREAS

It has been generally assumed, as mentioned previously, that areas 18 and 19 are visual associative areas. Long association fibers are very scarce, however. It seems likely, in the light of experimental work in the macaque, that association fibers within the striate area are very short and that interareal association fibers are sent only to area 18 (154, 164, 182). Physiological neuronography confirms this finding (87, 88). Area 18 is, therefore, perhaps the only visual associative area. It sends association fibers to areas 17 and 19 and to all parts of 20. In the macaque, the inferior part of 18 is connected with the upper part of 19; the upper part of 18, with lower 19 (182). Areas 8 and 18 appear to be interconnected. Areas 18 and 19 are interconnected with area 37, and this last area appears to project also to area 17. Areas 18 and 19 receive axons from areas 41, 42, and 22, the auditory cortex, and from area 21, a complex temporal-lobe association area. Area 38, on the temporal pole, may send axons to area 19. Area 19 appears to have intrinsic association fibers and is also related by afferent and efferent connections with area 24. Commissural fibers between areas 18 and 19 and their homologous areas are numerous in the macaque. In the chimpanzee, area 19 has more commissural fibers than does 18. Area 17 does not have such connections.

In summarizing the visual-association-fiber relationship, Crosby and Henderson reported that the lower parts of area 17, which receive impulses from inferior retinal quadrants, are related through area 18 with the dorsal part of area 19 (182). The upper parts of area 17 are related to the lower part of 19 and the intermediate part of 17, receiving impulses from both upper and lower retinal quadrants, is related to the intermediate zone of 19.

Projection fibers from these occipital areas have been worked out in some detail in the macaque (182). The medium-sized pyramids in the deeper part of lamina IV and the solitary cells of Meynert are considered the source of projection axons from area 17 (156). These efferent fibers from the occipital lobe compose the internal sagittal stratum of the optic radiations. Corticopontine fibers arise from area 17. Corticotectal fibers arise in areas 17, 18, and 19 and end in the ipsilateral superior colliculus especially. Corticotegmental fibers arise also from areas 17, 18, and 19 and end probably in the oculomotor nucleus, in the nucleus of Darkschewitsch, and in the interstitial nucleus of Cajal. Some corticotegmental fibers synapse in tegmental gray just dorsal to the medial geniculate, and from this site axons have been followed caudalward (182). It was thought that they were directed to the parabducens and abducens nuclei. Projections from area 19 to the bulbar inhibitory center in the medulla tegmentum have been demonstrated by physiological neuronography (508) (Fig. 262).

The relations of the occipital cortex to definite zones of the superior colliculus have been described by Crosby and Henderson in their studies in the macaque. The upper part of area 19 is related to the rostromedial half of the superior colliculus; the lower half of area 19, to the caudolateral end of the superior colliculus. The lower parts of 17 and 18 are related to the rostromedial part of the superior colliculus; the upper part of these areas, to the caudolateral part of the superior colliculus. From the mid-portion of area 19 and from certain parts of 17 and 18, not discretely identified, corticotegmental fibers are thought to pass to the parabducens nucleus. How these paths function in automatic ocular movements will be described later.

SOME FUNCTIONAL ASPECTS OF THE VISUAL MECHANISM

The act of vision is composed of several processes. These include the perception of light, the perception of color, the perception of space, or the recognition of the position in space of the sources of light stimuli, and the process of visual integration underlying psychic visual functions. It is of interest to know the role played in these processes by each of the several units of the visual system at retinal, geniculate, and cortical levels. Only some of these processes can be considered here. It has been observed in an earlier chapter that the various components of the somatic sensory path each contribute to the somatic sensory process. Specific types of receptors, variation in fiber size, selective arrangement of internuncials and secondary neurons, and finally several levels of integration combine to complete somatic sensory function. Within the organization of the visual mechanism at the retinal level, the organism possesses certain pigments, at least two types of receptors, and several types of primary, secondary, and associative neurons according to their size, morphology, and synaptic relations. Variation of component fiber size is also a character of the optic nerves. Crossing of some optic fibers, a specific and point-to-point relation between retina and geniculate with its distinctive laminar arrangement of cells, and a point-to-point relation between geniculate and visual cortex, where crossed and uncrossed impulses converge on a tiny area, are other features of the optic mechanism.

Two distinct mechanisms are present in

human vision. The scotopic mechanism functions predominantly in dim light; the photopic, in bright light. It has long been thought that the rods are the active receptors in scotopic vision and the cones in photopic. It may not be true, however, that rods are day-blind and cones are night-blind. Some overlapping of function may exist. The cones, usually considered the sole receptors engaged in color perception, may be aided also by some rods. Visual purple, in some manner, seems intimately concerned with the sensitivity of the rods. Some other pigment, not as yet definitely identified, may be concerned with the activation of cones. Vitamin A is concerned with the synthesis of visual purple, and individuals on vitamin-A-deficient diets will develop night blindness. It is of considerable importance to know, then, if similar photochemical processes are concerned in cone activity and if color blindness can be treated with some pigment.

Theories of Color Vision

The stumbling block in most of the theories of color vision is the lack of evidence that several morphologic types of cones are present in the retina. A variety of theories are extant, and one of the most popular is the **trichromatic hypothesis** of Young and Helmholtz. This theory assumes that three distinct sets of nerve fibers or processes (cones) are present in the retina. Each of these cones is supposed to be particularly responsive to light stimuli of a certain wave length, although it is responsive to the entire visible spectrum. These three particular wave-length sensitivities would correspond to each of the three primary colors. Long-wave-length receptors would be susceptible to red; medium-wave-length receptors, to green; short-wave-length receptors, to blue or violet. Unequal stimulations of the three receptor types would lead to the sensation of the remaining visible colors or hues. Equal stimulation of all three receptors would lead to the sensation of white. Absence of stimulation would lead to the sensation of black.

Variations of this theory have been offered, and even more types of receptors have been suggested. As many as seven types are necessary in one theory, and these have eight response curves (343). Crimson (with responses both in the red and in the violet zones), orange, yellow, green, blue-green, blue, and blue-violet receptors are postulated. At one retinal zone, certain of these receptors are most active; at another, certain others are most active. At the fovea, for example, orange, green, and blue-violet receptors are most active; at the periphery, only yellow and blue. It is considered possible by some physiologists that although a larger number of receptor types than three may be present, their activities may be combined in such a way that they provide no more than three types of fundamental response (310). A single long-wave response mechanism may result from a linking of several receptors having maximum responses in the red, the orange, and the yellow. In such linking of the greens and the blues, single medium- and short-wave-length responses would result, and the basic three responses of the trichromatic theory would be realized.

In view of the fact that morphologically different cones have not been described in the retina, some observers have looked to other retinal elements as furnishing the three variable receptors needed. In such fashion, the several types of bipolars and ganglion cells have been used. It is recognized that bipolars vary considerably in size, in dendritic morphology, and in manner of synaptic relations with rods and cones. In such a way, perhaps, three types of fibers conducting light impulses of three different wave lengths may exist.

Since the smallest experimental retinal lesion leads to detectable cell degeneration in each of three cell layers of the geniculate, and since each optic fiber terminates in only one layer, the three-fiber unit is considered the functional visual unit. Since anatomical differences in retinal receptors subserving color vision cannot be determined, it was suggested by Clark that the three cell laminae in each geniculate corresponding with each retina may be concerned with the three fundamental color sensations (152). He proposed that the two large-celled laminae, 1 and 2, one for each retina, serve as relay stations for the fibers concerned with appreciation of blue. Laminae 3 and 4, consisting of small cells, act as relays for another color, and laminae 5 and 6 for the remaining one of the three fundamental colors. Further correlations were made with reference to retinal representation in the geniculates and with the relative sensitivity of certain parts of the retina to color.

The Visual Fields

The extent of visibility possible by the two retinas at any given fixed position constitutes the visual fields. The refractive media of the eyes serve to bring impulses arising in the upper visual fields onto the lower retinas, impulses arising in the temporal-field quadrants onto the nasal retinas, and vice versa. The decussation of the optic-nerve fibers serves to bring all the impulses from the right fields to the left lateral geniculate. The left optic tract, in other words, carries impulses derived from the nasal (right) field of the left eye, and the temporal (right) field of the right eye (Fig. 283). Similarly, the left lateral geniculate projects solely to the left visual receptive cortex. The impulses from the left quadrants of each eye, resulting from the stimuli in the right quadrants of each field, thus reach the left visual receptive cortex. With the left visual cortex, therefore, one sees to the right; with the right visual cortex, to the left.

Function of Visual Areas

The striate cortex activity underlies the act of fusion, whereby the separate impressions from the two retinas are united into a single image. It is only in the striate cortex that the impulses from the two retinas come together. The perception of color is also a striate cortex function. The localization of objects in space with reference to the direct line of vision is a striate function, although the retinal optic mechanisms are fundamental in this process. The striate cortex also subserves the recognition of form and the discrimination of outline of objects (384).

The identification of the objects seen depends on integrations in other cortical tissue, and especially, in so far as visual impulses alone are concerned, in area 18. The interpretation of printed or written words is a function of the rostral occipital and posterior parietal cortex, in the left angular gyrus. The absolute localization of objects in space with particular reference of them to self is a function of tissue in both cortices, and particularly of posterior parietal and anterior occipital cortex.

That portion of the visual receptive cortex subserving the macula and central vision is relatively larger than that subserving the periphery of the retina. Anatomical and physiological studies indicate a point-to-point localization of the retina in the cortex. Since certain retinal receptors are related to more than one bipolar and ganglionic cell, however, and since each ganglionic cell axon terminates about five or six geniculate neurons, a diffusion of retinal impulses may take place, and impulses from each point of the retina may reach a relatively large area of the visual cortex. The functional projection of the retina appears to be punctate, however, and each cone in the fovea, at least, has one primary cortical locus (499, 773).

The visual cortex appears to have a certain amount of plasticity, however, and this is usually demonstrable in disease processes (384). As will be pointed out later, in cases of hemianopia due to striate cortex disease, macular vision may be subserved by extramacular parts of the visual cortex to the extent that the patient may be unaware of the hemianopia. This plasticity can also be observed in patients who have a chronically squinting eye. In such a condition asymmetric points of the two retinas are ordinarily stimulated, two cortical foci are also activated, and the patient sees two images or is said to have diplopia. In chronic deviations of a single eye the patient develops an extramacular false macula in that eye to correspond with the true macula of the normal eye, and the impulses from the false and true maculae are fused in the visual cortex. The patient thus overcomes his diplopia.

Utilizing the neural arcs outlined above, the occipital cortex, in response to impulses from the extrafoveal retinas, also promotes the involuntary or automatic movements of the eyes toward an object so located outside central vision. Fixation on objects at rest or in motion is maintained by the reflex mechanisms possible through the occipital cortex.

In addition to the fibers passing to the geniculates, the optic nerves contain pupillomotor fibers which pass to the pretectal region. These form the afferent limb of the pupillary light reflex described below. Other optic-nerve fibers pass into the superior colliculi as a feature of the mechanisms subserving automatic reflex movements of the eyes. Specific regions of the superior colliculus receive im-

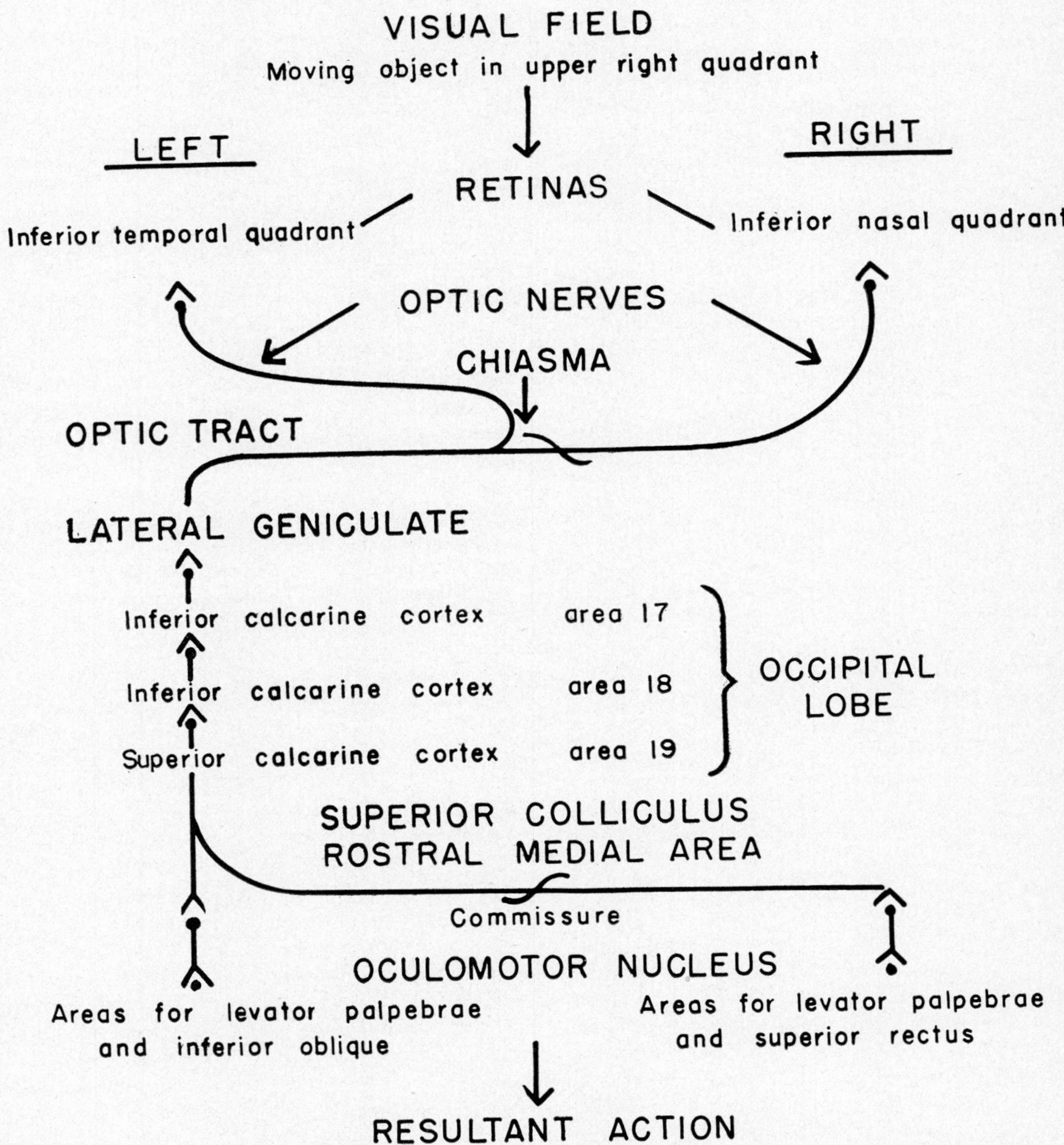

FIG. 286. Schema to show cortical control of ocular movements in upward direction. (*Based in part on data from Crosby and Henderson, J. Comp. Neurol., vol.* 88.)

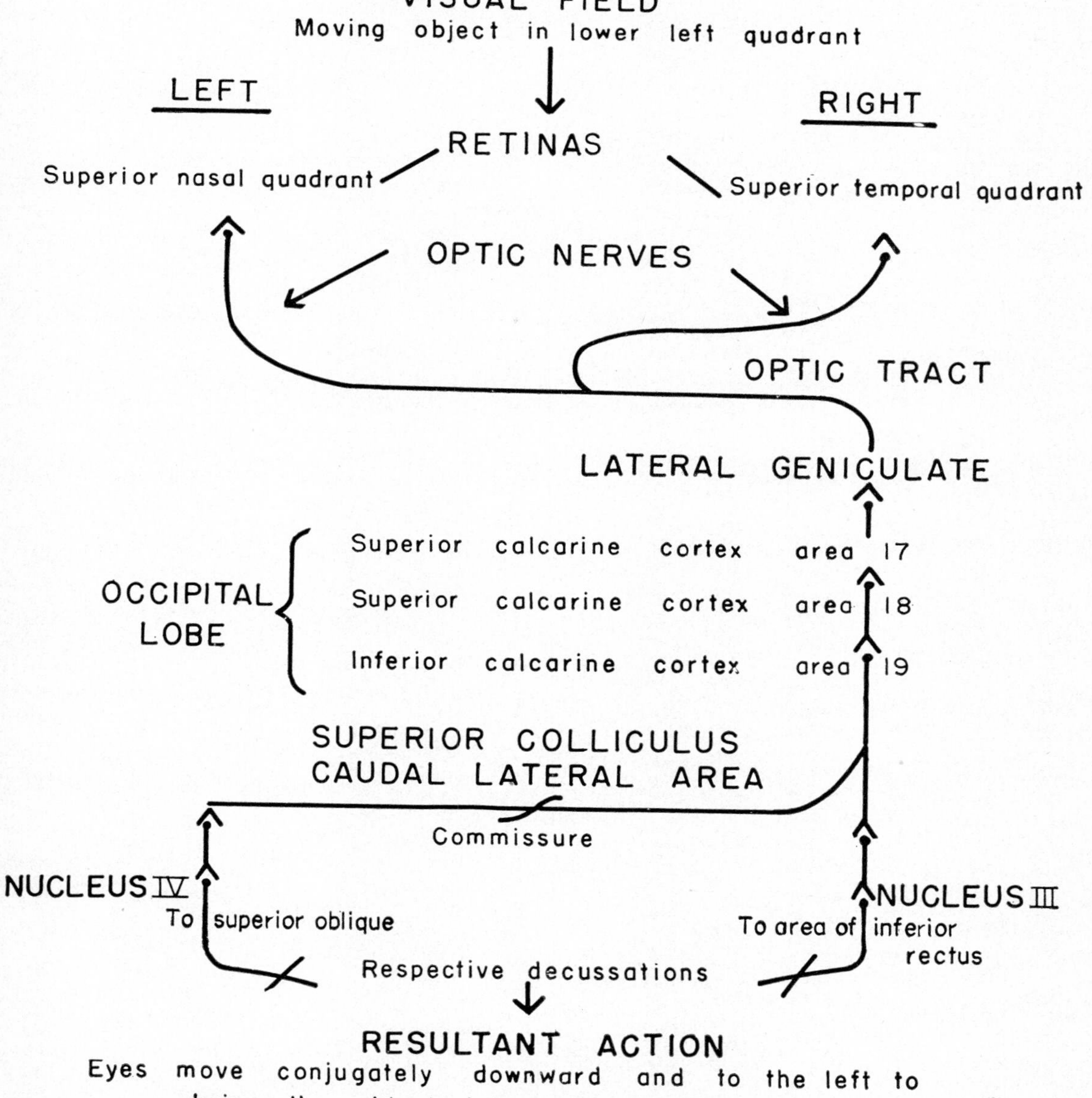

FIG. 287. Schema to show cortical control of ocular movements in downward direction. (*Based in part on data from Crosby and Henderson, J. Comp. Neurol., vol.* 88.)

pulses from specific retinal areas, and from specific regions of the visual cortex. From the inferior retina, receiving stimuli from the superior fields, the rostromedial portions of the superior colliculus receive impulses. Impulses from the superior fields reach the inferior calcarine cortex and, via area 18 synapses, the upper part of area 19. From this part of 19 corticotectal fibers have been traced to the rostromedial half of the superior colliculus. This region of the superior colliculus is related to the more rostral part of the oculomotor nucleus via tecto-oculomotor fibers. This part of the oculomotor nucleus is thought to innervate muscles which turn the eyes upward. In such fashion stimuli from the superior fields may evoke upward movements of the eyes (Fig. 286). Downward movements may be evoked by impulses from upper retinas passing to upper calcarine cortex; relays from there excite the inferior part of area 19, from which corticotectal fibers pass to the caudolateral end of the superior colliculus. Impulses via tecto-oculomotor tracts activate the caudal oculomotor neurons to initiate downward movements (Fig. 287). Other arcs subserve lateral movements of the eyes (Fig. 288).

Stimulation of Occipital Tissue

Electrical stimulations of the occipital cortex have proved the existence of such arcs for ocular movements. Stimulation of the dorsal portions of area 19 in monkeys produced upward movements of the eyes; that of lower portions of area 19, downward movements; and that of middle portions of area 19, lateral movements. Stimulation of the upper half of area 17 in the monkey evoked conjugate movements of the eyes downward and to the opposite side (182, 800). Stimulation of the lower part of area 17 produced eye movements upward and to the opposite side. Pure vertical and horizontal movements are probably initiated via area 19 and oblique movements from area 17, at least in the monkey. Foerster found that the human area 19 responded only to faradic stimulation (255). By stimulating this area he elicited lateral deviation of the eyes toward the opposite side, and the deviation was maintained for the duration of the stimulus (Fig. 239). On occasions he found the lateral movements combined with upward movements after stimulation of the inferior half of area 19. After stimulation of the superior half, the lateral movements were combined with downward movements. Thus, Foerster's results in humans do not agree with the results obtained in the macaque, if the area of stimulation agrees. Occasionally, pupillary dilatation was obtained with the eye movements in humans. With the ocular movements the patients experienced complex visual sensations. Foerster was unable to produce ocular movements in humans by stimulating area 17. Stimulation of the visual receptive cortex in humans, however, has produced visual hallucinations (255, 622). These are usually simple objects such as a ball, a line, a star, or color images of red, green, and yellow. Stimulations of such hallucinations have been effective over area 17 occasionally, and over 18 and 19 fairly often. The images have been seen in the right field when the left occipital region has been stimulated. Stimulation above the calcarine fissure has given lights in the lower visual fields, stimulation below the fissure has given lights in the upper visual fields, and stimulation at the occipital pole has produced lights directly in front.

The Visual Mechanisms Involved in the Light and Accommodation Reflexes

The pupillary diameter of an individual varies considerably during his waking state. It varies according to the intensity of the light about him, and it changes as he looks at far and near objects. It varies in accordance with the general systemic reaction of the individual. In strong light the pupillary diameters are small; in dim light or darkness, they are large. If a near object is looked at, the pupils are constricted, if a distant object, they are larger. In painful conditions or under circumstances of emotional stress or fear, the pupils may be large.

If a bright light is cast into an unfixed eye, both pupils will constrict. The response in the same eye is known as the **direct light response,** that in the opposite eye is the **consensual light response.** The anatomical details of these light reflexes have been analyzed in the macaque, and clinical evidence supports the belief that similar patterns exist in man (523). The afferent limb of the light reflex is composed of

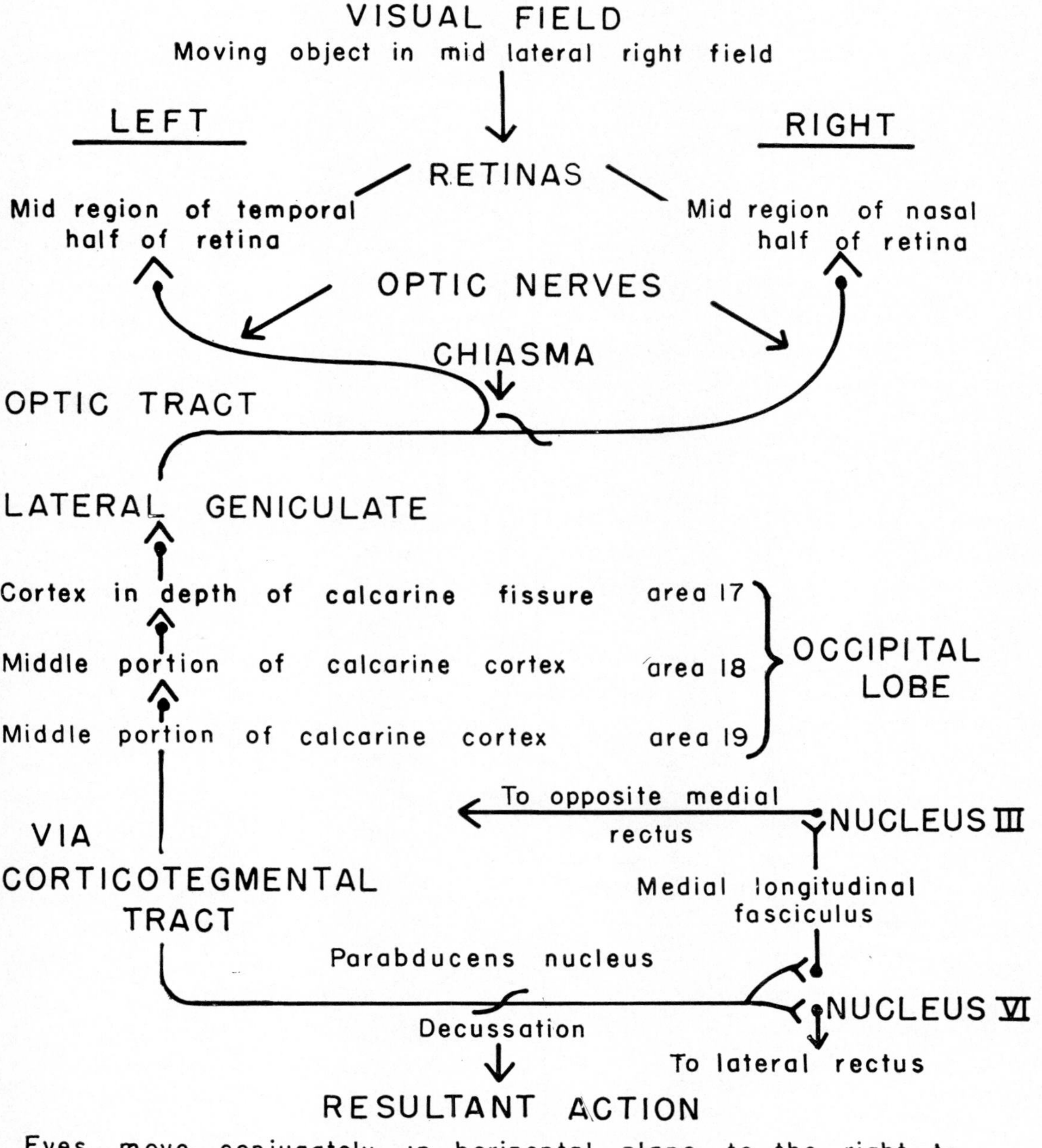

Fig. 288. Schema to show cortical control of ocular movements in horizontal plane. (*Based in part on data from Crosby and Henderson, J. Comp. Neurol., vol.* 88.)

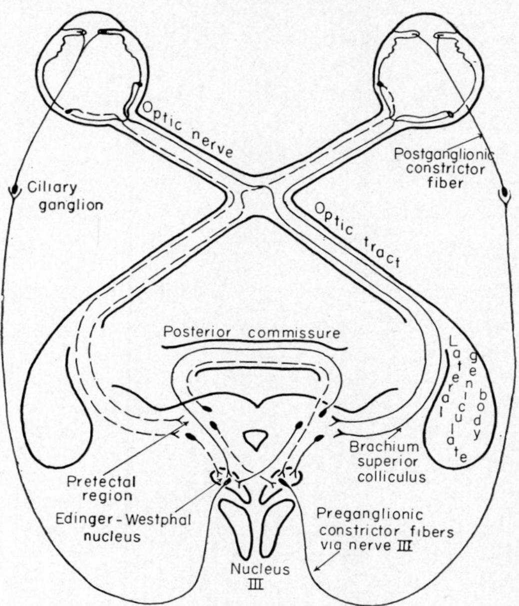

FIG. 289. Diagram of the light-reflex pathways. (*Based on data from Ranson, Magoun, and others.*)

the smaller fibers of the optic nerves. These fibers undergo a partial decussation at the chiasma, just as do the other optic-nerve elements. They leave the optic tracts and pass by way of the brachium of the superior colliculus to gain the pretectal area, where a synapse is afforded (Fig. 289). From the pretectal area, fibers relay the impulses to the nuclei of Edinger-Westphal. Some of these fibers pass via the posterior commissure to reach the opposite Edinger-Westphal nucleus, others pass ventrally to the cerebral aqueduct to gain the Edinger-Westphal nucleus of the same and opposite side. The consensual light reflex depends in part on the fibers crossing in the posterior commissure. From the Edinger-Westphal nuclei the constrictor impulses are sent out over fibers accompanying the oculomotor nerve. After a relay in the ciliary ganglion, the impulses are discharged via the short ciliary nerves to the pupillary sphincter muscles (Fig. 290). Constriction of the pupils in response to light is therefore a parasympathetic activity and involves brain stem reflex arcs.

Dilatation of the pupil in darkness is considered a function of the sympathetic nervous system. The afferent limb of this pupillary reflex is not known, although the superior colliculus or pretectal area may be involved. From the tectum, tectospinal relays may discharge the impulses to the preganglionic sympathetic neurons in the upper thoracic segments of spinal cord. From these preganglionic neurons, axons leave upper thoracic anterior spinal roots and communicating rami to gain the sympathetic trunk and finally the superior cervical ganglion in which they synapse. The postganglionic fibers arise in the superior cervical ganglion and reach the dilator muscles of the pupil via the arteries of the head and ultimately by a branch of the trigeminal nerve. The dilator muscles are poorly developed, according to Langworthy, and he assumes that the sympathetic fibers are more important for innervation of the arterioles of the ciliary process and iris (461, 465) (Fig. 290*B*). Changes in the arteriolar caliber are important in determining pupillary dilatation (see Chap. 7). Furthermore, it is known that the pupils dilate in response to pain after removal of the cervical sympathetic. Reflex inhibition of the oculomotor constrictor mechanism is considered at work here.

When the eyes are turned from a distant object to a near one, several activities take place to bring the latter into sharp focus. These activities constitute the process of **accommodation** and include pupillary constriction, an increase in the diameter of the lens, and a convergence of the eyes. The fully developed act of accommodation depends on visual impulses reaching the visual receptive cortex. From this level the effector impulses are discharged to the brain stem centers involved. Certain components of the act may involve brain stem arcs only. Pupillary constriction in accommodation may have a separate peripheral path from that subserving pupillary constriction in response to light. This has been referred to in an earlier section (see Chap. 9). The visual cortex presumably discharges to the posterior parts of the nuclei of Edinger-Westphal as well as to the nucleus of convergence. From the former nuclei axons pass with the oculomotor nerves but do not synapse in the ciliary ganglion. They relay instead in episcleral ganglia, from which postganglionic axons pass to the constrictor muscles (302, 581). Impulses bringing about an increase in the lens diameter also arise in the posterior portions of the Edinger-Westphal nuclei. Axons

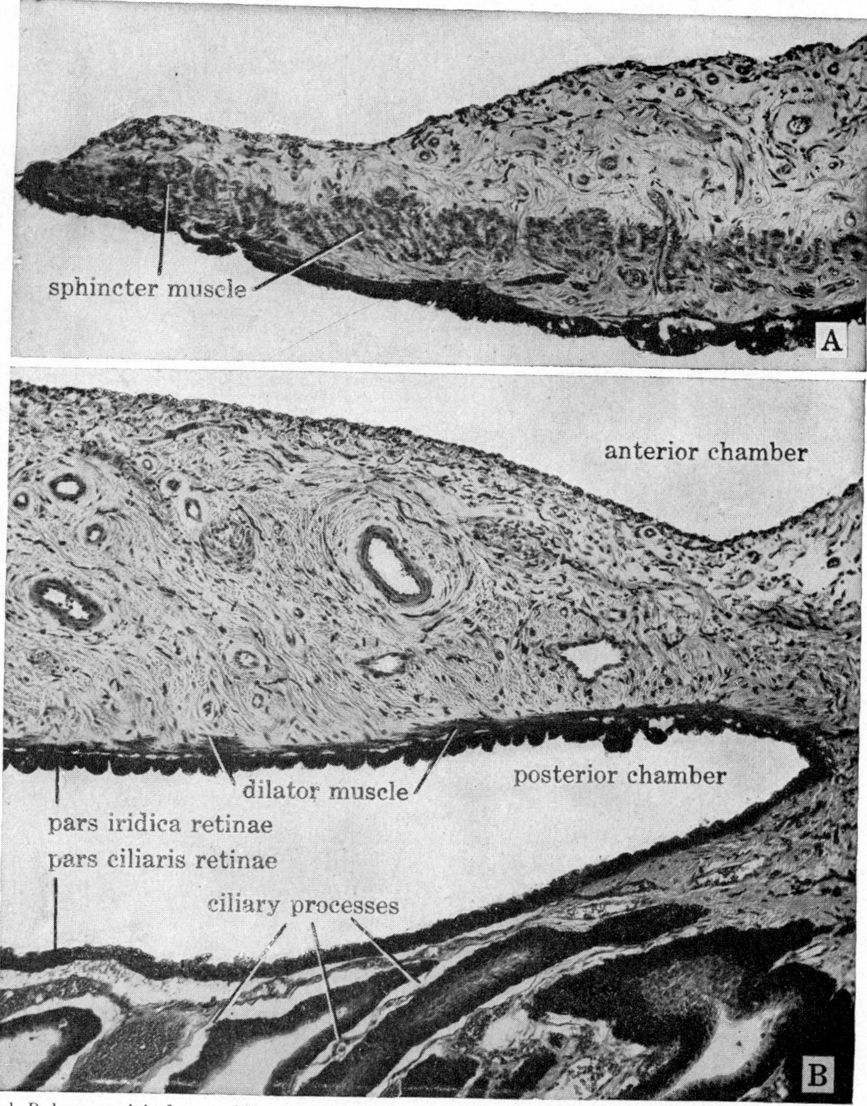

FIG. 290. *A* and *B*, human iris from a blue-eyed subject: *A*, inner rim of the iris showing its stroma, sphincter muscle, and pigmented epithelium on the posterior surface; *B*, peripheral one-third of the iris, the posterior chamber, and ciliary processes. Note the arterioles with thick adventitia, the dilator muscle of the iris and the pigmented epithelium of the pars iridica retinae. Specimen in the Piersol collection. Photomicrograph, ×125. (*After Nonidez and Windle, "Textbook of Histology," courtesy of McGraw-Hill Book Company, Inc.*)

from here, relaying in the ciliary ganglion or in episcleral neurons, discharge impulses to the ciliary muscle.

Changes in the lens with accommodation to near vision are brought about through the activity of the ciliary process and its muscle (Fig. 290*A*, *B*). This muscle contains meridional, radial, and circular fibers. From the ciliary process delicate fibers, the zonule of Zinn, run to the capsule of the lens. These fibers support the lens; they are stretched and tend to flatten the lens during distant vision. When a near object is focused on, however, the ciliary muscle contracts. By this contraction, especially of the circular muscle fibers, the ciliary process approaches the lens; the meridional fibers may also help by pulling forward the posterior part of the ciliary body where most of the zonule of Zinn fibers are inserted. These latter fibers are relaxed as a result, and the lens becomes more convex owing to its own plasticity and to that of its capsule. When the ciliary muscles relax, the zonule fibers again become taut, by virtue of the fact also that the ciliary process is pulled back by the elastic traction of the chorioid; the lens becomes flattened again for distant vision.

The convergence of the two eyes, in response to visual impulses reaching a cortical level, involves simultaneous contraction of the internal rectus muscles of each eye. Impulses from the cortex reach that part of the oculomotor nucleus constituting the nucleus of Perlia. This nucleus in turn discharges to the nucleus for each of the internal recti muscles.

The afferent impulses for the full act of accommodation may be of double origin: visual from the retinas, and proprioceptive from the ocular muscles, especially from the internal recti. The proprioceptive impulses arising from these muscles as a result of convergence may play a role in the initiation of the pupillary constriction and the changes in the lens diameter, but these two reactions are not dependent entirely on convergence.

The Control of Conjugate Movements of the Eyes

The two eyes customarily move together either laterally to right or to left, upward, downward, or inward (674). Such movements may occur volitionally, as a feature of the visual fixing or following activity, in response to vestibular stimulation, and occasionally in response to sound. Central regulating mechanisms exist for the control of such movements, and brain stem centers for lateral, upward, downward, and inward deviations have been described. Some of these have been alluded to above (Figs. 286, 287, 288).

In the vicinity of the abducens nucleus, on either side, are dorsally placed neurons near the floor of the fourth ventricle. These constitute the parabducens nuclei and probably serve as centers for lateral deviations, the right one for movements to the right and the left one for movements to the left. In order for the two eyes to turn laterally to the right, impulses must pass from the right parabducens to the right abducens nucleus and, via the medial longitudinal fasciculus, to the right oculomotor nucleus, especially that portion which innervates the left internal rectus muscle. From the right abducens and oculomotor nuclei, impulses are sent to the right external rectus and the left internal rectus and the eyes deviate to the right.

The frontal end of the superior colliculus appears to be concerned with eye movements in an upward direction. From this collicular region tecto-oculomotor fibers pass to the rostral part of the oculomotor nucleus, from which impulses are discharged to the ocular muscles responsible for movements in an upward direction, to right or left. The caudal end of the superior colliculus is concerned with eye movements in a downward direction. This collicular region discharges to the caudal end of the oculomotor nucleus, from which impulses are sent to the ocular muscles responsible for movements in a downward direction, right or left. The nucleus of Perlia constitutes the center for convergence. From it impulses pass to those portions of the oculomotor nucleus which innervate the internal recti.

Impulses arise from the frontal eye fields located in the precentral and immediately frontal gyri for the initiation of eye movements voluntarily. From the vicinity of area 8 and also from the precentral gyrus Penfield has been able to elicit deviations of the eyes in response to electrical stimulation (255, 622, 659). Frontal cortical impulses are discharged along corticobulbar tracts to the various brain stem centers for conjugate gaze. Stimulation from the more frontal focus usually produced rotation of the eyes to the contralateral side. In some instances the deviation of the eyes was associated with turning of the head (face) to the same direction. In certain cases, the eye movement was associated with eyelid movement or pupillary dilation. From the precentral eye focus, Penfield was able to produce deviation of the eyes to the ipsilateral side almost as frequently as to the contralateral, and deviation upward was obtained about half as frequently as were lateral movements. Convergence was obtained on one occasion. Turning of the head did not occur with eye deviations elicited from the precentral focus. Eyelid movements, closing, twitching, and opening, were obtained from loci very close to the central fissure. Penfield has also elicited eye movements to the opposite side and pupillary dilatation, especially, by stimulating within his "supplementary" motor area, just anterior to the precentral leg field on the medial hemispheric surface. Deviations of the head (face) to the opposite side and sometimes elevation of the contralateral arm were also obtained with eye movements from this area.

From areas 19 and 17 in the monkey, and probably also in man, corticotectal and corticotegmental fibers pass to the various brain stem centers for conjugate movements (182). These have been described above. Through these arcs, retinal impulses from the upper fields may lead to upward deviations of the eyes; impulses from the lower fields, to downward deviations; impulses from the right lateral fields, to lateral movements to the right; and so on. These corticotectal paths from the occipital cortex make it possible for the individual to deviate his eyes automatically toward objects falling into his peripheral visual fields and also enable him to follow moving objects.

Impulses from the vestibular nuclei, passing to the centers for conjugate movements either by the medial longitudinal fasciculus or via vestibulomesencephalic tracts, may also lead to eye movements. The right vestibular nuclei, for example, appear to be concerned primarily with movements toward the opposite side, in so far as horizontal movements are concerned. It is probably true that certain vestibular neurons are primarily concerned with vertical movements of the eyes (see Chap. 10).

Auditory impulses in certain animals may lead to conjugate deviations acting through either the superior olive or the inferior colliculus. From these centers impulses pass to the centers for conjugate movements. The necessary arc in man may involve the auditory cortex and corticotectal and corticotegmental fibers therefrom to the brain stem centers for conjugate movements.

In the normal individual the frontal eye fields appear to exert the strongest influence in the initiation of eye movements. The visual reflex following movements can be voluntarily interrupted at any time.

THE VISUAL DEFECTS RESULTING FROM INJURY TO THE OPTIC PATHWAYS

The visual fields can be mapped by the use of a perimeter or tangent screen. Lacking such equipment, the examiner can usually demonstrate visual-field defects by the confrontation method. The examiner, standing several feet in front of the patient and facing him, moves a finger or small object successively across the field of vision of one eye at a time. The patient is asked to cover the opposite eye and to fix the eye under examination directly ahead. The examiner successively moves the object from the periphery to the central fixation zone, covering ultimately all the quadrants of the visual field. Later the other eye may be tested in the same fashion. The central zone of the visual field corresponds to the macular area of the retina; the peripheral portions of the fields, to the periphery of the retina. A blind spot, corresponding to the optic papilla, can usually be demonstrated in the temporal half of the field near the central zone. Macular lesions produce **central scotomata.** Lesions involving macular and papilla regions produce **cecocentral scotomata.**

It should be noted at the outset that, with disorders producing blindness, the visual defect is usually expressed in terms of the visual fields rather than in terms of anatomical structure. The visual-field defect is opposite, right or left, nasal or temporal, superior or inferior, from the site of retinal or conducting element lesion. Visual disorders within the retina may result from disorder in the percipient elements, the rods and cones, or from obstructions in the nerve-fiber layer. If a local disorder involves the rods and cones, the visual-field defect, or scotoma, will agree with it in size and shape. If the disorder is in the nasal retina, the scotoma will, however, occur in the temporal field.

If the optic fibers are obstructed within the retina, the resulting scotoma may be large. Injury to a compact bundle of fibers near the optic papilla may result in a large arcuate defect or a complete quadrantic scotoma. Injuries to the fibers in the periphery of the retina may damage only a few axons, and the scotoma may be so small or so dispersed as to be unnoticed. Retinal disorder secondary to obstruction to one of the four major branches of retinal artery or vein sometimes produces quadrantic scotomata which may have sharp horizontal and vertical boundaries. Retinal lesions frequently betray themselves to ophthalmoscopic examination, while disorder in the conducting paths usually does not.

Visual-field Disturbances with Topical Lesions

It is pertinent to the present discussion to describe briefly some of the visual defects resulting from lesions along the conducting paths. If the arrangement of the fibers in the various portions of the optic system is recalled, the nature of the visual defect resulting from topical lesions can easily be surmised. Injury to the entire retinal blood supply or to a complete optic nerve will lead to complete blindness in the homolateral eye, and the direct pupillary light response will be absent. The pupil may constrict consensually, however, in response to light in the opposite eye. Laterally placed lesions of the optic nerve just behind the orbit may produce a central scotoma because of involvement of the papillomacular bundle, laterally situated at this point.

Injuries of an optic nerve distally, or near the chiasma, may produce homolateral defects in nasal or temporal quadrants alone, since the fibers are separating preparatory to the crossing of those from nasal retinas. The defects may be peripheral, central, or both. Lesions in the most distal part of an optic nerve may damage not only all the fibers of that nerve but also the crossing ventral nasal fibers of the other nerve which loop forward into it (Fig. 283). Such an immediately prechiasmal lesion will produce complete blindness in the homolateral eye and upper temporal-field blindness in the opposite eye (Fig. 291). Compression of an optic nerve within the orbit or within the cranial cavity may produce atrophy of the nerve, with varying degrees of visual defect. A tumor placed rostrally beneath the frontal lobe of one side may compress the homolateral optic nerve and produce optic atrophy while the other eye shows papilledema. Such a combination of ocular findings constitutes the so-called **Foster Kennedy syndrome.**

Other chiasmal lesions may produce characteristic defects, and **bitemporal hemianopia** is most often seen (Fig. 291). This would result from complete compression of the crossing nasal retinal fibers from each eye. The defect may begin as a quadrantic one, involving the upper temporal quadrants, especially, if the chiasmal compression is in its rostral portion wherein ventral retinal fibers cross. Tumors in and about the hypophysis or hypothalamus are most commonly associated with bitemporal hemianopia. Compression of the chiasma from a lateral border usually leads to a contralateral homonymous hemianopic defect, compression from the right side producing a left **homonymous hemianopia.** It will be observed that homonymous defects involve the right or left fields of the two eyes and result from injury to the fibers from the right or left halves of each retina. Since bitemporal hemianopia involves the right field of the right eye and the left field of the left eye, it is sometimes referred to as **heteronymous hemianopia.**

It is theoretically possible to produce a **binasal hemianopia** by compressing the lateral peripheries of the chiasma, but actually such a field defect is seldom seen. Aneurysms of the internal carotid artery of each side, compressing the chiasma, conceivably could produce such a picture. Injuries to the right optic tract, for example, just where it begins in the chiasma, not only may damage all the fibers of that tract, derived from the right half of each retina, but also may damage the dorsal nasal fibers of the right retina which loop back into the right tract before entering the left. The field defect resulting from injury to the right tract would be a left homonymous hemianopia, but the lower temporal quadrant of the right eye might also be blind. Complete destruction of an optic tract further behind the chiasma, while infrequent, produces a contralateral complete homonymous hemianopia which "splits the macula" in each eye. Lesions of the optic tracts not only produce hemianopic blindness but also are associated with a loss of the direct light reflex in the hemianopic fields. Such a loss of the light reflex is difficult to demonstrate without the proper instruments. Actually optic-tract lesions are more often incomplete, and the field defects in the two eyes are not usually congruous, since the crossed

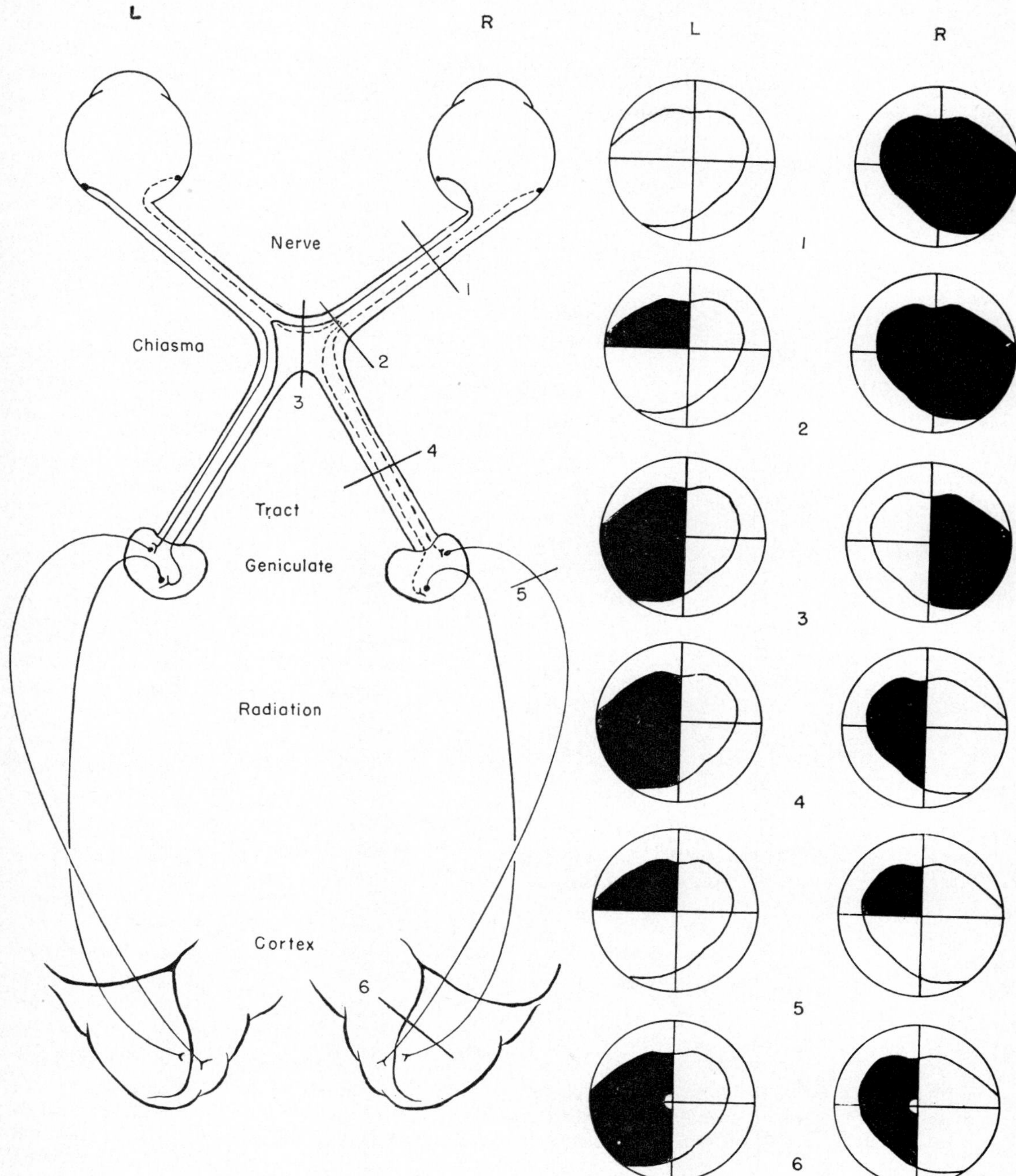

FIG. 291. Diagram to show visual-field defects with interruptions of optic pathways at various levels. Corresponding numbers are used at site of lesion and on field defect. The homonymous hemianopic defect in 4 has arbitrarily been made a "macula-splitting" one; that in 6, a "macula-sparing" one. In the lesion at 5 only the most ventral (in temporal lobe) fibers have been severed.

and uncrossed homologous fibers are not grouped together in the tracts.

Destruction of an entire geniculate or of an entire geniculocalcarine tract would likewise produce a contralateral homonymous hemianopia (Fig. 291). Isolated destruction of a lateral geniculate is rare, and such a destruction would not often be diagnosed clinically. The geniculocalcarine tract running within a great extent of temporal and inferior parietal lobes is more often subject to compression. It is worthy of note that compression of the geniculocalcarine tract may produce homonymous quadrantic defects early which later increase to become hemianopic (549, 702). For example, some centrally placed temporal-lobe neoplasms may destroy the ventrally placed fibers in the geniculocalcarine tract. These transmit impulses which arose in the inferior retinal quadrants. Such a destruction of these ventral fibers would produce, therefore, a superior contralateral **quadrantic** field defect. Such a visual-field finding takes on much importance in the localization of a suspected right-temporal-lobe neoplasm, since this lobe is relatively "silent" otherwise.

In similar fashion deep-seated neoplasms in the inferior parietal region may compress at first the superior fibers in the radiation, and a contralateral inferior quadrantic visual defect would be produced. These quadrantic defects, upper and lower, may or may not involve macular vision. The fibers transmitting macular impulses are thought to occupy the broad middle zone of the geniculocalcarine tract. Since the homologous crossed and uncrossed fibers are closely grouped in the distal portion of the geniculocalcarine tract, preparatory to their closely associated occipital termination, the homonymous hemianopia defects resulting from lesions in this zone of the tract are usually congruous.

With visual cortex lesions, again, it is possible to have contralateral homonymous quadrantic or hemianopic defects which are congruous. Lesions in the visual cortex sufficiently large to cause demonstrable visual-field defects serve to verify the point-to-point relationship between retina and visual cortex. Larger lesions give characteristic defects also. Destruction of inferior calcarine cortex would result in contralateral superior quadrantic visual defect, for example. It is occasionally noted in occipital lesions that the macula zone of the field is "spared," and in fact, some observers have used this "macula sparing" in otherwise hemianopic defects as a criterion for diagnosing geniculocalcarine or occipital lesions. They hold that "macula splitting" characterizes tract lesions. Examples of "macula sparing" in apparently complete visual cortex lesions have therefore produced a lively debate as to the mechanism at play, and bilateral representation of the macular areas in each visual cortex has been assumed (272, 324, 619). Such bilateral representation has been said to result from fibers crossing via the corpus callosum from one geniculocalcarine tract to the other. In reality no such crossing fibers have been demonstrated, and furthermore, experimental removal of one visual cortex results in complete degeneration of the corresponding lateral geniculate. It seems more likely that other factors than bilateral representation are at work in the "sparing of the macula" with occipital lesions. The supposedly complete occipital destruction or surgical removal may have been incomplete, and moreover the macular area in some individuals may be spread over a larger area of the visual cortex than that of the occipital pole, as is customary. Furthermore, a loss of optic fixation reflexes seen in occipital lesions may result in an eccentric fixation, and the "sparing of the macula" would appear. With hemianopia resulting from geniculocalcarine-tract or visual-cortex lesions, the pupillary light response is normal.

Homonymous hemianopic defects which develop suddenly are more often due to vascular disorder or trauma than to neoplasm or degenerative disorder. Vascular spasm or thrombosis may lead to a sudden homonymous hemianopic defect, and within a few hours or days the central vision may return, presumably because of a difference in blood supply to the occipital region, wherein the macula area is usually represented. The middle cerebral artery may share in the nourishment of the visual cortex. Sudden, or consecutively developing, bilateral homonymous hemianopia may occur in vascular disorder. After a few days of complete blindness vision may return in the central field. Occasionally the complete blindness may persist. Sometimes, in complete bilateral homonymous hemianopia of sudden origin, an entire half-field of vision may return. In such cases vascular disorder should be highly suspected.

A patient with homonymous hemianopia occasionally may be unaware of the diminution in his field of vision (384). To him his subjective field of vision has not diminished, although objectively it can be shown that it is halved and that the patient can see only half an object. He can compensate for this disability by psychologically completing the object seen if it is a familiar one. The patient may also extend his vision toward the blind side by using some retinal point other than the fovea in fixation. This new point is on the seeing side of the retina, and since it can be developed to serve as a fovea ordinarily does, it has been called a **pseudofovea.** By directing his gaze toward the blind side of the object which he is viewing and thus using the pseudofovea, the patient learns that he may see the object more fully than if he used the normal macular region. The pseudofovea usually disappears when the patient discovers his hemianopia.

In persisting complete cortical blindness the patient shows a loss of all visual sensation, a loss of reflex blinking to very bright illumination or threating gestures, a preservation of the pupillary constriction in response to light and to convergence, a normally appearing retina usually, and a retention of the normal mobility of the eye. In long-standing cases, the observation of the retina will demonstrate optic atrophy, presumably through the mechanism of transneuronal degeneration.

Occasionally, the beginning of a homonymous hemianopia may be noticed first through an extreme temporal sector defect, upper or lower, in one eye; or in an otherwise complete homonymous hemianopic defect, this sector may escape. Such occurrences have drawn attention to the location of the unpaired nasal fibers subserving the monocular vision of each eye. It is to be recalled that if the visual fields of the two eyes are superimposed, a small temporal sector of each field overlaps. This is served by nasal fibers. Within the geniculocalcarine tract these unpaired impulses from upper and lower retina are transmitted by fibers placed at the dorsal and ventral edges, respectively, of the radiation (Fig. 283). When homonymous hemianopia has been followed in its development, it has been observed that the defects for colored objects invariably appeared before disturbance for form and for black-and-white objects was noted (78, 79). It is also true that when the visual field is altered for colors or for a single color, it is also altered for white as well (78).

Visual Disturbances with Lesions in Visual Associative Areas

With destruction of the visual associative areas only, the patient may have visual disorder of a more complex nature. Although he "sees" objects, he has difficulty in identifying them, appreciating their significance. He has a visual agnosia. He also has difficulty in recognizing the absolute localization in space of objects seen. The identification of objects visually is disturbed when the lateral portion of the visual associative areas of the left hemisphere is destroyed. Left-sided or bilateral destruction in the vicinity of the angular gyrus may be associated with an inability to read (see Chap. 22). An inability to sort out and select various colors without being given their names may result from left-sided lesions also. Bilateral injuries of the angular gyri may lead to spatial disorientation (386). A patient thus afflicted cannot estimate the relative positions in space of objects or the positions of objects with relation to himself and therefore gropes about for them. Although he may see objects such as chairs or walls, he frequently runs into them since he cannot appreciate their direction or distance from him. Topographical memory is also disturbed, and the patient cannot describe his course through surroundings previously familiar to him. He may have difficulty in finding his way about his house or in telling how to move throughout it. Visual attention may also be defective with destructions in, or in front of, either angular gyrus, and the patient will not notice objects in the opposite field of vision.

Effect of Irritative Processes on Visual Paths

Thus far only the visual defects resulting from destructive lesions of the conducting paths and visual receptive and associative cortex have been described. Irritative lesions of the visual tracts may lead to visual hallucinations. These may result from irritation at any level from retina to visual cortex. It is usually true that the hallucinations resulting from visual cortex irritation (or electrical stimulation) are simple ones. Flashes of light, a star, a ball, or simple lines characterize such hallucinations. Visual hallucinations arising from irritation of posterior temporal tissue are more complex and consist of formed images such as people and animals. Visual memories may also be recalled by irritative lesions in the temporal region (see Chap. 22). Such irritative visual symptoms may precede a focal or generalized convulsive attack.

Disturbances of Conjugate Ocular Movements

Some disorders of the ocular movements may be touched upon (379). Destructive lesions of the frontal-lobe eye field of one hemisphere, or of projection paths therefrom, result in a deviation of the two eyes to the side of the lesion, and an inability to turn the eyes toward the opposite side. Usually in unilateral lesions the deviation persists only a few days, after which the eyes resume a mid-position. Some impairment in turning them voluntarily to the side opposite the lesion may persist longer. The improvement is related to an assumption by the normal hemisphere of the activity of the damaged one. Corticobulbar fibers are not completely crossed, it is to be recalled. Irritative lesions of these frontal centers produce periodic tonic deviations of the eyes toward the opposite side. Such deviations of the eyes, and sometimes of the head also, characterize focal seizures initiated from the region of area 8.

Since the frontal oculogyric centers normally supersede the occipital ones, some interesting features may occur with destruction of the former or of their projection paths. The ocular fixation reflexes, maintained by the occipital areas, become exaggerated, and this fact complicates the picture (382).

A patient suffering interruption of the projection fibers from the two frontal centers is unable to deviate his eyes on command or to turn them toward an object to his right, for example. Once he fixes on an object, however, he can follow it if it moves slowly and thus he deviates his eyes in directions not attainable on simple volition. Moreover, he cannot willfully deviate his eyes from an object on which his vision is fixed. He may be able to move his eyes from one spot on a piece of paper to another distant spot on the same sheet, provided a line connects the two, or he can move along a line of very closely approximated spots. In reading he is unable to deviate his eyes from the right end of one line to the beginning or left end of the next succeeding line. He may overcome this difficulty by placing a finger beneath the line being read and moving it along to and fro as he reads. He usually has deviations of the eyes when his head is turned, illustrating thus that ocular movement in response to labyrinthine stimulations is intact.

After acute unilateral removal of area 19 in man, Foerster reported that the eyes deviate temporarily to the same side and cannot be turned to the contralateral side (255). With chronic destructions of the occipital oculogyric centers, ocular-fixation movements are disturbed but the eyes can be moved voluntarily in any direction (382). It is difficult to study the disturbance of the visual reflex movements when the visual cortex is destroyed because of the associated loss of vision. If a patient has destruction of the corticotectal fibers at some point along their course to the brain stem, the difficulties in the visual reflexes are more readily apparent and especially so if he has bilateral lesions. He is unable to maintain fixation on an object if the object is moved or if he himself is moving. He cannot maintain fixation on an object that is far to one side of him. He may have difficulty in fusion and in accommodation.

Brain stem lesions may be associated with disorder of conjugate movements. These lesions are more often destructive than irritative, and therefore the deviation, if present, is a paralytic symptom rather than an irritative one. As a matter of fact, deviations of the eyes with brain stem lesions are relatively rare, and when present, they are usually permanent in contrast to the deviation resulting from cortical lesions (81). The paralysis of lateral conjugate movements toward the side of the lesion in pontine lesions is nearly always severe and permanent.

The brain stem center for lateral conjugate movements to the right is located near the right abducens nucleus as noted previously. Destruction of it results, therefore, in an inability to deviate the eyes horizontally to the right under any condition. If the destruction is in the connections between the center and the ipsilateral abducens nucleus, the external rectus of that side will not contract in horizontal conjugate movements, but the internal rectus of the opposite eye may. Similarly, if the lesion is in the medial longitudinal fasciculus, the external rectus may move normally in horizontal movements to that side, but the internal rectus of the opposite eye will not, since the impulses from the horizontal center cannot reach the oculomotor nucleus. The internal rectus, which does not move with the opposite external rectus in a conjugate movement, in such a case will contract, however, with the opposite internal rectus in a convergence movement.

Destructions of the nucleus of Perlia will lead to a paralysis of convergence. If the nuclei for the internal recti are not damaged, however, these muscles will continue to act in horizontal deviations. Lesions in the vicinity of the superior colliculus usually produce disorders of vertical conjugate movements (Parinaud's syndrome). The disorder may involve only elevation, only depression, or both. Disturbances of the pupillary activities may also be associated.

CHAPTER 22

THE AUDITORY PATHWAYS AND THE TEMPORAL LOBE

THE PRIMARY NEURONS for hearing are located in the spiral ganglion of the cochlear division of the eighth nerve. Peripheral processes of these neurons terminate about hair cells in the cochlea. The mechanism of stimulation of these cells is uncertain, but it is known that the apical portions of the cochlea respond to low tones and the basal portions to high tones. Secondary cochlear neurons are located in the dorsal and ventral cochlear nuclei, in the medulla. Secondary fibers ascend from these pairs of nuclei by way of three striae, to end especially in contralateral superior olives, trapezoid nuclei, nuclei of lateral lemnisci, and the inferior colliculi. To a lesser extent, secondary fibers end homolaterally in the same nuclei. The lateral lemniscus of each side contains fibers, therefore, carrying impulses from each cochlea. These end in the medial geniculate body of the thalamus, directly or indirectly, after a synapse in the inferior colliculus. Neurons in the medial geniculate body project onto the superior transverse temporal gyrus, where the cortical center for hearing is located.

Reflex movements of the head and eyes in response to cochlear impulses are possible through a connection of the cochlear nuclei with the superior olive and thence with the eye-muscle nuclei and upper cervical spinal neurons, via reticular synapses and medial longitudinal fasciculus, respectively. Reflexes are also possible through connections of the inferior colliculus with the motor nuclei of the brain stem and anterior horn cells of the spinal cord, through tectobulbar and tectospinal paths, respectively. Reflexes at a thalamic level probably also are possible and cortical mechanisms for turning the eyes in the direction of a sound also exist. Because secondary cochlear fibers from cochlear nuclei of one side ascend in both sides of the brain stem and because of the existence of several decussation paths, whereby each medial geniculate body and each temporal lobe receive impulses from each cochlea, unilateral lesions in either of these structures give only partial bilateral hearing disability.

External and Middle Ear

It is chiefly by way of the external ear and of the middle ear that sound waves reach the receptor organ in the inner ear, the cochlea. The human external ear, relatively immobile in most individuals, does not serve particularly for concentrating sound waves; the external auditory canal, however, serves not only for conduction, but also possibly for the amplification of sound. Stretched between the outer and middle ear is the **tympanic membrane,** or drum (Fig. 167). The drum may be set in vibration by sound waves, and it responds to a wide range of frequencies.

Attached to the inner surface of the drum is one of the three tiny ossicles, the **malleus** or hammer (Figs. 167, 292). The malleus articulates with the **incus** or anvil; the latter in turn articulates with the **stapes** or stirrup. The base or foot plate of the stirrup lies in the **oval window** leading to the inner ear. These three ossicles transmit the drum vibrations to the inner ear, and with the vibrations the stirrup is alternately pressed into the oval window and drawn out of it. Two striated muscles, attached to the ossicles, are present in the middle ear. The **tensor tympani** muscle is attached to the hammer handle, the **stapedius,** into the neck of the stapes (Fig. 292). The former is innervated by the trigeminal nerve; the latter, by the facial. The handle of the

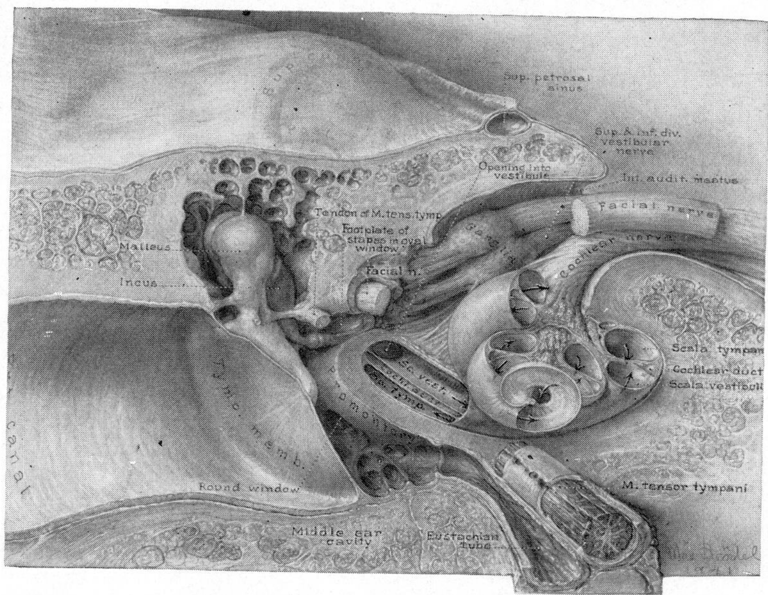

FIG. 292. A dissection of the middle and inner ear. (*After Brödel, courtesy of W. B. Saunders Company.*)

hammer is pulled inward by contraction of the tensor tympani. The neck of the stapes is pulled backward by the contraction of the stapedius, and the foot plate is thus rotated toward the tympanic cavity.

THE INTERNAL EAR

The **bony cochlea** is composed in humans of a basal vestibular portion and two and a half turns, wound around a spindle or **modiolus** (Figs. 167, 292). The bony cochlear canal is incompletely divided by the **lamina spiralis,** a bony ledge projecting from the modiolus. The partitions so formed are the **scala vestibuli** and the **scala tympani.** With the head in an upright position the scala vestibuli is lateral to the scala tympani.

The **membranous cochlear duct,** also spirally wound, is inserted into the lamina spiralis, and lies between the scala vestibuli and the scala tympani. The cochlear duct is filled with endolymph; the scalae, with perilymph. The outer wall of the cochlear duct is formed by the spiral cochlear ligament, adherent to bone; its base is a membranous continuation of the bony lamina spiralis, the so-called membranous lamina spiralis, or **basilar membrane** (Fig. 293). This separates the cochlear duct from the scala tympani. The upper wall of the cochlear duct is formed by **Reissner's vestibular membrane** which separates it from the scala vestibuli.

The endolymph of the cochlea may communicate with that of the sacculus of the vestibule through the **ductus reuniens** (Figs. 168, 170). The endolymphatic duct, leading from the sacculus, in turn ends as the endolymphatic sac lying between two layers of dura mater. The scalae, filled with perilymph, constitute the perilymphatic space. The scalae communicate with one another through the **helicotrema** at the apex of the bony cochlea. The perilymph of the scala vestibuli is continuous with that of the vestibule; the large end of the scala tympani, however, is closed over at the round window, separating it from the middle ear.

THE ORGAN OF CORTI

This structure constitutes the receptor organ of hearing. It is an epithelial ridge on the upper surface of the basilar membrane and therefore follows the spirals of the cochlea (Fig. 293). Its histologic structure is very complex, but fundamentally it is composed of two types of cells: supporting cells and sensory cells or hair cells. The supporting cells are of several varieties, but in general they are tall

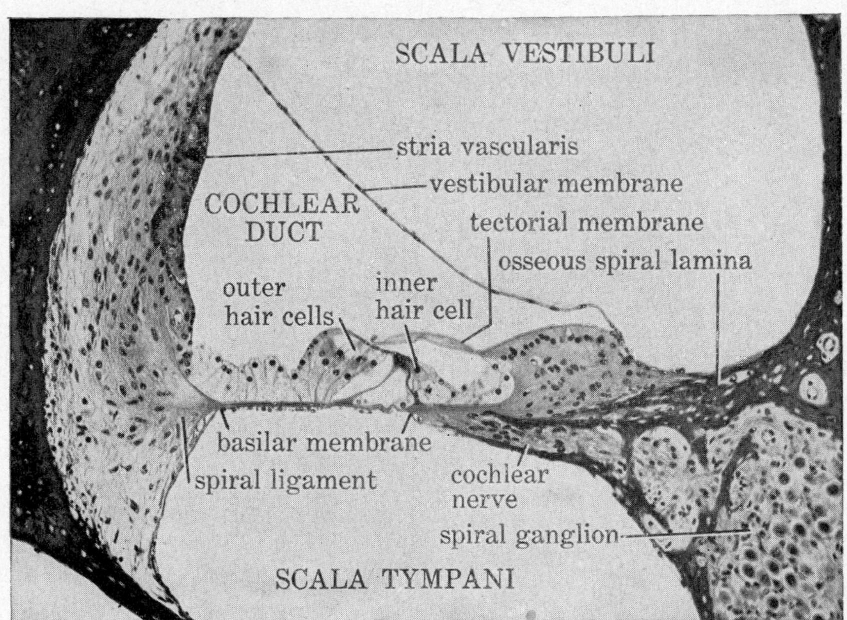

Fig. 293. Cochlear duct with spiral organ (Corti). Guinea pig. Photomicrograph, ×125. (*After Nonidez and Windle, "Textbook of Histology," courtesy of McGraw-Hill Book Company, Inc.*)

and extend through the depth of the epithelial surface. They have a cuticular plate on their distal ends. Although the distal portions of the cell bodies of supporting cells are separated by intercellular spaces, the cuticular edges are in contact and a continuous cuticular membrane is formed. This membrane has many perforations in it, however, because of the irregular shapes of the cuticular plates. Into these perforations are fitted the sensory, or hair, cells, which occupy the intercellular spaces between the supporting cells. The hair cells are short and do not reach the basilar membrane. Their outer surface is surmounted by many fine hairs. The **tectorial membrane** projecting from the edge of the bony lamina spiralis rests above or upon the hairs.

Within the central part of the organ of Corti is a tunnel formed by two columns of tall supporting cells abutting on one another. These cells are the inner and outer pillar cells. The hair cells, disposed on either side of the tunnel, are called inner and outer hair cells. The inner hair cells are arranged in a single row; the outer cells, in three rows. Inner cells number approximately 3,500; outer hair cells, approximately 20,000. Certain of the nerve fibers entering through the bony lamina spiralis run across the tunnel and end about the bases of the outer hair cells. Other nerve fibers end about the inner hair cells.

The Auditory Nerve and Nuclei

The **primary neurons** of the auditory nerve are located in the **spiral ganglion,** lying in the modiolus. The neurons are bipolar, and the dendrites coming from their contacts with hair cells run through the bony spiral lamina. The central processes of the ganglion cells run longitudinally in the modiolus toward its base, which forms the floor of the distal end of the internal auditory canal. This floor has small openings through which the nerve fibers pass into the auditory canal, where they join to form the auditory or cochlear nerve.

The peripheral processes of the ganglionic cells terminate by means of one of two types of fibers, the **radial** and **spiral fibers.** The radial fibers terminate about the internal hair cells, a single fiber ending about several cells. The spiral fibers may course for some distance longitudinally within the organ of Corti. They end about both internal and external hair cells, presumably. In such a way, a double innervation is furnished for certain internal hair cells in the cochlea, and these are therefore doubly represented in the nerve fibers.

The auditory nerve fibers change from the peripheral-nerve type of fiber to the central-path type in the subarachnoid space, just within the internal auditory meatus. This zone of the nerve, the **Obersteiner-Redlich zone,** is the point at which the myelin sheaths of all the fibers are interrupted, as a final node of Ranvier, and the neurolemmal sheath is replaced by glial-cell elements. Proximal to this zone, therefore, the fibers possess no neurolemma but are myelinated.

The auditory-nerve fibers enter the medulla laterally, just lateral and rostral to the restiform body. Two **cochlear nuclei,** the dorsal and ventral, are more or less continuous cell masses over the lateral surface of the restiform body (Figs. 294, 295). The incoming fibers divide into ascending and descending branches, the former ending chiefly in the ventral cochlear nucleus, the descending ones in the dorsal nucleus placed beneath the acoustic tubercle. The incoming fibers enter in orderly fashion but are twisted on themselves in an amount corresponding to the region of the cochlea from which they come. The apical cochlear fibers terminate in the ventral part of the dorsal cochlear nucleus and in the ventral nucleus, and the basal fibers end in the dorsal part of the dorsal cochlear nucleus (481). Some few fibers may end in higher auditory centers.

CENTRAL AUDITORY PATHS

Secondary auditory connections in man are not accurately known and have been inferred in part from those demonstrated in lower animals. The following description is based on evidence obtained in the macaque (61). From the dorsal and ventral cochlear nuclei, secondary fibers are grouped into three striae

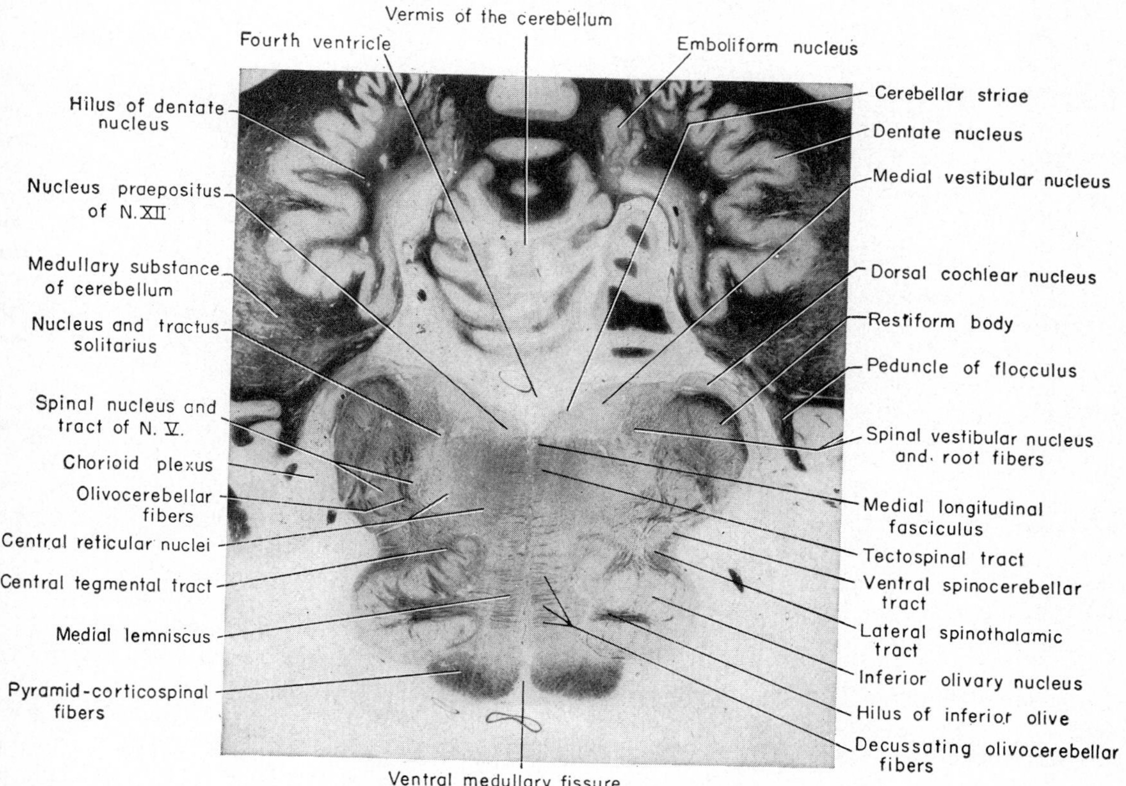

FIG. 294. Transverse section, A 381, of human brain stem through plane of lateral recess of fourth ventricle. Weigert. Photograph, ×2.5.

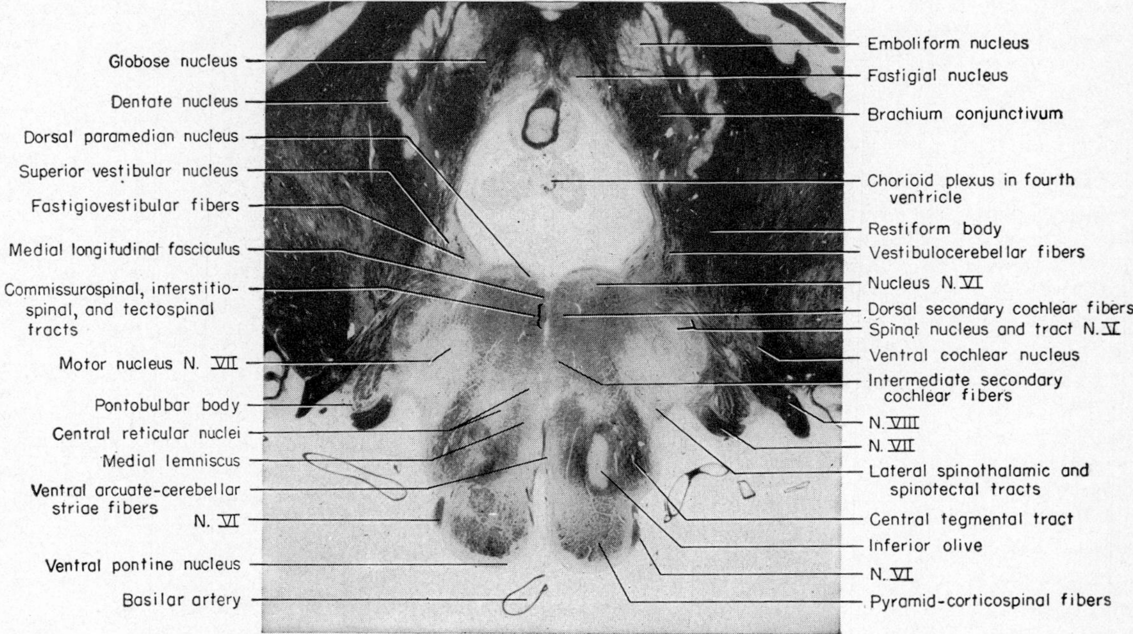

FIG. 295. Transverse section, A 463, of human brain stem through facial colliculus. Weigert. Photograph, ×2.5.

(Figs. 295, 296). A **dorsal stria** (decussation of Monakow) from the dorsal nucleus passes medially and traverses the median raphe ventral to the medial longitudinal fasciculus. An **intermediate stria** (decussation of Held) arising in the dorsal part of the ventral nucleus passes around the restiform body, turns medioventrally, and crosses the median raphe in an intermediate position. A **ventral stria** arises from the main portion of the ventral cochlear nucleus and passes directly medialward as the **trapezoid body** or tract. Scattered among the trapezoid fibers are neurons composing the **nuclei** of the **trapezoid body.** A bit rostrally located, and also dorsolaterally placed with reference to the bulk of trapezoid fibers, is the **superior olivary nucleus.**

Fibers from all three striae terminate in the contralateral superior olive and nuclei associated with the trapezoid body. Very likely some fibers or collaterals of the ventral stria also end in the homolateral superior olive and trapezoid nuclei. Some fibers of the dorsal stria en route across the medulla end in the reticular formation of the two sides. Those fibers of the three striae that do not end in superior olive, trapezoid nuclei, or reticular formation can be traced into the contralateral **lateral lemniscus** (Figs. 297, 298). Some of them end about neurons in the gray column located just medially to the lateral lemniscus, the **nuclei of the lateral lemniscus.** The remaining ascending secondary fibers end in the **nucleus** of the **inferior colliculus.** No secondary fibers ascend higher than this nucleus, and in comparison to the number of fibers leaving the cochlear nuclei, only a few reach the midbrain levels uninterrupted. No **direct** homolateral ascending fibers from cochlear nuclei have been adequately demonstrated, however (61). A prominent collection of **tertiary** fibers ascends in the lateral lemniscus from the homolateral superior olive and trapezoid nuclei, and undoubtedly some of these carry impulses arising in the ipsilateral cochlea. Some of these tertiary fibers reach the medial geniculate body uninterrupted, but most of them end in the inferior colliculus. The fibers arising in the superior olive end particularly in the nucleus of the lateral lemniscus in the cat (657).

THE SUPERIOR OLIVE

This nucleus constitutes an auditory relay center as well as an auditory reflex center

(Fig. 296). It receives auditory impulses from all three secondary striae. It sends axons into the reticular formation wherein synapses take place (657). The reticular neurons in turn discharge to the third, fourth, and sixth cranial nerve nuclei. Other axons from the superior olive enter the medial longitudinal fasciculus and travel spinalward to end in upper cervical segments. By virtue of these two discharge paths the superior olive can correlate eye and head movements in response to auditory impulses. Still other superior olivary axons pass to the trigeminal and facial motor nuclei. Through these fibers auditory impulses may reflexly lead to contraction of tensor tympani and stapedius muscles (501).

THE INFERIOR COLLICULUS

This structure includes a prominent central nucleus surrounded by a capsule of entering and emergent fibers ventromedially, dorsolaterally, and laterally (Fig. 299). Rostrally, the nucleus is continuous with periventricular gray. Aside from auditory impulses which reach the inferior colliculus via the lateral lemnisci, impulses from the cortical auditory areas also enter it. These latter travel in close association with the auditory radiations from the medial geniculate nucleus described below. The inferior colliculus may share with the superior colliculus the reception of sensory impulses of pain and tactile type from spinal and trigeminal nuclei via spinotectal tracts and collaterals from ventral trigeminal lemnisci, respectively. Similarly it may share impulses from the hypothalamus coming by way of the dorsal longitudinal fasciculus. The inferior collicular neurons relay auditory impulses to the ipsilateral medial geniculate nucleus by way of the brachium of the inferior colliculus; they discharge to the opposite inferior colliculus via the commissure interconnecting the two, and some of these crossing fibers may pass uninterrupted into the opposite medial geniculate nucleus. Certain inferior colliculus neurons project their axons rostrally to the ipsilateral superior colliculus as an acoustico-optic tract. Some axons may enter the habenula. Certain others project to the cerebellum. Finally, certain neurons contribute to tectobulbar and tectospinal tracts. Tectonigral fibers may be present also.

The nucleus of the inferior colliculus, when considered in the light of its connections, may constitute more than an auditory reflex center and auditory relay center. It may serve as a center in which pain and tactile impulses are interrelated with those of auditory nature. In view of the fact that the superior colliculus is much larger, that it receives sensory and hypo-

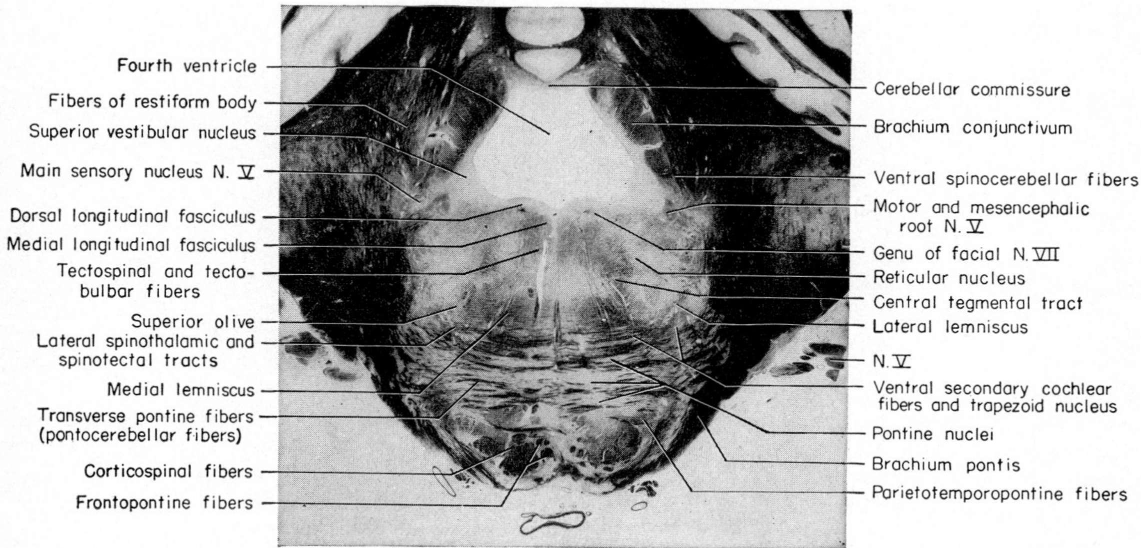

FIG. 296. Transverse section, A 520, of human brain stem slightly caudal to plane of entry of trigeminal nerve fibers. Weigert. Photograph, ×2.

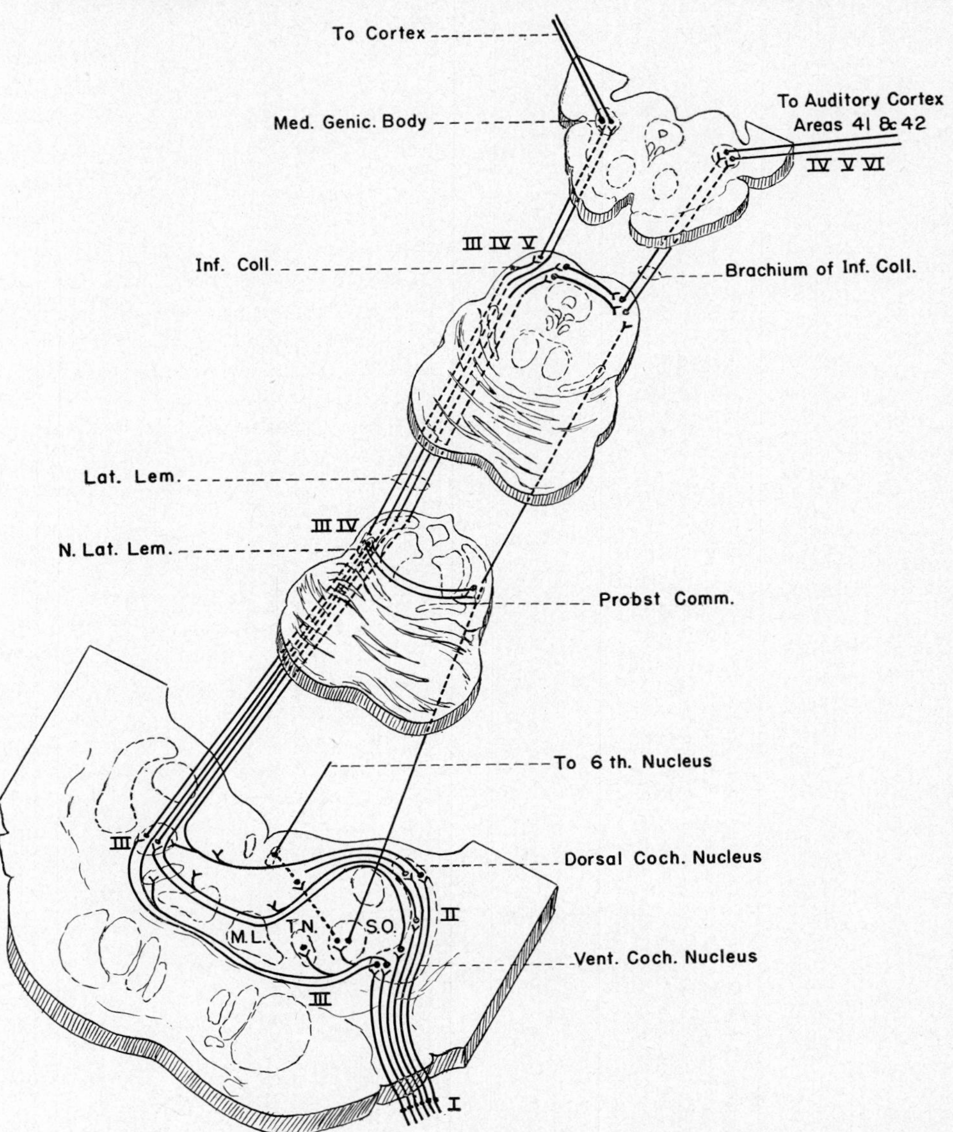

FIG. 297. Schema of auditory pathways based on data in the macaque and cat. The broken line arising in the superior olive represents fibers relaying in reticular nuclei before passing into the abducens nucleus. The synapses in the auditory paths are indicated by Roman numerals. *M.L.*, medial lemniscus; *S.O.*, superior olivary nucleus; *T.N.*, trapezoid nuclei.

thalamic impulses, as well as auditory impulses from the inferior colliculus, it may well be the more important integrating center. As such it may interrelate pain and tactile impulses with those of auditory, visual, and olfactory type. It also plays a part in the automatic movements of the eyes (see Chap. 21).

In addition to the commissure between the inferior colliculi, another is available to secondary and tertiary auditory impulses in upper pontine levels. This is the commissure of Probst, which interconnects the nuclei of the lateral lemnisci. These connections further provide means for bilateral representation of each cochlea in the higher auditory centers, and in consequence, unilateral destruction of any of

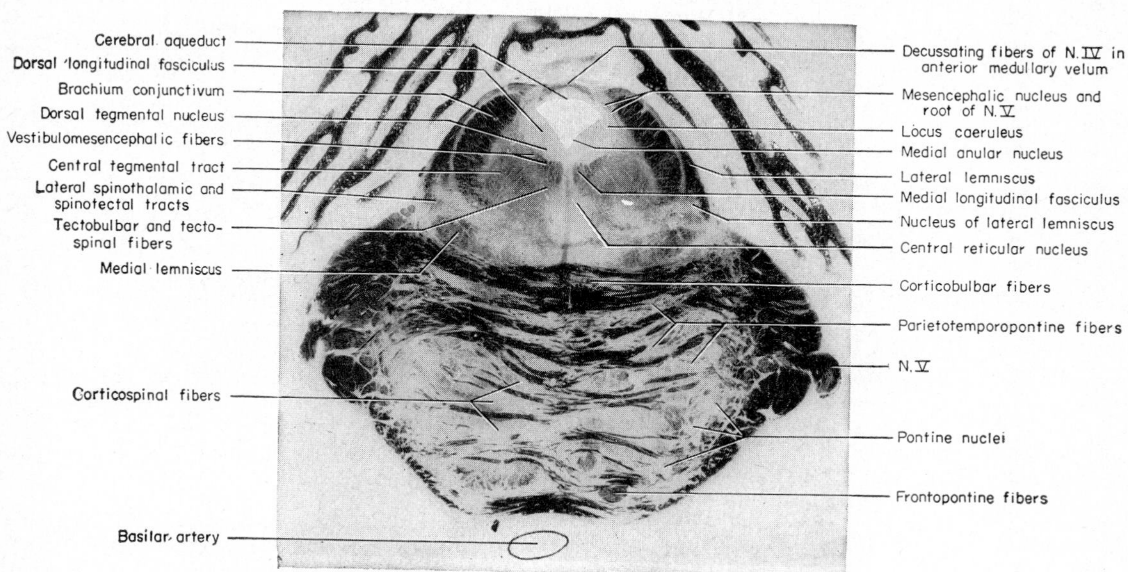

FIG. 298. Transverse section, A 678, of human brain stem at level of point of attachment of trigeminal nerve. Weigert. Photograph, ×2.5.

the auditory centers results in bilateral, although slight, hearing disturbances.

THE MEDIAL GENICULATE NUCLEUS

This thalamic center receives auditory impulses, predominantly of tertiary and quaternary orders, from ipsilateral and contralateral cochleae. The tertiary fibers have arisen in trapezoid nuclei, in nuclei of the lateral lemniscus, or in the inferior colliculus; the quaternary ones, from either of the last two sources.

The medial geniculate body is situated just dorsomedial to the lateral portion of the cerebral peduncle (Figs. 139, 147, 197, 200). It lies between the lateral geniculate body and the suprageniculate thalamic nucleus. A hilus through which fibers enter and emerge presents medially. The medial geniculate nucleus is composed of a large-celled medial part and a small-celled lateral one. The large-celled portion lies dorsal to the posteromedial ventral nucleus. The small-celled part lies dorsal to the posterolateral ventral nucleus. It does not extend as far caudally as does the magnocellular portion. The suprageniculate nucleus belongs to the intralaminar thalamic nuclei.

Certain medial geniculate neurons project directly, or via collaterals, to the inferior colliculus, others to the zona incerta region, and others to the pulvinar. The majority of the geniculate neurons, however, project to the **auditory receptive cortex** in the superior transverse temporal gyri. This auditory radiation traverses the retrolenticular and sublenticular portions of the posterior limb of the internal capsule (626). It passes beneath the ventral sulcus of the insula. In the human, the fibers in the dorsal part of the radiation end in the medial part of the cortical receptive area; those in the ventral part, in the lateral part of the cortical receptive area.

In the monkey, the termination of the auditory radiation has been worked out in more detail (792, 793). The ventral and posterior portions of the medial geniculate nucleus project to the anterior portion of the auditory receptive area; the dorsal and anterior portions project to the posterior part of the cortical area (Fig. 300). Lateral parts of the medial geniculate project to the lateral part of the cortical receptive area; medial parts, to the medial portion of the cortical area. By such an arrangement high tones would relay through cells in the dorsal and anterior portions; low tones, through the ventral and posterior portions. According to Riley, the auditory receptive area also projects to the medial geniculate nucleus (675).

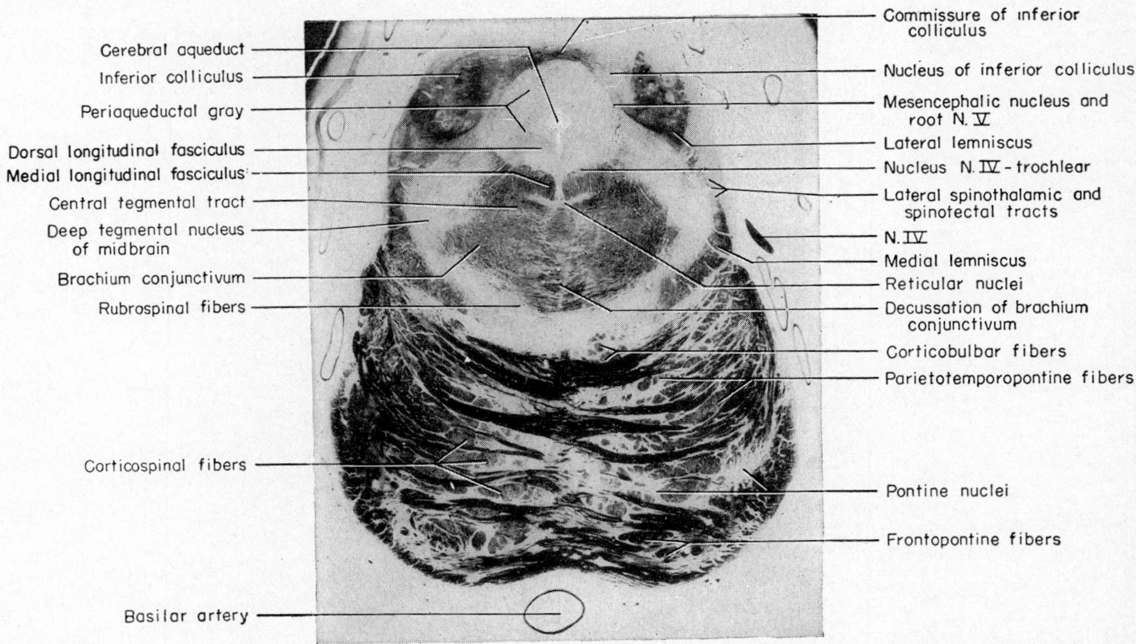

FIG. 299. Transverse section, A 798, of human brain stem through the inferior colliculus. Weigert. Photograph, ×2.5.

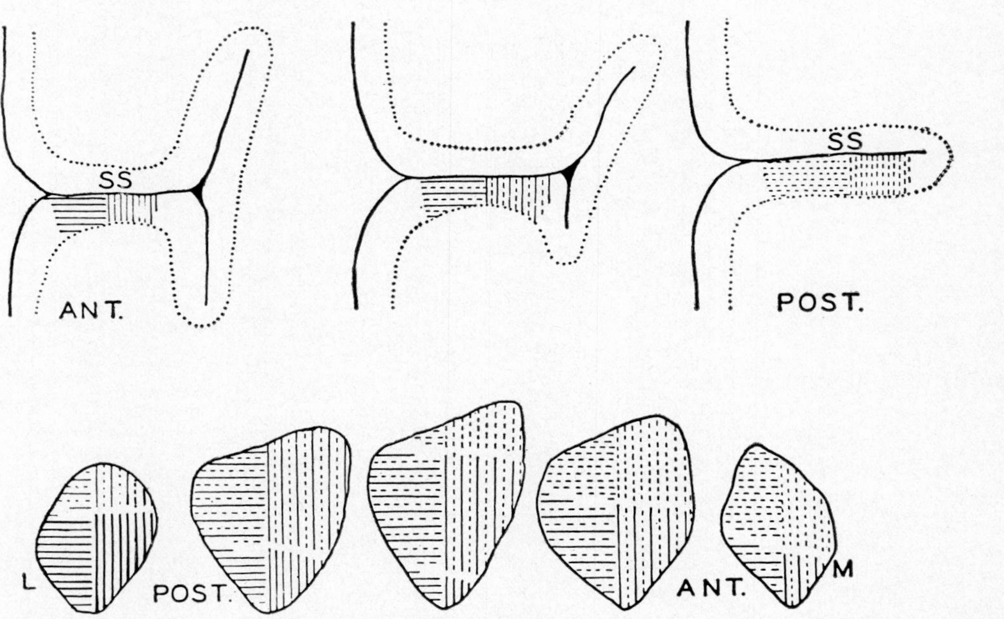

FIG. 300. The topographic relations between the medial geniculate body and the auditory receptive cortex in the macaque. The geniculate body, below, projects to the similarly marked part of the cerebral cortex, in the superior transverse temporal gyri. *L*, lateral surface of geniculate; *M*, medial surface; *SS*, sylvian fissure. (*After Walker, "The Primate Thalamus," The University of Chicago Press.*)

The Cortical Auditory Areas

On the superior surface of the superior temporal gyrus, near its posterior end, are usually one or two smaller gyri running transversely. These constitute the gyri of Heschl, and the more anterior one serves as the primary receptive cortical area for auditory impulses. The posterior one and the adjacent surface of the superior temporal gyrus complete the auditory area, serving chiefly as auditory associative regions. The auditory receptive cortex has been numbered area 41 by Brodmann. Area 42 is a small field lateral to 41 and surrounds it on anterior, lateral, and caudal borders (Figs 226, 227). Actually areas 41 and 42 are intermingled to a certain extent and show transitional areas (86). Area 42 is an auditory associative area. Medial to area 41 is area 52 bordering the insular cortex. The remaining part of the superior temporal gyrus exclusive of its rostral tip constitutes area 22, and that part immediately surrounding 41 and 42 is an auditory associative area. Area 41 is *TC* in Economo's symbols, 42 is *TB,* and 22 is *TA*. Area 52 is *TD*.

CYTOARCHITECTURE OF AUDITORY AREAS

The cortex of area 41 is typical koniocortex (Fig. 221*D*). All its layers contain small cells predominantly. The outermost layer contains few cells; the second and third are composed for the most part of small pyramidal cells, the former being more densely populated. Layer IV, the granular layer, is broad and is composed of granule cells rather closely packed, but arranged somewhat in columns. The fifth layer, or ganglionic layer, is lightly stained in Nissl preparations. The cells, small and medium-sized pyramids, are arranged in columns. The sixth layer contains many polymorphous and pyramidal cells and does not show columnar arrangement. Area 42 shows similar characteristics, but its pattern varies from point to point. Its third and fourth layers are not so wide as are the corresponding ones in area 41. Area 22 shows a tendency toward columnar arrangement (232, 233). The pyramidal cells of the third layer gradually increase in size in the deeper portion; the fourth, or granular, layer is narrow and is composed of small granule cells. The fifth, or ganglionic, layer contains medium-sized pyramids and is only moderately dense. The sixth layer is not striking.

CONNECTIONS OF THE AUDITORY AREAS

Area 41 receives the major part of the auditory radiation from the medial geniculate body. Area 42 may receive a few radiation fibers and is related to 41 by association fibers. Area 22 receives fibers from both 41 and 42. In comparing these auditory fields with the visual areas, 41 would compare with striate area 17, the visual receptive area; 42 would compare with the parastriate, and 22 with the preoccipital visual fields, 18 and 19 respectively.

Corticocortical connections of the auditory receptive cortex have been studied with the use of the physiological-neuronography technique (47, 764, 766). "Auditory receptive cortex" in these studies included areas 41 and at least a part of 42. This receptive cortex projected to the upper part of area 8, the frontal eye field; to the visual associative areas, 18 and 19; to the "face" area in the frontoparietal region, areas 6, 44, 43, and 1; to the superior and middle-temporal gyri, at least areas 22 and 21; and to the cortex just posterior to these gyri, area 37. The projection to area 22 was the most dense of these. Area 22 had corticocortical connections within its own boundaries, with the auditory receptive area, and with area 21. It appeared to project to area 45, to be mutually related with area 10, and to project to frontal and parietal opercular regions.

When that part of area 22 which is buried in the anterior bank of the superior temporal sulcus was investigated with physiological-neuronographic technique, many other connections were postulated on the basis of the "firing." These included discharges throughout the rest of 22 and to area 38, the temporal pole. Projections to area 37, to occipital areas 18 and 19, and to frontal areas 44, 45, and 8 were disclosed. The relations of this auditory associative area to that frontal region concerned with the production of speech should be noted. **Commissural fibers** via the posterior one-fourth of the corpus callosum interconnect the auditory receptive areas of the two hemispheres, but no callosal fibers were found connecting the areas 22. **Projection fibers** from the auditory receptive areas are scarce, and include corticogeniculate and corticotectal to the medial geniculate nucleus and inferior colliculus, respectively. These latter have been described in anatomical studies (182). They are closely associated with occipitotectal fibers for a part of their course.

TONOTOPIC LOCALIZATION

As mentioned above, a characteristic pattern exists in the terminations of the auditory radiations in the auditory receptive area. Such a pattern presumably underlies a tonotopic arrangement. It has been reported that high tones in the human are referred to the medial portion of the receptive area; low tones, anteriorly and laterally (626). More detailed information is available concerning tonotopic localization in the cat, macaque, and chimpanzee. The manner of representation according to frequency becomes more of a point-to-point one as the mammalian scale is ascended. The tonotopic representation has been determined by observation of loci demonstrating action potentials in response to certain sound frequencies and in response to stimulation of fixed points of the cochlea (7, 8, 860). In monkeys, for example, the apex of the cochlea, in which low tones are selectively picked up, projects to the most rostral part of the auditory cortex, the middle cochlear turn, to the auditory region lateral to the posterior end of the insula, and the basal coil, to the remainder. A secondary auditory area has been identified in the monkey medial to the primary receptive area (6, 811, 857). The tonotopic representation in the secondary area is the reverse of that in the primary, the basal coil of the cochlea (high frequencies) being represented rostrally and the apical portion (low frequencies) posteriorly (Fig. 273). In the chimpanzee, lower frequencies activated the anterolateral part of the primary acoustic area, 41; higher frequencies, the posteromedial portion (47, 483). No activity was seen in area 22 in response to acoustic stimulation, but some was observed in area 42.

RESULTS OF STIMULATION OF AUDITORY CORTEX IN HUMANS

Electrical stimulation of the human superior temporal gyrus has elicited a sensation of sound (616, 622) (Fig. 239). The sound was usually described as a cricket, a bell, a whistle, humming, buzzing, or a knocking. It was either high-pitched or low-pitched and was more often referred to the contralateral ear. Details of frequency localization were not worked out, and in fact, because of technical difficulties, most of the points stimulated lay in the associative areas in the lateral region of areas 42 and 22, rather than in the major auditory receptive area, 41. Occasionally, a patient reported a sensation of deafness, a diminution of hearing, or a sense of sounds heard becoming louder. It would appear that simple auditory impulses are perceived in the primary auditory area. More complex sounds are appreciated as a result of integration in cortical auditory associative cortex. Interpretation of sounds as speech occurs in this tissue in the dominant hemisphere, especially.

A sensation of movement of the whole body (vertigo) has also been elicited by stimulation of the superior temporal gyrus, especially (622). Less distinct vertiginous sensations have been produced by stimulation in parietal areas.

ANATOMICOPHYSIOLOGIC CORRELATIONS

It will be pertinent at this point to consider certain physiologic aspects of various parts of the auditory mechanism. The drum and ossicles are probably of equal efficiency throughout the pitch range normally. If conduction by the drum and ossicles is lost, transmission of sound by bone conduction through the skull is important. Good hearing is often possible without the tympanic membrane and the ossicles.

Contractions of the tensor tympani and the stapedius are elicited reflexly by sound stimuli and prevent too great excursions of the drum and stapes. Transmission of low tones is impaired by increased tension of the tensor and consequent rigidity of the ossicle chain. Relaxation of the ossicular chain resulting from cutting the tensor impairs transmission of high tones. The tensor becomes tetanized under the influence of a sound stimulus and remains thus during the extent of the stimulation. Reflex contraction appears more readily, the higher, the more unpleasant, and the more intense the sound. The role of the stapedius is a protective one also in that it contracts reflexly in response to sound. This reflex appears for all tones of the auditory scale, but noises produce the reflex more easily than do pure tones.

Some definite localization of tone reception

exists in the cochlea and this has been shown in several ways (185). Destructions of discrete areas of the cochlea in guinea pigs have been correlated with losses of response to specific frequencies of sound. Similarly, results of audiometer tests in humans, correlated with postmortem studies of their cochleae, have shown that definite areas of damage in the cochlea are associated with a loss of hearing of certain frequencies of sound (186). In such a way it has been shown that high tones are received in the basal part of the cochlea, low frequencies in the apical part.

A few points concerning the auditory paths are worthy of emphasis. It is apparent at once that they have more relay centers in their progress toward the thalamus and cortex than do the fibers of the ascending somatic sensory systems. On the basis of the experimental study of the auditory connections, the superior olive, nucleus of lateral lemniscus, and the nucleus of the inferior colliculus serve as relay and reflex centers. Projections from auditory cortex to superior colliculus underlie reflex ocular movements in response to sound. Further, projections from the auditory receptive cortex pass to the occipital area from which the corticotectal tract to the superior colliculus arises. Through such an arc an anatomical basis may be found for permitting automatic responses of the eyes to auditory stimuli, especially. Another point of interest is the contrast in diameter between the fine fibers of the dorsal and intermediate striae and the heavily myelinated ones of the ventral stria. The fiber diameter difference perhaps indicates fast and slow-conducting auditory systems. The approximately equal representation of the two cochleae in a single lateral lemniscus, colliculus, and medial geniculate would appear to represent a certain margin of safety in the auditory mechanism. Finally, the connections of the auditory receptive area to the visual associative area and to the frontal areas 6 and 44 appear to underlie cortical associations important in the mechanisms of speech to be described later.

The mechanics of stimulation of the hair cells apparently involve perilymph compression or movement. The stapes is inserted into the oval window and can transmit vibrations to the perilymph of the vestibule. This is in continuity with perilymph of the scala vestibuli. The scala vestibuli is in continuity, in turn, through the helicotrema with the scala tympani. This latter channel has its other end blocked off at the round window by a membrane, thus separating it from the middle ear. The membranous cochlear duct is between the two scalae, it is to be recalled, and pressure changes passing along the scala vestibuli to the scala tympani and back are in all likelihood reflected on the membranous cochlea. Beyond this, the further details involved in the stimulation of the hair cells are not agreed upon, but movement of either the tectorial membrane or the basilar membrane presumably occurs. In such a way the hair cells are distorted by contact with the tectorial membrane and stimulation takes place.

Though the neuroanatomical agents for hearing have been fairly well known for some time, arguments still exist concerning the mechanics of their working. The physiology of hearing usually centers around two chief theories, the "telephone" theory and the "resonance" theory. The former theory assumes vibration in response to sound waves, with the whole cochlea vibrating, the impulses being transmitted as such to auditory paths for analysis. The resonance theory of Helmholtz assumes a local reaction in the cochlea to certain frequencies, with the same spot always reacting to the same frequency. Sound is broken down in the cochlea into harmonics, and various points receive impulses which are distributed to auditory pathways. The latter theory perhaps has more proponents, but this theory alone is not sufficient as an explanation of all the principles involved in hearing.

Sound waves set up mechanical vibrations in the tympanic membrane, and these are transmitted to the inner ear by the ossicles. The activity of the ossicles is controlled somewhat by reflex contractions of the stapedius and tensor tympani muscles. As the foot plate of the stapes moves in the oval window and compresses perilymph, vibrations are set up in the basilar membrane. It seems most likely that the frequency of the sound waves determines the site of maximal amplitude of vibration in the basilar membrane. The selective frequency reception of low tones near the apical portion of the cochlea and high tones near the base forms the basis of discrimination of pitch (197). Electrical potentials, arising as a result of the mechanical vibration of the basilar membrane and organ of Corti, seem to be generated by the hair cells. The auditory nerve transmits impulses in a 1:1 relation to the activating sound waves in so far as the refractory period of the nerve fibers permits. The maximal frequency of transmission in a single fiber cannot exceed 1,000 per sec. (197). If tones of higher frequency are present, the nerve fibers respond to every second, third or fourth sound waves; if the frequencies are above 4,000 per sec., the nerve impulses are not synchronized with the sound waves. Loudness of sounds perceived is determined primarily by the number of active nerve fibers.

Clinical Disorders Involving the Auditory Paths

From the neuroanatomical connections, it is evident that a fair margin of safety is provided in the arrangement of central auditory fibers. Injuries to the central tracts of one side characteristically are associated with little hearing disorder. Isolated lesions in one cochlea give loss of hearing for certain tones in the ear of that side. Eighth-nerve injuries give a loss of hearing restricted to one ear. Cochlear disease is characterized by strong subjective noises, gradual onset of hearing disturbance, and restriction of high tones with normal hearing of low tones and comparatively good hearing for middle tones. Nerve disease may be characterized by more rapid onset of hearing loss, restriction of low tones, and normal or nearly normal perception of upper tones (748). Nerve deafness is occasionally a result of the action of toxins or drugs, such as quinine or certain antibiotics. The basal part of the cochlea, chiefly, is injured by loud explosions, while repeated noises involve mainly the upper parts (748). Injuries in the secondary, tertiary, and quaternary fibers give bilateral disturbances in the two ears, and the qualitative type of loss is difficult to ascertain. Such injuries may be secondary to neoplasm or to vascular disorder, especially in the distribution of the superior cerebellar artery, the collicular artery, or some branch of the posterior cerebral artery.

Injuries in the thalamic centers for hearing may be associated with a distortion and unpleasant character to the sounds heard by the patient. Such a disorder may be a feature of a gross thalamic syndrome. Aside from this type of hearing disorder, disease of the individual portions of the auditory paths does not show characteristic symptoms, and it is necessary to study the associated neural signs due to involvement of other neighboring tracts in order to localize the site of damage in a central hearing disorder.

Since each cortex receives fibers from both cochleae, destruction of one cortical area gives only slight disturbance of hearing bilaterally. According to Penfield, the chief auditory defect, if any, following a removal of the temporal lobe is one of inability to locate the source of sound (617). More often, removal of one temporal lobe does not lead to any noticeable auditory or equilibratory disorder. If the ablation includes intermediate or posterior temporal cortex, fibers of the optic radiations may be interrupted and an homonymous hemianopia or quadrantanopia will result. Bilateral destructions of the auditory receptive areas in humans are reported to give complete deafness. If the posterior part of the associative areas are destroyed on the left in a right-handed individual, an inability to interpret the meaning of sounds heard results. If the destruction involves the posterior part of area 22, word deafness may occur. This disability, acoustic verbal agnosia, constitutes a form of sensory aphasia (see later).

Diseases of the middle ear and ossicles give an impairment of hearing known as **middle-ear** or **conduction deafness** as contrasted to disorders in the auditory nerve fibers and cochlea, which lead to **nerve** or **perception deafness.** Acute middle-ear disease involving later the internal ear gives both auditory and vestibular disturbance. Disturbance of auditory or vestibular function alone frequently indicates nerve disease. In addition to the sign of deficit, or impairment of hearing, in diseases involving the cochlea, auditory nerve, or auditory pathways, a positive sign of irritation is frequently found. This is **tinnitus,** characterized by the presence of sounds heard subjectively by the patient in the absence of known stimulation. These sounds can be humming, whistling, crackling, or ringing in character, and they are frequently quite bothersome to the patient.

THE NONAUDITORY TEMPORAL REGION

The remaining neopallial portion of the temporal lobe is constituted chiefly by the middle and inferior temporal and the fusiform gyri. The rostral tip of the superior temporal gyrus is also included. The cortex covering the major part of the middle and inferior temporal gyri has been divided into areas 21 (*TE*1) and 20 (*TE*2), respectively, by Brodmann, although the areal boundaries do not coincide exactly with the sulci (Figs. 226, 227, 228). The temporal pole region is area 38 (*TG*). The fusiform gyrus is covered to the greatest extent by area 36 (*TF*). All these areas are anatomically similar in that they do not appear to receive fibers from the thalamus directly. They apparently receive their impulses chiefly from other cortical areas.

Cytoarchitecture

The cortex of the middle and inferior temporal gyri is fairly broad and shows a prominent radial arrangement of the cells (689) (Fig. 221*F*). The innermost two layers are relatively wider and more densely populated than the upper cell layers. Layer III of the middle-temporal-gyrus cortex contains larger pyramids than does the same layer in the inferior-temporal-gyrus cortex. Otherwise the two regions are quite similar. Layer I is divided into an outer cell-rich zone and an inner cell-poor one. The cells are for the most part small pyramids. Layer II is rather narrow, quite irregular, and not sharply set apart from III. It contains granules and small pyramids. Layer III is relatively narrow and subdivided into three sublayers. Its radial columnization is irregular. The component pyramidal cells are irregularly distributed, and they show a gradual increase in size as the deeper zone of the lamina is reached. Layer IV is of medium width and shows an arrangement of the cells into groups. The cells are granules and small pyramids. Layer V is densely populated and is broad. The cells are medium-sized and large pyramids. Layer VI is also thick and moderately dense, especially in the zone near V. It contains large spindles.

The cytoarchitecture of area 38 is quite different from that of the two areas just described. Its cellular density is lower, its third and fifth layers contain small cells, and the internal granular layer IV is thin and poorly developed.

The cortex of the fusiform gyrus (36) is also deep. The lamination is quite prominent, the columnar pattern fairly distinct. Cell population is fairly dense in all the layers, and the cells are preponderantly small. Lamina V is well developed and divisible into two sublayers.

Between the fusiform gyrus and the hippocampal gyrus in a small region, area 35, or *TH* of Economo and Koskinas. Its cortical pattern is quite similar to that of area 38 (689). It has a broad layer III, which is rather sparsely populated and is composed of medium-large pyramids. Layer IV is wide and dense and contains larger pyramids than does III. It is rather prominent.

Fiber Connections of the Nonauditory Neopallial Temporal Region

Physiological neuronography has been used predominantly in the demonstration of the corticocortical connections of the nonauditory temporal-lobe cortex. This technique has been applied on that cortex on the convexity of the gyri as well as on that buried in the sulci (625, 764, 767). The results of these studies are shown in Table 6. The details of the fiber connections will not be described here.

Table 6. Corticocortical Connections of the Nonauditory Temporal Cortex in the Macaque

Afferent	*Efferent*
20 ← 18	21 → 22, 36, 37, 39, 40, 18, 19, 45, 46
21 ← 41, 22	20 → 21, 22, 36, 46
37 ← 46, 39	37 → 21, 22, 36, 17, 18, 19, 7, 39, 40, 8, 10, 45, 46
	38 → 36, posterior orbital area, uncus, 21, 22, 44, 45, 10, 37, 19
	36 → 47, 36, 38, uncus

In summary, the nonauditory temporal cortex, especially areas 20, 21, and 37, is connected chiefly with associative cortex of frontal, parietal, and occipital lobes. Area 38 is connected with the posterior orbital cortex, wherein autonomic activity appears located, with the uncus, and with other temporal areas. The fusiform gyrus in part is connected with the olfactory regions of the temporal lobe, in part with the orbital portion of the frontal lobe. It would appear to be more closely related functionally, therefore, with the temporal pole region than with other temporal regions.

Commissural fibers via the corpus callosum pass from area 38 to its opposite counterpart, but no callosal-commissural fibers have been found for these other nonauditory temporal areas in the monkey and chimpanzee. Such commissural fibers as are present pass via the anterior commissure, apparently.

Projection fibers from the nonauditory portions of the temporal lobe also appear scarce, in the macaque at least (121, 695). Temporopontine fibers have been described by some observers but denied by others (769). They are usually recognized in the human. They take a sublenticular course to reach the posterior limb of the internal capsule and thence pass into the lateral portion of the basis pedunculi.

Results of Stimulation or Ablation of Nonauditory Neopallial Temporal Regions

Stimulation of this temporal region in animals has been singularly unproductive except for the results obtained from stimulation of area 38. When this area is stimulated in the monkey and proper attention is given to the pulse duration and the frequency of stimulation, respiratory movements are completely or partially inhibited. If partial, the inhibition affects mainly the amplitude of respiration; when complete, the arrest occurs with the thorax in the expiratory position and is not maintained beyond 25 to 30 sec. (421). Elevation of blood pressure after a latency of a few seconds could usually be produced from the same foci. Stimulation of the uncus gave similar respiratory and vasomotor alterations. It was found that these temporal foci are only part of a circle of cortical tissue from which such respiratory and vasopressor alterations could be obtained. The circle includes the anterior temporal operculum, the anterior insula, posterior orbital area, anterior perforated space, subcallosal area, and anterior cingular cortex. It should be noted that this circle of responsive areas is covered by allocortex or isocortex which is of a transitional or mesocortex type. Such transitional cortex is either agranular or sparsely granular. Because it was impossible to abolish the response on stimulation by cutting around any of these responsive areas, it was suggested that they probably have projections to a common subcortical region. These projections have not been identified anatomically, however.

Electrical stimulation of the tips of the temporal lobes (area 38) in a human under Pentothal anesthesia has been found to produce significant elevation of both the systolic and diastolic blood pressures (136, 137). This effect was perhaps exerted by way of connections from the temporal lobe tip to the hypothalamus, although it is not clear whether such connections are direct, or by way of a relay in certain of the olfactory regions of the brain, such as pyriform cortex.

Stimulation of other nonauditory temporal cortex in humans has elicited quite remarkable sensations. The stimulations have been more provocative in patients who have suffered convulsive disorders related to scars, injuries, or neoplasms in the temporal lobe (622). The patients usually had experienced major convulsive attacks preceded by some form of psychical sensation of hallucinatory or illusory character. This may have been characterized by a repeated dream, visual or auditory hallucination, or perceptual illusion involving distortion of visual or auditory perceptions. Some patients experienced a sense of familiarity with their perceptions, a feeling of having previously seen and experienced an event at hand even though such had not been the case (*déjà vu*). Others had a feeling of remoteness, of being far removed from their environment, or of thinking that the environment was absurd. It was possible often to reproduce these sensations by electrical stimulation over the diseased temporal cortex, and the foci have been found in any one of the temporal gyri, but usually over cortex outside the recognized auditory areas. In some instances the irritable foci apparently lay in the inferior parietal lobule or in the most rostral visual area, 19. Stimulation of nonauditory temporal cortex of the left hemisphere, in a region about 7 cm. posterior to the anterior tip of the temporal lobe and overlying middle temporal gyrus especially, resulted in an arrest of speech (622).

Ablations from the nonauditory portions of the temporal lobe have been of two sorts in macaques, involving removal of only superficial cortical tissue or of the entire cortex (10, 121). The most striking changes have been reported after bilateral temporal lobectomy. These emotional alterations apparently were due particularly to removal of the hippocampus and temporal tip. They have been described in Chap. 23. The superficial temporal cortex has been removed from macaques trained in visual form discrimination (9). It was learned that the ability of form discrimination was retained after bitemporal decortication and could also be acquired in the absence of the temporal lobes. If the occipital areas were removed first, the animals lost the form-discrimination ability but regained it; if bitemporal decortication was then carried out, the habit could not be regained with long retraining. These studies apparently demonstrate that the superficial temporal cortex assists in the neural activity underlying visual form discrimination, although the role played by the occipital tissue in this activity is greater.

Ablations of varying amounts of nonauditory temporal cortex have been made for the relief of a form of epilepsy. The incidence of psychomotor epilepsy seems to be related to some dysfunction in the nonauditory portions of the temporal lobe, particularly in the more rostral portion. This form of epilepsy is characterized by episodes of mental confusion, amnesia, or impairment of consciousness in which the patient performs some gross and poorly coordinated movement. The movements appear partially purposeful and may involve walking about, chewing motions, clenching of the hands, dressing, or disrobing. Occasionally the confusional period is preceded by an "uncinate attack" during which the patient may experience gustatory or olfactory hallucinations, and he may smack his lips. In the majority of patients experiencing such attacks a characteristic abnormal brain-wave pattern can be found from an anterior temporal focus, unilaterally or bilaterally (299, 362). The frequency with which the abnormality can be found is increased if electroencephalograms are made during natural or induced sleep. The wave pattern, either a burst of irregular sharp spikes or series of 6-per-sec. waves, is found during a clinical seizure and also between the seizures.

The correlation of psychomotor seizures, which are often refractory to medical treatment, with an abnormal electrical discharge in the anterior temporal region, has led some investigators to attempt a surgical treatment (51, 317). Varying amounts of the temporal-pole region have been removed. The best results seem to be obtained when a "lobectomy" is performed. This involves a removal of superior, middle, inferior, and fusiform gyri to a plane lying 3 to 3.5 cm. from the temporal pole. The inferior horn of the lateral ventricle is opened, but the hippocampus is spared. Such a procedure does not usually damage auditory cortex or that temporal region associated with speech activity. It is of further interest that the geniculocalcarine tract did not appear to be sectioned, although it is customarily believed that the ventral extension of this tract comes in close relationship with the tip of the temporal horn of the lateral ventricle. The patients who had bilateral operations, with one exception, did not show any of the behavioral disturbance noted in the monkeys from which both temporal lobes, including hippocampi, were removed. A lessening in the frequency of the psychomotor attacks has been noted as a result of temporal-lobe removal. It is true, however, that the majority of the patients must continue some form of drug treatment.

Aside from the evidence presented above, the nonauditory portion of the temporal lobe is relatively "silent" when diseased in so far as abnormal neurological signs are concerned. When the ventral fibers of the optic radiations, traversing the anterior temporal region, are damaged, the patient characteristically demonstrates an upper quadrantanopia. Temporal-lobe tumors are frequently associated with focal convulsive disorders, motor or sensory in type. This may be due directly to compression by the tumor of precentral and postcentral gyri, or indirectly to interference with the middle cerebral vascular supply to these regions. Occasionally "uncinate attacks" have been stressed in deep, medially placed temporal-lobe tumors. These are characterized by gustatory or olfactory hallucinations, or both, usually unpleasant in character, and dreamy states in which the patient may be confused, disoriented, subject to visual hallucinations and to a sensation of *déjà vu*. He may make licking movements or smack his lips. It is rare that all these symptoms plus those of auditory and aphasic nature occur in a single case. It is quite common that a few, or none, occur, especially subsequent to defects in the right temporal lobe.

Function of the Nonauditory Temporal Areas

The temporal lobe appears to be yielding slowly to analysis. Certainly auditory function is a part of its activity, and some vestibular control may be initiated there. The regulation of visceral activity seems a function of the anterior temporal region, an activity shared by other cortical regions and especially by the posterior orbital region and the anterior supracallosal cingular region, area 24. Certain rhinencephalic tissues of the temporal lobe subserve olfaction, while others, especially the hippocampus, appear to have a nonolfactory function, perhaps playing a role in the control of emotional expression. The function of the middle and inferior temporal and fusiform gyri is not known definitely. Judging from their connections with the associative regions of the parietal, occipital, and frontal cortex, it would appear that these temporal regions represent associative cortical tissue. They probably belong to the highest "level" of the cerebral cortex. The inability to catalogue their function may be due to the fact that they cooperate with other large areas of cortex in a common activity and much overlapping of responsibility exists. Such an idea seems supported by the report of mutual interests with occipital cortex in a visual-form-discrimination ability, as described above.

On the basis of Penfield's results of electrical stimulation of the nonauditory temporal lobe in humans, it would appear that this cortex contains neural patterns which have been formed as a result of some experience (622). The stimulating electrode is able to bring to consciousness a visual memory, an auditory memory, or a complex memory involving both types of activity. A memory of a significant previous experience is perhaps "stored" in the temporal lobe in the form of a chain of interrelated neurons (Fig. 301). In response to some later experience this memory may be brought to consciousness again, or may be remembered. The subsequent recalling of a memory pattern may result in an increase in the complexity of the pattern, through some new stimulus and the resulting neural integrative activity.

It would seem likely, therefore, that a simple record of a significant experience, whether it involves somatic sensory, auditory, visual, gustatory, or olfactory stimulation, is filed in the cerebral cortex. The regions in which the filing occurs are either within or adjacent the temporal lobe, and numerous association fibers interconnect them. A correlation of the various types of impulses into an over-all pattern or memory may take place originally in the temporal cortex, and the various components of the pattern—somatic, visual, or auditory—may be developed and added to in other cortical regions: posterior parietal, rostral occipital, and the like. The full development of any pattern component involves not only corticocortical association, but also corticothalamocortical associations.

The Cortical Regions Associated with Speech

In a similar way faculties of speech are developed. A child first perceives a sound or a name given to an object. He associates the sound with the object. Later he learns to utter this sound. His conversation consists of several isolated nouns or names. He proceeds from the utterance of single simple sounds to several sounds and to more complex sounds. He learns names for actions and also learns verbs and adjectives. He then becomes able to form the words into sentences. He later begins to correlate a written symbol with an object and becomes able to comprehend a series of such symbols. Then he develops the ability to express himself in writing. His speech gradually changes through these developmental stages from a sort of reflex parroting of single words in response to auditory or visual stimulation to a form characterized by more complex neural associations. He becomes able to understand commands of complex character, both seen and heard. He perceives, interprets, associates, and formulates ideas of his own, converting many of them into propositional speech. In the development of speech the child uses widely separated cortical areas, in frontal, parietal, temporal, and occipital lobes.

Presumably, these speech processes are developed in each hemisphere although the development in the left hemisphere is usually more advanced. Mechanisms underlying the production or emission of speech appear to have a frontal localization in the cortical speech centers. Mechanisms underlying the appreciation of spoken and written speech appear to have a more posterior localization in temporal and occipital lobes. These frontal, temporal, and occipital regions are interconnected, especially in the left hemisphere, by association fibers.

Broca first called attention to a frontal speech area in the posterior third of the second and third frontal convolutions after he had observed two patients with loss of ability to speak resulting, as he thought, from a restricted lesion to that area (98). Subsequent studies, however, have shown that those two patients had more extensive lesions than Broca surmised, and similarly, it is now often maintained that loss of motor speech (**motor aphasia**) cannot be accounted for by disease in such a restricted or localized area. It is customary, nevertheless, to refer to a posterior part of the inferior frontal gyrus on the left as **Broca's area,** although the boundaries of this area appear to vary with different investigators. Brodmann's area 44 is often referred to as Broca's area (85). In another description, Broca's area includes the triangular gyrus, together with the opercular and possibly the orbital portions of the inferior frontal gyrus (496). Certainly, an indefinite amount of cortical tissue in and adjacent the frontal opercular area, in the left inferior frontal convolution, is concerned with the production of articulate speech. This tissue is included in the "face" field of the motor strip and is rostral to that area from which movements of cranial muscles may be elicited.

That portion of area 22 in the left superior temporal gyrus, which is just posterior to areas 41 and 42, together with the adjacent portion of the middle temporal gyrus, is sometimes referred to as **Wernicke's area** (835). Destruction of this area leads to an inability to comprehend the spoken word, and occasionally the written word. A patient with such a destruction is not deaf or blind but is said to have word deafness or acoustic verbal agnosia and visual verbal agnosia. Agraphia is frequently present. This combination of speech disorders is sometimes called Wernicke's aphasia or **sensory aphasia.** Because the patient's comprehension of spoken speech is defective, his own speech is frequently irrelevant or jargonlike (**jargon aphasia**). Dejerine subsequently described an area in that left cortical region wherein angular gyrus, parietal, temporal, and occipital lobes meet, the destruction of which was associated with an inability to read (203, 204). A patient with such a destruction is also often said to have sensory aphasia or, particularly, word blindness or **alexia.** This is often a feature of Wernicke's aphasia, as noted previously. More complex forms of speech disorder have been described clinically but will not be included here. It is worth noting, however, that **anomia,** or the inability to name a familiar object, is a form of amnesic aphasia often observed in disease of the posterior part of the left temporal lobe.

That these various cortical regions are concerned with the production of speech is widely believed. The understanding of speech and the production of speech, however, do not depend on the activity of these individual cortical areas but on the development of, and adaptation of, cerebral association fibers, not only interconnecting these specific cortical areas with one another but also joining them with other cortical regions. It is possible to interfere with speech function by destroying either the specific cortical areas or their association fibers.

The sensory impulses, somatic, auditory, and visual, coming from the periphery, reach the primary receptive areas of each hemisphere. Objects may be visualized, their contour may be appreciated, or sounds may be heard in either hemisphere. The interpretation of the significance of the object or of the sound depends apparently on integration within the left hemisphere, particularly. Activity in the primary sensory receptive areas and sensory association areas precedes the activity in the frontal areas when speech is produced. The area from which the motor faculties of speech are primarily controlled has a left frontal location, as has been stated previously. From this frontal region impulses are discharged to subcortical mechanisms innervating laryngeal, pharyngeal, palatal, glossal, jaw, thoracic, and abdominal muscles.

It has been possible to innervate several of these peripheral mechanisms in animals and

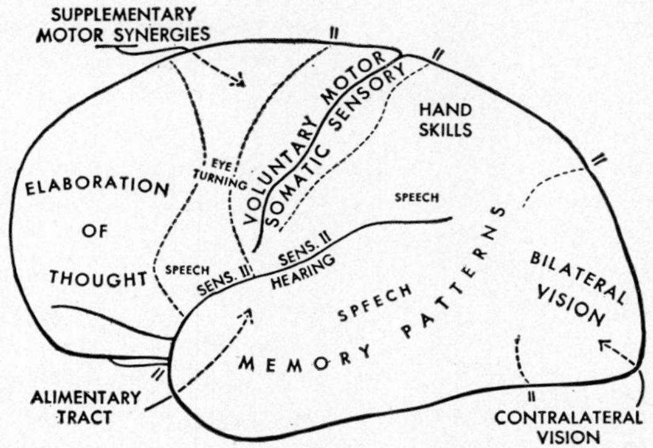

FIG. 301. Diagram to show the major functional regions of the human cerebral cortex. (*From Penfield and Rasmussen, "The Cerebral Cortex of Man," The Macmillan Company.*)

humans by electrical stimulation of one of several cortical regions. As a result of such complex innervations, the individual may vocalize. He utters a sound, usually a vowel sound, but does not produce words. Penfield, for example, has been able to produce vocalization by stimulating in either the precentral or postcentral "face" field in either the right or left hemisphere (622, 658). He has also produced vocalization by stimulating a region on the medial side of the superior frontal gyrus, about 4 cm. anterior to the central fissure. This region is also responsive bilaterally. Removal of these rolandic areas from either hemisphere results in transient anarthria. It does not produce aphasia.

Penfield has also been able to produce an arrest of speech by cortical stimulation of these rolandic and superior frontal regions, of either the right or left hemisphere (Fig. 301). It was possible to arrest speech by cortical stimulation of regions in addition to these, but only from foci in the dominant hemisphere. These dominant hemisphere foci were in the frontal, parietal, and temporal lobes. The frontal region was in the frontal opercular area; the parietal region was in the supramarginal gyrus; the temporal region, still indefinitely outilned, was in the posterior portion of the middle temporal gyrus, especially. During the stimulation of the frontal or parietal region, the patient was unable correctly to name objects shown him, although this ability returned as soon as the electrode was removed. These left hemispheric areas concerned with speech would appear able to utilize the rolandic articulation centers of either hemisphere (622). This use probably is brought about through a subcortically placed mechanism from which either rolandic area may be innervated. These results of electrical stimulation tend to confirm previous concepts concerning speech.

It would apear from these observations also that faculties for vocalization are present in each hemisphere and that those for the production of speech are present in the left, or dominant, hemisphere only. At least these speech processes are developed primarily in the left hemisphere in right-handed individuals. It is possible, however, for the processes to be developed in the right hemisphere in certain young individuals suffering destruction of the areas in the left. Older individuals are not able to transfer speech processes so easily. With restricted destruction within the left hemispheric speech areas, however, practically all patients can regain many of their speech faculties with retraining. It is worthy of note also that, in some patients, the removal of what appears to be area 44 does not produce motor aphasia (546).

CHAPTER 23

THE OLFACTORY SYSTEM

THE OLFACTORY SYSTEM of the human, in contrast to that of many animals, plays relatively an unimportant part in the life of the individual. The human who is rendered anosmic as a result of injury to, or disease in, the upper part of the nasal cavity is little handicapped. The individual with an intact olfactory system is only partially dependent on it for recognition of potential danger, for the sorting out of his food, and for searching out a suitable companion. And yet, the human olfactory system bestows upon him the ability rapidly to discern certain potentially harmful agents and the ability to anticipate pleasurably the joys of certain foods and companions or to reject them. Occasionally, moreover, the diagnosis of certain disorders of the nervous system is made easier by knowledge of an acquired anosmia.

In following the development of the cortex as the animal scale is ascended, it will be noted that the neopallium has greatly overshadowed the remaining more primitive portions, the archipallium and the paleopallium (Fig. 302). The entire pallial region, in species below reptiles, is dominated by the olfactory system. Scattered throughout it are large numbers of fibers derived from the olfactory bulb or from an anterior olfactory area (358). In reptiles a beginning division into separate pallial regions occurs, although the olfactory system continues to dominate these divisions. A dorsal region develops between a medially placed archipallium and a laterally placed paleopallium, and it receives a large proportion of nonolfactory fibers. This region occupies the locus of the mammalian neopallium. In mammals the entire pallial region is much enlarged, and those portions concerned with olfaction are separated from a nonolfactory portion. The olfactory portions are very large and complex in the lowest mammals, while the nonolfactory portion is relatively small. As the mammalian scale is ascended, however, the nonolfactory pallial region continues to develop, to become much larger proportionally, and to be more complex. The olfactory pallial regions show little or no advance in mammals and undergo certain changes in their disposition and organization coincident to the enlarging neopallium and the relative reduction of the peripheral olfactory apparatus.

Although certain of the neural structures which are thought to be involved in the transmission of olfactory impulses belong chiefly to those oldest regions of the pallium, it is not clear as yet to what extent in man, at least, they may participate in an olfactory activity. It seems likely, furthermore, that certain of these human archipallial and paleopallial regions are not completely devoted to olfactory activity, and others may, in fact, be little concerned with smell. The hippocampus, for example, reaches its highest development in microsmatic man, and it is well formed in certain anosmatic species. Certain portions of the amygdaloid complex show a relative increase in development in man, and the prepyriform area also shows a relative increase in development when compared to the reduced size of the olfactory bulb. These regions in man may therefore serve for more complex interrelations of olfactory and other types of impulses. The hippocampus may be concerned with associations and integrations of olfactory and other types of impulses at a cortical level.

The Olfactory Receptors

The olfactory membrane, a yellowish-brown area in the upper part of the nasal cavity, constitutes the peripheral organ of smell. This

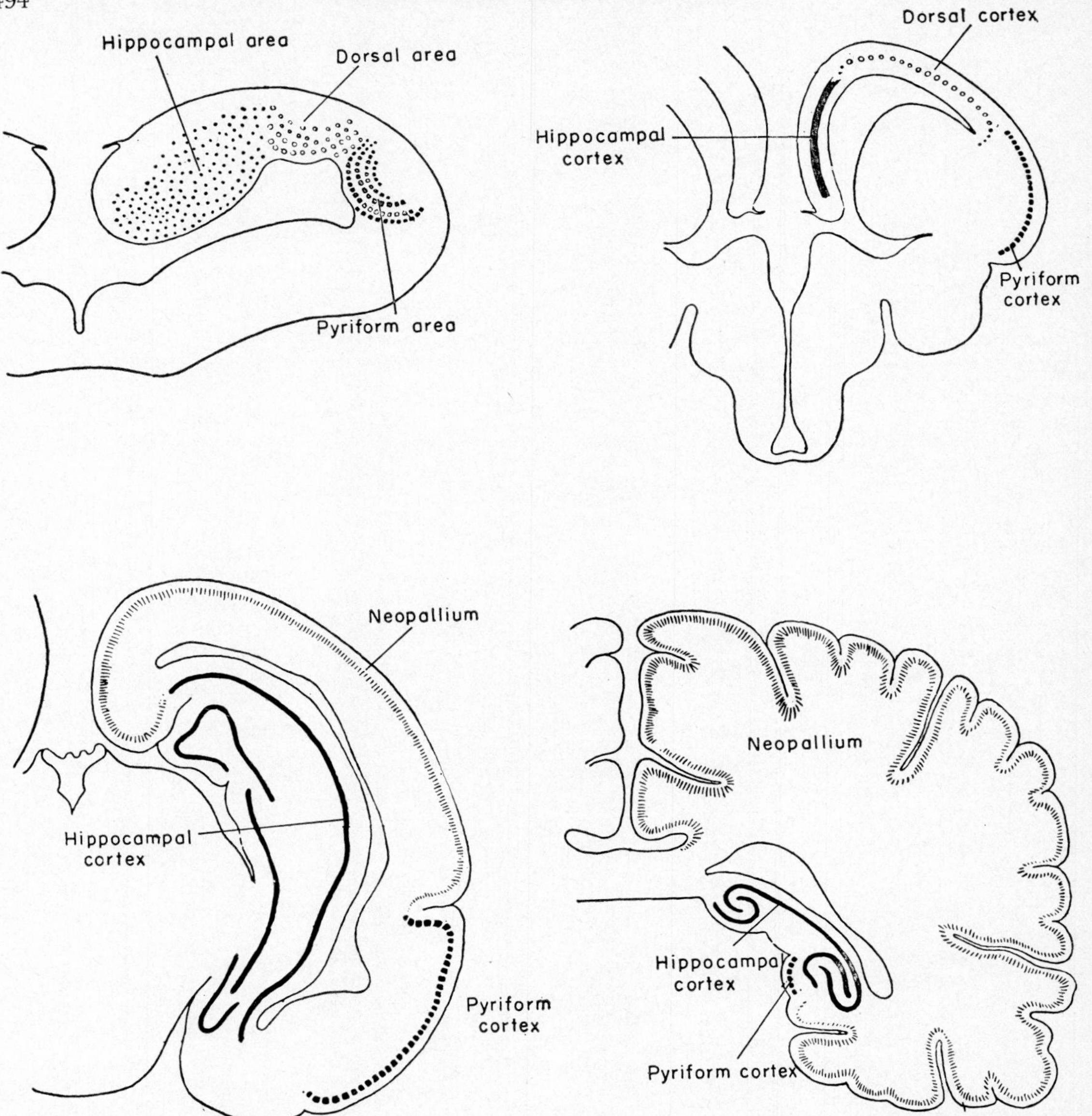

FIG. 302. Diagrams to show approximately the relative extent of the olfactory and nonolfactory pallial fields as seen in, cross sections of various vertebrate brains. Above, left, Necturus, with entire pallial field olfactory, ×16; above, right the box tortoise, Cistudo, with differentiated cortex, all of which is under olfactory influence, ×9; below, left, the opossum, Didelphis, with olfactory cortex (hippocampus and pyriform) more extensive than nonolfactory cortex (neopallium), ×5.5; below, right, human, with enlargement of neopallium and reduction of olfactory cortex, ×$\frac{2}{3}$. (*After Herrick, Proc. Nat. Acad. Sc., vol.* 19.)

colored area is of irregular outline and is on the middle upper third of the nasal septum and the adjacent superior concha on each side.

The olfactory receptors of various mammals have certain similar characteristics. They have a small cell body with a round nucleus surrounded by a small amount of cytoplasm. They show two processes: a coarse one, the olfactory rod, which terminates at the surface of the olfactory epithelium; and a finer one which passes centrally through the basement membrane of the epithelium. The coarse peripheral olfactory rod shows a terminal swelling from which arise 10 to 12 short olfactory hairs which usually are equipped with blunt tips as they terminate in the layer of mucus overlying the olfactory epithelium. The olfactory rods are evenly distributed over the surface of the olfactory epithelium except where the tubulo-alveolar mucous glands open on the surface. In the rabbit the density of the olfactory rods has been estimated as 150,000 per square millimeter of olfactory epithelium (165). The mucous glands serve to keep the olfactory epithelium moist, furnishing thereby a fluid medium for rendering into solution the gases or odors to smell. The olfactory endings are chemoreceptors.

The fine, centrally directed, unmyelinated processes of the olfactory cells pass vertically through the basement membrane. Several converge to form a small fasciculus of **olfactory-nerve** fibers as they approach the membrane. Each nerve fiber appears to serve only one receptor in the rabbit, and there is no overlap in the epithelial distribution of the different fasciculi of fibers (165). This is in contrast to the usual arrangement of sensory surfaces. The fascicles pierce the cribriform plate, and within the cranial cavity they form an intricate olfactory plexus. It appears likely that olfactory fibers from each local area of olfactory epithelium are distributed to a specific region of the olfactory bulb.

The Olfactory Bulb

The olfactory bulb of the human adult is a solid, flattened, ovoid mass composed of gray and white matter (Fig. 42). Its structure shows a laminar pattern although the layers are not as distinct as are those in the bulbs of lower mammals (398). Beginning along its ventral surface and proceeding into the substance of the bulb, eight layers showing variable development may be evident. The lowermost layer is composed of the olfactory nerve fibers, most of which enter the bulb at its anterior tip. Next is the glomerular layer wherein are found the synaptic formations or **glomeruli,** between the fine terminal branches of olfactory nerve fibers and the dendrites of cells which are more deeply placed.

Deep to the glomerular layer is the external granular layer containing a mixture of small granule cells and larger neurons which appear to be mitral cells that have migrated from the more deeply placed mitral layer (398). The external molecular layer, next in order, is of similar composition, but the outwandered mitral cells are more numerous. The dendrites of these mitral cells extend into the glomerular layer, where they end in tuftlike formations in relation to the incoming olfactory nerve fibers; their axons pass centrally.

The mitral cell layer, composed of large neurons, of miter shape, is next most deeply placed. The dendrites of these large mitral cells also extend into the glomerular layer to form synapses with the incoming olfactory nerve fibers. Their axons pass centrally.

Deep to the mitral layer are, successively, the internal molecular and internal granular layers, composed principally of small granule cells. Next comes the layer of mitral cell axons which will compose the olfactory tract.

The granule cells throughout the olfactory bulb serve an associative function; the small and large mitral cells are the secondary neurons in the olfactory pathway.

The Accessory Olfactory Bulb and Nervus Terminalis

An accessory olfactory bulb is lacking in the adult human brain, but within the dorsal part of the main olfactory bulb, caudally, a region is present in which no cell layers are found. It was suggested by Humphrey and Crosby that this region represents the usual position of an accessory bulb, and since a **vomeronasal nerve** is present in the human embryo, they consider that this rudimentary region of the bulb perhaps served as a relay for this primitive accessory olfactory nerve (398). A **nervus terminalis** extending from the region of the nasal septum and passing along with the olfactory nerve is also present in the human. Along its course peripherally are many neurons, and a ganglion is said to be present on it centrally as it lies medial to the olfactory bulb. The central fibers of the nervus terminalis enter the anterior perforated substance. It has been considered as a mixed sensory and autonomic nerve (600, 601).

The Olfactory Tracts

The olfactory tracts extend from the olfactory bulbs posteriorly to their point of

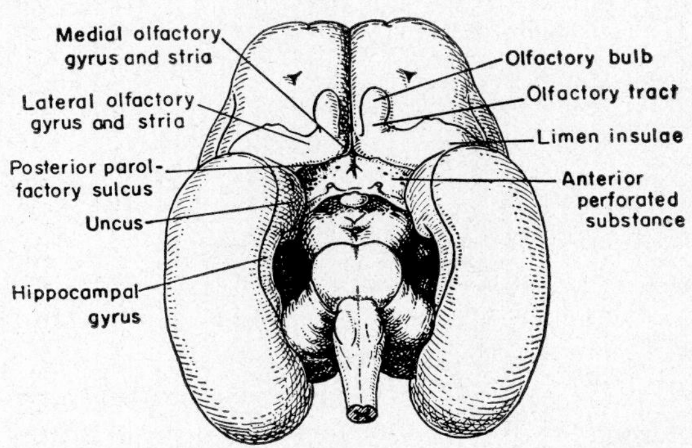

FIG. 303. Ventral view of brain of a human fetus of 20 cm.

apparent union with the anterior perforated substance and cerebral hemisphere (Fig. 304). In cross section each tract is triangular in shape, with the apex of the triangle directed dorsally into the olfactory sulcus. The central portion of the tracts is occupied by the axons of the mitral and tufted cells of the olfactory bulbs. In scattered groups, dorsally, laterally, medially and, to less extent, ventrally, are the cell bodies of the anterior olfactory nucleus. In the caudal end of the olfactory tract, a separation of fibers and gray into **lateral** and **medial olfactory striae** and **gyri** occurs, and these portions appear grossly to blend with the basal frontal lobe cortex, the anterior perforated substance, and the prepyriform cortex of the temporal lobe. An **intermediate olfactory stria** is poorly developed in the human. Within each olfactory tract are certain axons which have arisen in the opposite olfactory bulb and have crossed by way of the anterior commissure. These centrifugally directed fibers arise chiefly from the bulbar portion of the anterior olfactory nucleus of one side and end in the opposite olfactory bulb, among the cells of the internal granular layer (165).

Central Olfactory Nuclei

ANTERIOR OLFACTORY NUCLEUS

Before describing the course of the fibers in the olfactory tracts certain nuclear centers, related to them, should be described briefly. Within the olfactory bulbs, along the olfactory tracts, and within the base of the cerebral hemisphere at the caudal end of the olfactory tracts, an **anterior olfactory nucleus** is present, as noted previously. It is represented in man by discontinuous groups of neurons intermediate in size between the mitral cells and the granule cells of the olfactory bulb. At various positions along the olfactory tract, dorsal, medial, lateral, and ventral portions of the anterior olfactory nucleus may be identified. The anterior olfactory nucleus in part becomes continuous with neopallium, in part also with prepyriform gray, and also with the polymorphic layer of the olfactory tubercle (see later). It is not continuous, apparently, with the anterior continuation of the hippocampus (see later).

OLFACTORY TUBERCLE

The olfactory tubercle occupies that part of the basal hemisphere wall just posterior to the point of attachment of the olfactory tracts (Figs. 303, 304). It is included within the region most often identified by the numerous perforations made by entering blood vessels and known as the anterior perforated space. Its posterior boundary is formed by the **diagonal band of Broca** and its nucleus. The olfactory tubercle can be divided into rostral, middle, and caudal regions (183). Some investigators have considered it a rudimentary form of cortex. It usually shows three laminae, in its middle portion especially: an outermost **plexiform,** an intermediate **pyramidal,** or cortical layer, and an innermost **polymorph** layer. The pyramidal layer is composed of mixtures of granules and pyramidal cells for the most part. These are arranged in groups and often do not simulate a cortical band. The polymorph layer contains some large and small pyramidal cells and clusters of granules and is not always easily separated from the pyramidal layer. Collections of granule cells, referred to as **islands of Calleja,** are interspersed between these layers of the olfactory tubercle and the adjacent neopallial subcallosal gyrus and the overlying caudate nucleus. Lateral extensions of the olfactory tubercle approach the pyriform lobe region.

The olfactory tubercle receives fibers from the olfactory bulb or anterior olfactory nucleus and from the amygdaloid nuclei. It sends fibers into the stria medullaris thalami and the medial forebrain bundle. It may also discharge to the septal nuclei. With the physio-

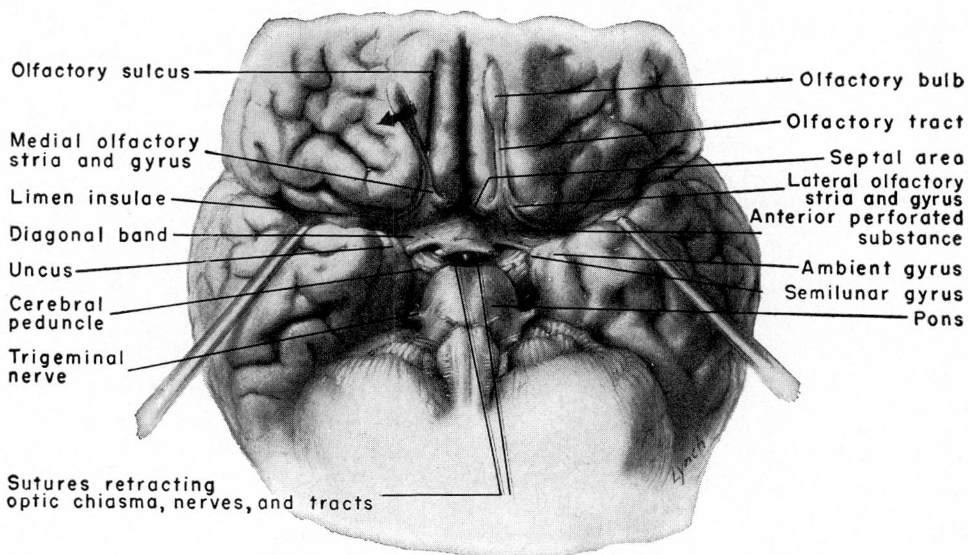

FIG. 304. Base of young human brain. The temporal poles and the optic chiasma are retracted in order to expose rhinencephalic structures.

logical-neuronography technique the olfactory tubercle has been shown to have connections with the medial orbital cortical region and the subcallosal (septal) area (638). It also is connected to posterior orbital cortical region, the anterior insula, temporal pole area, and periamygdaloid area. Less prominent connections with the amygdaloid nuclei and hippocampus region were indicated.

The substantia innominata of Reichert beneath the lenticular nucleus overlies the olfactory tubercle in part. The posterior extension of the latter blends with the **nucleus of the diagonal band of Broca.** This last gradually replaces the cortical and polymorph layers of the olfactory tubercle. The diagonal band appears usually as a stripe just in front of the optic tracts (Fig. 304). It runs between the medial, basal region of the caudal end of the frontal lobe and the amygdaloid complex within the frontal end of the temporal lobe.

THE SEPTAL AREA

This term refers to a basal region of the hemisphere which extends forward from the anterior commissure and lamina terminalis to the caudal end of the anterior olfactory nucleus. Overhanging it is the anterior continuation of the hippocampus, and beneath it and lateral to it is the olfactory tubercle. It includes the **subcallosal gyrus** and **parolfactory area** (Figs. 46*B*, 47). **Medial** and **lateral septal nuclei** have been described in this region in front of the anterior commissure. The medial septal nucleus becomes continuous with the nucleus of the diagonal band of Broca and its tract. Through this relationship it is connected with the amygdaloid complex. The lateral septal nucleus may be continuous over the commissure with neurons in the septum pellucidum. The septal nuclei may receive fibers via the medial olfactory stria from the olfactory bulb or anterior olfactory nucleus, directly or via a relay in the olfactory tubercle. The medial septal nucleus receives ascending fibers from the medial forebrain bundle, and it is believed to discharge fibers to the hippocampal cortex (423). The lateral nucleus receives corticoseptal fibers from the hippocampus and perhaps from the frontal-lobe cortex. It sends fibers to the olfactory tubercle and into the medial forebrain bundle. Axons from the septal nuclei also pass into the stria medullaris thalami. Physiological neuronography has revealed that the subcallosal area in the macaque is interconnected with that part of the cingular gyrus just in front of the genu of the corpus callosum (638). It is also interconnected with the medial orbital area of the cortex, the posterior orbital region, and the olfactory tubercle area.

This septal area just described is sometimes referred to as the precommissural part of the septum, although the term "septum" has only a regional connotation. The septum pellucidum which is behind the anterior commissure is sometimes referred to as the postcommissural part of the septum, and it may also sometimes contain nerve cells as noted above. The two septa pellucida may be fused, or a sizable space, the cavum septi pellucidi, sometimes designated the fifth ventricle, may be found between them.

THE AMYGDALOID COMPLEX

This is a large nuclear mass located above the tip of the inferior horn of the lateral ventricle within the frontal end of the temporal lobe (Figs. 212, 254). It is continuous medially with the cortex of the uncus and of the temporal lobe. Above it is the lenticular nucleus. Dorsorostrally it is continuous with the anterior perforated substance, and caudally it is in contact with the tail of the caudate nucleus (Fig. 250).

The human amygdaloid complex has been subdivided into **basolateral** and **corticomedial** groups of **nuclei,** and **anterior amygdaloid** and **cortico-amygdaloid areas** (183). The basolateral portion includes the very large lateral and basal, and accessory basal, nuclei. The basal and accessory basal nuclei are again subdivided in the human. These subdivisions and the large size of the lateral reflect their more advanced development in man as compared to their subprimate status.

In contrast to the increase in development of the basolateral group, the corticomedial group as a whole is relatively decreased in man, and certain of its subdivisions are poorly differentiated. This group includes cortical, medial, and central nuclei as well as the **nucleus of the lateral olfactory tract.** The cortical nucleus shows a relatively high development in man, and it has been identified as cortex in some accounts because of a laminar pattern in its component cells. The central nucleus is related to striatal gray, and its neurons are similar to those of the putamen. The nucleus of the lateral olfactory tract is the least well developed of the amygdaloid nuclei in man. It shows two portions, an anterior and a posterior. The larger posterior portion lies in close relation with the medial nucleus, and its elongated deeply stained neurons outline the fibers of the lateral olfactory tract. This nucleus is near the surface of the temporal lobe in the region of the semilunar gyrus.

The anterior amygdaloid area, the most rostral region of the amygdaloid complex, shows poor differentiation. It is traversed by fibers entering and leaving the amygdaloid complex.

The cortico-amygdaloid transition area, which presents on the brain surface, is composed of a mass of pyramidal and polymorph cells. It is connected with the pyriform cortex by strands of cells. It is also continuous with the superficial part of the medial division of the basal amygdaloid nucleus. This part of the basal nucleus is directly continuous with the lateral amygdaloid nucleus. The cortico-amygdaloid area is a transition zone, therefore, between the well-developed basolateral nuclei and the pyriform cortex. Since the cortico-amygdaloid area is also continuous in certain levels with the cortical amygdaloid nucleus, it serves to form continuity between this nucleus and the pyriform cortex, and between the cortical amygdaloid nucleus and the basolateral amygdaloid group. The pyriform lobe cortex and these last parts of the amygdaloid complex are related functionally, and it seems likely that they are related developmentally (420).

Several of the nuclei of the amygdaloid complex receive fibers from the olfactory bulb or the anterior olfactory nucleus. The corticomedial group of nuclei and the cortico-amygdaloid transition area receive olfactory fibers in the rabbit, while the basolateral nuclei do not. The amygdaloid nuclei are connected with the pyriform lobe cortex and with the olfactory tubercle, septal areas, and perhaps the anterior continuation of the hippocampus. The connections with these last three regions pass by way of the diagonal band of Broca. Certain of the amygdaloid nuclei appear to give rise to a part, at least, of the fibers of the stria terminalis.

This bundle of fibers courses through the central amygdaloid nucleus, and though the basal nucleus appears to contribute fibers to the bundle, the lateral does not. It is impossible, actually, to designate the origin of this tract, or to be certain about the limits of the so-called bed nucleus of the stria terminalis which presumably also contributes fibers to it. Although this nucleus is continuous with the central amygdaloid nucleus, its more rostral extra-amygdaloid extent in man is not clear. It is usually assumed, however, that the stria terminalis is an efferent tract from certain amygdaloid nuclei. By way of it they discharge to the septal area, preoptic area, hypothalamus, habenula, and opposite amygdaloid complex. The fibers to the habenula join the stria medullaris thalami; those to the opposite amygdaloid nuclei cross by way of the anterior commissure.

It is of interest that those amygdaloid nuclei showing the highest differentiation in man do not receive olfactory impulses directly from the olfactory bulb. Furthermore, the olfactory fibers reaching the central amygdaloid nuclei come by way of the anterior commissure in the rabbit, and some are crossed.

The Olfactory Cortical Regions

The cortical regions usually considered as related to the olfactory system are the pyriform lobe and the hippocampal formation. They are continuous through several transition regions. The pyriform lobe and hippocampal formation are subdivided.

THE PYRIFORM LOBE

As its name implies, the pyriform lobe is pear-shaped in certain forms. It includes the **lateral olfactory gyrus** and the greater portion, at least, of the **hippocampal gyrus.** In the brain of the human fetus, these two regions form an easily seen continuous mass (Fig. 303). Although their continuity still exists in the adult brain, it is less obvious because certain alterations in the contour of the pyriform lobe have taken place in association with the great development of the neopallial part of the temporal lobe. As the temporal lobe grows rostrally, the insula becomes depressed and the pyriform lobe is bent on itself. The bend, which forms the limen insulae, becomes buried with the insula in the depths of the sylvian fissure. The lateral olfactory gyrus can be seen as it extends laterally along the border of the anterior perforated space in the fully developed brain (Fig. 304). If the temporal pole is pulled away ventrally and laterally, it can be seen that the lateral olfactory gyrus takes a caudomedial turn at the limen insulae toward the inner surface of the temporal lobe, and its gray matter can be seen to be spread over the rostral end of the amygdaloid complex and to become continuous with the head of the hippocampal gyrus. Several small gyri can be seen in some brains where the lateral olfactory gyrus spreads over the amygdaloid complex. These are the **ambient** and **semilunar gyri** (Fig. 304).

The anterior end of the hippocampal gyrus is rolled upward and inward as a result of the developing neopallial changes. The rostromedial part of this gyrus is called the **uncus.** The rhinal fissure, which sometimes is continuous with the collateral, separates the anterior part of the hippocampal gyrus laterally from neopallial cortex (Fig. 305). It also extends up onto the medial surface of the temporal lobe and separates the head of the gyrus from the temporal pole.

The pyriform lobe is divided into several regions. The **prepyriform area** is often referred to as the lateral olfactory gyrus, which can be seen extending along the lateral olfactory stria to the rostral amygdaloid region. Fibers in the lateral olfactory stria, derived from the olfactory bulb and anterior olfactory nucleus, end in the prepyriform area. It is, therefore, an olfactory relay center for impulses of secondary and tertiary orders. Although the prepyriform area appears insignificant in size in the human, its size relative to that of the olfactory bulb is greater than is its relative size in comparison to the olfactory bulb of certain macrosmatic animals. It would appear that the prepyriform area serves to a greater extent as a correlation center in man than it does in animals with a greater developed smell sense.

The **periamygdaloid area** of the pyriform lobe is a small region included almost entirely in the semilunar gyrus (Fig. 304). It also receives fibers from the lateral olfactory stria.

The most posterior part of the pyriform lobe is the **entorhinal area** designated as area 28 by Brodmann (Fig. 226). This occupies the posterior part of the ambient gyrus and the major portion of the hippocampal gyrus anteriorly in man. The **perirhinal area,** which is area 35 in Brodmann's designation, is found in the depths of the rhinal fissure (Fig. 226). It serves as a transition area between allocortex and isocortex. At the caudal end of area 35, the **retrosubicular area,** area 48, is a separate transitional zone in man. Transition zones between the hippocampal gyrus and the hippocampus are found near and within the hippocampal fissure into which the hippocampal gyrus dips. These are, in order going from hippocampal gyrus to the hippocampus, the **presubiculum** and **subiculum** (Fig. 308). The former is usually included with the pyriform lobe; the latter, with the hippocampus.

PYRIFORM CORTEX. CYTOARCHITECTURE

As noted eleswhere, Brodmann divided the cortex into two major types, homogenetic and heterogenetic. These subdivisions correspond, respectively, to the isocortex and allocortex of Vogt. Homogenetic type of cortex is found in the neopallium. Heterogenetic cortex is found in the archipallium and paleopallium, or the hippocampal formation and the pyriform lobe, respectively.

Heterogenetic cortex was divided by Brodmann into three subtypes, **cortex primitivus, cortex rudimentarius,** and **cortex striatus.** The primitive cortex shows no lamination, the rudimentary cortex shows beginning lamination, and cortex striatus may show six or more layers in the adult. Primitive cortex is found, according to Brodmann, in the olfactory bulb, olfactory tubercle, and amygdaloid complex. Rudimentary cortex is found in the dentate gyrus, Ammon's horn, and subiculum. Cortex striatus is found in the prepyriform, entorhinal, perirhinal, presubicular, and retrosubicular regions. While the amount of heterogenetic cortex present in any mammal varies considerably with the development of the olfactory system, certain heterogenetic areas are found in some anosmatic animals and therefore must be related to other activity. Furthermore, some heterogenetic cortex reaches an advanced development in man, in whom olfactory function is relatively unimportant.

Lorente de Nó has criticized Brodmann's interpretations underlying his division of cortex into homogenetic (isocortex) and heterogenetic (allocortex) and his claim that the six-layered plan is characteristic of homogenetic cortex only (500). With proper stains, Lorente de Nó finds evidence of stratification of the cortex at embryonic stages in which Brodmann found none. He agrees to a division into allocortex and isocortex when it is made on the basis of the existence of a superficial layer of myelinated fibers, this layer being much more prominent in the allocortex. Furthermore, he finds six layers in some of Brodmann's heterogenetic or allocortex, although these layers do not correspond to the six layers of the homogenetic or isocortex. The cell types are fewer in the allocortex, and the arrangement of neuron chains is different. No cells are found in allocortex which are comparable to those of layers II and III of much of the isocortex. The simplest form of cortical pattern is found in the entorhinal region, where the six layers of cells and plexuses are separated into **external** and **internal laminae** (Fig. 221*G*). It is possible to interpret a common pattern of architecture in allocortex and isocortex if a simplification is made and the isocortex is considered an elaboration of the entorhinal pattern (500). Isocortex then also has external and internal laminae, but within these the development of the six laminae is more advanced and more cell types are found.

The entorhinal cortex of the pyriform lobe shows six laminae, as follows: lamina I, or plexiform layer; II, or layer of star cells; III, or layer of superficial pyramids and in the deeper portion, a dense plexus; IV, or layer of deep pyramids; V, or layer of small pyramids with recurrent axons; VI, or layer of polymorph cells (590). Laminae I to III inclusive compose the external lamina; IV to VI, the internal lamina. All the specific afferents end in the external lamina, and the same cells around which these end receive the recurrent collaterals from the axons arising in the internal lamina. Many axons arising in the external lamina extend to other cortical areas, many arising in the internal lamina are projected to subcortical centers (498).

The entorhinal cortex receives several types of afferent fibers from certain of the olfactory centers previously considered as well as from other regions of the allocortex. It does not receive fibers from the olfactory tract directly. The uncus receives fibers from the isocortical temporal pole region, 38, and the anterior end of the fusiform gyrus (767). The entorhinal cortex discharges fibers via the subiculum to the hippocampus, fibers to the frontal lobe by way of the uncinate fasciculus, and association fibers to neighboring cortical regions, including areas 21, 22, 36, 37, and 38 (764).

THE HIPPOCAMPAL FORMATION

The hippocampal formation in the human brain extends from the rostral, subcallosal septal region, over the corpus callosum and behind it, and down into the rostral end of the temporal lobe. Such a contour results from a displacement of the posterior (temporal) part of the hippocampus by the developing corpus callosum and neopallial temporal lobe. That part of the hippocampal formation related to the corpus callosum is greatly narrowed, and the most rostral extent, in the septal area, is often referred to as the **anterior continuation of the hippocampus** (395). The posterior or temporal portion of the hippocampal formation is a much broader band of tissue and is rolled into the inferior horn of the lateral ventricle for which it forms a floor (234). That part of the hippocampal formation which runs along the dorsal surface of the corpus callosum is called the **supracallosal gyrus** or **indusium griseum** (Figs. 139, 189).

The hippocampal formation is composed of the **hippocampus** or horn of Ammon, the **dentate gyrus,** and the **subiculum.** These divisions are obvious only in the temporal region. The **hippocampal fissure** separates the hippocampal formation and the adjacent pallium. In the temporal region it is interposed between hippocampal gyrus and hippocampal formation. In the supracallosal region, it is continuous with the callosal sulcus, which is interposed between the cingular gyrus and the supracallosal gyrus. In a transverse section through the hemisphere, at a plane wherein the temporal part of the hippocampal formation is well developed, the latter has loosely the appearance of a double U, a larger U embracing a smaller one and each having its open end directed medially (Fig. 308). The larger U represents the hippocampus; the smaller one, the dentate gyrus. The hippocampal fissure has hippocampal gyrus on its ventral or medial bank and dentate gyrus on its dorsal or lateral wall. The hippocampal gyrus is continuous through the presubiculum and subiculum with the hippocampus.

The hippocampus. The over-all length of the hippocampus, within the floor of the inferior horn of the lateral ventricle, is about 5 cm. (Fig. 306). The ependymal lining of the ventricle covers it. Beneath the ependyma a layer of myelinated fibers, the **alveus,** covers the hippocampus. This becomes continuous with the

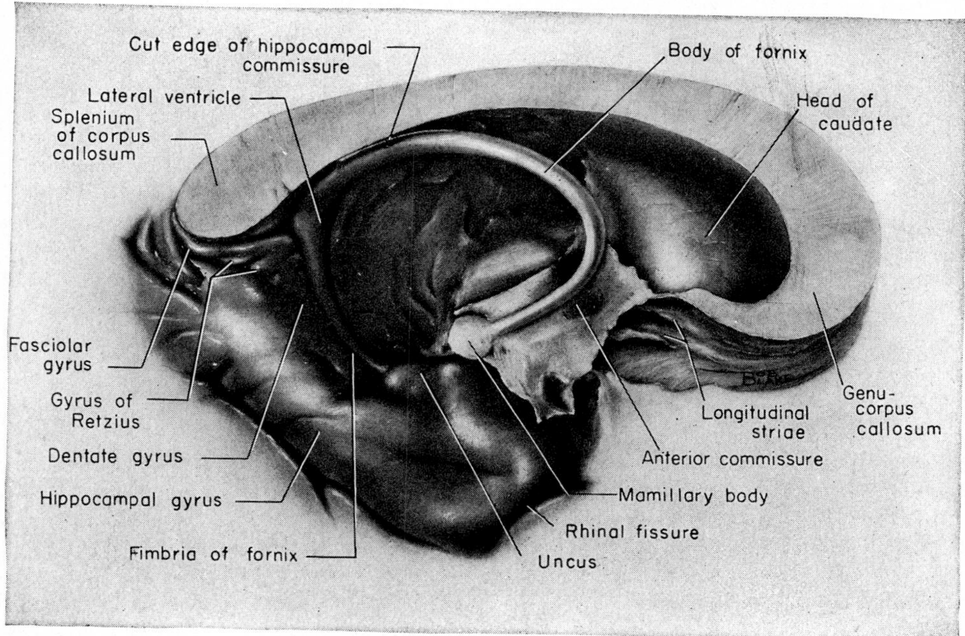

FIG. 305. The dentate gyrus and the fornix.

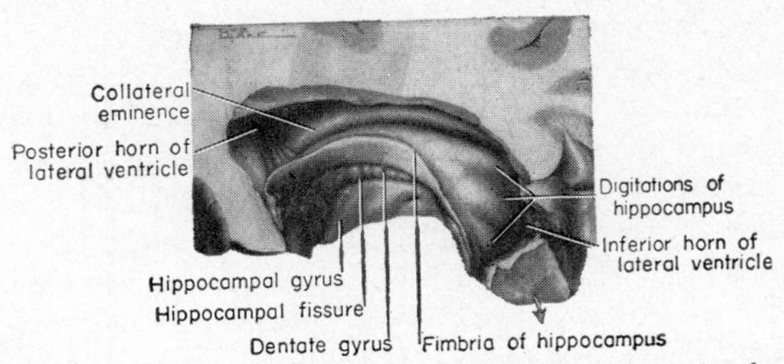

FIG. 306. A dissection to show the hippocampus in the floor of the inferior horn of the lateral ventricle.

fimbria along the medial border of the hippocampus. The fimbria is directed posteriorly and dorsally and is continued into the body of the **fornix.** The rostral end of the hippocampus is slightly expanded and is crossed by several grooves separating, between them, the digitations of the hippocampus. As noted above, the hippocampus extends posteriorly upward and around the splenium of the corpus callosum to be continuous with the supracallosal gyrus.

The dentate gyrus. The dentate gyrus, opposite the hippocampal gyrus across the hippocampal fissure, is a narrow band of cortex so grooved transversely as to come by its name (Figs. 305, 306). In a transverse section through the temporal lobe the dentate gyrus is seen to be surrounded by the hippocampus on all its sides except the medial (Fig. 308). This medial side comes to the surface in the hippocampal fissure, as noted above. The dentate gyrus is continuous with the hippocampus within the depths of the hippocampal fissure. It extends anteriorly to the notch of the uncus, where it turns. It is continued across the inferior surface of the uncus and spreads out over the medial surface of the latter as the **bands of Giacomini.** Posteriorly, the dentate gyrus is continuous through the **fasciolar gyrus** below and behind the splenium with the supracallosal gyrus (Fig. 305). The fasciolar gyrus occasionally shows small elevations on its posterior surface, and these are referred to as the **gyri of Anders Retzius.**

The supracallosal gyrus and longitudinal striae. Within the supracallosal gyrus of some forms it has been possible to recognize continuations of the hippocampus, dentate gyrus, and subiculum. Such continuity exists in the brain of the human fetus and can be seen in some infant brains (363).

The medial and lateral longitudinal striae accompany the supracallosal gyrus. The medial one is also known as the **stria of Lancisi;** the lateral one, as the **taenia tecta.** The supracallosal gyrus continues around the rostrum of the corpus callosum and merges into the subcallosal gyrus wherein its cells become associated with certain septal nuclei (Figs. 139, 197, 305, 307). This last part of the supracallosal gyrus is occasionally called the anterior continuation of the hippocampus, as noted previously. Beyond the subcallosal gyrus the longitudinal striae continue as a single fascicle which passes into the diagonal band of Broca.

CYTOARCHITECTURE OF THE HIPPOCAMPAL FORMATION

In proceeding from the hippocampal gyrus to the hippocampus and dentate gyrus, one encounters several distinct zones and a gradual change occurs from a cortical pattern of six layers to one of three. The six-layered scheme of the entorhinal region is primitive, and the individual laminae are not comparable to those of the isocortex, as noted previously. In passing from entorhinal zone to hippocampus, certain entorhinal layers drop out and others are rearranged in the various zones. These zones, beginning with the entorhinal region, include (in order) the parasubicular region, presubicular region, subicular region, prosubicular region, hippocampus, and dentate gyrus. The parasubicular and prosubicular zones, especially, are

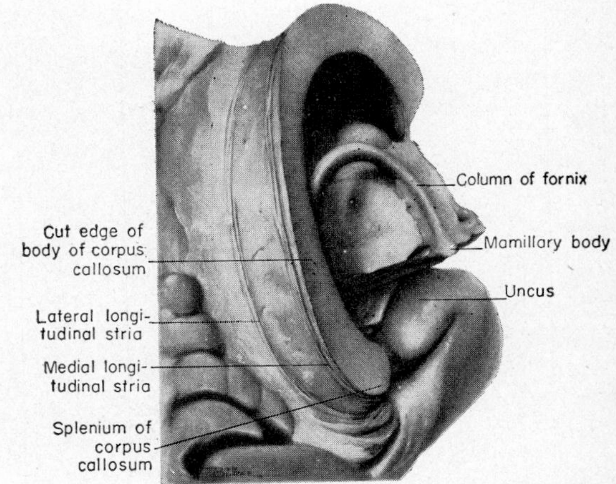

FIG. 307. Dissection to show the medial and lateral longitudinal striae on the dorsal surface of the corpus callosum.

zones of transition. The details of the finer architecture have been given by Lorente de Nó (498, 499). Only the hippocampus and dentate gyrus will be considered here.

Although the hippocampus shows three fundamental layers, the **external plexiform layer,** the **pyramidal layer,** and the **polymorphic cell layer,** several secondary laminae are formed by the arrangement of the axons and dendrites of the cells of the fundamental layers. These laminae are as follows, passing from alvear surface inward: the **stratum oriens,** the **stratum pyramidale,** the **stratum radiatum,** the **stratum lacunosum,** and the **stratum moleculare.** The last three are said to correspond to the molecular layer of the isocortex (498, 499). The hippocampus itself is divided into four zones by finer variations in intrinsic structure.

The fibers of the **alveus** arise in part in the entorhinal area and enter the hippocampus. Many others arise in the hippocampus and continue into the fornix, either as projection fibers or as commissural fibers to the opposite hippocampus. While in the alveus, collaterals arise from some of the projection and commissural axons and penetrate into the underlying hippocampal laminae. Some polymorphic cells, having migrated out from the stratum oriens, are found in the alveus.

The stratum oriens consists of fibers and polymorphic cells and is subdivided into an inferior and superior zone, the former being adjacent to the alveus. The inferior zone shows less complexity and contains fusiform or triangular cells, the dendrites of which ascend into the molecular layer and ramify within it. The superior zone contains the basal dendrites of the pyramid cells and collaterals of axons of those cells. These dendrites and axon collaterals form a plexus within this zone, and for this reason this sublayer is sometimes called the internal plexiform layer. Several varieties of cells are found in this sublayer. Some of them send their axons into the alveus, some axons ramify within the layer, and some extend into the pyramidal cell layer, which also receives some dendritic processes from those cells whose axons enter the alveus.

The pyramidal layer contains many large pyramids mixed with small pyramids and Golgi type II cells (Fig. 308). The large and small pyramids show differences in morphology and,

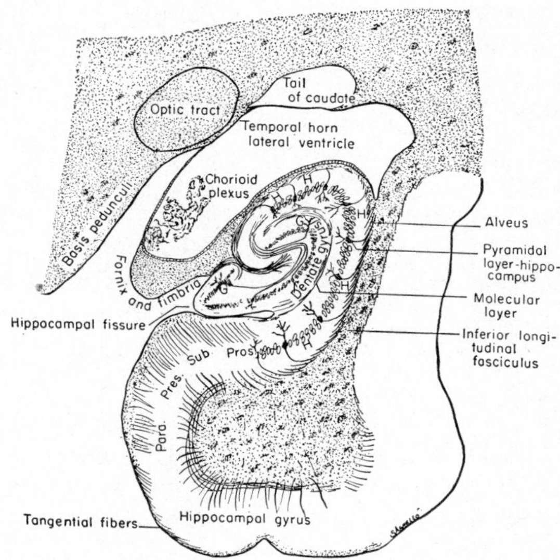

FIG. 308. Diagram for orientation of hippocampus and dentate gyrus. *G*, granule cell of dentate gyrus; *H*, hippocampus; *Para*, parasubiculum; *Pres.*, presubiculum; *Pros.*, prosubiculum; *Sub.*, subiculum.

especially, in dendritic development. Basal dendrites enter the stratum oriens to synapse with pyramidal axon collaterals there; apical dendrites enter the stratum radiatum, and some reach the molecular layer and synapse with axons of granule cells. The pyramidal axons descend through the stratum oriens wherein they give off collaterals and enter the alveus.

The stratum radiatum contains pyramidal, triangular, and fusiform cells. The axons of the pyramids enter the alveus. Axons of triangular and fusiform cells may arborize within the stratum radiatum or may enter either the stratum lacunosum or pyramidal layer to ramify. Some axon collaterals may reach either the stratum oriens or the stratum lacunosum, or even the molecular layer.

The stratum lacunosum contains many myelinated fibers and many small neurons. The fibers include collaterals from alvear axons, shorter collaterals from the axons of pyramidal cells, terminal fibers from the white substance, and terminals of certain pyramidal dendrites. The nerve cells have short ascending dendrites and descending ones which reach the stratum oriens; the axons pass in a horizontal direction and arborize within the stratum lacunosum.

The molecular, or external plexiform, layer

contains small neurons of Golgi type II and many fibers entering it from the external layer of the subiculum. Some of the fibers have traversed the cortex of the subiculum. The axons of the neurons have many branches and end within the layer.

The dentate gyrus also shows three laminae: an **outer molecular, a granular,** following the outline of a U with the open end directed toward the fimbria, and a **polymorph layer.** The molecular layer is continuous with that of the hippocampus around the depths of the hippocampal fissure. Its fibers include those entering from other regions to terminate, and dendritic processes of the granule cells below. Small cells are found superficially in the molecular layer; larger ones are more deeply placed. The axons of each type end within the layer, as do some of the dendrites, while other dendrites, especially of the deep cells, enter the granular or polymorph layers.

The granular layer is composed of small cells (Fig. 308). Their axons pass through the polymorph layer and enter the pyramidal layer of the hippocampus, wherein they end. Collaterals of the axons are given off in the granular layer and in the polymorph layer, and some turn back into the molecular layer. The granule-cell dendrites enter the molecular layer to divide and end.

The polymorph layer is thought to correspond in a general way to the layer of that name occurring elsewhere in the cerebral cortex. It contains several types of cells. So-called basket cells have radiating dendrites, and their axons pass into the molecular layer, through which they run and in which they give rise to basketlike collaterals which descend again into the granular layer. Other cells have short ascending axons, still others have short horizontal ones. Finally, modified pyramidal cells are also included in the polymorph layer. Their axons pass through the inferior part of the alveus into the fimbria and thus into the fornix (498, 499). The polymorph-layer pyramids are then the projection cells of the dentate gyrus; the granule cells can be considered as associative in that they send axons into the pyramidal layer of the hippocampus.

The **blood supply** of these olfactory structures should be mentioned. The olfactory bulb, tracts, striae, tubercle, and septal region are nourished by twigs from the anterior cerebral artery. The pyriform lobe and amygdaloid region are supplied by branches of the middle cerebral and anterior chorioidal, especially (Fig. 56). The hippocampus and dentate gyrus are supplied by the anterior chorioidal artery anteriorly and by the posterior cerebral artery posteriorly.

The Olfactory Pathways

Having completed the discussion of the various olfactory centers, it is now possible to return to the fibers of the olfactory tracts and follow them to these centers. The distribution and course of the olfactory fibers have been determined by anatomical and physiological methods. Many anatomical studies have been made in normal animal material. Other studies have utilized the Marchi and certain silver techniques in animals from which an olfactory bulb had been removed. Physiologic methods have utilized a recording of electrical potentials from various brain regions following electrical stimulation of the olfactory bulb or the introduction of odorous substances into the nasal cavity (16, 271, 344, 555, 685). Although certain differences exist in the results of the various investigators, in general, the agreement is fairly good, especially as concerns the experimental anatomical and physiological studies.

The fibers of the olfactory tracts are derived from the olfactory bulb directly and from the anterior olfactory nucleus. Certain of the axons arising in the latter nucleus pass via the anterior commissure to enter the olfactory tract and bulb of the opposite side. Certain axons arising in the olfactory bulb end in the anterior olfactory nucleus, which in turn discharges axons into the olfactory tracts. The olfactory tracts then may transmit olfactory impulses of secondary and tertiary orders. The fibers of the olfactory tracts of the human are divided into well-defined lateral and medial striae and an insignificant intermediate stria. The lateral and medial striae are accompanied by gray substance which composes lateral and medial olfactory gyri (Fig. 304). The lateral olfactory stria and gyrus runs along the lateral edge of the anterior perforated space to reach the prepyriform region. The medial olfactory stria and gyrus, less distinct macroscopically on the human brain, appears to become continuous with the cortex

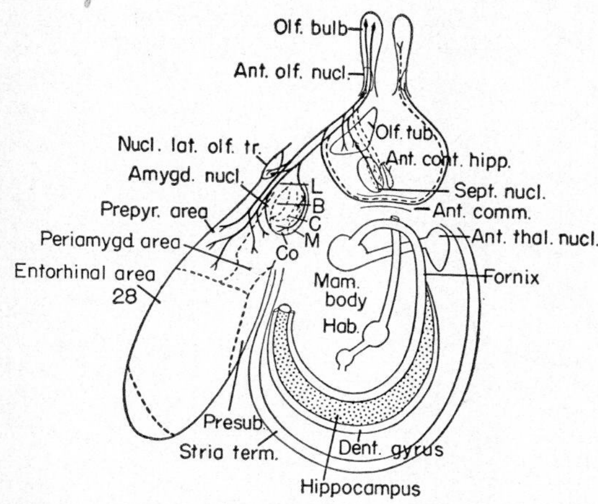

FIG. 309. The distribution of the afferent olfactory fibers from the olfactory bulb and anterior olfactory nucleus. Connections which are questionable are indicated by broken lines. *B*, basal; *C*, central; *Co*, cortical; *L*, lateral and *M* medial amygdaloid nuclei; *Ant. cont. hipp.*, anterior continuation of the hippocampus; *Prepyr. area*, prepyriform area; *Presub.*, presubiculum. (*After Brodal, Brain*, 70, *with outlines mainly after Allen, Am. J. Physiol., vol.* 128.)

of the subcallosal gyrus and parolfactory area. The intermediate stria appears to dip into the anterior perforated space. Hereafter in the discussion, its fibers will be included in the medial stria.

It appears certain that fibers of the lateral stria arising in the olfactory bulb or anterior olfactory nucleus terminate in the nucleus of the lateral olfactory tract, the medial, cortical, and central amygdaloid nuclei, the cortico-amygdaloid transition area, and the anterior part of the pyriform cortex, the prepyriform and periamygdaloid areas, in particular (101, 555). None appear to reach the entorhinal area. The fibers of the medial olfactory stria pass into the olfactory tubercle and into the anterior commissure. By way of the anterior commissure, olfactory fibers are bilaterally distributed to the nucleus of the stria terminalis and to the central amygdaloid nucleus (162). Some few medial stria fibers may pass to the septal area directly, or after a relay in the olfactory tubercle, to end in the medial septal nucleus. These were not found in the monkey (555). An insignificant number may reach the anterior continuation of the hippocampus (Fig. 309).

Since the prepyriform cortex and periamygdaloid area receive terminals of the lateral olfactory stria, they are thus considered by many authorities to be primary olfactory receptive cortex. It is of great interest that the olfactory impulses reach a cortical level without having traversed a thalamic relay, as do all other afferent impulses which reach cortical levels. The **primary olfactory cortex,** therefore, is to be found in the semilunar and in the anterior part of the ambient gyri.

These primary olfactory cortical regions send numerous axons into the entorhinal area (28) of the hippocampal gyrus. This latter region also receives many fibers from neighboring neopallial cortex. It is considered as secondary olfactory cortex, or **associative olfactory cortex,** in which olfactory impulses are integrated with other cortical impulses. The entorhinal area discharges axons via the uncinate fasciculus to the frontal lobe, and it is associated with regional temporal neopallial areas. It sends many axons into the hippocampus, and these will be discussed later.

OLFACTORY REFLEX MECHANISMS

It seems likely, therefore, that olfactory impulses gain conscious recognition via the pathways just outlined. Many olfactosomatic and olfacto-autonomic reflexes are possible, however, by other pathways that have been described.

Olfactory impulses are discharged into the olfactory tubercle, certain amygdaloid nuclei, and the nucleus of the lateral olfactory tract and possibly into the septal nuclei, directly or indirectly after a relay in the tubercle. The septal nuclei are interconnected by way of the diagonal band of Broca and its nucleus with amygdaloid nuclei. They also are said to contribute axons to the medial forebrain bundle, previously described (see Chap. 14). Furthermore, the septal nuclei contribute to the **stria medullaris thalami.** Many other nuclei also contribute to this bundle, including certain of the amygdaloid, some of those of the hypothalamus and preoptic area, the pulvinar, the globus pallidus, the nucleus of the lateral olfactory tract, and neurons in the pyriform-lobe cortex. The hippocampus may also send some axons into this tract by way of the fornix. The stria medullaris thalami fibers pass along the lateral wall of the third ventricle just below the taenia thalami (Figs. 139, 259). They end in the habenular ganglion of the same side chiefly, although some few fibers traverse the habenular commissure to end in the opposite habenular ganglion.

The **habenula** is usually described as being composed of two nuclei, a medial and a lateral (Figs. 201, 204, 210, 259). The cells of the lateral nucleus are smaller than those of the medial. On the basis of varying cell size and their arrangement, Marburg has subdivided the medial and lateral nuclei and describes five habenular nuclei in the human (530). Marburg described each of these nuclei as being in connection with a special fiber tract.

Olfactory impulses may reach the habenula via the stria medullaris thalami from the olfactory tubercle, septal nuclei, nucleus of the lateral olfactory tract, amygdaloid nuclei, and pyriform cortex and perhaps from the hippocampus. The nature of the impulses from the hippocampus may not be olfactory in type, however. Impulses of other nature reaching the habenula via the stria medullaris thalami come from the globus pallidus, hypothalamus, and pulvinar. The habenula is also interconnected with the tectum. By way of its connections with the tectum, the habenula may receive impulses of somatic sensory, auditory, and visual nature. The habenula would appear to be chiefly, therefore, an olfactosomatic correlation center. Some axons of the stria medullaris thalami pass over the habenular commissure to end in the opposite habenula. Interhabenular fibers also compose the commissure.

The chief efferent tract from the habenula is the **habenulopeduncular tract,** or the fasciculus retroflexus of Meynert (Figs. 201, 204). This bundle also includes axons from the **nucleus of the habenulopeduncular tract** located just ventral to the habenular groups, and some fibers from the pulvinar. The **interpeduncular nucleus** receives practically all the fibers of the habenulopeduncular tract (Figs. 137, 148). This nucleus extends from levels through the caudal third of the oculomotor nucleus to the pons. Its rostral part is just ventral to the ventral tegmental decussation. The emerging oculomotor roots and the substantia nigra are on its lateral border rostrally. The cells of the interpeduncular nucleus are both small and large, and they appear very pale in Nissl preparations. The interpeduncular nucleus discharges into certain reticular nuclei of the brain stem tegmentum, and especially into the **dorsal tegmental nucleus.** From this latter nucleus axons enter the **dorsal longitudinal fasciculus of Schütz,** and by way of this tract impulses may enter brain stem nuclei concerned with somatic and visceral activity. Olfactosomatic and olfactovisceral reflexes are then possible by these relays just outlined.

Another reflex relay system may involve the following centers. The septal nuclei and olfactory tubercle contribute axons to the medial forebrain bundle, as noted previously. This bundle courses posteriorly through the lateral preoptic and lateral hypothalamic areas to reach the midbrain tegmentum, at least, and it includes ascending as well as descending fibers. Olfactory impulses from the olfactory tubercle and septal nuclei, transmitted by way of this tract and its collaterals, may be brought into relation with the preoptic nucleus, with certain tuberal hypothalamic nuclei, with the mamillary nuclei, with certain extrapyramidal nuclei, and finally with reticular, autonomic, and somatic motor nuclei of the brain stem. The hypothalamic interrelations may afford integration of olfactory impulses with other visceral impulses from lower centers which reach the hypothalamus by way of ascending fibers of the medial forebrain bundle and by way of the mamillary peduncle.

Another link in the olfactory reflex paths may be afforded by way of the **stria terminalis** (Figs. 144, 202, 206). This tract appears to arise from the amygdaloid nuclei. The axons come especially from the basal nuclei, but also perhaps from the medial, cortical, and central amygdaloid nucleus as well (269). They follow the tail of the caudate nucleus as it runs in the roof of the inferior horn of the lateral ventricle. Visible grossly, they form a longitudinal cordlike elevation as they run in the sulcus between the caudate nucleus and the thalamus, dorsally. The fibers of the stria terminalis have been described as terminating in the septal region, in the preoptic area, and in the paraventricular nucleus of the hypothalamus. Some fibers are also said to enter the stria medullaris thalami, but such were not found in the cat (269). By way of the stria terminalis, it is possible, therefore, for olfactory nuclei again to play into those regions from which the medial forebrain bundle arises and, by this latter bundle, to be relayed to brain stem motor centers.

THE ANTERIOR COMMISSURE

A brief description of the anterior commissure is pertinent here, since it is in part concerned with olfactory connections. It is an old structure phylogenetically. As it crosses the median plane in the lamina terminalis, it is just rostral to the columns of the fornix, and it appears as a compact, oval bundle of fibers (Figs. 47, 305). Laterally, within the hemispheres it fans out, and two component parts, or anterior and posterior limbs, may be observed. On the basis of studies in animals the commissure is said to contain fibers interconnecting not only the olfactory bulbs and rhinencephalic areas but also certain neopallial regions (Fig. 313). Fibers have been described in the rat interconnecting the anterior olfactory nuclei (the "bulbar" component), the olfactory tubercles, all the pyriform cortex, the entorhinal areas, the bed nuclei of the stria terminalis, the nuclei of the basal amygdaloid nuclei, the cortico-amygdaloid transition areas, and certain neopallial regions (102).

The anterior limb of the commissure in the macaque contains fibers passing between the anterior olfactory nuclei and the olfactory tubercles (270). The posterior limb contains fibers interconnecting middle temporal gyri and probably also the inferior temporal gyri or the amygdaloid nuclei and hippocampal gyri. The middle and inferior temporal gyri, in the chimpanzee, also appear to be interconnected by way of the anterior commissure (50). Interstriatal fibers may also be present in the commissure.

THE CONNECTIONS OF THE HIPPOCAMPUS

If the entorhinal area serves as associative olfactory cortex, a different function must be served by the hippocampus, which heretofore—albeit without adequate justification, perhaps—has been considered to be olfactory cortex. Such an assumption has been based on its *supposed* reception of olfactory impulses from the olfactory bulb. A summary of its known fiber connections reveals three sources of **afferent** fibers to the hippocampus in addition to its commissural connections via the commissure of the fornix (Fig. 311). These include fibers reaching it from the supracallosal gyrus and striae, from the cingular gyrus, and from the entorhinal area. The fibers from the cingular gyrus presumably come from the posterior part of that gyrus only and end in the subiculum and hippocampus. The fibers reaching the hippocampus via the supracallosal striae are derived from neurons in the posterior portion of that gyrus only, and they enter the dentate gyrus and the hippocampus. It seems unlikely that the fibers of these two sources transmit olfactory impulses, since neither the cingular gyrus nor the supracallosal gyrus has been shown conclusively to be recipient of olfactory impulses from the olfactory bulbs. The direct connections of the medial olfactory stria with the septal nuclei have been questioned.

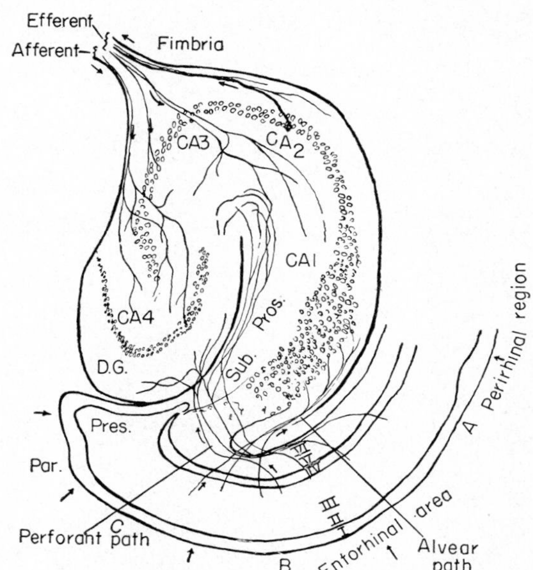

FIG. 310. The alvear and perforant paths entering the hippocampus. The fibers entering and leaving via the fimbria and hippocampal commissure are also included. The arrows *outside* the figure serve to divide the entorhinal area into three parts, *A*, *B*, *C*. The arrows *inside* the figure indicate direction of impulses. The four regions of the hippocampus are indicated *CA* 1 to 4. *D.G.*, dentate gyrus; *Par*, parasubiculum; *Pres.*, presubiculum; *Pros.*, prosubiculum; *Sub.*, subiculum. (*Modified after Lorente de Nó.*)

The entorhinal area sends many axons via the subiculum to the hippocampus and dentate gyrus. The entorhinal-hippocampal connections have been described in some detail by Cajal and Lorente de Nó (499, 644). Fibers from the

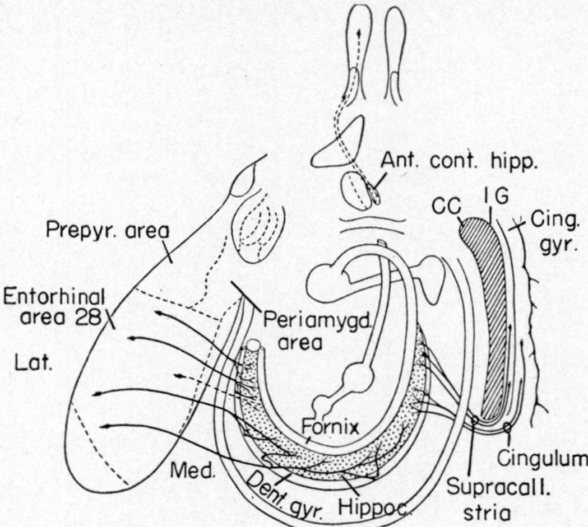

Fig. 311. The afferent paths to the hippocampus. *Ant. cont. hipp.*, anterior continuation of hippocampus; *CC*, corpus callosum; *Cing. gyr.*, cingular gyrus; *Hippoc.*, hippocampus; *IG*, indusium griseum; *Periamygd. area*, periamygdaloid area; *Prepyr. area*, prepyriform area; *Supracall. stria*, supracallosal stria. (*After Brodal, Brain, vol.* 70.)

medial part of the entorhinal area are distributed to the prosubiculum only and probably to the adjacent sector of the hippocampus. They constitute the **alvear path** (Fig. 310). Fibers from the lateral part of the entorhinal area constituting the **perforant path** traverse the external part of the subiculum to which they give collaterals. They continue into the molecular layer of the hippocampus and distribute to all hippocampal sectors except that portion adjacent the dentate gyrus. They also are distributed to the dentate gyrus, and possibly through it, to that hippocampus sector which does not receive them directly. It seems unlikely, on the basis of its afferent connections, that the hippocampus receives a significant number of olfactory impulses directly, or that its function is primarily concerned with olfaction. This will be discussed more fully below.

It seems most likely that the **fornix** represents the chief, if not the only, **efferent** path from the hippocampus, and it also appears likely that the fibers of the fornix are only efferent in type in relation to the hippocampus (26) (Fig. 312). On the basis of chromatolysis after section of the fornix in dogs, Allen reported that the fornix axons spring from the pyramidal cells of the hippocampus and from certain pyramidal cells of the polymorphic layer of the dentate gyrus. Axons arising in the prosubiculum have also been traced into the fornix (499). The major terminus of the fornix projection fibers is the homolateral medial mamillary nucleus. A few fibers from the fornix have been said to be distributed to each of the following: septal nuclei, nucleus of diagonal band, preoptic area, habenula, and rostral hypothalamic nuclei. Some axons arising in the hippocampus pass dorsal to the splenium of the corpus callosum in company with the striae of Lancisi. Certain of these penetrate the anterior portion of the corpus callosum, join fibers of the fornix, and distribute anteriorly to the anterior commissure to the septal region, nucleus of diagonal band, and perhaps to the preoptic area. This part of the fornix distributing anterior to the anterior commissure is called precommissural. Fornix fibers entering the anterior hypothalamus and mamillary nuclei are joined by axons penetrating the corpus callosum also. Fibers leaving the fornix

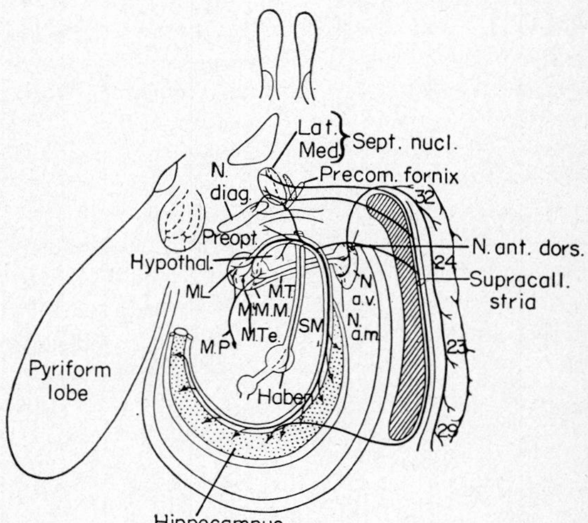

Fig. 312. Diagram to show efferent connections of the hippocampus and certain mamillary projections. *Haben.*, habenular nucleus; *ML*, lateral mamillary nucleus; *M.M.M.*, medial part of medial mamillary nucleus; *M.P.*, mamillary peduncle; *M.T.*, mamillothalamic tract; *M.Te.*, mamillotegmental tract; *N.a.m.*, anteromedial nucleus; *N.a.v.*, anteroventral nucleus of thalamus; *N. ant. dors.*, anterodorsal nucleus of thalamus; *N. diag.*, nucleus of diagonal band; *Precom. fornix*, precommissural fornix; *Preopt.*, preoptic area; *SM*, stria medullaris thalami; *Supracall. stria*, supracallosal stria. (*After Brodal, Brain, vol.* 70.)

are said to enter the stria medullaris thalami to reach the medial habenular nucleus (530).

Precommissural fornix fibers have been described as crossing the mid-line to end in septal, preoptic, and anterior hypothalamic nuclei. It seems likely that the relation between the hippocampus and mamillary nucleus and habenula is an uncrossed one, and that the hippocampus of one hemisphere can influence the septal area, preoptic area, and anterior hypothalamus of each side (101). Exact details of the relations between hippocampus and these various nuclei are lacking. The fornix also contains commissural fibers passing between the two hippocampi, and the majority of these cross in the commissure of the fornix, or **psalterium** (Fig. 305).

By way of its projections to the basal ventromedial nuclei and to the habenula, the hippocampus can influence the olfactory reflex mechanisms outlined previously. Other spheres of influence are admitted to it by way of the mamillary nuclei. These nuclei contribute many axons to the anterior nuclei of the thalamus by way of the mamillothalamic tract (see Chap. 14 and Figs. 199, 203, 210). Although each of the three divisions of the anterior thalamic nucleus receives mamillothalamic fibers, the anteroventral receives the major portion. The anteroventral thalamic nucleus, which shows a progressive development phylogenetically, makes up practically all of the anterior thalamic nuclei in man (777). The anterodorsal and anteromedial are quite reduced in size comparatively. The projections from the anterior thalamic nuclei are chiefly to the cingular gyrus, and an orderly projection has been described. The anteromedial nucleus projects to the anterior part of the cingular gyrus, to area 32 (160). The anteroventral nucleus projects chiefly to areas 23 and 24, and the anterodorsal nucleus, to the retrosplenial portion of the cingular gyrus, or area 29 (Fig. 264). Less complete projections have been reported in man (see Chap. 18). The cingular gyrus, at least its posterior part, projects in turn into the hippocampus and a closed circuit is thus formed (101). Area 24 of the cingular gyrus, as judged by physiological neuronography, projects to the caudate nucleus, to the bulbar inhibitory center, and also to area 32 (507, 816). By way of this projection to the caudate nucleus and to the reticular inhibitory

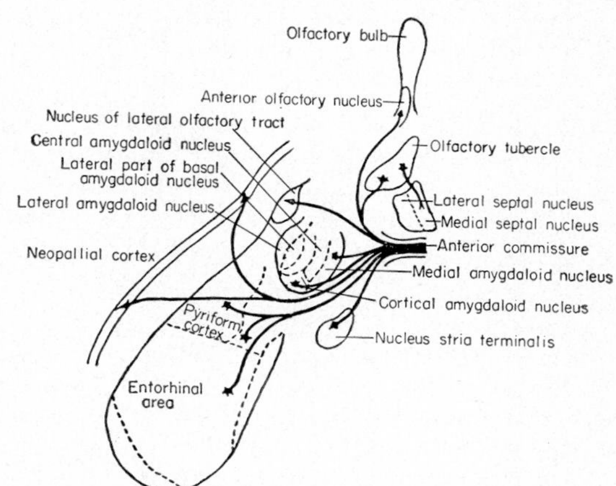

Fig. 313. Diagram of the components of the anterior commissure. (*After Brodal, J. Comp. Neurol., vol.* 88.)

center, the hippocampus may indirectly influence motor activity. Through its hypothalamic connections the hippocampus may also be related with the dorsomedial nucleus of the thalamus and, through this nucleus, with the prefrontal region.

By way of mamillotegmental connections to midbrain reticular nuclei, the hippocampus may also influence brain stem centers. It seems likely that hippocampal influence may be exerted even at a spinal level, since it would appear from transection experiments that descending hypothalamic projections are relayed spinalward by both the medial forebrain bundle and mamillotegmental connections.

Stimulation and Ablation Studies on the Olfactory Centers and Hippocampus

In efforts to learn something of the function of the olfactory centers, a variety of experiments has been performed. Some have involved stimulation of the olfactory regions in animals deprived of much of their neopallial tissue. Others have been concerned with a study of conditioned reflexes involving olfaction in animals with various parts of the neocortex and olfactory centers destroyed. Others have been concerned with behavioral and emotional change consequent to damage of tissue usually believed to be concerned with olfactory activity.

In cats from which neocortex had been removed, leaving only striatum, thalamus, and rhinencephalon intact, the basal olfactory areas and the pyriform lobe were stimulated (676). Sniffing, biting, chewing, licking, swallowing, and salivation were evoked, particularly from the pyriform lobe. It was assumed, therefore, that the feeding reflexes associated with olfaction are mediated through these basal olfactory areas and, especially, the pyriform lobe. It is worthy of note that the cingular gyrus was removed in these animals. If the hippocampus is involved in such reactions, its activity is not expressed through ths gyrus. Elevation of blood pressure and respiratory arrest have been produced by stimulating the uncus in the macaque (421).

In his olfaction studies with dogs, in which he applied the method of conditioned reflexes, Allen concluded that the olfactory discrimination necessary for a correct performance of his tests did not depend on the integrity of the hippocampus and fornix system. The pyriform-amygdaloid areas appeared to be in part essential for the necessary olfactory discrimination ability. Even if these areas were destroyed, however, the dogs retained a conditioned response to clove vapor, and they were able to select a packet of meat from a collection of packets containing nonfood articles. Lower olfactory centers appear to be involved also in these reactions. Bilateral frontal lobectomy interfered with the acquisition of olfactory reflexes involving the foreleg. The establishment of a negative conditioned response to asafetida and a conditioned differentiation, which involved a decision in 7 sec. whether to respond positively to cloves or negatively to asafetida, was prevented also by bilateral frontal ablation (24, 25). Bilateral removal of parietal, occipital, and temporal lobes (exclusive of hippocampi and pyriform areas) or removal of 90 to 100 per cent of the hippocampi did not alter the establishment of such reactions.

It has been observed that **sham rage** reactions could be induced in cats from which the forebrain had been removed, and it has been said that the reactions occurred in animals in which a frontal-lobe inhibition of the hypothalamus had been removed. In rage reactions it appeared that a generalized overactivity of sympathetic innervations occurred, and it was observed that such phenomena could be induced so long as the posterior hypothalamus was intact (54). Cats with bilateral lesions in the base of the frontal lobes just above the chiasma can also show "sham" rage (283). The effective lesion here may have been destruction of the olfactory tubercles. Spiegel and his coauthors were able to evoke sham rage in cats consequent to bilateral destruction of the olfactory tubercles or amygdaloid nuclei (746). In a reinvestigation of the experimental production of rage, Bard and Mountcastle have advanced some new ideas. In their recent analysis, they state that the production of rage reactions does not depend only on the removal of neocortex (58). They find that removal of neocortex leads to a state of placidity, if certain parts of the rhinencephalon and at least a part of the cingular gyrus is spared. They feel that some of these structures, when spared, inhibit the brain stem mechanisms concerned in the expression of anger. If the amygdaloid complex and pyriform lobe were removed bilaterally from a placid animal, a state of ferocity followed. It was reasoned that normally inhibitory influences originating in transitional cortex, such as that of the cingular gyrus, in the neocortex, and in the amygdaloid complex suppress the mechanisms underlying rage activity. They think that this inhibitory activity is expressed through the amygdaloid complex, and they further suspect that facilitatory activities arising in the neocortex are expressed through connections that do not involve the amygdaloid complex.

Of interest, in line with the above analysis, are the observations of Klüver and Bucy in monkeys from which both temporal lobes were removed (439). It seems likely that the amygdaloid complex would have been damaged in these removals. In these animals, usually quite wild and normally combative before operation, a tameness appeared. They showed a loss of certain natural fears for objects and reptiles. An increase in sexual activity, usually in the direction of perversions, was noted. It seems likely that these behavioral and emotional changes were related to the removal of the two hippocampi or of the temporal poles. It was also noted that these monkeys had a psychic visual blindness. They showed an increasing curiosity in visible objects and examined them orally repeatedly. They seemed unable to recognize the objects either by vision or by touch. The ablations involved perhaps also the visual associative areas, and this fact may have accounted for the visual disorder. That the removal of the hippocampus may have been related to the emotional change is suggested by extirpations from the temporal lobe in humans (51). In these latter removals the insula and hippocampus were spared, and the patients did not show changes comparable to those observed in the monkey.

Recently Thomson and Walker have investigated the behavioral effects in monkeys consequent to bilateral destruction of the amygdaloid nuclei, uncus, or hippocampi (775). For 4 or 5 months after the operations, some of their monkeys were tame, fearless, and asocial. They felt that the amygdaloid destruction was the significant lesion.

It may be true that the function of the hippocampus is not exactly the same in one species as it is in another. Allen reports that he did not observe any emotional changes in dogs from which he had removed the hippocampus or sectioned the fornix bilaterally (27). He feels that the hippocampus serves as an amplification mechanism for simpler olfactory reflexes, and in contrast to other investigators, he has been able to elicit respiratory, visceral, and muscular activity in dogs by stimulating the hippocampus with strong electrical or chemical stimuli. The stimulation of the hippocampus in man is without obvious response, while stimulation of the olfactory bulb elicits olfactory sensation (616).

The "uncinate" fits described clinically and mentioned previously in other chapters have been correlated with irritative phenomena in the vicinity of the uncus and hippocampal gyrus. In a complete form they may involve gustatory and olfactory hallucinatory experiences, smacking of the lips, and a dreamlike mental state. They do not appear to rise from irritation of the hippocampus, nor do all these symptoms mentioned arise from irritation of uncus and hippocampal gyrus. Taste appears to be represented cortically in the parietal operculum adjacent the insula, and the gustatory hallucinations probably arise from spread of irritation to this neighboring region. The dreamlike state presumably arises from activity in nonauditory and nonolfactory temporal regions.

The Function of the Olfactory System and the Hippocampus

In following the differentiation of the cerebral cortex, it has been noted that the olfactory system plays a dominant part in the lower animal scale. In the primates the olfactory system is reduced to a subordinate position. The organ of smell is described by Herrick as an exteroceptor and an interoceptor (358). The central connections for its interoceptive function are associated with the other neural mechanisms of feeding, nutrition, and reproduction. The pattern of these subcortical connections is similar and quite constant throughout the entire vertebrate scale. The exteroceptive function of the organ of smell is more important, since it warns of potentially harmful substances and enemies. It also guides the animal to mates and food. These exteroceptive functions are well performed in spite of a lack of any localization capacity of the olfactory sense. Other exteroceptors aid in the localization of olfactory stimuli. The olfactory sense can only evaluate the quality and intensity of odors. The reactions to these odors are only in small measure specific olfactory reflexes. To a much greater degree the reactions are expressed over effector mechanisms common to olfactory and other sensory systems. The responses depend on the combined action and may embody feeding, mating, or avoiding patterns. These responses result chiefly from subcortical activities. The olfactory system is associated with nonolfactory cortical regions by many association fibers, and these relations are present also in animals which have no peripheral olfactory apparatus. Olfactory impulses may therefore influence the activity of nonolfactory cortical regions in animals possessing a peripheral olfactory apparatus. In addition to its interoceptive functions, the olfactory system serves as an activator or sensitizer of the nervous system as a whole and, especially, of certain sensorimotor systems simultaneously influenced by other exteroceptors. The threshold of excitability may thus be lowered for all stimuli and specific types of response may be facilitated or suppressed (358).

In certain anosmic animals, such as the dolphin, which have no peripheral olfactory apparatus, the hippocampal cortex is well differentiated. Its function in these species and also in microsmatic man, in which it is also well developed, is not readily apparent. Furthermore, as noted above, it seems unlikely that the hippocampus is primarily directly concerned with an olfactory function, if its fiber connections are considered. Significant numbers of olfactory impulses appear to reach it only from the entorhinal area, which appears to be an olfactory associative region. Structurally, the hippocampus appears to be an effector region, and its large projection bundle passes to septal region, preoptic area, rostral hypothalamus, epithalamus, and mamillary region of the hypothalamus. Certain of these regions, habenula, septal nuclei, and mamillary nuclei, by way of their projections, can activate effector systems for the completion of pure olfactory reflexes and other more complex sensorimotor behavior. Others of these regions, preoptic area and hypothalamus, are concerned with autonomic activity. Finally, others of these hippocampal projection regions, hypothalamus and mamillary nuclei, are related by numerous fibers to thalamic nuclei, in turn related to the cerebral cortex. The dorsomedial nucleus, for example, receives many fibers from the hypothalamus and projects to prefrontal cortex; the anterior thalamic nuclei receive many fibers from the mamillary nuclei and project to the cingular gyrus. These are, in fact, closed circuits, since the cortical regions send fibers to the thalamic nuclei also.

It has been noted earlier that destruction of the hippocampi or section of the fornix bilaterally does not interfere with olfactory discrimination. Nor does bilateral degeneration of the anterior thalamic nuclei in rats interfere with olfactory discrimination (470). It is seldom that brain disease is so discretely localized as to destroy only the hippocampus. It is not possible, therefore, to state that olfactory disorder will arise from a hippocampal lesion, nor is it possible to localize accurately the site of an expected disorder that would produce a gnostic disturbance of smell. Cellular degeneration, due presumably to vascular disturbance, is relatively common in the hippocampus in a variety of intracranial disorders. Reports of olfactory disturbance in such cases are, however, very rare. Finally, histological alterations of the mamillary bodies (and other hypothalamic regions) occur clinically in nutritional deficiency states, and the patients may demonstrate alterations of consciousness, delirium, or amnesia, and confabulations (111). It would appear likely, therefore, that the hippocampus and anterior thalamic nuclei are not primarily concerned with olfaction alone, even though the former, through some of its connections, may be able to influence reflex activity initiated by olfactory and other exteroceptive impulses.

The results of studies involving either stimulation or ablation of the prefronto-orbital and cingular cortex suggest that these regions may be concerned in the control of emotional activity. Prefrontal activity appears to bestow on the individual the ability to anticipate and plan, and orbital cortex would appear able to summon into activity the visceral mechanisms necessary for the performance of the planned somatic motor response. The cingular gyrus, or at least a portion of it, area 24, is a strong suppressor of somatic motor activity under certain conditions and also appears to exert some influence on autonomic innervations. When it is destroyed experimentally, certain behavioral changes are noted (see Chap. 18). When it is the site of disease process, the patient may show disorders of affect (791, 817). Similarly, experimental destruction of the hippocampi or of the amygdaloid complex bilaterally in some species is followed by behavioral change. These cortical regions, orbital, cingular, and hippocampal, together with uncus, prepyriform area, and insula constitute a large circle of cortex interconnected by fiber systems and described histologically as being of transitional or primitive (allocortex) type. Each of them is perhaps also connected directly or indirectly with the hypothalamus. Although knowledge of their afferent connections is not as yet complete, it would appear justified to suspect that they have certain functional interrelationships. These functional interrelationships may subserve the cortical control of autonomic activity and especially of that autonomic activity underlying emotional reactions (518, 593).

The Examination of the Sense of Smell

It is not often in neurological examination that a measurement of olfactory ability is pertinent to the diagnosis. And yet, proof of some disorder of olfaction has aided in certain regional diagnoses. It usually suffices to test the patient's ability, through one nostril at the time, to perceive one or several test odors. The value of such tests is minimized if the patient has a cold or some local nasal disorder. Quantitative tests of the smell function have been devised by Elsberg and his colleagues

(239, 240, 241). In these tests a measured amount of a test odor is discharged into one nostril at the time, with the patient holding his breath at the moment. The least amount of the test odor required for recognition is denoted as the **minimal identifiable odor** (M.I.O.). After this has been established, a continuous stream of the odor is continued for 30 sec., or until fatigue sets in. The nostril is tested at 30-sec. intervals afterward with the M.I.O. in order to measure the duration of fatigue.

Using this test and correlating its results with the subsequently proved disorder, Elsberg and his colleagues felt it was useful in the localization of intracranial disorder. Diseases of the olfactory bulb or compression of the tract are associated with an increase in the M.I.O. in the nostril on that side (239, 240). More test substance is required for recognition. In intracerebral tumors the M.I.O. is normal, but the duration of fatigue is increased in the nostril of the diseased side, and with tumors near the mid-line, fatigue may persist for more than 10 min. Olfactory fatigue appears to be related to cortical activity. If a frontal-lobe tumor causes pressure on an olfactory tract also, there will be an increase both in the M.I.O. and in the duration of fatigue in the nostril on the side of the tumor. This applies to supratentorial tumors, especially, and the results of the tests are more accurate in tumors in, or about, the frontal or temporal lobe (752). These tests have not had the wide application they perhaps deserve.

An interesting observation has been made with reference to a transference of an olfactory stimulus to the other nostril (751). The Elsberg tests were used in a series of 12 patients later proved to have a unilateral cerebral tumor. After the establishment of the M.I.O., fatigue was induced, and the M.I.O. was then used at intervals. It was observed that although the substance was not perceived on the fatigued side, it was "transferred" to the opposite side and perceived there as if the test substance had actually been discharged into that nostril. It was demonstrated that in 9 of the 12 cases the odor was "transferred" from the nostril on the side of the cerebral tumor to the nostril on the sound side. Such a transference of stimuli from one side to the other has been referred to as **olfactory allesthesia,** and this phenomenon has been observed in unilateral disease involving somatic sensory, auditory, and visual paths as well.

Neurological Conditions Associated with Disorders of Olfaction

It has been shown that patients with the neurological complications of pernicious anemia are often anosmic (694). This is probably a manifestation of a peripheral neuropathy. Brain tumors, especially meningiomata, growing in the floor of the frontal fossa or along the sphenoidal ridge, are apt to compress an olfactory tract or its related structures. Aneurysms of the internal carotid or anterior cerebral arteries may compress the olfactory tracts, as may suprasellar tumors. Unilateral neoplasms involving the basal part of the frontal lobe or the rostromedial region of the temporal may be associated with complete anosmia, or with ipsilateral disorder only.

"Uncinate" fits are occasionally observed as a manifestation of irritation of the mediobasal part of the temporal lobe. The incidence of such fits in temporal-lobe disorders in general is not great. In patients who do suffer them, the site of irritation has usually been found to involve the uncus and immediately adjacent regions. It may be true, therefore, that the olfactory hallucinations result from the irritation of either the primary olfactory cortex or the entorhinal area. The smacking of the lips and the movements of the tongue and jaw associated with uncinate attacks may be related to spread of stimulation to subcortical reflex mechanisms from the uncus region. The dreamy state occasionally associated with the uncinate attack perhaps results from a spread of irritation to the middle and inferior temporal gyri or to the basal frontal region via the uncinate fasciculus.

BIBLIOGRAPHY

1. Abbie, A. A., 1933, The clinical significance of the anterior choroidial artery, *Brain,* **56**, 233–246.
2. Abbie, A. A., 1934, The morphology of the fore-brain arteries, with especial reference to the evolution of the basal ganglia, *J. Anat.,* **68**, 433–470.
3. Abd-el-Malek, Shafik, 1938, On the presence of sensory fibers in the ocular nerves, *J. Anat.,* **72**, 524–530.
4. Ackerly, S. Spafford, and Arthur L. Benton, 1948, Report of case of bilateral frontal lobe defect, *Research Publ., A. Nerv. & Ment. Dis.,* **27**, 479–504.
5. Adams, W. E., 1942, The blood supply of nerves. I. Historical review, *J. Anat.,* **76**, 323–341; II. The effects of exclusion of its regional source of supply on the sciatic nerve of rabbits, *J. Anat.,* **77**, 243–250.
6. Ades, H. W., 1943, A secondary acoustic area in the cerebral cortex of the cat, *J. Neurophysiol.,* **6**, 59–64.
7. Ades, H. W., and J. M. Brookhart, 1950, The central auditory pathway, *J. Neurophysiol.,* **13**, 189–205.
8. Ades, H. W., and R. Felder, 1942, The acoustic area of the monkey (*Macaca mulatta*), *J. Neurophysiol.,* **5**, 49–54.
9. Ades, H. W., and David Raab, 1946, Recovery of motor function after two-stage extirpation of area 4 in monkeys, *J. Neurophysiol.,* **9**, 55–60.
10. Ades, H. W., and David Raab, 1949, Effect of pre-occipital and temporal decortication on learned visual discrimination in monkeys, *J. Neurophysiol.,* **12**, 101–108.
11. Adler, Alexandra, 1933, Zur Topik des Verlaufes der Geschmackssinnsfasern und anderer afferenter Bahnen im Thalimus, *Ztscher. f. d. ges. Neurol. u. Psychiat.,* **149**, 208–220.
12. Adler, F. H., W. J. McNally, E. A. Stuart, and B. J. Alpers, 1941, Symposium on vertigo, *Tr. Am. Acad. Ophth.,* **46**, 33–54.
13. Adrian, E. D., 1928, "The Basis of Sensation. The Action of the Sense Organs," New York, Norton, 122 pp.
14. Adrian, E. D., 1935, "The Mechanism of Nervous Action. Electrical Studies of the Neuron," New York, Oxford, x + 103 pp.
15. Adrian, E. D., 1940, Double representation of the feet in the sensory cortex of the cat, *J. Physiol.,* **98**, 16P–18P.
16. Adrian, E. D., 1942, Olfactory reactions in the brain of hedgehog, *J. Physiol.,* **100**, 459–473.
17. Adrian, E. D., 1943, Afferent areas in the cerebellum connected with the limbs, *Brain,* **66**, 289–315.
18. Adrian, E. D., and B. H. C. Matthews, 1934, The Berger rhythm: Potential changes from the occipital lobes in man, *Brain,* **57**, 355–385.
19. Adson, Alfred W., 1924, The surgical treatment of glossopharyngeal neuralgia, *Arch. Neurol. & Psychiat.,* **12**, 487–506.
20. Akelaitis, A. J., 1941, Studies on the corpus callosum; Higher visual functions in each homonymous field following complete section of the corpus callosum, *Arch. Neurol. & Psychiat.,* **45**, 788–796.
21. Alexander, L., 1942, The vascular supply of the striopallidum, *Research Publ., A. Nerv. & Ment. Dis.,* 21, 77–132.
22. Alexander, L., and T. H. Suh, 1937, Arterial supply of lateral parolivary area of the medulla oblongata in man, *Arch. Neurol. & Psychiat.,* **38**, 1243–1260.
23. Alexander, W. F., 1940, The innervation of the biliary system, *J. Comp. Neurol.,* **72**, 357–370.
24. Allen, W. F., 1940, Effect of ablating the frontal lobes, hippocampi, and occipito-parieto-temporal (excepting pyriform areas) lobes on positive and negative olfactory conditioned reflexes, *Am. J. Physiol.,* **128**, 754–771.
25. Allen, W. F., 1941, Effect of ablating the pyriform-amygdaloid areas and hippocampi on positive and negative olfactory conditioned reflexes and on conditioned olfactory differentiation, *Am. J. Physiol.,* **132**, 81–92.
26. Allen, W. F., 1944, Degeneration in the dog's mammillary body and Ammon's horn following transection of the fornix, *J. Comp. Neurol.,* **80**, 283–291.
27. Allen, W. F., 1948, Fiber degeneration in Ammon's horn resulting from extirpations of the

pyriform and other cortical areas and from transection of the horn at various levels, *J. Comp. Neurol.*, **88**, 425–438.

28. Alpers, B. J., 1940, Personality and emotional disorders associated with hypothalamic lesions, *Research Publ., A. Nerv. & Ment. Dis.*, **20**, 725–752.
29. Anderson, Manuel, 1946, Diuresis by suggestion, *Brit. M. J.*, **1**, 776.
30. Andrew, Warren, and C. T. Ashworth, 1945, The adendroglia, *J. Comp. Neurol.*, **82**, 101–127.
31. Angulo y González, A. W., 1929, Is myelogeny an absolute index of behavorial capacity? *J. Comp. Neurol.*, **48**, 459–464.
32. Angulo y González, A. W., 1939, Histogenesis of the monopolar neuroblast and the ventral longitudinal path in the albino rat, *J. Comp. Neurol.*, **71**, 325–360.
33. Angulo y González, A. W., 1940, The differentiation of the motor cell columns in the cervical cord of albino rat fetuses, *J. Comp. Neurol.*, **73**, 469–488.
34. Anrep, G. V., and H. N. Segall, 1926, The regulation of the coronary circulation, *Heart*, **13**, 239–260.
35. Anson, B. J., and J. P. Nesselrod, 1936, Endolymphatic and associated ducts in man, *Arch. Otolaryng.*, **24**, 127–140.
36. Apter, Julia T., 1945, Projection of the retina on superior colliculus of cats, *J. Neurophysiol.*, **8**, 123–134.
37. Apter, Julia T., 1946, Eye movements following strychninization of the superior colliculus of cats, *J. Neurophysiol.*, **9**, 73–86.
38. Arey, L. B., 1937, The numerical relation of retinal ganglion cells to optic nerve fibers in vertebrates, *Anat. Rec.*, **70**, Suppl. 1, 85.
39. Atkinson, W. J., 1949, The anterior inferior cerebellar artery. Its variations, pontine distribution, and significance in the surgery of cerebello-pontine angle tumors, *J. Neurol., Neurosurg. & Psychiat.*, N.S. **12**, 137–151.
40. Babkin, B. P., and T. J. Speakman, 1950, Cortical inhibition of gastric motility, *J. Neurophysiol.*, **13**, 55–63.
41. Bach, L. M. N., and H. W. Magoun, 1947, The vestibular nuclei as an excitatory mechanism for the cord, *J. Neurophysiol.*, **10**, 331–337.
42. Bailey, P., 1942, Reflections aroused by an unusual tumor of the cerebellum, *J. Mt. Sinai Hosp.*, **9**, 299–310.
43. Bailey, P., 1948, "Intracranial Tumors," Springfield, Ill., Charles C Thomas, xxiv + 478 pp.
44. Bailey, P., 1948, Concerning cytoarchitecture of the frontal lobe of chimpanzee (*Pan satyrus*) and man (*Homo sapiens*), *Research Publ., A. Nerv. & Ment. Dis.*, **27**, 84–94.
45. Bailey, P., G. von Bonin, E. W. Davis, H. W. Garol, and W. S. McCulloch, 1944, Further observations on associational pathways in the brain of *Macaca mulatta, J. Neuropath. & Exper. Neurol.*, **3**, 413–415.
46. Bailey, P., G. von Bonin, E. W. Davis, H. W. Garol, W. S. McCulloch, E. Roseman, and A. Silveira, 1944, Functional organization of the medial aspect of the primate cortex, *J. Neurophysiol.*, **7**, 51–55.
47. Bailey, P., G. von Bonin, H. W. Garol, and W. S. McCulloch, 1943, Functional organization of temporal lobe of monkey (*Macaca mulatta*) and chimpanzee (*Pan satyrus*), *J. Neurophysiol.*, **6**, 121–128.
48. Bailey, P., G. von Bonin, H. W. Garol, and W. S. McCulloch, 1943, Long association fibers in cerebral hemispheres of monkey and chimpanzee, *J. Neurophysiol.*, **6**, 129–134.
49. Bailey, P., J. G. Dusser de Barenne, H. W. Garol, and W. S. McCulloch, 1940, Sensory cortex of chimpanzee, *J. Neurophysiol.*, **3**, 469–485.
50. Bailey, P., H. W. Garol, and W. S. McCulloch, 1941, Cortical origin and distribution of corpus callosum and anterior commissure in the chimpanzee (*Pan satyrus*), *J. Neurophysiol.*, **4**, 564–571.
51. Bailey, P., and F. A. Gibbs, 1951, The surgical treatment of psychomotor epilepsy, *J. A. M. A.*, **145**, 365–370.
52. Bailey, P., and W. H. Sweet, 1940, Effects on respiration, blood pressure and gastric motility of stimulation of orbital surface of frontal lobes, *J. Neurophysiol.*, **3**, 276–281.
53. Baker, A. B., Howard A. Matzke, and J. R. Brown, 1950, Poliomyelitis. III. Bulbar poliomyelitis; A study of medullary function, *Arch. Neurol. & Psychiat.*, **63**, 257–281.
54. Bard, P., 1928, A diencephalic mechanism for the expression of rage with special reference to the sympathetic nervous system, *Am. J. Physiol.*, **84**, 490–515.
55. Bard, P., 1933, Studies on the cerebral cortex. I. Localized control of placing and hopping reactions in the cat and their normal management by small cortical remnants, *Arch. Neurol. & Psychiat.*, **30**, 40–74.
56. Bard, P., 1938, Studies on the cortical representation of somatic sensibility, *Harvey Lect.*, **33**, 143–169.
57. Bard, P., 1941, "McCleod's Physiology in Modern Medicine," St. Louis, Mosby, 9th ed., 1256 pp.
58. Bard, P., and V. B. Mountcastle, 1947, Some

forebrain mechanisms involved in expression of rage with special reference to suppression of angry behavior, *Research Publ., A. Nerv. & Ment. Dis.*, **27**, 362–404.

59. Bard, P., C. N. Woolsey, R. S. Snider, V. B. Mountcastle, and R. B. Bromiley, 1947, Delimitation of central nervous mechanisms involved in motion sickness, *Federation Proc.*, **6**, 72.

60. Barnes, Stanley, 1901, Degenerations in hemiplegia: With special reference to a ventrolateral pyramidal tract, the accessory fillet and Pick's bundle, *Brain*, **24**, 463–501.

61. Barnes, W. T., H. W. Magoun, and S. W. Ranson, 1943, The ascending auditory pathway in the brain stem of the monkey, *J. Comp. Neurol.*, **79**, 129–152.

62. Barr, Murray L., 1948, Observations on the foramen of Magendie in a series of human brains, *Brain*, **71**, 281–289.

63. Barron, Donald H., personal communications.

64. Barron, Donald H., 1941, The functional development of some mammalian neuromuscular mechanisms, *Biol. Rev.*, **16**, 1–33.

65. Barron, Donald H., 1943, The early development of the motor cells and columns in the spinal cord of the sheep, *J. Comp. Neurol.*, **78**, 1–27.

66. Barron, Donald H., 1946, Observations on the early differentiation of the motor neuroblasts in the spinal cord of the chick, *J. Comp. Neurol.*, **85**, 149–169.

67. Barron, Donald H., 1948, Some effects of amputation of the chick wing bud on the early differentiation of the motor neuroblasts in the associated segments of the spinal cord, *J. Comp. Neurol.*, **88**, 93–127.

68. Beams, H. W., and R. L. King, 1935, The effects of ultracentrifuging the spinal ganglion cells of the rat with special reference to Nissl bodies, *J. Comp. Neurol.*, **61**, 175–189.

69. Beaton, L. E., and C. R. Leininger, 1943, Spinal distribution of thermoregulatory pathways in the monkey, *J. Neurophysiol.*, **6**, 37–38.

70. Beaton, L. E., C. R. Leininger, and W. A. McKinley, 1943, Thermoregulatory pathways in the cat brain stem, *J. Neurophysiol.*, **6**, 29–35.

71. Beattie, J., G. R. Brow, and C. N. H. Long, 1930, Physiological and anatomical evidence for the existence of nerve tracts connecting the hypothalamus with spinal sympathetic centres, *Proc. Roy. Soc., London*, **B. 106**, 253–275.

72. Beck, E., 1949, A cytoarchitectural investigation into the boundaries of cortical areas 13 and 14 in the human brain, *J. Anat.*, **83**, 147–157.

73. Beck, E., 1950, The origin, course, and termination of the prefronto-pontine tract in the human brain, *Brain*, **73**, 368–391.

74. Beck, E., T. McLardy, and A. Meyer, 1949, Anatomical comments on psychosurgical procedures, *Digest Neurol. & Psychiat., Inst. of Living*, **17**, 570.

75. Beckett, S., and E. Gellhorn, 1948, Role of acetylcholine in the activity of sensori-motor and suppressor areas of the cortex, *Am. J. Physiol.*, **153**, 113–120.

76. Bell, Eric, and L. J. Karnosh, 1949, Cerebral hemispherectomy. Report of a case ten years after operation, *J. Neurosurg.*, **6**, 285–293.

77. Benda, C. E., and S. Cobb, 1942, On the pathogenesis of paralysis agitans (Parkinson's disease), *Medicine*, **21**, 95–142.

78. Bender, M. B., and M. G. Kanzer, 1939, Dynamics of homonymous hemianopias and preservation of central vision, *Brain*, **62**, 404–421.

79. Bender, M. B., and I. Strauss, 1937, Defects in visual field of one eye only in patients with a lesion of one optic radiation, *Arch. Ophth.*, N.S. **17**, 765-787.

80. Berger, H., 1929, Über das Elektrenkephalogramm des Menschen, *Arch. f. Psychiat.*, **87**, 527–570.

81. Bielschowsky, A., 1935, Lectures on motor anomalies of the eyes. III. Paralysis of the conjugate ocular movements of the eyes, *Arch. Ophth.*, N.S. **13**, 569–583.

82. Bishop, George H., 1947, Neural mechanisms of cutaneous sense, *Physiol. Rev.*, **26**, 77–102.

83. Blum, M., A. E. Walker, and T. C. Ruch, 1943, Localization of taste in the thalamus of *Macaca mulatta*, *Yale J. Biol. & Med.*, **16**, 175–192.

84. Bodian, D., 1937, The structure of the vertebrate synapse. A study of the axon endings on Mauthner's cell and neighboring centers in the goldfish, *J. Comp. Neurol.*, **68**, 117–159.

85. Bonin, G. von, 1949, Architecture of the precentral motor cortex and some adjacent areas, Chap. II in "The Precentral Motor Cortex," ed. by Paul C. Bucy, 2d ed., Urbana, University of Illinois Press, pp. 8–82.

86. Bonin, G. von, 1950, "Essay on the Cerebral Cortex," Springfield, Ill., Charles C Thomas, xiii + 150 pp.

87. Bonin, G. von, H. W. Garol, and W. S. McCulloch, 1941, Functional organization of occipital lobe, *Anat. Rec.*, **79**, Suppl. 1, 10.

88. Bonin, G. von, H. W. Garol, and W. S. McCulloch, 1942, The functional organization of the occipital lobe, *Biol. Symposia*, **7**, 165–192.

89. Börnstein, W. S., 1940, Cortical representation

of taste in man and monkey, *Yale J. Biol. & Med.,* **12,** 719–736; **13,** 133–156.

90. Bosma, J. F., and Ernst Gellhorn, 1946, Electromyographic studies of muscular coordination on stimulation of motor cortex, *J. Neurophysiol.,* **9,** 263–274.

91. Botterell, E. H., and J. F. Fulton, 1938, Functional localization in the cerebellum of primates. Three papers, *J. Comp. Neurol.,* **69,** 31–87.

92. Boyd, Edith, 1941, "Outline of Physical Growth and Development," Minneapolis, Burgess Publishing Co., 43 pp., 43 plates, 33 tables.

93. Boynton, E. P., and Marion Hines, 1933, On the question of threshold in stimulation of the motor cortex, *Am. J. Physiol.,* **106,** 175–182.

94. Bremer, F., 1949, Considérations sur l'origine et la nature des "ondes" cérébrales, *Electroencephalog. & Clin. Neurophysiol.,* **1,** 177–193.

95. Breusch, S. R., 1944, The distribution of myelinated afferent fibers in the branches of the cat's facial nerve, *J. Comp. Neurol.,* **81,** 169–191.

96. Breusch, S. R., and L. B. Arey, 1942, The number of myelinated and unmyelinated fibers in the optic nerve of vertebrates, *J. Comp. Neurol.,* **77,** 631–665.

97. Brickner, R. M., 1934, An interpretation of frontal lobe function based upon the study of a case of partial bilateral frontal lobectomy, *Research Publ., A. Nerv. & Ment. Dis.,* **13,** 259–351.

98. Broca, P., 1861, Nouvelle observation d'aphémie produite par une lésion de la moitié postérieure des deuxième et troisième circonvolutions frontales, *Bull. Soc. anat. de Paris,* **6,** 398.

99. Brodal, A., 1940, Experimentelle Untersuchungen über die olivo-cerebellare Lokalisation, *Ztschr. f. d. ges. Neurol. u. Psychiat.,* **169,** 1–153.

100. Brodal, A., 1947, Central course of afferent fibers for pain in facial, glossopharyngeal, and vagus nerves. Clinical observations, *Arch. Neurol. & Psychiat.,* **57,** 292–306.

101. Brodal, A., 1947, The hippocampus and the sense of smell. A review, *Brain,* **70,** 179–222.

102. Brodal, A., 1948, The origin of the fibers of the anterior commissure in the rat. Experimental studies, *J. Comp. Neurol.,* **88,** 157–205.

103. Brodal, A., and J. Jansen, 1946, The pontocerebellar projection in the rabbit and cat. Experimental investigations, *J. Comp. Neurol.,* **84,** 31–118.

104. Brodmann, K., 1909, "Vergleichende Lokalisationslehre der Grosshirnrinde in ihren Prinzipien dargestellt auf Grund des Zellenbaues," Leipzig, Barth, xii + 324 pp.

105. Bronk, Detlev W., R. F. Pitts, and M. G. Larrabee, 1940, Role of hypothalamus in cardiovascular regulation, *Research Publ., A. Nerv. & Ment. Dis.,* **20,** 323–341.

106. Brooks, C. McC., and J. C. Eccles, 1947, An electrical hypothesis of central inhibition, *Nature, London,* **159,** 760–764.

107. Brooks, C. McC., E. F. Lambert, and P. Bard, 1942, Experimental production of obesity in the monkey (*Macaca mulatta*), *Federation Proc.,* **1,** 11.

108. Brouwer, B., 1918, Klinisch-anatomische Untersuchungen über den Oculomotoriuskern, *Ztschr. f. d. ges. Neurol. u. Psychiat.,* **40,** 152–193.

109. Brouwer, B., 1923, Experimentell-anatomische Untersuchungen über die Projektion der Retina auf die primaren Opticuszenten, *Schweiz. Arch. f. Neurol. u. Psychiat.,* **13,** 118–137.

110. Brouwer, B., 1934, Projection of the retina on the cortex in man, *Research Publ., A. Nerv. & Ment. Dis.,* **13,** 529–534.

111. Brouwer, B., 1947, Positive and negative aspects of hypothalamic disorders, *Proc. d. k. Nederl. Akad. v. Wetensch.,* **50,** 3–15.

112. Brouwer, B., and W. P. C. Zeeman, 1926, The projection of the retina in the primary optic neuron in monkeys, *Brain,* **49,** 1–35.

113. Brown, Meyer, and G. K. Yacorzynski, 1942, Studies of the sensation of vibration, *Arch. Neurol. & Psychiat.,* **47,** 813–820.

114. Bucy, P. C., 1938, Studies on the human neuromuscular mechanism. II. Effect of ventromedial chordotomy on muscular spasticity in man, *Arch. Neurol. & Psychiat.,* **40,** 639–662.

115. Bucy, P. C., 1942, Cortical extirpation in the treatment of involuntary movements, *Research Publ., A. Nerv. & Ment. Dis.,* **21,** 551–595.

116. Bucy, P. C., 1942, The neural mechanisms of athetosis and tremor, *J. Neuropath. & Exper. Neurol.,* **1,** 224–239.

117. Bucy, P. C., 1949, Effects of extirpation in man, Chap. XIV in "The Precentral Motor Cortex," ed. by P. C. Bucy, 2nd ed., Urbana, University of Illinois Press, pp. 353–394.

118. Bucy, P. C., 1949, Relation to abnormal involuntary movements, Chap. XV in "The Precentral Motor Cortex," ed. by P. C. Bucy, 2d ed., Urbana, University of Illinois Press, pp. 395–408.

119. Bucy, P. C., and T. J. Case, 1937, Athetosis. II. Surgical treatment of unilateral athetosis, *Arch. Neurol. & Psychiat.,* **37,** 983–1020.

120. Bucy, P. C., and J. F. Fulton, 1933, Ipsilateral representation in the motor and premotor cortex in monkeys, *Brain,* **56,** 318–342.

121. Bucy, P. C., and H. Klüver, 1940, Anatomic

changes secondary to temporal lobectomy, *Arch. Neurol. & Psychiat.*, **44**, 1142–1146.

122. Cameron, D. Ewen, and Miguel D. Prados, 1948, Symposium on gyrectomy. Part 2. Bilateral frontal gyrectomy: Psychiatric results, *Research Publ., A. Nerv. & Ment. Dis.*, **27**, 534–536.

123. Campbell, A. W., 1905, "Histological Studies on the Localization of Cerebral Function," New York, Cambridge, xix + 360 pp.

124. Cannon, B. W., L. E. Beaton, and S. W. Ranson, Jr., 1943, Nature of paresis following lateral corticospinal section in monkeys, *J. Neurophysiol.*, **6**, 425–429.

125. Cannon, W. B., 1939, The argument for chemical mediation of nerve impulses, *Science*, **90**, 521–527.

126. Carmichael, E. Arnold, and H. H. Woollard, 1933, Some observations on the fifth and seventh cranial nerves, *Brain*, **56**, 109–125.

127. Carrea, Paul M. E., and F. A. Mettler, 1947, Physiologic consequences following extensive removals of the cerebellar cortex and deep cerebellar nuclei and effect of secondary cerebral ablations in the primate, *J. Comp. Neurol.*, **87**, 169–288.

128. Carrea, Paul M. E., Magdalena Reissig, and F. A. Mettler, 1947, The climbing fibers of the simian and feline cerebellum. Experimental inquiry into their origin by lesions of the inferior olives and deep cerebellar nuclei, *J. Comp. Neurol.*, **87**, 321–356.

129. Castro, F. De, 1932, Sympathetic ganglia. Normal and pathological, Sec. VII in "Cytology and Cellular Pathology of the Nervous System," ed. by Wilder Penfield, New York, Hoeber, Vol. I, 317–380.

130. Caton, R., 1875, The electric current of the brain, *Brit. M. J.*, **2**, 278.

131. Cawthorne, E. A., G. Fitzgerald, and C. S. Hallpike, 1924, Studies in human vestibular function. II. Observations on directional preponderance of caloric nystagmus ("Nystagmus-bereitschaft") resulting from unilateral labyrinthectomy, *Brain*, **65**, 138–160.

132. Chambers, W. W., 1947, Electrical stimulation of the interior of the cerebellum in the cat, *Am. J. Anat.*, **80**, 55–93.

133. Chang, H.-T., and T. C. Ruch, 1947, Topographical distribution of spinothalamic fibres in the thalamus of the spider monkey, *J. Anat.*, **81**, 150–164.

134. Chang, H.-T., and T. C. Ruch, 1949, The projection of the caudal segments of the spinal cord to the lingula in the spider monkey, *J. Anat.*, **83**, 303–307.

135. Chang, H.-T., T. C. Ruch, and A. A. Ward, Jr., 1947, Topographical representation of muscles in motor cortex of monkeys, *J. Neurophysiol.*, **10**, 39–56.

136. Chapman, W. P., K. E. Livingston, and J. L. Poppen, 1950, Effect upon blood pressure of electrical stimulation of tips of temporal lobes in man, *J. Neurophysiol.*, **13**, 65–71.

137. Chapman, W. P., K. E. Livingston, and J. L. Poppen, 1950, An observation of the effect of the electrical stimulation of the temporal lobes on blood pressure in man, *J. Nerv. & Ment. Dis.*, **111**, 430–434.

138. Chapman, W. P., A. S. Rose, and H. C. Solomon, 1948, Measurements of heat stimulus producing motor withdrawal reaction in patients following frontal lobotomy, *Research Publ., A. Nerv. & Ment. Dis.*, **27**, 754–768.

139. Chorobski, J., and W. Penfield, 1932, Cerebral vasodilator nerves and their pathway from the medulla oblongata, *Arch. Neurol. & Psychiat.*, **28**, 1257–1289.

140. Clark, G., 1948, The mode of representation in the motor cortex, *Brain*, **71**, 320–331.

141. Clark, G., 1949, Suppression and facilitation—a review, *Quart. Chicago Med. School*, **10**, 14–26.

142. Clark, G., K. L. Chow, C. C. Gillaspy, and D. A. Klotz, 1949, Stimulation of anterior limbic region in dogs, *J. Neurophysiol.*, **12**, 459–463.

143. Clark, G., and S. C. Wang, 1939, The liberation of a pressor hormone following stimulation of the hypothalamus, *Am. J. Physiol.*, **127**, 597–601.

144. Clark, G., and J. W. Ward, 1948, Responses elicited from the cortex of monkeys by electrical stimulation through fixed electrodes, *Brain*, **71**, 332–342.

145. Clark, S. L., 1939, Responses following electrical stimulation of the cerebellar cortex in the normal cat, *J. Neurophysiol.*, **2**, 19–35.

146. Clark, S. L., and J. W. Ward, 1937, Electrical stimulation of the cortex cerebri of cats. Responses elicitable in chronic experiments through implanted electrodes, *Arch. Neurol. & Psychiat.*, **38**, 927–943.

147. Clark, W. E. L., 1926, The mammalian oculomotor nucleus, *J. Anat.*, **60**, 426–448.

148. Clark, W. E. L., 1932, A morphological study of the lateral geniculate body, *Brit. J. Ophth.*, **16**, 264–284.

149. Clark, W. E. L., 1932, Structure and connections of the thalamus, *Brain*, **55**, 406–470.

150. Clark, W. E. L., 1932, An experimental study of thalamic connections in the rat, *Philos. Tr. Roy. Soc., London*, **B. 222**, 1–28.

151. Clark, W. E. L., 1935–1936, The topography

and homologies of the hypothalamic nuclei in man, *J. Anat.*, **70**, 203–214.

152. Clark, W. E. L., 1940, Anatomical basis of colour vision, *Nature, London,* **146**, 558–559.

153. Clark, W. E. L., 1940, The nervous and vascular relations of the pineal gland, *J. Anat.*, **74**, 471–492.

154. Clark, W. E. L., 1941, Observations on the association fibre system of the visual cortex and the central representation of the retina, *J. Anat.*, **75**, 225–235.

155. Clark, W. E. L., 1941, The laminar organization and cell content of the lateral geniculate body in the monkey, *J. Anat.*, **75**, 419–433.

156. Clark, W. E. L., 1942, The cells of Meynert in the visual cortex of the monkey, *J. Anat.*, **76**, 369–376.

157. Clark, W. E. L., 1942, The visual centres of the brain and their connexions, *Physiol. Rev.*, **22**, 205–232.

158. Clark, W. E. L., 1948, The connexions of the frontal lobes in the brain, *Lancet,* **1**, 353–356.

159. Clark, W. E. L., J. Beattie, G. Riddoch, and N. M. Dott, 1938, "The Hypothalamus," Edinburgh, Oliver & Boyd, xii + 211 pp.

160. Clark, W. E. L., and R. H. Boggan, 1933, On the connections of the anterior nucleus of the thalamus, *J. Anat.*, **67**, 215–226.

161. Clark, W. E. L., and R. H. Boggan, 1935, The thalamic connections of the parietal and frontal lobes of the brain in the monkey, *Philos. Tr. Roy. Soc., London,* **B. 224**, 313–359.

162. Clark, W. E. L., and M. Meyer, 1947, The terminal connexions of the olfactory tract in the rabbit, *Brain,* **70**, 304–328.

163. Clark, W. E. L., and G. G. Penman, 1933, The projection of the retina in the lateral geniculate body, *Proc. Roy. Soc., London,* **B. 114**, 291–313.

164. Clark, W. E. L., and S. Sunderland, 1939, Structural changes in the isolated visual cortex, *J. Anat.*, **73**, 563–574.

165. Clark, W. E. L., and R. T. T. Warwick, 1946, The pattern of olfactory innervation, *J. Neurol., Neurosurg. & Psychiat.*, N.S. **9**, 101–111.

166. Clarke, J. Lockhart, 1851, Researches into the structure of the spinal cord, *Philos. Tr. Roy. Soc.*, London, volume for 1851, Part II, pp. 607–621.

167. Coghill, G. E., 1929, Anatomy and the Problem of Behavior, New York, Cambridge, xii + 113 pp. See also "Studies," 1914–1936, Parts I to XII, *J. Comp. Neurol.*, **24**, 161–233; **26**, 247–340; **37**, 37–70, 71–120; **40**, 47–94; **41**, 95–151; **42**, 1–16; **45**, 227–247; **51**, 311–375; **53**, 147–168; **57**, 327–357; **64**, 135–167.

168. Coghill, G. E., 1938, Early movement of the opossum with special reference to the walking gait, *Proc. Soc. Exper. Biol. & Med.*, **39**, 31–35.

169. Coghill, G. E., 1940, "Early Embryonic Somatic Movements in Birds and in Mammals Other than Man," Monographs of the Society for Research in Child Development, Washington, D.C., National Research Council. Vol. V, No. 2, Serial No. 25, pp. 1–48.

170. Conel, J. LeRoy, 1941, "The Postnatal Development of the Human Cerebral Cortex," Vol. II, "The Cortex of the One Month Infant," Cambridge, Mass., Harvard University Press, viii + 136 pp., 108 plates.

171. Connor, G. J., 1941, Functional localization within the anterior cerebellum, *Proc. Soc. Exper. Biol. & Med.*, **47**, 205–207.

172. Cooper, Sybil, and Peter M. Daniel, 1949, Muscle spindles in human extrinsic eye muscles, *Brain,* **72**, 1–24.

173. Cooper, Sybil, and C. S. Sherrington, 1940, Gower's tract and spinal border cells, *Brain,* **63**, 123–134.

174. Corbin, K. B., 1940, Observations on the peripheral distribution of fibers arising in the mesencephalic nucleus of the fifth cranial nerve, *J. Comp. Neurol.*, **73**, 153–177.

175. Corbin, K. B., and Frank Harrison, 1939, The sensory innervation of the spinal accessory and tongue musculature in the rhesus monkey, *Brain,* **62**, 191–197.

176. Corbin, K. B., and Frank Harrison, 1942, Further attempts to trace the origin of afferent nerves to the extrinsic eye muscles, *J. Comp. Neurol.*, **77**, 187–190.

177. Corbin, K. B., F. C. Harrison, and C. Wigginton, 1941, Elicitation of the "pseudomotor contracture" in the tongue by intramedullary stimulation, *Arch. Neurol. & Psychiat.*, **45**, 271–281.

178. Corbin, K. B., and R. K. Oliver, 1942. The origin of fibers to the grape-like endings in the insertion third of the extra-ocular muscles, *J. Comp. Neurol.*, **77**, 171–186.

179. Covell, W. P., and G. H. Scott, 1928, Experimental study of relation between granules stainable with neutral red and Golgi apparatus in nerve cells, *Anat. Rec.*, **38**, 377–400.

180. Crawford, M. P., J. F. Fulton, C. F. Jacobsen, and J. B. Wolfe, 1948, Frontal lobe ablation in chimpanzee: A resume of "Becky" and "Lucy," *Research Publ., A. Nerv. & Ment. Dis.*, **27**, 3–58.

181. Critchley, M., 1930, The anterior cerebral artery and its syndromes, *Brain,* **53**, 120–165.

182. Crosby, E. C., and J. W. Henderson, 1948, The mammalian midbrain and isthmus regions.

II. Fiber connections of the superior colliculus. B. Pathways concerned in automatic eye movements, *J. Comp. Neurol.*, **88**, 53–91.

183. Crosby, E. C., and T. Humphrey, 1941, Studies of the vertebrate telencephalon. II. The nuclear pattern of the anterior olfactory nucleus, tuberculum olfactorum and the amygdaloid complex in adult man, *J. Comp. Neurol.*, **74**, 309–352.

184. Crosby, E. C., and R. T. Woodburne, 1943, The nuclear pattern of the nontectal portions of the midbrain and isthmus in primates, *J. Comp. Neurol.*, **78**, 441–482.

185. Crowe, S. J., 1935, Symposium: Tone localization in the cochlea, *Ann. Otol., Rhin. & Laryng.*, **44**, 737–837.

186. Crowe, S. J., S. R. Guild, and L. M. Polvogt, 1934, Observations on pathology of high tone deafness, *Bull. Johns Hopkins Hosp.*, **54**, 315–380.

187. Cuajunco, F., 1940, Development of the neuromuscular spindle in human fetuses, *Contrib. Embryol.*, xxviii (Carnegie Inst. Wash. Publ. 518), 95–128.

188. Cuajunco, F., 1942, Development of the human motor end plate, *Contrib. Embryol.*, xxx (Carnegie Inst. Wash. Publ. 541), 127–152.

189. Curtis, A. H., and H. F. Helmholtz, 1911, The study of the anterior horn cells of an abrachius and their relation to the development of the extremities, *J. Comp. Neurol.*, **21**, 323–344.

190. Curtis, A. H., B. J. Anson, F. L. Ashley, and Tom Jones, 1942, The anatomy of the pelvic autonomic nerves in relation to gynecology, *Surg., Gynec. & Obstet.*, **75**, 743–750.

191. Curtis, H. J., 1940, Intercortical connections of the corpus callosum as indicated by evoked potentials, *J. Neurophysiol.*, **3**, 407–413.

192. Cushing, Harvey, 1902, Some experimental and clinical observations concerning states of increased intracranial tension, *Amer. J. M. Sc.*, **124**, 375–400.

193. Dale, H. H., 1939, Physiology of the nervous system, *Science*, **90**, 393–394.

194. Dandy, W. E., 1933, Physiological studies following extirpation of the right cerebral hemisphere in man, *Bull. Johns Hopkins Hosp.*, **53**, 31–51.

195. Dandy, W. E., 1937, Ménière's disease. Its diagnosis and treatment, *South. M. J.*, **30**, 621–623.

196. Danis, P. C., 1948, The functional organization of the third nerve nucleus in the cat, *Amer. J. Ophth.*, **31**, 1122–1131.

197. Davis, H., 1939, Physiology of hearing, Chap. 1 in "Loose Leaf Medicine of the Ear," ed. by E. P. Fowler, New York, Nelson.

198. Davis, H., P. A. Davis, A. L. Loomis, E. N. Harvey, and G. Hobart, 1937, Changes in human brain potentials during the onset of sleep, *Science*, **86**, 448–450.

199. Davis, Loyal E., 1923, The deep sensibility of the face, *Arch. Neurol. & Psychiat.*, **9**, 283–305.

200. Davison, Charles, 1940, Disturbances of temperature regulation in man, *Research Publ., A. Nerv. & Ment. Dis.*, **20**, 774–823.

201. Davison, Charles, 1942, The role of the globus pallidus and substantia nigra in the production of rigidity and tremor, *Research Publ., A. Nerv. & Ment. Dis.*, **21**, 267–333.

202. Davison, W. C., 1949, *"The Compleat Pediatrician,"* 6th ed., Durham, N.C., Duke University Press, vi + 256 pp.

203. Dejerine, J., 1906, L'aphasie sensorielle; Sa localisation et sa physiologie pathologique, *Presse méd.*, **14**, 437–439; **14**, 453–457.

204. Dejerine, J., 1901, "Anatomie des Centres Nerveux," Paris, J. Rueff, Vol. 2, p. 51 (also Figs. 376 and 377, p. 544).

205. Delgado, J. M. R., 1948, Report on respiratory centers of frontal lobes, *Research Publ., A. Nerv. & Ment. Dis.*, **27**, 433–437.

206. Delgado, J. M. R., and R. B. Livingston, 1948, Some respiratory, vascular, and thermal responses to stimulation of orbital surface of frontal lobe, *J. Neurophysiol.*, **11**, 39–55.

207. Dempsey, E. W., and Morison, R. S., 1942, The production of rhythmically recurrent cortical potentials after localized thalamic stimulation, *Am. J. Physiol.*, **135**, 293–300.

208. Denny-Brown, D., and E. H. Botterell, 1948, The motor functions of the agranular frontal cortex, *Research Publ., A. Nerv. & Ment. Dis.*, **27**, 235–345.

209. Denny-Brown, D., and E. G. Robertson, 1933, The state of the bladder and its sphincters in complete tranverse lesions of the spinal cord and cauda equina, *Brain*, **56**, 397–463.

210. Dey, F. L., 1943, Genital changes in female guinea pigs resulting from destruction of the median eminence, *Anat. Rec.*, **87**, 85–90.

211. Dickson, L. M., 1940, The development of nerve endings in the respiratory muscles of the sheep, *J. Anat.*, **74**, 268–276.

212. Dow, R. S., 1938, Efferent connections of the flocculo-nodular lobe in *Macaca mulatta*, *J. Comp. Neurol.*, **68**, 297–305.

213. Dow, R. S., 1938, Effect of lesions in the vestibular part of the cerebellum in primates, *Arch. Neurol. & Psychiat.*, **40**, 500–520.

214. Dow, R. S., 1939, Cerebellar action potentials in response to stimulation of various afferent connections, *J. Neurophysiol.*, **2**, 543–555.

215. Dow, R. S., 1942, The evolution and anatomy of the cerebellum, *Biol. Rev.*, **17**, 179–220.

216. Dunsmore, R. H., and M. A. Lennox, 1950, Stimulation and strychninization of supracallosal anterior cingulate gyrus, *J. Neurophysiol.*, **13**, 207–214.

217. Dusser de Barenne, J. G., 1933, The mode and site of action of strychnine in the nervous system, *Physiol. Rev.*, **13**, 325–335.

218. Dusser de Barenne, J. G., 1934, Origin of the motor reactions produced by electrical stimulation of the cerebral cortex, *Arch. Neurol. & Psychiat.*, **31**, 1129–1138.

219. Dusser de Barenne, J. G., H. W. Garol, and W. S. McCulloch, 1941, The "motor" cortex of the chimpanzee, *J. Neurophysiol.*, **4**, 287–303.

220. Dusser de Barenne, J. G., H. W. Garol, and W. S. McCulloch, 1942, Physiological neuronography of the corticostriatal connections, *Research Publ., A. Nerv. & Ment. Dis.*, **21**, 246–266.

221. Dusser de Barenne, J. G., and W. S. McCulloch, 1938, Functional organization in the sensory cortex of the monkey (*Macaca mulatta*), *J. Neurophysiol.*, **1**, 69–85.

222. Dusser de Barenne, J. G., and W. S. McCulloch, 1938, Sensorimotor cortex, nucleus caudatus and thalamus opticus, *J. Neurophysiol.*, **1**, 364–377.

223. Dusser de Barenne, J. G., and W. S. McCulloch, 1941, Suppression of motor response obtained from area 4 by stimulation af area 4*s*, *J. Neurophysiol.*, **4**, 311–323.

224. Dusser de Barenne, J. G., and O. Sager, 1931, Über die sensiblen Funktionen des Thalamus opticus der Katze, *Ztschr. f.d. ges. Neurol. u. Psychiat.*, **133**, 231–272.

225. Dusser de Barenne, J. G., and O. Sager, 1937, Sensory functions of the optic thalamus of the monkey (*Macacus rhesus*). Symptomatology and functional localization investigated with the method of local strychninization, *Arch. Neurol. & Psychiat.*, **38**, 913–926.

226. Ebin, Judah, 1949, Combined lateral and ventral pyramidotomy in treatment of paralysis agitans, *Arch. Neurol. & Psychiat.*, **62**, 27–47.

227. Eccles, J. C., 1945, An electrical hypothesis of synaptic and neuromuscular transmission, *Nature, London*, **156**, 680–683.

228. Eccles, J. C., 1947, Acetylcholine and synaptic transmission in the spinal cord, *J. Neurophysiol.*, **10**, 197–204.

229. Echols, D. H., and J. H. Maxwell, 1934, Superior laryngeal neuralgia relieved by operation, *J. A. M. A.*, **103**, 2027–2028.

230. Economo, C. von, 1926, Ein Koeffizient für die Organisationshöhle der Grosshirnrinde, *Klin. Wchnschr.*, **5**, 593–595.

231. Economo, C. von, 1926, Die Bedeutung der Hirnwindung, *Allg. Ztschr. f. Psychiat.*, **84**, 123–132.

232. Economo, C. von, 1929, "The Cytoarchitectonics of the Human Cerebral Cortex," trans. by S. Parker (Humphrey Milford), New York, Oxford, xii + 186 pp.

233. Economo, C. von, and G. Koskinas, 1925, "Die Cytoarchitektonik der Hirnrinde der erwachsenen Menschen," Vienna, Springer, 810 pp., atlas with 112 plates.

234. Edinger, Ludwig, 1890, "Twelve Lectures on the Structure of the Central Nervous System," 2d ed., revised, trans. by W. H. Vittum, ed. by C. E. Riggs, Philadelphia, Davis, xii + 230 pp.

235. Edwards, E. A., 1931, Anatomic variations of the cranial venous sinuses. Their relation to the effect of jugular compression in lumbar manometric tests, *Arch. Neurol. & Psychiat.*, **26**, 801–814.

236. Einarson, Larus, 1933, Notes on the morphology of the chromophil material of nerve cells and its relation to nuclear substances, *Am. J. Anat.*, **53**, 141–175.

237. Einarson, Larus, 1935, Histological analysis of the Nissl pattern and substance of nerve cells, *J. Comp. Neurol.*, **61**, 101–133.

238. Elliott, H. Chandler, 1943, Studies on the motor cells of the spinal cord. II. Distribution in the normal human fetal cord, *Am. J. Anat.*, **72**, 29–38.

239. Elsberg, Charles A., 1935, The sense of smell. XI. The value of quantitative olfactory tests for the localization of supratentorial tumors of the brain. A preliminary report, *Bull. Neurol. Inst. New York*, **4**, 511–522.

240. Elsberg, Charles A., and Earl D. Brewer, 1935, The sense of smell. X. A detailed description of the technique of two olfactory tests used for the localization of supratentorial tumors of the brain, *Bull. Neurol. Inst. New York*, **4**, 501–510.

241. Elsberg, Charles A., and Hyman Spotnitz, 1942, Value of quantitative olfactory tests for localization of supratentorial disease, *Arch. Neurol. & Psychiat.*, **48**, 1–12.

242. Erlanger, J., and H. S. Gasser, 1937, "Electrical Signs of Nervous Activity," Philadelphia, University of Pennsylvania Press, x + 221 pp.

243. Evans, J. P., 1935, A study of the sensory defects resulting from excision of cerebral substance in humans, *Research Publ., A. Nerv. & Ment. Dis.*, **15**, 331–370.

244. Falconer, Murray A., 1948, Relief of intractable pain of organic origin by frontal lobot-

omy, *Research Publ., A. Nerv. & Ment. Dis.*, **27**, 706–714.

245. Favill, J., 1929, The relationship of eye muscles to semicircular canal currents in rotationally induced nystagmus, *Research Publ., A. Nerv. & Ment. Dis.*, **6**, 530–546.

246. Feiling, Anthony, 1913–1914, On the bulbar nuclei, with special reference to the existence of a salivary centre in man, *Brain*, **36**, 255–265.

247. Ferrier, D., 1876, "The Functions of the Brain," New York, Putnam, 2nd., xxiii + 498 pp.

248. Finley, Knox H., 1940, Angio-architecture of the hypothalamus and its peculiarities, *Research Publ., A. Nerv. & Ment. Dis.*, **20**, 286–309.

249. Fitzgerald, G., and C. S. Hallpike, 1942, Studies in human vestibular function: I. Observations on the directional preponderance ("Nystagmusbereitschaft") of caloric nystagmus resulting from cerebral lesions, *Brain*, **65**, 115–137.

250. Fitzgerald, James E., and W. F. Windle, 1942, Some observations on early human fetal movements, *J. Comp. Neurol.*, **76**, 159–167.

251. Foerster, O., 1927, "Die Leitungsbahnen des der Schmerzzustande," Berlin, Urban & Schwarzenberg, viii + 360 pp.

252. Foerster, O., 1931, The cerebral cortex in man, *Lancet*, **2**, 309–312.

253. Foerster, O., 1933, The dermatomes in man, *Brain*, **56**, 1–39.

254. Foerster, O., 1936, Symptomatologie der Erkrankungen des Rückenmarks und seiner Wurzeln, in "Handbuch der Neurologie," by O. Bumke and O. Foerster, Berlin, Springer, Vol. 5, pp. 1–403.

255. Foerster, O., 1936, Motorische Felder und Bahnen, in "Handbuch der Neurologie," by O. Bumke and O. Foerster, Berlin, Springer, Vol. 6, pp. 1–352

256. Foerster, O., 1936, Sensible corticale Felder, in "Handbuch der Neurologie," by O. Bumke and O. Foerster, Berlin, Springer, Vol. 6, pp., 358–448.

257. Foerster, O., 1936, The motor cortex in man in the light of Hughlings Jackson's observations, *Brain*, **59**, 135–159.

258. Foerster, O., O. Gagel, and W. Mahoney, 1936, Über die Anatomie und Pathologie der Pupillarinnervation, *Verhandl. d. deutsch. Gesellsch. f. inn. Med.*, **48**, 386–398.

259. Foerster, O., O. Gagel, and D. Sheehan, 1933, Veränderungen an den Endösen im Rückenmark des Affen nach Hinterwurzeldurchschneidung, *Ztschr. f. d. ges. Anat.*, **101**, 553–565.

260. Foix, C., and P. Hillemand, 1925, Les syndromes de la région thalamique, *Presse méd.*, **33**, 113–117.

261. Foix, C., and P. Hillemand, 1925, Les artères de l'axe encéphalique jusqu'au diencéphale inclusivement, *Rev. neurol.*, **II**, 705–739.

262. Foix, C., and M. Levy, 1927, Les ramollissements sylviens, *Rev. neurol.*, **II**, 1–51.

263. Fontaine, René, and L. G. Herrmann, 1932, Clinical and experimental basis for surgery of the pelvic sympathetic nerves in gynecology, *Surg., Gynec. & Obstet*, **54**, 133–163.

264. Forbes, A., 1939, Problems of synaptic function, *J. Neurophysiol.*, **2**, 465–472.

265. Forbes, H. S., 1940, Physiologic regulation of the cerebral circulation, *Arch. Neurol. & Psychiat.*, **43**, 804–814.

266. Forbes, H. S., and S. Cobb, 1938, Vasomotor control of cerebral vessels, *Brain*, **61**, 221–233.

267. Forbes, H. S., and H. G. Wolff, 1928, Cerebral circulation. III. The vasomotor control of the cerebral vessels, *Arch. Neurol. & Psychiat.*, **19**, 1056–1086.

268. Ford, F. R., 1937, "Diseases of the Nervous System in Infancy, Childhood and Adolescence," Springfield, Ill., Charles C Thomas, xxiv + 953 pp.

269. Fox, C. A., 1943, The stria terminalis, longitudinal association bundle and precommissural fornix fibers in the cat, *J. Comp. Neurol.*, **79**, 277–295.

270. Fox, C. A., R. R. Fisher, and S. J. Desalva, 1948, The distribution of the anterior commissure in the monkey (*Macaca mulatta*). Experimental studies, *J. Comp. Neurol.*, **89**, 245–277.

271. Fox, C. A., W. A. McKinley, and H. W. Magoun, 1944, An oscillographic study of olfactory system of cats, *J. Neurophysiol.*, **7**, 1–16.

272. Fox, J. C., and W. J. German, 1936, Macular vision following cerebral resection, *Arch. Neurol. & Psychiat.*, **35**, 808–826.

273. Frankenhaeuser, B., 1951, Limitations of method of strychnine neuronography, *J. Neurophysiol.*, **14**, 73–79.

274. Freeman, W., 1949, Transorbital lobotomy, *Digest Neurol. & Psychiat., Inst. of Living*, **16**, 398.

275. Freeman, W., and J. W. Watts, 1939, Interpretation of function of frontal lobes based upon observations in 48 cases of prefrontal lobotomy, *Yale J. Biol. & Med.*, **11**, 527–539.

276. Freeman, W., and J. W. Watts, 1947, Retrograde degeneration of the thalamus following prefrontal lobotomy, *J. Comp. Neurol.*, **86**, 65–93.

277. Freeman, W., and J. W. Watts, 1948, Pain mechanisms and the frontal lobes: A study of

prefrontal lobotomy for intractable pain, *Ann. Int. Med.*, **28**, 747–754.

278. FREEMAN, W., and J. W. WATTS, 1950, "Psychosurgery in the Treatment of Mental Disorders and Intractable Pain," 2d ed., Springfield, Ill., Charles C Thomas, xxviii + 598 pp.

279. FRENCH, J. D., O. SUGAR, and J. G. CHUSID, 1948, Corticocortical connections of the superior bank of the sylvian fissure in the monkey (*Macaca mulatta*), *J. Neurophysiol.*, **11**, 185–192.

280. FRITSCH, G., and E. HITZIG, 1870, Über die elektrische Erregbarkeit des Grosshirns, *Arch. f. Anat. u. Physiol.*, **37**, 300–332.

281. FULTON, J. F., 1937, A note on Francesco Gennari and the early history of cytoarchitectural studies of the cerebral cortex, *Bull. Inst. Hist. Med.*, **5**, 895–913.

282. FULTON, J. F., 1949, "Physiology of the Nervous System," 3d ed., revised, New York, Oxford, x + 667 pp.

283. FULTON, J. F., and F. D. INGRAHAM, 1929, Emotional disturbances following experimental lesions of the base of the brain (pre-chiasmal), *J. Physiol.*, **67**, xxvii–xxviii.

284. FULTON, J. F., E. G. T. LIDDELL, and D. McK. RIOCH, 1930, The influence of unilateral destruction of the vestibular nuclei upon posture and the knee jerk, *Brain*, **53**, 327–343.

285. FULTON, J. F., and D. SHEEHAN, 1935, The uncrossed lateral pyramidal tract in higher primates, *J. Anat.*, **69**, 181–187.

286. GARDNER, ERNEST, and H. M. CUNEO, 1945, Lateral spinothalamic tract and associated tracts in man, *Arch. Neurol. & Psychiat.*, **53**, 423–430.

287. GAROL, H. W., and P. C. BUCY, 1944, Suppression of motor response in man, *Arch. Neurol. & Psychiat.*, **51**, 528–532.

288. GASSER, H. S., 1935, Conduction in nerves in relation to fiber types, *Research Publ., A. Nerv. & Ment. Dis.*, **15**, 35–59.

289. GASTAUT, H., J. ROGER, and Y. GASTAUT, 1948, Les formes expérimentales de l'épilepsie humaine: L'épilepsie induite par la stimulation lumineuse intermittente rythmée ou épilepsie photogénique, *Rev. neurol.*, **80**, 161–183.

290. GELLHORN, E., 1948, The influence of alterations in posture of the limbs on cortically induced movements, *Brain*, **71**, 26–33.

291. GELLHORN, E., and L. THOMPSON, 1944, The influence of muscle pain on cortically induced movements, *Am. J. Physiol.*, **142**, 231–239.

292. GERARD, M. W., 1923, Afferent impulses of the trigeminal nerve, *Arch. Neurol. & Psychiat.*, **9**, 306–338.

293. GERARD, R. W., 1931, Nerve conduction in relation to nerve structure, *Quart. Rev. Biol.*, **6**, 59–83.

294. GERSH, ISADORE, and DAVID BODIAN, 1943, Some chemical mechanisms in chromatolysis, *J. Cell. & Comp. Physiol.*, **21**, 253–280.

295. GESELL, A., C. S. AMATRUDA, B. M. CASTNER, and H. THOMPSON, 1939, "Biographies of Child Development," New York, Hoeber, xvii + 328 pp.

296. GESELL, A., H. M. HALVERSON, H. THOMPSON, F. L. ILG, B. M. CASTNER, L. B. AMES, and C. S. AMATRUDA, 1940, "The First Five Years of Life. A Guide to the Study of the Preschool Child," New York, Harper, xiii + 393 pp.

297. GESELL, A., and H. THOMPSON, 1934, "Infant Behavior: Its Genesis and Growth," New York, McGraw-Hill, viii + 343 pp.

298. GESELL, A., and H. THOMPSON, 1938, "The Psychology of Early Growth," New York, Macmillan, vii + 290 pp.

299. GIBBS, E. L., F. A. GIBBS, and B. FUSTER, 1948, Psychomotor epilepsy, *Arch. Neurol. & Psychiat.*, **60**, 331–339.

300. GIBBS, F. A., and E. L. GIBBS, 1950, "Atlas of Electroencephalography," 2d ed., Cambridge, Mass., Addison-Wesley Press, iv + 324 pp.

301. GIBBS, F. A., E. L. GIBBS, and W. G. LENNOX, 1938, Cerebral dysrhythmias of epilepsy, *Arch. Neurol. & Psychiat.*, **39**, 298–314.

302. GIVNER, ISADORE, 1939, Episcleral ganglion cells, *Arch. Ophth.*, N.S. **22**, 82–88.

303. GLEES, P., 1942, Observations on the structure of the connective tissue sheaths of cutaneous nerves, *J. Anat.*, **77**, 153–159.

304. GLEES, P., 1944, The anatomical basis of corticostriate connexions, *J. Anat.*, **78**, 47–51.

305. GLEES, P., 1945, Interrelation of the striopallidum and the thalamus in the macaque monkey, *Brain*, **68**, 331–346.

306. GLEES, P., and W. E. L. CLARK, 1941, The termination of optic fibres in the lateral geniculate body of the monkey, *J. Anat.*, **75**, 295–308.

307. GLEES, P., and J. COLE, 1950, Recovery of skilled motor functions after small repeated lesions of motor cortex in macaque, *J. Neurophysiol.*, **13**, 137–148.

308. GLEES, P., J. COLE, C. W. M. WHITLEY, and H. CAIRNS, 1950, The effects of lesions in the cingular gyrus and adjacent areas in monkeys, *J. Neurol., Neurosurg. & Psychiat.*, N.S. **13**, 178–190.

309. GLEES, P., and P. D. WALL, 1946, Fibre connections of the subthalamic region and the centromedian nucleus of the thalamus, *Brain*, **69**, 195–208.

310. GRANIT, R., 1947, "Mechanisms of the Retina.

With an Appendix on Electroretinography," New York, Oxford, xxiii + 412 pp.

311. GRANT, F. C., R. A. GROFF, and F. H. LEWY, 1940, Section of the descending spinal root of the 5th cranial nerve, *Arch. Neurol. & Psychiat.*, **43**, 498–509.

312. GRANT, F. C., and L. M. WEINBERGER, 1941, Experiences with intramedullary tractotomy. I. Relief of facial pain and summary of operative results, *Arch. Surg.*, **42**, 681–692.

313. GREEN, J. D., 1946, The adenohypophysis and the central nervous system, *Alexander Blain Hosp. Bull.*, **5**, 186–193.

314. GREEN, J. D., 1947, Some aspects of the anatomy and function of the pituitary gland with especial reference to the neurohypophysis, *Alexander Blain Hosp. Bull.*, **6**, 128–142.

315. GREEN, J. D., 1948, The histology of the hypophyseal stalk and median eminence in man with special reference to blood vessels, nerve fibers and a peculiar neurovascular zone in this region, *Anat. Rec.*, **100**, 273–296.

316. GREEN, J. D., and G. W. HARRIS, 1949, Observation of the hypophysio-portal vessels of the living rat, *J. Physiol.*, **108**, 359–361.

317. GREEN, J. R., R. E. H. DUISBERG, and W. B. MCGRATH, 1951, Focal epilepsy of psychomotor type, *J. Neurosurg.*, **8**, 157–172.

318. GRINKER, R. R., W. R. INGRAM, and S. W. RANSON, 1939, The hypothalamus—A review, *Psychosom. Med.*, **1**, 19–92.

319. GRUNDFEST, HARRY, 1946, The origin of electrical activity from spinal afferent stimulation of the inferior olive of cats, *Federation Proc.*, **5**, 38.

320. GRUNDFEST, HARRY, and BERRY CAMPBELL, 1942, Origin, conduction, and termination of the spino-cerebellar tract in cats, *J. Neurophysiol.*, **5**, 275–294.

321. GUILD, S. R., 1927, The circulation of the endolymph, *Am. J. Anat.*, **39**, 57–82.

322. HAGGQUIST, GOSTA, 1940, A contribution to the question of the nervous and muscular substratum of the muscle tone, *Acta med. Scandinav.*, **104**, 8–20.

323. HALLPIKE, C. S., and H. CAIRNS, 1938, Observations on the pathology of Ménière's syndrome, *J. Laryng. & Otol.*, **53**, 625–655.

324. HALSTEAD, W. C., A. E. WALKER, and P. C. BUCY, 1940, Sparing and non-sparing of "macular" vision associated with occipital lobectomy in man, *Arch. Ophth.*, N.S. **24**, 948–966.

325. HAMMOND, W. S., and C. L. YNTEMA, 1947, Depletions in the thoraco-lumbar sympathetic system following removal of neural crest in the chick, *J. Comp. Neurol.*, **86**, 237–265.

326. HAMPSON, J. L., 1949, Relationships between cat cerebral and cerebellar cortices, *J. Neurophysiol.*, **12**, 37–50.

327. HAMPSON, J. L., C. R. HARRISON, and C. N. WOOLSEY, 1945, Somatotopic localization in anterior lobe and lobulus simplex of cerebellum in cat and dog, *Federation Proc.*, **4**, 31.

328. HAMPSON, J. L., C. R. HARRISON, and C. N. WOOLSEY, 1946, Somatotopic localization in the cerebellum, *Federation Proc.*, **5**, 41.

329. HARDMAN, JAMES, 1949, First impressions on topectomy, *Digest Neurol. & Psychiat., Inst. of Living*, **17**, 512.

330. HARE, KENDRICK, 1947, The nervous control of the release of pituitrin, *Federation Proc.*, **6**, 123.

331. HARE, W. K., H. W. MAGOUN, and S. W. RANSON, 1937, Localization within the cerebellum of reactions to faradic cerebellar stimulation, *J. Comp. Neurol.*, **67**, 145–182.

332. HARLOW, HARRY F., and PAUL H. SETTLAGE, 1948, Effect of extirpation of frontal areas upon learning performance of monkeys, *Research Publ., A. Nerv. & Ment. Dis.*, **27**, 446–459.

333. HARLOW, J. M., 1848, Passage of an iron rod through the head, *Boston M. & S. J.*, **39**, 389–393.

334. HARLOW, J. M., 1868, Recovery from the passage of an iron bar through the head, *Mass. M. Soc. Publ.*, **2**, 327–346.

335. HARRIS, A. J., R. HODES, and H. W. MAGOUN, 1944, The afferent path of the pupillodilator reflex in the cat, *J. Neurophysiol.*, **7**, 231–243.

336. HARRIS, G. W., 1948, Neural control of the pituitary gland, *Physiol. Rev.*, **28**, 139–179.

337. HARRISON, FRANK, 1940, The hypothalamus and sleep, *Research Publ., A. Nerv. & Ment. Dis.*, **20**, 635–656.

338. HARRISON, R. G., 1907, Observations of the living developing nerve fiber, *Anat. Rec.*, **1**, 116–118.

339. HARRISON, R. G., 1910, The outgrowth of the nerve fiber as a mode of protoplasmic movement, *J. Exper. Zool.*, **9**, 787–848.

340. HARRISON, R. G., 1924, Neuroblast versus sheath cell in the development of peripheral nerves, *J. Comp. Neurol.*, **37**, 123–205.

341. HARRISON, R. G., 1935, On the origin and development of the nervous system studied by the methods of experimental embryology (The Croonian Lecture), *Proc. Roy. Soc., London*, **B. 118**, 155–196.

342. HARTMANN, J. F., 1948, Mitochrondria in nerve cell-bodies following section of axones, *Anat. Rec.*, **100**, 49–59.

343. HARTRIDGE, H., 1950, The polychromatic theory, pp. 279–288 in "Recent Advances in the Phys-

iology of Vision," Philadelphia, Blakiston, xxi + 401 pp.

344. Hasama, Bun-ichi, 1934, Ueber die elektrischen Begleiterscheinungen an der Riechsphäre bei der Geruchsempfindung, *Pflüger's Arch. f.d. ges. Physiol.*, **234**, 748–755.

345. Hausman, L., 1939, Pure flaccid hemiplegia uncomplicated by sensory defect, *Tr. Am. Neurol. A.*, **65**, 217–219.

346. Hayne, R., R. Meyers, and J. R. Knott, 1949, Characteristics of electrical activity of human corpus striatum and neighboring structures, *J. Neurophysiol.*, **12**, 185–195.

347. Head, Henry, 1920, "Studies in Neurology," New York, Oxford, Vol. I, ix + 329 pp.; Vol. II, viii + 330–862.

348. Head, Henry, and G. Holmes, 1911, Sensory disturbances from cerebral lesions, *Brain*, **34**, 102–254.

349. Head, Henry, and G. Riddoch, 1917, The automatic bladder, excessive sweating and some other reflex conditions in gross injuries of the spinal cord, *Brain*, **40**, 188–263.

350. Heath, R. G., D. A. Freedman, and F. A. Mettler, 1947, Striatal removal without previous cortical ablation: Release, disorientation, metabolic disturbance, *Federation Proc.*, **6**, 126.

351. Heath, R. G., and J. L. Pool, 1948, Bilateral fractional resection of frontal cortex for the treatment of psychoses, *J. Nerv. & Ment. Dis.*, **107**, 411–429.

352. Hebb, D. O., and W. Penfield, 1940, Human behavior after extensive bilateral removal from the frontal lobes, *Arch. Neurol. & Psychiat.*, **44**, 421–438.

353. Hecaen, H., M. David, and J. Talairach, 1947, L'Aire "suppressive" du cortex prémoteur chez l'homme, *Rev. neurol.*, **79**, 726–732.

354. Heimbecker, Peter, and H. L. White, 1941, Hypothalamico-hypophysial system and its relation to water balance in the dog, *Am. J. Physiol.*, **133**, 582–593.

355. Henneberg, R., 1910, Messung der Oberflächenausdehnung der Grosshirnrinde, *J. f. Psychol. u. Neurol.*, **17**, 144–158.

356. Henry, C. E., 1949, EEG changes following transorbital lobotomy and cortical undercutting, *Digest Neurol. & Psychiat., Inst. of Living*, **17**, 365.

357. Herren, R. Y., and Leo Alexander, 1939, Sulcal and intrinsic blood vessels of human spinal cord, *Arch. Neurol. & Psychiat.*, **41**, 678–687.

358. Herrick, C. Judson, 1933, The functions of the olfactory parts of the cerebral cortex, *Proc. Nat. Acad. Sc.*, **19**, 7–14.

359. Hess, W. R., 1947, Vegetative Funktionen und Zwischenhirn, *Helvet. physiol. et. pharm. acta*, Suppl. IV, 65 pp.

360. Hetherington, A. W., and S. W. Ranson, 1940, Hypothalamic lesions and adiposity in the rat, *Anat. Rec.*, **78**, 149–172.

361. Hetherington, A. W., and S. W. Ranson, 1942, The relation of various hypothalamic lesions to adiposity in the rat, *J. Comp. Neurol.*, **76**, 475–499.

362. Hill, Denis, 1949, The electroencephalographic concept of psychomotor epilepsy: A summary, *Digest Neurol. & Psychiat., Inst. of Living*, **17**, 560.

363. Hines, Marion, 1922, Studies in the growth and differentiation of the telencephalon in man. The fissura hippocampi, *J. Comp. Neurol.*, **34**, 73–171.

364. Hines, Marion, 1927, Nerve and muscle, *Quart. Rev. Biol.*, **2**, 149–180.

365. Hines, Marion, 1929, On cerebral localization, *Physiol. Rev.*, **9**, 462–574.

366. Hines, Marion, 1934, Cytoarchitecture of the cerebral cortex in man, *Research Publ., Nerv. & Ment. Dis.*, **13**, 26–37.

367. Hines, Marion, 1936, The anterior border of the monkey's (*Macaca mulatta*) motor cortex and the production of spasticity, *Am. J. Physiol.*, **116**, 76.

368. Hines, Marion, 1937, The "motor" cortex, *Bull. Johns Hopkins Hosp.*, **60**, 313–336.

369. Hines, Marion, 1940, Movements elicited from precentral gyrus of adult chimpanzee by stimulation with sine wave currents, *J. Neurophysiol.*, **3**, 442–446.

370. Hines, Marion, 1943, Control of movements by the cerebral cortex in primates, *Biol. Rev.*, **18**, 1–31.

371. Hines, Marion, 1949, Significance of the precentral motor cortex, Chap. XVIII in "The Precentral Motor Cortex," ed. by P. C. Bucy, 2d ed., Urbana, University of Illinois Press, pp. 461–499.

372. Hines, Marion, personal communications.

373. Hines, Marion, and E. P. Boynton, 1940, The maturation of "excitability" in the precentral gyrus of the young monkey (*Macaca mulatta*), *Contrib. Embryol.*, xxviii (Carnegie Inst. Wash. Publ. 518), 309–451.

374. Hodes, R., and H. W. Magoun, 1942, Autonomic responses to electrical stimulation of the forebrain and midbrain with special reference to the pupil, *J. Comp. Neurol.*, **76**, 169–189.

375. Hodes, R., and H. W. Magoun, 1942, Pupillary and other responses from stimulation of the frontal cortex and basal telencephalon of the cat, *J. Comp. Neurol.*, **76**, 461–473.

376. Hoefer, P. F. A., 1942, Physiology of motor innervation in the dyskinesias, *Research Publ., A. Nerv. & Ment. Dis.*, **21**, 502–528.

377. Hoff, E. C., and H. E. Hoff, 1934, Spinal terminations of the projection fibres from the motor cortex of primates, *Brain*, **57**, 454–474.

378. Hogg, I. D., 1941, Sensory nerves and associated structures in the skin of human fetuses of 8 to 14 weeks of menstrual age correlated with functional capability, *J. Comp. Neurol.*, **75**, 371–410.

379. Holmes, Gordon, 1921, Palsies of the conjugate ocular movements, *Brit. J. Ophth.*, **5**, 241–250.

380. Holmes, Gordon, 1922, Clinical symptoms of cerebellar disease, and their interpretations, *Lancet*, **1**, 1177–1182, 1231–1237; **2**, 59–65, 111–115.

381. Holmes, Gordon, 1927, Disorders of sensation produced by cortical lesions, *Brain*, **50**, 413–427.

382. Holmes, Gordon, 1938, The cerebral integration of the ocular movements, *Brit. M. J.*, **2**, 107–112.

383. Holmes, Gordon, 1939, The cerebellum of man, *Brain*, **62**, 1–30.

384. Holmes, Gordon, 1944, The organization of the visual cortex in man (Ferrier Lecture), *Proc. Roy. Soc. London*, **B. 132**, 348–361.

385. Holmes, Gordon, and Henry Head, 1911, A case of lesion of the optic thalamus with autopsy, *Brain*, **34**, 255–271.

386. Holmes, Gordon, and Gilbert Horrax, 1919, Disturbances of spatial orientation and visual attention with loss of stereoscopic vision, *Arch. Neurol. & Psychiat.*, **1**, 385–407.

387. Holmes, Gordon, and W. T. Lister, 1916, Disturbances of vision from cerebral lesions, with special reference to the cortical representation of the macula, *Brain*, **39**, 34–73.

388. Holmes, Gordon, and W. Page May, 1909, On the exact origin of the pyramidal tracts in man and other mammals, *Brain*, **32**, 1–43.

389. Holmes, Gordon, and P. Sargent, 1915, Injuries of the superior longitudinal sinus, *Brit. M. J.*, **2**, 493–498.

390. Holmes, Gordon, and T. G. Stewart, 1908, On the connection of the inferior olives with the cerebellum in man, *Brain*, **31**, 125–137.

391. Holtfreter, J., 1933, Die totale Exogastrulation, eine Selbstablösung des Ektoderms vom Entomesoderm. Entwicklung und funktionelles Verhalten nervenloser Organe, *Wilhelm Roux, Arch. f. Entwicklungsmech. d. Organ*, **129**, 669–793.

392. Hooker, D., 1942, Fetal reflexes and instinctual processes, *Psychosom. Med.*, **4**, 199–205.

393. Hooker, D., 1944, The origin of overt behavior, University of Michigan Lecture No. 1, 38 pp.

394. Huber, G. C., E. C. Crosby, R. T. Woodburne, L. A. Gillilan, J. O. Brown, and B. Tamthai, 1943, The mammalian midbrain and isthmus regions. Part I. The nuclear pattern, *J. Comp. Neurol.*, **78**, 129–534.

395. Humphrey, T., 1940, The development of the olfactory and the accessory olfactory formations in human embryos and fetuses, *J. Comp. Neurol.*, **73**, 431–468.

396. Humphrey, T., 1944, Primitive neurons in the embryonic human central nervous system, *J. Comp. Neurol.*, **81**, 1–45.

397. Humphrey, T., 1947, Sensory ganglion cells within the central canal of the embryonic human spinal cord, *J. Comp. Neurol.*, **86**, 1–35.

398. Humphrey, T., and E. C. Crosby, 1938, The human olfactory bulb, *Mich. Univ. Hosp. Bull.*, **4**, 61–62.

399. Hunt, J. R., 1909, The sensory system of the facial nerve and its symptomatology, *J. Nerv. & Ment. Dis.*, **36**, 321–350.

400. Hunt, J. R., 1937, Geniculate neuralgia. Neuralgia of the nervus facialis, *Arch. Neurol. & Psychiat.*, **37**, 252–285.

401. Hunter, John, and H. H. Jasper, 1949, Effects of thalamic stimulation in unanaesthetized animals, *Electroencephalog. & Clin. Neurophysiol.*, **1**, 305–324.

402. Hurst, E. W., 1929, The histology of experimental poliomyelitis, *J. Path. & Bact.*, **32**, 457–477.

403. Hyde, J., S. Beckett, and E. Gellhorn, 1949, Acetylcholine and convulsive activity, *J. Neurophysiol.*, **12**, 17–27.

404. Hydén, Holger, 1943, Protein metabolism in the nerve cell during growth and function, *Acta physiol. Scandinav.*, **6**, Suppl. 17, 1–136.

405. Hyndman, O. R., 1941, Physiology of the spinal cord. I. Role of the anterior column in hyperreflexia, *Arch. Neurol. & Psychiat.*, **46**, 695–703.

406. Hyndman, O. R., 1943, Physiology of the spinal cord. II. The influence of chordotomy on existing motor disturbances, *J. Nerv. & Ment. Dis.*, **98**, 343–358.

407. Hyndman, O. R., and C. Van Epps, 1939, Physiological effects of anterior chordotomy. Possibility of differential section of the spinothalamic tract, *Arch. Surg.*, **38**, 1036–1053.

408. Hyndman, O. R., and Julius Wolkin, 1943, Anterior chordotomy. Further observations on physiologic results and optimum manner of performance, *Arch. Neurol. & Psychiat.*, **50**, 129–148.

409. Ingram, W. R., 1940, Nuclear organization and

chief connections of the primate hypothalamus, *Research Publ., A. Nerv. & Ment. Dis.*, **20**, 195–244.

410. Ingvar, Sven, 1928, Studies in Neurology. I. The phylogenetic continuity of the central nervous system. II. On cerebellar function, *Bull. Johns Hopkins Hosp.*, **43**, 315–367.

411. Jacobsen, C. F., 1934, Influence of motor and premotor area lesions upon the retention of skilled movements in monkeys and chimpanzees, *Research Publ., A. Nerv. & Ment. Dis.*, **13**, 225–247.

412. Jakob, A., 1925, The anatomy, clinical syndromes and physiology of the extrapyramidal system, *Arch. Neurol. & Psychiat.*, **13**, 596–620.

413. Jansen, J., and A. Brodal, 1940, Experimental studies on the intrinsic fibers of the cerebellum. II. The corticonuclear projection, *J. Comp. Neurol.*, **73**, 267–321.

414. Jasper, H. H., 1949, Diffuse projection systems: The integrative action of the thalamic reticular system, *Electroencephalog. & Clin. Neurophysiol.*, **1**, 405–419.

415. Jasper, H. H., 1949, The electroencephalography in neurosurgery, *Digest Neurol. & Psychiat., Inst. of Living*, **17**, 559.

416. Jasper, H. H., and Jan Droogleever-Fortuyn, 1947, Experimental studies on the functional anatomy of petit mal epilepsy, *Research Publ., A. Nerv. & Ment. Dis.*, **26**, 272–298.

417. Jefferson, Geoffrey, 1931, Glossopharyngeal neuralgia, *Lancet*, **2**, 397–399.

418. Jefferson, Geoffrey, 1938, On the saccular aneurysms of the internal carotid artery in the cavernous sinus, *Brit. J. Surg.*, **26**, 267–302.

419. Jefferson, J. M., 1940, A study of the subcortical connexions of the optic tract system of the Ferret, with special reference to gonadal activation by retinal stimulation, *J. Anat.*, **75**, 106–134.

420. Johnston, J. B., 1923, Further contributions to the study of the evolution of the forebrain, *J. Comp. Neurol.*, **35**, 337–481; V. Survey of forebrain morphology, *J. Comp. Neurol.*, **36**, 143–192.

421. Kaada, B. R., K. H. Pribram, and J. A. Epstein, 1949, Respiratory and vascular responses in monkeys from temporal pole, insula, orbital surface, and cingulate gyrus. A preliminary report, *J. Neurophysiol.*, **12**, 347–356.

422. Kahn, E. A., 1947, The role of the dentate ligaments in spinal cord compression and the syndrome of lateral sclerosis, *J. Neurosurg.*, **4**, 191–199.

423. Kappers, C. U. A., G. C. Huber, and E. C. Crosby, 1936, "The Comparative Anatomy of the Nervous System of Vertebrates," New York, Macmillan, Vol. I, xvii + 864 pp.; Vol. II, xi + 865–1845.

424. Katz, L. N., and K. Jochim, 1939, Observations on the innervation of the coronary vessels of the dog, *Am. J. Physiol.*, **126**, 395–401.

425. Keegan, J. Jay, 1943, Dermatome hypalgesia associated with herniation of intervertebral disc, *Arch. Neurol. & Psychiat.*, **50**, 67–83.

426. Keegan, J. Jay, and Frederic D. Garrett, 1948, The segmental distribution of the cutaneous nerves in the limbs of man, *Anat. Rec.*, **102**, 409–437.

427. Keene, M. F. L., and E. E. Hewer, 1927, Observations on the development of the human suprarenal gland, *J. Anat.*, **61**, 302–324.

428. Keith, W. S., 1932, Glossopharyngeal neuralgia, *Brain*, **55**, 357–366.

429. Keller, A. D., 1942, Elimination of the pars nervosa without eliciting diabetes insipidus, *Endocrinology*, **30**, 408–422.

430. Kennard, Margaret A., 1944, Experimental analysis of the functions of the basal ganglia in monkeys and chimpanzees, *J. Neurophysiol.*, **7**, 127–148.

431. Kennard, Margaret A., 1945, Focal autonomic representation in the cortex and its relation to sham rage, *J. Neuropath. & Exper. Neurol.*, **4**, 295–304.

432. Kennard, M. A., and J. F. Fulton, 1942, Corticostriatal interrelations in monkey and chimpanzee, *Research Publ., Nerv. & Ment. Dis.*, **21**, 228–245.

433. Kennard, M. A., H. R. Viets, and J. F. Fulton, 1934, The syndrome of the premotor cortex in man. Impairment of skilled movements, forced grasping, spasticity and vasomotor disturbances, *Brain*, **57**, 69–84.

434. Kennedy, Foster, 1940, Medical syndromes of the hypothalamus, *Research Publ., A. Nerv. & Ment. Dis.*, **20**, 864–874.

435. Kershman, John, 1938, The medulloblast and the medulloblastoma. A study of human embryos, *Arch. Neurol. & Psychiat.*, **40**, 937–967.

436. Kershman, John, 1939, Genesis of microglia in the human brain, *Arch. Neurol. & Psychiat.*, **41**, 24–50.

437. Kimmel, D. L., 1945, Efferent fibers of the substantia nigra in the cat, *Anat. Rec.*, **91**, 284.

438. Kingsbury, B. F., 1922, The fundamental plan of the vertebrate brain, *J. Comp. Neurol.*, **34**, 461–491.

439. Klüver, H., and P. Bucy, 1939, Preliminary analysis of functions of the temporal lobes in

monkeys, *Arch. Neurol. & Psychiat.,* **42,** 979–1000.

440. Knight, G. C., 1934, The relation of the extrinsic nerves to the functional activity of the esophagus, *Brit. J. Surg.,* **22,** 155–168.

441. Knighton, R. S., 1950, Thalamic relay nucleus for the second somatic sensory receiving area in the cerebral cortex of the cat, *J. Comp. Neurol.,* **92,** 183–191.

442. Kramer, S. P., 1912, On the function of the circle of Willis, *J. Exper. Med.,* **15,** 348–363.

443. Kremer, W. F., 1947, Autonomic and somatic reactions induced by stimulation of the cingular gyrus in dogs, *J. Neurophysiol.,* **10,** 371–379.

444. Krieg, W. J. S., 1932, The hypothalamus of the albino rat, *J. Comp. Neurol.,* **55,** 19–89.

445. Kristiansen, Kristian, and G. Courtois, 1949, Rhythmic electrical activity from isolated cerebral cortex. *Electroencephalog. & Clin. Neurophysiol.,* **1,** 265–272.

446. Kuffler, S. W., and R. W. Gerard, 1947, The small-nerve motor system to skeletal muscle, *J. Neurophysiol.,* **10,** 383–394.

447. Kuffler, S. W., C. C. Hunt, and J. B. Quilliam, 1951, Function of medullated small-nerve fibers in mammalian ventral roots: Efferent muscle spindle innervation, *J. Neurophysiol.,* **14,** 29–54.

448. Kuffler, S. W., Y. Laporte, and R. E. Ransmeier, 1947, The function of the frog's small nerve motor system, *J. Neurophysiol.,* **10,** 395–408.

449. Kuhlenbeck, H., and R. N. Miller, 1949, The pretectal region of the human brain, *J. Comp. Neurol.,* **91,** 369–407.

450. Kuhn, Robert A., 1950, Functional capacity of the isolated human spinal cord, *Brain,* **73,** 1–51.

451. Kuhn, R. A., and M. B. Macht, 1949, Some manifestations of reflex activity in spinal man with particular reference to the occurrence of extensor spasam, *Bull. Johns Hopkins Hosp.,* **84,** 43–75.

452. Kuntz, A., 1936, The autonomic nervous system. Essential anatomy, *J. A. M. A.,* **106,** 345–350.

453. Kuntz, A., 1949, "The Neuroanatomic Basis of Surgery of the Autonomic Nervous System," Springfield, Ill., Charles C Thomas, 83 pp.

454. Kuntz, A., and C. A. Richins, 1946, Components and distribution of nerves of parotid and submandibular glands, *J. Comp. Neurol.,* **85,** 21–32.

455. Langley, J. N., 1893, Preliminary account of the arrangement of the sympathetic nervous system based chiefly on observations upon pilomotor nerves, *Proc. Roy Soc.,* **52,** 547–556.

456. Langley, J. N., 1903, The autonomic nervous system, *Brain,* **26,** 1–26.

457. Langley, J. N., 1921, "The Autonomic Nervous System," Cambridge, Heffer, 80 pp.

458. Langley, L. L., and J. A. Whiteside, 1951, Mechanisms of accommodation of urinary tone, *J. Neurophysiol.,* **14,** 147–152.

459. Langworthy, O. R., 1928, The behavior of pouch young opossums correlated with the myelination of the tracts in the nervous systems, *J. Comp. Neurol.,* **46,** 201–247.

460. Langworthy, O. R., 1930, Medullated tracts in the brain stem of a seven-month human fetus, *Contrib. Embryol.,* xxi (Carnegie Inst. Wash. Publ. 407), 37–52.

461. Langworthy, O. R., 1943, General principles of autonomic innervation, *Arch. Neurol. & Psychiat.,* **50,** 590–602.

462. Langworthy, O. R., and H. M. Fox, 1937, Thalamic syndrome. Syndrome of posterior cerebral artery. A review, *Arch. Int. Med.,* **60,** 203–224.

463. Langworthy, O. R., and L. C. Kolb, 1933, The encephalic control of tone in the musculature of the urinary bladder, *Brain,* **56,** 371–382.

464. Langworthy, O. R., L. C. Kolb, and L. G. Lewis, 1940, "Physiology of Micturition," Baltimore, Williams & Wilkins, viii + 232 pp.

465. Langworthy, O. R., and Luis Ortega, 1943, The Iris. Innervation of the iris of the albino rabbit as related to its function. Theoretical discussion of abnormalities of the pupils observed in man, *Medicine,* **22,** 287–362.

466. Larsell, O., 1936, The development and morphology of the cerebellum in the opossum. II. Later development and adult, *J. Comp. Neurol.,* **63,** 251–291.

467. Larsell, O., 1937, The cerebellum: A review and interpretation, *Arch. Neurol. & Psychiat.,* **38,** 580–607.

468. Larsell, O., 1947, The development of the cerebellum in man in relation to its comparative anatomy, *J. Comp. Neurol.,* **87,** 85–129,

469. Larsell, O., 1951, "Anatomy of the Nervous System," 2d ed., New York, Appleton-Century-Crofts, xiv + 520 pp.

470. Lashley, K. S., and R. W. Sperry, 1943, Olfactory discrimination after destruction of the anterior thalamic nuclei, *Am. J. Physiol.,* **139,** 446–450.

471. Lassek, A. M., 1940, The human pyramidal tract. II. A numerical investigation of the Betz cells of the motor area, *Arch. Neurol. & Psychiat.,* **44,** 718–724.

472. Lassek, A. M., 1947, The pyramidal tract: Basic considerations of corticospinal neurons,

Research Publ., A. Nerv. & Ment. Dis., **27,** 106–128.

473. Leão, A. A. P., 1944, Spreading depression of activity in the cerebral cortex, *J. Neurophysiol.,* **7,** 359–390.

474. Leão, A. A. P., and R. S. Morison, 1945, Propagation of spreading cortical depression, *J. Neurophysiol,* **8,** 33–45.

475. Leksell, Lars, 1945, The action potential and excitatory effects of the small ventral root fibres to skeletal muscle, *Acta physiol. Scandinav.,* Suppl. **31,** 1–84.

476. Lennox, William G., 1946, "Science and Seizures," New York, Harper, xiii + 258 pp.

477. Lennox, W. G., E. L. Gibbs, and F. A. Gibbs, 1940, Inheritance of cerebral dysrhythmia and epilepsy, *Arch. Neurol. & Psychiat.,* **44,** 1155–1183.

478. Levin, P. M., 1949, Efferent fibers, Chap. V in "The Precentral Motor Cortex," ed. by P. C. Bucy, 2d ed., Urbana, University of Illinois Press, pp. 135–148.

479. Levin, P. M., and F. K. Bradford, 1938, The exact origin of the corticospinal tract in the monkey, *J. Comp. Neurol.,* **68,** 411–422.

480. Lewis, D., and W. E. Dandy, 1930, The course of the nerve fibers transmitting the sensation of taste, *Arch. Surg.,* **21,** 249–288.

481. Lewy, F. H., and H. Kobrak, 1936, Neural projection of cochlear spirals on primary acoustic centers, *Arch. Neurol. & Psychiat.,* **35,** 839–852.

482. Leyton, A. S. F., and C. S. Sherrington, 1917, Observations on the excitable cortex of the chimpanzee, orangutan and gorilla, *Quart. J. Exper. Physiol.,* **11,** 135–222.

483. Licklider, J. C. R., and K. D. Kryter, 1942, Frequency-localization in the auditory cortex of the monkey, *Federation Proc.,* **1,** 51.

484. Lindsay, J. R., 1947, Effect of obliteration of the endolymphatic sac and duct in the monkey, *Arch. Otolaryng.,* **45,** 1–13.

485. Lindsley, D. B., J. W. Bowden, and H. W. Magoun, 1949, Effect upon the EEG of acute injury to the brain stem activating system, *Electroencephalog. & Clin. Neurophysiol.,* **1,** 475–486.

486. Lindsley, D. B., L. H. Schreiner, and H. W. Magoun, 1949, An electromyographic study of spasticity, *J. Neurophysiol.,* **12,** 197–205.

487. Livingston, R. B., W. P. Chapman, K. E. Livingston, and L. Kraintz, 1948, Stimulation of orbital surface of man prior to frontal lobotomy, *Research Publ., A. Nerv. & Ment. Dis.,* **27,** 421–432.

488. Livingston, R. B., J. F. Fulton, J. M. R. Delgado, E. Sachs, Jr., S. J. Brendler, and G. D. Davis, 1948, Stimulation and regional ablation of orbital surface of frontal lobe, *Research Publ., A. Nerv. & Ment. Dis.,* **27,** 405–420.

489. Lloyd, D. P. C., 1941, Activity in neurons of the bulbospinal correlation system, *J. Neurophysiol.,* **4,** 115–134.

490. Lloyd, D. P. C., 1941, The spinal mechanism of the pyramidal system in cats, *J. Neurophysiol.,* **4,** 525–546.

491. Lloyd, D. P. C., 1942, Mediation of descending long spinal reflex activity, *J. Neurophysiol.,* **5,** 435–458.

492. Lloyd, D. P. C., 1944, Functional Organization of the spinal cord, *Physiol. Rev.,* **24,** 1–17.

493. Lloyd, D. P. C., 1946, Facilitation and inhibition of spinal motoneurons, *J. Neurophysiol.,* **9,** 421–438.

494. Lloyd, D. P. C., 1946, Integrative pattern of excitation and inhibition in two-neuron reflex arcs, *J. Neurophysiol.,* **9,** 439–444.

495. Lloyd, D. P. C., and H.-T. Chang, 1948, Afferent fibers in muscle nerves, *J. Neurophysiol.,* **11,** 199–207.

496. Lockard, Isabel, 1948, Certain developmental relations and fiber connections of the triangular gyrus in primates, *J. Comp. Neurol.,* **89,** 349–386.

497. Locke, C. E., and H. C. Naffziger, 1924, The cerebral subarachnoid system, *Arch. Neurol. & Psychiat.,* **12,** 411–418.

498. Lorente de Nó, R., 1933, Studies on the structure of the cerebral cortex. I. The area entorhinalis, *J. f. Psychol. u. Neurol.,* **45,** 381–438.

499. Lorente de Nó, R., 1934, Studies on the structure of the cerebral cortex. Continuation of study of ammonic system, *J. f. Psychol. u. Neurol.,* **46,** 113–177.

500. Lorente de Nó, R., 1949, Cerebral cortex: Architecture, intracortical connections, motor projections, Chap. XV in "Physiology of the Nervous System," by J. F. Fulton, 3d ed., New York, Oxford, pp. 288–330.

501. Lorente de Nó, R., and A. S. Harris, 1933, Experimental studies in hearing threshold of reflexes of muscles of middle ear, *Laryngoscope,* **43,** 315–326.

502. McCulloch, W. S., 1944, The functional organization of the cerebral cortex, *Physiol. Rev.,* **24,** 390–407.

503. McCulloch, W. S., 1947, Modes of functional organization of the cerebral cortex, *Federation Proc.,* **6,** 448–452.

504. McCulloch, W. S., 1948, Some connections of the frontal lobe established by physiological neuronography, *Research Publ., A. Nerv. & Ment. Dis.,* **27,** 95–105.

505. McCulloch, W. S., 1949, Cortico-cortical con-

nections, Chap. VIII in "The Precentral Motor Cortex," ed. by P. C. Bucy, 2d ed., Urbana, University of Illinois Press, pp. 211–242.

506. McCulloch, W. S., and H. W. Garol, 1941, Cortical origin and distribution of corpus callosum and anterior commissure in the monkey (*Macaca mulatta*), *J. Neurophysiol.*, **4**, 555–563.

507. McCulloch, W. S., C. Graf, and H. W. Magoun, 1946, A cortico-bulbo-reticular pathway form area 4*s*, *J. Neurophysiol.*, **9**, 127–132.

508. McCulloch, W. S., and Elwood Henneman, 1948, The projection of area 19 to the reticular formation, *Federation Proc.*, **7**, 79.

509. McLardy, T., 1948, Projection of the centromedian nucleus of the human thalamus, *Brain*, **71**, 290–303.

510. McLardy, T., 1950, Uraemic and trophic deaths following leucotomy: Neuroanatomical findings, *J. Neurol., Neurosurg. & Psychiat.*, N.S., **13**, 106–114.

511. McLardy, T., 1950, The thalamic projection to frontal cortex in man, *J. Neurol., Neurosurg. & Psychiat.*, N.S. **13**, 198–202.

512. McLardy, T., and A. Meyer, 1949, Anatomical correlates of improvement after leucotomy, *J. Ment. Sc.*, **95**, 182–196.

513. McMichael, J., 1945, Spinal tracts subserving micturition in case of Erb's spinal paralysis, *Brain*, **68**, 162–164.

514. McNally, W. J., 1927, Some experiments upon the utricle, *Tr. Am. Otol. Soc.*, **23**, 99.

515. McNally, W. J., and J. Tait, 1925, Ablation experiments on the labyrinth of the frog, *Am. J. Physiol.*, **75**, 155–179.

516. McNally, W. J., and J. Tait, 1933, Some results of section of particular nerve branches to the ampullae of the four vertical semicircular canals of the frog, *Quart. J. Exper. Physiol.*, 23, 147–196.

517. Macht, M. B., and R. A. Kuhn, 1948, Responses to thermal stimuli mediated through the isolated spinal cord, *Arch. Neurol. & Psychiat.*, **59**, 754–778.

518. MacLean, P. D., 1949, Psychosomatic disease and the "visceral brain." Recent developments bearing on the Papez theory of emotion, *Psychosom. Med.*, **11**, 338–353.

519. Mangus, R., 1924, "Korperstellung," Berlin, Springer, xiii + 740 pp.

520. Magoun, H. W., 1940, Descending connections from the hypothalamus, *Research Publ., A. Nerv. & Ment. Dis.*, **20**, 270–285.

521. Magoun, H. W., 1944, Bulbar inhibition and facilitation of motor activity, *Science*, **100**, 549–550.

522. Magoun, H. W., 1949, discussion on "Diffuse projection systems: The integrative action of the thalamic reticular system" by H. Jasper, *Electroencephalog. & Clin. Neurophysiol.*, **1**, 419–420.

523. Magoun, H. W., D. Atlas, W. K. Hare, and S. W. Ranson, 1936, The afferent path of the pupillary light reflex in the monkey, *Brain*, **59**, 234–249.

524. Magoun, H. W., and L. E. Beaton, 1942, The salivatory motor nuclei in the monkey, *Am. J. Physiol.*, **136**, 720–725.

525. Magoun, H. W., F. Harrison, J. R. Brobeck, and S. W. Ranson, 1938, Activation of heat loss mechanisms by local heating of the brain, *J. Neurophysiol.*, **1**, 101–114.

526. Magoun, H. W., and Mary Ranson, 1942, The supraoptic decussations in the cat and monkey, *J. Comp. Neurol.*, **76**, 435–459.

527. Magoun, H. W., and R. Rhines, 1946, An inhibitory mechanism in the bulbar reticular formation, *J. Neurophysiol.*, **9**, 165–171.

528. Magoun, H. W., and R. Rhines, 1947, "Spasticity. The Stretch-reflex and Extrapyramidal Systems," Springfield, Ill., Charles C Thomas, 59 pp.

529. Malmo, R. B., 1942, Interference factors in delayed response in monkeys after removal of frontal lobes, *J. Neurophysiol.*, **5**, 295–308.

530. Marburg, Otto, 1944 The structure and fiber connections of the human habenula, *J. Comp. Neurol.*, **80**, 211–233.

531. Markee, J. E., C. H. Sawyer, and W. H. Hollinshead, 1946, Activation of the anterior hypophysis by electrical stimulation in the rabbit, *Endocrinology*, **38**, 345–357.

532. Marsh, Gordon, and H. W. Beams, 1946, In vitro control of growing chick nerve fibers by applied electric current, *J. Cell. & Comp. Physiol.*, **27**, 139–157.

533. Marshall, C., and A. E. Walker, 1950, The electroencephalographic changes after hemispherectomy in man, *Electroencephalog. & Clin. Neurophysiol.*, **2**, 147–156.

534. Marshall, W. H., 1949, Suppressor action on primary sensory projection reactions, *Federation Proc.*, **8**, 107.

535. Marshall, W. H., 1950, The relation of dehydration of the brain to the spreading depression of Leão, *Electroencephalog. & Clin. Neurophysiol.*, **2**, 177–186.

536. Matthews, B. H. C., 1933, Nerve endings in mammalian muscle, *J. Physiol.*, **78**, 1–53.

537. Melville, E. V., and Kendrick Hare, 1945, Antidiuretic material in the supraoptic nucleus, *Endocrinology*, **36**, 332–339.

538. Merritt, H., and M. Finland, 1930, Vascular

lesions of the hindbrain (lateral medullary syndrome), *Brain,* **53,** 290–305.

539. Mettler, F. A., 1935, Corticifugal fiber connections of the cortex of *Macaca mulatta. a.* The occipital region, *J. Comp.,* **61,** 221–256; *b.* The parietal region, *J. Comp. Neurol.,* **62,** 263–291; *c.* The frontal region, *J. Comp. Neurol.,* **61,** 509–542; *d.* The temporal region, *J. Comp. Neurol.,* **63,** 25–47.

540. Mettler, F. A., 1940, Extrapyramidal function, *J. Nerv. & Ment. Dis.,* **92,** 141–150.

541. Mettler, F. A., 1942, Relation between pyramidal and extrapyramidal function. *Research Publ., A. Nerv. & Ment. Dis.,* **21,** 150–227.

542. Mettler, F. A., 1945, Fiber connections of the corpus striatum of the monkey and baboon, *J. Comp. Neurol.,* **82,** 169–204.

543. Mettler, F. A., 1947. Extracortical connections of the primate frontal cerebral cortex. I. Thalamocortical connections, *J. Comp. Neurol.,* **86,** 95–118. II. Corticifugal connections, *J. Comp. Neurol.,* **86,** 119–166.

544. Mettler, F. A., 1948, "Neuroanatomy," 2d ed., St. Louis, Mosby, 536 pp.

545. Mettler, F. A., 1948, The nonpyramidal motor projections from the frontal cerebral cortex, *Research Publ., A. Nerv. & Ment. Dis.,* **27,** 162–199.

546. Mettler, F. A. (editor), 1949, "Selective and Partial Ablation of the Frontal Cortex. A Correlative Study of its Effects on Human Psychotic Subjects," Columbia-Greystone Associates, New York, Hoeber, xiv + 517 pp.

547. Mettler, F. A., H. Ades, E. Lipman, and E. A. Culler, 1939, The extrapyramidal system: An experimental demonstration of function, *Arch. Neurol. & Psychiat.,* **41,** 984–995.

548. Mettler, F. A., and C. C. Mettler, 1941, Role of the neostriatum, *Am. J. Physiol.,* **133,** 594–601.

549. Mettler, F. A., and C. C. Mettler, 1942, The effects of striatal injury, *Brain,* **65,** 242–255.

550. Meyer, A., 1907, The connections of the occipital lobes and the present status of the cerebral visual affections, *Tr. A. Am. Physicians,* **22,** 7–16.

551. Meyer, A., and E. Beck, 1945, Neuropathological problems arising from prefrontal leucotomy, *J. Ment. Sc.,* **91,** 411–425.

552. Meyer, A., E. Beck, and T. McLardy, 1947, Prefrontal leucotomy: A neuroanatomical report, *Brain,* **70,** 18–49.

553. Meyer, A., and T. McLardy, 1948, Posterior cuts in prefrontal leucotomy: A clinico-pathological study, *J. Ment. Sc.,* **94,** 555–564.

554. Meyer, M., 1949, Study of efferent connexions of the frontal lobe in the human brain after leucotomy, *Brain,* **72,** 265–296.

555. Meyer, M., and A. C. Allison, 1949, An experimental investigation of the connexions of the olfactory tracts in the monkey, *J. Neurol., Neurosurg. & Psychiat.,* N.S. **12,** 274–286.

556. Meyers, R., 1942, The modification of alternating tremors, rigidity and festination by surgery of the basal ganglia, *Research Publ., A. Nerv. & Ment. Dis.,* **21,** 602–665.

557. Meyers, R., 1942, Surgical interruption of the pallidofugal fibers. Its effect on syndrome of paralysis agitans and technical consideration in its application, *New York State J. Med.,* **42,** 317–325.

558. Meyers, R., D. B. Sweeney, and J. T. Schwidde, 1950, Hemiballismus: Etiology and surgical treatment, *J. Neurol., Neurosurg. & Psychiat.,* N.S. **13,** 115–126.

559. Miller, F. R., G. W. Stavraky, and G. A. Woonton, 1940, Effects of eserine, acetylcholine and atropine on the electrocorticogram, *J. Neurophysiol.,* **3,** 131–138.

560. Minkowski, M., 1920, Über den Verlauf, die Endigung und die zentrale Repräsentation von gekreuzten und ungekreuzten Sehnervenfasern bei einigen Säugetieren und beim Menschen, *Schweiz. Arch. f. Neurol. u. Psychiat,* **6,** 201–252.

561. Minkowski, M., 1923–1924, Etude sur les connections anatomiques des circonvolutions rolandiques, pariétales et frontales, *Schweiz. Arch. f. Neurol. u. Psychiat.,* **12,** 71–104, 227–268; **14,** 255–278; **15,** 97–132.

562. Moersch, F. P., and J. W. Kernohan, 1939, Hemiballismus: A clinico-pathologic study, *Arch. Neurol. & Psychiat.,* **41,** 365–372.

563. Monrad-Krohn, G. H., 1924, On the dissociation of voluntary and emotional innervation in facial paresis of central origin, *Brain,* **47,** 22–35.

564. Monrad-Krohn, G. H., 1934, "The Clinical Examination of the Nervous System," 6th ed., New York, Hoeber, xix + 234 pp.

565. Morel, F., 1947, La massa intermedia ou commissure grise, *Acta anat.,* **4,** 203–207.

566. Morison, R. S., and E. W. Dempsey, 1942, A study of thalamocortical relations, *Am. J. Physiol.,* **135,** 281–292.

567. Morison, R. S., and E. W. Dempsey, 1943, Mechanism of thalamocortical augmentation and repetition, *Am. J. Physiol.,* **138,** 297–308.

568. Morison, R. S., K. H. Finley, and G. N. Lothrop, 1943, Spontaneous electrical activity of the thalamus and other forebrain structures, *J. Neurophysiol.,* **6,** 243–254.

569. Morton, Guy, Andre Cipriani, and D. Mc-

Eachern, 1947, Mechanism of motion sickness, *Arch. Neurol. & Psychiat.*, **57**, 58–70.

570. Moruzzi, Guiseppe, 1940, Paleocerebellar inhibition of vasomotor and respiratory carotid sinus reflexes, *J. Neurophysiol.*, **3**, 20–32.

571. Moruzzi, Guiseppe, and H. W. Magoun, 1949, Brain stem reticular formation and activation of the EEG, *Electroencephalog. & Clin. Neurophysiol.*, **1**, 455–473.

572. Müller, J., 1826, "Zur vergleichenden Physiologie des Gesichtssinnes des Menschen und der Thiere nebst einem Versuch über die Bewegungen der Augen und über den menschlichen Blick," Leipzig, Cnobloch, xxxii + 462 pp.

573. Munro, Donald, 1945, The rehabilitation of patients totally paralyzed below the waist, with special reference to making them ambulatory and capable of earning their living. I. Anterior rhizotomy for spastic paraplegia, *New England J. Med.*, **233**, 453–461.

574. Munro, Donald, 1946, The rehabilitation of patients totally paralyzed below the waist, with special reference to making them ambulatory and capable of earning their own living. II. Control of urination, *New England J. Med.*, **234**, 207–216.

575. Munro, Donald, 1948, Rehabilitation of veterans paralyzed as the result of injury to the spinal cord and cauda equina, *Am. J. Surg.*, **75**, 3–18.

576. Murphy, J. P., and E. Gellhorn, 1945, The influence of hypothalamic stimulation on cortically induced movements and on action potentials of the cortex, *J. Neurophysiol.*, **8**, 341–364.

577. Murphy, J. P., and E. Gellhorn, 1945, Further investigations on diencephalic-cortical relations and their significance for the problem of emotion, *J. Neurophysiol.*, **8**, 431–447.

578. Nachmansohn, D., 1945, Role of acetylcholine in mechanism of nerve activity, *Vitamins & Hormones*, **3**, 337–377.

579. Nachmansohn, D., and B. Meyerhof, 1941, Relation between electrical changes during nerve activity and concentration of choline esterase, *J. Neurophysiol.*, **4**, 348–361.

580. Nathan, P. W., and M. C. Smith, 1951, The centripetal pathway from the bladder and urethra within the spinal cord, *J. Neurol., Neurosurg. & Psychiat.*, N.S. **14**, 262–280.

581. Nathan, P. W., and J. W. A. Turner, 1942, Efferent pathway for pupillary contraction, *Brain*, **65**, 343–351.

582. Niemer, W. T., and H. W. Magoun, 1947, Reticulospinal tracts influencing motor activity, *J. Comp. Neurol.*, **87**, 367–379.

583. Nims, L. F., and F. E. Nulsen, 1947, Interaction of cerebral cortex and cerebellum, *Federation Proc.*, **6**, 170.

584. Nonidez, J. F., 1935, Innervation of the thyroid gland. III. Distribution and termination of the nerve fibers in the dog, *Am. J. Anat.*, **57**, 135–169.

585. Norman, R. M., 1945, Thalamic degeneration following bilateral premotor frontal lobe atrophy of the Strümpell type, *J. Neurol., Neurosurg. & Psychiat.*, N.S. **8**, 52–56.

586. Nulsen, F. E., S. P. W. Black, and C. G. Drake, 1948, Inhibition and facilitation of motor activity by the anterior cerebellum, *Federation Proc.*, **7**, 86–87.

587. Obrador, S., 1943, Effect of hypothalamic lesions on electrical activity of the cerebral cortex, *J. Neurophysiol.*, **6**, 81–84.

588. O'Connor, W. J., and E. B. Verney, 1942, The effect of removal of the posterior lobe of the pituitary on the inhibition of water diuresis by emotional stress, *Quart. J. Exper. Physiol.*, **31**, 393–408.

589. O'Connor, W. J., and E. B. Verney, 1944, The effect of increased activity of the sympathetic system in the inhibition of water diuresis by emotional stress, *Quart. J. Exper. Physiol.*, **33**, 77–90.

590. O'Leary, James L., 1937, Structure of the primary olfactory cortex of the mouse, *J. Comp. Neurol.*, **67**, 1–31.

591. Olszewski, Jerzy, 1950, On the anatomical and functional organization of the spinal trigeminal nucleus, *J. Comp. Neurol.*, **92**, 401–413.

592. Papez, J. W., 1926, Reticulospinal tracts in the cat. Marchi method, *J. Comp. Neurol.*, **41**, 365–399.

593. Papez, J. W., 1937, A proposed mechanism of emotion, *Arch. Neurol. & Psychiat.*, **38**, 725–743.

594. Papez, J. W., 1942, A summary of fiber connections of the basal ganglia with each other and with other portions of the brain, *Research Publ., A. Nerv. & Ment. Dis.*, **21**, 21–68.

595. Papez, J. W., H. G. Bull, and W. A. Stotler, 1940, Cortical softening with atrophy of internal capsule and dorsal thalamus. Connections of the ventral lateral nucleus of the thalamus, *Arch. Neurol. & Psychiat.*, **44**, 977–989.

596. Papez, J. W., and W. A. Stotler, 1940, Connections of the red nucleus, *Arch. Neurol. & Psychiat.*, **44**, 776–791.

597. Paton, L., and G. Holmes, 1910, The pathology of papilledema, *Brain*, **33**, 389–432.

598. Patton, H. D., and T. C. Ruch, 1946, The relation of the foot of the pre- and postcentral gyrus to taste in the monkey and chimpanzee, *Federation Proc.*, **5**, 79.

599. Patton, H. D., T. C. Ruch, and A. E. Walker, 1944, Experimental hypogeusia from Horsley-Clarke lesions of the thalamus in *Macaca mulatta, J. Neurophysiol.,* **7,** 171–184.

600. Pearson, A. A., 1941, The development of the nervus terminals in man, *J. Comp. Neurol.,* **75,** 39–66.

601. Pearson, A. A., 1941, The development of the olfactory nerve in man, *J. Comp. Neurol.,* **75,** 199–217.

602. Pearson, A. A., 1944, The oculomotor nucleus in the human fetus, *J. Comp. Neurol.,* **80,** 47–63.

603. Pearson, A. A., 1945, Further observations on the intramedullary sensory type neurons along the hypoglossal nerve, *J. Comp. Neurol.,* **82,** 93–100.

604. Pearson, A. A., 1947, The roots of the facial nerve in human embryos and fetuses, *J. Comp. Neurol.,* **87,** 139–159.

605. Pearson, A. A., 1949, The development and connections of the mesencephalic root of the trigeminal nerve in man, *J. Comp. Neurol.,* **90,** 1–46.

606. Peele, T. L., 1942, Cytoarchitecture of individual parietal areas in the monkey (*Macaca mulatta*) and the distribution of the efferent fibers, *J. Comp. Neurol.,* **77,** 693–737.

607. Peele, T. L., 1944, Acute and chronic parietal lobe ablations in monkeys, *J. Neurophysiol.,* **7,** 269–286.

608. Penfield, W., 1920, Alterations of the Golgi apparatus in nerve cells, *Brain,* **43,** 290–305.

609. Penfield, W., 1924, Oligodendroglia and its relation to classical neuroglia, *Brain,* **47,** 430–452.

610. Penfield, W., 1929, Diencephalic autonomic epilepsy, *Arch. Neurol. & Psychiat.,* **22,** 358–374.

611. Penfield, W., 1932, Neuroglia: Normal and pathological, Sec. 9 in "Cytology and Cellular Pathology of the Nervous System," New York, Hoeber, Vol. II, 421–480.

612. Penfield, W., 1936, The cerebral cortex and consciousness, *Harvey Lect.,* **32,** 35–69.

613. Penfield, W., 1947, Some observations on the cerebral cortex of man, *Proc. Roy. Soc., London,* **B. 134,** 329–347.

614. Penfield, W., 1948, Symposium on gyrectomy. Part I. Bilateral frontal gyrectomy and postoperative intelligence, *Research Publ., A. Nerv. & Ment. Dis.,* **27,** 519–533.

615. Penfield, W., and E. Boldrey, 1937, Somatic motor and sensory representation in the cerebral cortex of man as studied by electrical stimulation, *Brain,* **60,** 389–443.

616. Penfield, W., and T. C. Erickson, 1941, "Epilepsy and Cerebral Localization. A Study of the Mechanism, Treatment and Prevention of Epileptic Seizures," Springfield, Ill., Charles C Thomas, x + 623 pp.

617. Penfield, W., and J. P. Evans, 1934, Functional defects produced by cerebral lobectomies, *Research Publ., A. Nerv. & Ment. Dis.,* **13,** 352–377.

618. Penfield, W., and J. P. Evans, 1935, The frontal lobe in man: A clinical study of maximum removals, *Brain,* **58,** 115–133.

619. Penfield, W., J. P. Evans, and J. A. MacMillan, 1935, Visual pathways in man with particular reference to macular representation, *Arch. Neurol. & Psychiat.,* **33,** 816–834.

620. Penfield, W., and F. McNaughton, 1940, Dural headache and innervation of the dura mater, *Arch. Neurol. & Psychiat.,* **44,** 43–75.

621. Penfield, W., and T. Rasmussen, 1949, Vocalization and arrest of speech, *Arch. Neurol. & Psychiat.,* **61,** 21–27.

622. Penfield, W., and T. Rasmussen, 1950, "The Cerebral Cortex of Man. A Clinical Study of Localization of Function," New York, Macmillan, xv + 248 pp.

623. Penfield, W., and J. S. M. Robertson, 1943, Growth asymmetry due to lesions of the postcentral cerebral cortex, *Arch. Neurol. & Psychiat.,* **50,** 405–430.

624. Peterson, E. W., H. W. Magoun, W. S. McCulloch, and D. B. Lindsley, 1949, Production of postural tremor, *J. Neurophysiol.,* **12,** 371–384.

625. Petr, R., L. B. Holden, and J. Jirout, 1949, The efferent intercortical connections of the superficial cortex of the temporal lobe (*Macaca mulatta*), *J. Neuropath. & Exper. Neurol.,* **8,** 100–103.

626. Pfeifer, R. A., 1936, Pathologie der Hörstrahlung und der corticalen Hörsphäre, in "Handbuch der Neurologie," by O. Bumke and O. Foerster, Berlin, Springer, Vol. 6, pp. 533–626.

627. Pitts, R. F., 1940, The respiratory center and its descending pathways, *J. Comp. Neurol.,* **72,** 605–625.

628. Pitts, R. F., 1942, The function of components of the respiratory complex, *J. Neurophysiol.,* **5,** 403–413.

629. Polyak, S. L., 1928, An experimental study of the association callosal, and projection fibers of the cerebral cortex of the cat, *J. Comp. Neurol.,* **44,** 197–258.

630. Polyak, S. L., 1933, A contribution to the cerebral representation of the retina, *J. Comp. Neurol.,* **57,** 541–617.

631. Polyak, S. L., 1941, "The Retina," Chicago, University of Chicago Press, x + 607 pp.

632. POLYAK, S. L., and R. HAYASHI, 1936, The cerebral representation of the retina in the chimpanzee, *Brain,* **59,** 51–60.

633. POOL, J. L., 1943, Effects of electrical stimulation of the human cerebellar cortex. A preliminary note, *J. Neuropath. & Exper. Neurol.,* **2,** 203–204.

634. POOL, J. L., and J. RANSOHOFF, 1949, Autonomic effects on stimulating rostral portion of cingulate gyri in man, *J. Neurophysiol.,* **12,** 384–392.

635. POPA, G., and U. FIELDING, 1930, A portal circulation from the pituitary to the hypothalamic region, *J. Anat.,* **65,** 88–91.

636. POPPEN, J. L., 1948, Prefrontal lobotomy, *Digest Neurol. & Psychiat., Inst. of Living,* **16,** 403–408.

637. PREYER, W., 1885, "Specielle Physiologie des Embryo," Leipzig. ("Embryonic Motility and Sensitivity," trans. by G. E. Coghill and W. K. Legner, 1937, Monographs of the Society for Research in Child Development, National Research Council, Washington, D.C., Vol. II, No. 6, Serial No. 13, 115 pp.)

638. PRIBRAM, K. H., M. A. LENNOX, and R. H. DUNSMORE, 1950, Some connections of the orbito-fronto-temporal, limbic and hippocampal areas of *Macaca mulatta, J. Neurophysiol.,* **13,** 127–135.

639. PUTNAM, T. J., 1926, Studies on the central visual system. IV. The details of the organization of the geniculostriate system in man, *Arch. Neurol. & Psychiat.,* **16,** 638–707.

640. PUTNAM, T. J., 1938, Results of treatment of athetosis by section of the extrapyramidal tracts in the spinal cord, *Arch. Neurol. & Psychiat.,* **39,** 258–275.

641. PUTNAM, T. J., 1940, Relief from unilateral paralysis agitans by section of the lateral pyramidal tract, *Arch. Neurol. & Psychiat.,* **44,** 950–976.

642. PUTNAM, T. J., 1942, Operative treatment of diseases characterized by involuntary movements (tremor, athetosis), *Research Publ., A. Nerv. & Ment. Dis.,* **21,** 666–696.

643. RACHMATULLIN, Z. C., 1936, Die Entwicklung der Meissnerschen Körperchen in der Menschenhaut, *Ztschr. f. mikr.-anat. Forsch.,* **40,** 445–454.

644. RAMÓN Y CAJAL, S., 1909–1911, "Histologie du système nerveux de l'homme et des vertébrés," 2 vols., Paris, A. Maloine.

645. RANEY, RUPERT B., 1939, A hitherto undescribed surgical procedure relieving attacks of angina pectoris, *J. A. M. A.,* **113,** 1619–1623.

646. RANSON, S. W., 1915, Unmyelinated nerve-fibres as conductors of protopathic sensation, *Brain,* **38,** 381–389.

647. RANSON, S. W., 1936, Some functions of the hypothalamus, *Harvey Lect.,* **32,** 92–121.

648. RANSON, S. W., 1939, Somnolence caused by hypothalamic lesions in the monkey, *Arch. Neurol. & Psychiat.,* **41,** 1–23.

649. RANSON, S. W., 1940, Regulation of body temperature, *Research Publ., A. Nerv. & Ment. Dis.,* **20,** 342–399.

650. RANSON, S. W., and P. R. BILLINGSLEY, 1916, Afferent spinal paths and the vasomotor reflexes. Studies in vasomotor reflex arcs IV, *Am. J. Physiol.,* **42,** 16–35.

651. RANSON, S. W., and H. W. MAGOUN, 1939, The hypothalamus, *Ergebn. Physiol., biol. Chem., u. exper. Pharmakol.,* **41,** 56–163.

652. RANSON, S. W., and S. W. RANSON, Jr., 1942, Efferent fibers of the corpus striatum, *Research Publ., A. Nerv. & Ment. Dis.,* **21,** 69–76.

653. RASMUSSEN, A. T., 1940, Effects of hypophysectomy and hypophysial stalk resection on the hypothalamic nuclei of animals and man, *Research Publ., A. Nerv. & Ment. Dis.,* **20,** 245–269.

654. RASMUSSEN, A. T., and W. T. PEYTON, 1941, The location of the lateral spinothalamic tract in the brain stem of man, *Surgery,* **10,** 699–710.

655. RASMUSSEN, A. T., and W. T. PEYTON, 1946, Origin of the ventral external arcuate fibers and their continuity with the striae medullares of the fourth ventricle of man, *J. Comp. Neurol.,* **84,** 325–337.

656. RASMUSSEN, A. T., and W. T. PEYTON, 1948, The course and termination of the medial lemniscus in man, *J. Comp. Neurol.,* **88,** 411–424.

657. RASMUSSEN, G. L., 1946, The olivary peduncle and other fiber projections of the superior olivary complex, *J. Comp. Neurol.,* **84,** 141–219.

658. RASMUSSEN, T., and W. PENFIELD, 1947, Further studies of the sensory and motor cerebral cortex of man, *Federation Proc.,* **6,** 452–460.

659. RASMUSSEN, T., and W. PENFIELD, 1948, Movement of head and eyes from stimulation of human frontal cortex, *Research Publ., A. Nerv. & Ment. Dis.,* **27,** 346–361.

660. RAY, B. S., J. C. HINSEY, and W. A. GEOHEGAN, 1943, Observations on the distribution of the sympathetic nerves to the pupil and upper extremity as determined by stimulation of the anterior roots in man, *Ann. Surg.,* **118,** 647–655.

661. REICHERT, F. L., and E. J. POTH, 1933, Recent knowledge regarding the physiology of the glossopharyngeal nerve in man with an analysis of its sensory, motor, gustatory and secretory functions, *Bull. Johns Hopkins Hosp.,* **53,** 131–139.

662. Renyi, G. S. de, 1929, The structure of cells in tissues as revealed by microdissection. II. The physical properties of the living axis cylinder in the myelinated nerve fiber of the frog, *J. Comp. Neurol.,* **47,** 405–426.

663. Renyi, G. S. de, 1932, Architecture of the nerve cell as revealed by microdissection, Sec. XXXIII in "Special Cytology," ed. by E. V. Cowdry, 2d ed., New York, Hoeber, pp. 1369–1402.

664. Rexed, Bror, 1944, Contributions to the knowledge of the post-natal development of the peripheral nervous system in man, *Acta psychiat. et neurol.,* Suppl. **33,** 1–206.

665. Rhines, R., and H. W. Magoun, 1946, Brain stem facilitation of cortical motor response, *J. Neurophysiol.,* **9,** 219–229.

666. Rhines, R., and W. F. Windle, 1941, The early development of the fasciculus longitudinalis medialis and associated secondary neurons in the rat, cat, and man, *J. Comp. Neurol.,* **75,** 165–189.

667. Richards, Glenn A., Jr., H. Burr Steinbach, and T. F. Anderson, 1943, Electron microscope studies of squid giant nerve axoplasm, *J. Cell. & Comp. Physiol.,* **21,** 129–143.

668. Richter, Curt P., 1946, Instructions for using the cutaneous resistance recorder, or "dermometer," on peripheral nerve injuries, sympathectomies, and paravertebral blocks, *J. Neurosurg.,* **3,** 181–191.

669. Richter, Curt P., 1947, Cutaneous areas denervated by upper thoracic and stellate ganglionectomies determined by the electrical skin resistance method, *J. Neurosurg.,* **4,** 221–232.

670. Richter, Curt P., and Marion Hines, 1938, Increased general activity produced by prefrontal and striatal lesions in monkey, *Brain,* **61,** 1–16.

671. Richter, Curt P., and B. G. Woodruff, 1941, Changes produced by sympathectomy in the electrical resistance of the skin, *Surgery,* **10,** 957–970.

672. Riddoch, G., 1917, The reflex functions of the completely divided spinal cord in man, compared with those associated with less severe lesions, *Brain,* **40,** 264–402.

673. Rienhoff, W. F., and L. N. Gay, 1938, Treatment of intractable bronchial asthma by bilateral resection of the posterior pulmonary plexus, *Arch. Surg.,* **37,** 456–469.

674. Riley, H. A., 1930, The central nervous system control of the ocular movements and the disturbances of the mechanism, *Arch. Ophth.,* N.S. **4,** 640–661; 885–910.

675. Riley, Henry A., 1943, "An Atlas of the Basal Ganglia, Brain Stem, and Spinal Cord" (based on myelin-stained material), Baltimore, Williams & Wilkins, ix + 708 pp.

676. Rioch, David McK., and Charles Brenner, 1937, Experiments on the corpus striatum and rhinencephalon, *J. Comp. Neurol.,* **68,** 491–507.

677. Rio-Hortega, P. del, 1932, Pineal gland, Sec. XIV in "Cytology and Cellular Pathology of the Nervous System," ed. by Wilder Penfield, New York, Hoeber, pp. 635–704.

678. Rio-Hortega, P. del, 1939, The microglia, *Lancet,* **1,** 1023–1026.

679. Robertis, E. De, and F. O. Schmitt, 1948, An electron microscope analysis of certain nerve axon constituents, *J. Cell. & Comp. Physiol.,* **31,** 1–24.

680. Robinson, M. F., W. Freeman, and J. W. Watts, 1949, Personality changes after psychosurgery, *Digest Neurol. & Psychiat., Inst. of Living,* **17,** 558.

681. Rogers, L., 1947, The function of the circulus arteriosus of Willis, *Brain,* **70,** 171–178.

682. Romanes, G. J., 1941, The development and significance of the cell columns in the ventral horn of the cervical and upper thoracic spinal cord of the rabbit, *J. Anat.,* **76,** 112–130.

683. Romanes, G. J., 1942, The spinal cord in a case of congenital absence of the right limb below the knee, *J. Anat.,* **77,** 1–5.

684. Romanes, G. J., 1947, The prenatal medullation of the sheep's nervous system, *J. Anat.,* **81,** 64–81.

685. Rose, J. E., and C. N. Woolsey, 1943, Potential changes in the olfactory brain produced by electrical stimulation of the olfactory bulb, *Federation Proc.,* **2,** 42.

686. Rose, J. E., and C. N. Woolsey, 1948, The orbito-frontal cortex and its connections with the mediodorsal nucleus in rabbit, sheep, and cat, *Research Publ., A. Nerv. & Ment. Dis.,* **27,** 210–232.

687. Rose, J. E., and C. N. Woolsey, 1948, Structure and relations of limbic cortex and anterior thalamic nuclei in rabbit and cat, *J. Comp. Neurol.,* **89,** 279–347.

688. Rose, J. E., and C. N. Woolsey, 1949, Organization of the mammalian thalamus and its relationships to the cerebral cortex, *Electroencephalog. & Clin. Neurophysiol.,* **1,** 391–402.

689. Rose, M., 1935, Cytoarchitektonik und Myeloarchitektonik der Grosshirnrinde, in "Handbuch der Neurologie," by O. Bumke and O. Foerster, Vol. I, Berlin, Springer, pp. 588–778.

690. Rowbotham, G. F., 1939, Observations on the effects of trigeminal denervation, *Brain,* **62,** 364–380.

691. Ruch, T. C., M. Blum, and J. Brobeck, 1941,

Taste disturbances from thalamic lesions in monkeys, *Am. J. Physiol.*, **133**, P433–P434.

692. Ruch, T. C., and H. D. Patton, 1946, The relation of the deep opercular cortex to taste, *Federation Proc.*, **5**, 89–90.

693. Ruch, T. C., and H. A. Shenkin, 1943, The relation of area 13 on the orbital surface of frontal lobes to hyperactivity and hyperphagia in monkeys, *J. Neurophysiol.*, **6**, 349–360.

694. Rundles, R. W., personal communications.

695. Rundles, R. W., and J. W. Papez, 1938, Fiber and cellular degeneration following temporal lobectomy in the monkey, *J. Comp. Neurol.*, **68**, 267–296.

696. Russell, D. S., A. H. E. Marshall, and F. B. Smith, 1948, Microgliomatosis. A form of reticulosis affecting the brain, *Brain*, **71**, 1–15.

697. Russell, W. Ritchie, 1948, Functions of the frontal lobes, *Lancet*, **1**, 356–360.

698. Rylander, G., 1943, Mental changes after excision of cerebral tissue. A clinical study of 16 cases of resections in the parietal, temporal, and occipital lobes, *Acta psychiat. et neurol.*, Suppl. 25, 1–81.

699. Rylander, G., 1948, Personality analysis before and after frontal lobotomy, *Research Publ., A. Nerv. & Ment. Dis.*, **27**, 691–705.

700. Sachs, Ernest, Jr., S. J. Brendler, and J. F. Fulton, 1949, The orbital gyri, *Brain*, **72**, 227–240.

701. Sand, R., 1903, Beitrag zur Kenntnis der corticobulbaren und corticopontinen Pyramidenfasern beim Menschen, *Arb. a. d. neurol. Inst. a. d. Wien. Univ.*, **10**, 185–222.

702. Sanford, H. S., and H. L. Bair, 1939, Visual disturbances associated with tumors of the temporal lobe, *Arch. Neurol. & Psychiat.*, **42**, 21–43.

703. Sauer, F. C., 1935, Mitosis in the neural tube, *J. Comp. Neurol.*, **62**, 377–405.

704. Sauer, F. C., 1935, The cellular structure of the neural tube, *J. Comp. Neurol.*, **63**, 13–23.

705. Sawyer, C. H., 1943, Cholinesterase and the behavior problem in Amblystoma. I. The relationship between the enzyme and early motility. II. The effect of inhibiting cholinesterase, *J. Exper. Zool.*, **92**, 1–29.

706. Scarff, J. E., 1940, Primary cortical centers for movements of upper and lower limbs in man; Observations based on electrical stimulation, *Arch. Neurol. & Psychiat.*, **44**, 243–299.

707. Scarff, J. E., and J. L. Pool, 1947, Factors causing mass spasms after transection in the cord in man: A reexamination, *Arch. Neurol. & Psychiat.*, **57**, 261–263.

708. Schlesinger, B., 1939, Venous drainage of the brain, with special reference to galenic system, *Brain*, **62**, 274–291.

709. Schmitt, F. O., 1950, The structure of the axon filaments of the giant nerve fibers of Loligo and Myxicola, *J. Exper. Zool.*, **113**, 499–516.

710. Schmitt, F. O., and R. S. Bear, 1939, The ultrastructure of the nerve axon sheath, *Biol. Rev.*, **14**, 27–50.

711. Schreiner, L. H., D. B. Lindsley, and H. W. Magoun, 1949, Role of brain stem facilitatory systems in the maintenance of spasticity, *J. Neurophysiol.*, **12**, 207–216.

712. Schwartz, H. G., and G. Weddell, 1938, Observations on the pathways transmitting the sensation of taste, *Brain*, **61**, 99–115.

713. Scoville, W. B., 1949, Selective cortical undercutting as a means of modifying and studying frontal lobe function in man. Preliminary report of forty-three operative cases, *J. Neurosurg.*, **6**, 65–73.

714. Seddon, H. J., 1948, A review of work on peripheral nerve injuries in Great Britain during World War II, *J. Nerv. & Ment. Dis.*, **108**, 160–168.

715. Seddon, H. J., P. B. Medawar, and H. Smith, 1943, Rate of regeneration of peripheral nerves in man, *J. Physiol.*, **102**, 191–215.

716. Sheehan, Donal, 1940, The hypothalamus and gastrointestinal regulation, *Research Publ., A. Nerv. & Ment. Dis.*, **20**, 589–616.

717. Sheehan, Donal, 1941, The autonomic nervous system, *Ann. Rev. Physiol.*, **3**, 399–448.

718. Sheehan, D., and J. Pick, 1943, The rami communicantes in the rhesus monkey, *J. Anat.*, **77**, 125–139.

719. Shenkin, H. A., M. H. Harmel, and S. S. Kety, 1948, Dynamic anatomy of the cerebral circulation, *Arch. Neurol. & Psychiat.*, **60**, 240–252.

720. Shenkin, H. A., and F. H. Lewey, 1944, Taste aura preceding convulsions in a lesion of the parietal operculum, *J. Nerv. & Ment. Dis.*, **100**, 352–354.

721. Shenkin, H. A., R. B. Woodford, F. A. Freyhan, and S. S. Kety, 1947, Effects of frontal lobotomy on cerebral blood flow and metabolism, *Research Publ., A. Nerv. & Ment. Dis.*, **27**, 823–831.

722. Sheps, Jack G., 1945, The nuclear configuration and cortical connections of the human thalamus, *J. Comp. Neurol.*, **83**, 1–56.

723. Sherman, Irving C., and Alex J. Arieff, 1948, Dissociation between pain and temperature in spinal cord lesions, *J. Nerv. & Ment. Dis.*, **108**, 285–292.

724. Sherrington, C. S., 1898, Decerebrate rigidity

and reflex coordination of movements, *J. Physiol.*, **22**, 319–332.

725. Sherrington, C. S., 1898, Experiments in examination of the peripheral distribution of the fibres of the posterior roots of some spinal nerves. Part II. *Philos. Tr., roy. Soc., London*, **B. 190**, 45–186.

726. Sherrington, C. S., 1906, "The Integrative Action of the Nervous System," London, Constable, xvi + 411 pp.

727. Sinclair, D. C., 1948, Observations on sensory paralysis produced by compression of a human limb, *J. Neurophysiol.*, **11**, 75–92.

728. Sjoqvist, O., 1938, Studies on pain conduction in the trigeminal nerve: A contribution to the surgical treatment of facial pain, *Acta psychiat. et neurol.*, Suppl. 17, 1–139.

729. Sloan, N., and H. Jasper, 1950, The identity of spreading depression and "suppression," *Electroencephalog. & Clin. Neurophysiol.*, **2**, 59–78.

730. Sloan, N., and H. Jasper, 1950, Studies of the regulatory functions of the anterior limbic cortex, *Electroencephalog. & Clin. Neurophysiol.*, **2**, 317–328.

731. Smith, W. K., 1945, The functional significance of the rostral cingular cortex as revealed by its responses to electrical excitation, *J. Neurophysiol.*, **8**, 241–255.

732. Smyth, G. E., 1939, The systemization and central connections of the spinal tract and nucleus of the trigeminal nerve, *Brain*, **62**, 41–87.

733. Snider, R. S., 1945, Electro-anatomical studies on a tectocerebellar pathway, *Anat. Rec.*, **91**, 299.

734. Snider, R. S., and E. Eldred, 1948, Cerebral projections to the tactile, auditory, and visual areas of the cerebellum, *Anat. Rec.*, **100**, 714.

735. Snider, R. S., W. S. McCulloch, and H. W. Magoun, 1949, A cerebello-bulboreticular pathway for suppression, *J. Neurophysiol.*, **12**, 325–334.

736. Snider, R. S., and H. W. Magoun, 1949, Facilitation produced by cerebellar stimulation, *J. Neurophysiol.*, **12**, 335–345.

737. Snider, R. S., H. W. Magoun, and W. S. McCulloch, 1947, A suppressor cerebello-bulbo-reticular pathway from anterior lobe and paramedian lobules, *Federation Proc.*, **6**, 207.

738. Snider, R. S., and A. Stowell, 1944, Receiving areas of the tactile, auditory, and visual systems in the cerebellum, *J. Neurophysiol.*, **7**, 331–357.

739. Snider, R. S., and C. N. Woolsey, 1941, Extensor rigidity in cats produced by simultaneous ablation of the anterior lobe of the cerebellum and the pericruciate areas of the cerebral hemispheres, *Am. J. Physiol.*, **133**, P454.

740. Speidel, C. C., 1932, Studies on living nerves. I. The movements of individual sheath cells and nerve sprouts correlated with the process of myelin-sheath formation in amphibian larvae, *J. Exper. Zool.*, **61**, 279–331.

741. Speidel, C. C., 1935, Studies of living nerves. Phenomena of nerve irritation and recovery, degeneration and repair, J. *Comp. Neurol.*, **61**, 1–80.

742. Spemann, H., 1938, "Embryonic Development and Induction," New Haven, Yale University Press, 401 pp.

743. Spencer, W. G., 1894, The effect produced upon respiration by faradic excitation of the cerebrum in the monkey, dog, cat, and rabbit, *Philos. Tr., roy. Soc., London*, **B. 185**, 609–657.

744. Spiegel, E. A., 1932, Cortical center of labyrinth, *J. Nerv. & Ment. Dis.*, **75**, 504–512.

745. Spiegel, E. A., 1934, Labyrinth and cortex. Electroencephalogram in stimulation of the labyrinth, *Arch. Neurol. & Psychiat.*, **31**, 469–482.

746. Spiegel, E. A., H. R. Miller, and M. J. Oppenheimer, 1940, Forebrain and rage reactions, *J. Neurophysiol.*, **3**, 538–548.

747. Spiegel, E. A., and J. B. Price, 1939, Origin of the quick component of labyrinthine nystagmus, *Arch. Otolaryng.*, **30**, 576–588.

748. Spiegel, E. A., and I. Sommer, 1944, "Neurology of the Eye, Ear, Nose and Throat," New York, Grune & Stratton, xi + 667 pp.

749. Spiegel, E. A., H. L. Wycis, M. Marks, and A. J. Lee, 1947, Stereotaxic apparatus for operations on the human brain, *Science*, **106**, 349–350.

750. Spielmeyer, W., 1906, Hemiplegie bei intakter Pyramidenbahn (intrakortikall Hemiplegie), *München. Med. Wchnschr.*, **53**, 1404–1407.

751. Spillane, John D., 1938, Olfactory alloaesthesia, *Brain*, **61**, 393–401.

752. Spillane, John D., 1939, Clinical investigation of olfactory function in brain tumour patients, *Brain*, **62**, 213–221.

753. Spiller, W. G., 1932, Corticonuclear tracts for associated ocular movements, *Arch. Neurol. & Psychiat.*, **28**, 251–271.

754. Sprague, J. M., 1946, Distribution of the axons from the motor cell groups in the spinal cord of the fetal sheep, *J. Comp. Neurol.*, **85**, 127–139.

755. Sprague, J. M., L. H. Schreiner, D. B. Lindsley, and H. W. Magoun, 1948, Retic-

ulospinal influences on stretch reflexes, *J. Neurophysiol.*, **11**, 501–507.

756. Starzl, T. E., and H. W. Magoun, 1951, Organization of the diffuse thalamic projection system, *J. Neurophysiol.*, **14**, 133–146.

757. Stead, E. A., R. V. Ebert, John Romano, and J. V. Warren, 1942, Central autonomic paralysis, *Arch. Neurol. & Psychiat.*, **48**, 92–107.

758. Stern, K., 1938, Note on the nucleus ruber magnocellularis and its efferent pathway in man, *Brain*, **61**, 284–289.

759. Stopford, J. S. B., 1916, The arteries of the pons and medulla oblongata, *J. Anat.*, **50**, 131–164, 255–280.

760. Stopford, J. S. B., 1927, Disturbances of sensation following section and suture of a peripheral nerve, *Brain*, **50**, 391–398.

761. Straus, W. L., and A. B. Howell, 1936, The spinal accessory nerve and its musculature, *Quart. Rev. Biol.*, **11**, 387–405.

762. Streit, Paul H., 1942, Tic douloureux of the glossopharyngeal nerve, *Arch. Otolaryng.*, **36**, 704–712.

763. Strong, Oliver S., 1936, Some observations on the course of the fibers from Clarke's column in the normal human spinal cord, *Bull. Neurol. Inst., New York*, **5**, 378–386.

764. Sugar, O., L. V. Amador, and B. Griponissiotes, 1950, Corticocortical connections of the walls of the superior temporal sulcus in the monkey (*Macaca mulatta*), *J. Neuropath. & Exper. Neurol.*, **9**, 179–185.

765. Sugar, O., J. G. Chusid, and J. D. French, 1948, A second motor cortex in the monkey (*Macaca mulatta*), *J. Neuropath. & Exper. Neurol.*, **7**, 182–189.

766. Sugar, O., J. D. French, and J. G. Chusid, 1948, Corticocortical connections of the superior surface of the temporal operculum in the monkey (*Macaca mulatta*), *J. Neurophysiol.* **11**, 175–184.

767. Sugar, O., R. Petr, L. V. Amador, and B. Griponissiotes, 1950, Corticocortical connections of the cortex buried in intraparietal and principal sulci of monkey (*Macaca mulatta*), *J. Neuropath. & Exper. Neurol.*, **9**, 430–437.

768. Suh, T. H., and Leo Alexander, 1939, Vascular system of the human spinal cord, *Arch. Neurol. & Psychiat.*, **41**, 659–677.

769. Sunderland, S., 1940, The projection of the cerebral cortex on the pons and cerebellum in the macaque monkey, *J. Anat.*, **74**, 201–226.

770. Sweet, W. H., G. C. Cotzias, J. Seed, and P. Yakovlev, 1948, Gastrointestinal hemorrhages, hyperglycemia, azotemia, hyperchloremia and hypernatremia following lesions of the frontal lobe in man, *Research Publ., A. Nerv. & Ment. Dis.*, **27**, 795–822.

771. Szentagothai, John, and Tibor Kiss, 1949, Projection of dermatomes on the substantia gelatinosa, *Arch. Neurol. & Psychiat.* **62**, 734–744.

772. Szymonowicz, W., 1933, Über die Entwicklung der Nervendigungen in der Haut des Menschen, *Ztschr. f. Zellforsch. u. mikr. Anat.*, **19**, 356–382.

773. Talbot, S. A., and W. H. Marshall, 1941, Physiological studies on neural mechanisms of visual localization and discrimination, *Am. J. Ophth.*, **24**, 1255–1264.

774. Thompson, C. E., and A. C. Witham, 1948, Paroxysmal hypertension in spinal cord injuries, *New England J. Med.*, **239**, 291–294.

775. Thomson, Alfredo F., and A. E. Walker, 1951, Behavioral alterations following lesions of the medial surface of the temporal lobe, *Arch. Neurol. & Psychiat.*, **65**, 251–252.

776. Toennies, J. F., 1939, Conditioning of afferent impulses by reflex discharges over the dorsal roots, *J. Neurophysiol.*, **2**, 515–525.

777. Toncray, J. E., and W. J. S. Krieg, 1946, The nuclei of the human thalamus. A comparative approach, *J. Comp. Neurol.*, **85**, 421–459.

778. Torkildsen, A., 1934, The gross anatomy of the lateral ventricles, *J. Anat.*, **68**, 480–491.

779. Torkildsen, A., 1939, A new palliative operation in cases of inoperable occlusion of the Sylvian aqueduct, *Acta psychiat. et neurol.*, **14**, 221.

780. Tower, Sarah S., 1940, Units for sensory reception in cornea, with notes on nerve impulses from sclera, iris, and lens, *J. Neurophysiol.*, **3**, 486–500.

781. Tower, Sarah S., 1940, Pyramidal lesion in the monkey, *Brain*, **63**, 36–90.

782. Tower, Sarah S., 1949, The pyramidal tract, Chap. VI in "The Precentral Motor Cortex," ed. by P. C. Bucy, 2d ed., Urbana, University of Illinois Press, pp. 151–172.

783. Tower, Sarah S., and Marion Hines, 1935, Dissociation of the pyramidal and extrapyramidal functions of the frontal lobe, *Science*, **82**, 376.

784. Trueta, J., A. E. Barclay, K. J. Franklin, P. M. Daniel, and M. M. L. Prichard, 1947, "Studies of the Renal Circulation," Oxford, Blackwell, xix + 187 pp.

785. Trueta, J., P. Daniel, A. E. Barclay, K. J. Franklin, and M. M. L. Prichard, 1946, Renal pathology in the light of recent neurovascular studies, *Lancet*, **2**, 237–238.

786. Tyler, David B., and P. Bard, 1949, Motion sickness, *Physiol. Rev.* **29**, 311–369.

787. Verhaart, W. J. C., 1949, The central tegmental tract, *J. Comp. Neurol.*, **90**, 173–192.

788. Vernet, Maurice, 1918, Syndrome du trou déchiré postérieur, *Rev. neurol.*, 2(34), 117–148.

789. Verney, E. B., 1948, Agents determining and influencing the functions of the pars nervosa of the pituitary, *Brit. M. J.*, **2**, 119–123.

790. Vogt, C., and O. Vogt, 1919, Allgemeine Ergebnisse unserer Hirnforschung, *J. f. Psychol. u. Neurol.*, **25**, 279–461.

791. Vonderahe, A. R., 1943, Anatomic basis of emotion, *Ohio State M. J.*, **39**, 325–330.

792. Walker, A. E., 1937, The projection of the medial geniculate body to the cerebral cortex in the macaque monkey, *J. Anat.*, **71**, 319–331.

793. Walker, A. E., 1938, "The Primate Thalamus," Chicago, University of Chicago Press, xviii + 321 pp.

794. Walker, A. E., 1938, An oscillographic study of the cerebello-cerebral relationships, *J. Neurophysiol.*, **1**, 16–23. Preliminary note (1937), *J. Physiol.*, **90**, 39P–41P.

795. Walker, A. E., 1939, The origin, course and terminations of the secondary pathways of the trigeminal nerve in primates, *J. Comp. Neurol.*, **71**, 59–89.

796. Walker, A. E., 1940, The spinothalamic tract in man, *Arch. Neurol. & Psychiat.*, **43**, 284–298.

797. Walker, A. E., 1949, Afferent connections, Chap. IV in "The Precentral Motor Cortex," ed. by P. C. Bucy, 2d ed., Urbana, University of Illinois Press, pp. 113–132.

798. Walker, A. E., 1949, Symposium: Thalamocortical relationships. Concluding remarks, *Electroencephalog. & Clin. Neurophysiol.*, **1**, 451–454.

799. Walker, A. E., 1949, Cerebral pedunculotomy for the relief of involuntary movements. I. Hemiballismus, *Acta psychiat. et neurol.*, **24**, 723–729.

800. Walker, A. E., and T. A. Weaver, 1940, Ocular movements from the occipital lobe in the monkey, *J. Neurophysiol.*, **3**, 353–357.

801. Wall, P. D., P. Glees, and J. F. Fulton, 1951, Corticofugal connexions of posterior orbital surface in Rhesus monkey, *Brain*, **74**, 66–71.

802. Waller, W. H., 1940, Progression movements elicited by subthalamic stimulation, *J. Neurophysiol.*, **3**, 300–307.

803. Walshe, F. M. R., 1921, On the disorders of movement resulting from loss of postural tone, with special reference to cerebellar ataxy, *Brain*, **44**, 539–556.

804. Walshe, F. M. R., 1924, Review of "Körperstellung" of R. Magnus, *Brain*, **47**, 383–390.

805. Walshe, F. M. R., 1930, Intracranial tumours. A critical review, *Quart. J. Med.*, **24**, 587–640.

806. Walshe, F. M. R., 1935, On the syndrome of the premotor cortex (Fulton) and the definition of the terms "premotor" and "motor" with a consideration of Jackson's views on cortical representation of movements, *Brain*, **58**, 49–80.

807. Walshe, F. M. R., 1942, The anatomy and physiology of cutaneous sensibility, *Brain*, **65**, 48–112.

808. Walshe, F. M. R., 1942, The giant cells of Betz, the motor cortex, and the pyramidal tract: A critical review, *Brain*, **65**, 409–461.

809. Waltner, Jules G., 1948, Barrier membrane of the cochlear aqueduct, *Arch. Otolaryng.*, **47**, 656–669.

810. Walzl, E. M., and V. Mountcastle, 1949, Projection of vestibular nerve to cerebral cortex of the cat, *Am. J. Physiol.*, **159**, 595.

811. Walzl, E. M., and C. N. Woolsey, 1943, Cortical auditory areas of the monkey as determined by electrical excitation of nerve fibers in the osseous spiral lamina and by click stimulation, *Federation Proc.*, **2**, 52.

812. Wang, S. C., and G. Clark, 1940, Decussation of the sacral autonomic pathways of the bladder from the hypothalamus, *Am. J. Physiol.*, **130**, 74–80.

813. Wang, S. C., G. Clark, F. L. Dey, and S. W. Ranson, 1940, Further study on the gastrointestinal motility following stimulation of the hypothalamus, *Am. J. Physiol.*, **130**, 81–88.

814. Wang, S. C., and S. W. Ranson, 1939, Descending pathways from the hypothalamus to the medulla and spinal cord. Observations on blood pressure and bladder responses, *J. Comp. Neurol.*, **71**, 457–472.

815. Ward, A. A., Jr., 1947, Decerebrate rigidity, *J. Neurophysiol.*, **10**, 89–103.

816. Ward, A. A., Jr., 1948, The cingular gyrus: Area 24, *J. Neurophysiol.*, **11**, 13–23.

817. Ward, A. A., Jr., 1948, The anterior cingulate gyrus and personality, *Research Publ., A. Nerv. & Ment. Dis.*, **27**, 438–445.

818. Ward, A. A., Jr., and W. S. McCulloch, 1947, The projection of the frontal lobe on the hypothalamus, *J. Neurophysiol.*, **10**, 309–314.

819. Ward, A. A., Jr., W. S. McCulloch, and H. W. Magoun, 1948, Production of an alternating tremor at rest in monkeys, *J. Neurophysiol.*, **11**, 317–330.

820. Ward, A. A., Jr., J. K. Peden, and O. Sugar, 1946, Corticocortical connections in the monkey

with special reference to area 6, *J. Neurophysiol.*, **9**, 453–461.

821. Ward, A. A., Jr., and H. L. Reed, 1946, Mechanism of pupillary dilatation elicited by cortical stimulation, *J. Neurophysiol.*, **9**, 329–335.

822. Ward, J. W., and V. LeQuire, 1950, Responses elicited by electrical stimulation of the gyrus cingulus in unanaesthetized cats, *Anat. Rec.*, **106**, 91.

823. Watts, J. W., and W. Freeman, 1948, Frontal lobotomy in the treatment of unbearable pain, *Research Publ., A. Nerv. & Ment. Dis.*, **27**, 715–722.

824. Watts, J. W., *et al.*, 1949, Proceedings of the first postgraduate course in psychosurgery, *Digest Neurol. & Psychiat., Inst. of Living*, **17**, 407–454.

825. Weddell, G., 1941, The pattern of cutaneous innervation in relation to cutaneous sensibility, *J. Anat.*, **75**, 346–367.

826. Weddell, G., 1941, The multiple innervation of sensory spots in the skin, *J. Anat.*, **75**, 441–446.

827. Weddell, G., B. Feinstein, and R. E. Pattle, 1944, The electrical activity of voluntary muscle in man under normal and pathological conditions, *Brain*, **67**, 178–257.

828. Weddell, G., J. A. Harpman, D. G. Lambley, and L. Young, 1940, The innervation of the musculature of the tongue, *J. Anat.*, **74**, 255–267.

829. Weddell, G., D. C. Sinclair, and W. H. Feindel, 1948, An anatomical basis for alterations in quality of pain sensibility, *J. Neurophysiol.*, **11**, 99–110.

830. Weed, L. H., 1938, Meninges and cerebrospinal fluid, *J. Anat.*, **72**, 181–215.

831. Weinberger, L. M., and F. C. Grant, 1941, Precocious puberty and tumors of the hypothalamus, *Arch. Int. Med.*, **67**, 762–792.

832. Weinberger, L. M., and F. C. Grant, 1942, Experiences with intramedullary tractotomy, *Arch. Neurol. & Psychiat.*, **48**, 355–381.

833. Weiss, P., 1941, Nerve patterns; Mechanics of nerve growth, *Growth* (suppl.), **5**, 163–203.

834. Weiss, P., and Hsi Wang, 1936, Neurofibrils in living ganglion cells of the chick, cultivated in vitro, *Anat. Rec.*, **67**, 105–117.

835. Wernicke, C., 1874, "Der aphasische Symptomencomplex. Eine psychologische Studie auf anatomischer Basis," Breslau, Cohn und Weigert, 72 pp.

836. Wheatley, M. D., 1944, The hypothalamus and affective behavior in cats, *Arch. Neurol. & Psychiat.*, **52**, 296–316.

837. Whittier, J. R., and F. A. Mettler, 1949, Studies on the subthalamus of the Rhesus monkey. I. Anatomy and fiber connections of the subthalamic nucleus of Luys, *J. Comp. Neurol.*, **90**, 281–317. II. Hyperkinesia and other physiologic effects of subthalamic lesions, with special reference to the subthalamic nucleus of Luys, *J. Comp. Neurol.*, **90**, 319–372.

838. Williams, D. J., 1936, The origin of the posterior cerebral artery, *Brain*, **59**, 175–180.

839. Williams, J. M., and W. Freeman, 1951, Amygdaloidectomy for the suppression of auditory hallucinations, *Med. Ann. District of Columbia*, **20**, 192–196.

840. Wilson, W. C., and H. W. Magoun, 1945, The functional significance of the inferior olive in the cat, *J. Comp. Neurol.*, **83**, 69–77.

841. Windle, W. F., 1926, Non-bifurcating nerve fibers of the trigeminal nerve, *J. Comp. Neurol.*, **40**, 229–240.

842. Windle, W. F., 1940, "Physiology of the Fetus," Philadelphia, Saunders, xiii + 249 pp.

843. Windle, W. F., and R. E. Baxter, 1935, Development of reflex mechanisms in the spinal cord of albino rat embryos. Correlations between structure and function, and comparisons with the cat and the chick, *J. Comp. Neurol.*, **63**, 189–209.

844. Winkelman, N. M., and A. Silverstein, 1934, Trophic disturbances of the limbs in retrorolandic lesions, *Research Publ., A Nerv. & Ment. Dis.*, **13**, 485–528.

845. Winkler, C., 1927, "Opera omnia, Manuel de neurologie," Haarlem, Netherlands, E. F. Bohn, Vol. 8, p. 10.

846. Winokur, G. L., S. A. Trufant, R. B. King, and J. L. O'Leary, 1950, Thalamocortical activity during spreading depression. *Electroencephalog. & Clin. Neurophysiol.*, **2**, 79–90.

847. Wislocki, G. B., and L. S. King, 1936, The permeability of the hypophysis and hypothalamus to vital dyes, with a study of the hypophyseal vascular supply, *Am. J. Anat.*, **58**, 421–472.

848. Wohlfahrt, S., 1932, Die vordere Zentralwindung bein Pyramidenbahnläsionen verschiedner Art, *Acta med. Scandinav.*, Suppl. **46**, 1–234.

849. Wolff, H. G., and H. L. Blumgort, 1929, The cerebral circulation. VI. The effect of normal and of increased intracranial cerebrospinal fluid pressure on the velocity of intracranial blood flow, *Arch. Neurol. & Psychiat.*, **21**, 795–804.

850. Woodburne, R. T., E. C. Crosby, and R. E. McCotter, 1946, The mammalian midbrain and isthmus regions. Part II. The fiber connections. A. The relations of the tegmentum of

the midbrain with the basal ganglia in *Macaca mulatta, J. Comp. Neurol.,* **85**, 67–92.

851. Woodhall, Barnes, 1939, Anatomy of the cranial blood sinuses with particular reference to the lateral, *Laryngoscope,* **49**, 966–1010.

852. Woodhall, Barnes, J. W. Devine, Jr., and D. Hart, 1941, Homolateral dilatation of the pupil, homolateral paresis and bilateral muscular rigidity in the diagnosis of extradural hemorrhage, *Surg., Gynec. & Obst.,* **72**, 391–398.

853. Woollard, H. H., G. Weddell, and J. A. Harpman, 1940, Observations on the neurohistological basis of cutaneous pain, *J. Anat.,* **74**, 413–440.

854. Woolsey, C. N., 1938, Representation in the motor cortex of flexor and extensor muscles of the leg, *Am. J. Physiol.,* **123**, 221–222.

855. Woolsey, C. N., 1947, Patterns of sensory representation in the cerebral cortex, *Federation Proc.,* **6**, 437–441.

856. Woolsey, C. N., and H.-T. Chang, 1947, Activation of the cerebral cortex by antidromic volleys in the pyramidal tract, *Research Publ., A. Nerv. & Ment. Dis.,* **27**, 146–161.

857. Woolsey, C. N., and D. Fairman, 1946, Contralateral, ipsilateral, and bilateral representation of cutaneous receptors in somatic areas I and II of the cerebral cortex of pigs, sheep and other mammals, *Surgery,* **19**, 684–702.

858. Woolsey, C. N., W. H. Marshall, and P. Bard, 1942, Representation of cutaneous tactile sensibility in the cerebral cortex of the monkey as indicated by evoked potentials, *Bull. Johns Hopkins Hosp.,* **70**, 399–441.

859. Woolsey, C. N., W. H. Marshall, and P. Bard, 1943, Note on organization of the tactile sensory area of cerebral cortex of chimpanzee, *J. Neurophysiol.,* **6**, 287–291.

860. Woolsey, C. N., and E. M. Walzl, 1942, Topical projection of nerve fibers from local regions of the cochlea to the cerebral cortex of the cat, *Bull. Johns Hopkins Hosp.,* **71**, 315–344.

861. Yacorzynski, G. K., and Loyal Davis, 1945, An experimental study of the functions of the frontal lobes in man, *Psychosom. Med.,* **7**, 97–107.

862. Young, J. Z., 1942, The functional repair of nervous tissue, *Physiol. Rev.,* **22**, 318–374.

863. Young, J. Z., 1945, Structure, degeneration and repair of nerve fibers, *Nature, London,* **156**, 132–136.

864. Young, J. Z., 1946, Effects of use and disuse on nerve and muscle, *Lancet,* **2**, 109–113.

865. Youngstrom, K. A., 1940, A primary and a secondary somatic motor innervation in amblystoma, *J. Comp. Neurol.,* **73**, 139–151.

866. Youngstrom, K. A., 1941, Acetylcholine esterase concentration during the development of the human fetus, *J. Neurophysiol.,* **4**, 473–477.

867. Youngstrom, K. A., 1944, Intramedullary sensory type ganglion cells in the spinal cord of human embryos, *J. Comp. Neurol.,* **81**, 47–53.

868. Youngstrom, K. A., B. Woodhall, and R. Graves, 1941, Acetylcholine esterase content of brain tumors, *Proc. Soc. Exper. Biol. & Med.,* **48**, 555–557.

869. Zimmerman, H. M., 1940, Temperature disturbance and the hypothalamus, *Research Publ., A. Nerv. & Ment. Dis.,* **20**, 824–840.

870. Zollinger, R., 1935, Removal of left cerebral hemisphere. Report of a case, *Arch. Neurol. & Psychiat.,* **34**, 1055–1064.

VISUAL AIDS

THE MOTION PICTURES listed below and on the following pages can be used to supplement much of the material in this book. It is suggested, of course, that each film be reviewed before it is used in order to determine its suitability for a particular group. Immediately following the title of each film are the names of its producer and distributor (sometimes the same), and these individuals and organizations are identified in the list of sources at the end of the bibliography. In many instances, the films can be borrowed or rented from local or state 16mm film libraries. (A nationwide list of these local sources is given in "A Directory of 2002 16mm Film Libraries," available for fifty cents from the Superintendent of Documents, Washington 25, D.C.) All of the motion pictures are 16mm films and, unless otherwise indicated, sound and black-and-white.

This bibliography is not inclusive. Film users should examine various specialized catalogs of medical films such as the following:

"Medical Motion Pictures Approved by the College." Chicago, American College of Surgeons, 1953.

"Professional Motion Picture Films." Topeka, Kansas, Academy-International of Medicine.

"Psychological Cinema Register." State College, Pennsylvania, Pennsylvania State University, 1952.

"Medical Films and Film Strips of the Armed Forces." Washington, U.S. Armed Forces Institute of Pathology, 1953.

"Films in Psychiatry, Psychology and Mental Health." Chicago, Medical Audio-Visual Institute of the Association of American Medical Colleges, 1953.

Anatomy of the Brain (MP; Sarnoff/UWF; 15min silent). Dissection of the brain and demonstration of the dura and pacchionian bodies, falx cerebri, corpus callosum, olfactory bulbs and tract optic chiasma, anterior cerebral vessels, pituitary body, optic nerves, oculomotor and abducens nerves. Septum pellucidum, 3rd and 4th ventricles, medulla, pons, 6th nerve, gasserian ganglion, trigeminal, 7, 8, 9, 10, 11 and 12th nerves, cerebellum, pia, and arachnoid are demonstrated.

The Brain (MP; Brandon; 75min silent). Structure of the brain, cranial nerves, embryonic development, ventricles, fissures and convolutions, cerebral hemispheres, etc. Based on studies of Pavlov. Russian labels with English subtitles.

Cerebellar Disorders, Disorders Involving the Lower Motor Neurons, and Convulsive States (MP; USPHS/PCR; 17min silent). Shows symptoms of nystagmus in Friedreich's ataxia, past pointing in case of head injury scarring cerebellum, pendulous knee jerk in case of cerebellar tumor, anterior horn disease, radial nerve paralysis, median nerve paralysis, and peripheral facial paralysis. Presents several epileptiform seizures of various types and etiology. For medical personnel. (Introduction to Clinical Neurology Series, No. 3)

Development of the Nervous System in Vertebrates and Invertebrates (MP; Brandon; 30-min, silent). Traces the development of the brain of fish to the brain of man.

Disorders of the Extra-pyramidal System and the Posterior Columns (MP; USPHS/PCR; 20min silent). Presents cases of parkinsonism, chronic epidemic encephalitis, Huntington's chorea, Sydenham's chorea, congenital athetosis, choreo-athetosis, striate rigidity, tabetic ataxia, and tabes dorsalis. For medical personnel. (Introduction to Clinical Neurology Series, No. 2)

Experimental Psychology of Vision (MP; IFB; 16min silent). Chief phenomena and techniques of research in visual perception, including phi phenomenon, optical illusions, color constancy, eye movements, perception span, and digit span.

Functional Syndromes with Pronounced Physical Symptoms (MP; USPHS/PCR; 17min silent). Presents functional cases in which physical symptoms not caused by neurological impairment play a major part—hysterical epileptiform seizures, hysterical pseudohemiplegia, functional tremors, and tics. Stresses the contrast between functional and organic paralysis cases in carrying out purposeful acts with partially paralyzed members. (Introduction to Clinical Neurology series, No. 4)

Functions of the Nervous System (MP; PCR; 13min). Description of central nervous system; cranial, cervical, thoracic, lumbar, and sacral connections; sympathetic ganglia; sense organs; and mechanism of muscular coordination.

General Neurological Examination and Clinical Signs of Disorders of the Pyramidal System (MP; USPHS/PCR; 19min silent). Reviews gross anatomy of the brain; demonstrates minimal neurological examination of cranial nerves, motor coordination, reflexes, and sensation; presents clinical signs of disorders of the pyramidal system; and shows two cases of hemiplegia with internal hydrocephalus, x-rays being presented to show the seat of impairment. For medical personnel. (Introduction to Clinical Neurology series, part 1)

Integrative Aspects of the Nervous System. Part 2: The Motor System (MP; USA; 47min color). Portrays means by which the nervous system is believed to make use of "feed back" and "scanning" mechanism in nerve impulses.

Mechanics of the Brain (MP; Brandon; 60min silent). Demonstrates the fundamental processes of the psychology of the nervous system.

Motor Disorders in Nervous Diseases (MP; Herz and Putnam; Columbia). Ten films all silent, with following titles and running times:

Abnormal Involuntary Movements (30min)
Disorders of Gait (37min)
Disorders of Coordination (41min)
Muscle Status (30min)
Reflexes (30min)
Skilled Acts (30min)
Oculomotor Disorders (30min)
Facial Palsy (26min)
Disorders of the Vestibular System (26min)
Disorders of the Motor Trigeminal, Spinal Accessory, and Hypoglossal Nerve (22min)

The Nervous System (MP; Brandon; 3½hrs silent). In parts dealing with the development of the nervous system, reflex action, the spinal cord, the brain, and conditioned reflexes and behavior.

The Nervous System (MP; EBF; 11min). Elementary demonstration of structure and function of spinal cord, medulla, midbrain, thalamus, cerebrum, and membrane theory of conduction.

Neuro-Ophthalmological Conditions: Pathological Ocular Manifestations of Clinical Interest (MP; NYU; 18min). Abnormal neurological conditions associated with pathological signs relating to vision.

The Role of the Hypothalamus in Emotion and Behavior (MP; Masserman/PCR; 27min). Illustrates Horsley-Clarke technique for inserting electrodes into hypothalamus of cats and effects of such stimulation. Concludes that hypothalamus may integrate pathways of effective expression, but does not serve as source of "drive" or as "center" of emotion.

The Spinal Cord (MP; Brandon; 30min silent). Illustrates the complete structure and functions of the spinal cord. Based on studies of Pavlov. Russian labels with English subtitles.

SOURCES OF FILMS LISTED

Brandon—Brandon Films, Inc., 200 W. 57th St., New York 19

Columbia—Columbia University, Educational Films, 413 W. 117th St., New York 27

EBF—Encyclopedia Britannica Films, Inc., Wilmette, Ill.

Herz and Putnam—Ernst Hertz, M.D., and Tracy J. Putnam, M.D., New York (Films distributed by Columbia University)

IFB—International Film Bureau, Inc., 57 E. Jackson Blvd., Chicago 4, Ill.

Masserman—Jules H. Masserman, M.D., Chicago, Ill. (Films distributed by Psychological Cinema Register)

NYU—New York University, Film Library, 26 Washington Pl., New York 14

PCR—Psychological Cinema Register, Pennsylvania State University, State College, Pa.

Sarnoff—Jacob Sarnoff, M.D., Brooklyn, N.Y. (Films distributed by United World Films)

USA—U.S. Army, Armed Forces Institute of Pathology, Washington 25, D.C.

USPHS—U.S. Public Health Service, Washington 25, D.C. (Films distributed by Psychological Cinema Register)

UWF—United World Films, Inc., 1445 Park Ave., New York 29

INDEX

Q

R

U

V

W

X

Z